CAMPER STOP

EUROPE

2015

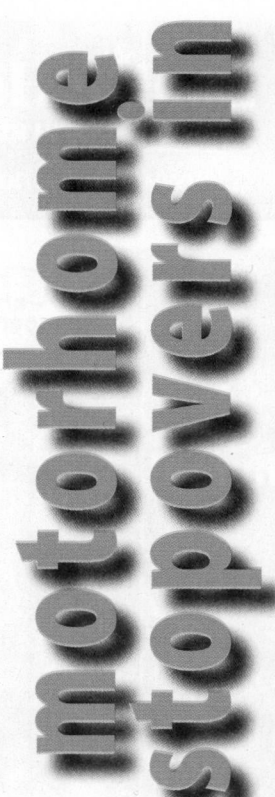

motorhome stopovers in

United Kingdom
The Netherlands
Belgium
Luxemburg
France
Spain
Portugal
Denmark
Germany
Switzerland
Austria
Italy
Slovenia
Croatia
Greece

Publisher - Herausgeber - Éditeur - Editore

Facile Media

COLOPHON

A publication of:

Facile Media, Oss
Landweerstraat-Zuid 109
5349 AK Oss
Postbus 555
NL-5340 AN Oss
tel: +31 412 65 68 85

Chief editor
Anne van den Dobbelsteen

The draft of this version is saved
in October 2014

Comments or suggestions can
be sent to the publisher:

Facile Media
Postbus 555, NL-5340 AN Oss
Tel.: +31 412 65 68 85
E-mail: info@camperstop.com
Internet: www.camperstop.com

ISBN 978-90-76080-41-3

Copyright 2014 Facile Media

Preface

Since 1996, Facile Media has been publisher of European motorhome guides. As of 2005, the information about motorhome stopovers in Europe is available in a multilingual version.

And now, this Camperstop Europe 2015 is already the third release of the full English version.

Our guides contain indispensable information about motorhome stopovers, service facilities and tourist information in the main European motorhome countries.

Traveling with "Camperstop Europe" will be a pleasant experience and a relaxed vacation in your motor home. We therefore wish you happy motorhome season, with many pleasant and surprising travels in 2015.

Anne van den Dobbelsteen
Chief editor

Reliable information
Every summer, 50 teams of Facile Media drive all across Europe to inspect the motorhome stopovers. The inspections take place according to predefined guidelines. The inspections by these specially trained motorhome enthusiasts have made it possible to make the information in the guide as up-to-date as possible. More than 8000 motorhome stopovers and 6072 illustrative photos are the result.

Unique way to find the motorhome sites
The motorhome stopovers can be easily located on the 40 maps. Next to each map, you'll find a location name index with map referral and a page number where the location can be found in the guide. In addition, the type of motorhome stopover is indicated. In a glance, you'll be able to see whether it is the type of stopover you had in mind. In order to provide you with additional information, the location is described extensively on the relevant page, usually with a picture.

GPS-data sets on your navigation system
In addition to this guide, you can order datasets online, which you can download. The sets can be uploaded to the most common navigation systems. This allows you to drive to the motorhome stopovers listed in this guide without any effort. More information about this is available on page 8.

Table of contents

Table of contents

How to use the guide

Searching in a region

In the table of contents, at the beginning of the guide, one can search a region in preferred country. On the page of the region a map indicates the different departments/provinces with a reference to the pages.

Maps

On pages 10-11 the countries are divided into sections. The number in each box is the number of the map. On the map the red dots indicate the location of the town. Next to each map an index is published with the places on maps. The index shows the name, type of stopover, map code and page number of each location. This way the description of the motorhome stopover can be found quickly and easy.

Searching for a town

Places identified in this guide can be found under the name of the local town in the alphabetical index at the back. Use the index like a dictionary to look for specific towns, the facilities offered, map references and relevant page numbers.

Country specific rules

When travelling you have to take into account that each country has its own rules and regulations. These rules are written on the first page of each countries section.

Advise

It is recommended not to wait to long to look for an overnight stop. It could be that chosen motorhome stopover is already full and you have to go looking for an alternative.

How to use the guide

Description motorhome stopover

The information per motorhome stopover always begins with a colored block containing the type of stopover, town name and reference to the map. Directly below the name, address, GPS coordinates mostly followed by a picture. Beneath the picture you find the following information: number of pitches, rate, facilities and opening period. After that, if known, distances to city centre, shop, restaurant etc. Specific information of the motorhome stopover and a brief route description.

Motorhome facilities

 MOTORHOME PARK
This symbol indicates a motorhome park, a park designed for motorhomes with a range of facilities.

 OFFICIAL MOTORHOME STOPOVER
This symbol indicates an area suitable for overnight parking

 OVERNIGHT PARKING TOLERATED
In some countries tolerated places are mentioned. This means that it is officially prohibited but is being tolerated by local authorities. Therefore the local or national situation may change at any time. Nevertheless these places are listed because they were frequently being used by motorhomes at the time of writing.

 OVERNIGHT STAY IN HARBOUR/MARINA
Motorhome stopover in or near harbour or marina, often with a beautiful view.

 OVERNIGHT STAY AT FARM/VINEYARD
Farms and vineyards that welcome motorhomes, you may be encouraged to sample and buy their fare.

 OVERNIGHT STAY AT RESTAURANT
Motorhomes are allowed to stopover on the car park of a hotel, restaurant or bar. You should expect to dine or drink in the bar. Some restaurants insist on you having dinner. Sometimes a nominal charge is asked for the overnight stay.

 OVERNIGHT STAY AT SPA
A growing number of spas and thermal baths offer stopovers to motorhomes.

 OVERNIGHT STAY AT ZOO/MUSEUM/ AMUSEMENT PARK
Motorhomes are allowed to stopover on the car park of a zoo, museum or amusement park. Entrance is not always obligated.

 OVERNIGHT STAY AT COMPANY/ ENTERPRISE
Overnight stay, mostly inside the gates, at companies/ enterprises.

 OVERNIGHT STAY OUTSIDE THE CAMPSITE
Motorhomes are allowed to stopover on the parking place outside the gate of a campsite.

 CAMPSITE
Overnight stay on a campsite.

 CAR-PARK
Motorhome parking bays, suitable for daytime use only. Often in large cities and/or tourist towns, charges may apply.

Other symbols

- ⅃ Motorhome stopover, number of pitches and rate
- ⬆ Signposted on the spot
- ➡ Signposted in town
- ⬆ No signs to indicate the motorhome stopover

Payment
- 🅿 Collector parking fee
- 🅿 Parking meter
- 💳 Payment only with a credit/debit card
- 💳 Payment with cash and credit/debit card

S **Service facilities**
This symbol indicates that there are service facilities available.

- 🚰 drinking water
- grey water dump
- Ch chemical toilet disposal point
- charging battery
- electricity available
- WC toilets
- showers
- washing machine/ dryer on the spot
- wifi access point

GPS - convenience

Downloading GPS-coordinates

Downloads of the gps-coordinates for the motorhome stopovers listed in this guide are available from www.camperstop.com. The files are suitable for most navigation systems. The data that appears on the screen gives the town name and page number in this guide so you can look up the details of the facilities very easily.

The downloadable files list the stopovers and most of the other facilities mentioned in the guide. Therefore it could be a stopover with or without service facilities, a place with service facilities only, but also a tourist information office or a campsite.

You can easily check for your nearest stopover, the navigation system will list the stopovers by distance. Use the guide to see what facilities are available. Once a choice has been made you can navigate to there without a problem.

The costs for downloading are € 3.25 per country/dataset. The Netherlands/Belgium/Luxembourg are sold as one country, also Austria/Switzerland and Spain/Portugal are treated the same.

Full downloading instructions are found on at www.camperstop.com. There are different downloads of several navigation systems.

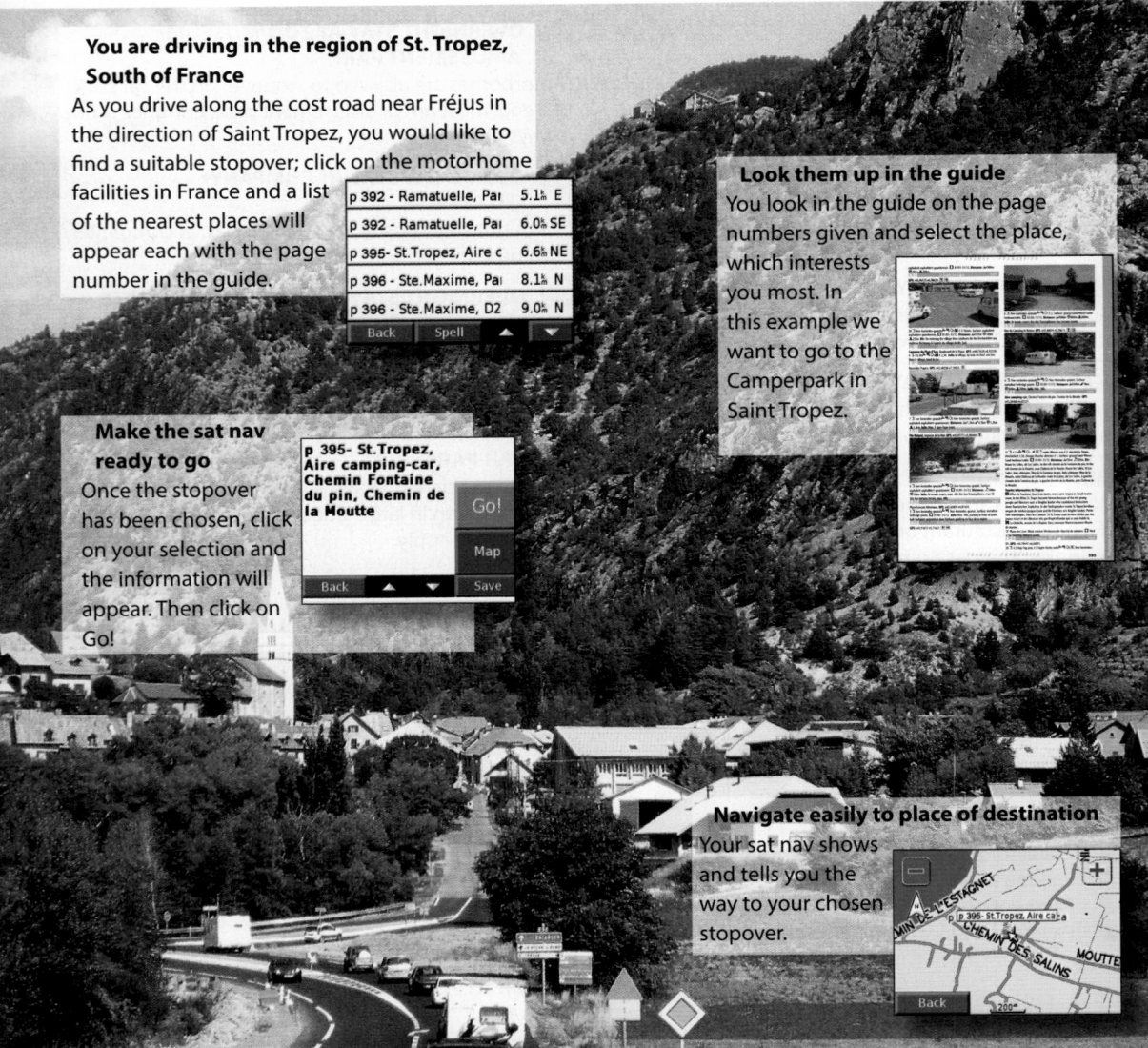

You are driving in the region of St. Tropez, South of France

As you drive along the cost road near Fréjus in the direction of Saint Tropez, you would like to find a suitable stopover; click on the motorhome facilities in France and a list of the nearest places will appear each with the page number in the guide.

p 392 - Ramatuelle, Par	5.1ᵏᵐ E
p 392 - Ramatuelle, Par	6.0ᵏᵐ SE
p 395- St.Tropez, Aire c	6.6ᵏᵐ NE
p 396 - Ste.Maxime, Par	8.1ᵏᵐ N
p 396 - Ste.Maxime, D2	9.0ᵏᵐ N
Back	Spell	▲	▼

Look them up in the guide

You look in the guide on the page numbers given and select the place, which interests you most. In this example we want to go to the Camperpark in Saint Tropez.

Make the sat nav ready to go

Once the stopover has been chosen, click on your selection and the information will appear. Then click on Go!

p 395- St.Tropez, Aire camping-car, Chemin Fontaine du pin, Chemin de la Moutte

Go!
Map
Back ▲ ▼ Save

Navigate easily to place of destination

Your sat nav shows and tells you the way to your chosen stopover.

Driving regulations in Europe

Each country has different driving rules. For motorhomes sometimes there are different regulations. Here below an overview with maximum speed limits for motorhomes.

Per country there are also different rules as for warning triangles, security vests or driving with daily lights. Here below this information at a glance.

Country	within towns	single carriageway		expressway		motorway		compulsory in your vehicle:
		<3,5T	>3,5T	<3,5T	>3,5T	<3,5T	>3,5T	
GB Great Britain	30 (48km)	50 (80km)		70 (112km)		70 (112km)		Speed limits in mph.
NL The Netherlands	50	80		100	80	130	80	warning triangle — >3,5 ton = motorhome on truck basis.
B Belgium	50	90				120	90	warning triangle, security vest, fire extinguisher, first aid kit
L Luxemburg	50	90	75			130	90	warning triangle, security vest — Speed limits on a dry road.
F France	50	80		110	100	130	110	warning triangle, security vest — Speed limits on a dry road. Safety vest also for bicycles.
ES Spain	50	80		90	80	100	90	warning triangle, security vest — Set of spare bulbs.
P Portugal	50	100	90			120	110	warning triangle, daily lights
DK Denmark	50	80	70	110	80	130	80	warning triangle, daily lights
D Germany	50	100	80	130	100	130	100	security vest, first aid kit — 130km/h is a recommended speed limit.
CH Switzerland	50	80		100		120	100	warning triangle, daily lights
A Austria	50	100	70			130	80	warning triangle, security vest, first aid kit — A10-A12-A13-en A14 : 22-05h max. 110km/h.
I Italy	50	90	80	110	80	130	100	warning triangle, security vest, daily lights — Speed limits on a dry road. * Suburban.
SLO Slovenia	50	90	80	100	80	130	80	warning triangle, fire extinguisher — Set of spare bulbs.
HR Croatia	50	90	80	110	90	130	90	warning triangle, security vest, first aid kit — Set of spare bulbs.
GR Greece	50	90		110	90	120		warning triangle, fire extinguisher, first aid kit

Legend: warning triangle — security vest — fire extinguisher — first aid kit — daily lights — recommended

Information is based on information available in September 2014.

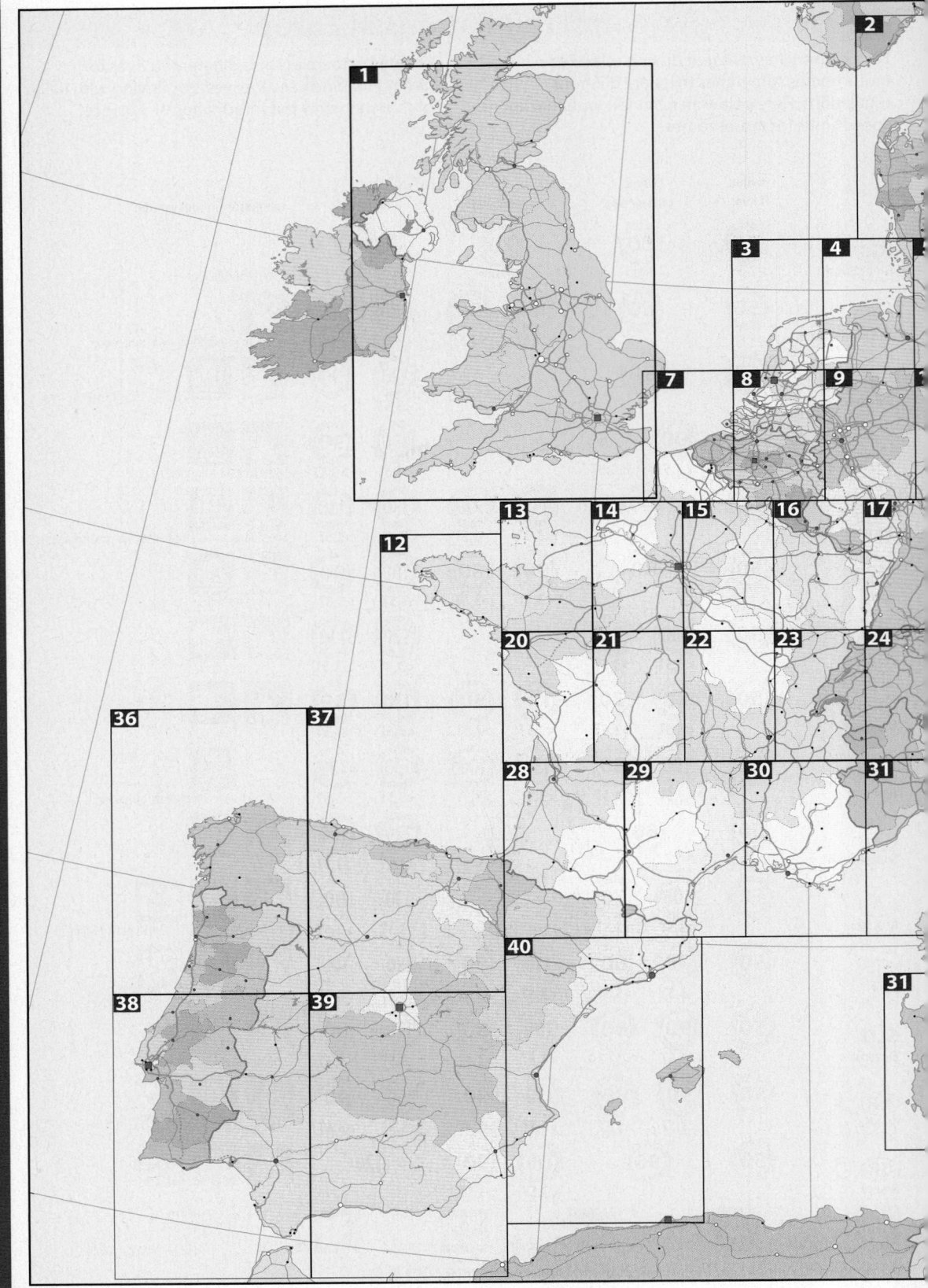

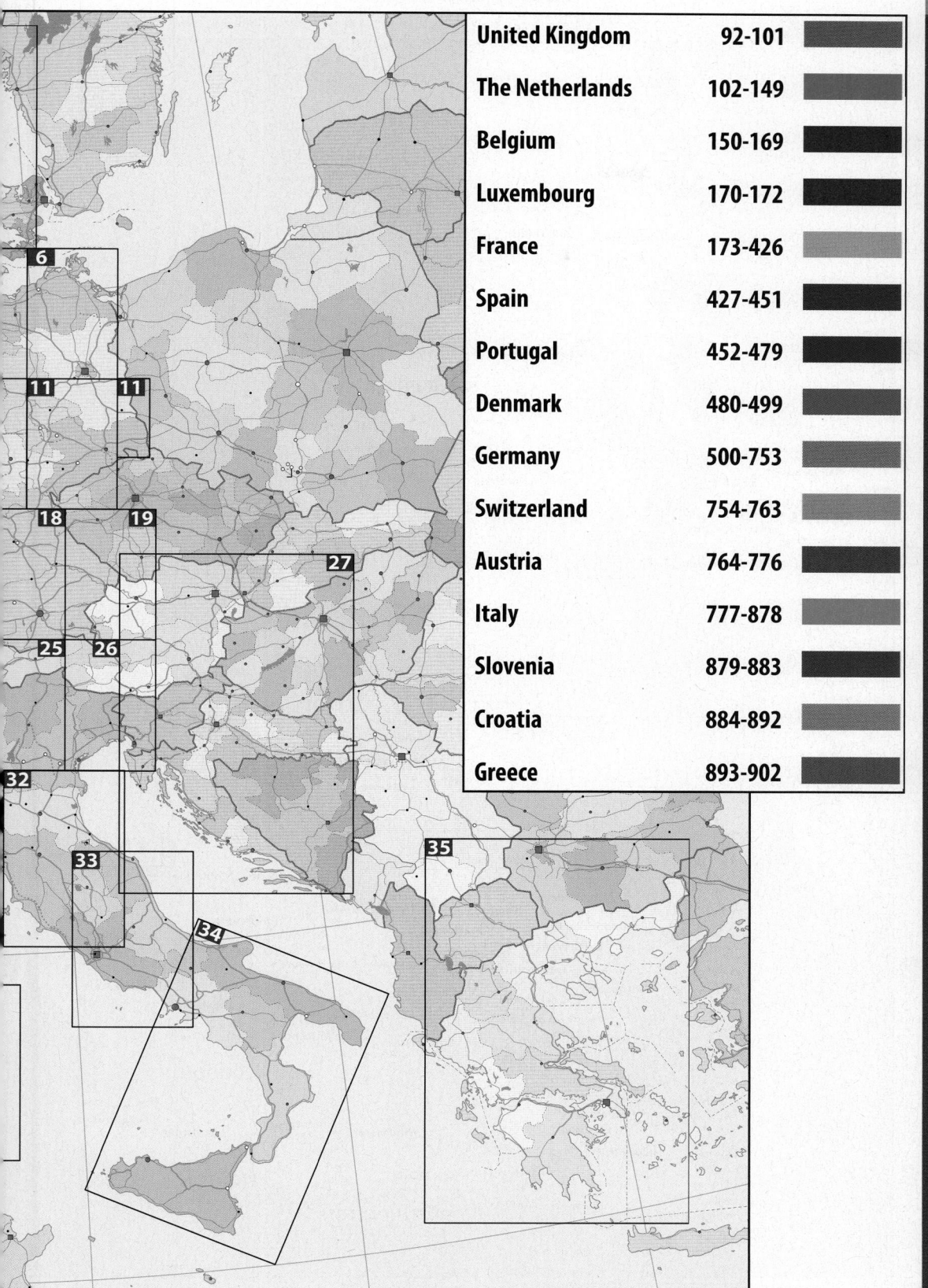

United Kingdom	**92-101**
The Netherlands	**102-149**
Belgium	**150-169**
Luxembourg	**170-172**
France	**173-426**
Spain	**427-451**
Portugal	**452-479**
Denmark	**480-499**
Germany	**500-753**
Switzerland	**754-763**
Austria	**764-776**
Italy	**777-878**
Slovenia	**879-883**
Croatia	**884-892**
Greece	**893-902**

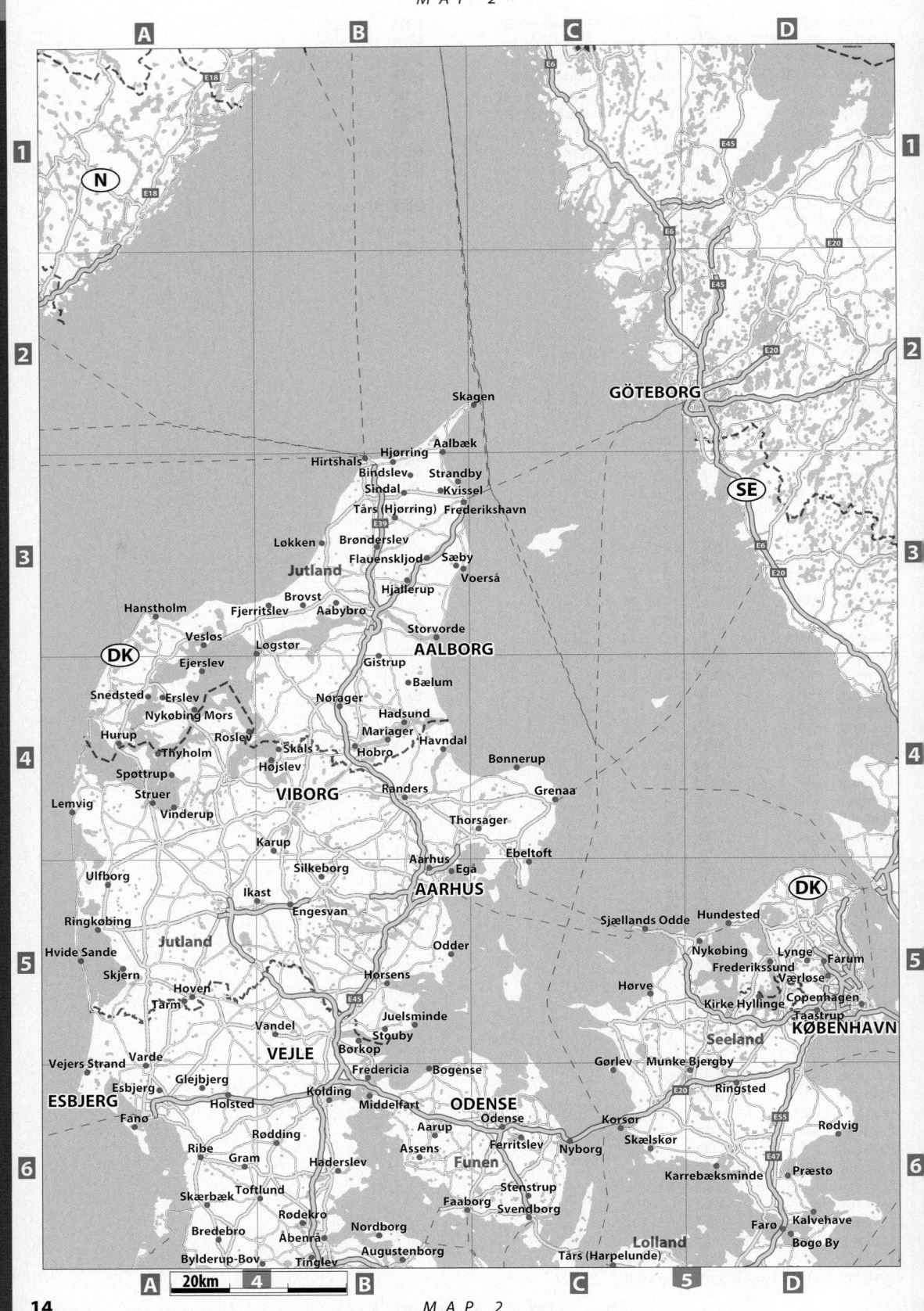

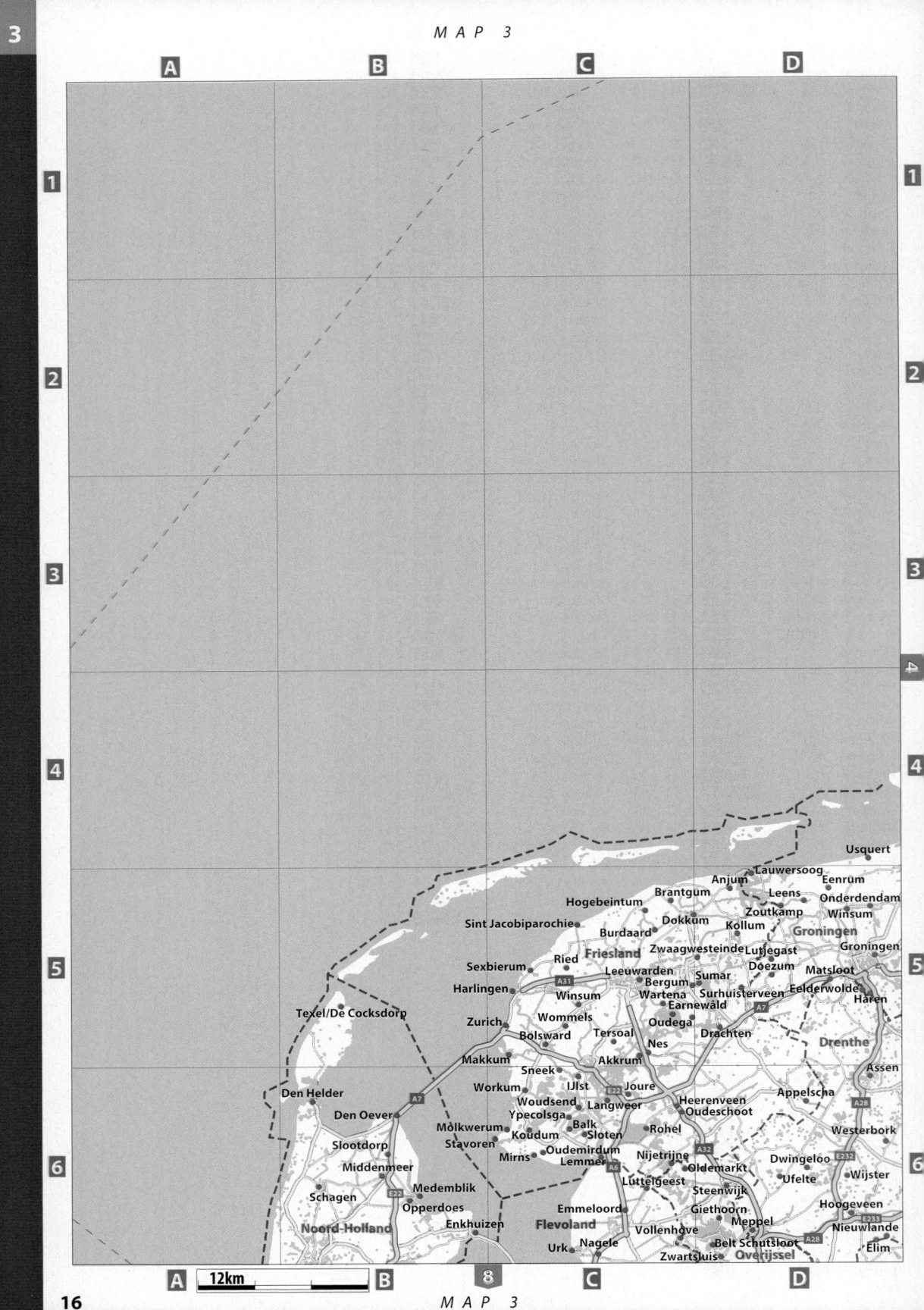

A   **B**   **C**   **D**

1   **1**

2   **2**

3   **3**

4

4   **4**

Usquert

Lauwersoog   Eenrum
Anjum
Brantgum   Leens   Onderdendam
Hogebeintum   Zoutkamp   Winsum
Sint Jacobiparochie   Dokkum   **Groningen**
Burdaard   Kollum
Ried   **Friesland**   Zwaagwesteinde   Lutjegast   Groningen
Sexbierum   Leeuwarden   Doezum   Matsloot

5   Harlingen   Winsum   Bergum   Sumar   Surhuisterveen   Eelderwolde   **5**
  Wartena   Haren
Zurich   Wommels   Earnewald   A7
  Bolsward   Tersoal   Oudega
Texel/De Cocksdorp   Nes   Drachten   **Drenthe**
Makkum   Akkrum
  Sneek   Assen
Den Helder   Workum   IJlst   Joure   Heerenveen   Appelscha
Den Oever   A7   Langweer   Oudeschoot   A28
  Woudsend   Ypecolsga   Rohel   Westerbork
Slootdorp   Molkwerum   Balk   A32
Middenmeer   Stavoren   Koudum   Sloten   Nijetrijne   Dwingeloo   E232

6   Mirns   Oudemirdum   Oldemarkt   Ufelte   Wijster   **6**
Schagen   E22   Lemmer   Luttelgeest   Steenwijk
Medemblik   Hoogeveen
Opperdoes   Emmeloord   Giethoorn   E233
  Enkhuizen   **Flevoland**   Vollenhove   Meppel   Nieuwlande
Noord-Holland   Urk   Nagele   Belt Schutsloot   **Overijssel**   Elim
  Zwartsluis

MAP 5

MAP 5

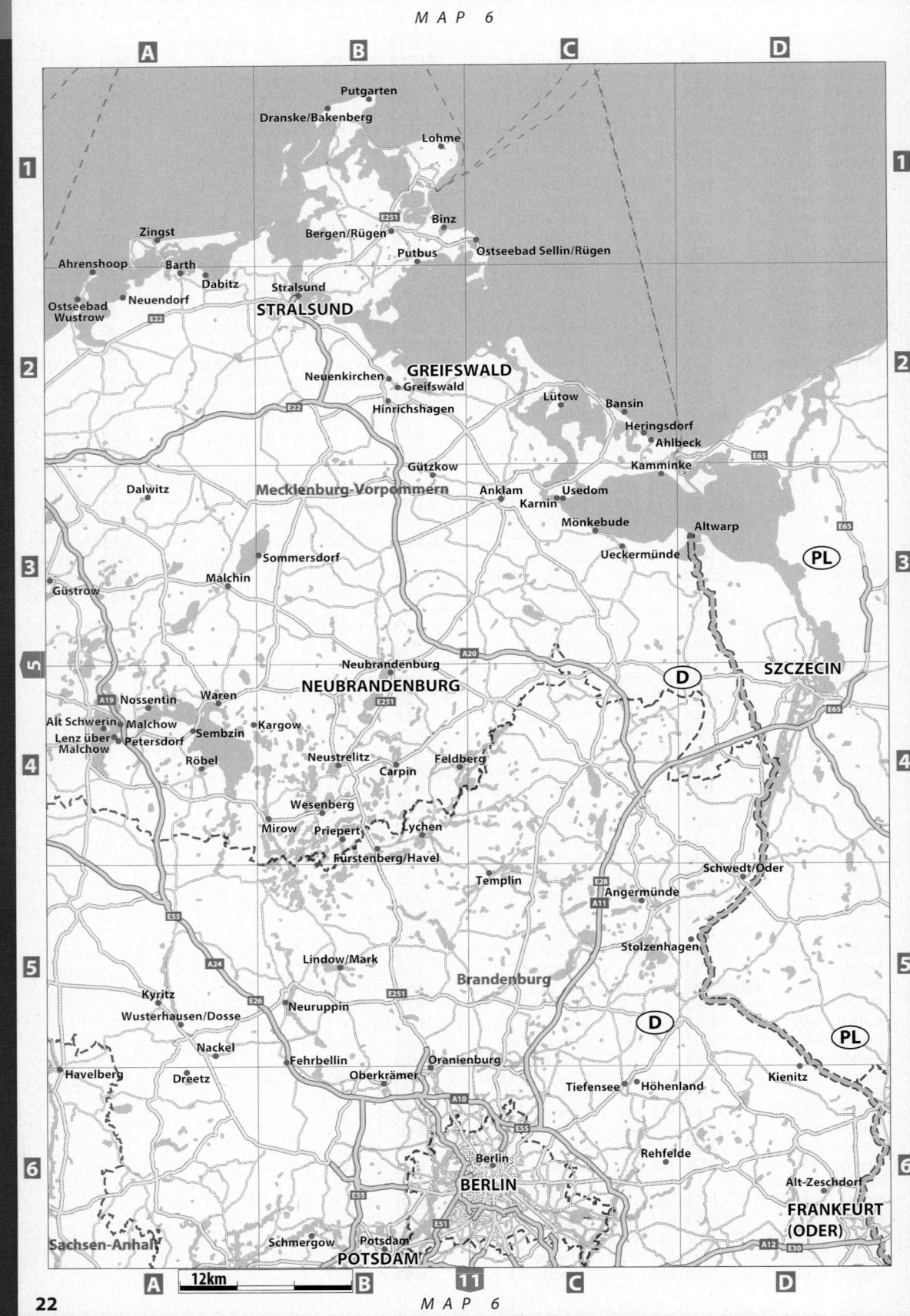

A B C D

1

UK

2

Ouddorp

3 Zierikzee

Kamperland
Oostkapelle
Wolphaartsdijk
Middelburg
Zeeland
NL
Breskens
Hansweert
Knokke-Heist
Groede
Kloosterzande
Terneuzen
Zeebrugge
St.Laureins
Vogelwaarde
Axel
Sas van Gent
Assenede
Westdorpe
BRUGGE
Brugge
Maldegem
Eeklo
Oudenburg
Beernem
Aalter
Lokeren
Westende
Gistel
GENT
Nieuwpoort
Aartrijke
Wingene
Gentbrugge
Veurne
Diksmuide
Berlare
DUNKERQUE
Vlaanderen
Grand-Fort-Philippe
Kortemark
Zulte
Oye-plage
Gravelines
B
Roeselare
Gavere
Calais
Hondschoote
Langemark- Poelkappele
Sint-Eloois-Vijve
CALAIS
Bergues
Harelbeke
Wissant
Poperinge
Zonnebeke
Kortrijk
Geraardsbergen
Tardinghen
F
Cassel
Mesem
Wervik
Ambleteuse
Mouscron
Arques
Bailleul
Dottignies
Lessines
Boulogne-sur-Mer
Leers Noord
Wallonie
Lahamaide
Le Portel
LILLE
Leuze-en-Hainaut
Equihen-Plage
B
Hardelot
Longfossé
Aubechies
Tournai/Doornik
Beloeil
Le Touquet-Paris Plage
Richebourg
Quevaucamps
Stella-plage
Embry
Blaton
Harchies
Nimy
Merlimont
Montreuil-sur-Mer
Bernissart
Quaregnon
Berck-sur-Mer
Lens
Hornu
Mons/Bergen
Fort-Mahon Plage
Quend
F
Quend-plage-les-Pins
Nuncq-Hautecôte
Bavay
Le Crotoy
Picardie
Arras
Boussois

Nord-Pas-de-Calais

12km

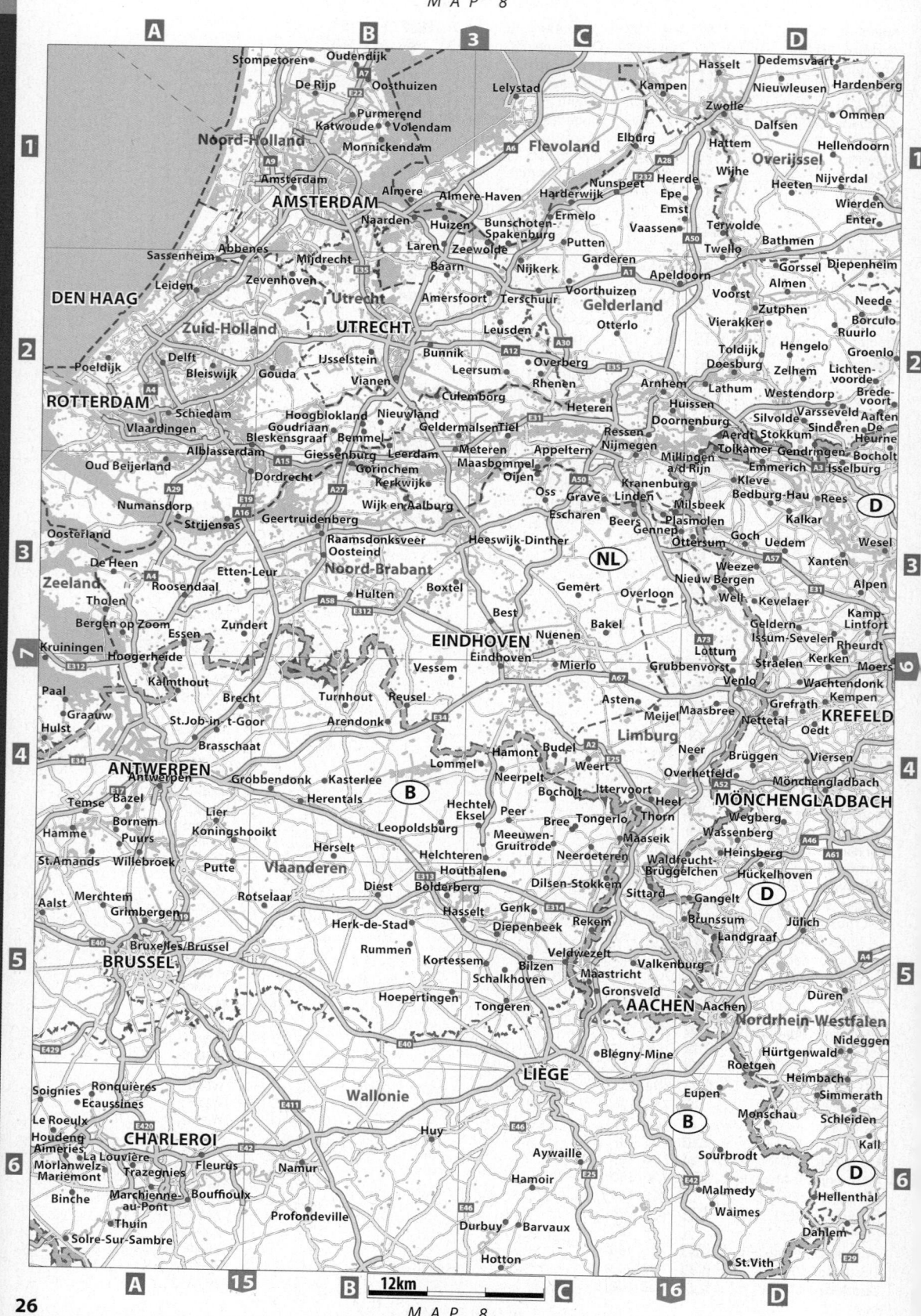

MAP 8

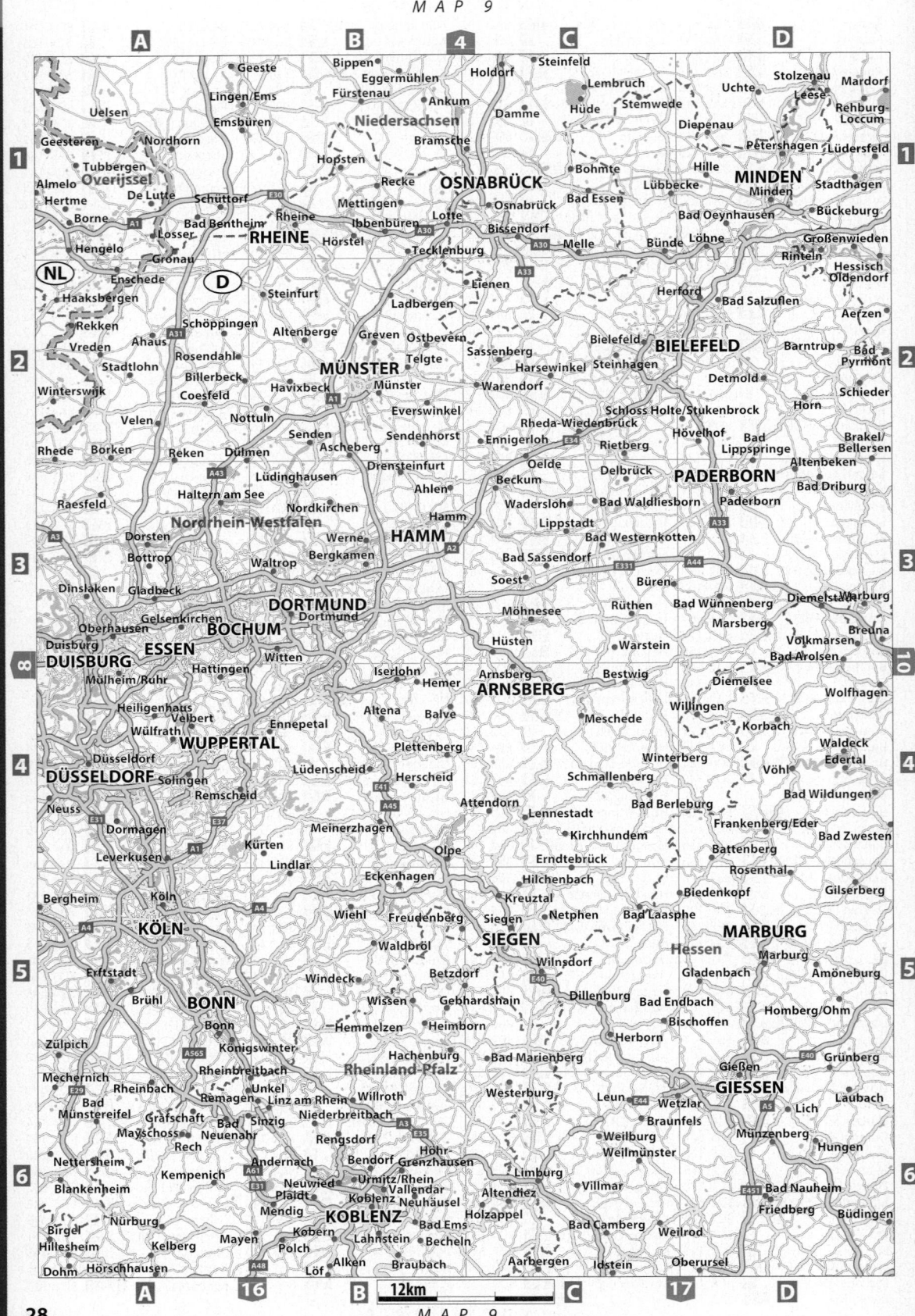

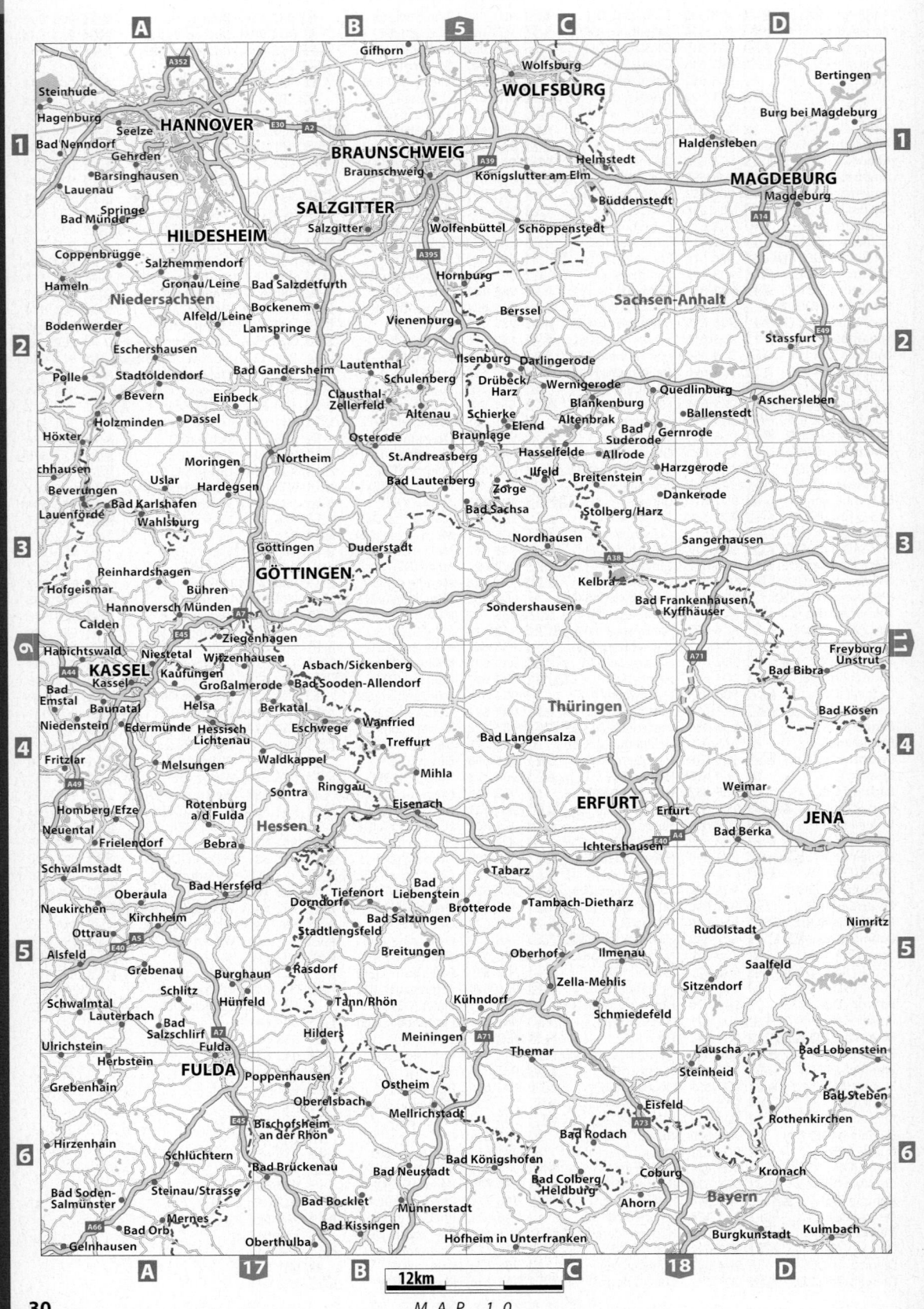

A　　B　　6　　C　　D

1

Brandemburg
Werder Havel
Kloster Lehnin
E30
A2
E55
A10

Storkow/Mark
Bad Saarow

1

Luckenwalde

Brandenburg

Sachsen-Anhalt
E36
Lübbenau
Burg/Spreewald
COTTBUS
Kolkwitz

DESSAU-
ROSSLAU
Coswig/Anhalt
Wörlitz
Lutherstadt Wittenberg
A15
2

Dessau-Roßlau
Oranienbaum-
Wörlitz
Bergwitz
Klein-Ossnig
Altdöbern

Prettin
A13
Dollenchen

Bitterfeld
Senftenberg
Brieske
Geierswalde
Elsterheide

E49
Bad Düben

Brachwitz
Halle/Saale
E51

3

HALLE
(SAALE)
A9

Merseburg
LEIPZIG
Leipzig
A14
Rothersdorf
Diesbar-Seusslitz

Dresden
Dresden
E55
Heidenau
Königstein

Braunsbedra
A38

10
Weissenfels
Bad Lausick

Naumburg/Saale
Selb
Zeitz
Königsfeld-Stollsdorf
Sachsen
A17

4

E49
Freiberg

Bad Klosterlausnitz

Reichenbach
A4
E40
CHEMNITZ
Dennheritz
Amtsberg
Hermsdorf
USTI NAD
LABEM
E442

Thüringen
ZWICKAU
D
Seiffen

Neustadt/Orla
Marienberg

Linda
Zeulenroda
A72
Grünhain
11a
A15
E36

5

E441

Schleiz
E51
A9
PLAUEN
Breitenbrunn
Oberwiesenthal
E442
Bad Muskau
D
CZ

Zwota
E49
CZ
Sachsen
Biehain

6

Naila
Hof/Saale
Adorf
Bad Elster
A4
E40
GÖRLITZ

Bayern
KARLOVY
VARY

Kirchenlamitz
E49
Ebersbach/Sachsen

Marktleuthen
Thierstein
Hohenberg/Eger
Arzberg
E48
E48
E49
Zittau

A　　18　　B　　C　　12km　　D

A B C D

1

Pleumeur-Bodou
Plestin-les-Grèves
Trégastel
Trébeurden
Pleubian
Ploubazlanec
St.Pol-de-Léon
Roscoff
Santec
Plougasnou
Tréguier
Lézardrieux
Paimpol
Plouézec
Kerlouan
Guissény
Plouguerneau
Portsall
Goulven
Le Folgoët
Plouescat
Penzé
Carantec
La Roche-Derrien
Plouha
Plévenon
Lannilis
Bourg-Blanc
Plabennec
St.Derrien
Landivisiau
Morlaix
Binic
Erquy
Fréhel
Lampaul-Plouarzel
Plouarzel
Ploumoguer
Locmaria-Plouzané
St.Renan
Landerneau
St.Servais
Guimiliau
St.Thégonnec
Belle-Isle-en-Terre
Guingamp
Pléneuf-Val-André
St.Cast-le-Guildo

2

Le Conquet
Brest
La Martyre
Bretagne
Trémuson
Plérin
Planguenoual
Plougonvelin
BREST
Plougastel-Daoulas
Commana
Callac
Hillion
Camaret-sur-Mer
Saint-Rivoal
Huelgoat
Quintin
Meslin
Bretagne
Crozon
Poullaouen
Lanfains
St.Carreuc
Carhaix-Plouguer
Moncontour
Plonévez-Porzay
Maël-Carhaix
Rostrenen
Saint-Gelven
Plessala
Cléden-Cap-Sizun
Châteauneuf-du-Faou
Cléden-Poher
Glomel
Saint Aignan
Loudéac
Plémet

3

Plogoff
Primelin
Pont-Croix
Locronan
Guiscriff
Priziac
Le Croisty
Silfiac
Noyal-Pontivy
Neulliac
Saint Gérand
St.Barnabé
La Chèze
Audierne
Landudec
Scaër
Le Faouët
Guern
Pontivy
Gueltas
Rohan
Mauron
QUIMPER
Kernascléden
Pluméliau
Réguiny
Les Forges
Paimpont
Pont-l'Abbé
Plomelin
Combrit
Concarneau
Le Trévoux
Quimperlé
Baud
Radenac
Josselin
Campénéac
Penmarch
Trégunc
Pont-Aven
Clohars-Carnoët
LORIENT
Locminé
Loctudy
Fouesnant
Névez
Moëlan-sur-Mer
Guidel
Languidic

13

Larmor-Plage
Locmiquelic
Brech
Locqueltas
Sérent
Malestroit
Ploemeur
Port-Louis
Riantec
Plouhinec
Auray
VANNES
St.Guyomard
Elven
Rochefort-en-Terre
Gâvres
Étel
Belz
Crac'h
Sulniac
Berric
Malansac
Erdeven
Vannes
Theix

4

Carnac
Locmariaquer
Arzon
Larmor-Baden
Brillac
Damgan
Marzan
La Roche-Bernard
Saint-Pierre-Quiberon
St.Gildas-de-Rhuys
Sarzeau
Penvins
Arzal
Quiberon
Pénestin
Assérac
Piriac-sur-Mer
La Turballe
Guérande
Le Croisic
La Baule
SAINT-NAZAIRE
Batz-sur-Mer
Saint-Nazaire

5

St.Michel-Chef-Chef
La Plaine-sur-Mer
Préfailles
Pornic
La Bernerie-en-Retz
Noirmoutier-en-l'Ile
Bouin
Beauvoir-sur-Mer
Notre-Dame-de-Monts
St.Jean-de-Monts
Pays de la Loire
St.Hilaire de Riez

6

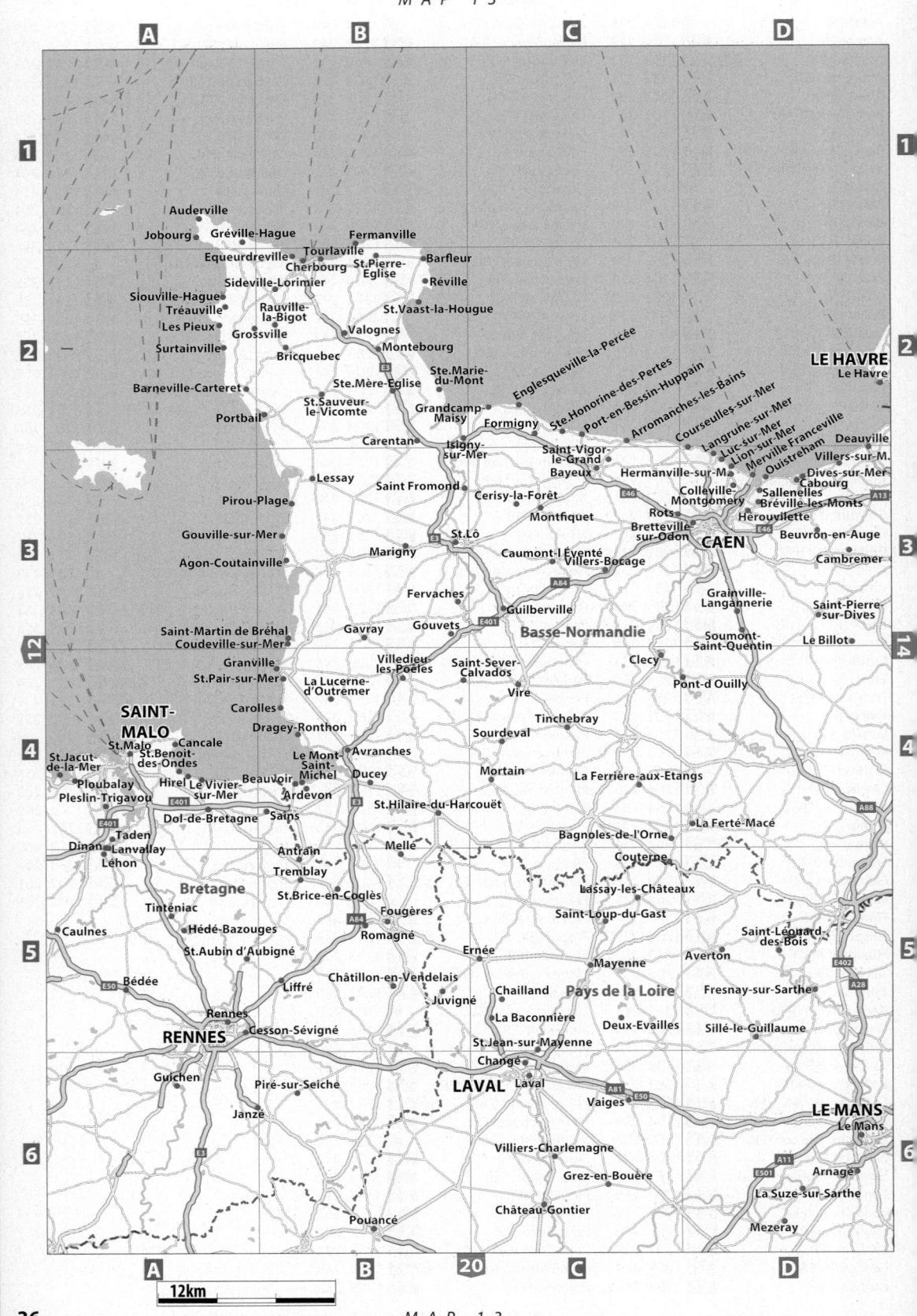

MAP 13

A   B   C   D

Auderville
Jobourg   Gréville-Hague
Equeurdreville   Tourlaville   Fermanville
Cherbourg   St.Pierre-Eglise   Barfleur
Sideville-Lorimier   Réville
Siouville-Hague   Rauville-la-Bigot
Tréauville   St.Vaast-la-Hougue
Les Pieux   Grossville   Valognes
Surtainville   Bricquebec   Montebourg

LE HAVRE
Le Havre

Barneville-Carteret   Ste.Marie-du-Mont
St.Sauveur-le-Vicomte   Englesqueville-la-Percée
Portbail   Ste.Mère-Eglise   Ste.Honorine-des-Pertes
Grandcamp-Maisy   Port-en-Bessin-Huppain   Arromanches-les-Bains
Formigny   Courseulles-sur-Mer   Langrune-sur-Mer   Luc-sur-Mer
Carentan   Isigny-sur-Mer   Saint-Vigor-le-Grand   Lion-sur-Mer   Merville Franceville
Lessay   Bayeux   Hermanville-sur-M.   Ouistreham   Deauville
Villers-sur-M.
Saint Fromond   Cerisy-la-Forêt   Colleville-Montgomery   Sallenelles   Dives-sur-Mer
Pirou-Plage   Montfiquet   Rots   Bréville-les-Monts   Cabourg
St.Lô   Bretteville-sur-Odon   Hérouvillette   Beuvron-en-Auge
Gouville-sur-Mer   CAEN
Agon-Coutainville   Marigny   Caumont-l'Éventé   Cambremer
Villers-Bocage
Grainville-Langannerie
Fervaches   Saint-Pierre-sur-Dives
Saint-Martin de Bréhal   Guilberville   Le Billot
Coudeville-sur-Mer   Gavray   Gouvets   Basse-Normandie   Soumont-Saint-Quentin
Granville   Villedieu-les-Poêles   Saint-Sever-Calvados   Clecy
St.Pair-sur-Mer   La Lucerne-d'Outremer   Pont-d'Ouilly
Carolles   Vire
Dragey-Ronthon   Tinchebray
SAINT-MALO   Sourdeval
St.Malo   Cancale   Le Mont-Saint-Michel   Avranches   Mortain   La Ferrière-aux-Etangs
St.Jacut-de-la-Mer   St.Benoit-des-Ondes   Ducey
Ploubalay   Hirel   Le Vivier-sur-Mer   Beauvoir
Pleslin-Trigavou   Ardevon   St.Hilaire-du-Harcouët
Dol-de-Bretagne   Sains   La Ferté-Macé
Taden   Bagnoles-de-l'Orne
Dinan   Lanvallay   Antrain   Melle   Couterne
Léhon   Tremblay   Lassay-les-Châteaux
Bretagne   St.Brice-en-Coglès   Saint-Loup-du-Gast
Tinténiac   Fougères   Saint-Léonard-des-Bois
Caulnes   Hédé-Bazouges   Romagné   Averton
St.Aubin d'Aubigné   Ernée   Mayenne   Fresnay-sur-Sarthe
Bédée   Liffré   Châtillon-en-Vendelais   Chailland   Pays de la Loire   Sillé-le-Guillaume
Juvigné   La Baconnière   Deux-Evailles
RENNES   Cesson-Sévigné   St.Jean-sur-Mayenne
Guichen   Changé   LE MANS
Piré-sur-Seiche   LAVAL   Laval   Le Mans
Janzé   Vaiges
Villiers-Charlemagne   Arnage
Grez-en-Bouère   La Suze-sur-Sarthe
Pouancé   Château-Gontier   Mezeray

12   14
1   2   3   4   5   6

A   B   20   C   D

12km

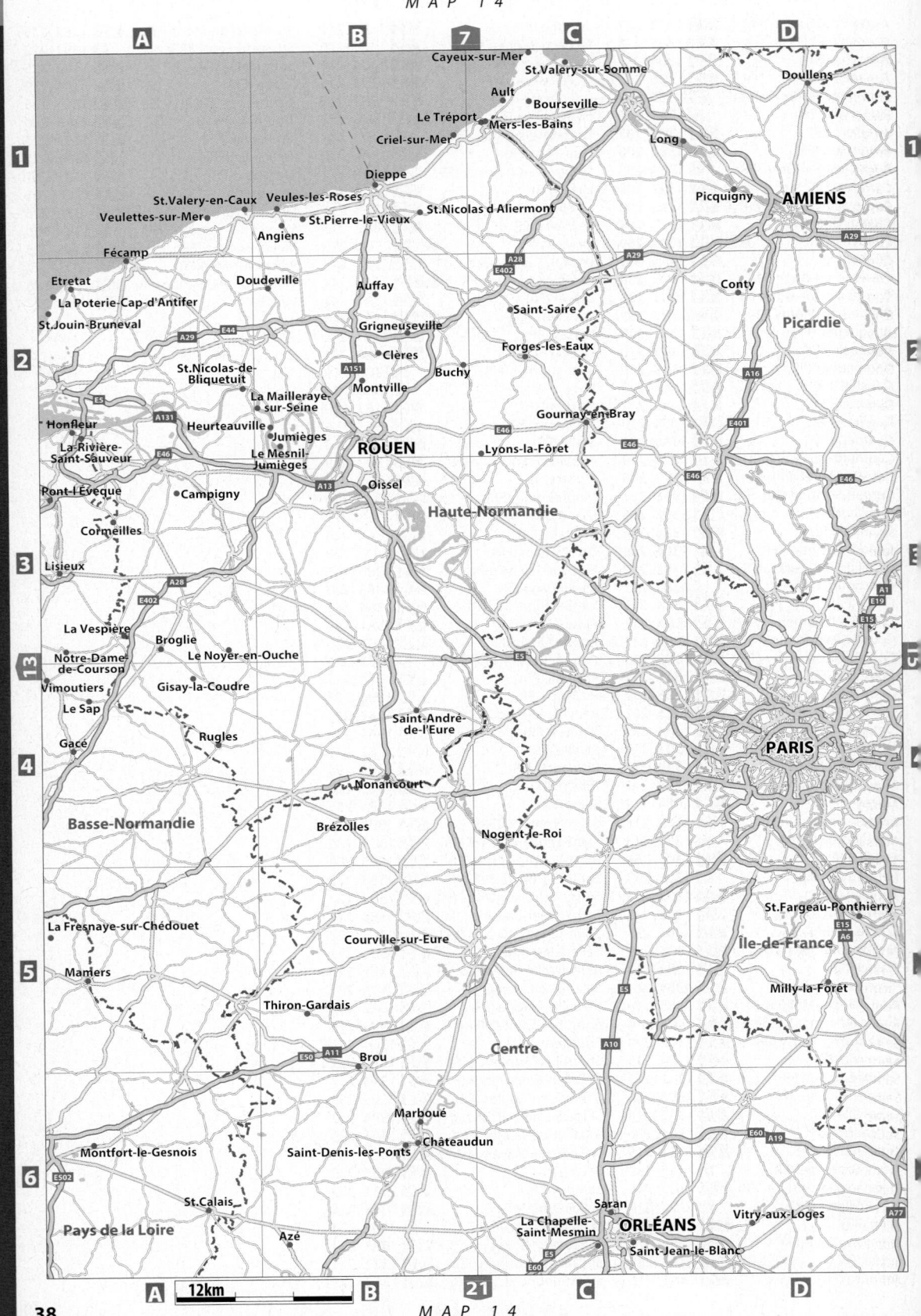

Cayeux-sur-Mer
St.Valéry-sur-Somme
Doullens
Ault
Bourseville
Le Tréport
Mers-les-Bains
Criel-sur-Mer
Long
AMIENS
Dieppe
Picquigny
St.Valéry-en-Caux
Veules-les-Roses
Veulettes-sur-Mer
St.Pierre-le-Vieux
St.Nicolas d'Aliermont
Angiens
Conty
Fécamp
Picardie
Etretat
Doudeville
Auffay
La Poterie-Cap-d'Antifer
St.Jouin-Bruneval
Saint-Saire
A29 A44
Grigneuseville
St.Nicolas-de-Bliquetuit
Clères
Forges-les-Eaux
Buchy
A151
La Mailleraye-sur-Seine
Montville
Honfleur
Heurteauville
Gournay-en-Bray
La-Rivière-Saint-Sauveur
Jumièges
E46
Lyons-la-Fôret
Le Mesnil-Jumièges
ROUEN
Pont-l'Évêque
Campigny
Oissel
A13
Haute-Normandie
Cormeilles
Lisieux
A28
E402
La Vespière
Broglie
Le Noyer-en-Ouche
Notre-Dame-de-Courson
Gisay-la-Coudre
Vimoutiers
Saint-André-de-l'Eure
Le Sap
Rugles
Gacé
Nonancourt
Basse-Normandie
Brézolles
Nogent-le-Roi
La Fresnaye-sur-Chédouet
St.Fargeau-Ponthierry
Courville-sur-Eure
Île-de-France
Mamers
Milly-la-Fôret
Thiron-Gardais
Centre
Brou
A10
Marboué
Châteaudun
A19
Montfort-le-Gesnois
Saint-Denis-les-Ponts
E502
St.Calais
Saran
Vitry-aux-Loges
Pays de la Loire
Azé
La Chapelle-Saint-Mesmin
ORLÉANS
Saint-Jean-le-Blanc
PARIS

12km

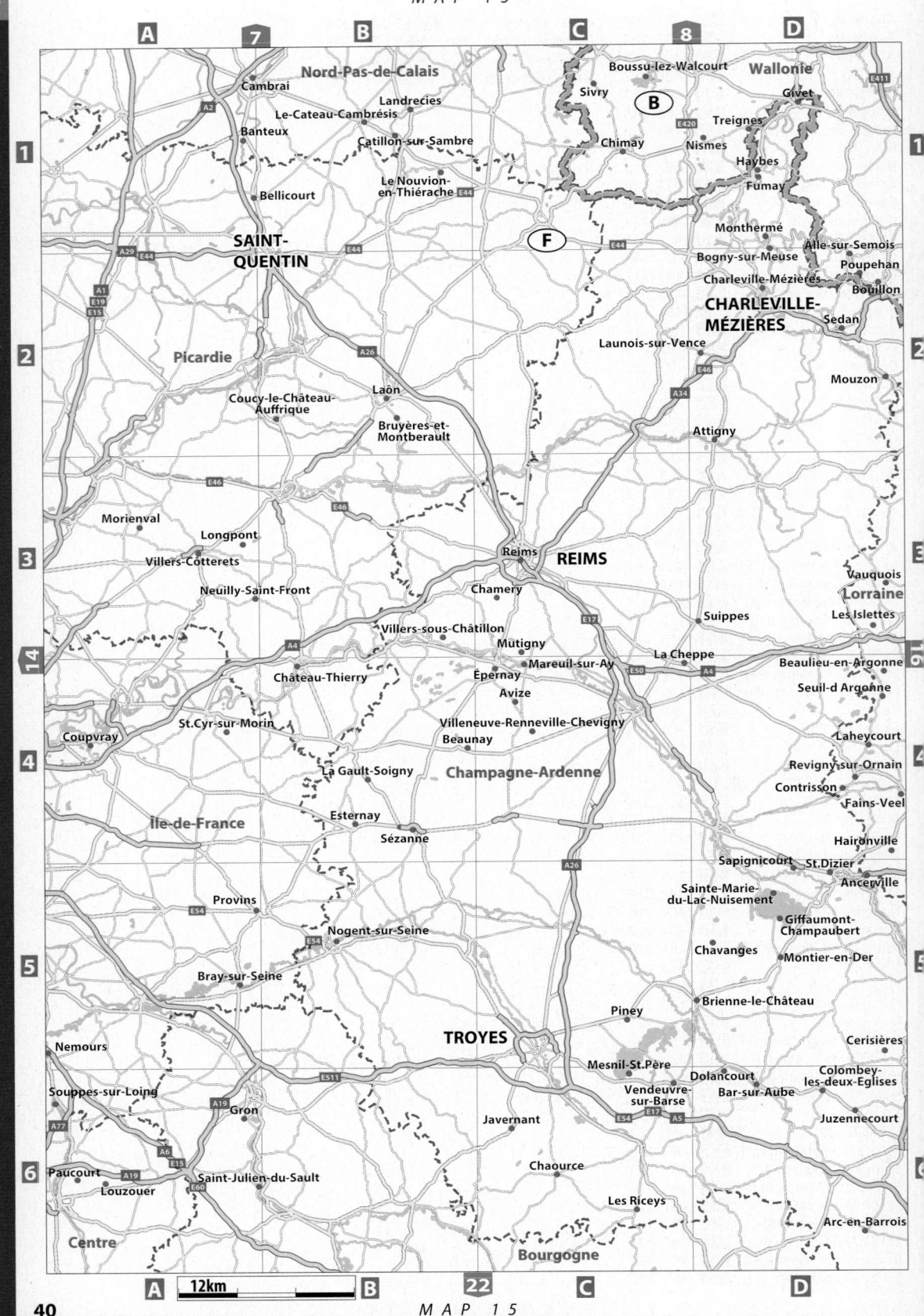

A 7 B C 8 D

Nord-Pas-de-Calais

Boussu-lez-Walcourt **Wallonie**

Cambrai

Sivry Givet

Landrecies Treignes

Le-Cateau-Cambrésis E420

Banteux Chimay Nismes Haybes

Catillon-sur-Sambre Fumay

Bellicourt Le Nouvion-
en-Thiérache E44

Monthermé Alle-sur-Semois

**SAINT-
QUENTIN** E44 Bogny-sur-Meuse Poupehan

F Charleville-Mézières Bouillon

**CHARLEVILLE-
MÉZIÈRES** Sedan

Picardie Launois-sur-Vence

Mouzon

Coucy-le-Château-
Auffrique Laon

Bruyères-et-
Montberault Attigny

Morienval

Longpont Vauquois

Villers-Cotterets **Lorraine**

Neuilly-Saint-Front Reims **REIMS** Les Islettes

Chamery

Suippes Beaulieu-en-Argonne

Villers-sous-Châtillon La Cheppe

Mutigny Seuil-d'Argonne

Château-Thierry Mareuil-sur-Ay

Épernay Laheycourt

Avize Revigny-sur-Ornain

St.Cyr-sur-Morin Villeneuve-Renneville-Chevigny Contrisson

Coupvray Beaunay Fains-Veel

La Gault-Soigny **Champagne-Ardenne** Haironville

Île-de-France Sapignicourt St.Dizier

Esternay Anceville

Sézanne Sainte-Marie-
du-Lac-Nuisement

Provins Giffaumont-
Champaubert

Nogent-sur-Seine Chavanges Montier-en-Der

Bray-sur-Seine

Piney Brienne-le-Château

Nemours Cerisières

Mesnil-St.Père Colombey-
les-deux-Eglises

Souppes-sur-Loing Dolancourt

Gron Vendeuvre-
sur-Barse Bar-sur-Aube

Javernant Juzennecourt

Paucourt Chaource

Louzouer **TROYES**

Saint-Julien-du-Sault Les Riceys Arc-en-Barrois

Centre **Bourgogne**

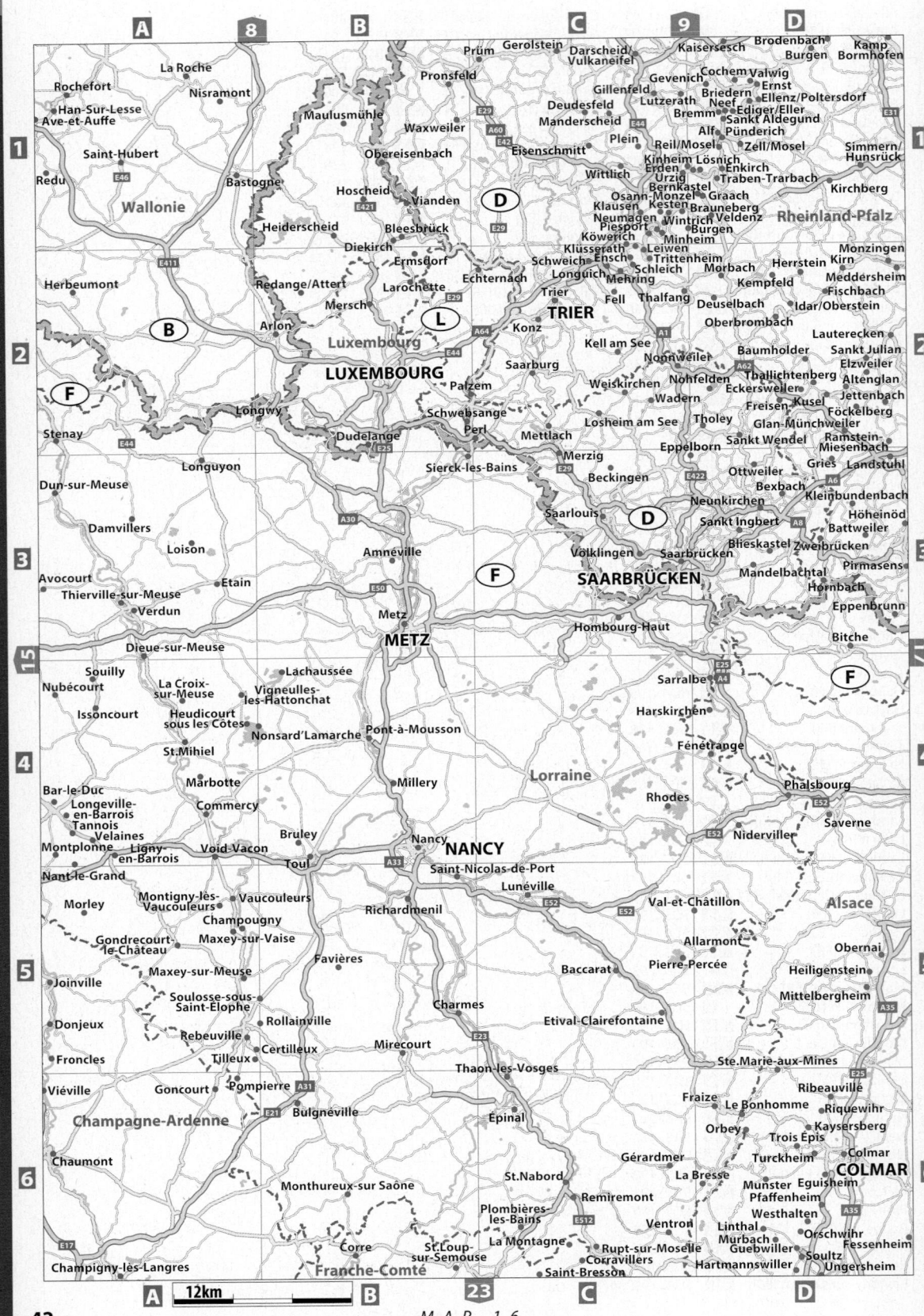

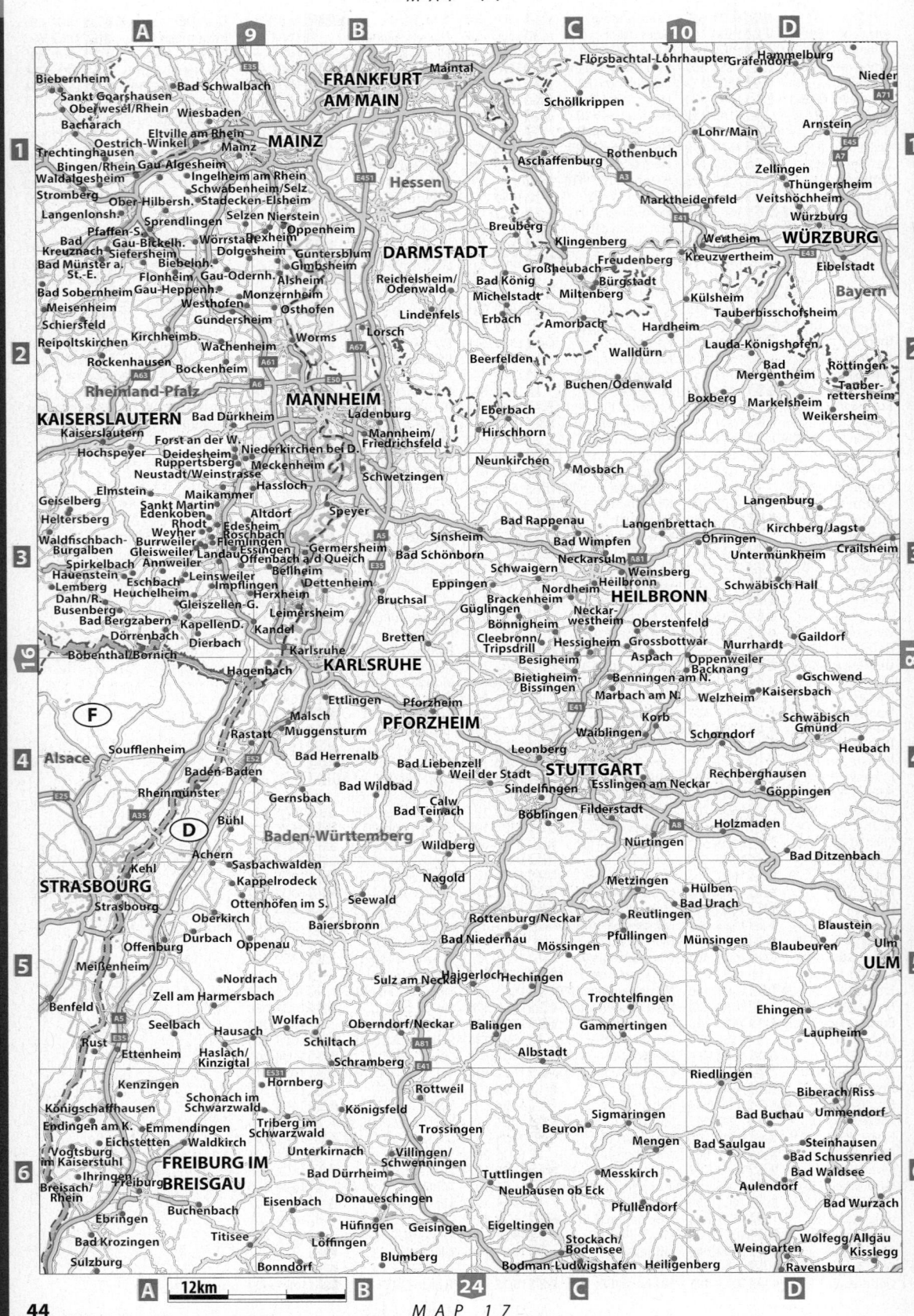

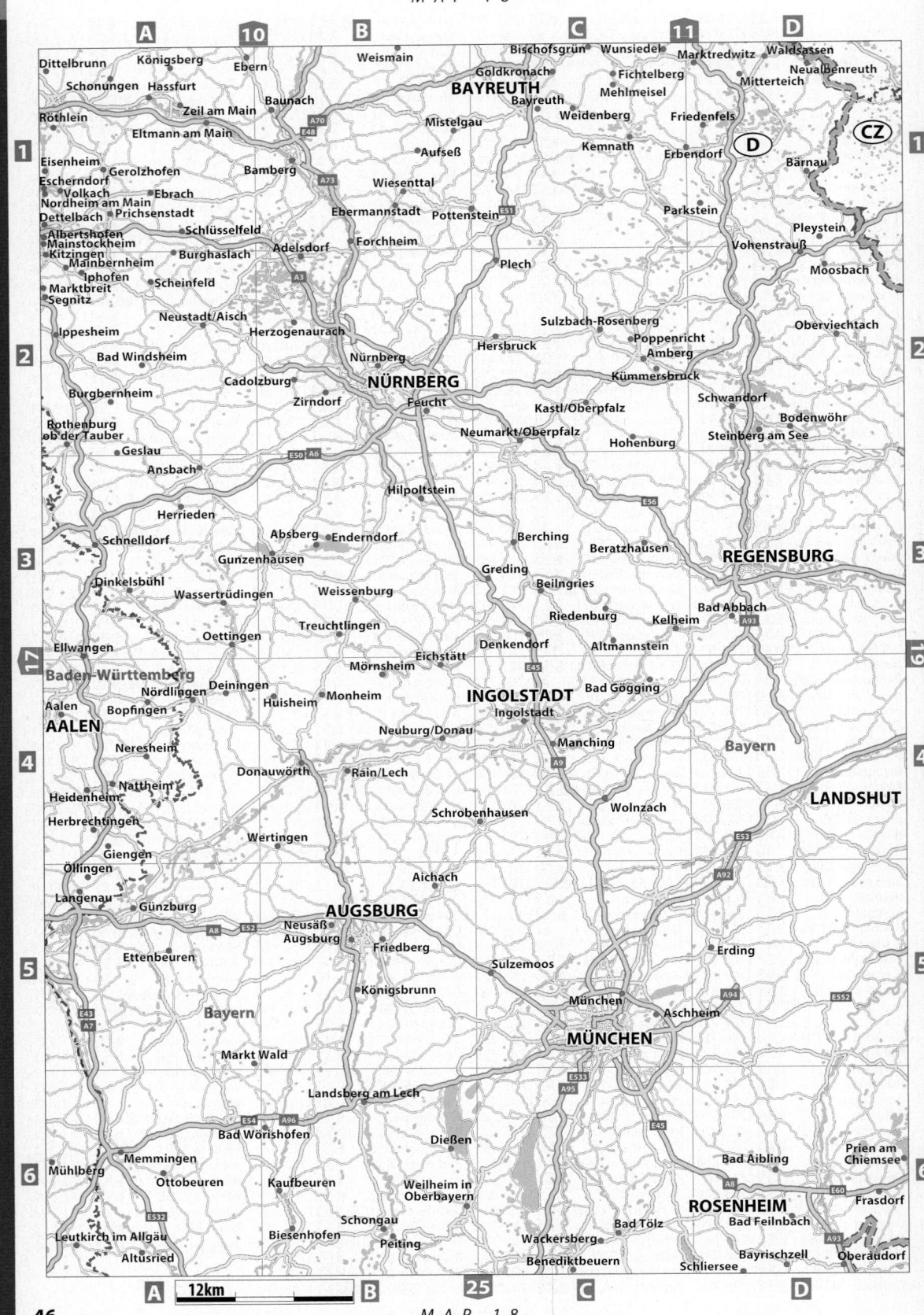

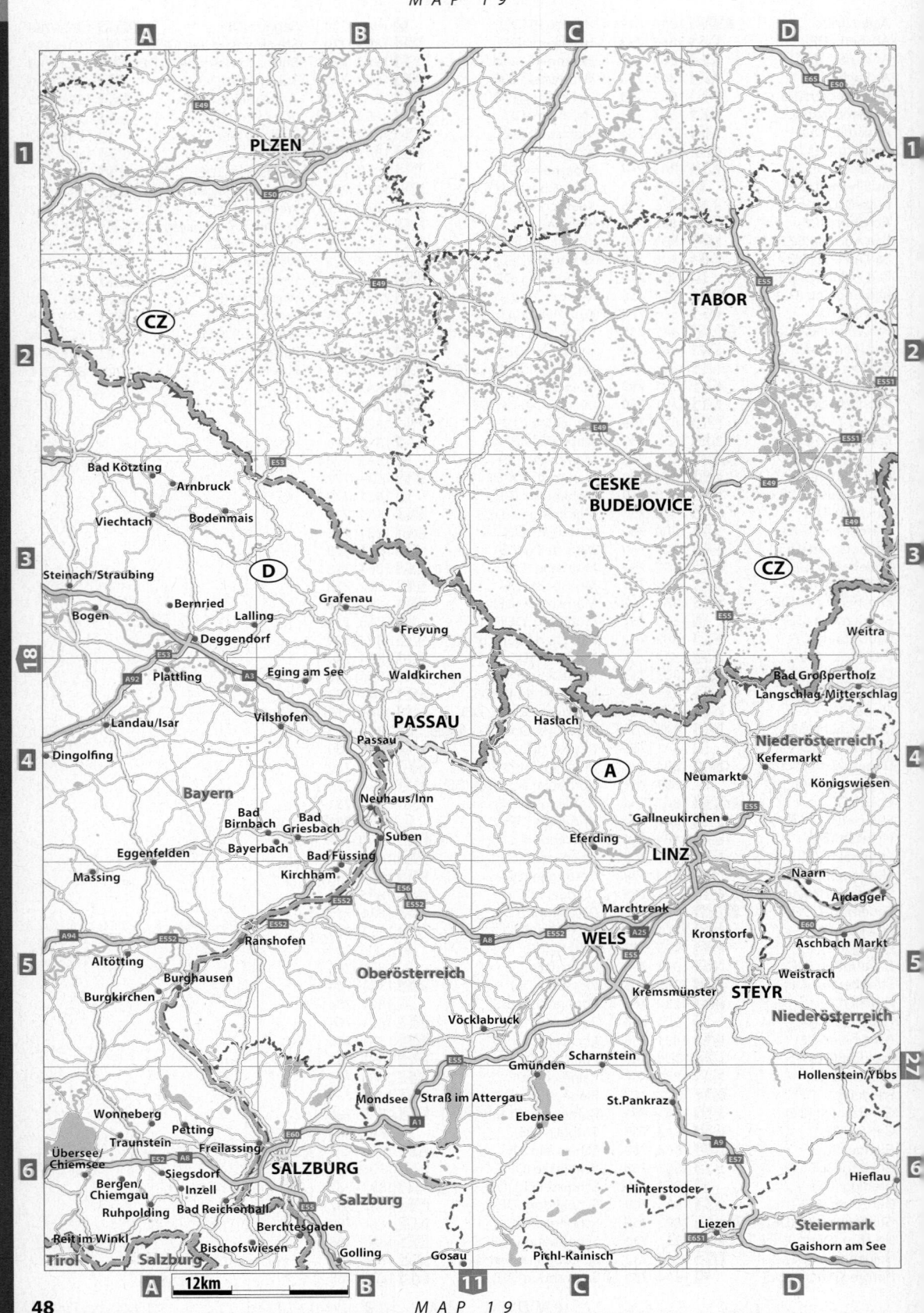

MAP 19

A B C D

PLZEN

CZ

TABOR

CESKE
BUDEJOVICE

CZ

Bad Kötzting
Arnbruck
Viechtach
Bodenmais

D

Steinach/Straubing
Bernried
Lalling
Bogen
Deggendorf

Grafenau

Freyung

Weitra

Plattling
A92

Eging am See

Waldkirchen

Bad Großpertholz
Langschlag Mitterschlag

Landau/Isar
Vilshofen

PASSAU

Haslach

Niederösterreich

Dingolfing

Passau

Kefermarkt

A

Neumarkt

Königswiesen

Bayern

Neuhaus/Inn

Gallneukirchen

Bad
Birnbach
Bad
Griesbach
Bayerbach
Bad Füssing

Suben

Eferding

LINZ

Naarn

Ardagger

Eggenfelden

Massing

Kirchham

Marchtrenk

Aschbach Markt

Ranshofen

WELS
A25

Kronstorf

Altötting
Burghausen

Oberösterreich

Weistrach

Burgkirchen

A94

Kremsmünster

STEYR

Niederösterreich

Vöcklabruck

Hollenstein/Ybbs

Gmünden

Scharnstein

St.Pankraz

Wonneberg
Petting
Traunstein
Freilassing

Mondsee

Straß im Attergau

Ebensee

Übersee/
Chiemsee

Siegsdorf

Inzell

SALZBURG

Salzburg

Bergen/
Chiemgau

Hinterstoder

Hieflau

Ruhpolding

Bad Reichenhall

Liezen

Steiermark

Reit im Winkl

Berchtesgaden

Tirol

Bischofswiesen

Golling

Salzburg

Gosau

Pichl-Kainisch

Gaishorn am See

A 12km B 11 C D

A B 13 C D

1 1

2 2

3 3

21

4 4

5 5

6 6

Redon
Combree
Segré
Chenillé-Changé
Bazouges-sur-le-Loir
Durtal
La Flèche
Guenrouet
Jans
Nozay
Angrie
Gené
Feneu
Briollay
Villeveque
Baugé
Blain
Riaille
St.Mars-La-Jaille
Montreuil-Juigné
Pellouailles-les-Vignes
Le Guédéniau
Nort-sur-Erdre
ANGERS
Angers
A85
Champtocé-sur-L.
Bouchemaine
La Daguenière
Gizeux
Viaud
Liré
St.Georges-sur-L.
St.Saturnin-sur-L.
St.Rémy-la-Varenne
Champtoceaux
Chalonnes-sur-L.
Brissac-Quincé
Longué-Jumelles
Nantes
La Chapelle-Saint-Florent
St.Aubin-de-Luigné
Faye d'Anjou
St.Clément-des-Levées
Chênehutte-Trèves-Cunault
Rouans
Rablay sur Layon
Saulgé l'Hôpital
Restigné
St.Hilaire-de-Chaléons
La Poitevinière
Chanzeaux
Chavagnes les Eaux
Dampierre-sur-Loire
Chouzé-sur-Loir
Valanjou
Martigné-Briand
Parnay
Montsoreau
Le Pallet
Mouzillon
Aubigné-sur-Layon
Le Coudray Macouard
Turquant
Avoine
Bourgneuf-en-Retz
Maisdon-sur-Sèvre
Doué-la-Fontaine
St.Cyr-en-Bourg
Fontevraud-l'Abbaye
St.Philbert-de-Grandlieu
Vihiers
Concourson-sur-Layon
Le Vaudelnay
Montreuil-Bellay
Centre
La Séguinière
Le Puy-Notre-Dame
Champigny-sur-Veude
Pays de la Loire
CHOLET
Loudun
Challans
Chavagne-en-Paillers
Chambretaud
Les Epesses
Thouars
St.Gilles-Croix-de-Vie
Mesnard-la-Barotière
Les Herbiers
St.Amand-sur-Sèvre
Angliers
Le Poiré-sur-Vie
Belleville-sur-Vie
Vendrennes
St.Michel-Mont-Mercure
Bressuire
Venansault
Les Essarts
Pouzauges
LA ROCHE-SUR-YON
Brétignolles-sur-Mer
La Meilleraie-Tillay
Thurageau
Olonne-sur-Mer
La Roche-sur-Yon
Chantonnay
Parthenay
Vasles
POITIERS
Les Sables-d'Olonne
Moutiers-sur-le-Lay
Vouvant
Château-d'Olonne
Mervent
Foussais-Payré
Talmont-Saint-Hilaire
Jard-sur-Mer
St.Vincent-sur-Jard
Luçon
Fontenay-le-Comte
Pamproux
Château-Larcher
Saint-Michel-en-l'Herm
Fontaines
Bougon
La Tranche-sur-Mer
Chaille-les-Marais
Maillezais
Benet
Coulon
Niort
La-Mothe-St.Héray
Gencay
L'Aiguillon-sur-Mer
Maillé
Arçais
Magné
NIORT
Chey
Couhé
Les Portes-en-Ré
St.Clément-des-Baleines
St.Hilaire-la-Palud
Lezay
Le Bois-Plage-en-Ré
Saint-Martin-de-Ré
Mauzé-sur-le-Mignon
Celles-sur-Belle
Rivedoux-Plage
LA ROCHELLE
La Rochelle
Poitou-Charentes
Aytré
Angoulins
St.Germain-de-Marencennes
Sauzé-Vaussais
Châtelaillon-Plage
Chef-Boutonne
Londigny
St.Denis-d'Oléron
Fouras
Saint Laurent de la Prée
Aulnay
Ruffec
La Brée-les-Bains
Port-des-Barques
Saint-Pierre-d'Oléron
Rochefort
Tonnay-Charente
Dolus-d'Oléron
Soubise
St.Jean-d'Angély
Aigre
Le Château d'Oléron
Echillais
Le Grand Village Plage
St.Agnant
St.Trojan-les-Bains
Hiers-Brouage
Cellefrouin
Bourcefranc-le-Chapus
Marennes
St.Pochaire
Poitou-Charentes
Agris
Nieulle-sur-Seudre
Saint Césaire
Cherves-Richemont
Rouillac
Les Mathes/La Palmyre
Saintes
St.Yrieix-sur-Charente
La Rochefoucauld
Saujon
Cognac
Meschers-sur-Gironde
Genté
Nersac
Le Verdon-sur-Mer
Pons
Segonzac
La Couronne
Soulac-sur-Mer
Mortagne-sur-Gironde
Criteuil la Magdeleine
St.Génis-de-Saintonge
Montalivet-les-Bains
Valeyrac
Jonzac
Aquitaine
Aquitaine

A 12km B 28 C D

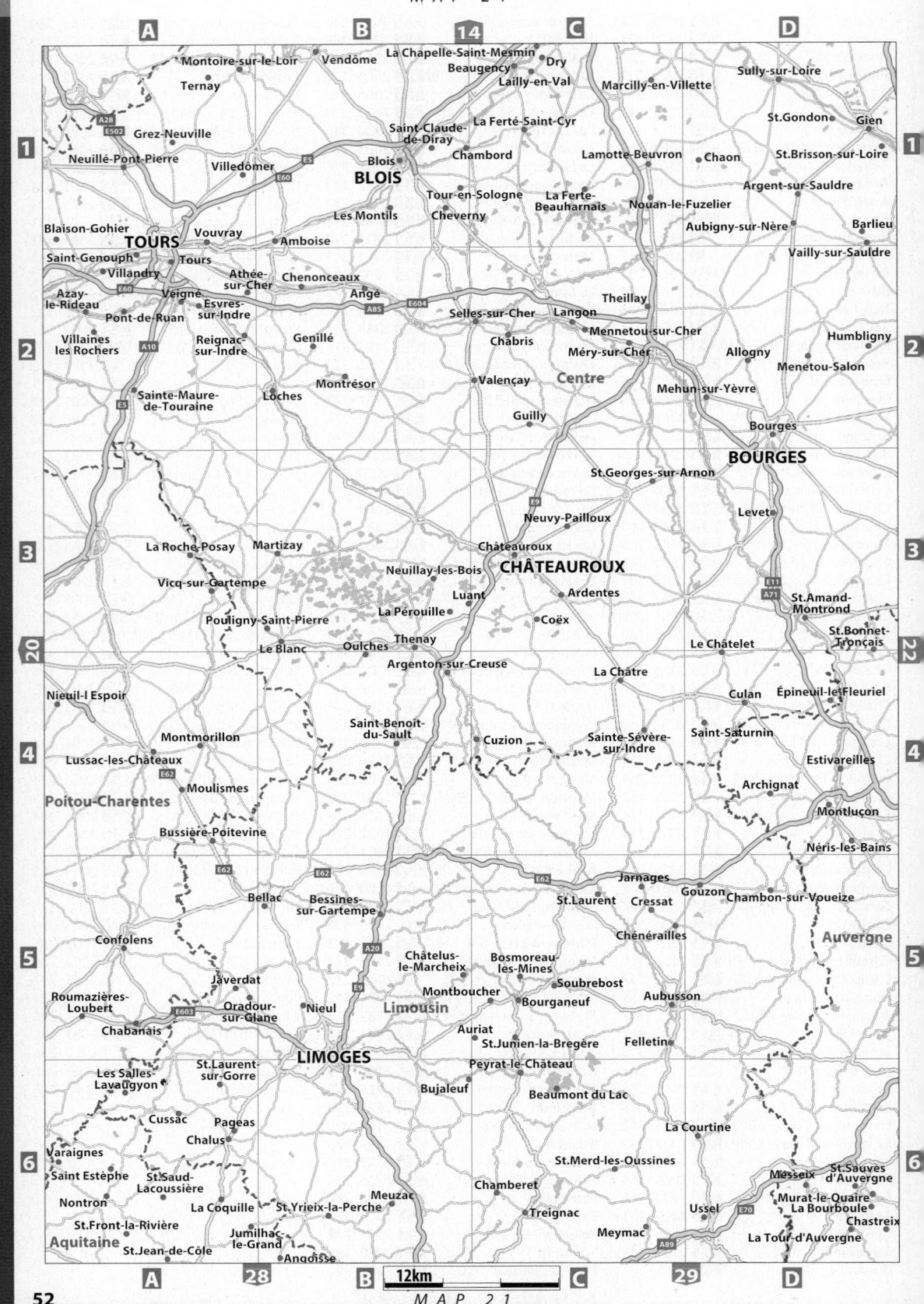

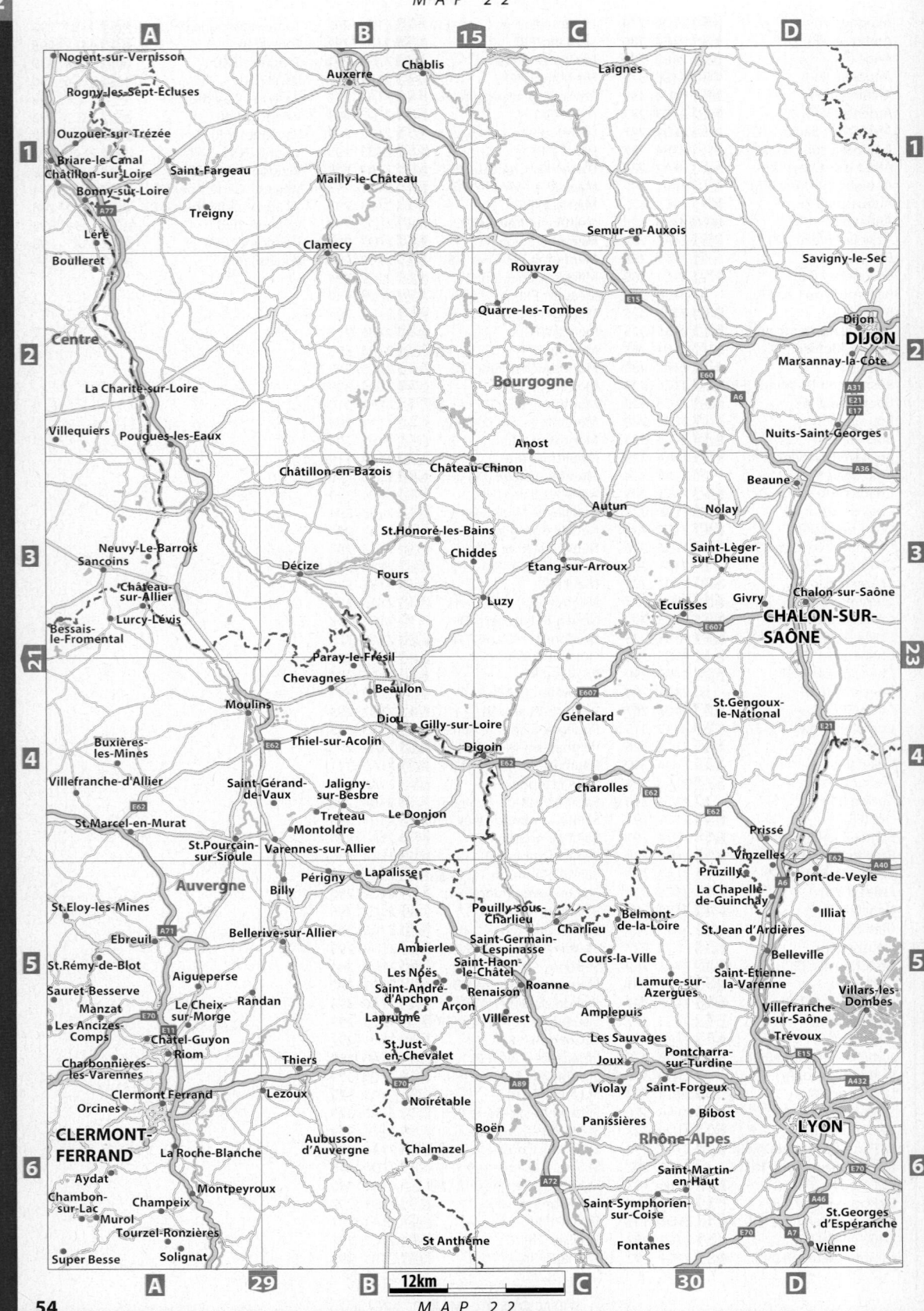

Nogent-sur-Vernisson

Rogny-les-Sept-Écluses

Chablis

Auxerre

Laignes

Ouzouer-sur-Trézée

1

Briare-le-Canal
Châtillon-sur-Loire   Saint-Fargeau

Mailly-le-Château

Savigny-le-Sec

Bonny-sur-Loire

A77

Léré   Treigny

Dijon

DIJON

Boulleret

Clamecy

Semur-en-Auxois

E15

Centre

Marsannay-la-Côte

2

Rouvray

A6   A31

E21
E17

La Charité-sur-Loire

Bourgogne

Quarre-les-Tombes

E60

Villequiers   Pougues-les-Eaux

Anost

Nuits-Saint-Georges

A36

Châtillon-en-Bazois   Château-Chinon

Beaune

Autun   Nolay

Neuvy-Le-Barrois   St.Honoré-les-Bains

Saint-Léger-
sur-Dheune

3

Sancoins

Décize   Chiddes

Château-
sur-Allier   Fours   Étang-sur-Arroux

Chalon-sur-Saône

21

Lurcy-Lévis   Luzy

Écuisses   Givry

CHALON-SUR-

Bessais-
le-Fromental

E607   **SAÔNE**

Paray-le-Frésil

Chevagnes   Beaulon

St.Gengoux-
le-National

4

Moulins   Diou

Gilly-sur-Loire   E607

Génelard

Thiel-sur-Acolin   Digoin

Buxières-
les-Mines   E62

E21

Villefranche-d'Allier   Saint-Gérand-
de-Vaux   Jaligny-
sur-Besbre   Charolles   E62

St.Marcel-en-Murat   E62   Treteau   E62

St.Pourçain-
sur-Sioule   Montoldre   Le Donjon   Prissé

Varennes-sur-Allier   Vinzelles   E62   A40

Auvergne   Périgny   Lapalisse   Pruzilly   Pont-de-Veyle

Billy   La Chapelle-
de-Guinchay   A6

St.Eloy-les-Mines   Pouilly-sous-
Charlieu   Belmont-
de-la-Loire   St.Jean d'Ardières   Illiat

Ebreuil   Bellerive-sur-Allier   Charlieu   Belleville

A71   Ambierle   Saint-Germain-
Lespinasse   Cours-la-Ville

5

St.Rémy-de-Blot   Les Noës   Saint-Haon-
le-Châtel   Lamure-sur-
Azergues   Saint-Étienne-
la-Varenne   Villars-les-
Dombes

Sauret-Besserve   Aigueperse   Saint-André-
d'Apchon   Renaison   Roanne

Manzat   Randan   Arçon   Amplepuis   Villefranche-
sur-Saône

Le Cheix-
sur-Morge   Laprugne   Villerest   Les Sauvages   Trévoux

Les Ancizes-
Comps   E70   Joux   Pontcharra-
sur-Turdine   E15

E11   Châtel-Guyon

Charbonnières-
les-Varennes   Riom   Thiers   St.Just-
en-Chevalet   Saint-Forgeux   A432

Lezoux   Violay   **LYON**

Rhône-Alpes   Bibost

Clermont Ferrand   E70   Panissières

Orcines   Noirétable

CLERMONT-   Boën   Saint-Martin-
en-Haut

6

FERRAND   La Roche-Blanche   Aubusson-
d'Auvergne   A89   St.Georges
d'Espérance

Aydat   Montpeyroux   Chalmazel   Saint-Symphorien-
sur-Coise   A46

Chambon-
sur-Lac   Champeix   A72   A7

Murol   St Anthème   Fontanes   Vienne

Super Besse   Tourzel-Ronzières   Solignat

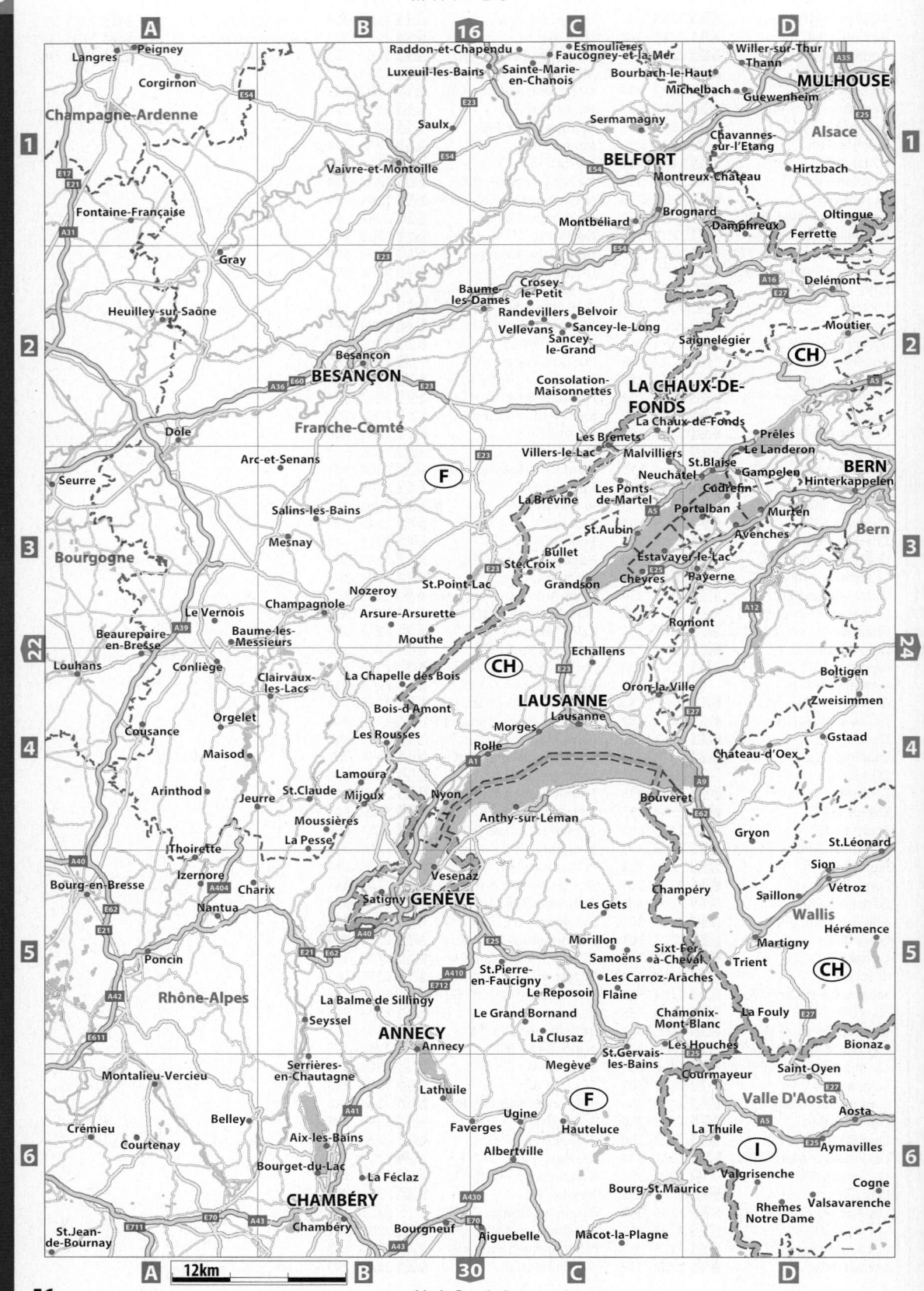

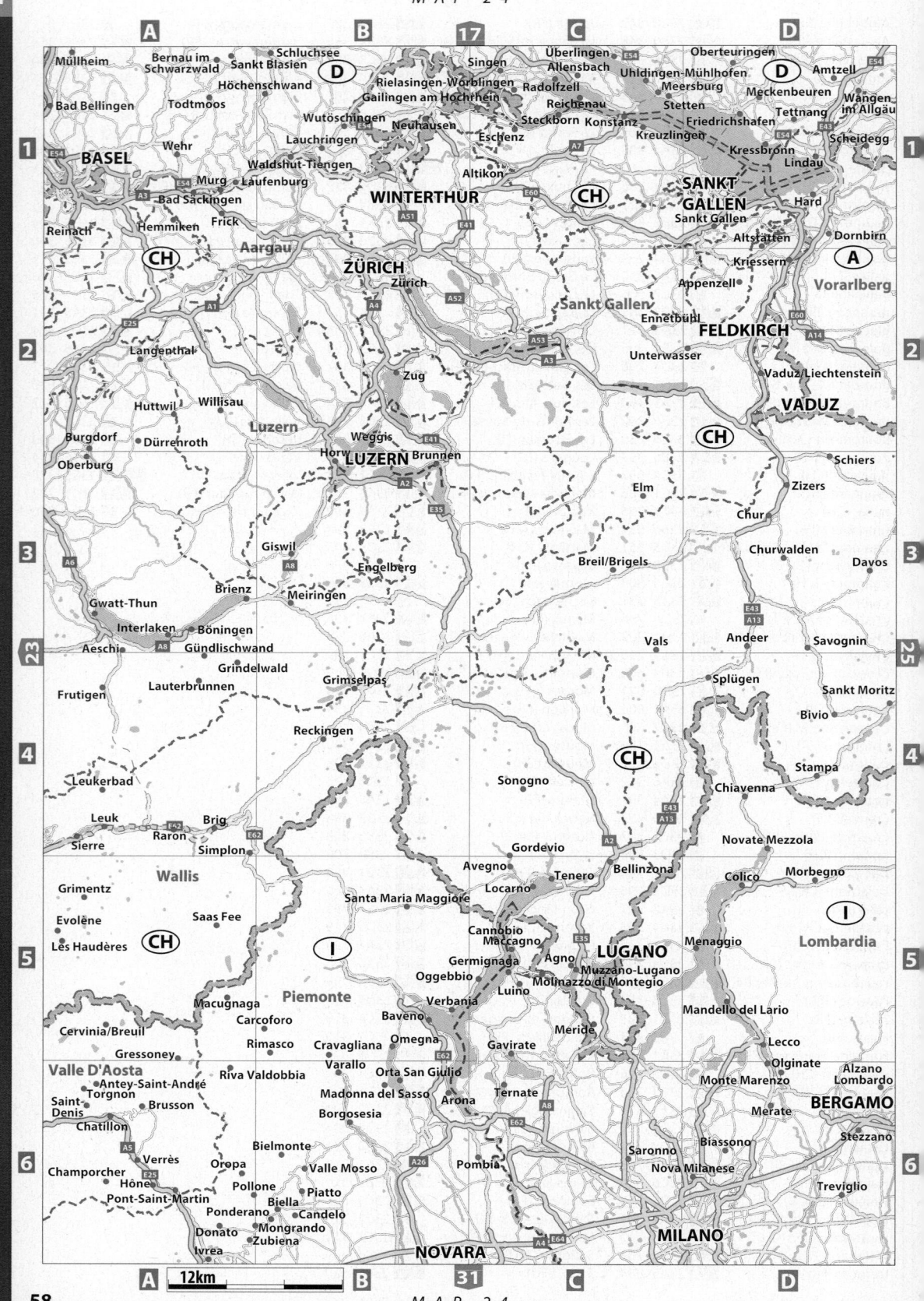

MAP 25

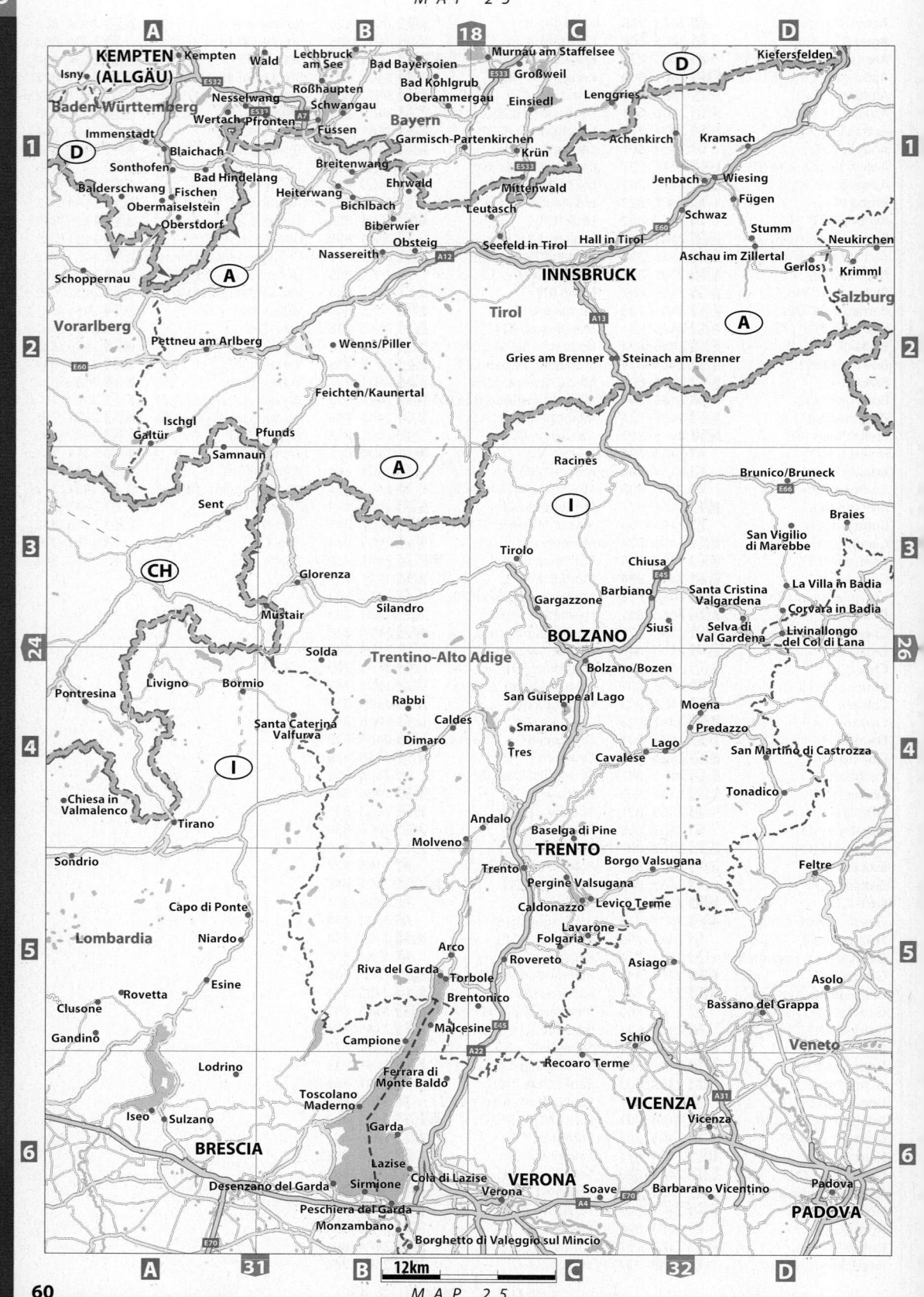

A

B

18

C

D

KEMPTEN (ALLGÄU)
Isny
Kempten
Wald
Lechbruck am See
Bad Bayersoien
Murnau am Staffelsee
Kiefersfelden
D
Baden-Württemberg
Nesselwang
Roßhaupten
Bad Kohlgrub
Großweil
Schwangau
Oberammergau
Lenggries
Immenstadt
Wertach Pfronten
Füssen
Bayern
Blaichach
Breitenwang
Garmisch-Partenkirchen
Krün
Achenkirch
Kramsach
D
Sonthofen
Ehrwald
Krün
Jenbach
Wiesing
Balderschwang
Bad Hindelang
Heiterwang
Mittenwald
Fügen
Obermaiselstein
Fischen
Bichlbach
Leutasch
Schwaz
Oberstdorf
Biberwier
Stumm
Obsteig
Seefeld in Tirol
Hall in Tirol
Neukirchen
Schoppernau
Nassereith
A12
INNSBRUCK
Aschau im Zillertal
Gerlos
Krimml
A
Salzburg
Vorarlberg
Tirol
Pettneu am Arlberg
Wenns/Piller
A13
E60
Gries am Brenner
Steinach am Brenner
A
Feichten/Kaunertal
A
Ischgl
Galtür
Pfunds
Racines
I
Samnaun
Brunico/Bruneck
E66
Sent
Braies
San Vigilio di Marebbe
CH
Tirolo
Chiusa
E45
Glorenza
Gargazzone
Barbiano
Santa Cristina Valgardena
La Villa in Badia
Mustair
Silandro
Siusi
Corvara in Badia
Solda
Selva di Val Gardena
Livinallongo del Col di Lana
Trentino-Alto Adige
BOLZANO
Pontresina
Livigno
Bormio
Bolzano/Bozen
Rabbi
San Guiseppe al Lago
Moena
Santa Caterina Valfurva
Caldes
Smarano
Predazzo
Chiesa in Valmalenco
Dimaro
Tres
Lago
San Martino di Castrozza
I
Cavalese
Tirano
Tonadico
Andalo
Sondrio
Molveno
Baselga di Pine
TRENTO
Capo di Ponte
Trento
Borgo Valsugana
Feltre
Lombardia
Niardo
Pergine Valsugana
Caldonazzo
Levico Terme
Esine
Arco
Lavarone
Rovetta
Riva del Garda
Folgaria
Asiago
Clusone
Torbole
Rovereto
Asolo
Gandino
Brentonico
Bassano del Grappa
Lodrino
Malcesine
E45
Schio
Recoaro Terme
Veneto
Campione
A22
Ferrara di Monte Baldo
Toscolano Maderno
VICENZA
A31
Garda
Iseo
Sulzano
Vicenza
BRESCIA
Lazise
Cola di Lazise
VERONA
Barbarano Vicentino
Padova
Desenzano del Garda
Sirmione
Verona
Soave
A4
E70
PADOVA
Peschiera del Garda
Monzambano
Borghetto di Valeggio sul Mincio

A

31

B

12km

C

32

D

MAP 26

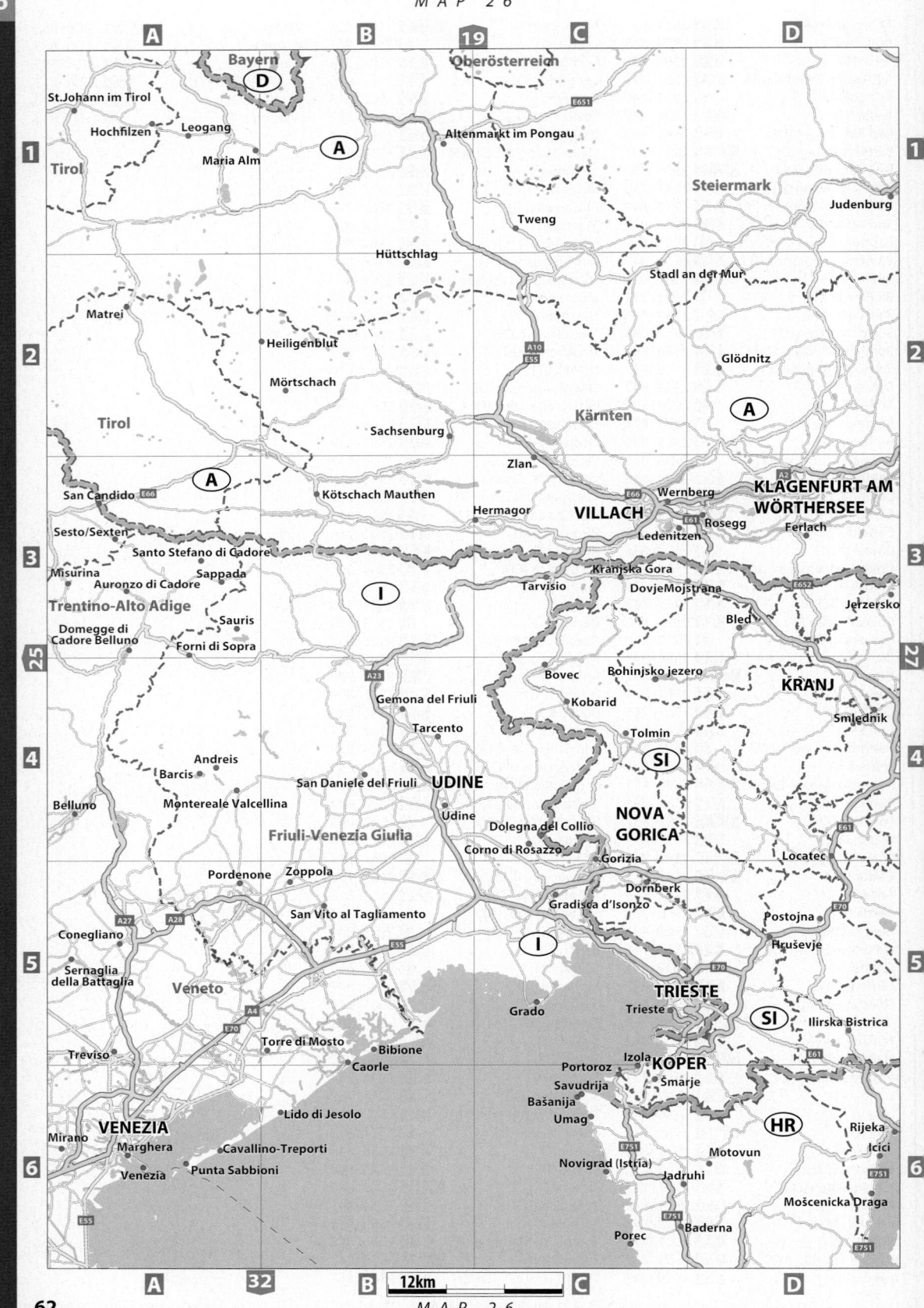

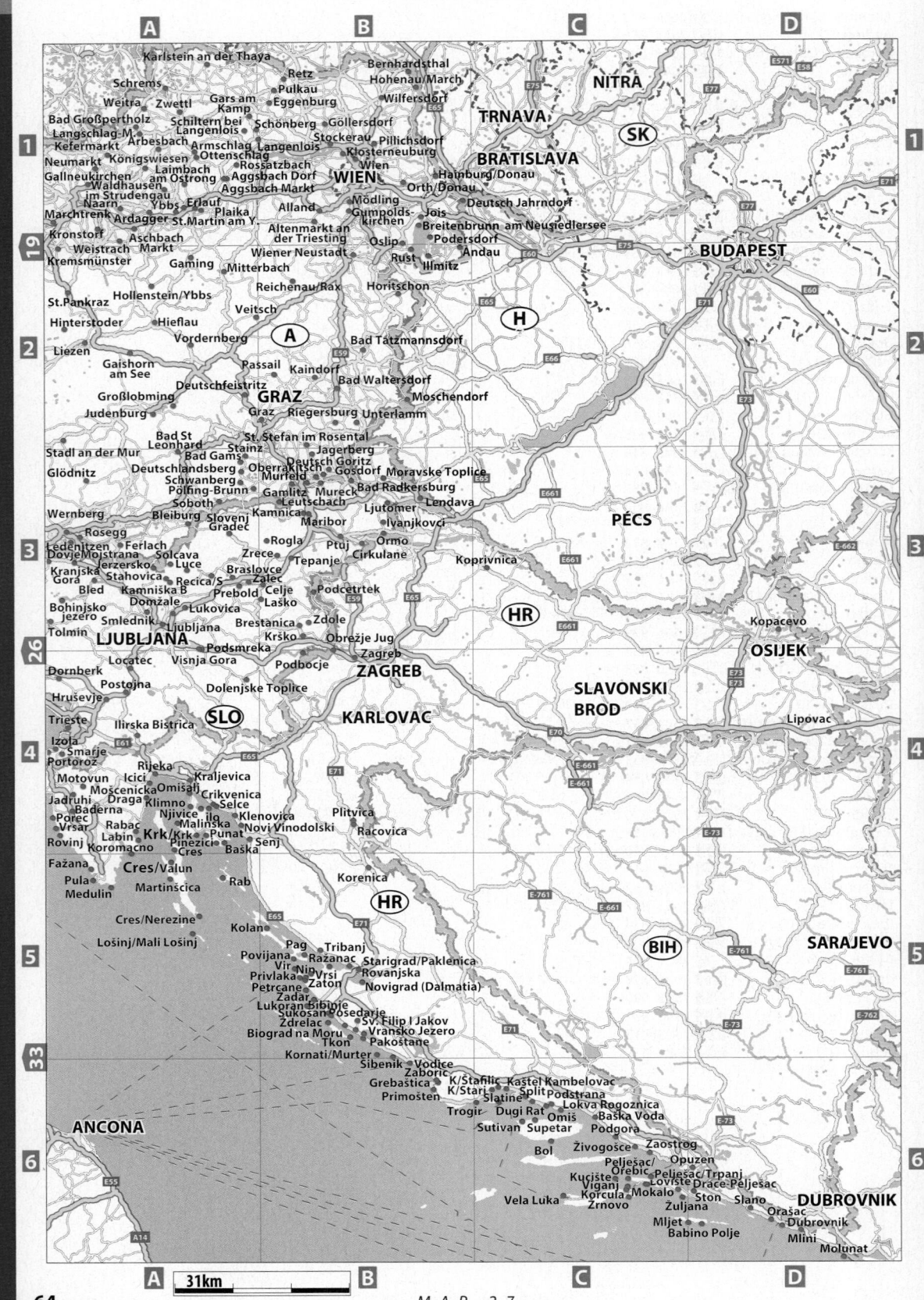

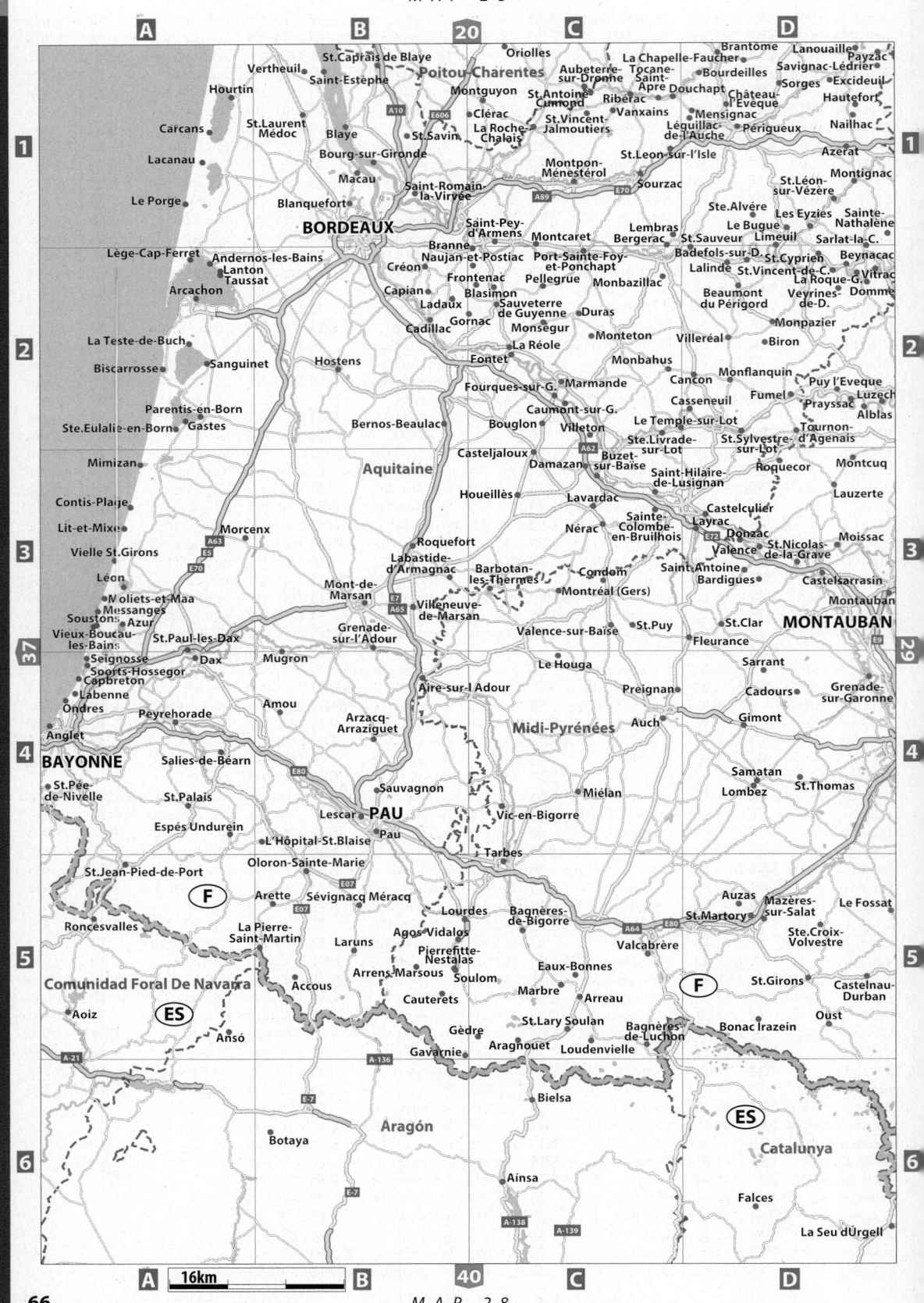

MAP 29

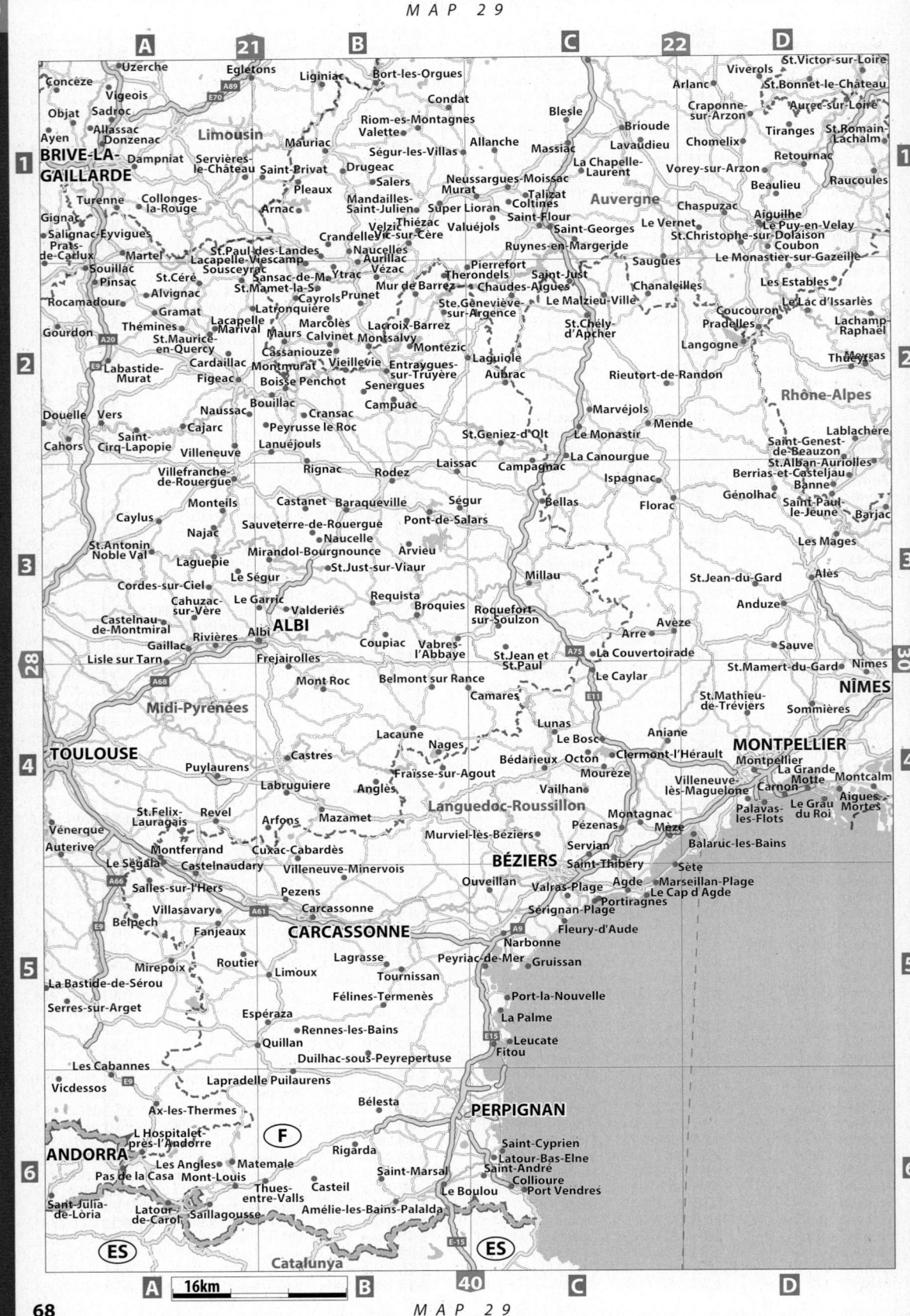

MAP 29

16km

A   **B**   23   **C**   **D**

Reventin-Vaugris
Eyzin-Pinet
Val d'Isère
Ceresole Reale

Planfoy
Le Bessat
Le Cheylas
Allevard
Les Menuires
F

Boulieu-
les-Annonay
St.Désirat
Hauterives
Prapoutel-les-Sept-Laux
St.Jean-de-Maurienne
Chiusa di
San
Michele

St.Bonnet-
le-Froid
Beausemblant
Sassenage
GRENOBLE
Les Karellis
Susa
Chianocco

Lalouvesc
Saint-Romain-d'Ay
Chamrousse
Vaujany
Valloire
Villar Focchiardo
Sestriere

St.Félicien
Gervans
St.Donat-sur-l'Herbasse
Lans-en-Vercors
Alpe d'Huez
Le Monêtier-
les-Bains
Sant Antonino di Susa
Usseaux
Avigliana
Giaveno

Arlebosc
Tournon-sur-Rhône
Villards-de-Lans
Les Deux-Alpes
Névache
Fenestrelle
Pragelato

Saint-
Agrève
Colombier-le-Jeune
Romans-sur-Isère
Saint-Théoffrey
La Salle-les-Alpes
Montgenèvre
Cesana Torinese
Prarostino

Lamastre
St.Romain-de-Lerps
St.Jean-en-Royans
Briançon
Prali

Le Cheylard
Cornas
Vassieux-
en-Vercors
Treffort
Villar Pellice
Bibiana
Cavour

VALENCE
Bouvante
Rhône-Alpes
Gresse-en-Vercors
Puy-Saint-Vincent
St.Véran
Crissolo
Barge

Grane
Die
Chichilianne
Orcières-Merlette
Saint-Crépin
Pontechianale
Sanfront

Privas
Crest
Saillans
Veynes
La Roche-
des-Arnauds
Gap
Chorges
Savines-le-Lac
Le Lauzet-Ubay
Melle
Piemonte

Marsanne
Puy-Saint-Martin
Selonnet
Pra-Loup
Jausiers
Barcelonnette
Pietraporzio

Alba-la-
Romaine
Aubignas
Charols
Provence-Alpes-
Côte d'Azur
Uvernet-Fours
Vinadio

Vogüé
Montélimar
Le Teil
Montbrison-sur-Lez
Laragne-
Montéglin
Allos
St.Etienne-
de-Tinée
Valdieri

Valvignères
St.Thomé
Valréas
Nyons
Colmars-les-Alpes

Balazuc
Vallon-
Pont-
d'Arc
Viviers
Donzère
Les Granges-
Gontards
Clansayes
Visan
Mirabel-aux-Baronnies
Sisteron
Guillaumes
Valberg

St.Rémèze
Bourg-St.A.
St.Paul-Trois-C.
Aiguèze
Bollène
Suze-la-Rousse
St.Restitut
Vaison-la-Romaine
Château-Arnoux-
Saint-Auban
Digne-les-Bains
F

Orgnac
l'Aven
St.Just-
d'Ardèche
Sablet
Montbrun-
les-Bains
St.André-les-Alpes

Bagnols-sur-Cèze
Gigondas
Malaucène
Sault
Banon
Annot
Puget Theniers

Chusclan
Sarrians
Bédoin
Carpentras

Laudun-l'Ardoise
AVIGNON
Malemort-
du-Comtat
Dauphin
Moustiers
Ste.Marie
Castellane

Remoulins
Avignon
Fontaine-
de-Vaucluse
Gordes
Roussillon
St.Michel-
l'Observatoire
Villeneuve
Riez
Les Salles-
sur-Verdon
Caille
Thorenc

Comps
Vallabrègues
Ménerbes
Gréoux-
les-Bains
Ste.Croix-
de-Verdon
Trigance
La Bastide

Beaucaire
Oppède-
le-Vieux
Sénas
Esparron de Verdon
Comps-
sur-Artuby
St.Laurent-du-Var

Bellegarde
Fontvieille
Puyvert
Vinon sur
Verdon
Quinson
Fayence
NICE

St.Gilles
Arles
Pélissanne
St.Paul-
lez-Durance
Bagnols-en-Forêt
CANNES

Stes.Maries-
de-la-Mer
St.Martin-
de-Crau
AIX-EN-
PROVENCE
Sillans-la-Cascade
La Motte

Salin-de-Giraud
Greasque
Provence-Alpes-Côte d'Azur
Le Thoronet
Les Arcs-
sur-Argens
Les Issambres

Port Saint-Louis-
du-Rhône
Sausset-
les-Pins
MARSEILLE
Plan-de-la-Tour
Ste.Maxime

Carro
Carry-le-Rouet
Gémenos
Grimaud
St.Tropez

Marseille
Cuges-les-Pins
Cavalière
Ramatuelle

Six-Fours-les-Plages
La Crau
Hyères
La Londe-les-Maures

St.Mandrier
TOULON

A 16km   **B**   **C**   **D**

MAP 31

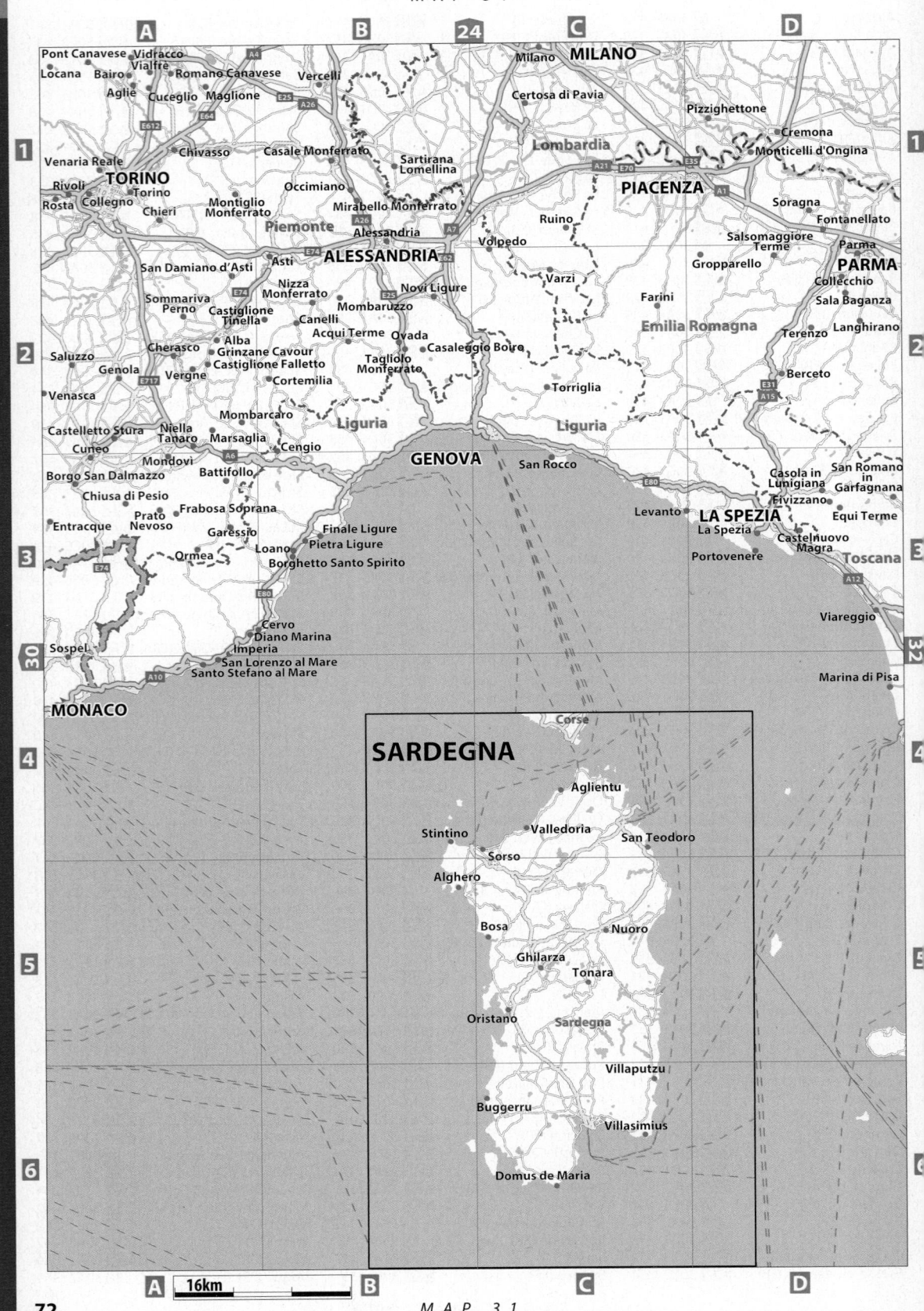

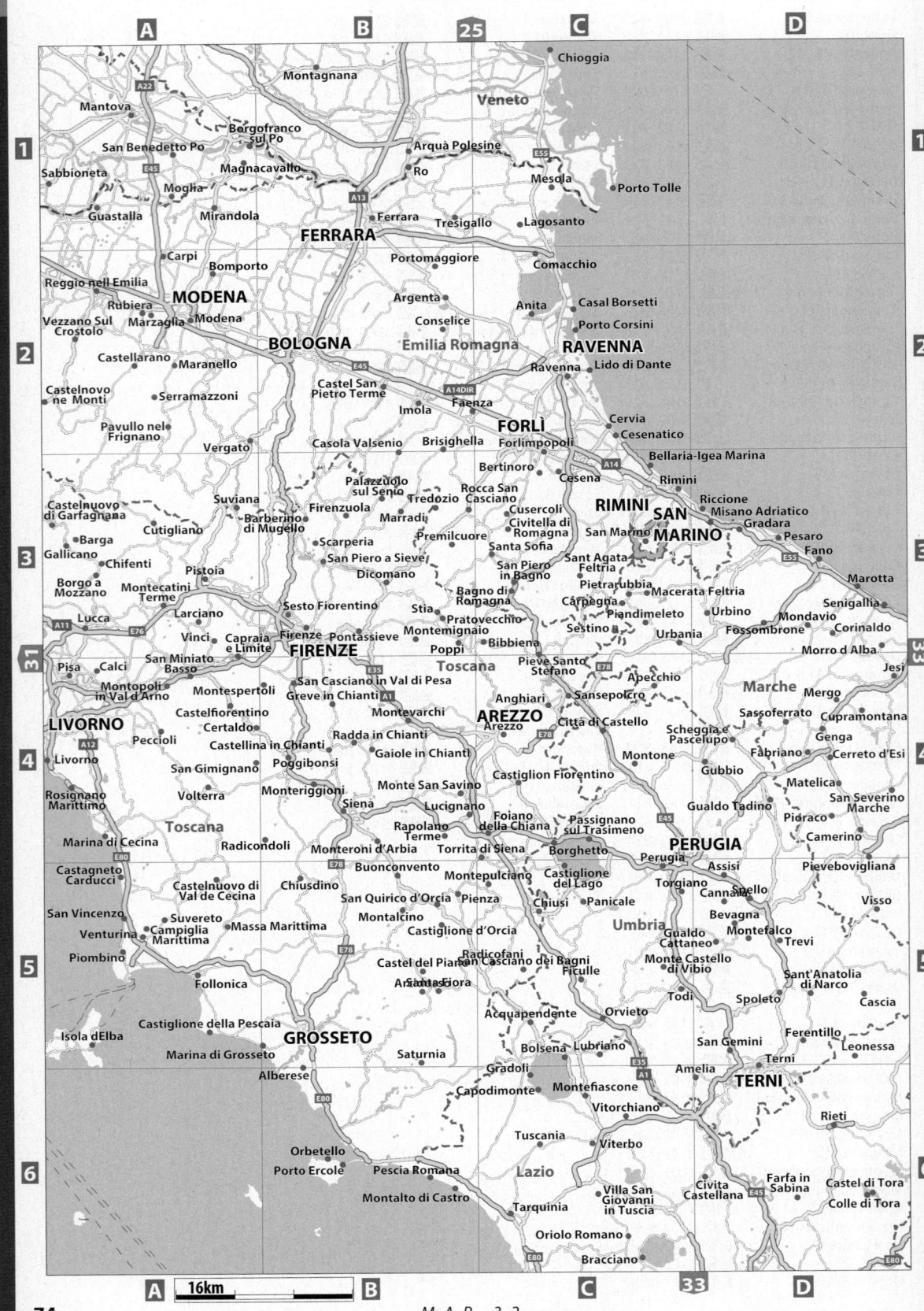

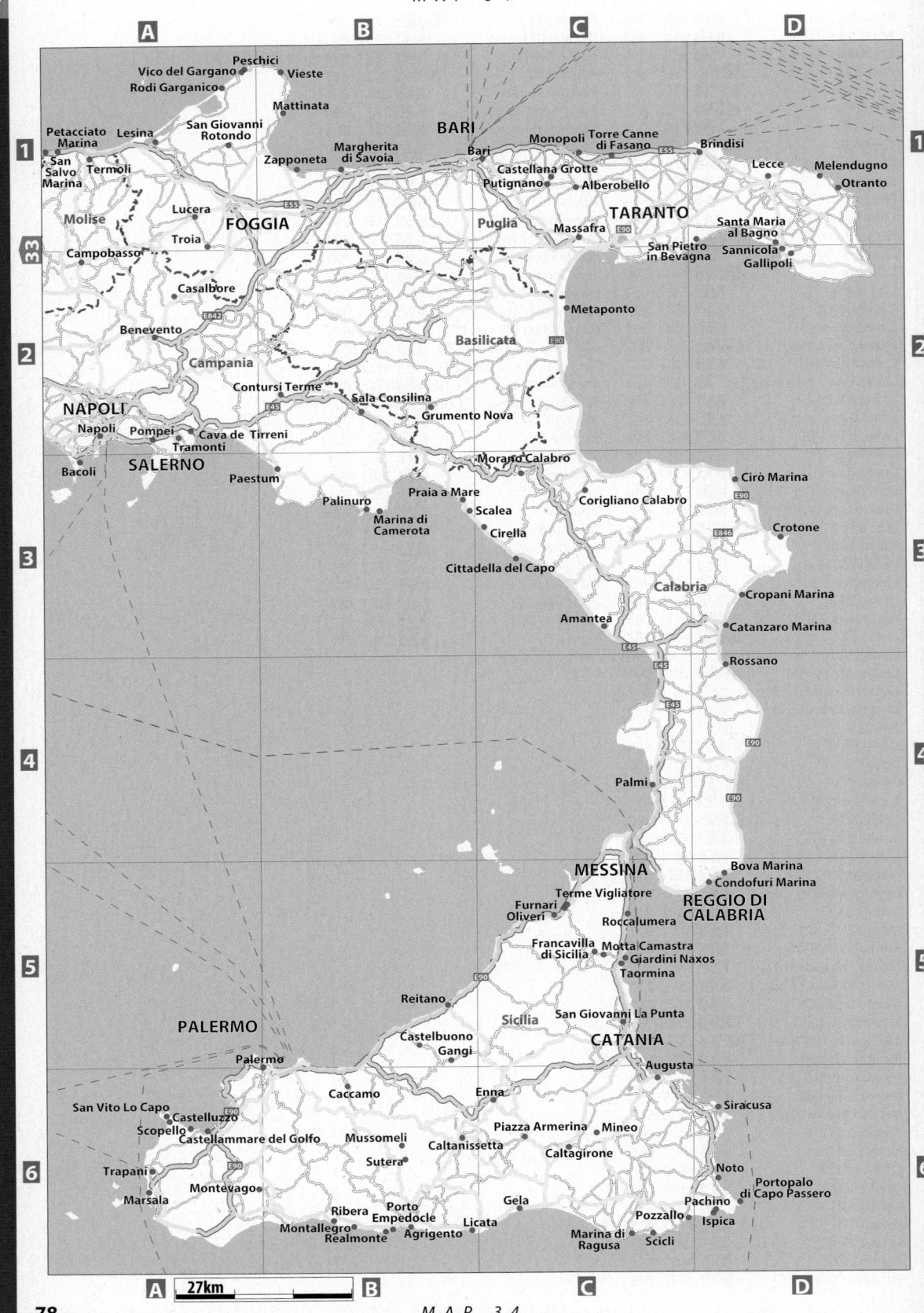

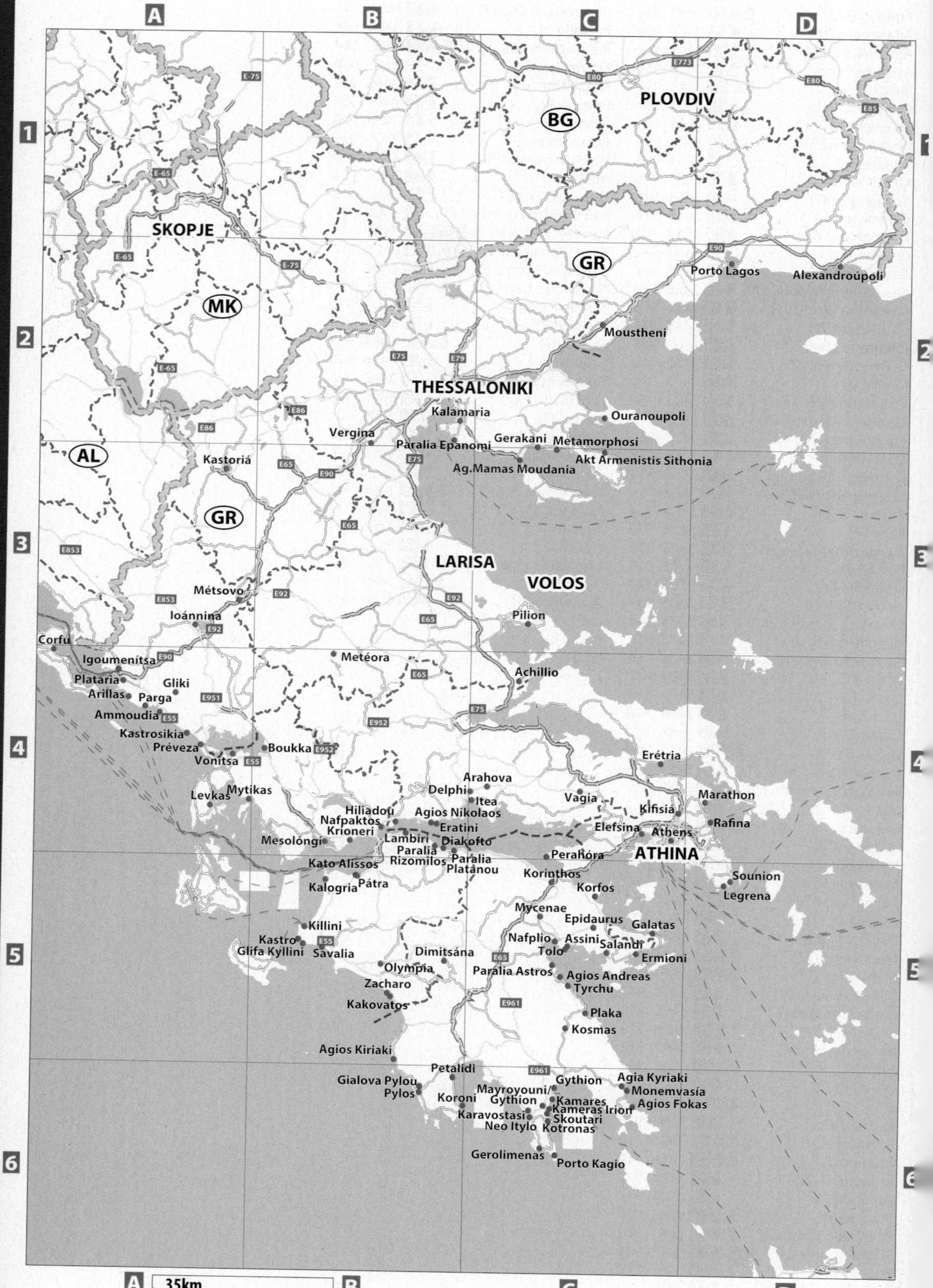

MAP 35

A   **B**   **C**   **D**

1

PLOVDIV

BG

SKOPJE

GR

MK

Porto Lagos

Alexandroúpoli

2

Moustheni

AL

Kalamaria

Ouranoupoli

Vergina

Paralia Epanomi   Gerakani   Metamorphosi

Kastoriá

THESSALONIKI

Akt Armenistis Sithonia

Ag.Mamas Moudania

GR

3

Métsovo

LARISA

VOLOS

Ioánnina

Pilion

Corfu

Metéora

Igoumenitsa

Plataria   Gliki

Achillio

Arillas   Parga

Ammoudia

Kastrosikia

4

Préveza   Boukka

Vonitsa

Erétria

Levkas   Mytikas

Arahova

Marathon

Delphi

Itea   Vagia   Kifisia

Hiliadou   Agios Nikolaos

Rafina

Nafpaktos   Eratini   Elefsina   Athens

Krioneri   Lambiri   Diakofto

Mesolóngi   Paralia   Paralia   ATHINA

Rizomilos   Platánou

Kato Alissos   Perahóra

Korinthos   Sounion

Kalogria   Pátra   Korfos   Legrena

5

Killini   Mycenae   Galatas

Epidaurus

Kastro   Nafplio   Assini

Glifa Kyllini   Tolo   Salandi   Ermioni

Savalia   Dimitsána

Olympia   Paralia Astros   Agios Andreas

Zacharo   Tyrchu

Kakovatos   Plaka

Kosmas

Agios Kiriaki

Petalidi   Gythion   Agia Kyriaki

Gialova Pylou   Mayroyouni   Monemvasía

Pylos   Koroni   Gythion   Kamares   Irion   Agios Fokas

Karavostasi   Kameras   Skoutari

Neo Itylo   Kotronas

6

Gerolimenas   Porto Kagio

A   35km   **B**   **C**   **D**

MAP 35

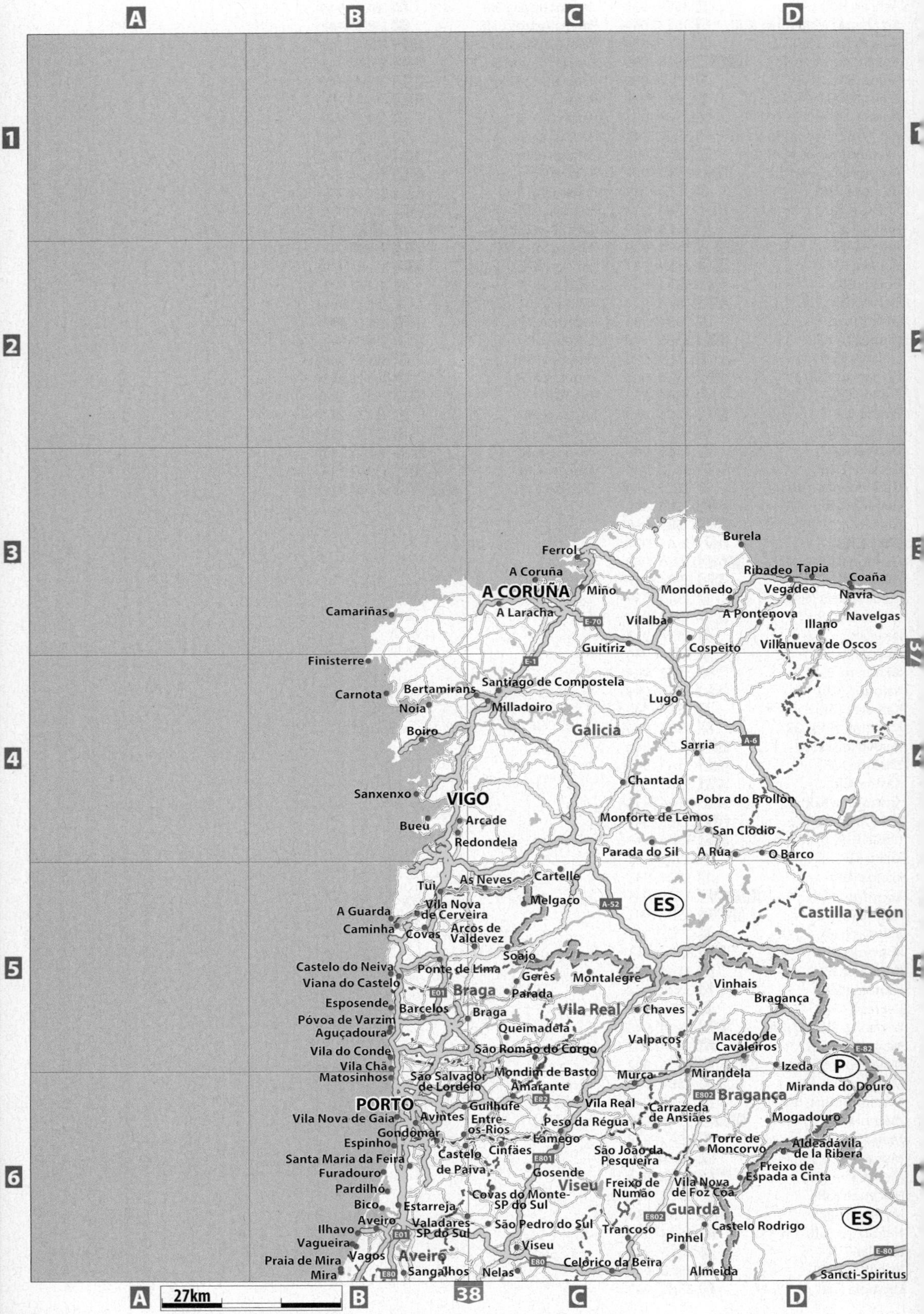

A
B
C
D
1
2
3
4
5
6
37
Burela
Ferrol
A Coruña
Ribadeo
Tapia
Coaña
A CORUÑA
Miño
Mondoñedo
Vegadeo
Navia
Camariñas
A Laracha
A Pontenova
Navelgas
Vilalba
Illano
E-70
Guitiriz
Cospeito
Villanueva de Oscos
Finisterre
E-1
Santiago de Compostela
Carnota
Bertamirans
Lugo
Noia
Milladoiro
Boiro
Galicia
A-6
Sarria
Chantada
Sanxenxo
VIGO
Pobra do Brollón
Bueu
Arcade
Monforte de Lemos
San Clodio
Redondela
Parada do Sil
A Rúa
O Barco
Cartelle
As Neves
Tui
Melgaço
Vila Nova de Cerveira
A-52
ES
A Guarda
Castilla y León
Caminha
Arcos de Valdevez
Covas
Soajo
Castelo do Neiva
Ponte de Lima
Viana do Castelo
Gerês
Montalegre
Vinhais
Braga
Parada
E01
Esposende
Bragança
Barcelos
Braga
Vila Real
Chaves
Póvoa de Varzim
Queimadela
Aguçadoura
Macedo de Cavaleiros
Valpaços
Vila do Conde
São Romão do Corgo
E-82
Vila Chã
Izeda
P
Matosinhos
São Salvador de Lordelo
Mondim de Basto
Murça
Mirandela
Amarante
Miranda do Douro
PORTO
E82
E802
Bragança
Vila Real
Guilhufe
Carrazeda de Ansiães
Vila Nova de Gaia
Avintes
Entre-os-Rios
Mogadouro
Gondomar
Peso da Régua
Lamego
Torre de Moncorvo
Aldeadávila de la Ribera
Espinho
Cinfães
São João da Pesqueira
Santa Maria da Feira
Castelo de Paiva
E801
Freixo de Espada a Cinta
Furadouro
Gosende
Pardilho
Viseu
Freixo de Numão
Vila Nova de Foz Côa
Covas do Monte-SP do Sul
Bico
Estarreja
E802
Guarda
Aveiro
ES
Valadares-SP do Sul
São Pedro do Sul
Trancoso
Castelo Rodrigo
Ilhavo
E01
Pinhel
Vagueira
Viseu
Vagos
Aveiro
E-80
Praia de Mira
Celorico da Beira
E80
Mira
E80
Sangalhos
Nelas
Almeida
Sancti-Spiritus
38
27km

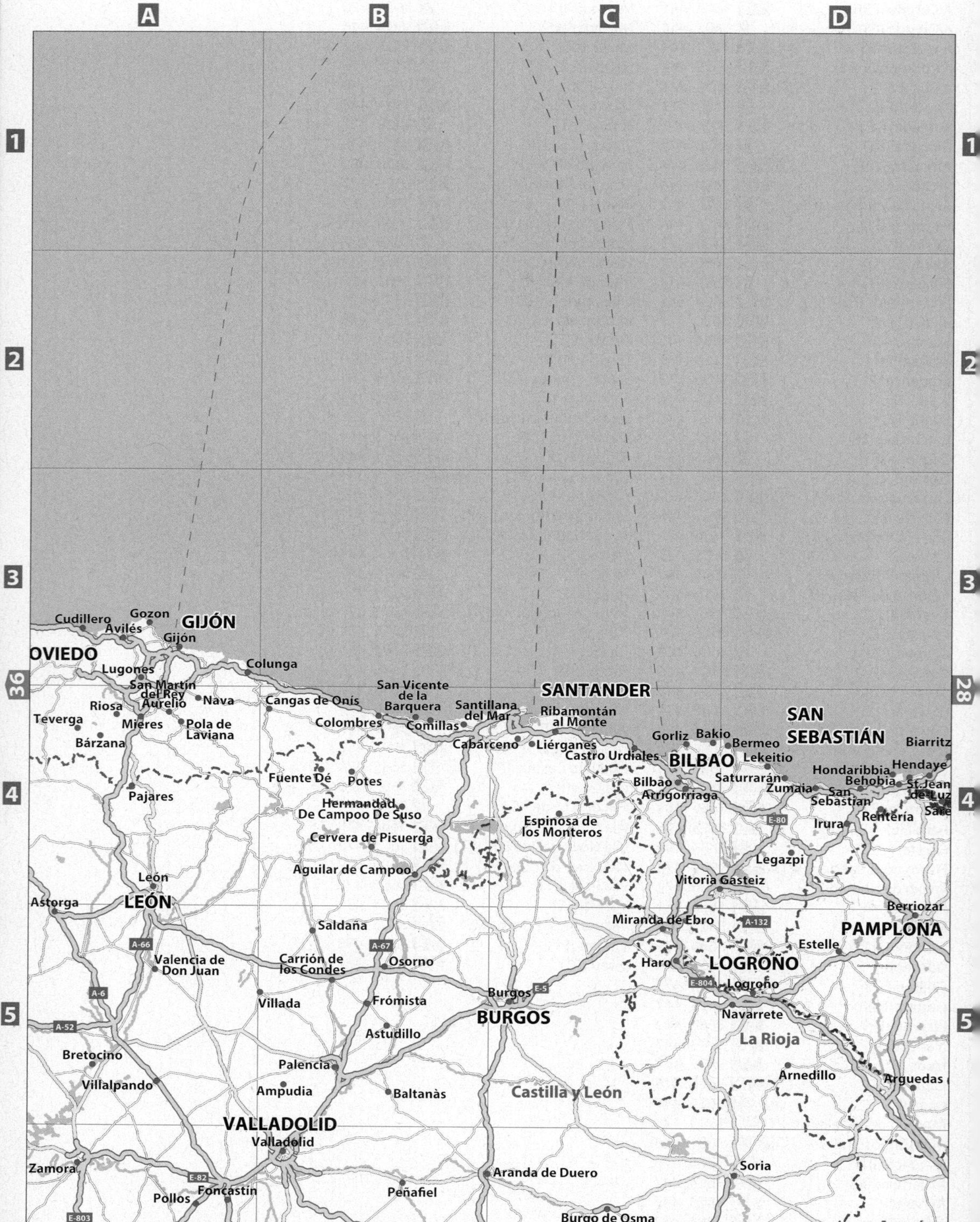

A   B   C   D

1   1

2   2

3   3

36   28

Cudillero Gozon
Avilés Gijón GIJÓN
OVIEDO Gijón
Lugones Colunga
San Martin
del Rey
Riosa Aurelio Nava Cangas de Onis San Vicente
Teverga Mieres Pola de Colombres de la Santillana SANTANDER
Bárzana Laviana Barquera del Mar Ribamontán
Comillas al Monte SAN
Cabárceno Liérganes SEBASTIÁN
Fuente Dé Potes Gorliz Bakio Biarritz
Pajares Castro Urdiales Bermeo Lekeitio
Hermandad Bilbao BILBAO Hondaribbia Hendaye
De Campoo De Suso Arrigorriaga Saturrarán Behobia St-Jean
Espinosa de Zumaia de Luz Sale
Cervera de Pisuerga los Monteros San Réntería
E-80 Sebastián
Aguilar de Campoo Irura
Legazpi
León Vitoria Gásteiz
Astorga LEÓN Berriozar
Miranda de Ebro A-132
Saldaña PAMPLONA
A-66 Carrión de Osorno Estelle
Valencia de los Condes Haro LOGROÑO
Don Juan Burgos E-5 E-804 Logroño La Rioja
A-6 Villada Frómista BURGOS Navarrete
Astudillo
A-52 Bretocino Palencia Arnedillo
Villalpando Ampudia Baltanàs Castilla y León Arguedas
VALLADOLID
Zamora Valladolid Soria
E-82 Aranda de Duero
Pollos Foncastin Peñafiel Aragón
E-803 Cuellar Burgo de Osma Almazán
A-66 E-80 Olmedo Sepúlveda
Coca
SALAMANCA Ariza
Cabrerizos Turégano A-15
Salamanca Castilla-La Mancha
Terradillos A-50

4   4

5   5

6   6

MAP 38

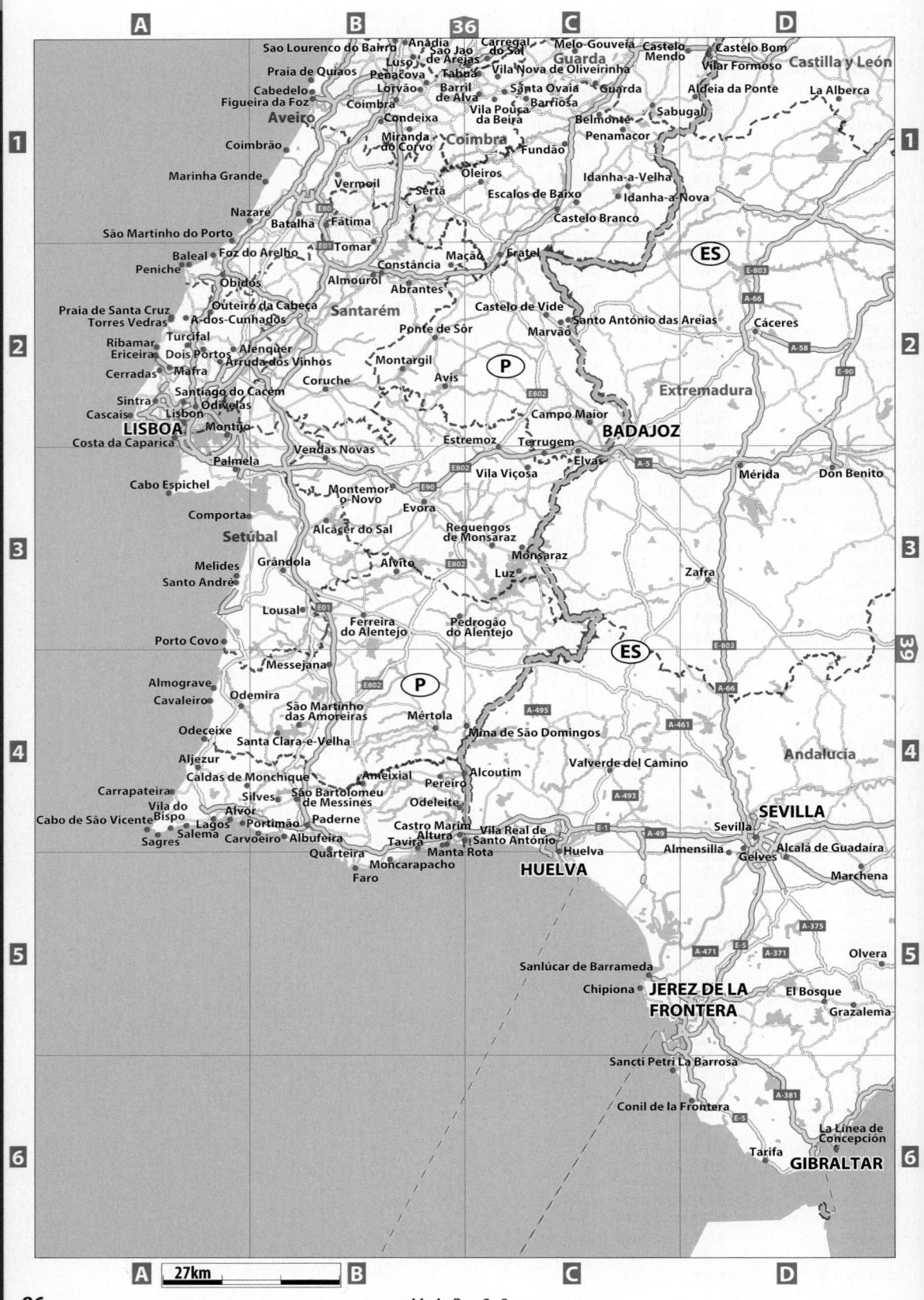

MAP 38

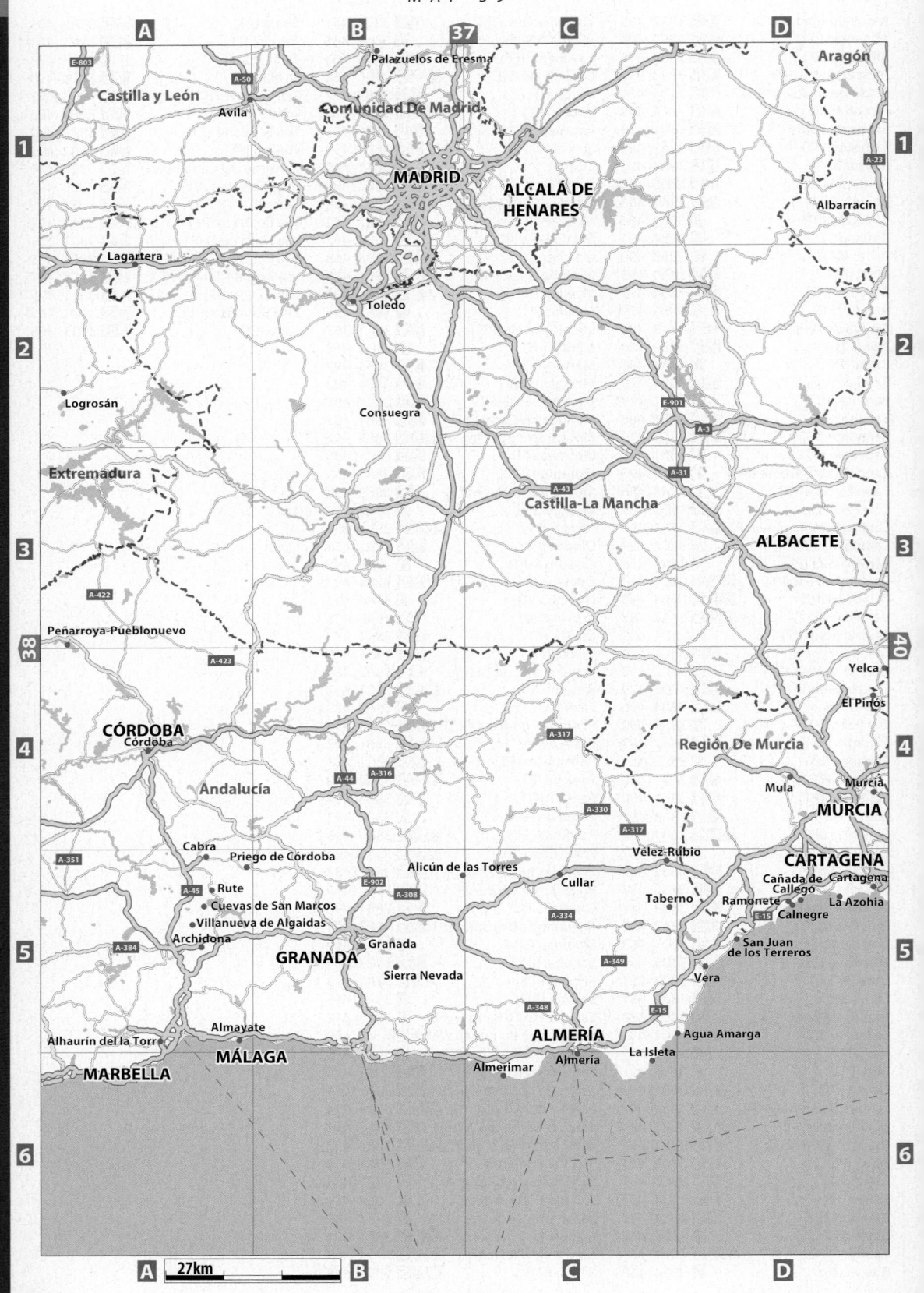

Aragón

Castilla y León

E-803

A-50
Avila

Palazuelos de Eresma

Comunidad De Madrid

MADRID

ALCALÁ DE
HENARES

A-23
Albarracín

Lagartera

Toledo

Logrosán

Consuegra

E-901

A-3

Extremadura

A-43

A-31

Castilla-La Mancha

ALBACETE

A-422

Peñarroya-Pueblonuevo

A-423

Yelca

El Piñós

CÓRDOBA
Córdoba

A-317

Región De Murcia

Andalucía

A-44   A-316

A-330

Mula

Murcia

MURCIA

A-317

Cabra

Priego de Córdoba

Alicún de las Torres

Cullar

Vélez-Rubio

CARTAGENA

A-351

E-902   A-308

Taberno

Cañada de
Callego

Cartagena

Rute
A-45

Cuevas de San Marcos

Villanueva de Algaidas

A-334

Ramonete

La Azohia

E-15   Calnegre

Archidona

A-384

Granada

GRANADA

Sierra Nevada

A-349

San Juan
de los Terreros

Vera

Alhaurín del la Torr

Almayate

MÁLAGA

A-348

ALMERÍA

E-15

Agua Amarga

MARBELLA

Almerimar

Almería

La Isleta

38

40

1

2

3

4

5

6

1

2

3

4

5

6

A   B   C   D

A   27km   B   C   D

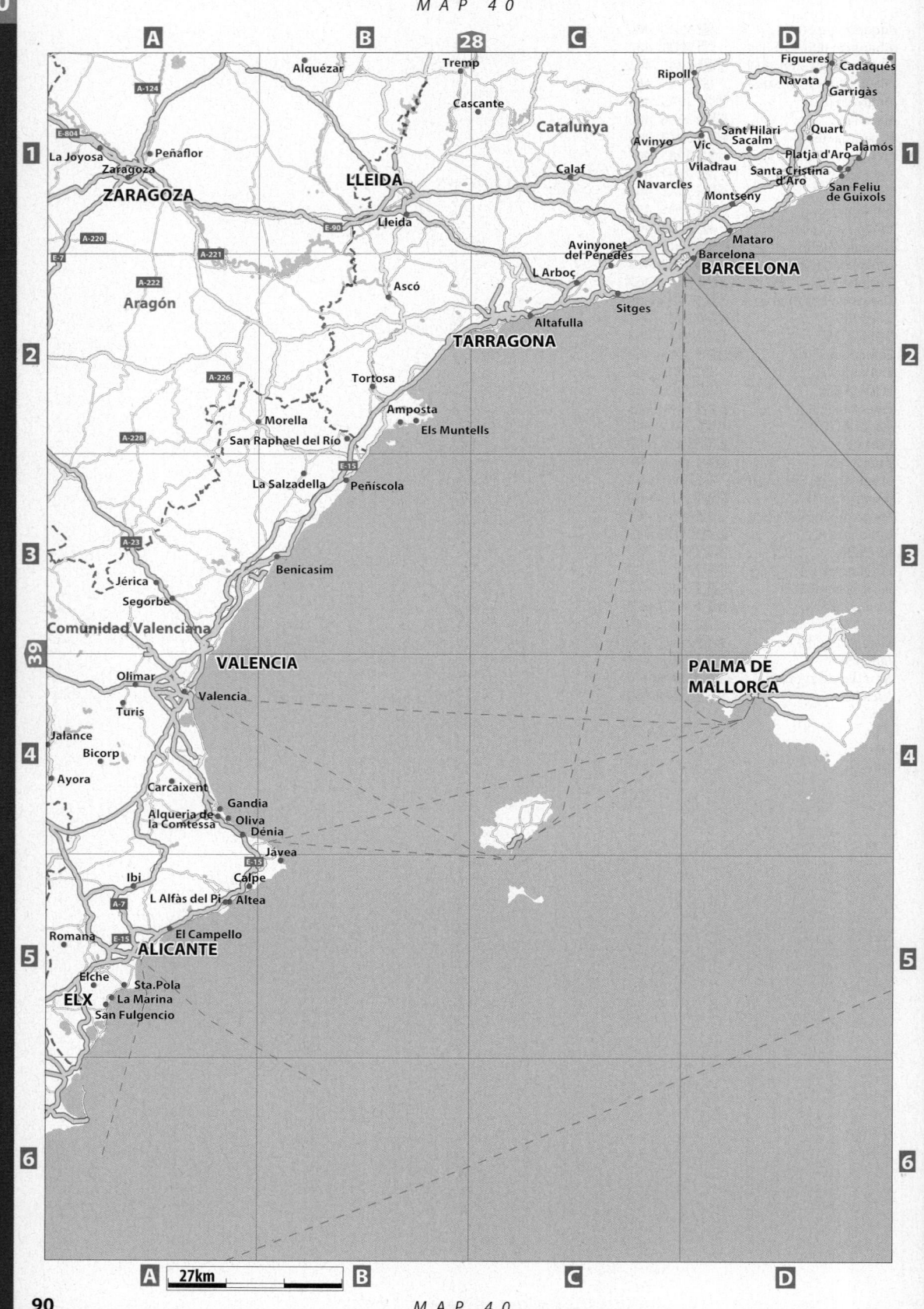

UNITED KINGDOM

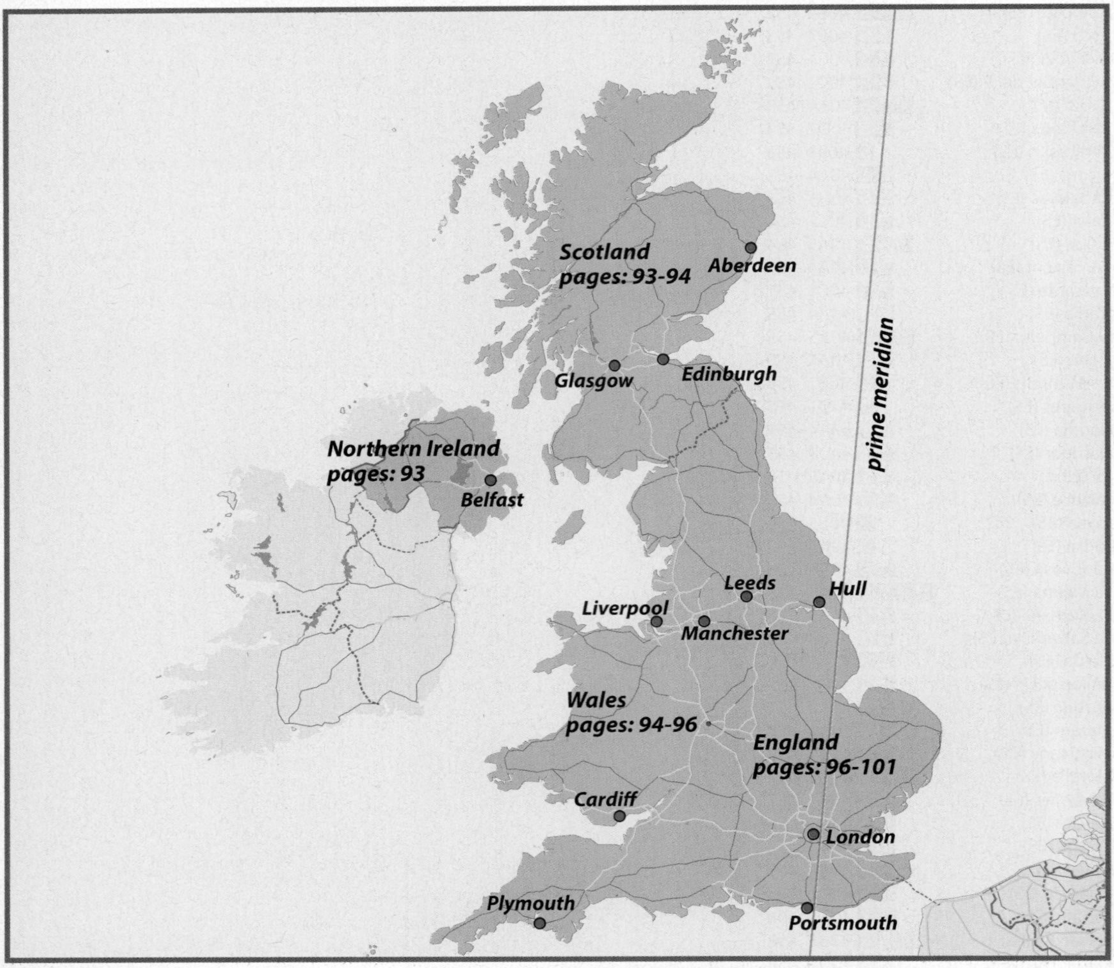

Scotland
pages: 93-94

Aberdeen

Glasgow   Edinburgh

Northern Ireland
pages: 93

Belfast

prime meridian

Leeds   Hull

Liverpool
Manchester

Wales
pages: 94-96

England
pages: 96-101

Cardiff

London

Plymouth

Portsmouth

Capital: London
Government: Constitutional monarchy
Official Language: English
Population: 64,100,000 (2013)
Area: 244,820 km²

General information
Dialing code: 0044
General emergency: 112
Currency: Pound sterling (GBP),
£1 = € 1,28, € 1 = £0.78 (October 2014)

Regulations for overnight stays
Wild camping is forbidden in the UK. Motorway
service stations allow overnight parking.

Additional public holidays 2015
March 17 St. Patricksday (Northern Ireland)
April 3 Good Friday
April 6 Easter monday
May 1 Labour Day
May 4 Early May Bank Holiday
May 25 Spring Bank Holiday
July 12 Orangemens' Day (Northern Ireland)
August 31 Summer Bank Holiday
October 31 Halloween
November 51 Guy Fawkes Day
December 26 Boxing Day

Great Britain

Northern Ireland

⚟S   Aghadowey   1A3

Golf Car Park, Brown Trout Golf and Country Inn, 209 Agivey Road, A54. **GPS**: n55,02413 w6,59985.
⚟free ⚟.
Remarks: Max. 48h.

⚟   Antrim   1A3

The Ramble Inn, 236 Lisnevenagh Road. **GPS**: n54,76198 w6,24265.
⚟free.
Distance: ⚟Antrim 7km.

⚟   Ballinamallard   1A3

Ballinamallard Football Club, Ferney Park. **GPS**: n54,41474 w7,60092.

⚟free. **Surface:** gravel.
Distance: ⚟1,5km.
Tourist information Ballinamallard:
⚟ Ballinamallard River, Kilgortnaleague Bridge, A35 Enniskillen > Irvinestown. Wild Salmon and Trout River.

⚟   Ballymoney   1A3

Anglers' Rest, 139 Vow Road. **GPS**: n54,99087 w6,56672.
⚟free.
Distance: ⊗on the spot.
Tourist information Ballymoney:
⚟ Leslie Hill Open Farm, 9, Macfin Road. Living history on the farm, picnic area, playground, Tea-room etc. ⚟ Easter-31/05: Su-Bank Holidays 14-18h, 01/06-30/06: Sa-Su 14-18h, 01/07-31/08: Mo-Sa 11-18h, Su 14-18h.
⚟ Old Bushmills Distillery, Main Street, Bushmills. World's oldest licensed whiskey distillery. ⚟ Mo-Sa 9.30-17h, Su 12-17h ⚟ Good Friday, 12/07, 25-26/12, 31/12-01/01.

⚟S   Broughshane   1A3

Houston Mills, Buckna road. **GPS**: n54,89352 w6,20076.⚟.

⚟free ⚟£1 ⚟Ch ⚟ (4x)£1.
Location: Central, noisy. **Surface:** asphalted.
Distance: ⚟on the spot ⊗on the spot.
Remarks: Coins at supermarket.

⚟S   Carrickfergus   1A3

Carrickfergus Harbour Car Park, Rodgers Quay. **GPS**: n54,71177 w5,8119.
⚟free ⚟£1 ⚟Ch ⚟£1.
Remarks: Coins at harbourmaster and tourist office.

⚟S   Donaghadee   1A3

The Commons Parks, Millisle Road. **GPS**: n54,63475 w5,5312.⚟.
⚟free ⚟£2/100liter ⚟ ⚟£2/h. **Surface:** asphalted.
Distance: ⚟on the spot ⚟on the spot ⚟on the spot ⊗on the spot ⚟on the spot.
Remarks: Coins at petrol station.

⚟   Newtownards   1A3

Daft Eddys, Sketrick Island. **GPS**: n54,48812 w5,64807.

⚟free.
Distance: ⚟Newtownards 17km.
Tourist information Newtownards:
⚟ Somme Heritage Centre, 233 Bangor Road, Conlig, A21. The centre examines Ireland's role in the 1st World War.
⚟ Castle Espie Wildfowl And Wetlands Centre, 78 Ballydrain Road, Comber.
⚟ 01/01-31/12 ⚟ 23-25/12.

⚟S   Portrush   1A2

Sandhill Drive. **GPS**: n55,20107 w6,65253.
10 ⚟ ⚟£1,25/100liter ⚟Ch ⚟£1,25/kWh. ⚟ ⚟ **Location:** Simple, central. **Surface:** asphalted.
Distance: ⚟on the spot ⚟600m.

⚟S   Whitehead   1A3

Bentra Golf Club, Slaughterford Road. **GPS**: n54,75908 w5,72012.⚟.
⚟free ⚟£1 ⚟Ch. **Surface:** asphalted.
Distance: ⚟1km ⚟1,5km ⊗150m.

Scotland

⚟   Aberdeen   1C1

Hazelhead Park, Hazledene Road. **GPS**: n57,13987 w2,17956.

⚟free. **Surface:** asphalted.
Distance: ⚟200m ⊗400m ⚟400m.

⚟S   Ballachulish   1B1

Glencoe, A82 Ballachulish > Achallader. **GPS**: n56,63295 w4,82744.

⚟£15 ⚟.
Remarks: Parking ski-lifts.

⚟   Dufftown   1C1

Castle Road. **GPS**: n57,45325 w3,12912.

GB

+20 🛏free. **Surface:** asphalted.
Distance: 🚶400m ⊗400m 🚰400m.

| 🏠 | **Dumfries** | 1B3 |

P Long Stay, White Sands. **GPS:** n55,06722 w3,6125.

10 🛏free. **Surface:** asphalted. 🅿 01/01-31/12
Distance: 🚶100m 🚂on the spot ⊗on the spot 🚰100m.

| 📶S | **Dunthulm** 🌿⚓🏔🐚 | 1A1 |

Isle of Skye. **GPS:** n57,65020 w6,40459.
12 🛏£12 🚿Ch WC. **Surface:** metalled.
Distance: 🚂on the spot.
Remarks: Nearby Dunthulm Castle.

| 📶S | **Easdale** 🌿⚓🏔🐚 | 1B2 |

Souvenir shop, Ellenabeich, Isle of Seil. **GPS:** n56,29540 w5,6462.

10 🛏£10 🚿Ch WC. **Surface:** metalled.
Distance: 🚶on the spot 🚂on the spot ⊗on the spot 🚐on the spot.

| 📶 | **Fettercairn** | 1C1 |

Car Park Bowling Club, Fettercairn, Laurencekirk. **GPS:** n56,84971 w2,57306.
🛏.

Tourist information Fettercairn:
👁 Fettercairn Distillery Visitor Centre Information, Distillery Road. One of Scotland's oldest malt whiskey distilleries. 🅿 01/05-30/09, Mon-Sa 10-14.30h.
🅃 free.

| 🏠 | **Givran** | 1B2 |

Harbour street- Henriettastreet. **GPS:** n55,24324 w4,85869.

50 🛏free. **Surface:** asphalted. 🅿 01/01-31/12
Distance: 🚶100m ⛱sandy beach 50m ⊗50m.

| **New Abbey** 🌿🏔 | 1B3 |

Parking Sweetheart Abbey, A710, Main Street. **GPS:** n54,98070 w3,61966.

6 🛏free. **Surface:** metalled.

| 🏠 | **Oban** 🚢 | 1B2 |

Longsdale Car park, Longsdale Road. **GPS:** n56,41997 w5,46846.
± 10 🛏free. **Location:** Simple, central. **Surface:** asphalted.
🅿 01/01-31/12
Distance: 🚶400m ⛱300m ⊗50m 🚰400m.

| | **Rhugarbh** 🏔 | 1B2 |

Parking Scottish Sea Life Sanctuary, A828 Rhugharb - Barcaldine.
GPS: n56,51731 w5,34679.

10 🛏free. **Surface:** metalled.

Wales

| 📶S | **Abergynolwyn** | 1B4 |

Riverside Guest House, Llanegryn Street. **GPS:** n52,64584 w3,95856.⬆

5 🛏£10/night 🚿Ch included 🔌£6/night. 🚽
Location: Rural, comfortable, central, quiet. **Surface:** grassy/metalled.
🅿 01/01-31/12
Remarks: Arrival <18h, narrow entrance (2.6m), Snowdonia National Park.

| 📶S | **Brecon** | 1B5 |

The Watton Car Park, Heol Gouesnou. **GPS:** n51,94609 w3,38531.⬆

25 🛏£0.50/h, max. £2.50 8-18h, overnight stay free WC free,150m.

GB

Location: Urban, simple, quiet. **Surface:** asphalted. ◻ 01/01-31/12
Distance: ⌂on the spot ⛟on the spot.
Remarks: 1 night per 7 nights.

| | Brecon | 1B5 |

Canal Road Car/Coach-Lorry Park, Canal Road. **GPS:** n51,94486 w3,38993.⬆️.

10 ⏱8-18h parking rate, overnight stay free. ⛺ **Location:** Urban, simple,
central, quiet. **Surface:** asphalted. ◻ 01/01-31/12
Distance: ⌂100m ⛟100m.
Remarks: 1 night per 7 nights.

| | Brecon | 1B5 |

The Promenade Car Park, Fenni-Fach Rd. **GPS:** n51,95089 w3,4036.⬆️.

25 ⏱8-18h parking rate, overnight stay free. ⛺ **Location:** Urban, simple,
isolated, quiet. **Surface:** asphalted. ◻ 01/01-31/12
Distance: ⌂600m ⚓on the spot ⛟700m.
Remarks: 1 night per 7 nights.

| | S | Builth Wells | 1B5 |

The Groe Car Park, The Strand. **GPS:** n52,14969 w3,40252.⬆️.

20 ⏱8-18h parking rate, overnight stay free WC. ⛺ **Location:** Urban, simple,
quiet. **Surface:** asphalted. ◻ 01/01-31/12
Distance: ⌂on the spot ⚓on the spot ⌂on the spot.
Remarks: 1 night per 7 nights.

| | Builth Wells | 1B5 |

Smithfield Car Park, Brecon Rd. **GPS:** n52,14714 w3,40261.⬆️.

50 ⏱8-18h parking rate, overnight stay free. ⛺ **Location:** Urban, simple,
central. **Surface:** asphalted. ◻ 01/01-31/12

Distance: ⌂200m.
Remarks: 1 night per 7 nights.

| | | Crickhowell | 1B5 |

Beaufort Street Car Park, Greenhill Way. **GPS:** n51,85838 w3,13557.⬆️.

8 ⏱8-18h parking rate, overnight stay free. ⛺ **Location:** Urban, simple,
central, quiet. **Surface:** asphalted. ◻ 01/01-31/12
Distance: ⌂50m.
Remarks: 1 night per 7 nights.

| | S | Hay-on-Wye | 1B5 |

Oxford Road Car Park, Oxford Road. **GPS:** n52,07316 w3,12592.⬆️.

25 ⏱£0.50/h, max. £2.50 8-18h, overnight stay free WC free. ⛺
Location: Urban, simple, central, quiet. **Surface:** asphalted.
◻ 01/01-31/12
Distance: ⌂150m ⊗150m ⛟150m ⌂on the spot.
Remarks: 1 night per 7 nights.

| | S | Knighton | 1B5 |

Bowling Green Lane Car Park, Bowling Green Lane. **GPS:** n52,34324 w3,04553.
⬆️.

30 ⏱£0.50/h, max. £2.50 8-18h, overnight stay free WC free. ⛺
Location: Rural, simple, central, quiet. **Surface:** asphalted.
◻ 01/01-31/12
Distance: ⌂200m ⛟300m ⌂on the spot.
Remarks: 1 night per 7 nights.

| | | Llandrindod Wells | 1B5 |

High Street Car Park, High Street. **GPS:** n52,24151 w3,38042.⬆️.

30 ⌁8-18h parking rate, overnight stay free. 🚐 **Location:** Urban, simple, central. **Surface:** asphalted. 📅 01/01-31/12
Distance: 🚶150m 🚐on the spot.
Remarks: 1 night per 7 nights, max. 6m.

⑤ Llanidloes 1B5
Mount Street Car Park, Mount Lane. **GPS:** n52,44750 w3,53938.⬆️.

12 ⌁8-18h parking rate, overnight stay £5. 🚐 **Location:** Urban, simple, central, quiet. **Surface:** asphalted. 📅 01/01-31/12
Distance: 🚶on the spot ⊗100m 🚰100m 🚐100m.
Remarks: 1 night per 7 nights.

⑤ Moelfre 1B4
Lligwy Bay. **GPS:** n53,35910 w4,26132.
⌁£10/night.
Remarks: Beach parking.

🍴⑤ Nantgaredig 1B5
Railway Hotel, B4310. **GPS:** n51,86533 w4,18976.⬆️.
5 ⌁£5 WC. 📅 01/01-31/12

⑤ Newton 1B5
Back Lane Car Park, Back Lane. **GPS:** n52,51534 w3,31735.⬆️.

40 ⌁8-18h parking rate, overnight stay £5 WCfree. 🚐 **Location:** Urban, simple, central, quiet. **Surface:** asphalted. 📅 01/01-31/12
Distance: 🚶150m ⊗on the spot 🚐on the spot.
Remarks: 1 night per 7 nights.

⑤ Newton 1B5
The Gravel Car Park, Heol Les Herbiers. **GPS:** n52,51421 w3,31167.⬆️.

25 ⌁8-18h parking rate, overnight stay £5. 🚐 **Location:** Urban, simple, central. **Surface:** asphalted. 📅 01/01-31/12
Distance: 🚶250m ⊗50m 🚐250m.
Remarks: 1 night per 7 nights.

⑤ Presteigne 1B5
Hereford Street Car Park, Hereford Street. **GPS:** n52,27245 w3,00488.⬆️.

10 ⌁8-18h parking rate, overnight stay free WC free. 🚐 **Location:** Urban, simple, central, quiet. **Surface:** asphalted. 📅 01/01-31/12
Distance: 🚶100m 🚐on the spot.
Remarks: 1 night per 7 nights, max. 6m.

⑤ Welshpool 1B5
Berriew Street Car Park, Berriew Rd. **GPS:** n52,65875 w3,14806.⬆️.

30 ⌁8-18h parking rate, overnight stay £5 WCfree. 🚐 **Location:** Urban, simple, central, quiet. **Surface:** asphalted. 📅 01/01-31/12
Distance: 🚶200m 🚰500m.
Remarks: 1 night per 7 nights.

⑤ Welshpool 1B5
Church Street Car Park, Church Street. **GPS:** n52,66031 w3,1438.⬆️.

25 ⌁8-18h parking rate, overnight stay £5 WCfree. 🚐 **Location:** Urban, simple, central, quiet. **Surface:** asphalted. 📅 01/01-31/12
Distance: 🚶150m 🚰300m.
Remarks: 1 night per 7 nights.

England

⑤ Abingdon 1C5
Rye Farm Pay & Display car park, Bridge Street, A415.
GPS: n51,66746 w1,27799.⬆️.

8 ⌁£7.30/24h WC. 🚐 **Location:** Urban, simple. **Surface:** asphalted.
📅 01/01-31/12
Distance: 🚶500m ⊗500m 🚰800m.
Remarks: Max. 24h, first call or mail, carparks@southandvale.gov.uk,

01235 547665.

Aldershot 1C6

Parsons Barracks Car park, Ordnance Road. **GPS**: n51,24979 w0,75731.
£1. **Surface**: asphalted. 01/01-31/12

Ambleside 1C3

Miller Field Motorhome Camping, Rothay Rd. **GPS**: n54,42898 w2,96586.
50 £10 Ch.
Location: Rural, comfortable, quiet. **Surface**: grassy.
Distance: 200m Lake Windmere 800m on the spot on the spot.
Remarks: At Lake District National Park.

Appledore 1B6

Churchfields Car Park, The Quay. **GPS**: n51,05464 w4,19135.

25 £5 18-10h, £3 day. WC free. **Location**: Urban, simple, quiet.
Surface: asphalted. 01/01-31/12
Distance: 150m 50m 200m.
Remarks: Max. 2 nights, min. 6m space between motorhomes.

Bakewell 1C4

Car Park, Asford Lane, Monsal Head. **GPS**: n53,24015 w1,72325.
£10.
Distance: on the spot.

Bideford 1B6

Riverbank (long stay) Car Park, Kingsley road. **GPS**: n51,02086 w4,20386.

20 £5 18-10h, £3 day. **Location**: Urban, simple, quiet.
Surface: asphalted. 01/01-31/12
Distance: 1,5km 50m 500m 1km 500m.
Remarks: Max. 2 nights, min. 6m space between motorhomes.

Bourton-on-the-Water 1C5

Bourton Rovers, Rissington Road. **GPS**: n51,87995 w1,7513.

5 £10 Ch WC free, Password at the bar.
Location: Rural, simple, central, quiet. **Surface**: grassy. 01/01-31/12
Distance: 500m 500m 500m.

Bourton-on-the-Water 1C5

Bourton Vale Car & Coach Park, Station Rd. **GPS**: n51,88512 w1,75471.

10 9-18h parking rate, overnight stay £8 WC free. **Location**: Urban,
simple, central, quiet. **Surface**: asphalted. 01/01-31/12
Distance: 200m on the spot on the spot.

Bury St.Edmunds 1D5

Ram Meadow Carpark Annexe, Cotton Lane. **GPS**: n52,24775 e0,71893.

5 £2.20 8-18h, overnight stay free WC free. **Location**: Urban, simple,
central, quiet. **Surface**: asphalted. 01/01-31/12
Distance: 300m 300m 300m.
Remarks: Max. 1 night.

Canterbury 1D6

Canterbury Coach Park, Kingsmead Road. **GPS**: n51,28554 e1,08492.

12 £10/12h WC free. **Location**: Urban. **Surface**: asphalted.
01/01-31/12
Distance: 650m 650m.

Canterbury 1D6

New Dover Road Park&Ride, New Dover Road. **GPS**: n51,26199 e1,10258.

24 £3 Ch included WC free.
Location: Rural, simple, isolated, quiet. **Surface**: asphalted.
Acces Mo-Sa 6.30-20.30h, exit 24/24
Distance: Vintage Inn on the spot.
Remarks: Max. 24h, bus to city centre incl.

Cheltenham 1C5

The Gloucester Old Spot, Tewkesbury Road, A4109. **GPS**: n51,93325 w2,14881.

5 🛏 free, use of a meal obligated 🚰 WC included, during opening hours.
Location: Rural, simple, isolated. **Surface:** gravel/sand. 🅿 01/01-31/12
Distance: 🚶 500m ⊗ on the spot.

| 🛏 S | **Chester** 🌿🚿🍴 | 1B4 |

Car Park, Little Roodee, Castle Road. **GPS:** n53,18447 w2,89245.
🛏 £5.80/day £1.50/night 🚰 WC.
Distance: 🚶 3,5km.
Remarks: Along the Dee river, gate closed from 22.30-6h.

| 🛏 | **Cirencester** | 1C5 |

Old Cricklade Road lorry park, Cricklade Road. **GPS:** n51,70760 w1,955.🔼.

20 🛏 £6.20. 🚐 **Location:** Urban, simple. **Surface:** asphalted.
🅿 01/01-31/12
Distance: 🚶 1,5km ⊗ 50m 🚉 150m.
Remarks: Near McDonalds.

| 🍴 S | **Cirencester** | 1C5 |

The Crown Inn, High Street, Cerny Wick. **GPS:** n51,66264 w1,88933.🔼.

5 🛏 £10 🚰 🚽 Ch 🧹 WC during opening hours. 🚙 **Location:** Rural, simple.
Surface: grassy/metalled. 🅿 01/01-31/12
Distance: ⊗ on the spot.

| 🍴 | **Crediton** | 1B6 |

Thelbridge Cross Inn, Thelbridge. **GPS:** n50,89530 w3,72228.
6 🛏 £5. **Location:** Isolated, quiet. **Surface:** asphalted.
Distance: 🚶 14km ⊗ on the spot.

| 🛏 | **Darlington** | 1C3 |

Car Park, Chesnut Street. **GPS:** n54,52993 w1,54758.
🛏 £4/day £2/night. **Surface:** metalled.
Distance: 🚶 700m 🚶 4,7km.

| 🛏 S | **Exeter** | 1B6 |

Huntisbeare, Oak Road, Aylesbeare. **GPS:** n50,72816 w3,33599.🔼.

5 🛏 £12/night 🚰🚽 Ch 🧹 WC included. 🚙 **Location:** Rural, simple,
isolated, quiet. **Surface:** metalled. 🅿 01/01-31/12
Distance: 🚶 1,5km 🚉 1,5km.
Remarks: Arrival <18h.

| 🍴🍴 | **Great Missenden** | 1C5 |

The Black Horse, Aylesbury Road. **GPS:** n51,71019 w0,71215.
5 🛏 guests free. **Surface:** metalled.
Distance: 🚶 800m ⊗ on the spot.

| 🛏 S | **Hayling Island** | 1C6 |

West Beach Car Park, Sea Front. **GPS:** n50,78530 w1,0007.🔼.

40 🛏 8-22h parking rate, max. £6, overnight stay £10, 01/03-01/10 £20
🚰 free Ch WC 🚽 At TI, 7 Sea-Front (600m). 🚐 **Location:** Rural, simple, quiet.
Surface: grassy/gravel. 🅿 01/01-31/12
Distance: 🏊 on the spot ⊗ on the spot 🚌 600m.
Remarks: Max. 72h.

| 🛏 | **Holsworthy** | 1B6 |

The Manor Car Park, Western Road. **GPS:** n50,81133 w4,35282.🔼.

12 🛏 £5 18-10h, £3 day. 🚐 **Location:** Urban, simple, quiet.
Surface: asphalted. 🅿 01/01-31/12
Distance: 🚶 on the spot ⊗ 150m 🚉 150m.
Remarks: Max. 2 nights.

| 🛏 | **Holy Island** | 1C2 |

Lindisfarne Causeway. **GPS:** n55,67815 w1,87552.
5 🛏. **Surface:** metalled.

| 🛏 S | **Huntingdon** | 1D5 |

Wellsbridge Motorhomes Sales, Ramsey Forty Foot, Ramsey.
GPS: n52,47540 w0,08834.🔼.

GB

5 🚐 £5 🔌 WC. 🚽 **Location:** Rural, simple, isolated, quiet.
Surface: asphalted. ☐ 02/01-23/12
Distance: 🚌 on the spot.

[🍇][S] Ipswich 1D5

Burnt House Farm, Wash Lane, Witnesham. **GPS**: n52,11418 e1,20094. [↑][→].

5 🚐 £8 🚰 🗑 Ch 🔌 WC included. 🚽 **Location:** Rural, comfortable, isolated, quiet. **Surface:** grassy/metalled. ☐ 01/01-31/12
Distance: 🏙 2km 🍴 2km.

[🍴] Ipswich 1D5

Orwell Crossing Lorry Park, A14 Eastbound, Nacton. **GPS**: n52,02473 e1,22678. [↑].

20 🚐 £12. 🚽 💳 **Location:** Highway, simple, noisy. **Surface:** asphalted.
☐ 01/01-31/12
Distance: 🍴 on the spot.

[🍴] Ivybridge 1B6

Lee Mill Services, A38. **GPS**: n50,38493 w3,97041. [↑][→].
10 🚐 £8/night. 🚽 **Location:** Simple, noisy. **Surface:** asphalted.
☐ 01/01-31/12
Distance: 🍴 on the spot 🛒 500m.

[🚐][S] Maidstone 🛒 1D6

Maidstone Services, M20. **GPS**: n51,26568 e0,61588. [↑].
8 🚐 £20 WC 🚿 📶 against payment. 🚗 💳 **Location:** Highway, simple, noisy.
Surface: asphalted. ☐ 01/01-31/12
Distance: ⛽ 200m 🍴 on the spot.

Tourist information Maidstone:
[M] Museum of Kent Life, Lock Lane, Sandling. History and traditions of Kent.
☐ 14/02-05/11, 10-17h.

[🚐] Marazion ⛱ 〰 1A6

Car Park, Kings Road. **GPS**: n50,12415 w5,47587. [↑].

12 🚐 £10. 🚽 **Location:** Simple, quiet. **Surface:** metalled.
☐ 17-09h ◙ 9-17h
Distance: 🏙 50m ⛱ on the spot 🍴 100m 🚌 100m.
Remarks: Parking at sea, nearby Saint Michael's Mount, not suitable for big motorhomes. Follow Marazion Car Parkings.

Tourist information Marazion:
👁 🏰 Saint Michael's Mount. Rocky island with medieval castle and church.
☐ 01/04-31/10.

[🚐][S] Mevagissey ⛱ 1A6

Willow Car & Coach Park, Valley Road. **GPS**: n50,27155 w4,79044. [↑].

10 🚐 10-18h parking rate, overnight stay £7.50 🚰 on demand. 🚽
Location: Urban, simple, central. **Surface:** metalled. ☐ 01/01-31/12
Distance: 🏙 150m ⛱ 1km 🍴 300m.

[🍇][S] New Milton 1C6

New Lane Orchard, New Lane, Bashley. **GPS**: n50,77182 w1,6645. [↑].

5 🚐 £13 🚰 🗑 Ch included 🔌. 🚽 **Location:** Rural, comfortable, isolated, quiet. **Surface:** grassy/metalled. ☐ 01/01-31/12
Distance: 🏙 400m ⛱ 6,5km 🎣 on the spot 🚶 New Forest.
Remarks: Arrival <18h.

[🍇][S] Newnham on Severn 1C5

Elton Farm, Littledean Road, A4151. **GPS**: n51,82355 w2,44753. [↑].
5 🚐 £5 🚰 🗑 Ch. 🚽 **Location:** Rural, simple, isolated. **Surface:** grassy.
☐ 01/01-31/12
Distance: 🎣 on the spot 🚌 on the spot.

[🚐][S] Newton Abbot 1B6

Sunnyside, Yvonne Bassett, Totnes Road, A381, Ipplepen.
GPS: n50,48591 w3,63376. [↑].

GB

5 ⬛£6/night ⌁ ▦ Ch ⚷ WC included. ⛟ **Location:** Rural, simple, quiet.
Surface: grassy/metalled. ▢ 01/01-31/12
Distance: ⬛100m.
Remarks: Arrival <18h.

| 🛉 S | **Oldham** | 1C4 |

The Hawthorn, Roundthorn Road. **GPS:** n53,53352 w2,08637.
5 ⬛£9 ⚷ £2,50/night WC ⬛.
Distance: ⬛3km.

| S | **Pickering** | 1C3 |

Antiques Centre, Southgate. **GPS:** n54,24413 w0,78026.
5 ⬛£10 ⌁ Ch. **Location:** Simple. **Surface:** asphalted. ▢ 01/01-31/12
Distance: ⊗500m.

| 🛉 | **Praa Sands** | 1A6 |

Car Park, Castle Drive. **GPS:** n50,10375 w5,38888.
⬛against payment.

| 🛉 S | **Rake** | 1C6 |

The Flying Bull, London Road. **GPS:** n51,04419 w0,85418.
⬛£5 ⌁ ▦ WC 📶. **Location:** Rural, isolated, quiet. **Surface:** grassy.
▢ 01/01-31/12
Distance: ⬛3km ⊗on the spot.

| 🛉 S | **Scarborough** | 1D3 |

South Moor Farm, Dalby Forest Drive. **GPS:** n54,30049 w0,61169. ⬆.
5 ⬛£10 ⌁ ▦ Ch. **Location:** Rural, simple. **Surface:** grassy.
▢ 01/01-31/12

| 🛉 S | **Sewerby** | 1D4 |

The Ship Inn, Cliff Road. **GPS:** n54,10167 w0,16411.
5 ⬛£15 ⌁ ▦ Ch. **Surface:** unpaved.
Distance: ⊗on the spot.

| 🛉 S | **St. Ives** | 1D5 |

The Seven Wives, Ramsey road. **GPS:** n52,33193 w0,07634. ⬆.

5 ⬛£5 ⌁ ▦ Ch ⚷ £6/night WC. ⛟ **Location:** Urban, simple, central.
Surface: metalled. ▢ 01/01-31/12
Distance: ⬛1,4km ⊗on the spot.

| 🛉 | **St. Jidgey** | 1A6 |

Halfway House Inn. **GPS:** n50,48949 w4,89943.
4 ⬛£10, guests free.
Location: Rural, isolated, quiet. **Surface:** grassy.
Distance: ⊗on the spot.

| S | **St.Austell** | 1A6 |

Edgemoor, Enniscaven, St.Dennis. **GPS:** n50,39636 w4,8676. ⬆.

---

5 ⬛£5/night ⌁ ▦ Ch WC included. ⛟ **Location:** Comfortable, quiet.
Surface: grassy/metalled. ▢ 01/01-31/12
Distance: ⬛St.Austell 14,5km 🚲on the spot 🧍on the spot.
Remarks: Arrival <18h.

| 🛉 | **Stratford-upon-Avon** 🌼 | 1C5 |

Stratford Marina Car Park, Bridgeway. **GPS:** n52,19280 w1,70154. ⬆.

10 ⬛9-18h £8, overnight stay £15. 🚐 ⛟ **Location:** Urban, simple, central.
Surface: asphalted. ▢ 01/01-31/12
Distance: ⬛200m ⊗200m ⬛200m.

| 🛉 S | **Stratford-upon-Avon** 🌼 | 1C5 |

The New Inn Hotel, Clifford Chambers. **GPS:** n52,16929 w1,7168. ⬆.

5 ⬛£8 ⌁ ⚷ £4,80. ⛟ 📖 **Location:** Rural, simple. **Surface:** grassy.
▢ 01/01-31/12
Distance: ⊗on the spot ⬛on the spot.

Tourist information Stratford-upon-Avon:
🛈 Birthplace of William Shakespeare.

| 🛉 S | **Tarrington** | 1C5 |

The Tarrington Arms, Ledbury road. **GPS:** n52,06473 w2,5604.

5 ⬛free WC free. **Location:** Rural, simple. **Surface:** metalled.
Distance: ⬛200m ⊗on the spot.

| S | **Tenby** | 1A5 |

Carew Airfield & Pavilion, Sageston. **GPS:** n51,69362 w4,80973. ⬆.

GB

5 🛏£15-20/night 🚰🚽Ch 🚿 WC included. 🚐 **Location:** Comfortable, quiet. **Surface:** concrete. 🔲 01/01-31/12
Distance: 🛥150m ⚓8km ⊗500m ⛽1,5km 🚌1,5km.

🅂	Thaxted	1D5

Margaret Street Car Park, Margaret Street. **GPS:** n51,95530 e0,34328. ⬆.

2 🛏free WC free. **Location:** Urban, simple, central, quiet. **Surface:** concrete. 🔲 01/01-31/12
Distance: 🚶150m 🚌150m.
Remarks: Max. 48h in fortnight.

🅂	Tintagel ⛟	1A6

King Arthur's Car Park, Fore Street. **GPS:** n50,66356 w4,75129. ⬆.
50 🛏£3 10.00-16h, £3 16-10h WC . 🚐 **Location:** Simple. **Surface:** asphalted. 🔲 16-10h
Distance: 🚶on the spot ⊗on the spot 🚌100m.
Remarks: Opposite Tintagel Old Post Office.

	Tintagel ⛟	1A6

Mayfair Car Park, Fore Street. **GPS:** n50,66329 w4,75103. ⬆.
50 🛏£2 8.00-20h, £3.50 20-08h. 🚐 **Location:** Urban, simple, central.
Surface: asphalted/grassy. 🔲 01/01-31/12
Distance: 🚶on the spot ⊗100m.
Remarks: Next to King Arthur's Car Park.

	Tintagel ⛟	1A6

Sword in Stone Car Park, Bossine Rd. **GPS:** n50,66257 w4,74763. ⬆.
20 🛏£2 10.00-20h, £3.50 20-10h. 🚐 **Location:** Urban, simple.
Surface: asphalted. 🔲 01/01-31/12
Distance: 🚶150m ⊗250m.

Tourist information Tintagel:
👁 Tintagel Old Post Office, Fore Street. 600 year-old traditional Cornish Longhouse.
🏰 King Arthur's Castle, Castle Road. 🔲 10-17/18h 🔘 24-26/12, 01/01.

	Torrington	1B6

Sydney House Car Park, South Street. **GPS:** n50,95121 w4,14438. ⬆.

20 🛏£5 18-10h, £3 day. 🚐 **Location:** Urban, simple, quiet.
Surface: asphalted. 🔲 01/01-31/12
Distance: 🚶300m ⊗250m ⛽250m.
Remarks: Max. 2 nights, min. 6m space between motorhomes.

	Westward Ho! ⛟🌊	1B6

Main Car Park, Golf Links Rd. **GPS:** n51,04069 w4,23728. ⬆.

8 🛏£5 18-10h, £7 day. 🚐 **Location:** Urban, simple, central, quiet.
Surface: asphalted. 🔲 01/01-31/12
Distance: 🚶on the spot ⚓200m ⊗200m ⛽150m.
Remarks: Max. 5000kg, min. 6m space between motorhomes.

🍴🅂	Whaplode St. Catherines	1D5

The Bleu Bell Inn, Cranesgate S. **GPS:** n52,75956 w0,0155. ⬆.
5 🛏£5, free with a meal 🚰🚽Ch 🚿 (2x)£2,50/night. 🚐 **Location:** Simple.
🔲 01/01-31/12 🔘 Mo
Distance: ⊗on the spot.

	Winchester	1C6

Car Park, Worthy Lane, B3044. **GPS:** n51,06396 w1,31632.
🛏£4.
Remarks: Max. 24h.

🅂	Yeovil	1B6

Cartgate Truckstop and Picnic Area, A303/A3088 roundabout.
GPS: n50,96926 w2,74087. 🏕 .

20 🛏free WC 📶 Password at the restaurant. **Location:** Highway, simple, noisy.
Surface: asphalted/metalled. 🔲 01/01-31/12
Distance: 🚶15km ⊗on the spot.

GB

THE NETHERLANDS

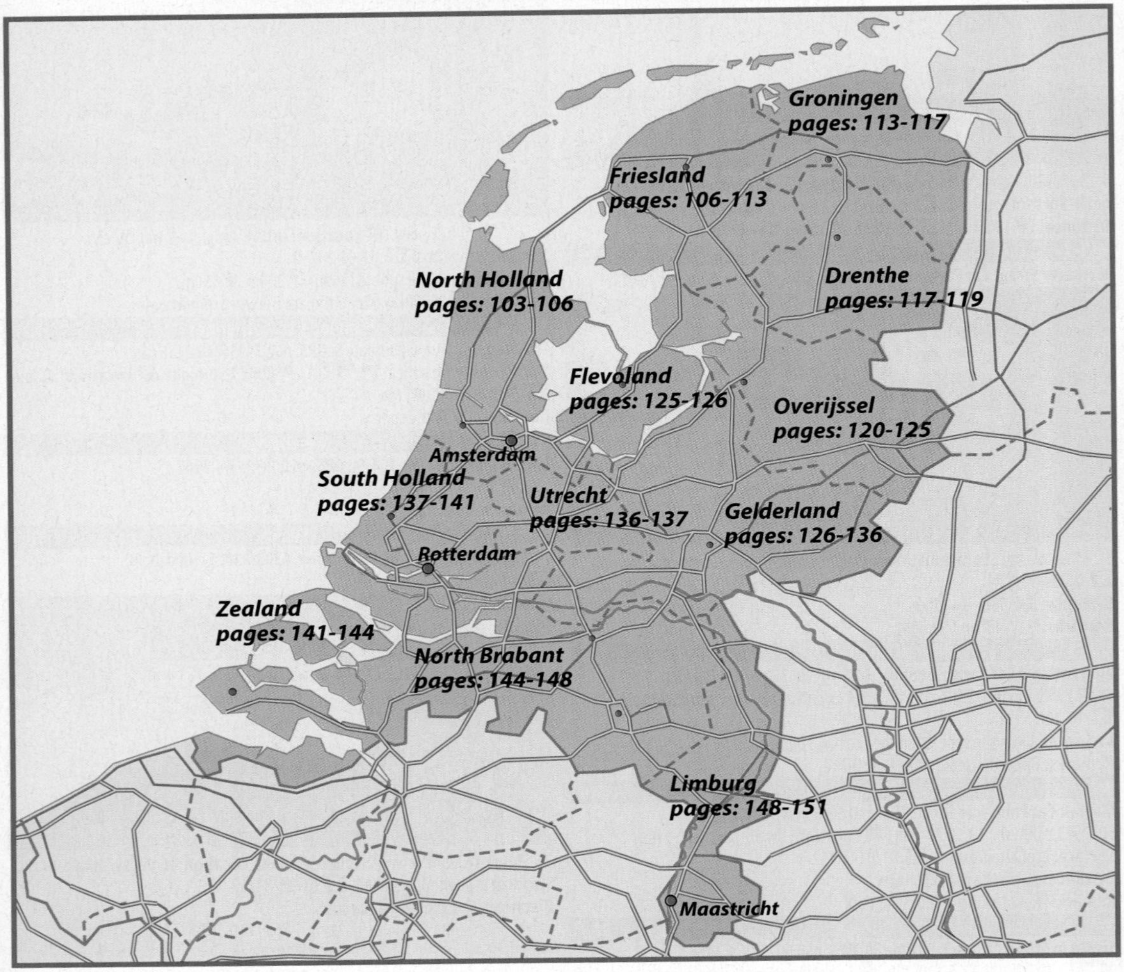

Groningen
pages: 113-117

Friesland
pages: 106-113

North Holland
pages: 103-106

Drenthe
pages: 117-119

Flevoland
pages: 125-126

Overijssel
pages: 120-125

Amsterdam

South Holland
pages: 137-141

Utrecht
pages: 136-137

Gelderland
pages: 126-136

Rotterdam

Zealand
pages: 141-144

North Brabant
pages: 144-148

Limburg
pages: 148-151

Maastricht

NL

Capital: Amsterdam
Government: Constitutional monarchy
Official Language: Dutch
Population: 16,805,000 (2013)
Area: 41, 526 km²

General information
Country dial code: 0031
General emergency: 112
Currency: Euro
Credit cards are not accepted everywhere.

Regulations for overnight stays
Wild camping is forbidden in the Netherlands. Several motorhome-friendly municipalities have regulated facilities where overnight parking is allowed.

Additional public holidays 2015
April 27 King's day
May 5 Liberation day
May 25 Pentecost Monday
December 26 Boxing day

North Holland

☕S Abbenes 🌿✿ 8A2
Hoeve 't Groene Hart, Kaagweg 50. **GPS:** n52,22630 e4,61911.⬆

15 🚐€ 10, Apr-May € 12, 2 pers. incl 🚰🔌Ch included 💦
(6x)€2/24h,10Amp WC€0,50 🚽€1 🔊. 🚿 **Location:** Rural, comfortable, quiet.
Surface: grassy/gravel. ◻ 15/03-01/11
Distance: 🚶4km 🏊900m 🛒1,5km ⊗1,5km 🚊4km 🚆Leiden
<> Amsterdam 🚲 on the spot 🎣 on the spot.
Remarks: Bicycle rental € 11/day.

☕S Amsterdam 🌿✿🍺 8B1
Amsterdam City Camp, Papaverweg 55. **GPS:** n52,39847 e4,90010.⬆

60 🚐€ 15, Jul/Aug € 20, 2 pers. Incl 🚰€2/100liter 🔌Ch 💦 (30x)€3,10Amp
🔊included 📷.🛒📷 **Location:** Urban, comfortable. **Surface:** metalled.
◻ 01/01-31/12
Distance: 🚶2km 🛒20m ⊗100m 🚊1km 🛒1,5km 🚆500m.
Remarks: Video surveillance, free ferry to city centre.

△S Amsterdam 🌿✿🍺 8B1
Het Amsterdamse Bos, Kleine Noorddijk 1, Amsterdam-zuid.
GPS: n52,29271 e4,82171.
100 🚐€ 9 + € 5/pp 🚰🔌Ch 💦€4,50 WC 🔌📷. ◻ 15/03-01/12
Distance: 🚶1km on the spot ⊗on the spot 🚊on the spot 🚆100m.

☕S Amsterdam 🌿✿🍺 8B1
Fam. Ackermann, Lutkemeerweg 149, Amsterdam-Osdorp.
GPS: n52,36358 e4,77240.⬆

16 🚐€ 10-12, 2 pers.incl, >7m: +€ 1/m 🚰€3 🔌Ch 💦€4,50/day.
🚿
Surface: metalled.
◻ 01/01-31/12
Distance: 🚶10km city centre 🚊2km 🚆Tram > Amsterdam 1,2km.
Remarks: Via Osdorperweg, special license.

Tourist information Amsterdam:
ℹ VVV, Stationsplein 10 en Leidseplein 1, www.iamsterdam.com. City Card
gives entrance to museums, public transport, boattrip on the canals etc.,
24h/€ 47, 48h/€57, 72h/€ 67, available at VVV.

👁 Canalbus. Boat trip on the canals. 🎫 € 13.
⚔ Stelling van Amsterdam. Forts built to protect Amsterdam.
🎭 Albert Cuyp, Albert Cuyp. Market with over 260 stalls.
◻ daily ◼ Su.
🎭 Antiek, Noordermarkt. ◻ Sa 9-17h.
😊 Artis. City-zoo. ◻ 9-17/18h.
🛍 Villa Arena. Furniture mall, 80 shops.
◻ Tue-Sa 10-18h, Mo 13-18h.

☕S De Rijp 🌊 8B1
Bloembolbedrijf Stoop, Zuiddijk 34. **GPS:** n52,54813 e4,83416.

4 🚐€ 7 🚰€1/100liter 💦 (4x)€2/day. 🚿 **Location:** Rural, simple, quiet.
Surface: concrete. ◻ 01/01-31/12
Distance: 🚶3km 🏊200m 🛒200m ⊗3km 🚊3km.

⚓S Den Helder 🌊 3B6
Willemsoord, Willemsoord 47. **GPS:** n52,96134 e4,76856.⬆

15 🚐€ 10 🚰€0,50/80liter 🔌Ch 💦 (3x) 🚽€0,50 🔊€3. 🚿
Location: Simple, central, quiet. **Surface:** metalled.
◻ 01/01-31/12
Distance: 🚶400m 🏊300m 🛒300m ⊗400m 🚊1km 🚆600m.
Remarks: Max. 48h, caution key sanitary € 15, ferry boat to Texel 500m.

⚓S Den Oever 🌊 3B6
Haventerrein Oostkade, Oostkade 3. **GPS:** n52,93395 e5,03974.⬆

10 🚐€ 10 🚰€0,50/100liter 🔌€0,50 Ch 💦 (8x) WC 🔌included. 🚿
Location: Highway, simple, isolated, noisy. **Surface:** metalled.
◻ 01/01-31/12
Distance: 🚶500m 🏊1,4km 🏊200m 🛒offshore fishing ⊗500m 🚊500m
🚆on the spot.
Remarks: At old harbour, max. 3 days, saturday-morning fishmarket.

☕S Enkhuizen 🌿✿🍺 3B6
Gependam, Dirck Chinaplein. **GPS:** n52,69806 e5,29005.⬆

6 🗲 € 10,50/12-12h ⌐ WC € 0,20 🗋 € 1. 🖳 **Location:** Urban, simple, central.
Surface: asphalted.
◻ 01/01-31/12
Distance: 🚰1km 🏊on the spot ⛽on the spot ⊗100m 🛒1km 🔲100m.
Remarks: Max. 48h.

Tourist information Enkhuizen:
Ⓜ Zuiderzeemuseum. Historical little town. ◻ Apr-autumn holiday 10-17/18h.

| ⚓ S | Hoorn 🌿 ◢ | 8B1 |

Jachthaven Hoorn, Visserseiland 221. **GPS:** n52,63467 e5,05676. ⬆.

20 🗲 € 13,75 ⌐ 🔌 Ch 💧 WC included 🗋 € 0,50. 🚿 ◢ **Location:** Quiet.
Surface: metalled. ◻ 01/04-31/10
Distance: 🚰500m ◢ 2,8km 🏊on the spot ⊗100m 🛒on the spot.
Remarks: Check in at harbourmaster.

| 🖳 | Huizen ◢ | 8B1 |

Recreatieterrein Wolskamer, IJsselmeerstraat. **GPS:** n52,30860 e5,24046. ⬆.

8 🗲free. **Location:** Simple, quiet. **Surface:** grassy. ◻ 01/01-31/12
Distance: 🚰1km 🏊200m ⛽200m 🛒1km 🛒Lidl 300m 🚲on the spot
🚶on the spot.
Remarks: Max. 48h, service at harbourmaster.

Tourist information Huizen:
⛲ ◻ Sa.

| 🖳 | Katwoude | 8B1 |

De Simonehoeve, Wagenweg 2. **GPS:** n52,48620 e5,03196. ⬆.

10 🗲free. **Location:** Simple. **Surface:** asphalted. ◻ 01/01-31/12
Distance: 🚰2km 🏊2km ⛽2km ⊗on the spot 🛒2km 🔲100m.
Remarks: Cheese farm, nearby Hotel Volendam, free guided tour.

| 🖳 S | Laren | 8B1 |

Sportcomplex De Biezem, Schapendrift 64. **GPS:** n52,25717 e5,23884.

2 🗲free ⌐ 🔌 Ch WC 🗋. **Surface:** metalled. ◻ 01/01-31/12
Distance: ◢1km.
Remarks: Max. 1 night.

| ⚓ S | Medemblik 🌿 ◢ | 3B6 |

Haven Medemblik, Pekelharinghaven 50. **GPS:** n52,77139 e5,11361. ⬆.

3 🗲 € 8 + € 0,70/pp tourist tax 🔌 Ch 💧 € 1,75 🗋. 🚿 ◢ **Location:** Simple,
quiet. **Surface:** metalled. ◻ 01/01-31/12
Distance: 🚰1km 🏊200m ⛽on the spot ⊗50m 🛒1km 🚲50m
🚶on the spot.
Remarks: Max. 48h, check in at harbourmaster.

Tourist information Medemblik:
Ⓜ Museum Stoomtram. Steam tram museum: Hoorn-Medemblik.

| ⚓ S | Middenmeer | 3B6 |

Jachthaven Middenmeer, Havenstraat. **GPS:** n52,81236 e4,99112. ⬆.

7 🗲 € 10 ⌐ 🔌 Ch 💧 WC included 🗋 🔲 € 5/2 💧 € 2. **Location:** Comfortable.
Surface: metalled. ◻ 01/01-31/12
Distance: 🚰500m ◢ 1,7km 🏊50m ⛽50m ⊗500m 🔲150m
🚲on the spot.
Remarks: Max. 48h, check in at harbourmaster.

| ⚓ S | Monnickendam 🌿 ◢ | 8B1 |

Jachthaven Waterland, Galgeriet 5a. **GPS:** n52,45920 e5,04059. ⬆.

6 🛏 € 17,50 ⚹stay 🔧Ch ⚹€0,50/2kWh WC ⬛🔲€4,50 📶included.
Location: Urban, simple, quiet. **Surface:** metalled. ⬛ 30/04-15/10
Distance: 🚶500-800m ⚹on the spot ⊗on the spot.
Remarks: Check in at harbourmaster, caution sepkey € 20, bookins in peak season.

⚓S   Naarden 🌿⚹🛶   8B1
Jachthaven Naarden, Onderwal 4. **GPS:** n52,30874 e5,14703.⬆.

10 🛏 € 12.50 + € 2/pp tourist tax ⚹🔧Ch ⚹WC ⬛€5/3 📶included.
⚹🌊**Location:** Rural, comfortable, quiet. **Surface:** grassy/metalled.
⬛ 01/01-31/12
Distance: 🚶Naarden-vesting (fortress) 2,3km ⚹600m ⚹500m lake Gooi
⊗on the spot ⚹on the spot ⚹on the spot.
Tourist information Naarden:
Ⓜ Vestingmuseum. Fortress museum. ⬛ 01/03-31/10 Tue-Fri 10.30-17h,
weekend 12-17h, summer Mo-Fri, 01/11-28/02 Su 12-17h.

Oosthuizen   8B1
Recreatieknooppunt Oosthuizen, Hoornse Jaagweg. **GPS:** n52,57609 e4,99719. ⬆.

2 🛏free. **Location:** Rural, isolated, noisy. **Surface:** asphalted.
⬛ 01/01-31/12
Distance: 🚶250m ⚹on the spot ⚹on the spot ⊗200m ⚹500m ⚹100m
> Volendam ⚹on the spot ⚹on the spot.
Remarks: Max. 48h.

🛏S   Opperdoes   3B6
Imkerij de Bijenstal, Zwarte pad. **GPS:** n52,76255 e5,08027.

3 🛏€ 11,10, 2 pers.incl ⚹stay ⚹(2x)€3,50 📶. ⚹**Location:** Rural, simple, isolated, quiet. **Surface:** gravel.
Distance: 🚶500m ⚹2km ⚹300m ⚹500m. **Remarks:** Boat rental.
Tourist information Opperdoes:
Ⓜ Museum stoomtram, Medemblik. Steam tram museum: Hoorn-Medemblik.
Ⓣ € 12.

🚻   Oudendijk 🛶   8B1
Bruin Eetcafé Les Deux Ponts, Slimdijk 2. **GPS:** n52,60462 e4,95983.⬆.

10 🛏free, use of a meal obligated. **Location:** Rural, simple, quiet.
Surface: gravel. ⬛ 01/01-31/12 ⬛ Tue
Distance: 🚶2km ⚹on the spot ⚹on the spot ⊗on the spot.

🛏S   Purmerend 🏺🛶   8B1
Het Bolwerk, Nieuwstraat. **GPS:** n52,50681 e4,95049.⬆.

5 🛏€ 6,90 ⚹€1 ⚹€0,15/h. 🏠**Location:** Urban, simple, quiet.
Surface: metalled. ⬛ 01/01-31/12 ⬛ water: 01/11-01/04
Distance: 🚶200m ⊗200m.
Remarks: Max. 72h, tuesday morning market.
Tourist information Purmerend:
⚹ Centrum. ⬛ Tue.

⚓S   Schagen 🌿⚹🏺🛶   3B6
Jachthaven Schagen, Lagedijkerweg 2B. **GPS:** n52,79088 e4,78746.⬆.

15 🛏€ 5,10 + € 0,80/pp tourist tax ⚹€0,50/100liter 🔧Ch ⚹€1,50
WC ⬛€0,50 ⬛€4/4 📶€1. ⚹**Surface:** metalled. ⬛ 01/01-31/12
Distance: 🚶500m ⚹on the spot ⊗400m ⚹500m.
Remarks: Check in at harbourmaster, caution key sanitary building € 15.
Tourist information Schagen:
⚹ West Friese Folkloremarkt. Folkore market. ⬛ Jun-Jul-Aug: Thu.

🛏S   Slootdorp   3B6
De Tulpentuin, Wierweg 7. **GPS:** n52,85627 e5,01010.⬆.

NL

10 ⌼€ 10 ⌁▤Ch ⚲ (14x) WC ⌁ included. ▥ **Location:** Rural, isolated, quiet. **Surface:** gravel. ◯ 01/01-31/12
Distance: ⌁Wieringerwerf 2km ⌁2,6km ⌁Deen 1,9km.
Remarks: At tulip grower.

⍟	**Stompetoren**	8B1

Het Schermer Wapen, Oterlekerweg 3. **GPS:** n52,61285 e4,82096. ⬆ .

4 ⌼free, use of a meal obligated. **Location:** Urban, simple. **Surface:** gravel.
◯ 01/01-31/12 ◉ Wed
Distance: ⌁500m ⊗on the spot ⌁500m.

▣	**Texel/De Cocksdorp**	3B5

De Krim, Roggeslootweg 6. **GPS:** n53,15110 e4,85996.
10 ⌼€ 16-€ 26. **Surface:** metalled. ◯ 01/01-31/12

▣ S	**Volendam** ❀ ⛴ ▨	8B1

Marinapark Volendam, De Pieterman 1. **GPS:** n52,48944 e5,05972. ⬆➡ .

36 ⌼€ 6 10-17h, € 14 17-10h ⌁▤Ch ⚲ included ◉€5 ⌁. ▥
Location: Comfortable, quiet.
Surface: grasstiles/metalled.
◯ 01/01-31/12
Distance: ⌁1,5km ⌁50m ⌁50m ⊗300m ⌁300m ⌁300m.

Tourist information Volendam:
ℹ VVV, Zeestraat 37, www.vvv-volendam.nl. Old fishermen's village.
M Volendams Museum, Zeestraat 41. Life and Work in Volendam, 1800-1900.
◯ Easter-autumn holiday 10-17h.

Friesland

▣ S	**Akkrum**	3C5

Tusken de Marren, Ulbe Twijnstrawei 31. **GPS:** n53,04853 e5,82577.

20 ⌼€ 12,50 ⌁€0,50/100liter ▤Ch ⚲€2/night WC ⌁€0,50/time ⌁free.
Surface: grassy/metalled. ◯ 15/03-01/11
Distance: ⌁200m ⌁on the spot ⌁on the spot ⌁700m ⌁500m.
Remarks: Information at harbourmaster, boat rental.

▣ S	**Anjum**	3D5

It Tún-Hûs, Bantswei 1a. **GPS:** n53,37751 e6,12999. ⬆➡ .

8 ⌼€ 10 ⌁▤Ch ⚲ ⌁. **Surface:** metalled. ◯ 01/04-01/11
Distance: ⌁300m ⊗350m ⌁550m.

▣ S	**Appelscha** ▨	3D6

De Compagnonshoeve, Vaart Noordzijde 104. **GPS:** n52,95222 e6,36278. ⬆ .

10 ⌼€ 8 ⌁▤Ch ⚲€1,50 ⌁included. ▥ **Location:** Rural, simple, quiet.
Surface: grassy. ◯ 01/01-31/12
Distance: ⌁on the spot ⌁3km ⌁on the spot ⊗200m ⌁400m ◉400m
⌁50m.

▣ S	**Balk** ⛴ ▨	3C6

Jachthaven Lutsmond, Sleatemar 1a. **GPS:** n52,90389 e5,59694.

10 ⌼€ 10 excl. tourist tax ⌁▤Ch ⚲€2,50 WC ⌁. **Surface:** grassy.
◯ 01/01-31/12
Distance: ⌁1km ⌁on the spot ⌁on the spot ⊗nearby ⌁1km.

▣ S	**Bergum** ❀ ⛴ ▨	3C5

Camperterrein Prinses Margriet Kanaal, Opperdijk van Veenweg 22.
GPS: n53,18643 e6,00176. ⬆➡ .

NL

25 ⌇ € 10/night ⛽ 🗑 Ⓒincluded 🚿 €2/night 📶1h free, 1 day €7,50.
🚐 **Location:** Urban, comfortable, quiet. **Surface:** grassy/metalled.
🗓 01/01-31/12
Distance: 🛒2km 🏊2km ⛽on the spot ⊗2km 💊2km 🏥on the spot
🚲on the spot 🚶on the spot.

| ⚓ S | Bergum 🌿🏖🚣 | 3C5 |

Jachthaven Burgumerdaam, Bergumerdaam 51. **GPS**: n53,18705 e5,99299.⬆

10 ⌇ € 10 ⛽ €0,50/100liter 🗑 Ⓒh 🚿 €0,50/kWh WC 🚽€0,50/5minutes
🚿€3,50/3,50 📶included. 🚐 **Location:** Urban, comfortable, central, quiet.
Surface: metalled. 🗓 15/03-01/11
Distance: 🛒500m 🏊500m ⛵5km ⛽on the spot ⊗500m 💊500m
🏥500m 🚲on the spot 🚶on the spot.
Remarks: Max. 72h.

| 🚐 S | Bolsward 🌿 | 3C5 |

Camperplaats Half-Hichtum, Hichtumerweg 14. **GPS**: n53,07365 e5,52253.⬆

6 ⌇ € 14 ⛽ 🗑 Ⓒh 🚿 WC 🚽included 🚿€3,50/time 📶. 🚐 **Location:** Rural,
comfortable, quiet. **Surface:** grassy/metalled. 🗓 01/04-01/11
Distance: 🛒1km 🏊1,3km ⛵6km ⛽500m ⊗1km 💊1km 🏥200m
🚲on the spot 🚶on the spot.

| 🚐 S | Brantgum | 3C5 |

Camperplaats Veldzicht, Veldbuurtsterweg 9. **GPS**: n53,35556 e5,93632.⬆

20 ⌇ € 11 ⛽ 🗑 Ⓒh 🚿 📶included. 🚐 **Location:** Rural, comfortable,
isolated, quiet. **Surface:** grassy/metalled. 🗓 01/01-31/12
Distance: 🛒Dokkum 7km ⛽2km ⊗3km 💊3km 🏥on the spot
🚶on the spot.

Remarks: Ferry boat to Ameland 3km.

| 🚐 S | Burdaard 🚣 | 3C5 |

Jachthaven Mouneheim, Mounewei 17. **GPS**: n53,29711 e5,88261.⬆.

12 ⌇ € 10 ⛽ 🗑 Ⓒh 🚿 €1/night, 10Amp WC 🚽€0,50/5minutes 🚿€4,50/2,50
📶included. 🚐 **Location:** Rural, comfortable, quiet. **Surface:** grassy/gravel.
🗓 01/01-31/12
Distance: 🛒on the spot 🏊2km ⛵on the spot ⛽on the spot ⊗100m
💊500m 🏥2km 🚲on the spot 🚶on the spot.
Remarks: Passerby € 1/100l.

| 🚐 | Dokkum 🌿 | 3C5 |

Kalkhuisplein, Kalkhuisplein. **GPS**: n53,32650 e6,00936.⬆.

3 ⌇ € 5. 🚐 **Location:** Urban, simple, quiet. **Surface:** metalled.
🗓 15/03-31/12
Distance: 🛒500m 🏊1km ⛵20m ⛽20m ⊗1km 💊1km 🏥1km
🚲on the spot 🚶on the spot.
Remarks: Max. 1 night, only overnight stays 18-9h.

| | Drachten | 3D5 |

VV Drachten, Gauke Boelensstraat. **GPS**: n53,10289 e6,08832.⬆.

5 ⌇ free. **Surface:** asphalted.
Distance: 🛒500m 💊500m.

| 🚐 S | Earnewâld | 3C5 |

Eilansgrien. **GPS**: n53,12958 e5,93630.⬆ ➡.

5 ⌇ € 5,40 + € 0,80/pp tourist tax ⛽ 🗑 Ⓒh 🚿 stay WC 🚽€0,50 🚿€3,50/3,50
📶. **Surface:** asphalted. 🗓 01/01-31/12
Distance: 🛒200m 🏊500m 💊200m.

Remarks: Max. 72h, sanitary/washing machine at tourist office (Summer season).

Harlingen 3C5

Tsjerk Hiddesluizen, Nieuwe Vissershaven 17. **GPS**: n53,17938 e5,41731.

10 €7,50 €1 Ch (16x)€1/2kWh WC . **Surface:** asphalted.
Distance: 500m 500m 500m 100m.
Remarks: Max. 72h, laundromat/toilets/shower 500m.

Heerenveen 3C6

Thialf, Pim Mulierlaan 1. **GPS**: n52,93843 e5,94495.

4 free. **Surface:** metalled.
01/01-31/12 during event
Distance: 2km 2km 2km.
Remarks: On parking ground of skating rink, max. 72h.

Heerenveen 3C6

De Koningshof, Prinsenweg 1. **GPS**: n52,94759 e5,94438.

4 free. **Surface:** asphalted. 01/01-31/12
Distance: 1km on the spot 4km 500m.
Remarks: Large parking near A32, max. 72h.

Heerenveen 3C6

Gemeentewerf, Venus 4. **GPS**: n52,96663 e5,93502.
free. Mon-Fri 9-15u

Hogebeintum 3C5

Bezoekerscentrum Terp Hegebeintum, Pijpkedijk 4. **GPS**: n53,33612 e5,85266.

4 free. **Location:** Simple, isolated. **Surface:** asphalted.
Distance: 4km.
Remarks: Parking information centre/VVV, highest mound in the Netherlands, max. 2 days, ferry boat to Ameland 3km.

IJlst 3C6

De Tsjalk, De Tsjalk. **GPS**: n53,00846 e5,62741.

4 free WC free €0,50/5minutes. **Location:** Urban, simple, central, quiet. **Surface:** metalled. 01/01-31/12
Distance: 200m on the spot 200m 200m 200m on the spot on the spot.

Joure 3C6

Jachthaven, Grienedyk. **GPS**: n52,97210 e5,78836.

4 € 16,50 €0,50/70liter €3 €1. **Surface:** metalled.
01/03-01/11
Distance: 500m 50m.
Remarks: Max. 72h.

Kollum 3D5

Jachthaven de Rijd, Cantecleer 2. **GPS**: n53,28727 e6,15139.

12 €9 Ch €1,50/night,10Amp WC €1/time included.
Location: Urban, simple, central, quiet. **Surface:** metalled.
01/05-01/10
Distance: on the spot on the spot 500m 500m 500m on the spot on the spot.
Remarks: Max. 72h.

Koudum 3C6

De Kuilart, De Kuilart 1. **GPS**: n52,90305 e5,46706.

10 + 2 🚐 € 10, Quick-Stop € 8 🚰🔌Ch included 🔌€1/night,6 Amp
WC 🚽€0,35/5minutes 📶€4,40/2,35 📶. 🚿 **Location:** Rural, luxurious,
noisy. **Surface:** grassy/metalled. ⬛ 01/01-07/05, 22/05-05/07, 25/08-31/12
◉ holidays
Distance: 🛒1,5km 🏊on the spot 🚶on the spot ⊗on the spot 🚆1km
🚌1km 🚲on the spot 🎣on the spot.

⚓S	Langweer 🏊🛶	3C6

Brandweerkazerne, Pontdyk. **GPS:** n52,96000 e5,71972. ⬆️

4 🚐free. **Location:** Simple. **Surface:** metalled. ⬛ 01/01-31/12
Distance: 🛒500m 🏊500m ⊗500m 🚆500m.
Remarks: Max. 72h.

⚓S	Langweer 🏊🛶	3C6

Passantenhaven Langweer, Pontsdyk. **GPS:** n52,96091 e5,72240. ⬆️

3 🚐€ 7,50 + € 1/pp tourist tax 🚰€0,20 🔌Ch 🔌€2 WC 🚽€0,50
📶€3,50/3,50 📶.
Surface: grassy. ⬛ 01/04-31/10
Distance: 🛒500m 🏊on the spot 🚶on the spot ⊗500m 🚆500m 🚌500m.

🚐S	Leeuwarden 🌿🏊🛶	3C5

Prinsentuin, Wissesdwinger 1. **GPS:** n53,20528 e5,79659. ⬆️

4 🚐€ 9,08 🚰🔌Ch 🔌€0,34/kWh,6 Amp WC 🚽📶€4,31/3 📶included.
🏠 **Location:** Urban, comfortable, central, quiet. **Surface:** metalled.
⬛ 01/01-31/12 ◉ sanitary building: 01/11-01/04
Distance: 🛒on the spot 🚲2km 🏊on the spot 🚶on the spot ⊗on the spot
🚆on the spot 🚌on the spot 🎣on the spot 🏃on the spot.

🚐S	Leeuwarden 🌿🏊🛶	3C5

Harlingertrekweg. **GPS:** n53,19839 e5,77098. ⬆️

5 🚐free. **Location:** Noisy. **Surface:** metalled. ⬛ 01/01-31/12
Distance: 🛒1km ⊗1km 🚆1km 🚌500m.

🚐S	Leeuwarden 🌿🏊🛶	3C5

Taniaburg, Vierhuisterweg 72. **GPS:** n53,21955 e5,79286. ⬆️➡️

8 🚐€ 11,10 🚰🔌Ch 🔌€2,40/night,6 Amp WC 🚽📶€2,50/3
📶 included. 🚿 **Location:** Rural, comfortable, quiet. **Surface:** grassy/gravel.
⬛ 01/04-01/11
Distance: 🛒3km 🚲1km 🏊on the spot 🚶on the spot 🚆500m 🚌500m
🚲on the spot 🏃on the spot.
Remarks: Canoe and bicycle rental.

⚓S	Leeuwarden 🌿🏊🛶	3C5

Leeuwarder Jachthaven, Jachthavenlaan 3. **GPS:** n53,19886 e5,83019. ⬆️➡️

6 🚐€ 12,50 🚰🔌Ch 🔌WC 🚽€1/5minutes 📶included. 🚿
Location: Urban, comfortable, isolated, quiet. **Surface:** grassy/gravel.
⬛ 01/01-31/12
Distance: 🛒2,5km 🚲1km 🏊on the spot 🚶on the spot ⊗500m 🚆500m
📶300m 🚲on the spot 🏃on the spot.
Remarks: Check in at harbourmaster.

⚓S	Lemmer 🌿🏊🛶	3C6

Jachthaven Lemmer, Plattedijk 4-12. **GPS:** n52,84708 e5,69696. ⬆️

29 🚐€ 13, 2 pers.incl, tourist tax € 1/pp 🚰€0,50 🔌Ch 🔌€0,50 WC 🚽€0,50.
Surface: metalled. ⬛ 01/01-31/12
Distance: 🛒1km 🚲2,7km 🏊on the spot 🚆1km.

⚓S	Lemmer 🌿🏊🛶	3C6

Watersportcentrum Tacozijl, Plattedijk 20. **GPS:** n52,85104 e5,68189.

NL

20 ⌀ € 12 ⌂ ⌧ Ch ⌨ €3 WC ⌐included �“ ⌘.
Surface: grassy/metalled.
⬛ 01/01-31/12
Distance: ⌷centre 2,2km ⌥3km ⌇on the spot.
Tourist information Lemmer:
⌑ Ir. D.F. Woudagemaal. The biggest steam pumpingstation of Europe.

⌂⬛S Makkum ⌇⌧⌐ 3C5
Gemeentehaven Makkum, Workumerdijk 2. **GPS:** n53,05329 e5,40317.⬆.

2 ⌀ € 10 Ch WC ⌐included ⌘€2/2. ⌧
Location: Urban, simple, central, noisy. **Surface:** metalled.
⬛ 01/04-31/10 ⌧ service: 01/11-01/04
Distance: ⌷100m ⌐on the spot ⌧400m ⌘950m ⌐950m ⌧on the spot ⌧on the spot.
Remarks: Max. 72h.

⌐S Mirns ⌇⌧ 3C6
De Braamberg, Murnserdyk. **GPS:** n52,85249 e5,48190.⬆.

10 ⌀ € 10 + € 1/pp tourist tax ⌂ ⌧ Ch included ⌨ €2 WC ⌐⌘.
Location: Rural. **Surface:** gravel. ⬛ 01/01-31/12
Distance: ⌇beach 250m.

⌀S Molkwerum 3C6
Camperplaats 't Seleantsje, 't Seleantsje 2. **GPS:** n52,90419 e5,39493.⬆.

18 ⌀ € 10 ⌂ ⌧ Ch ⌨ WC included ⌐€0,50/6minutes ⌘€4/2,50 ⌘€5/day.
⌧ **Location:** Rural, comfortable, quiet. **Surface:** grasstiles. ⬛ 15/03-01/11
Distance: ⌷300m ⌇on the spot ⌐on the spot ⌧on the spot ⌘4km ⌐1km ⌧on the spot ⌧on the spot.

⌀S Nes 3C5
Manege Nes, Burdineweg 2. **GPS:** n53,05468 e5,85558.⬆⌐.

10 ⌀ €3 ⌂ ⌧ Ch ⌨ €2/night,16 Amp WC ⌘included. ⌧ **Location:** Rural, simple, quiet. **Surface:** grassy/metalled. ⬛ 01/01-31/12
Distance: ⌷700m ⌥1km ⌇10km ⌐50m ⌧700m ⌘700m ⌐700m ⌧on the spot ⌧on the spot.
Remarks: At manege.

⌐ Nijetrijne 3C6
Paviljoen Driewegsluis, Lindedijk 2a. **GPS:** n52,83261 e5,92467.

⌀customers free.
Distance: ⌐on the spot ⌧on the spot.

⌂⬛S Oudega ⌐ 3C5
Jachthaven Oudega, Roundeel. **GPS:** n53,12315 e5,99961.⬆.

2 ⌀ € 7 ⌂ ⌨ €1/100liter ⌨ €1 ⌐€0,50. **Location:** Simple. **Surface:** grassy.
⬛ 01/04-01/11
Distance: ⌷200m ⌧200m ⌘200m.
Remarks: Max. 48h.

⌀S Oudemirdum ⌧ 3C6
Landgoed de Syme, Jan Schotanuswei 106a, via Oude Balksterweg.
GPS: n52,85746 e5,51115.⬆⌐.

2 ⌀ € 5 ⌂ included ⌨ €2,50/night. ⌧ **Location:** Rural, simple, isolated, quiet. **Surface:** grassy/metalled. ⬛ 01/01-31/12
Distance: ⌷4km ⌇6km ⌐6km ⌧4km ⌘4km ⌧on the spot ⌧on the spot.

NL

C S Oudeschoot 3C6

Woutersbergje, Van Bienemalaan 15-17. **GPS:** n52,93544 e5,96009. ⬆➡.

15 🚐 € 10,40 🚰 🍽 Ch 🧹 € 2/night,6 Amp WC 🚿 € 3/1 📶 included. 🛁 **Location:** Rural, comfortable, central, quiet. **Surface:** grassy/metalled. 📅 01/01-31/12
Distance: 🚲 3,5km 🍴 300m 🛒 on the spot 🚶 on the spot.

S Ried 3C5

Jachthaven it Kattegat, Berlikumerweg 13. **GPS:** n53,22416 e5,59330.

3 + 4 🚐 € 9,50. 🛁 **Location:** Rural, simple, quiet. **Surface:** grassy/metalled. 📅 01/04-01/10
Distance: 🚲 on the spot ⛵ 500m ⚓ on the spot 🍴 on the spot 🛒 500m 🛴 on the spot 🚶 on the spot.

S Rohel 3C6

Aktiviteitenboerderij, Vierhuisterweg 29. **GPS:** n52,90337 e5,84540.

5 🚐 € 15 🚰 🍽 Ch 🧹 WC 🚿 included. **Location:** Quiet. **Surface:** metalled. 📅 01/01-31/12
Distance: ⚓ on the spot 🍴 on the spot ⊗ on the spot 🛒 on the spot.

Sexbierum 3C5

Restaurant Liauckama State, Liauckamaleane 2. **GPS:** n53,22028 e5,47656.

5 🚐 € 10, free for clients. **Surface:** grassy/gravel. 📅 01/01-31/12
Distance: 🚲 1km 🍴 1km 🛒 1km.

S Sint Jacobiparochie 3C5

Zeedijk, Zwarte Haan. **GPS:** n53,30915 e5,63051. ⬆.

25 🚐 free. **Surface:** grassy. 📅 01/01-31/12
Distance: 🚲 Sint Jacobiparochie 8km 🌊 Wadden Sea ⊗ 100m 🛒 on the spot 🚶 on the spot.

⚓ S Sloten 3C6

Jachthaven Lemsterpoort, Jachthaven 7. **GPS:** n52,89265 e5,64486. ⬆➡.

10 🚐 € 12 🚰 € 0,50/100liter 🍽 Ch 🧹 € 2,50/24h,6 Amp WC 🚿 € 1/5minutes 📶 included. 🛁 **Location:** Urban, comfortable, quiet. **Surface:** grassy/metalled. 📅 01/01-31/12
Distance: 🚲 100m ⛵ 2km ⚓ on the spot 🍴 on the spot ⊗ 100m 🛒 100m 🛴 500m 🛒 on the spot 🚶 on the spot.

🍴 S Sneek 3C6

Amicitia Hotel Sneek, Alexanderstraat. **GPS:** n53,02378 e5,67595. ⬆➡.

10 🚐 € 7,50, free with a meal 🚰 🍽 Ch 🧹 📶 included. **Surface:** metalled. 📅 01/01-31/12
Distance: 🚲 1,5km 🍴 400m 🛒 8km ⊗ on the spot.
Remarks: Reservation during Sneek sailing week: : info@amicitiahotel.nl, 1st week of August.

⚓ S Sneek 3C6

Jachthaven Holiday Boatin, Eeltjebaasweg 3. **GPS:** n53,02184 e5,56702. ⬆.

4 🚐 € 12 🚰 🍽 Ch 🧹 € 1/night,10Amp WC 🚿 📶 included. 🛁 **Location:** Urban, comfortable, quiet. **Surface:** concrete. 📅 01/01-31/12
Distance: 🚲 3,6km ⛵ 2km ⚓ on the spot 🍴 on the spot ⊗ 4km 🛒 2km, bakery 300m 🛒 300m 🛒 on the spot 🚶 on the spot.

⚓ S Stavoren 3C6

Marina Stavoren, Suderstrand 2. **GPS:** n52,87398 e5,36762. ⬆.

NL

20 ⛽ € 12,50 + € 1/pp tourist tax, dog € 1 🚰 Ch ♨ (4x)€2 WC 📶 included.
Surface: metalled. 📷 01/04-31/10
Distance: 🛒300m 🏊on the spot 🍴on the spot ⊗on the spot 🚮300m
🚌500m 🚲on the spot 🎣on the spot.

🚐S	Sumar	3D5

Recreatiecentrum Bergumermeer, Solcamastraat 30.
GPS: n53,19044 e6,02316. ⬆➡

10 ⛽ € 18 🚰 Ch ♨ WC 📶 included. 🚿 **Location:** Rural, luxurious,
quiet. **Surface:** grassy/metalled. 📷 01/04-31/10
Distance: 🛒5km.

📷	Sumar	3D5

Recreatiecentrum Bergumermeer, Solcamastraat-30.
GPS: n53,19044 e6,02316.

1 ⛽ € 8 17-10h. 📷 01/04-31/10

🚐S	Surhuisterveen	3D5

Zwembad Wettervlecke, Badlaan 3. **GPS:** n53,17987 e6,16124. ⬆

5 ⛽ € 5 🚰€1 ♨€1 WC 📶 included. **Surface:** grassy.
Distance: 🛒500m 🚮500m.

🚐S	Tersoal	3C5

Watersportbedrijf Lege Geaen, Buorren 2. **GPS:** n53,07729 e5,74360. ⬆➡

6 ⛽ € 10 🚰 Ch ♨€2,50/night WC 📶included. 🚿 **Location:** Rural,
comfortable, quiet. **Surface:** grassy/gravel. 📷 01/01-31/12
Distance: 🛒8km 🚲1,5km 🏊on the spot 🍴on the spot ⊗1,5km 🚮8km
🚌on the spot 🎣on the spot.

⛴S	Wartena	3C5

Jachthaven Wartena, Stukenwei. **GPS:** n53,15145 e5,90532.

10 ⛽ € 10 🚰€0,50/100 ♨ Ch WC 📷€1 🚮€6 📶. **Location:** Central.
Surface: grassy/metalled. 📷 01/01-31/11
Distance: 🛒200m 🏊on the spot 🍴on the spot ⊗500m 🚮500m
🚌on the spot 🎣on the spot.
Remarks: Bicycle rental.

⛴S	Winsum	3C5

Camperplaats Winsum, Skans 12. **GPS:** n53,15177 e5,63111. ⬆

4 ⛽ € 12 🚰 Ch ♨ included WC 📷. **Location:** Simple.
📷 01/01-31/12

⛴S	Wommels	3C5

Jachthaven Wommels, Terp 14. **GPS:** n53,10957 e5,58765. ⬆

5 ⛽ € 10 🚰 Ch ♨ WC included 📷€0,50. 🚿 **Location:** Simple.
Surface: grassy/metalled. 📷 01/04-01/10
Distance: 🛒300m 🏊on the spot 🚮100m.
Remarks: Market 100m, museum 200m.
Tourist information Wommels:
🏕 📷 Tue-morning.

⛴S	Workum	3C6

Jachthaven Bouwsma, Moleburren 11. **GPS:** n52,98230 e5,45518. ⬆

NL

6 ⬛€ 10 🚿 🍴 Ch 🔌 €2,50/night, 6 Amp WC ⬛€1/7minutes 💧€8/0 📶included. 🚮
Location: Urban, central, quiet. **Surface:** grassy/metalled.
📅 01/04-31/10
Distance: 🚲750m ⛵1,5km 🚌on the spot ⊗500m 🛒500m 🚂200m 🚶on the spot 🏊on the spot.
Tourist information Workum:
Ⓜ Jopie Huisman Museum, Noard 6. Autodidact, paintings and drawings.
📅 01/04-31/10 10-17h, 01/03-30/11 + Su 13-17h.

Woudsend 3C6
Recreatiecentrum De Rakken, Lynbaen 10. **GPS:** n52,94649 e5,62732. ⬆➡

15 ⬛€ 17,50 + € 1/pp tourist tax 🚿 🍴Ch 🔌 WC ⬛included 💧€4,50/2,50 📶. **Surface:** grassy/metalled. 📅 15/03-15/10
Distance: 🚲200m ⛵2,5km 🚌200m ⊗200m 🛒200m.

Ypecolsga 3C6
Camperplaats Waterloo, Nr. 19. **GPS:** n52,92758 e5,59549. ⬆

13 ⬛€ 10, 2 pers.incl 🚿 🍴Ch 🔌 WC ⬛use sanitary €1,50/pp 💧€4,50/2 📶included. **Surface:** grasstiles. 📅 01/01-31/12
Distance: 🚲3km ⛵1km 🚌1km ⊗3,5km 🛒3,5km 🚂nearby 🚶on the spot.

Zurich 3C5
Camperplaats Zurich, Caspar di Roblesdijk 3. **GPS:** n53,11235 e5,39335. ⬆

3 ⬛€ 3. 🚮 **Location:** Urban, simple, central, noisy. **Surface:** metalled.
📅 01/01-31/12
Distance: 🚲on the spot ⛵1,5km ⛵on the spot 🚌on the spot

🚶on the spot 🏊on the spot.
Remarks: Max. 72h.

Zwaagwesteinde 3D5
Camperpark Kuikhorne, Kuikhornsterweg 31. **GPS:** n53,24124 e6,01875. ⬆➡

25 ⬛€ 9, 2 pers.incl 🚿€0,50 🍴 Ch 🔌 €1 WC ⬛€0,50 💧€4/3 📶€1. 🚮
Surface: asphalted/grassy. 📅 15/03-01/11
Distance: 🚲2km 🚌on the spot ⊗2km, pizzeria within walking distance 🛒2km. **Remarks:** Max. 72h, boat rental.

Groningen

Appingedam 4A5
Camperplaats Appingedam, Farmsumerweg 21. **GPS:** n53,32062 e6,86689. ⬆

10 ⬛free 🚿 🍴free 🔌€1/kWh, 10Amp. **Location:** Urban, simple, central, noisy. **Surface:** metalled. 📅 01/01-31/12
Distance: 🚲750m 🚌Damsterdiep ⊗500m 🛒500m 🚂on the spot 🚶on the spot 🏊on the spot.
Remarks: Max. 72h.

Blijham 4A5
Camperpark Turfstee, Turfweg 28. **GPS:** n53,11118 e7,02912. ⬆

55 ⬛€ 10 + € 0,75 tourist tax 🚿 🍴 Ch 🔌 WC ⬛€0,50 💧€7,50/0 📶included.
Location: Rural, comfortable, isolated. **Surface:** grassy/gravel.
Distance: 🚲3km ⊗3km 🛒3km 🚂on the spot 🚶on the spot.

Delfzijl 4A5
Zeebadweg, Zeebadweg. **GPS:** n53,33582 e6,92650. ⬆

NL

4 ⌁free.
Distance: 🛒500m ⚓on the spot 🛒on the spot ⊗100m 🚰300m.

| ⛵S | **Doezum** | 3D5 |

Landgoed Jonker, Provincialeweg 133a. **GPS**: n53,20411 e6,26018.⬆️➡️.

60 ⌁€ 10, 2 pers.incl 🚐 Ch ✂(20x)€1,50/night WC🚽 📶included.
Location: Luxurious.
Surface: grassy/metalled.
🅿️ 01/01-31/12 ◉ facilities 01/10-31/03
Distance: 🛒1,5km 🛒on the spot 🚴on the spot 🚶on the spot.
Tourist information Doezum:
👁 Abel Tasman Kabinet, Kompasstraat 1, Grootegast. Local archaeological museum seafarer Abel Tasman. 🅿️ Thu-Sa 13.30-16.30h.

| ⚓S | **Eenrum** | 3D5 |

Jachthaven De Dobbe, Dobbepad. **GPS**: n53,36311 e6,45151.⬆️➡️.

4 ⌁€ 3 + € 3/pp + € 1,15/pp tourist tax 🚐Ch ✂€2 WC included 🚽€0,50.
🚴 **Location:** Rural, simple, quiet. **Surface:** grassy/metalled.
Distance: 🛒500m 🛒on the spot ⊗500m 🚰500m.
Remarks: Check in at harbourmaster.

| ⛵ | **Groningen** | 3D5 |

Sportcentrum Kardinge, Bieskemaar. **GPS**: n53,23946 e6,59680.⬆️.

15 ⌁free. **Location:** Rural, simple, quiet. **Surface:** metalled.
🅿️ 01/01-31/12
Distance: 🛒3km 🚰1km 🛒on the spot.
Remarks: Max. 72h.
Tourist information Groningen:
👁 Prinsenhof en prinsenhoftuin. 🅿️ 15/03-15/10.

| ⛵ | **Haren** | 3D5 |

De Lijste, Meerweg. **GPS**: n53,16298 e6,57878.⬆️.
10 ⌁free. **Surface:** grassy.
Distance: 🏊1,3 ⚓no bathing ⊗250m.

| ⛵S | **Lauwersoog** | 3D5 |

Lauwersmeerplezier, Kustweg 30. **GPS**: n53,40625 e6,20044.

14 ⌁€ 15, 2 pers.incl 🚐 ✂ WC🚽included ◉€3. **Surface:** grassy/metalled.
🅿️ 01/01-31/12
Distance: 🛒500m ⚓on the spot 🛒on the spot ⊗500m 🚰500m.

| ⚓S | **Lauwersoog** | 3D5 |

Havenkantoor Lauwersoog, Haven 2. **GPS**: n53,40819 e6,19768.⬆️➡️.

2 ⌁€ 1,50/m 🚐Ch ✂ WC🚽included. 🚿 **Location:** Urban, simple, quiet.
Surface: metalled. 🅿️ 01/01-31/12
Distance: 🛒on the spot ⊗on the spot 🛒on the spot 🚴on the spot 🚶on the spot.

| ⚓S | **Lauwersoog** | 3D5 |

Jachthaven Noordergat, Noordergat 1. **GPS**: n53,40493 e6,20311.⬆️➡️.

30 ⌁€ 14 🚐 Ch included ✂€2,10/24h 🚽€0,50/5minutes ◉€3/2,50. 🚴
Location: Rural, simple, quiet. **Surface:** concrete.
🅿️ 01/01-31/12
Distance: 🛒on the spot ⊗on the spot 🚴on the spot 🚶on the spot.
Tourist information Lauwersoog:
🌿 Lauwersmeergebied. Breeding area for birds and recreation area. 🅿️ 01/04-31/10 Tue-Su 11-17h.

| ⛵S | **Leens** | 3D5 |

Leenstertillen. **GPS**: n53,35066 e6,37002.⬆️.

15 ⌁€ 6/pp 🚐Ch WC🚽included. 🚴 **Location:** Rural, simple, quiet.
Surface: grassy. 🅿️ 01/01-31/12
Distance: 🛒1,5km ⚓50m 🛒50m ⊗1,5km 🚰1,6km.

| 🍴S | **Losdorp** | 4A5 |

Restaurant Eemhaven, Schafferweg 29. **GPS**: n53,37214 e6,84411.⬆️.

4 🍴consuming is appreciated 🚰🗑Ch 🔌€5,customers WC 📶free 🗑.
Location: Rural, simple, quiet. **Surface:** metalled. ⬛ 01/01-31/12 ⬜ Mo
Distance: 🚲2km 🚂2km 🚌1km 🛒on the spot 🚶on the spot.
Remarks: Code wifi in restaurant.

⚓🅂 | **Lutjegast** | 3D5
't Kompas, Kompasstraat 1. **GPS:** n53,23498 e6,25972.

5 🍴free. **Surface:** metalled. ⬛ 01/01-31/12
Distance: 🚲on the spot 🛒on the spot 🚌200m 🚌on the spot.
Remarks: Behind the club-building.

⚓🅂 | **Midwolda** ⛵ | 4A5

Blauwestadhoeve - Midwolda

info@blauwestadhoeve.nl - www.blauwestadhoeve.nl

Paved motorhome pitches
Rural location
Wifi

Blauwestadhoeve, Hoofdweg 156. **GPS:** n53,19424 e7,00751.
6 🍴€10 🚰€2,25 🗑€1,50 Ch€1,50 🔌(6x)€1,45 WC€1 🗑€1 📶€1,45 🗑.
Location: Rural. **Surface:** grassy/metalled. ⬛ 01/01-31/12
Distance: 🚲250m 🚴2km 🏊900m 🛒500m 🛒100m 🚌250m 🚌100m
🛒on the spot 🚶on the spot.

⚓🅂 | **Midwolda** ⛵ | 4A5
Jachthaven Midwolda, Strandweg 1. **GPS:** n53,19727 e7,02610. 🔼.

5 🍴€12 🚰€0,50 🗑Ch 🔌€4/day 📶. **Location:** Rural, comfortable, quiet.

Surface: grassy. ⬛ 01/04-31/10
Distance: 🚲city centre 1km 🏊on the spot ⊗on the spot 🛒on the spot
🚌on the spot 🛒on the spot.
Remarks: View at Lake Oldambt.

⚓🅂 | **Musselkanaal** 🍴🧁 🗑 | 4A6
Jachthaven Spoordok, Havenkade 1. **GPS:** n52,92694 e7,01389. 🔼➡.

35 🍴€9 🚰€0,50/100liter 🗑Ch 🔌(35x) WC 🗑included. 🗑 **Location:**
Rural, comfortable, quiet. **Surface:** grassy/metalled. ⬛ 01/04-31/10
Distance: 🚲500m 🏊on the spot 🛒on the spot ⊗on the spot 🚌nearby
🚌on the spot 🛒on the spot.
Remarks: Max. 72h.

⚓🅂 | **Onderdendam** ⛵ | 3D5
Watersportvereniging Onderdendam, Warffumerweg 12.
GPS: n53,33652 e6,58600. 🔼.

6 🍴€6 + €1/pp 🚰🗑Ch 🔌(6x)€2,50 WC included 🗑€0,50. **Location:**
Simple, quiet. **Surface:** grassy/metalled.
Distance: 🚲500m 🏊on the spot 🛒on the spot ⊗500m 🚌500m.

⚓🅂 | **Onstwedde** | 4A5
Holte 9. **GPS:** n53,05021 e7,04459. 🔼.

5 🍴€3 🚰🗑Chincluded 🔌€2. 🗑 **Location:** Rural, simple.
Surface: grassy. ⬛ 01/01-31/12
Distance: 🚲1km ⊗1km 🚌1km 🚌1km 🛒bike junction.

⚓🅂 | **Sellingen** 🍴 | 4A6
Camperpark Westerwolde, Zevenmeersveenweg 1a. **GPS:** n52,95412 e7,13174.

10 🍴€8 + €1/pp tourist tax 🚰€1 🗑Ch WC 🗑included ⬛€4.

NL

Location: Rural, simple, quiet. **Surface:** grassy.
⬛ 01/01-31/12
Distance: 🚶1km ⬤on the spot 🍴1km 🚲1km 🐾on the spot ⅄on the spot.
Remarks: Arrival after 7pm.

| ⬛S | **Sellingen** 🍴 | 4A6 |

De Barkhoorn, Beetserweg 6. **GPS:** n52,94617 e7,13421.⬆️

5 🏕€ 9 + tourist tax, dog € 3 ⚡€3,50. **Location:** Rural, simple, quiet.
Surface: grasstiles.
⬛ 01/04-31/10 ⬤ 01/07-22/08

| ⬛S | **Slochteren** ⚓ | 4A5 |

Duurswoldje, Edserweg. **GPS:** n53,20051 e6,79020.⬆️➡️

7 🏕€7 🚰🪣Ch⚡included. **Location:** Rural, simple, quiet.
Surface: grassy. ⬛ 01/01-31/12
Distance: 🚶500m ⬤on the spot ⊗on the spot 🍴1km 🚲on the spot.
Remarks: Covered picnic area, small stock accommodation.

| ⬛S | **Stadskanaal** | 4A5 |

De Roo Campers, Unikenkade 1. **GPS:** n53,03556 e6,87617.⬆️ .

10 🏕€5 🚰🪣Ch WC included ⬜.
Location: Rural, simple, quiet. **Surface:** grassy.
⬛ 01/01-31/12
Distance: 🚶8km ⚓4km ⬤on the spot ⬤on the spot ⊗8km 🍴8km.

Tourist information Stadskanaal:
ℹ️ Pagedal, www.stadskanaal.nl. Daytime recreation.

| ⬛S | **Ter Apel** ⚓ | 4A6 |

Jachthaven De Runde, Oosterkade 5. **GPS:** n52,87179 e7,07329.⬆️ .

10 🏕€ 7,50 + € 1,50 tourist tax 🚰€0,50 🪣Ch⚡WC⬜€0,50
⬜€4/2 📶free,5h. **Location:** Rural, comfortable, quiet. **Surface:** grassy.
⬛ 01/01-31/12
Distance: 🚶1km ⚓on the spot ⬤on the spot ⊗on the spot 🍴1km
🚲500m 🐾on the spot.
Remarks: Wifi 5h free.

| ⬛ | **Usquert** ⚓ | 3D4 |

't Zielhuis, Zijlweg. **GPS:** n53,43203 e6,58396.⬆️

+10 🏕free. **Location:** Rural, simple, isolated, quiet. **Surface:** gravel.
⬛ 01/01-31/12
Distance: 🚶Usquert 4,5km ⚓Wadden Sea ⬤on the spot ⊗on the spot.

| ⬛S | **Veendam** ⚓ | 4A5 |

Borgerswold, Flora 2. **GPS:** n53,10637 e6,84826.⬆️➡️

60 🏕€ 9/night 🚰🪣Ch⚡WC⬜📶included. 🐾
Location: Rural, simple, quiet.
Surface: grassy.
⬛ 01/01-31/12
Distance: 🚶2km ⚓beach 50m ⬤on the spot ⊗2km 🍴1km 🚲1,5km
🐾on the spot.

Tourist information Veendam:
🏛 Museumspoorlijn STAR, Parallelweg 4, Veendam. Museum railway line,
tickets available at railwaystation. ⬛ 01/04-31/10, 27/12-03/01. ⬜ round
trip € 9,50.
🏛 Veenkoloniaalmuseum, Museumplein 5. History of the peat, shipping and
industry.
⬛ Tue-Fri 11-17h, Sa-Su 13-17h ⬛ 01/09-30/06 Mo.

| ⬛⬛S | **Winschoten** 🌿⚓ | 4A5 |

Hotel Café Restaurant Bowling In den Stallen, Oostereinde 10.
GPS: n53,15371 e7,06528.⬆️ .

10 🏕consuming is appreciated 🚰⚡on demand 📶🗑. **Location:** Rural,
simple, quiet. **Surface:** asphalted/metalled.
Distance: 🚶1km ⚓600m ⬤600m ⊗on the spot 🍴1km 🚲600m.

| ⚓S | **Winschoten** 🌿⚓ | 4A5 |

Jachthaven de Rensel, Hellingbaan 4. **GPS:** n53,14405 e7,04760.⬆️

NL

10 ⬛€ 0,75/m, tourist tax € 0,80/pp ⬛€0,50 ⬛ Ch ⬛ WC included.
Location: Simple, quiet.
Surface: concrete.
⬛ 01/01-31/12
Distance: ⬛800m ⬛200m McDonalds ⬛200m AH.
Tourist information Winschoten:
⬛ Stoomgemaal, Winschoter Oostereinde. Steam-engine 1895.

| ⬛S | **Winsum** | 3D5 |

Jachthaven/Camping Marenland, Winsumerstraatweg.
GPS: n53,33177 e6,51015. ⬛⬛.

10 ⬛€ 15 ⬛ Ch ⬛ €3/night, 4 Amp WC ⬛ €6,50/0 ⬛ included, at restaurant. ⬛ **Location:** Urban, comfortable, quiet. **Surface:** grassy/metalled.
⬛ 01/04-01/11
Distance: ⬛300m ⬛200m ⬛on the spot ⬛on the spot ⬛500m ⬛200m ⬛ on the spot ⬛Pieterpad.

| ⬛S | **Zoutkamp** | 3D5 |

Jachthaven Hunzegat, Strandweg 17. **GPS:** n53,34114 e6,29406. ⬛.

10 ⬛€ 12,50 + tourist tax ⬛ Ch, dump chem. toilet only with biodegradable liquid ⬛ (10x), 4A WC included ⬛€0,50 ⬛€7,40/0 ⬛.
Location: Rural, comfortable, quiet. **Surface:** grassy/metalled.
⬛ 01/01-31/12
Distance: ⬛1km ⬛on the spot ⬛on the spot ⬛500m ⬛500m ⬛300m ⬛ on the spot.
Remarks: Bread-service.
Tourist information Zoutkamp:
⬛ Zeehondencrèche, Hoofdstraat 94a, Pieterburen. Sanctory to cure sick seals.
⬛ 9-18h. ⬛ € 4,50.

| ⬛S | **Zuidbroek** | 4A5 |

De Broeckhof, W.A. Scholtenweg 18. **GPS:** n53,16118 e6,86054. ⬛.

3 ⬛free ⬛ Ch ⬛ WC ⬛ ⬛ free. **Location:** Rural, simple, central, quiet.
Surface: metalled.
⬛ 01/01-31/12 ⬛ 3rd week Jun
Distance: ⬛500m ⬛on the spot ⬛on the spot ⬛1km ⬛on the spot ⬛on the spot ⬛ on the spot.
Remarks: Max. 72h.

Drenthe

| ⬛S | **Assen** ⬛ | 3D6 |

Van Hobokenstraat 5. **GPS:** n53,00030 e6,57123. ⬛.

5 ⬛free ⬛€0,50/100 ⬛ € 1. **Location:** Simple. **Surface:** metalled.
⬛ 01/01-31/12
Distance: ⬛1km ⬛50m ⬛500m.
Remarks: Max. 72h.

| ⬛S | **Barger Compascuum** | 4A6 |

Nationale Veenpark, Berkenrode 4. **GPS:** n52,75504 e7,02546. ⬛.

20 ⬛€ 6 + € 1,20/pp tourist tax ⬛ included. **Location:** Rural, simple, quiet.
Surface: grassy. ⬛ 01/05-31/10
Distance: ⬛100m ⬛on the spot ⬛ on the spot.
Remarks: Max. 3x24h, after visiting Veenpark 2nd night free.
Tourist information Barger Compascuum:
⬛ Veenpark-Wereld van Veen, Berkenrode 4. Life and Work in peat area, 160 acres of nature, peat and villages. ⬛ 01/04-31/10 10-17h, 01/07-31/08 10-18h.
⬛ >5: € 14.

NL

Borger 4A6

Nuuverstee - Borger

nuuverstee@live.nl - www.nuuverstee.nl

Rural location
Ideal base for walking and cycling
Bread-service

Nuuverstee, Rolderstraat 4. **GPS**: n52,92633 e6,77447. ⬆️➡️
6 🅿️ € 15 ⛽🔌 Ch 🚿 (6x),10Amp WC 🚿 included. ♿
Location: Rural, luxurious. **Surface**: grassy/metalled. 🔵 01/02-31/12
Distance: 🚶800m 🚲600m 🏊2km 🛒500m 🍽️600m 🍺1km 🚌500m
🚲 on the spot 🚶 on the spot.

Dwingeloo 3D6

Torentjeshoek, Leeuweriksveldweg 1. **GPS**: n52,81927 e6,36077. ⬆️➡️

6 🅿️ € 12-14 2p incl. + tourist tax ⛽€1/100liter 🚰 Ch 🚿€1/night,10Amp
WC 🚿 included,on camp site. ♿ **Location**: Rural, luxurious, quiet.
Surface: grassy/metalled. 🔵 01/01-31/12
Distance: 🚶2km 🚲2km 🏊200m 🛒200m 🍽️2km 🍺2km 🚌1km
🚲 on the spot 🚶 on the spot.
Remarks: Arrival >16h, departure <11h.

Eelderwolde 3D5

Scandinavisch Dorp, Oude Badweg 1. **GPS**: n53,16984 e6,55391. ⬆️

5 🅿️free. **Location**: Rural, simple, quiet. **Surface**: asphalted/grassy.
🔵 01/01-31/12 🍴 Restaurant: Tue, 01/10-01/04 Mo-Tue
Distance: 🚶2km 🚲5km 🏊500m 🛒on the spot 🍽️on the spot 🍺2km
🚌200m 🚲on the spot 🚶on the spot.

Eext 4A6

Schaopvolte, Stationsstraat 60a. **GPS**: n53,00007 e6,72862. ⬆️

10 🅿️€ 7,50 + tourist tax ⛽€1 🚰 Ch 🚿(6x)€1/4kWh WC 🚿€0,50
🚿€4,50 🔌€2/day. **Location**: Rural, simple, quiet. **Surface**: grassy/gravel.
🔵 01/04-01/11
Distance: 🚶2km.

Elim 3D6

De Barswieke, Barsweg 9. **GPS**: n52,67144 e6,57821. ⬆️

10 🅿️€ 6 ⛽🚰 Chincluded 🚿€1,50 WC 🚿. **Surface**: grassy.
🔵 01/01-31/12
Distance: 🚶1km 🍺1km.

Emmen 4A6

Kerkhoflaan- van Schaikweg. GPS: n52,78091 e6,90330. ⬆️➡️

10 🅿️free.
Location: Urban, simple.
Surface: gravel/metalled.
🔵 01/01-31/12
Distance: 🚶1km 🍽️Albert Heijn 600m.
Remarks: Behind hotel Eden, max. 72h, zoo Emmen 900m.

Tourist information Emmen:
ℹ️ Noorder Dierenpark, Hoofdstraat 18. Zoo. 🔵 from 10h.

Hoogeveen 3D6

Terpweg 3. GPS: n52,72639 e6,50040. ⬆️

3 🅿️free. **Location**: Rural, simple, isolated. **Surface**: metalled. 🔵 01/01-31/12
Distance: 🚶2km 🚲2,2km 🍽️100m 🍺1km 🚌1km.
Remarks: At sports park, max. 72h.

NL

Matsloot · 3D5
Camping Pool, Matsloot 1a. GPS: n53,19354 e6,44980. ⬆

10 €10 Ch WC included. **Location:** Rural, simple, isolated, quiet. **Surface:** metalled. 01/01-31/12
Distance: 5km on the spot on the spot.
Remarks: On Leekster lake.

Meppel · 3D6
Jachthaven, Westeinde 32. GPS: n52,69615 e6,18096. ⬆

15 €7,70, 2 pers.incl. €0,50 Ch €0,50/kWh WC €3/3. **Location:** Urban, comfortable, central, quiet. **Surface:** grassy. 01/01-31/12
Distance: 500m on the spot on the spot on the spot 400m.

Nieuwlande · 3D6
Bonenstee, Brugstraat 87. GPS: n52,67889 e6,61194. ⬆

20 €6 Ch (6x)€1,50 WC €1 included. **Location:** Rural.
Surface: grassy/metalled. 01/04-31/10
Distance: 2km 4km 4km 2km 2km 100m bike junction on the spot.
Remarks: Max. 72h.

Noord-Sleen · 4A6
De Kalverweide, Zweeloërstraat 1. GPS: n52,79330 e6,79475. ⬆

10 €12 Ch WC included. **Location:** Rural, comfortable, quiet. **Surface:** grassy. 01/01-31/12
Distance: 500m on the spot on the spot.
Remarks: Use of sauna against payment.

Oosterhesselen · 4A6
Sauna Hesselerbrug, Verlengde Hoogeveensevaart 32. GPS: n52,73535 e6,72029.

use of sauna obligatory. **Surface:** metalled.
Distance: 4km 4km.

Ufelte · 3D6
De Blauwe Haan, Weg achter de es 11. GPS: n52,80220 e6,27264. ⬆ ➡

6 €12 Ch €2,50/night,10Amp WC included. **Location:** Rural, luxurious, quiet. **Surface:** grassy/metalled. 01/04-31/10
Distance: 5km 2km 3km 3km 2,5km 5km 2km on the spot on the spot.

Westerbork · 3D6
Landgoed het Timmerholt, Gagelmaat 4. GPS: n52,86850 e6,61748. ⬆ ➡

4 €10, 19/07-02/08 €12,50 Ch included WC €1,50/pppd €1,50/pppd €3,90/2,75 h. **Location:** Rural, luxurious, quiet. **Surface:** grassy/metalled. 01/01-31/12
Distance: 2km 4km on the spot on the spot on the spot 2km 2km on the spot on the spot.
Tourist information Westerbork:
Ⓜ Herinneringscentrum Kamp Westerbork, Oosthalen 8, Hooghalen. Mo-Fri 10-17h, Sa-Su 13-17h, 01/07-31/08 11-17h.

Wijster · 3D6
Grondsels, Grondselweg 7. GPS: n52,80143 e6,49025. ⬆

10 €5 Ch €2 WC included. **Location:** Rural, simple, isolated, quiet. **Surface:** grassy/metalled. 15/03-31/10

Distance: 🚲3km ⛱on the spot ⊗3km 🛒5km 🚏on the spot.

Overijssel

⚓S | **Almelo** | 9A1

De Grenzen, Havenkade. **GPS**: n52,36000 e6,65694.⬆

3 🏕€ 4,50 🔌€2 🚰Ch ⬛€0,50 🔲€2,25/2,25. **Surface:** asphalted.
🅿 01/01-31/12
Distance: 🚲300m 🚤on the spot ⊗200m 🛒200m 🚏100m.
Remarks: Max. 72h, check in at harbourmaster.

Tourist information Almelo:
🛈 Centrumplein. 🅿 Thu 8-16h, Sa 8-17h.

⛺ | **Bathmen** 🏕🍴 | 8D1

Prinses Margrietlaan. **GPS**: n52,25025 e6,29927.⬆

2 🏕free. **Location:** Urban, simple, central, quiet. **Surface:** metalled.
🅿 01/01-31/12
Distance: 🚲1km 🚴2,5km ⊗1km 🛒1km 🚏on the spot 🚶on the spot.
Remarks: Parking gymnasium.

🍴S | **Belt Schutsloot** | 3D6

Café-Restaurant de Belt, Havezatheweg 4. **GPS**: n52,66774 e6,05189.

10 🏕free for clients WC 🚿. **Surface:** asphalted. 🅿 01/01-31/12
Distance: 🚲3km ⛱1km 🚤1km ⊗on the spot 🛒3km.
Remarks: North of Zwartsluis, at Belter- and Beulakerwijde.

⛺ | **Borne** | 9A1

Parking de Koem, De Koem. **GPS**: n52,29957 e6,75800.⬆

1 🏕€ 5/24h. **Surface:** metalled. 🅿 01/01-31/12

Distance: 🚲on the spot ⊗50m 🛒on the spot.
Remarks: Max. 72h, money in envelope in mail box at townhall.

⛺ | **Dalfsen** 🌿🏕🍴🍺 | 8D1

Stationsweg 4. **GPS**: n52,49944 e6,25949.⬆

5 🏕€ 5 + € 0,85/pp tourist tax. 🚿 **Location:** Rural, simple, central, quiet.
Surface: grasstiles. 🅿 01/01-31/12
Distance: 🚲500m ⊗500m 🛒800m 🚏on the spot 🚶on the spot
🚶on the spot.
Remarks: Max. 48h, service on campsite.

⛺S | **Dalfsen** 🌿🏕🍴🍺 | 8D1

Starnbosch, Sterrebosweg 4. **GPS**: n52,47538 e6,26336.⬆➡

7 🏕€ 10 + € 0,85/pp tourist tax 🔌🚰Ch 🚿(8x) WC included
⬛€0,40/5minutes 🔲€5/0,50 📶€1/1h. 🚿 **Location:** Rural, comfortable,
quiet. **Surface:** grassy/sand. 🅿 01/01-31/12
Distance: 🚲4km ⊗on the spot 🛒4km 🚏3,3km 🚴on the spot
🚶on the spot.

⛺S | **De Lutte** 🍺 | 9A1

Erve Velpen, Beuningerstraat 25. **GPS**: n52,33224 e7,01197.⬆

20 🏕€ 9, 2 pers.incl 🔌🚰Ch 🚿€2 ⬛€1/8minutes 📶included. 🚿
Location: Rural, comfortable, isolated, quiet. **Surface:** grassy.
🅿 01/01-31/12
Distance: 🚲4km ⊗300m 🚴bike junction 🚶on the spot.

⛺S | **Dedemsvaart** | 8D1

Camperplaats Dedemsvaart, Langewijk 112. **GPS**: n52,60435 e6,45108.⬆

10 🏕€ 6,50 🔌€1,50 🚰 🚿€2,50 📶. 🚿 **Surface:** metalled.

◯ 01/01-31/12
Distance: 🚶700m ⊗300m 🚊200m.
Remarks: Max. 48h.

🏕S Diepenheim 🏕🍴 8D2
Camperpark Diepenheim, Esweg 6. **GPS:** n52,18307 e6,57872.

30 🛏€ 11 + € 1/pp tourist tax 🚰🛢Ch 💧,6Amp WC 🗑 📶included 🛒.
Surface: grassy/metalled. ◯ 01/01-31/12
Distance: 🚶2km 🏊on the spot 🛒on the spot ⊗2km 🚊2km 🚲on the spot
🏕on the spot.

🍴S Diepenheim 🏕🍴 8D2
't Holt, Hengevelderweg 1A. **GPS:** n52,19500 e6,59186. 🔼.

3 🛏€ 5, free for clients 🚰🛢Ch free. **Surface:** metalled.
◯ 01/01-31/12
Distance: 🚶3km ⊗on the spot 🚊3km.
Remarks: Golf court (pitch+putt).

🍴 Diepenheim 🏕🍴 8D2
In de Kokkerieje, Grotestraat 94. **GPS:** n52,19923 e6,55452. 🔼.

🛏free with a meal. ◯ Mo-Tue
Distance: 🚶on the spot 🛒1km 🚊500m.
Remarks: Parking behind restaurant.

🏕 Enschede 🏕🍴 9A2
Diekmanterrein, Weggelhorstweg. **GPS:** n52,20543 e6,90096. 🔼.

5 🛏free. **Location:** Urban, simple, simple, isolated, quiet. **Surface:** asphalted.
◯ 01/01-31/12
Distance: 🚶2km 🚴 1,4km 🚌on the spot.

🏕 Enschede 🏕🍴 9A2
De Loeks, Moorvenweg 2a. **GPS:** n52,17757 e6,86599. 🔼➡️.

15 🛏€ 7, 01/04-31/10 € 15 🚰🛢Ch 💧WC 🗑included. 🛒
Location: Rural, isolated, quiet. **Surface:** grassy/metalled.
◯ 01/01-31/12 ◯ sanitary 01/11-31/03
Distance: 🚶3km 🚊1km on the spot 🏕on the spot.

🏕 Enter 🍴 8D1
Werfstraat. GPS: n52,29808 e6,58271. 🔼.

3 🛏free. **Location:** Urban, simple. **Surface:** grassy/gravel.
◯ 01/01-31/12
Distance: 🚶600m 🏊on the spot 🛒on the spot ⊗600m 🚊700m
🚲on the spot 🏕on the spot.
Remarks: Max. 72h.

🍴S Geesteren 🍴 9A1
Zalencentrum Spalink, Koelenbeekweg 10. **GPS:** n52,44060 e6,69555.

15 🛏€ 8,50 🚰🛢Ch 💧WC 🗑. **Surface:** grassy/gravel. ◯ 01/01-31/12
Distance: 🚶3,5km ⊗on the spot 🚊3,5km 🚲on the spot 🏕on the spot.
Remarks: Guests free.

🏕S Giethoorn 🌺 3D6
Passantenhaven Zuidercluft, Vosjacht 1G. **GPS:** n52,72134 e6,07449.

30 🛏€ 12, 2 pers.incl., 1/11-1/4 € 6 🚰€0,50/100liter 🛢Ch 💧€1/2kWh
WC 🗑€0,50. **Surface:** grassy. ◯ 01/01-31/12
Distance: 🚶1km 🏊on the spot 🛒on the spot.
Remarks: Check in at harbourmaster, water closed during wintertime.

NL

Giethoorn 🏴 3D6

Camperplaats Haamstede, Kanaaldijk 17. **GPS**: n52,72828 e6,07570. ⬆️➡️

35 € 11, 2 pers.incl €0,50 Ch €2 WC €0,50. **Location:** Rural, comfortable, central, quiet. **Surface:** grassy.
🅾️ 01/04-31/10
Distance: 2km 1km 20m 1km 1km on the spot on the spot.

Giethoorn 🏴 3D6

Camperresort Bodelaeke, Vosjacht 10A. **GPS**: n52,71703 e6,07668. ⬆️
99 € 14 2 pers.incl, dog € 3,50 €0,50/100liter Ch €3 WC €6/4
Location: Rural, comfortable.
Surface: grasstiles/grassy.
🅾️ 02/03-31/10
Distance: 1km on the spot on the spot.

Tourist information Giethoorn:
ℹ️ VVV, Eendrachtsplein 1, www.kopvanoverijssel.nl. Village in nature reserve De Weerribben, Dutch Venice, boat trips possible.

Haaksbergen 9A2

Camping Scholtenhagen - Haaksbergen

campingscholtenhagen@planet.nl - www.campingscholtenhagen.nl

Electricity at each pitch
Located in nature reserve
Excellent location for city visit

Camping Scholtenhagen, Scholtenhagenweg 30. **GPS**: n52,14820 e6,72467.
24 € 10 Ch (24x),6Amp WC €0,85 €5,25/1 included.
Surface: grassy. 🅾️ 01/03-30/09
Distance: 2km 7km 3km 2km 2,5km 1km on the spot on the spot.
Remarks: Max. 72h.

Haaksbergen 9A2

Henk Pen Caravans en Kampeerauto's, Westsingel 2.
GPS: n52,14917 e6,71167.

2 free free. **Surface:** asphalted. 🅾️ 01/01-31/12

Distance: 1km on the spot on the spot 1km.
Remarks: Motorhome dealer.

Hardenberg 8D1

De Kuserbrink, Parkweg. **GPS**: n52,57746 e6,62927. ⬆️

4 € 10 €0,50/100liter Ch (4x)€1/kWh. **Location:** Rural, comfortable, central, quiet. **Surface:** grasstiles. 🅾️ 01/01-31/12
Distance: centre 500m on the spot on the spot.
Remarks: Max. 72h.

Hardenberg 8D1

Fam. Pullen, Allemansweg 1a, Collendoorn. **GPS**: n52,58845 e6,59146. ⬆️

20 € 8,50 Ch included. **Location:** Rural, comfortable, isolated, quiet. **Surface:** grassy. 🅾️ 01/01-31/12
Distance: 3km 3km bike junction on the spot.
Remarks: Dog on leads.

Hasselt 🏴 8D1

Jachthaven de Molenwaard, Van Nahuysweg 151. **GPS**: n52,59367 e6,08741. ⬆️➡️

10 € 8,50 + € 0,70/pp tourist tax Ch (10x)€2/1night
WC €0,50/6minutes €3,75/3,75 included. **Location:** Luxurious, quiet. **Surface:** metalled. 🅾️ 01/01-31/12
Distance: 500m on the spot on the spot 500m 500m 500m on the spot on the spot.
Remarks: Check in at harbourmaster.

Heeten 8D1

De Baanbreker, Speelmansweg 8. **GPS**: n52,36026 e6,31190. ⬆️➡️

NL

10 ⧖ € 4 🚰 €1 🚽 €0,50 Ch €0,50 💧 €1,50. **Surface:** metalled.
⬛ 01/01-31/12
Distance: 🚶2km ⊗2km 🛒2km 🚲on the spot 🏃on the spot.

| ⬛S | Hellendoorn | 8D1 |

Camperplaats Hancate, Zuidelijke Kanaaldijk. **GPS:** n52,43418 e6,44060. ⬆➡

10 ⧖ € 10 🚰 🚽 Ch 💧 (4x) 📶 included. **Location:** Rural, simple, quiet.
Surface: grassy. ⬛ 01/01-31/12
Distance: 🚶5km 🛒on the spot ⊗100m 🚗200m 🚲on the spot
🏃on the spot.

| ⬛S | Hengelo | 9A1 |

Camperplaats Eulerhook, Vöckersweg 19. **GPS:** n52,24652 e6,75365. ⬆➡

15 ⧖ € 8 🚰 🚽 Ch 💧 WC 📶 included. **Location:** Rural, luxurious,
noisy. **Surface:** grassy/metalled. ⬛ 01/01-31/12
Distance: 🚶4km ⊿2km 🛒500m ⊗4km 🛒3km 🚗1km 🚲on the spot
🏃on the spot.
Remarks: Nearby motorway.

| ⬛S | Hertme | 9A1 |

Camperpark Rabo Scheele, Hertmerweg 37. **GPS:** n52,32663 e6,74691. ⬆➡

25 ⧖ € 12, 2 pers.incl 🚰 🚽 Ch 💧 WC 📶 included. **Location:** Rural,
comfortable, quiet. **Surface:** grassy/metalled. ⬛ 01/01-31/12
Distance: 🚶Hertme 500m, Borne 2km 🛒100m ⊗500m 🛒2km 🚗2km
🚲on the spot 🏃on the spot.

| ⬛S | Kampen | 8C1 |

Burgemeester Berghuisplein 1. **GPS:** n52,55268 e5,91356. ⬆

25 ⧖ € 7,50 🚰 🚽 Ch WC included 💡€0,50/6minutes. 🚿 **Location:** Urban,
comfortable, central, quiet. **Surface:** metalled.
⬛ 01/01-31/12
Distance: 🚶historical centre 500m ⊿1,5km 🛒1,5km ⊗900m 🛒1km
🚲on the spot 🏃on the spot.
Remarks: Max. 72h, entrance code sanitary building at town hall.

Tourist information Kampen:
ℹ VVV, Oudestraat 151, www.vvvkampen.nl. Former Hanseatic town on the
IJssel.

| ⬛ | Losser | 9A1 |

Brilmansdennen, Bookholtlaan. **GPS:** n52,26917 e7,01361. ⬆➡

3 ⧖ free. **Surface:** metalled. ⬛ 01/01-31/12
Distance: 🚶1km.
Remarks: At sports park, max. 72h.

| ⬛ | Nieuwleusen | 8D1 |

Koninging Julianalaan. **GPS:** n52,58213 e6,28076. ⬆

3 ⧖ free. **Location:** Urban, simple. **Surface:** metalled.
⬛ 01/01-31/12
Distance: 🚶300m 🚲on the spot 🏃on the spot.
Remarks: Max. 48h.

| ⬛ | Nijverdal | 8D1 |

De Wilgenweard, Sportlaan 6. **GPS:** n52,37118 e6,46538. ⬆➡

3 ⧖ € 5 + € 0,50/pp tourist tax. 🚿 **Surface:** grasstiles/metalled.
⬛ 01/01-31/12
Distance: 🚶500m ⊿on the spot 🛒on the spot ⊗on the spot 🛒500m
🚗200m 🚲on the spot 🏃on the spot.

| 🍴 | Oldemarkt | 3C6 |

Vaartjes partycentrum, Kruisstraat 86-88. **GPS:** n52,82095 e5,96698. ⬆➡

NL

10 🎦 free for clients. **Surface:** asphalted. 🔲 01/01-31/12
Distance: 🚶200m ⚓on the spot 🚪on the spot ⚡200m.

| 🎦S | Ommen 🌿(m) | 8D1 |

Landgoed De Stekkenkamp, Beerzerweg 3. **GPS:** n52,51128 e6,43933.⬆➡.

8 🎦 € 7,50 + € 0,83/pp tourist tax 🔥€0,50/4minutes 🔌 Ch 🚿 (8x).
Location: Rural, simple, quiet. **Surface:** grasstiles/grassy.
🔲 01/01-31/12
Distance: 🚶1,2km ⚓1,2km 🚪1,2km ⚡1,2km 🛒1,2km.
Remarks: At historical farmhouse, max. 72h.

| 🎦 | Steenwijk 🌿 | 3D6 |

Jachthaven, Houthaven. **GPS:** n52,78627 e6,10006.⬆➡.

20 🎦 € 10 🔥🔌 🚿€1. **Surface:** grassy. 🔲 01/01-31/12
Distance: 🚶1km ⚓on the spot 🚪on the spot ⚡300m.
Remarks: Check in at harbourmaster.

| 🎦 | Tubbergen | 9A1 |

De Vlaskoel, Sportlaan 3. **GPS:** n52,41043 e6,78316.⬆.

2 🎦 free. **Location:** Simple, simple. **Surface:** metalled.
🔲 01/01-31/12
Distance: 🚶500m 🚪600m ⚡600m 🎿on the spot 🚶on the spot.
Remarks: At swimming pool.

| 🎦S | Vollenhove 🌿⛵ | 3C6 |

Recreatiecentrum 't Akkertien, Op de Voorst, Noordwal 3.
GPS: n52,67609 e5,93914.

20 🎦 € 8 🔥🔌 Ch 🚿 included.
🔲 01/01-31/12
Distance: 🚶900m ⚓on the spot 🚪on the spot ⚡400m 🛒peak season.

| ⚓S | Vollenhove 🌿⛵ | 3C6 |

De Haven. GPS: n52,68277 e5,94862.⬆.

6 🎦 € 12 🔥🔌 Ch 🚿€1 WC 🚽€0,50. **Surface:** metalled.
🔲 01/01-31/12
Distance: 🚶100m ⚓100m ⚡1km.
Remarks: Check in at harbourmaster.

| 🎦S | Wierden 🌿⛵(m) | 8D1 |

De Huurne, Zandinksweg 22. **GPS:** n52,34899 e6,57191.

10 🎦 € 10 🔥🔌 Ch 🚿 included. 🔲 01/01-31/12
Distance: 🚶2km ⚓3km ⚡2km 🛒700m.
Remarks: Max. 3 nights, max 3,5t.

| 🎦S | Wierden 🌿⛵(m) | 8D1 |

Wijngaard Baan, Kloosterhoeksweg 15. **GPS:** n52,32172 e6,56709.

24 🎦 € 11,50 🔥🔌 Ch 🚿 WC 🚽. **Surface:** metalled. 🔲 01/01-31/12
Distance: 🚶3km 🚪on the spot 🚪on the spot ⚡3km 🎿on the spot
🚶on the spot.
Remarks: Vineyard.

| ⚓S | Wijhe 🌿⛵🍽 | 8D1 |

Passantenhaven, Veerweg. **GPS:** n52,38639 e6,12830.⬆.

NL

10 ⌂ € 6 + € 0,45/pp tourist tax ⌐ 🗑 Ch WC included 🗑. 🚻
Location: Simple, central. **Surface:** asphalted/metalled.
🔲 01/04-01/10
Distance: 500m ⌁on the spot ⌁on the spot ⊗500m 🍴500m
🚲on the spot 🅿on the spot.
Remarks: Max. 3 nights.
Tourist information Wijhe:
🏠 Marktplein. 🔲 Tue-morning.

| 🏞 S | Zwartsluis | 3D6 |

Voetbalvereniging DESZ, Clingellanden. **GPS:** n52,64437 e6,07810.

15 ⌂ € 5 ⌐ 🗑 Ch. **Surface:** gravel. **Remarks:** Service at marina.
Tourist information Zwartsluis:
👁 Stoomgemaal Mastenbroek, Kamperzeedijk 5, Genemuiden. Pumping-
engine, 1856.

| 🏞 | Zwolle 🌾🏠 | 8D1 |

Turfmarkt. **GPS:** n52,51326 e6,10380. ⬆

7 ⌂ mo-sa 8-18h € 4/day, free overnight stay. 🅿 **Location:** Urban, simple,
central. **Surface:** metalled. 🔲 01/01-31/12
Distance: 800m ⊗1km 🍴650m 🚲on the spot 🅿on the spot.
Remarks: Max. 72h.

| 🏞 S | Zwolle 🌾🏠 | 8D1 |

Jachthaven de Hanze, Holtenbroekerdijk 44. **GPS:** n52,53056 e6,07527. ⬆➡

15 ⌂ € 8 + € 0,60/pp tourist tax ⌐ 🗑 Ch (15x)€ 0,50/kWh
WC included 🗑 € 1/7minutes. 🚻 **Location:** Rural, comfortable, central, quiet.

Surface: grassy/metalled. 🔲 01/01-31/12
Distance: 2,5km 2km ⌁on the spot ⌁on the spot ⊗1km 🍴1km
🚲500m 🅿on the spot.
Remarks: Max. 72h.
Tourist information Zwolle:
👁 Sassenpoort, Koestraat 46. Medieval gate building. 🔲 Wed-Fri 14-17h,
Sa-Su 12-17h.
😊 Ecodrome, Willemsvaart 19. Theme park, history of nature, geology.
🔲 01/04-31/10 10-17, 01/11-31/03 Wed, Sa, Su 10-17h.

Flevoland

| ⛵S | Almere 🌾🐚 | 8B1 |

Marina Muiderzand, IJmeerdijk 4. **GPS:** n52,34302 e5,13521. ⬆➡

10 ⌂ € 13,50 ⌐ 🗑 Ch 🔌 WC 🗑 📷€5/3 🚿included 🧺. **Surface:** asphalted.
🔲 01/05-30/09
Distance: 8km ⌁on the spot ⌁on the spot ⊗on the spot 🍴on the spot
🚲1km.
Remarks: Check in at harbourmaster.

| 🏞 S | Almere-Haven 🏠🐚 | 8B1 |

WSV Almere, Sluiskade 11. **GPS:** n52,33257 e5,21715. ⬆

40 ⌂ € 11, 2 pers.incl ⌐ 🗑 Ch 🔌 (12x)€ 0,50/2kWh WC 🗑 📷€5 🚿included.
🚻 **Location:** Urban, simple. **Surface:** grassy. 🔲 01/01-31/12
Distance: ⌁on the spot ⊗on the spot 🍴200m 🚲on the spot.

| ⛵S | Almere-Haven 🏠🐚 | 8B1 |

Haven, Sluis. **GPS:** n52,33366 e5,22170. ⬆

2 ⌂ € 1,05/m per night ⌐ 🗑 Ch WC 🗑 € 0,50. **Surface:** metalled.
🔲 02/05-04/09
Distance: ⌁on the spot 🔌1km ⌁on the spot ⊗on the spot 🍴1km.
Remarks: Max. 72h, check in at harbourmaster.
Tourist information Almere-Haven:
🏠 De Brink. 🔲 Fri 9-16h.

| 🏞 S | Emmeloord | 3C6 |

Camperplaats Emmeloord, Casteleynsweg 1. **GPS:** n52,73981 e5,77235.
10 ⌂ € 9 ⌐included 🔌 € 2/day. **Surface:** grassy. 🔲 11/04-31/10

| 🏞 | Lelystad 🏠🐚 | 8C1 |

P Houtribhoek, Houtribslag. **GPS:** n52,54630 e5,45750. ⬆➡

NL

4 🆓 free. **Surface:** metalled.
🅾 01/01-31/12
Distance: 🚮2km 🏊on the spot 🛒on the spot ⊗on the spot ⚓2km.
Remarks: Max. 48h.

Tourist information Lelystad:
〰 Oostvaardersplassen. 6000 acres of lakes, mud fields, reed swamps, hiking route 5km and cycle route 35 km.
🛍 Batavia Stad, Bataviaplein 60. Outlet-shopping.
🛒 daily 10-18h. 🅃 free, parking € 2,50/4h.

| 🅲 🆂 | Luttelgeest | 3C6 |

Recreatie en Horeca bedrijf Craneburcht, Kuinderweg 52.
GPS: n52,78304 e5,84331.

10 🆓 € 10. **Surface:** metalled. 🅾 01/03-30/11 ⚫ winter: Mo-Tue
Distance: 🚮200m ⊗on the spot ⚓7km.
Remarks: Arrival >17h, departure <10h.

| 🆂 | Nagele | 3C6 |

Afslag Nagele, Han Stijkelweg 11. **GPS:** n52,65278 e5,68417.⬆

10 🆓 € 11 🚰 🔌 Ch 🚿 € 2 WC 🗑 included. 🚜 **Location:** Comfortable, isolated, quiet. **Surface:** grassy/metalled. 🅾 01/01-31/12
Distance: 🚮3km.
Remarks: Max. 72h.

| 🆂 | Urk 〰 | 3C6 |

Haven, Burgemeester Schipperkade. **GPS:** n52,66040 e5,59975.⬆

24 🆓 € 15 🚰 🔌 Ch 🚿 (18x) WC 🗑 📶 included. 🚜

Surface: metalled.
🅾 01/01-31/12
Distance: 🚮200m ⊗100m ⚓100m, bakery 300m.

Tourist information Urk:
ℹ VVV, Wijk 3 2, www.vvvflevoland.nl. Old fishermen's village, former island.
Ⓜ Het Oude Raadhuis, Wijk 2 2. Regional museum. 🅾 01/04-31/10 Mo-Fr 10-17h, Sa 10-16h, 01/03-30/11 Mo-Sa 10-16h.
🕊 Urkerhard. 🅾 Sa 8.30-13h.
🚶 Stegentocht/Ginkiestocht. Guided walk, reservation at Touristinfo Urk.
🅃 € 4.

| 🆂 | Zeewolde | 8C1 |

Camperpark De Wielewaal, Wielseweg 9. **GPS:** n52,25981 e5,43727.

50 🆓 € 11 + € 1,50/pp tourist tax 🚰 🔌 Ch included 🚿 € 2 WC 🗑 against payment. **Surface:** metalled. 🅾 01/01-31/12
Distance: 🚮7km 🏊on the spot 🛒on the spot ⚓7km.

Gelderland

| 🆂 | Aalten | 8D2 |

't Noorden, Lichtenvoordsestraatweg 44. **GPS:** n51,93326 e6,58221.⬆

4 🆓 € 10 🚰 € 1/80liter 🔌 Ch 🚿 included WC free. 🚽
Location: Rural. **Surface:** gravel.
🅾 01/01-31/12
Distance: 🚮700m ⊗on the spot.

Tourist information Aalten:
👁 Wijngoed De Hennepe, Romienendiek 3. Guided tour and tastery. 🅾 shop Tue-Fr 13.30h-sunset, Sa 10h, guided tour/tasting Jul/Aug We 15h.
🕊 Hoge Blik. 🅾 Thu 8-12h.

| 🅲 🆂 | Aerdt | 8D2 |

De Aerdtse Wacht, Heuvelakkersestraat 18. **GPS:** n51,88634 e6,08861.⬆

4 🆓 € 10 🚰 € 1/80liter 🔌 Ch 🚿 . 🚽 **Location:** Rural. **Surface:** metalled.
🅾 01/01-31/12
Distance: 🚮on the spot 🛒on the spot 🚲on the spot 🚶on the spot.

| 🆂 | Almen | 8D2 |

De Nieuwe Aanleg, Scheggertdijk 10. **GPS:** n52,16711 e6,29744.⬆➡

NL

12 🍴€ 12 ⛽€0,75/100liter 🔌Ch 🚿(12x)included WC 🚽€0,75/5minutes
📶 🔌 ♨ **Location:** Rural, comfortable, quiet. **Surface:** metalled.
🅿 01/01-31/12
Distance: 🚶2km ⛰on the spot 🍴on the spot ⊗on the spot 🚊2km
🚃on the spot 🚲on the spot 🚶on the spot. **Remarks:** At the Twentekanaal.

Tourist information Almen:
👁 Mosterdmakerij Boesveld, Dorpsstraat 39. Mustard factory.
🅿 Tue-Fri 13.30-17h, Sa 9-16h.

🚐S	Apeldoorn 🍲🍴	8C2

Malkander, Dubbelbeek 38. **GPS:** n52,18305 e5,96673.⬆.

4 🍴free. **Location:** Simple, isolated. **Surface:** metalled.
🅿 01/01-31/12, 15-09h
Distance: 🚶2km ⊗150m 🚊1km.
Remarks: At swimming pool.

🍴S	Appeltern	8C3

Herberg 't Mun - Appeltern

info@mun.nl - www.mun.nl
Beautiful view
Restaurant with regional specialties
Walking and bicycle area

Herberg 't Mun, Molenstraat 10, Blauwe Sluis. **GPS:** n51,84048 e5,56360.
50 🍴€ 5 ⛽🔌Ch 🔌(12x)€2,6Amp WC 📶included.
Location: Rural, simple, isolated, quiet. **Surface:** grassy/metalled.
🅿 01/01-31/12
Distance: 🚶2km ⛰300m 🍴Trout farm ⊗on the spot 🚊2km
🚃on the spot 🚲on the spot 🚶on the spot.
Remarks: Show-garden Appeltern 3km.

🚐S	Arnhem 🍲	8C2

Nieuwe Kade. **GPS:** n51,97290 e5,91644.
4 🍴€ 9 🔌€0,50/kWh. 🏠 **Surface:** metalled. 🅿 01/01-31/12
Distance: 🚶1km 🚲4,7km ⊗200m.
Remarks: Along the Rhine river.

🚐	Bemmel ⬆🍴	8B2

Dijkstraat/Wardstraat. **GPS:** n51,88972 e5,00000.⬆➡.

3 🍴free. **Location:** Urban, simple, central, quiet. **Surface:** metalled.
🅿 01/01-31/12
Distance: 🚶400m ⊗400m 🚊400m ⛰400m 🛵on the spot 🚶on the spot.
Remarks: Max. 72h.

🚐S	Borculo	8D2

Hambroekplas, Hambroekweg 10. **GPS:** n52,11573 e6,53758.⬆.

4 🍴€ 10 ⛽€1/80liter 🔌Ch 🚿included. 🏠 **Location:** Rural, comfortable,
quiet. **Surface:** gravel. 🅿 01/03-31/10
Distance: 🚶500m ⛰150m ⊗50m 🚲on the spot 🚶on the spot.

🚐S	Borculo	8D2

Bruggink Campers, Kamerlingh Onnestraat 19. **GPS:** n52,12281 e6,52682.

6 🍴free 🚿on demand. **Surface:** metalled. 🅿 01/01-31/12, 18-9h
Distance: 🚶1,5km ⛰2km 🍴500m ⊗1,5km 🚊1,5km.

🚐S	Bredevoort 🌿🍴	8D2

P2, recreatieplaats Slingeplas, Kruittorenstraat 10b. **GPS:** n51,94749 e6,62346.
⬆➡.

8 🍴€ 10 ⛽€1/80liter 🔌Ch 🚿(8x)included. 🏠
Location: Rural, comfortable, quiet. **Surface:** metalled.
🅿 01/01-31/12
Distance: 🚶200m ⛰100m ⊗400m 🚊500m.
Remarks: Max. 72h.

Tourist information Bredevoort:
ℹ City with half-timbered houses.
🏛 Book market. 🅿 3rd Sa of the month 10-17.

⚓S — **Culemborg** 🌿⚓🍴〰 8B2

Jachthaven de Helling, Beusichemsedijk. **GPS:** n51,96117 e5,22148. ⬆➡

20 🛏 € 14, 1,55 pers.incl, € 1,55/pp tourist tax 🚰€0,50/100liter
Ch 🔌 WC 🚻€0,50 💧€4/4 📶included. **Surface:** grassy/sand.
📅 01/04-01/11
Distance: 🚶500m 🏊on the spot 🎣on the spot ⊗on the spot 🍽500m
🚉1,5km.
Remarks: Check in at harbourmaster.

🛏S — **De Heurne** 8D2

De Haar, Casperstraat 14. **GPS:** n51,89802 e6,50035. ⬆

± 10 🛏€ 10 🚰€1/80liter Ch 🔌 📶included. 🌳 **Location:** Rural, quiet.
Surface: grassy. 📅 01/01-31/12
Distance: 🚶1km 🚴8km.
Remarks: Filling station gas bottles 300m.

⚓S — **Doesburg** 🌿⚓🍴〰 8D2

Jachthaven Doesburg, Turfhaven. **GPS:** n52,01109 e6,13368. ⬆➡

6 🛏€ 7,50 🚰 Ch 🔌 (6x)€0,50/kWh WC included 🚿€0,50/4minutes.
🌳 **Location:** Urban, comfortable, central, quiet. **Surface:** concrete.
📅 01/01-31/12
Distance: 🚶500m 🏊4km 🎣on the spot ⊗500m ⊗1km 🚉500m
⊗on the spot 🎣on the spot.
Remarks: Check in at harbourmaster.

🛏 — **Doornenburg** 🌿 8D2

Kerkstraat. **GPS:** n51,89416 e6,00129. ⬆

3 🛏free. **Location:** Rural, quiet. **Surface:** metalled. 📅 01/01-31/12

Distance: 🚶400m ⊗200m cafetaria ⊗200m 🚉400m ⚓on the spot.
Remarks: Max. 3 days, view on castle Doornenburg.

⚓S — **Elburg** 🌿⚓🍴〰 8C1

Gemeentehaven Elburg, Havenkade 1. **GPS:** n52,45110 e5,82933. ⬆

18 🛏€ 7,85 + € 1,05/pp tourist tax 🚰 Ch 🔌€0,50/24h
WC 🚻€0,50 📶included. 🌳 **Location:** Comfortable, central, quiet.
Surface: grasstiles/metalled. 📅 01/01-31/12
Distance: 🚶250m 🏊on the spot 🎣on the spot ⊗300m ⊗300m
🚉on the spot ⚓on the spot 🎣on the spot.
Remarks: Max. 3 days, water closed during wintertime.

🛏S — **Emst** 8C1

De Kievit, Zwarteweg 20. **GPS:** n52,30344 e5,99320. ⬆➡

15 🛏€ 10, 2 pers.incl, extra pers € 1,50 🚰 Ch 🔌€2/night,6 Amp
📶included. 🌳 **Location:** Rural, simple, quiet. **Surface:** grassy/metalled.
📅 01/01-31/12
Distance: 🚶3km 🏊1km 🎣1km ⚓on the spot 🎣on the spot.

⚓S — **Emst** 8C1

Recreatiepark 't Smallert, Smallertsweg 8. **GPS:** n52,30910 e5,98126. ⬆

20 🛏€ 5 🚰free. **Surface:** metalled. 📅 01/01-31/12
Distance: 🚶2km ⊗on the spot.
Remarks: Check in on arrival.

🛏 — **Epe** 8C1

Pastoor Somstraat. **GPS:** n52,34965 e5,98331. ⬆

3 🛏free. **Location:** Urban, simple. **Surface:** metalled. 📅 01/01-31/12
Distance: 🚶on the spot 🏊3km ⊗on the spot ⊗on the spot.

Ermelo 8C1
Camperpark Strand Horst, Buitenbrinkweg 82. **GPS:** n52,31181 e5,56643. ⬆.

40 🛏 € 10, 2 pers.incl 🚰 🔌 Ch 💧 (50x) WC 🧺€0,50/6minutes 📶 included. 🔧 **Location:** Rural, comfortable, noisy. **Surface:** grassy/metalled.
⬛ 01/03-31/10
Distance: 🚶4km 🏊50m 🌊200m 🛒200m ⊗500m 🚊4km.

Garderen 8C2
Hotel Restaurant Overbosch, Hooiweg 23. **GPS:** n52,22577 e5,70504. ✈.

10 🛏 € 7,50 💧 €2,50/24h 📶. 🔧 🚲 **Location:** Rural, simple, quiet.
Surface: gravel. ⬛ 01/01-31/12
Distance: 🚶1km ⊗on the spot 🚊1km 🚌on the spot 🚴on the spot
🚶on the spot.
Remarks: Use of a meal desired.

Garderen 8C2
Gasterij Zondag, Apeldoornsestraat 163-165. **GPS:** n52,21443 e5,70696. ✈.

10 🛏free.
Location: Rural. **Surface:** gravel.
⬛ 01/01-31/12 ⬤ Restaurant:Tue
Distance: 🚶2km 🏊3,5km ⊗on the spot 🚴on the spot 🚶on the spot.
Remarks: Max. 1 night, entrance next to restaurant, restaurant visit appreciated.

Geldermalsen 8B2
Kostverlorenkade. GPS: n51,88421 e5,28985.

1 🛏free. **Surface:** metalled.
Distance: 🚶100m 🏊3,6km 🌊on the spot 🛒on the spot ⊗on the spot.

Remarks: Parking at departure excursion boat.

Gendringen 8D2
Willem Alexanderplein. GPS: n51,86999 e6,37948. ⬆.

2 🛏free. **Location:** Simple. **Surface:** asphalted. ⬛ 01/01-31/12
Distance: 🚶200m ⊗100m 🚊500m.
Remarks: Max. 72h.

Gendringen 8D2
Diekshuus, Ulftseweg 4a. **GPS:** n51,87397 e6,38489. ⬆.

4 🛏 € 10 🚰€1 🔌 💧 included. 🚐 **Location:** Rural, simple. **Surface:** gravel.
⬛ 01/01-31/12
Distance: 🚶600m ⊗600m.
Remarks: At manege.

Gorssel 8D2
De Vlinderhoeve, Bathmenseweg 7. **GPS:** n52,21825 e6,26255. ⬆➡.

5 🛏 € 14 🚰 🔌 Ch 💧 WC 🧺€5/1,50 📶included. 🔧
Location: Rural, luxurious, quiet. **Surface:** forest soil. ⬛ 01/04-31/10
Distance: 🚶8km 🏊on the spot ⊗on the spot 🚊on the spot 🚴on the spot
🚶on the spot.

Groenlo 8D2
Camping Marveld, Elshofweg 6. **GPS:** n52,03698 e6,63187. ⬆.

4 🛏 € 10 🚰€1/80liter 🔌 Ch 💧. **Surface:** metalled. ⬛ 01/01-31/12

Harderwijk 8C1
P Parkweg, Parkweg. **GPS:** n52,34088 e5,62977. ⬆.

3 🛏free. **Location:** Urban, simple. **Surface:** metalled.
⭕ 01/01-31/12
Distance: 🚲1,2km 🚣3km ⊗1,3km 🛒800m.

3 🛏free. **Location:** Rural, simple, isolated, quiet. **Surface:** gravel/metalled.
⭕ 01/01-31/12
Distance: 🚲2km ⊗2km 🛒2km 🚌2km 🚴on the spot 🚶on the spot.
Remarks: Max. 72h.

| 🛏S | Hattem | 🌿⚓🍰 | 8D1 |

Jachthaven Hattem, Geldersedijk 20. **GPS:** n52,47699 e6,06945.⬆️.

| 🛏 | Huissen | 🌿⚓🍰 | 8C2 |

Looveer. GPS: n51,93578 e5,94467.⬆️➡️.

22 🛏S€ 8,50 + € 1,25/pp tourist tax 🚰🔌Ch 🚿(4x)€2 WC 🚽€0,50/8minutes 🚿€3,50/3 📶included. **Location:** Urban, comfortable, central, quiet.
Surface: grasstiles/grassy. ⭕ 01/01-31/12
Distance: 🚲200m 🏊on the spot 🛒on the spot ⊗200m 🛒200m 🚌50m 🚴on the spot 🚶on the spot.
Remarks: Max. 72h, check in at harbourmaster.

3 🛏free. **Location:** Simple, central. **Surface:** grasstiles/metalled.
⭕ 01/01-31/12
Distance: 🚲200m 🏊200m 🛒200m ⊗200m 🚌500m 🚴on the spot 🚶on the spot.
Remarks: Max. 72h.

| 🍴S | Heerde | 🌿⚓🍰 | 8D1 |

Brasserie Meet & Eat, Eperweg 55. **GPS:** n52,37084 e6,02079.

| 🛏S | Kerkwijk | | 8B3 |

Hippisch Centrum Bommelerwaard, Jan Stuversdreef 1-3.
GPS: n51,78876 e5,19929.⬆️.

10 🛏free, use of a meal desired 🚰🚿(2x)included WC 📶📹.
Surface: grassy/gravel. ⭕ Su (01/10-30/04)
Distance: 🚲3km 🏊1,5km 🛒1,5km ⊗on the spot 🛒2km 🚌100m.

| 🛏 | Hengelo | | 8D2 |

Elderinkweg 1-9. **GPS:** n52,04457 e6,30377.⬆️.

4 🛏€ 10 🚿 WC 📶included. **Surface:** metalled. ⭕ 01/01-31/12 ⭕ Su

| ⚓S | Lathum | 🍴⚓ | 8D2 |

Jachthaven 't Eiland, De Muggenwaard 16. **GPS:** n51,98819 e6,04462.⬆️➡️.

2 🛏free. **Surface:** asphalted. ⭕ 01/01-31/12
Distance: 🚲500m 🚌100m.
Remarks: Next to sports fields, max. 24h.

| 🛏 | Heteren | | 8C2 |

Steenkuil, N837. **GPS:** n51,95456 e5,73094.⬆️.

20 🛏€ 8,50 🚰🔌Ch 🚿(20x)€1,50/day WC included 🚽€0,50/4minutes 📶€3/day. 🚿 **Location:** Rural, comfortable, quiet. **Surface:** grassy/metalled.
⭕ 01/01-31/12
Distance: 🚲1km 🚴5km 🏊on the spot 🛒on the spot ⊗on the spot 🛒1km 🚴500m 🚶on the spot 🎣on the spot.
Remarks: Max. 48h.

| 🛏 | Lichtenvoorde | | 8D2 |

't Meekenesch, Kerkhoflaan 5. **GPS:** n51,99305 e6,56831.⬆️.

NL

3 ⏚free. **Surface:** metalled. ◻ 01/01-31/12
Distance: ⚓1km 🚗100m.
Remarks: Parking swimming pool, max. 72h.

| 🅿️S | Maasbommel 🌿🌸🍽 | 8C3 |

Saletmeubelen, Kapelstraat 30. **GPS:** n51,82459 e5,53193.⬆️.

5 ⏚€ 10 🔌🔋Ch 🧹 📶included. ◻ 01/01-31/12
Distance: ⚓300m 🏊1km 🍴1km ⊗1km 🛒300m.

| 🍴 | Meteren | 8B2 |

Restaurant den Tol, Rijksstraatweg 80. **GPS:** n51,85759 e5,28009.

5 ⏚free.
Remarks: Use of a meal desired.

| 🅿️S | Millingen a/d Rijn | 8D2 |

't **Crumpse Hoekje**, Crumpsestraat 28. **GPS:** n51,85624 e6,03145.⬆️➡️.

6 ⏚€ 6,50 + tourist tax € 0,75/pp 🔌€1/90liter 🔋Ch 🧹 (6x)€2/day WCfree
💧€1. 🌼 **Location:** Rural, luxurious, quiet. **Surface:** gravel.
◻ 01/01-31/12
Distance: ⚓1,4km 🚲2km ⊗1,4km 🛒1,4km.

| 🅿️ | Neede | 8D2 |

Den Blanken, Diepneheimseweg 44. **GPS:** n52,18013 e6,58603.⬆️➡️.

4 ⏚€ 10 🔌€1/80liter 🔋Ch 🧹included. ▮🅿️ **Location:** Quiet.
Surface: grassy. ◻ 01/01-31/12 🐕on the spot 🚶on the spot.

| 🍴S | Neede | 8D2 |

Café restaurant De Olde Mölle, Diepenheimseweg 21.
GPS: n52,14153 e6,61035.

8 ⏚€ 10 🔌€1/80liter 🔋Ch 🧹 . **Surface:** metalled. ◻ 01/01-31/12
Distance: ⊗on the spot.

| 🍴S | Neede | 8D2 |

Partycentrum 't Haantje, Borculoseweg 111. **GPS:** n52,13437 e6,59886.⬆️ .

5 ⏚€ 5, free with a meal 🔌🔋 🧹 WCincluded. **Surface:** gravel.
Distance: ⚓600m ⊗on the spot 🛒500m 🚗on the spot.
Remarks: Rental of electric scooters and bicycles.

| 🅿️ | Nijkerk | 8C2 |

Camperplaats Nijkerk, Watergoorweg 31. **GPS:** n52,22641 e5,47711.⬆️.

2 ⏚free. **Location:** Urban, simple, noisy. **Surface:** metalled.
◻ 01/01-31/12
Distance: ⚓500m 🚴2km 🏊2km 🚲500m ⊗500m 🛒500m 🚗200m
🐕on the spot 🚶on the spot.

| 🅿️S | Nijmegen 🌿🍃🍽 | 8C2 |

Lindenberghaven, Waalkade. **GPS:** n51,84889 e5,86936.⬆️.

NL

6 🕭 € 20 🚰 🛁 (6x)€0,50/kWh. 🏪 ♻
Location: Urban, simple, central, noisy. **Surface:** metalled.
🔲 01/05-01/09 🔵 during the Four Days Marche
Distance: �foon the spot ⚓on the spot ⛴on the spot.
Remarks: Along the river Waal, max. 72h.

🏊S		Nunspeet 🌿⛲🍴🎧		8C1

Camperplaats De Zwaan, Hardenbrinkweg 46. **GPS:** n52,37901 e5,75363. ⬆➡

35 🕭 € 13 🚰🍽Ch 🛁 (45x)WC 🗑€3/3 📶included. 🚻
Location: Rural, comfortable, luxurious, quiet. **Surface:** grasstiles/grassy.
🔲 01/01-31/12
Distance: 🚍2,5km 🚲3,5km ⛵2,5km ⚓2,5km ⚾1km ⛴2km 🚗900m
🚴Zwanenroute ⚫on the spot.
Remarks: No arrival on Sunday.

🍴S		Nunspeet 🌿⛲🍴🎧		8C1

Routiers Nunspeet, Rijksweg A28. **GPS:** n52,36199 e5,77061. 🔼 .

🕭free WC 🗑. **Surface:** asphalted. 🔲 01/01-31/12
Remarks: Use of sanitary free with a meal.

Tourist information Nunspeet:
⚫ 🔲 Thu-morning.

©S		Otterlo ⛲🎧		8C2

De Wije Werelt, Arnhemseweg 100-102. **GPS:** n52,08592 e5,77319.

16 🕭 € 18 🚰🍽Ch 🛁included WC 🗑📶. 🚻 **Location:** Rural, simple.
Surface: grassy. 🔲 01/04-01/11
Distance: 🚍2km ⚓on the spot ⛴campsite supermarket 🚴on the spot
⚫on the spot.

Remarks: Max. 2 nights.
Tourist information Otterlo:
Ⓜ Kröller Möller Museum. Collection.

🕭		Putten ⛲🍴🎧		8C1

Brinkstraat. **GPS:** n52,26244 e5,60756. 🔼.

2 🕭free. **Location:** Urban, simple, central. **Surface:** metalled.
🔲 01/01-31/12
Distance: 🚍200m ⊗300m ⛴300m 🚗250m 🚴on the spot ⚫on the spot.
Remarks: Max. 48h.

Tourist information Putten:
⚫ 🔲 Wed.

🎧		Rekken		9A2

Grensovergang, Oldenkotseweg. **GPS:** n52,09783 e6,75568. 🔼 .

5 🕭 € 5. **Surface:** metalled. 🔲 01/01-31/12
Distance: 🚍on the spot ⊗on the spot ⛴on the spot.
Remarks: Max. 72h, cycle and hiking routes.

🕭S		Ressen		8C2

De Woerdt, Woerdsestraat 4. **GPS:** n51,88867 e5,87215.

15 🕭 € 7,50 + € 1/pp tourist tax 🛁 (10x)included. 🚻
Location: Rural. **Surface:** grassy/metalled.
🔲 01/01-31/12
Distance: 🚍2km 🚲3,6km ⛴2km.
Remarks: Regional products, pitches in the orchard.

©S		Ruurlo		8D2

Camping Tamaring, Wildpad 3. **GPS:** n52,10239 e6,44257. 🔼.

NL

2 ⛺ € 10 🚰 €1/80liter 🔌 Ch 🧹 included. 🚐 **Location:** Simple.
Surface: forest soil. ⬜ 01/01-31/12
Distance: 🚶2km 🚴on the spot 🚶on the spot.
Remarks: Max. 8M.

| 🅿️ | **Silvolde** | 8D2 |

Parking de Paasberg, Terborgseveld. **GPS:** n51,91633 e6,37194.⬆️.

4 ⛺ free. **Location:** Urban. **Surface:** metalled. ⬜ 01/01-31/12
Distance: 🚶city centre 1km ⊗300m.
Remarks: Parking at swimming pool, max. 72h.

| ⓒⓢ | **Sinderen** | 8D2 |

Biezenhof, Kapelweg 42a. **GPS:** n51,90370 e6,45285.⬆️.

4 ⛺ € 10 🚰 €1/80liter 🔌 Ch 🧹 included. 🚐 **Location:** Rural, simple.
Surface: gravel. ⬜ 01/01-31/12

| 🅿️ⓢ | **Sinderen** | 8D2 |

Natuurlijkbuiten, Toldijk 11. **GPS:** n51,91297 e6,42384.

2 ⛺ € 12 🚰 🔌 🧹 (2x)included. **Location:** Rural. **Surface:** grassy/gravel.
⬜ 01/01-31/12
Distance: 🚶3km 🏊3km ⛵on the spot ⊗3km 🛒3km 🚌2km
🚴on the spot 🚶on the spot.
Remarks: Bread-service.

Camping Brockhausen, Eltenseweg 20. **GPS:** n51,87778 e6,21167.⬆️.
4 ⛺ € 10 🚰 €1/80liter 🔌 Ch 🧹 included 🚿€2,50/day. 🚐
Location: Rural. **Surface:** grasstiles. ⬜ 01/01-31/12
Distance: 🚶800m 🚴500m 🛒2,5km 🚌2km 🚴on the spot 🚶on the spot.
Remarks: At the edge of the forest, max. 2 nights, bread-service.

| 🅿️ⓢ | **Terschuur** | 8C2 |

Camperplaats Groot Westerveld, Leemweg 2. **GPS:** n52,16819 e5,53239.⬆️.

4 ⛺ € 7,50 🚰 🔌 Ch 🧹 €2,50/night,10Amp WC 🚿included. 🚽
Location: Rural, simple, quiet. **Surface:** grassy/metalled. ⬜ 01/03-30/09
Distance: 🚶1,5km 🏊4km 🛒2km ⊗3km ⛵2km 🚌1km 🚴on the spot
🚶on the spot.

| 🍴 | **Terwolde** 🏕 | 8D1 |

Dorpsstraat 53, N792. **GPS:** n52,28173 e6,09962.⬆️.

2 ⛺ free. **Location:** Simple, central, quiet. **Surface:** metalled.
⬜ 01/01-31/12
Distance: 🚶100m ⊗on the spot 🚌on the spot 🚴on the spot 🚶on the spot.

| 🍴ⓢ | **Tiel** | 8C2 |

Parking Waalkade, Waalkade. **GPS:** n51,88518 e5,44079.⬆️.

NL

4 ⌁ € 5,10. 🚰 **Surface:** asphalted. ⬛ 01/01-31/12
Distance: 🛒500m ⛱on the spot 🚰on the spot ⊗on the spot ⛲500m 🚰on the spot.
Remarks: Max. 2 nights, cash payment.

| 🛉S | Toldijk | 8D2 |

Prinsen, Hardsteestraat 4. **GPS:** n52,04489 e6,21737.⬆.

2 ⌁ € 6 🚰🔌Ch included ⚡(1x)€2,50.🚽
Location: Rural, simple, quiet. **Surface:** grassy.
⬛ 01/01-31/12
Distance: 🛒1,5km ⛱5km 🚰5km ⊗1,5km ⛲2km 🚰300m 🚶on the spot.
Remarks: Max. 3 nights.

| 🛉S | Tolkamer 🌿🚰🍴🛒 | 8D2 |

Europakade, Europakade. **GPS:** n51,85122 e6,09938.⬆➡.

15 ⌁ € 7,50 + € 0,80/pp tourist tax ⚡(6x)€1/kWh.🚽 **Location:** Simple,
central, quiet. **Surface:** metalled.
⬛ 01/01-31/12 🔲 high water
Distance: 🛒200m ⊗150m ⛲200m 🚰500m 🚲on the spot 🚶on the spot.
Remarks: Max. 48h.

| 🍴 | Tolkamer 🌿🚰🍴🛒 | 8D2 |

De Swaenebloem, Bijland 3. **GPS:** n51,86268 e6,07800.

⌁free with a meal. ⬛ 01/01-31/12
Distance: 🛒Lobith 3,5km ⛱100m 🚰on the spot ⊗on the spot.
Remarks: Max. 2 nights, charging point for electric bicycles.

| 🛉 | Twello 🚰🍴🍵 | 8D2 |

Jachtlustplein 7. **GPS:** n52,23439 e6,09847.⬆.

1 ⌁free. **Location:** Urban, simple, central, quiet. **Surface:** metalled.
⬛ 01/01-31/12
Distance: 🛒100m ⊗100m ⛲100m 🚰on the spot 🚲on the spot
🚶on the spot.

| 🛒 | Vaassen 🌿🍵 | 8C1 |

Julianalaan. **GPS:** n52,29040 e5,96550.⬆.

4 ⌁free. **Location:** Simple. **Surface:** asphalted.
Distance: 🛒on the spot ⊗100m.
Remarks: Max. 48h.

| 🛒 | Varsseveld | 8D2 |

Pallandtbad, Pallandstraat 4. **GPS:** n51,94444 e6,46639.

4 ⌁free. **Surface:** metalled. ⬛ 01/01-31/12
Distance: 🛒200m ⊗200m ⛲200m 🚰200m.
Remarks: Max. 24h.

| 🛒S | Vierakker 🚰🍵 | 8D2 |

Hanzestadcampers, Vierakkersestraatweg 19. **GPS:** n52,10659 e6,24122.⬆.

3 ⌁ € 7,50 🚰🔌Ch ⚡(3x)🔊included.🚽 **Location:** Rural, simple, quiet.
Surface: gravel. ⬛ 01/01-31/12
Distance: 🛒500m ⊗1km ⛲500m 🚰500m.

| 🛉S | Voorst | 8D2 |

De Adelaar, Rijksstraatweg 49. **GPS:** n52,17760 e6,14150.⬆.

10 ⬛€ 12,50 🔌🔧 Ch 🔧 (10x)€2 WC 🚻€0,50 💧€4/4 🚰. **Location:** Rural.
Surface: grassy/metalled. ⬛ 01/01-31/12
Distance: 🚶500m 🚲7km ⛱on the spot 🛒on the spot ⊗150m 🍴1km.
Remarks: Incl. use camp-site facilities.

| Ⓒ Ⓢ | Voorst | 8D2 |

Boerderij de Kolke, Klarenbeekseweg 30. **GPS:** n52,17355 e6,13318.

16 ⬛€6 🔌🔧 Ch included 🔧€1. **Surface:** grassy/metalled.
Remarks: Regional products.

| Ⓒ Ⓢ | Voorthuizen 👥 | 8C2 |

Ackersate, Harremaatweg 26. **GPS:** n52,18683 e5,62547.⬆

5 ⬛€ 14, 2 pers.incl 🔌🔧 Ch 🔧 WC included 🚻€1 💧€5,50, on camp site 🚰.
🐕 **Location:** Rural, simple. **Surface:** metalled. ⬛ 01/04-27/10
Distance: 🚶1,3km 🚲4,2km ⊗on the spot 🍴on the spot 🐴 on the spot
🏃on the spot.

| ⬛ Ⓢ | Westendorp 👥 | 8D2 |

Recreatieoord Hippique, Doetinchemseweg 141. **GPS:** n51,94964 e6,42084.⬆

4 ⬛€ 10 🔌€1/80liter 🔧 Ch 🔧 included WC 🚻€2 💧€5/5 🚰.🔌
Surface: grasstiles. ⬛ 01/01-31/12
Distance: 🚶500m ⊗500m 🍴3km 🚲600m 🐴 on the spot.
Remarks: Arrival 9><20h.

| ⬛ Ⓢ | Winterswijk | 9A2 |

Landgoed Kreil, Heenkamppieperweg 1. **GPS:** n51,93573 e6,67907.⬆

2 ⬛€ 10 🔌€1/80liter 🔧 Ch 🔧 included 🚰 against payment. 🚐 **Location:**
Rural, isolated. **Surface:** metalled. ⬛ 01/03-31/10
Distance: 🚶Breedevoort 4,5km 🚶Located on estate.

| Ⓒ Ⓢ | Winterswijk | 9A2 |

Camping Ten Hagen, Waliënsestraat 139A. **GPS:** n51,99131 e6,71898.⬆.

4 ⬛€ 10 🔌€1/80liter 🔧 Ch 🔧 included. **Location:** Rural, simple, isolated,
quiet. **Surface:** grassy. ⬛ 01/01-31/12
Distance: 🚶city centre 3km ⛱lake.
Remarks: Max. 24h, manufacturer of wooden clogs.

| Ⓒ Ⓢ | Winterswijk | 9A2 |

Vreehorst, Vreehorstweg 43. **GPS:** n51,95028 e6,69251.⬆.

4 ⬛€ 10 🔌€1/80liter 🔧 Ch 🔧 included. 🚐 **Location:** Rural, comfortable.
Surface: gravel. ⬛ 01/01-31/12
Distance: 🚶3,6km.

| ⬛ | Zelhem | 8D2 |

Carpoolplaats, Stikkenweg/N330. **GPS:** n51,99893 e6,34541.⬆.

2 ⬛free. **Surface:** asphalted. ⬛ 01/01-31/12
Distance: 🚶1km.
Remarks: Max. 24h.

| ⬛ Ⓢ | Zutphen 🌿🍽 | 8D2 |

Houtwal. **GPS:** n52,13565 e6,19866.⬆.

NL

8 €10 €1/80liter Ch included. **Surface:** metalled. 01/01-31/12
Distance: 1km.
Remarks: Nearby police station, max. 48h, beautiful view.

Zutphen 8D2
IJsselkade. **GPS:** n52,14037 e6,19119.

2 €7,80, Sunday free. **Surface:** metalled. 01/01-31/12
Distance: 1km.
Remarks: Motorhome max. 6m, max. 48h.
Tourist information Zutphen:
Groenmarkt-Houtmarkt-Zaadmarkt. Thu 8-12h, Sa 8-17h.
Lange Hofstraat. Farmers market. Thu 8-13h.

NL

Utrecht

Amersfoort 8C2
Aan de Eem, Klein Koppel. **GPS:** n52,16210 e5,37829.

3 €1,10/meter WC included. **Location:** Urban, noisy.
Surface: metalled. 01/01-31/12
Distance: 600m 500m 500m on the spot.
Remarks: At fire-station, max. 24h.

Baarn 8B2
De Zeven Linden, Zevenlindenweg 4. **GPS:** n52,19721 e5,24838.

3 €10 €2,50 Ch €5/time. **Location:** Simple.
Surface: metalled. 01/04-01/11
Distance: 2km 1km 2km 300m on the spot on the spot.

Bunnik 8B2
Camping de Boomgaard, Parallelweg 9. **GPS:** n52,06065 e5,19943.

6 €7,50 Ch WC €2. **Surface:** metalled. 01/04/31/10
Distance: 3km 800m.
Remarks: Arrival >17h departure <10h check in at reception next morning, use camp-site facilities allowed.

Bunschoten-Spakenburg 8C1
Jachthaven Nieuwboer, Westdijk 36. **GPS:** n52,26070 e5,37238.

8 €15, 2 pers.incl Ch WC €3,50/time included.
Location: Rural, simple, comfortable, quiet. **Surface:** grassy.
01/01-31/12
Distance: 800m 6km 100m 700m 700m 700m
on the spot on the spot.

IJsselstein 8B2
Jachthaven Marnemoende, Noord IJsseldijk 107b. **GPS:** n52,04583 e5,01861.

7 €15 Ch WC €4/2 included. **Location:** Rural, comfortable, luxurious, quiet. **Surface:** gravel. 01/01-31/12
Distance: 2km on the spot on the spot on the spot 2km 2km on the spot.

Leersum 8C2
Touché, Rijksstraatweg 54. **GPS:** n52,00974 e5,43507.

5 free. **Location:** Urban, simple. **Surface:** gravel. 01/01-31/12 Mo
Distance: 200m on the spot 200m on the spot on the spot.

Leusden 8C2

De Mof, Arnhemseweg 95. **GPS:** n52,10654 e5,41445. 🔼 .

5 🍖 free, use of a meal desired. **Location:** Rural, simple. **Surface:** gravel.
🔲 01/01-31/12 ⊙ Mon, Tue
Distance: 🚶4km 🚴 4km ⊗on the spot 🚌 on the spot 🚲 on the spot.
Remarks: First check in at restaurant.

Mijdrecht 8B2

Rondweg. **GPS:** n52,20804 e4,86879. 🔼➡️ .

4 🍖 free. **Location:** Urban, simple, noisy. **Surface:** metalled.
🔲 01/01-31/12
Distance: 🚶500m 🚴500m 🚊500m 🚌500m.
Remarks: Max. 48h.

Overberg 8C2

De Holle Boom, Dwarsweg 63. **GPS:** n52,02914 e5,50061. 🔼 .

5 🍖 free with a meal.
Location: Rural, simple, quiet. **Surface:** gravel.
Distance: 🚶on the spot ⊗on the spot 🚲on the spot 🚶on the spot.

Rhenen 8C2

Restaurant 3 Zussen, Kerkewijk-zuid 115. **GPS:** n52,00682 e5,54006.

5 🍖 free. **Location:** Rural, simple. **Surface:** asphalted.
🔲 01/01-31/12
Distance: 🚶1km Veenendaal ⊗on the spot 🚊1km 🚌on the spot
🚲 on the spot 🚶on the spot.
Remarks: Use of a meal desired.

Vianen 8B2

Kanaalweg, P1. **GPS:** n51,99549 e5,09620.

4 🍖 free. **Surface:** metalled.
🔲 01/01-31/12
Distance: 🚶500m.
Remarks: During events: Hazelaarplein, max. 48h.

Tourist information Vianen:
ℹ️ VVV, Voorstraat 97, www.vvv-vianen.nl. Historical centre.
⚓ Voorstraat (zuid). 🔲 Wed 10-16h.

South Holland

Alblasserdam 8A2

Haven 4. **GPS:** n51,86106 e4,65799. 🔼 .

10 🍖 € 10 🔌 €0,50 🚰 Ch WC 🍖.
Surface: asphalted.
🔲 01/01-31/12
Distance: 🚶500m 🚴 1,3km ⊗on the spot 🚊500m.
Remarks: At cultural centre 'Landvast', Kinderdijk ± 4,5km, check in at
harbourmaster, sanitary in harbour building against payment.
Tourist information Alblasserdam:
👁 Molens, Nederwaard 1, Kinderdijk. World famous mill-area.
🔲 01/07-31/08 Sa, 1st Sa of the month.
⚓ Wilgenplein. 🔲 Mo-afternoon.

Bleiswijk 8A2

Jan van de Heidenstraat. **GPS:** n52,01415 e4,53411. 🔼 .

2 🍖 free. **Location:** Urban. **Surface:** metalled. 🔲 01/01-31/12
Distance: 🚶300m 🚴 5km ⊗500m 🚊Jumbo 400m.
Remarks: Next to fire-station.

Bleskensgraaf 8B2

Farm Nescio, Elzenweg 19. **GPS:** n51,85674 e4,75266. 🔼 .

NL

8 € 14 WC included. **Location:** Rural, comfortable, isolated, quiet.
Surface: metalled. 01/01-31/12
Distance: 2,5km 1,5km 1,5km 1km 2,5km.
Remarks: Possibility of guided tour.

S Delft 8A2

Delftse Hout, Korftlaan 5. **GPS**: n52,01772 e4,37945.

20 € 20-28 Ch (20x) €6,50/time included.
Location: Urban, comfortable, central. **Surface:** grasstiles.
01/04-01/11
Distance: 1,5km 1,2km 500m on the spot on the spot on the spot summer > centre on the spot on the spot.
Remarks: Check in at reception campsite.

Tourist information Delft:
VVV, Hippolytusbuurt 4, www.delft.nl. Historical centre with canals and merchant houses. church 01/03-31/10 Mo-Sa 9-18h, 01/11-28/02 Mo-Sa 11-16h.

S Dordrecht 8A3

Camperplaats Stadswerven, Maasstraat. **GPS**: n51,81793 e4,68750.

12 Mo-Sa € 6,50/24h, Su free €1 Ch. **Location:** Simple, quiet.
Surface: metalled. 01/01-31/12
Distance: city centre 3km 5km on the spot on the spot 3km 1km waterbus.
Remarks: Max. 72h, near Noah's Ark.

Dordrecht 8A3

Weeskinderendijk 5. **GPS**: n51,80861 e4,65611.

2 € 1/4h, first 24h free. **Location:** Urban, simple, noisy. **Surface:** metalled.
01/01-31/12
Distance: 500m 500m 500m 100m.
Remarks: Max. 72h.

S Giessenburg 8B2

Boerenterras De Groot, A.M.A. Langeraadweg 9. **GPS**: n51,85327 e4,92205.

8 € 10 WC included.
Location: Rural, simple, isolated, quiet. **Surface:** concrete.
01/01-31/12
Distance: 1,5km 3km on the spot 1,5km 3,5km on the spot.

S Giessenburg 8B2

Halfomhoeve, Bovenkerkseweg 76/78. **GPS**: n51,84628 e4,87548.

3 € 10 included WC .
Location: Rural, simple, isolated, quiet. **Surface:** concrete. 01/01-31/12
Distance: 2km 3km on the spot 1,5km 1,5km on the spot on the spot.

S Giessenburg 8B2

Landscheiding Giessenburg, Landscheiding 1. **GPS**: n51,84753 e4,92294.

6 € 10 Ch WC included. **Location:** Rural, comfortable, isolated, quiet. **Surface:** grassy/metalled. 01/01-31/12
Distance: 2km 2km 2km on the spot on the spot.

S Gorinchem 8B3

WSV Merwede, Buiten de Waterpoort 8. **GPS**: n51,82697 e4,96477.

16 € 10 Ch included €0,75 €5/4. **Location:** Comfortable, isolated, quiet. **Surface:** gravel/metalled.

NL

◆ 01/01-31/12
Distance: 🚶500m 🏊on the spot 🛒on the spot ✛300m 🍺1km
🍴on the spot.
Remarks: Max. 72h, check in at harbourmaster.

Tourist information Gorinchem:
ℹ VVV, Grote Markt 17, www.gorinchem.nl. Historical centre with city walls.
✠✛ Slot Loevestein, Loevestein 1, Poederoijen. Castle, 14th century.
◆ 01/05-30/09 Tue-Fri 11-17h Sa-Su-Mo-holidays 13-17h, 01/10-30/04 Sa-Su 13-17h.
⚘ Grote Markt. ◆ Mo 8.30-12.30h.

Gouda   8B2
Parking Klein Amerika, Fluwelensingel. **GPS:** n52,01185 e4,71576. ⬆

30 🍴 € 8 🔌🚰Ch 🚿 (12x) WC included. 🚐
Location: Urban, simple, quiet.
Surface: metalled.
◆ 01/01-31/12
Distance: 🚶300m.
Remarks: Max. 3 days.

Tourist information Gouda:
ℹ VVV, Markt 27, www.vvvgouda.nl. Historical centre with 300 monuments, famous for its Gouda-cheese.
👁 Kaaswaag, Markt. History of the Gouda cheese. ◆ 01/04-30/09 13-17h, Thu 10-17h.
⚘ Markt. ◆ Thu 8.30-13h, Sa 8.30-17h.
⚘ Montmartre, Markt. Antiques and flea market. ◆ 01/05-30/09 We 9-17h.

Goudriaan   8B2
Boerderij de Verwondering, De Hoogt 14. **GPS:** n51,89150 e4,90741. ⬆

2 🍴 € 10 🔌🚰Ch 🚿📶included. 🚿 **Location:** Rural, simple, isolated.
Surface: concrete.
Distance: 🚶2,5km 🍺7km.

Hoogblokland   8B2
Landwinkel De Bikkerhoeve, Bazeldijk 66. **GPS:** n51,89716 e4,99563.

6 🍴 € 10 🔌🚰Ch 🚿WC included. 🚿 **Location:** Rural, simple, isolated, quiet. **Surface:** concrete. ◆ 01/03-31/10
Distance: 🚶2km 🏊1,4km ✛2km 🍺2km 🚌on the spot 🍴on the spot.

Leerdam   8B2
De Galgenwaard, Lingedijk 8a, Oosterwijk. **GPS:** n51,87451 e5,07311. ⬆

3 🍴 € 8 WC. 🚿 **Location:** Rural, simple, quiet. **Surface:** metalled.
◆ 01/04-01/10
Distance: 🚶Leerdam 2km 🏊on the spot 🛒on the spot ✛300m
🍴Along the river Linge.
Remarks: Opening hours 7-22h, passenger ferry across the Linge.

Leerdam   8B2
Groenzoom, Lingedijk. **GPS:** n51,88296 e5,08671. ⬆

2 🍴free. **Location:** Rural, simple. **Surface:** asphalted.
◆ 01/01-31/12
Distance: 🚶1km 🛒on the spot ✛1km 🍴on the spot.

Leerdam   8B2
Parking Glasmuseum, Lingedijk. **GPS:** n51,88288 e5,08670. ⬆

3 🍴free. **Location:** Urban, simple. **Surface:** metalled.
◆ 01/01-31/12
Distance: 🚶2,5km ✛2,5km 🍺2,5km 🍴on the spot.
Remarks: In front of Lingedijk 27, small pitches.

Leerdam   8B2
Jachthaven Oude Horn, Sundsvall 1. **GPS:** n51,88984 e5,09532. ⬆

3 🍴free. **Location:** Urban, simple. **Surface:** gravel.
◆ 01/01-31/12
Distance: 🚶300m ✛300m 🍺300m.
Remarks: Max. 72h.

NL

Leiden 🏖️⛵🏠 8A2

P Haagweg, Haagweg 6. **GPS**: n52,15963 e4,47852. ⬆️ .

15 🚐€ 12/24h. **Location:** Urban. **Surface:** metalled. ⬜ 01/01-31/12
Distance: 🚶800m 🚲800m 🚆800m 🚌Free bus to centre.
Remarks: Along railwayline, video surveillance, free shuttle (till 2am).

51 🚐€ 8-10/12h, € 14,50-18/24h + tourist tax € 0,81/pp, dog € 3,50/
day 🚰€3,50/100liter 🚽 Ch 🔌 (51x)€3/24h WC 🚿included 🧺 🍽️
Location: Rural, luxurious, isolated, quiet. **Surface:** grassy/metalled.
⬜ 01/01-31/12
Distance: 🚶500m ⛵1km ⊗on the spot 🚆on the spot 🚴on the spot.

🚐S Nieuwland 8B2

De Grienduil, Geer 25. **GPS**: n51,90106 e5,02622.⬆️

4 🚐€ 10 🚰🚽Ch 🔌 WC 🚿included. 🚴 **Location:** Simple, quiet.
Surface: gravel. ⬜ 01/01-31/12
Distance: 🚶on the spot ⊗2km 🚆4km 🚴on the spot 🚶on the spot.
Remarks: In winter limited services.

🚐S Poeldijk 🛥️ 8A2

Booma Recreatie, Vredebestlaan 14b. **GPS**: n52,02464 e4,21242.⬆️ .

10 🚐€ 5 🚰🚽Chincluded 🔌 (10x)€2/day. 🚴 **Location:** Rural, simple,
quiet. **Surface:** gravel. ⬜ 01/01-31/12
Distance: 🚶800m 🚴50m ⊗800m 🚆800m 🚌800m 🚴on the spot
🚶on the spot.

⛴️S Numansdorp 🛥️ 8A3

Fort Buitensluis, Fortlaan 10. **GPS**: n51,71727 e4,43866.
5 🚐€ 15 🚰🚽Ch 🚿included. **Surface:** unpaved.
⬜ 01/04-01/10
Distance: 🚶1,5km 🚴5km ⛵on the spot 🚣on the spot ⊗1,5km
🚴on the spot 🚶on the spot.
Remarks: At Hollands Diep, golf court 3km.

🚐 Oud Beijerland 🛥️🏖️🛥️ 8A3

De Oude Tol, Randweg 31a. **GPS**: n51,82933 e4,39585.⬆️

4 🚐free. **Location:** Rural, simple, isolated, quiet. **Surface:** asphalted.
⬜ 01/01-31/12
Distance: 🚶2km ⛵on the spot ⊗100m 🚴on the spot 🚶on the spot.
Remarks: Arrival >16h, max. 24h.

⛴️S Sassenheim 🛥️🛥️ 8A2

Jachthaven Jonkman, Jonkman 1. **GPS**: n52,22074 e4,54476.⬆️ .

6 🚐€ 15 🚰€0,50 🚽Ch 🔌€1 WC 🚿€0,50 🛁€5 🚿included. 🚴
Location: Comfortable. **Surface:** grassy/gravel. ⬜ 15/03-01/11
Distance: 🚶2km 🚴1km ⛵on the spot 🚣on the spot ⊗on the spot 🛁2km
🚴on the spot.
Remarks: Check in at harbourmaster.

🚐 Schiedam 🛥️🏖️🏠🛥️ 8A2

Doeleplein 1. GPS: n51,91972 e4,40111.⬆️ .

🚐 Ouddorp 🏖️🛥️ 7D3

Drive-in Camperpark Klepperduinen, Vrijheidsweg 1.
GPS: n51,81724 e3,89850.⬆️➡️ .

2 🚐€ 6,60. 🔌 **Location:** Urban, simple, central, quiet. **Surface:** metalled.
⬜ 01/01-31/12
Distance: 🚶500m 🚴1,5km ⛵on the spot 🚣on the spot ⊗500m 🛁500m
🚌500m.
Remarks: Max. 72h.

NL

Schiedam 8A2

Noordvest 40. **GPS**: n51,91926 e4,39372. ↑.

6 🚐 € 6,60. 🚰 **Location:** Urban, simple, central, quiet. **Surface:** metalled.
◻ 01/01-31/12
Distance: city centre 100m.
Remarks: Max. 72h.

Tourist information Schiedam:
Ⓜ Het Jenever Museum, Lange Haven 74-76. Making distilled spirits. ◻ Tue-Sa 12-17h, Su 13-17h.
⚓ Lange Kerkstraat. ◻ Fri 9-16h.

Strijensas 8A3

Jachthaven Strijensas, Sassendijk 6. **GPS**: n51,71472 e4,58735. ↑ →.

6 🚐 € 7 ⛽ €0,50/100liter 🔲 Ch 🧹 €2,50 WC 🔲 €1. 🚿 **Surface:** asphalted.
◻ 01/01-31/12
Distance: 500m on the spot on the spot on the spot.
Remarks: Max. 72h.

Vlaardingen 8A2

Parking Deltabrug, Oosthavenkade 81. **GPS**: n51,90364 e4,34769. ↑.

4 🚐 free. **Location:** Urban, noisy. **Surface:** metalled.
◻ 01/01-31/12
Distance: 1km on the spot 50m 100m 500m.
Remarks: Along railwayline, max. 48h.

Zevenhoven 8B2

Camperplaats Zevenhoven, Noordeinde 36. **GPS**: n52,19475 e4,77305. ↑.

5 🚐 € 10 ⛽ Ch 🧹 included. 🚿 **Location:** Rural, comfortable.

Surface: grassy/metalled. ◻ 01/01-31/12
Distance: 1km 1km on the spot on the spot.

Zealand

Axel 7D4

P Watertoren, Kinderdijk 4. **GPS**: n51,25972 e3,91028. ↑.

2 🚐 free. **Location:** Urban, simple, noisy. **Surface:** metalled.
◻ 01/01-31/12
Distance: 500m on the spot on the spot 500m on the spot on the spot.
Remarks: Max. 24h.

Tourist information Axel:
⚓ Noordstraat. ◻ Sa 8-16h.

Breskens 7D4

Roompot Recreatie, Nieuwe Sluisweg. **GPS**: n51,40193 e3,54420. ↑.

10 🚐 € 14 ⛽ 🔲 Ch included WC 🔲 📶 🚿 **Location:** Rural, comfortable, quiet. **Surface:** metalled. ◻ 01/01-31/12
Distance: 500m 400m 100m 100m on the spot on the spot.
Remarks: Servicepoint at camping Zeebad, ferry to Vlissingen 500m (pedestrian/bicycles).

Tourist information Breskens:
👁 Vismijn, Kaai 1. ◻ Mo-Fri 8-17h, auction Mo-Thu 15h, Fri 8h.

Graauw 8A4

Zandbergsestraat. **GPS**: n51,32519 e4,10420. ↑.

7 🚐 free. **Location:** Rural, simple, quiet. **Surface:** gravel/sand.
◻ 01/01-31/12
Distance: 400m 400m on the spot.
Remarks: Max. 72h.

Groede 7D4

De Ploeg, Parking Zuid, Voorstraat 47. **GPS**: n51,38232 e3,51268. ↑.

NL

40 🚐 € 5 17-10h, € 12,50/24h ⛽🚰 Ch ✦ (35x)€2,50/night WC 🚻 🔲.
🚿 **Location:** Comfortable, central, quiet. **Surface:** grasstiles/metalled.
📷 01/04-01/10 🔘 22-7h
Distance: 🚶100m 🏊3km ⊗100m 🛒100m 🚌100m > Terneuzen
🚲 on the spot 🚶 on the spot.
Remarks: Caution € 10, sanitary/washing machine at campsite.

| 📷 | Groede 🌿⛽🚣 | 7D4 |

Strandcamping Groede, Zeeweg 1. **GPS**: n51,39632 e3,48719.⬆️.

50 🚐 € 0,80/h. 🔲 🚿 **Location:** Rural, simple, quiet. **Surface:** gravel.
📷 01/01-31/12
Distance: 🚶Groede 3km 🏊sandy beach 200m ⊗60m 🛒on the spot
🚲 on the spot 🚶 on the spot.

| 🚐 | Hansweert 🌿⛽🚣 | 7D3 |

Westhavendijk. **GPS**: n51,44483 e4,00629.⬆️.

5 🚐free. **Location:** Rural, simple, isolated, quiet. **Surface:** asphalted.
📷 01/01-31/12
Distance: 🚶250m 🚣4km 🏊on the spot 🚲 on the spot 🚶 on the spot.

| ⚓ | Hulst 🌿⛽🍽 | 8A4 |

Parkeerterrein Havenfort, Havenfort. **GPS**: n51,27700 e4,04912.

15 🚐 € 0,80/h, mo-sa 9-17h, su 12-18h. 🔲 🚿 **Surface:** metalled.
📷 01/01-31/12
Distance: 🚶on the spot 🚊25m ⊗150m 🛒150m 🚌200m.
Remarks: Max. 72h, shops open on Sunday.
Tourist information Hulst:
ℹ️ VVV, Grote Markt 19, www.bezoekhulst.nl. Fortified city with city walls,

---

shops open on Sunday.

| 🚐S | Kamperland ⛽🚣 | 7D3 |

Camperpark Zeeland - Kamperland

info@camperparkzeeland.nl - www.camperparkzeeland.nl

Located directly at lake
Paved and flat motorhome pitches
Located in nature reserve

Camperpark Zeeland, Campensweg 5. **GPS**: n51,57495 e3,65236.⬆️➡️.
102 🚐 € 14,50-19,50 ⛽€0,20/min 🚰 Ch ✦ (75x)€4/24h,16Amp
WC 🚻€0,25/min 🔘€6/4 📶included 🚿.🔲🚿 **Location:** Rural, comfortable,
luxurious, quiet. **Surface:** grassy/gravel. 📷 01/01-31/12
Distance: 🚶3km 🚣2km 🏊50m 🚊50m ⊗100m 🛒4km 🚌2km
🚲 on the spot 🚶 on the spot.

| 📷S | Kamperland ⛽🚣 | 7D3 |

Roompot Beach Resort, Mariapolderseweg 1. **GPS**: n51,58972 e3,71666.

20 🚐 € 6 10-17h, € 14 17-10h ⛽🚰 Ch ✦ WC 🚻🔲€4,50/1,20 📶 🚿.
Surface: asphalted. 📷 01/01-31/12
Distance: 🚶3km 🏊500m 🚊500m ⊗500m 🛒500m 🚌1km.

| 🚐 | Kloosterzande | 7D4 |

Hulsterweg. **GPS**: n51,36555 e4,02121.⬆️.

2 🚐free. **Location:** Rural, simple, central, quiet. **Surface:** metalled.
📷 01/01-31/12
Distance: 🚶500m ⊗80m 🛒700m 🚲 on the spot 🚶 on the spot.

| 🔺S | Kruiningen | 8A4 |

Den Inkel, Polderweg 12. **GPS**: n51,43485 e4,04448.
6 🚐 € 15-21 ⛽🚰 Ch ✦ WCincluded. 📷 01/01-31/12

| 🚐S | Kruiningen | 8A4 |

Landwinkel de Plantage, Kaasgat 4a. **GPS**: n51,46865 e4,04445.

NL

8 🛏 € 12,50 ⚡ 🔌 Ch 💧 €2,50/night,10Amp WC 🗑included 🔲 .
Surface: grassy. 🔲 01/01-31/12
Distance: 🛒3km 🏊3km 🍴3km ⊗3km 🚉on the spot 🚌1km
🚲on the spot 🚶on the spot.

| 📷 S | Middelburg 🌿🎣🍴🏊 | 7D3 |

Hof van Tange, Hof van Tange. **GPS:** n51,49688 e3,60474. ⬆️.

6 🛏 € 9,50, Su/holidays free WC € 0,50/time. 🔲🚐
Location: Simple, central, quiet. **Surface:** gravel/sand.
🔲 01/01-31/12 🔲 1st week Aug
Distance: 🛒on the spot 🏄5km 🍴500m 🚉300m 🚌on the spot
🚲on the spot 🚶on the spot.
Remarks: Motorhome <6m, max. 48h.

| 📷 S | Middelburg 🌿🎣🍴🏊 | 7D3 |

Oude Veerseweg. **GPS:** n51,50071 e3,62842. ⬆️.

5 🛏 free ⚡ €1 🔌 💧 (4x)€1. **Location:** Comfortable, central, quiet.
Surface: metalled. 🔲 01/01-31/12
Distance: 🛒1km 🍴100m ⊗500m 🚉1km 🚲on the spot.

| 📷 | Middelburg 🌿🎣🍴🏊 | 7D3 |

Kanaalweg. **GPS:** n51,49432 e3,61519. ⬆️.

3 🛏 € 9,50. 🚐 **Location:** Urban, simple, central, noisy. **Surface:** concrete.
🔲 01/01-31/12
Distance: 🛒500m 🏊on the spot 🍴on the spot 🚉500m 🚲on the spot.
Remarks: Max. 48h.

| 🍴 | Oosterland 🌿 | 8A3 |

Wok van Zeeland, Rijksweg 6. **GPS:** n51,65767 e4,05336. ⬆️ .

3 🛏 free. **Location:** Simple, isolated, noisy. **Surface:** asphalted.
🔲 01/01-31/12
Distance: 🛒2km ⊗on the spot.
Remarks: Only overnight stays.

| 📷 S | Oostkapelle | 7D3 |

De Pekelinge, Landmetersweg 1. **GPS:** n51,55725 e3,55139. ⬆️.
20 🛏 € 18,50-27,50 ⚡ 🔌 Ch included. 🚲 ✂️
Location: Simple, isolated, quiet. **Surface:** gravel/sand. 🔲 27/03-01/11
Distance: 🛒nearby 🏊nearby ⊗on the spot 🚉on the spot.
Remarks: Arrival >20h departure <10h, max. 1 night.

| ⚓ | Paal | 8A4 |

Jachthaven, Zeedijk van de van Alsteinpolder. **GPS:** n51,35331 e4,10937. ⬆️.

4 🛏 free. **Location:** Rural. **Surface:** asphalted/metalled. 🔲 01/01-31/12
Distance: 🛒100m 🏊on the spot 🍴on the spot ⊗on the spot 🚲on the spot
🚶on the spot.
Remarks: Max. 72h.

| 📷 | Sas van Gent 🌿🍴 | 7D4 |

Kanaaleiland, Oostkade. **GPS:** n51,22527 e3,80246. ⬆️.

2 🛏 free. **Surface:** metalled.
Distance: 🛒100m ⊗100m 🚉100m.
Remarks: Max. 24h.

Tourist information Sas van Gent:
🗺 Keizer Karelplein. 🕐 Tue 9-16h.

| 📷 | Terneuzen 🌿🎣🍴🏊 | 7D4 |

Oostsluis, Binnenvaartweg. **GPS:** n51,33555 e3,82117. ⬆️.

NL

4 ⌶free. **Location:** Rural, simple, isolated, quiet. **Surface:** grassy/metalled.
◯ 01/01-31/12
Distance: 🚰500m ➤on the spot ⊗500m 🚗200m 🚲on the spot
🚶on the spot.
Remarks: Max. 24h.
Tourist information Terneuzen:
👁 Portaal van Vlaanderen, Zeevaartweg 11. Interactive Visitors Centre at the
Terneuzen Locks, guided tour and boat excursions. ◯ Apr-Jun We, July-Aug
Tue-We-Thu, guided tour 13.30h.
⚑ Markt. ◯ Sa 9-16h.

⊞S	Tholen ◿	8A3

Jachthaven, Contre Escarpe 4. **GPS:** n51,53112 e4,22390.⬆.

4 ⌶€ 7,50, service incl. € 10 🚰⚡Ch 🚿 WC 🔊. **Surface:** metalled.
◯ 01/03-01/10
Distance: 🚰100m ⊗100m 🚗100m.

⌷	Vogelwaarde	7D4

Populierenstraat. **GPS:** n51,32562 e3,97758.⬆.

2 ⌶free. **Location:** Urban, simple, quiet. **Surface:** metalled.
◯ 01/01-31/12
Distance: 🚰on the spot 🚗on the spot 🚲on the spot 🚶on the spot.

⌷	Westdorpe	7D4

De Baeckermat, Bernhardstraat. **GPS:** n51,22917 e3,82167.⬆.

2 ⌶free. **Location:** Rural, simple, quiet. **Surface:** metalled.
◯ 01/01-31/12
Distance: 🚰500m ➤on the spot ⊗100m 🚗500m 🚗on the spot
🚲on the spot 🚶on the spot.
Remarks: Max. 24h.

ⓒⓢ	Wolphaartsdijk ⚘⚓◿	7D3

Camping 't Veerse Meer, Veerweg. **GPS:** n51,54325 e3,81253.⬆.

7 ⌶€ 15/22 🚰⚡Ch 🚿 (5x) WC ⊡on camp site 🔘on camp site 🔊included.
🚿 **Location:** Rural, comfortable, isolated, quiet.
◯ 01/01-31/12 ◉ 15/11-15/12
Distance: 🚰1,5km ⊿100m ➤100m 🚱100m 🚗on the spot 🚲on the spot
🚶on the spot.

⌶S	Zierikzee ⚘⚓◿	7D3

De Zandweg, Zandweg 30. **GPS:** n51,65691 e3,91210.⬆.

12 ⌶€ 12,50 🚰⚡Ch 🚿 (12x),10Amp 🔊included. 🚿 **Location:** Rural,
comfortable, central, noisy. **Surface:** asphalted. ◯ 01/01-31/12
Distance: 🚰800m ⊿on the spot ➤on the spot ⊗350m 🚱1km 🚗350m
🚲on the spot.

North Brabant

⌶S	Asten	8C4

Camperpark Wetland, Tureluurweg 7. **GPS:** n51,36687 e5,84214.⬆➡.

50 ⌶€ 8,30, 2 pers.incl 🚰⚡Ch 🚿 (37x)€1,50 WC ⊡ 🔘€2/2 🔊included.
Location: Rural. **Surface:** grassy/metalled. ◯ 01/01-31/12
Distance: 🚰2km 🚤4km ⊿9km ➤5km ⊗2km 🚱1,5km 🚲on the spot
🚶on the spot.
Remarks: Located in nature reserve De Groote Peel.

⌷	Bakel	8C3

De Beekakker. GPS: n51,50061 e5,74377.⬆.
2 ⌶free. **Location:** Simple. **Surface:** metalled. ◯ 01/01-31/12
Distance: 🚰500m 🚲on the spot 🚶on the spot.
Remarks: At gymnasium.

⌶S	Beers	8C3

Kerkeveld 10. **GPS:** n51,73302 e5,82955.⬆.

NL

10 ⌂ € 6 ⟷ ◻ Ch ⟷ WC ◻ included. ◻ **Surface:** metalled.
◻ 01/01-31/12

Bergen op Zoom 8A3

De Boulevard Noord. **GPS:** n51,48735 e4,27708. ⬆.

5 ⌂ free. **Surface:** metalled. ◻ 01/01-31/12
Distance: 1km 3,8km on the spot ⊗ on the spot.
Remarks: Max. 72h. On the level of restaurant 'La Playa'.
Tourist information Bergen op Zoom:
◻ De Markiezenhof, Steenbergsestraat 8. Medieval city palace. ◻ Tue-Su 11-17h.

Best 8C3

Carpoolplaats De Wilg. **GPS:** n51,52106 e5,39423. ⬆.
3 ⌂ free. **Location:** Isolated. **Surface:** metalled. ◻ 01/01-31/12
Distance: 150 m.
Remarks: Max. 24h.

Boxtel 8B3

Dennenoord, Dennendreef 5. **GPS:** n51,59770 e5,28661. ⬆.

4 ⌂ € 12,50, 2 pers.incl ⟷ ◻ Ch ⟷ WC ◻ ◻ €4 ⟷ included. ◻ **Location:**
Rural, simple, isolated. **Surface:** metalled. ◻ 01/01-31/12
Distance: 4km 4km.
Remarks: Max. 3 nights.

Budel 8C4

Camperplaats Budel, Heikantstraat 16. **GPS:** n51,26163 e5,59007.

5 ⌂ € 6,50 + € 1/pp tourist tax ⟷ ◻ Ch included ⟷ €2,50/day,4Amp.
Location: Urban. **Surface:** grassy. ◻ 01/01-31/12

Distance: 800m 2km 600m ⊗800m 800m 600m
on the spot on the spot.

De Heen 8A3

Akkermans leisure&golf, Heensemolenweg 23. **GPS:** n51,60654 e4,24547. ⬆.

10 ⌂ € 12,50 ⟷ ◻ Ch ⟷ (16x) WC ◻ included ⟷ ⟷ ◻ ⟷
Location: Rural, comfortable, isolated, quiet. **Surface:** asphalted/metalled.
◻ 01/01-31/12
Distance: ⊗ on the spot on the spot on the spot.

Eindhoven 8C4

P+R Meerhoven, Sliffertsestraat 304. **GPS:** n51,43507 e5,42444.

10 ⌂ first 24h € 3, € 10/24h ◻ Ch WC free. ◻ ⟷ **Location:** Simple.
Surface: metalled. ◻ 01/01-31/12
Distance: 4km on the spot ⊗200m 500m on the spot
on the spot on the spot.
Remarks: Free bicycles available.

Escharen 8C3

Bar Bistro De Brouwketel, Hoogeweg 9. **GPS:** n51,74152 e5,73376. ⬆.

15 ⌂ free. **Surface:** grassy. ◻ 01/01-31/12

Etten-Leur 8A3

Jachthaven Turfvaart, Westpolderpad 6. **GPS:** n51,59512 e4,65102.

18 ⌂ € 10, 01/03-30/09 € 15 ⟷ €0,50/100liter ◻ Ch ⟷ WC included ◻ €1
⟷ free. **Surface:** grassy/metalled. ◻ 01/01-31/12
Distance: 1,5km ⊗ on the spot 500m.
Tourist information Etten-Leur:
◻ ◻ Mo-morning.

⚡S **Geertruidenberg** 🌿🌊 **8B3**

Statenlaan 2. **GPS**: n51,70333 e4,86333.⬆.

2 🚐free 🪑. **Surface:** metalled. 🔌 15/03-31/10
Distance: 🚶500m ⊶on the spot ⊗on the spot 🛒500m.
Remarks: Max. 24h.

⚡S **Geertruidenberg** 🌿🌊 **8B3**

WSV Geertruidenberg, Statenlaan 15. **GPS**: n51,70362 e4,86311.⬆.

8 🚐€ 10 🚰🪑Ch🧹WC 🚽◉📶included. **Location:** Comfortable, quiet.
Surface: gravel. 🔌 01/05-31/10
Distance: 🚶500m 🚲3km ⊶on the spot ⊗on the spot 🛒500m.
Remarks: Max. 3 days, max. 9m, only cash payment.

🍴 **Gemert** **8C3**

Koksehoeve, Koksedijk 25. **GPS**: n51,57380 e5,65846.

10 🚐free, use of a meal obligated. **Location:** Rural, simple, isolated, quiet.
Surface: metalled. 🔌 01/01-31/12 ◉ Wed
Distance: 🚶2km.

⚡ **Grave** 🌿🌊 **8C3**

Koninginnedijk. **GPS**: n51,76178 e5,73676.⬆➡.

🚐free. **Location:** Simple, central, quiet. **Surface:** gravel.
🔌 01/01-31/12
Distance: 🚶100m ⊶100m ⊗150m 🛒150m.
Remarks: Max. 72h.

🍴S **Heeswijk-Dinther** **8C3**

De Leygraaf, Meerstraat 45A. **GPS**: n51,66445 e5,47511.⬆.
4 🚐€ 11,20 🚰🪑Ch🧹included WC 🚽€2,50/time. **Location:** Rural,

comfortable. **Surface:** grassy. 🔌 01/01-31/12
Distance: 🚶1,5km 🚲6km ⊗on the spot 🐾on the spot 🚶on the spot.

⚡ **Hoogerheide** **8A4**

METO parking, Huijbergseweg. **GPS**: n51,42318 e4,33452.
5 🚐free. **Location:** Simple. **Surface:** metalled. 🔌 01/01-31/12
Distance: 🚶800m ⊗800m 🛒800m.

⚡S **Hoogerheide** **8A4**

Fa. Broos, Buitendreef 4, De Kooi. **GPS**: n51,42522 e4,34656.⬆.

5 🚐free 🚰🪑🧹(3x)free. 🪣 **Location:** Rural, simple, isolated.
Surface: metalled. 🔌 01/01-31/12
Distance: 🚶3km 🚲3km ⊗3km 🛒3km 🐾on the spot 🚶on the spot.

🍴S **Hulten** **8B3**

Restaurant Stad Parijs, Rijksweg 6. **GPS**: n51,56996 e4,96446.

15 🚐free 🚽€0,75. **Location:** Rural, simple, quiet. **Surface:** asphalted.
🔌 01/01-31/12
Distance: ⊗on the spot.
Remarks: Free, use of a meal obligated.

⚓S **Linden** 🌊 **8C3**

Jachthaven Brasker, Hardweg 15. **GPS**: n51,75182 e5,82740.⬆.

11 🚐€ 10, 2 pers.incl, tourist tax € 0,70/pp 🚰🪑Ch🧹€1,50/day WC 🚽€1
📶€2/day. **Surface:** grassy. 🔌 15/04-15/10
Distance: ⊿on the spot ⊶on the spot ⊗on the spot 🛒on the spot.
Remarks: Check in at harbourmaster 9-12h, 15-18h, caution key sanitary
building € 20.

△S **Mierlo** 👫 **8C4**

Boscamping 't Wolfsven, Patrijslaan 4. **GPS**: n51,43888 e5,59000.
6 🚐from € 16 🚰🪑🧹WC 🚽◉€4,50/1,20 📶🚿. **Surface:** asphalted.
🔌 26/03-21/10
Distance: 🚶3km ⊿150m ⊶150m ⊗1km 🛒on the spot 🚗1km.

⚡S **Nuenen** **8C3**

Oude Landen, Pastoorsmast 12. **GPS**: n51,46429 e5,56023.⬆.
5 🚐free 🪑. **Surface:** grassy. 🔌 01/01-31/12 ◉ July
Distance: 🚶1,7km 🚲800m 🛒900m.
Remarks: Max. 5 days a month.

🍴S **Oijen** 🌊 **8C3**

Speciaalbierbrouwerij Oijen, Oijensebovendijk. **GPS**: n51,81049 e5,53126.

NL

3 🛏 € 10, free with a meal 🛒 🔧 included. **Location:** Rural, simple, quiet. **Surface:** grassy/gravel. ⬜ 01/01-31/12 **Distance:** 🚲 on the spot 🛒 on the spot ⊗ on the spot 🛶 on the spot 🎿 on the spot.

15 🛏 voluntary contribution 🛒 🛍 Ch 🔧 €2. **Location:** Quiet. **Surface:** grassy. ⬜ 01/01-31/12 **Distance:** 🚶 2,5km 🚲 4km ⊗ 2,5km 🛒 2,5km 🛶 on the spot 🎿 on the spot.

🛏 S	Oosteind	8B3

Camperplaats Oosteind, Ter Horst 19. **GPS:** n51,64705 e4,88326. ⬆️.

🛏	Raamsdonksveer	8B3

De Uilendonck, Lageweg 8, Raamsdonk. **GPS:** n51,68540 e4,91380. ⬆️.

4 🛏 € 8 🛒 🛍 Ch 🔧 included. **Location:** Rural, comfortable, isolated. **Surface:** grassy. ⬜ 01/01-31/12 **Distance:** 🚶 2km 🚲 1km ⊗ 500m.

3 🛏 free. **Location:** Rural, simple, isolated, quiet. **Surface:** metalled. ⬜ 01/01-31/12 **Distance:** 🚶 1km 🛶 on the spot.

🛏 S	Oss	8C3

Van Venrooy Motorhomes, Galliërsweg 39. **GPS:** n51,75981 e5,55642. ⬆️.

🛏	Raamsdonksveer	8B3

Kloosterweg 1. **GPS:** n51,68908 e4,87582. ⬆️.

2 🛏 free 🛒 🔧 free. **Surface:** metalled. ⬜ 01/01-31/12

🛏	Oss	8C3

Sportpark Rusheuvel. GPS: n51,77657 e5,52409. ⬆️.

4 🛏 free. **Surface:** metalled. **Distance:** 🚶 800m ⊗ on the spot 🚰 800m. **Remarks:** Parking at sports park.

🍴 S	Reusel	8B4

Café-Restaurant de Klok, Turnhoutseweg 32. **GPS:** n51,35564 e5,14272. ⬆️.

🛏 free, 20-8h € 5,60, tourist tax incl. 🚐 **Surface:** metalled. ⬜ 01/01-31/12 **Distance:** 🚶 750m ⊗ 750m 🚰 AH 500m. **Remarks:** Max. 3 nights.

🛏 S	Overloon	8C3

Van Well, Roosendaalseweg 1. **GPS:** n51,56377 e5,91995.

3 🛏 free 🛒 🔧 WC 🚰 free. **Location:** Simple. **Surface:** metalled. ⬜ 01/01-31/12 **Distance:** 🚶 2km. **Remarks:** Use of a meal desired.

🍴	Reusel	8B4

De Wekker, Wilhelminalaan 97. **GPS:** n51,36187 e5,17339.

NL

NL

5 🔲Free, use of a meal obligated. **Location:** Simple, quiet. **Surface:** sand. 🅾 01/01-31/12 🔘 Wed
Distance: ⊗on the spot.

| 📷S | Roosendaal 🔱 | 8A3 |

Mobildrôme, Argon 31-33. **GPS:** n51,56333 e4,46278.

8 🔲free 🔌€0,50 🚰 Ch 💧€0,50. **Surface:** metalled.
Distance: ⊾2km 🚲1,1km 🚊2km.

Tourist information Roosendaal:
🏠 Rosada, A17, afrit 19. Factory outlet.

| ©S | Vessem | 8B4 |

Eurocamping Vessem, Zwembadweg 1. **GPS:** n51,41197 e5,27490.⬆.

40 🔲€6/€9 🔌€1/80liter 🚰Ch 💧€0,60/kWh 🔥€0,50 📶€5/day.
Location: Rural. **Surface:** grassy. 🅾 01/01-31/12
Distance: ⊾1,5km 🚲7km 🏊5km ⛴on the spot ⊗1,5km 🚊on the spot
🚐300m 🐾on the spot 🎣on the spot.

| 📷S | Wijk en Aalburg | 8B3 |

Bakkerij Hardeman, Torenstraat 4. **GPS:** n51,75976 e5,13123.

3 🔲€5 🔌🚰Ch 💧WC 📶included. 🅾 01/01-31/12
Distance: ⊾on the spot 🎣on the spot.

| ©S | Zundert 🔱((((| 8A3 |

Museum de Scooter, Heischoorstraat 4. **GPS:** n51,49025 e4,64532.

10 🔲€10 🔌🚰Ch 💧WC 📶included. 🅾 01/01-31/12
Distance: ⊾2,8km 🚲A1 7km 🐾on the spot 🎣on the spot.
Remarks: Reservation during flower parade: museum@lambretta-nl.net.

Limburg

| 📷 | Brunssum | 8D5 |

Schutterspark P1, Heidestraat 20. **GPS:** n50,94582 e5,98385.

10 🔲free. **Surface:** metalled. 🅾 01/01-31/12
Distance: ⊾1,5km ⊗100m Schuttershuuske.
Remarks: Max. 72h, barefoot path.

| 📷 | Gennep | 8C3 |

Martinusplein. GPS: n51,69985 e5,97206.⬆.

5 🔲free. **Location:** Urban, simple, quiet. **Surface:** metalled.
🅾 01/01-31/12
Distance: ⊾100m 🚲4,6km 🏊200m ⊗150m 🚊bakery 100m, supermarket 250m 🐾on the spot 🎣on the spot.
Remarks: Max. 72h.

| 📷 | Gronsveld | 8C5 |

A2 Campeercentrum, Veilingweg 13. **GPS:** n50,80632 e5,72201.
4 🔲free.
Distance: ⊾500m 🚲1,1km.
Remarks: Industrial area, only overnight stays.

| 📷S | Grubbenvorst | 8D4 |

Het Kompas, Meerlosebaan 7. **GPS:** n51,42861 e6,12889.⬆.

39 🔲€12 🔌🚰Ch 💧(39x),4Amp 📶included. **Location:** Rural.

Surface: grassy/gravel. 🔲 01/03-30/11
Distance: 🚶2km 🚮500m ⊗2km 🛒2km 🚌1km 🚲on the spot 🧍on the spot.

| 🍴 | **Heel** | 8C4 |

Koffieterras De Tump, Heelderweg 13. **GPS:** n51,17698 e5,88315. ⬆️.

5 🛏 € 7. **Surface:** grassy. 🔲 01/05-31/10 ⬤ Mo
Distance: 🚶1km 🏊on the spot.
Remarks: Max. 48h.

| 🚽 S | **Ittervoort** | 8C4 |

Camperplaats Ittervoort, Brigittastraat 31. **GPS:** n51,17565 e5,82228. ⬆️.

15 🛏 € 9,10, 2 pers.incl 🔌 🚰included 🚿 €2,50 🔋1/day. **Location:** Rural, simple. **Surface:** grassy. 🔲 01/01-31/12
Distance: 🚶Ittervoort 500m, Thorn 2km 🚲 2,6km 🛒Jan Linders 750m.
Remarks: Vineyard Thorn 600m.

| 🅿 S | **Landgraaf** | 8D5 |

De Watertoren, Kerkveldweg 1. **GPS:** n50,91016 e6,07300. ⬆️.

6 🛏€ 10, peak season € 15 + € 0,90/pp tourist tax 🔌€1/90liter 🚰Ch 🚿 included 🔋. **Location:** Simple, isolated, quiet. **Surface:** grassy/gravel. 🔲 01/01-31/12

| 🚽 S | **Lottum** 🍴 | 8D3 |

Camperplek IndeVerte, Horsterdijk 97. **GPS:** n51,45130 e6,13144. ⬆️➡️.

50 🛏€ 12 🔌€1/100liter 🚰Ch 🚿 (50x) 🗑€1 ⬤€4 🔋included. **Location:** Comfortable, isolated, quiet. **Surface:** grassy. 🔲 01/01-31/12
Distance: 🚶3km.

| 🍴 | **Maasbree** 🌳 | 8D4 |

Restaurant Boszicht, Provincialeweg 2. **GPS:** n51,36395 e6,07980. ⬆️.

3 🛏Free, use of a meal obligated. **Location:** Simple, noisy. **Surface:** gravel.
Distance: 🚶2km 🚲 2km ⊗on the spot.

| ⚓S | **Maastricht** | 8C5 |

Maastricht Marina, Hoge Weerd 20. **GPS:** n50,82389 e5,69944.

10 🛏€ 15, 01/06-31/08 € 17,50 🔌🚰Ch 🚿 (10x),6Amp
WC ⬤ 🔋included. **Surface:** gravel/metalled. 🔲 01/03-31/10
Distance: 🚶1km 🚲3km 🏊on the spot ⊗150m 🛒2km 🚌1km 🚲on the spot 🧍on the spot.
Remarks: Max. 72h.

| 🛏S | **Meijel** | 8C4 |

Nieuwehof, Vieruitersten 25. **GPS:** n51,35410 e5,89717. ⬆️➡️.

29 🛏€ 10 + € 1/pp 🔌🚰Ch 🚿 WC included 🗑🔋on demand. 🚿
Location: Rural, comfortable, quiet. **Surface:** grassy/sand. 🔲 01/01-31/12
Distance: 🚶1,8km 🚲14km 🚲on the spot 🧍on the spot.

| 🛏 | **Milsbeek** | 8C3 |

Toeristisch knooppunt de Diepen, Zwarteweg 60. **GPS:** n51,73788 e5,95510. ⬆️🧍.

10 🛏free. **Surface:** grassy/sand.
Distance: ⊗on the spot.
Remarks: Next to Eethuis de Diepen.

| 🍴 | **Neer** | 8D4 |

Café Restaurant Boothuis de Troost, Hanssum 47. **GPS:** n51,25964 e6,00380.

4 🛏€ 7,50, guests free. **Surface:** metalled.

NL

Neer 8D4

Jachthaven Hanssum, Hanssum 40b. **GPS:** n51,25778 e6,00361.

5 ⛺ € 7,50 ⛽ Ch 🚿 WC ⬛. **Surface:** grassy/metalled.
Distance: 🏊3km ⛵on the spot ⊗200m.
Remarks: Max. 48h, service near marina.

Nieuw Bergen 8D3

Camperplaats Bos&Heide, Op de Paal 4. **GPS:** n51,59008 e6,07269.

25 ⛺ € 6,50 + € 1/pp tourist tax ⛽included 🔌 Ch 🚿 (15x)€2 WC.
Surface: grassy. 🅾 01/03-31/10
Distance: 🏊1,5km ⛵2km ⊗1,5km 🛒1,5km.
Remarks: Located in nature reserve Maasduinen.

Ottersum 8D3

Bier-Café Restaurant Old Inn, Siebengewaldseweg 13.
GPS: n51,68935 e6,00728.

20 ⛺free. **Surface:** metalled. 🅾 01/01-31/12

Plasmolen 8C3

Eldorado, Witteweg 18. **GPS:** n51,73284 e5,91639.

13 ⛺€ 15,50 2 pers.incl, dog € 2 ⛽€1/100liter 🔌 Ch 🚿 (13x)€0,50/kWh
WC included ⬛€1 ⬛€3 🔌€5/24h.
Location: Rural, comfortable, quiet. **Surface:** grassy.
🅾 01/01-31/12 ⬤ **Service:** winter
Distance: 🏊200m ⛵8km ⛵on the spot ⛵on the spot ⊗200m 🛒200m
🚲 on the spot 🚶 on the spot.
Remarks: Check in at Eldorado Boatshop Witteweg 9, max. 72h.

Sittard 8C5

De Nieuwe Hateboer, Sportcentrumlaan. **GPS:** n51,00794 e5,88150.⬆

10 ⛺free ⛽🔌 Ch WC use sanitary facilities at swimming pool ⬛.
Surface: asphalted. 🅾 01/01-31/12
Distance: 🏊2km ⛵6,2km ⊗2km 🛒2km 🚌100m 🚶on the spot.
Remarks: At swimming pool, register via SMS (licence plate number)
+31 6 27 82 55 82, max. 48h.

Thorn 8C4

Waterstraat. **GPS:** n51,15860 e5,84403.⬆

3 ⛺€ 2,50/9-18h. **Surface:** gravel. 🅾 01/01-31/12
Distance: 🏊150m ⊗150m.
Remarks: Max. 24h.

Tourist information Thorn:
ℹ VVV, Wijngaard 14, www.lekker-genieten.nl. The white village, with
historical centre and Gothic collegiate church.

Valkenburg 8C5

Camperplaats Valkenburg aan de Geul, Heunsbergerweg 1.
GPS: n50,86037 e5,83148.
30 ⛺€ 15-21 ⛽€1/100liter 🔌 Ch 🚿 (30x)€0,60/kWh, 16Amp WC included
⬛€0,70/time ⬤€4,75/2,25 🔌€2,50/24h 🌊. **Location:** Rural, comfortable,
quiet. **Surface:** grassy/metalled. 🅾 01/01-31/12
Distance: 🏊500m ⛵2km ⛵1,5km ⛵1,5km ⊗on the spot 🛒500m
🚌500m 🚲on the spot 🚶on the spot.
Remarks: Maastricht 15km.

Valkenburg 8C5

Burgemeester Henssingel. **GPS:** n50,86361 e5,83725.

6 🚐 € 1,60/h 10-20h.
Surface: metalled.
🗓 01/01-31/12
Distance: 🏙300m.

Tourist information Valkenburg:
[i] VVV, Th.Dorrenplein 5, www.vvvzuidlimburg.nl. Popular holiday resort.
👁 Gemeentegrot, Cauberg 4. Marl caves.
[M] Steenkolenmijn, Daalhemerweg 31. Visiting a gallery of a mine.
🗓 01/04-30/11 10-17, 01/11-07/01 + weekend, guided tour 12h, 13.30h, 15h, remaining 14h.

🚐 [S] Venlo 8D4

De Boswesels, Weselseweg 43. **GPS**: n51,39279 e6,20032. ⬆ ➡.

16 🚐 € 10 🚰 🚽 Ch 🔌 (16x) 📶 included. 🧺 **Location:** Simple.
Surface: grassy. 🗓 01/04-01/11
Distance: 🏙3,5km 🛒 0,5km 🍴1,8km.

⚓ [S] Venlo 8D4

Jachthaven, Jachthavenweg 50. **GPS**: n51,39245 e6,14854. ⬆.

20 🚐 € 12,50 🚰 🚽 🔌 10Amp WC 🚿 included 🧺 € 3/2 📶. **Surface:** metalled.
🗓 01/04-30/10
Distance: 🏙Venlo centre 4km 🛒 3,5km 🚌 500m.
Remarks: Max. 48h, check in at harbourmaster.

🚐 [S] Weert 8C4

Suffolkweg Zuid 30. **GPS**: n51,25435 e5,69283. ⬆.

20 🚐 € 8, 2 pers incl., 1 pers + € 2 🚰 🚽 Ch included 🔌 € 2.

Remarks: Max. 72h.

🚐 [S] Well 8D3

Camperplaats De Wellsche Hut, Wezerweg 13. **GPS**: n51,58687 e6,12344. ⬆.

18 🚐 € 10 🚰 🚽 Ch 🔌 WC included 🧺.
Surface: metalled.
🗓 01/01-31/12
Distance: 🏙4km 🏖6km 🍴on the spot.
Remarks: At mountainbike trail, dog on leads, nature reserve Maasduinen.

⚓ [S] Well 8D3

Jachthaven 't Leuken, De Kamp 7a. **GPS**: n51,56361 e6,06360. ⬆.

30 🚐 € 10 🚰 🚽 Ch 🔌 WC 🚿 included. **Location:** Simple, quiet.
Surface: grassy. 🗓 01/04-01/11
Distance: 🏙Well 2km 🛒 11km 🏖on the spot 🎣on the spot 🍴on the spot.
Remarks: Acquatic sports area.

NL

BELGIUM

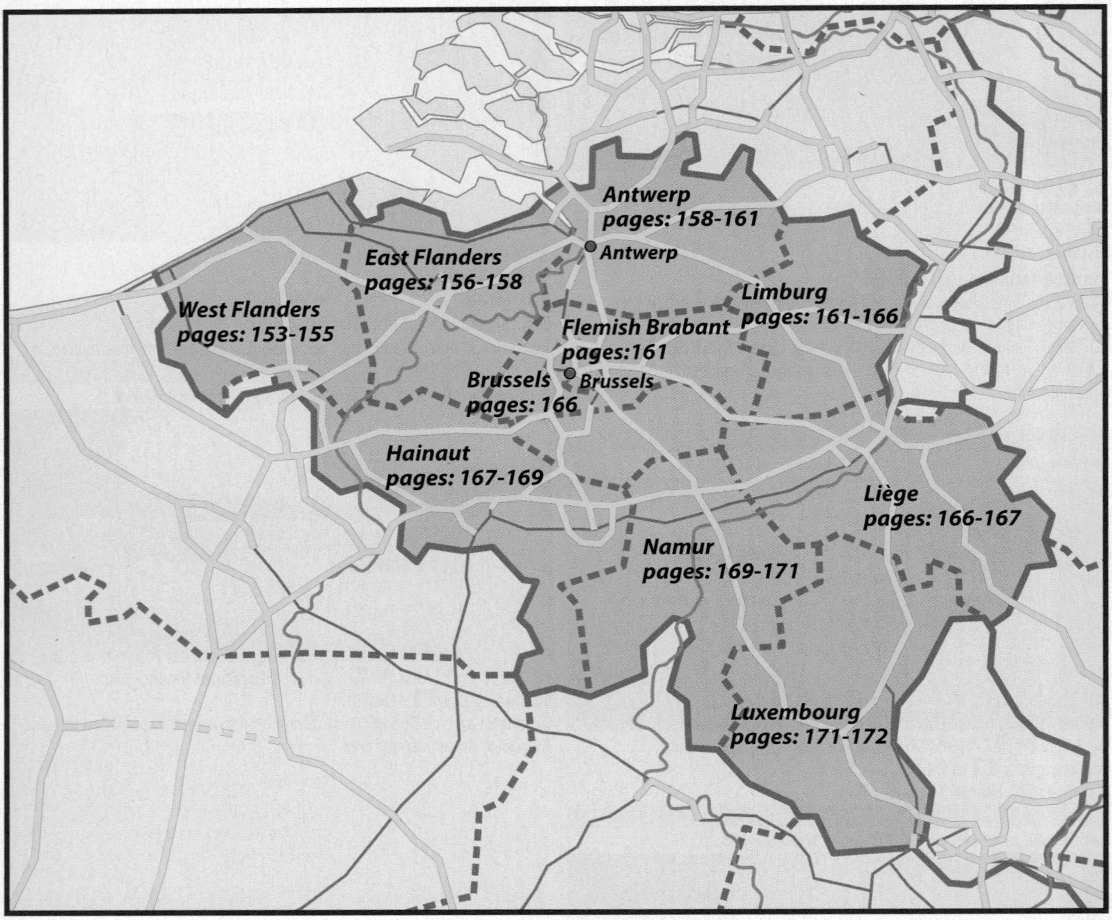

BE

Antwerp
pages: 158-161

● Antwerp

East Flanders
pages: 156-158

Limburg
pages: 161-166

West Flanders
pages: 153-155

Flemish Brabant
pages:161

Brussels
pages: 166

● Brussels

Hainaut
pages: 167-169

Liège
pages: 166-167

Namur
pages: 169-171

Luxembourg
pages: 171-172

Capital: Brussels
Government: Constitutional monarchy
Official Language: Dutch/Flemish, French and German
Population: 11,200.000 (2014)
Area: 30,518 km²

General information
Dialling code: 0032
General emergency: 112
Currency: Euro

Regulations for overnight stays
Wild camping is forbidden.

Additional Public Holidays 2015
May 1 Labour Day
July 11 Feast Flemish Community
July 21 National Day
August 15 Assumption Day
September 27 Feast of the Walloon Region
November 1 All Saints' Day
November 11 Armistice Day 1918

West Flanders

Aartrijke · 7C4

Sint-Aarnoutstraat. **GPS**: n51,11341 e3,08983. ⬆️.

3 free. **Surface:** asphalted. 🅿️ 01/01-31/12
Distance: 400m ⊗80m 🚲50m.

Beernem · 7C4

Kanaaloever Beernem, Oude Vaartstraat. **GPS**: n51,13482 e3,33427. ⬆️.

6 € 10/24h ⚡ Ch (4x) WC included, sanitary at harbour building. 🔧
Location: Rural. **Surface:** metalled. 🅿️ 01/01-31/12
Distance: 1,9km.
Remarks: Max. 72h, only exact change.

Brugge · 7C4

Bargeweg. **GPS**: n51,19633 e3,22544. ⬆️➡️.

5 € 5. Location: Rural, isolated, quiet. **Surface:** grassy.
🅿️ 01/01-31/12
Distance: 5km.
Remarks: Bread-service.

Gistel · 7C4

Sportstraat. **GPS**: n51,16112 e2,96495. ⬆️.

2 free ⚡ Ch free. **Surface:** metalled.
Distance: 1km 3,3km on the spot on the spot.
Remarks: Parking behind swimming pool, key service at swimming pool, many walking and bicycle area.

Harelbeke · 7C5

Kampeerautoterrein De Dageraad, Stasegemsesteenweg 21.
GPS: n50,84396 e3,31057.

8 € 5 ⚡ Ch included WC € 1,25 free. 🔧
Surface: metalled.
🅿️ 01/01-31/12
Distance: 1,6km 4,5km 700m 100m.
Remarks: Parking next to midget golf, service during opening hours: 8-20h.

Knokke-Heist · 7C4

Holiday, Natiënlaan 72. **GPS**: n51,33612 e3,28866.
10 € 18 01/10-30/06 € 20 01/07-30/09 ⚡ Ch WC included.
Surface: metalled. 🅿️ 01/10-28/10
Distance: 1km.

Kortemark · 7C5

Sporthal Kortemark, Ichtegemstraat 2a. **GPS**: n51,03201 e3,04168. ⬆️.

59 € 15, € 22,50 01/04-30/09 €0,50 Ch included 🔧
Location: Urban, simple, central. **Surface:** metalled.
🅿️ 01/01-31/12
Distance: within walking distance on the spot.
Remarks: Max 3,5t, monitored parking.

Tourist information Brugge:
ℹ️ Brugge City Card gives for free entrance on among other things 27 museums, boat trips and many discounts on purchases. € 43.
ℹ️ Toerisme Brugge, 't Zand 34, www.brugge.be. City with medieval character, hiking itinerary available at Tourist office.
👁 Boat excursion from Bruges to Damme with the `Lamme Goedzak', departure Noorweegse Kaai.
👁 Brouwerij Halve Maan, Walplein 26. Town brewery. 🅿️ 10-18h. € 7,50.
Ⓜ Diamantmuseum, Katelijnestraat 43. Diamond museum. 🅿️ 10.30-17.30h.
😊 Boudewijnpark, Alfons De Baeckerstraat 12, Sint-Michiels. Attractions park with dolphinarium, seal island etc., in winter large skating rink covered.

Diksmuide · 7C4

Nesthof, Zijdelingstraat 2a. **GPS**: n51,07178 e2,86422. ⬆️.

BE

2 🛏free ⚡€2 💧€2 Ch. **Surface:** metalled. ☐ 01/01-31/12
Distance: 🚶500m 🚌on the spot.
Remarks: Max. 48h.

🛏 S | Kortrijk 🌿 | 7C5
Kampeerautoterrein Broeltorens, Damkaai. **GPS:** n50,83120 e3,26818.⬆️.

8 🛏€ 10/24h ⚡💧Ch ✎ included. 🚽♻ **Location:** Urban.
Surface: metalled. ☐ 01/01-31/12
Distance: 🚶centre 400m ✖100m.

Tourist information Kortrijk:
ℹ️ Dienst Toerisme, Sint-Michielsplein 5, www.kortrijk.be. Historical little town with Beguine convent.

🛏 S | Langemark- Poelkappele | 7C5
Boezingestraat 51a. **GPS:** n50,90944 e2,91763.⬆️.

8 🛏€ 12 ⚡💧Ch ✎ (4x)included 🔌€1/time. 🚿 **Location:** Urban, simple.
Surface: grasstiles. ☐ 01/01-31/12
Distance: ✖on the spot 🚶on the spot.
Remarks: Max. 72h, check in at reception sports centre.

🛏 S | Mesen | 7C5
Kerkstraat. **GPS:** n50,76391 e2,89825.⬆️.

3 🛏free. **Surface:** metalled. ☐ 01/01-31/12
Distance: 🚶on the spot ✖frituur 200m 🍺100m.
Remarks: In front of church, max. 24h.

🛏 S | Nieuwpoort 🌿 | 7C4
De Zwerver, Brugsesteenweg 29, N367. **GPS:** n51,12988 e2,76576.⬆️.

28 🛏€ 0,50/h ⚡€0,50/50liter 💧Ch ✎ included,10Amp WC 🔌€4/time.

🚽 **Surface:** grassy. ☐ 01/01-31/12
Distance: 🚶within walking distance ⛵3,3km.

🛏 S | Oudenburg | 7C4
Carpool, Stationsstraat. **GPS:** n51,19387 e3,00567.

🛏free ⚡€2 💧€2 Ch. **Surface:** metalled.
Distance: ⛵800m.
Remarks: P service max. 30 min.

Tourist information Oudenburg:
⛪ ☐ Wed-afternoon.

🛏 | Poperinge 🌿 | 7B5
Oudstrijdersplein. **GPS:** n50,85300 e2,72300.

🛏. 📷 Fri
Distance: 🚶500m 🛒50m.

🛏 | Roeselare | 7C5
O.L. Vrouwenmarkt. **GPS:** n50,94786 e3,13450.⬆️.

1 🛏free. **Surface:** metalled. ☐ 18-9h, 01/01-31/12h
Distance: 🚶200m 🚌on the spot.
Remarks: Max. 1 night.

🛏 | Roeselare | 7C5
Trakelweg. **GPS:** n50,94438 e3,13320.⬆️.

10 🛏free. **Location:** Urban. **Surface:** asphalted. ☐ 01/01-31/12
Distance: 🚶1km 🚲on the spot 🚶on the spot.
Remarks: No camping activities.

Sint-Eloois-Vijve   7D5
Kampeerautoterrein Leiekamper, Leiesas 15. **GPS:** n50,90879 e3,40468.

8 € 5 €1/100liter included,16Amp. 01/01-31/12
Distance: 400m 400m 1km on the spot on the spot.
Remarks: Max. 72h.

Veurne   7B4
Kaaiplaats/Lindendreef. **GPS:** n51,07052 e2,66484.

6 free WC€0,50 €1,50,sanitary at harbour building. **Surface:** metalled.
Distance: on the spot 2km.
Remarks: Max. 6,5m.

Wervik   7C5
Kampeerautoterrein De Balokken, De Balokken. **GPS:** n50,77456 e3,03705.

8 € 10/72h €1/100liter Ch included. 01/01-31/12
Distance: 1km on the spot on the spot cafetaria 700m bakery.
Remarks: On leisure island, max. 72h.

Westende   7C4
Kompas kampeerautoterrein, Strandjuttersdreef. **GPS:** n51,15594 e2,76019.

35 20h € 11-16,50, 44h € 19,50-29,50 Ch included.
Surface: grasstiles/metalled. 01/01-31/12
Distance: on the spot 1km Taverne, Frituur on the spot.

Westende   7C4
Sint Laureinsstrand, Koning Ridderdijk. **GPS:** n51,16655 e2,76447.

10 € 5/day. **Surface:** asphalted. 01/01-31/12
Distance: Westende 1,4km on the spot on the spot Coast Tram.
Remarks: Beach parking.

Wingene   7C4
Smart - ijs BVBA, Noordakkerstraat 1a. **GPS:** n51,07377 e3,26515.

6 € 6, guests Bistro free Ch included. **Location:** Rural.
Surface: gravel.
Distance: 2km bike junction.
Remarks: Max. 72h.

Zeebrugge   7C4
Baron de Maerelaan. **GPS:** n51,32821 e3,18452.

9 free. **Surface:** metalled.
Distance: on the spot 350m 100m.

Zeebrugge   7C4
Kustlaan. **GPS:** n51,33350 e3,20777.

7 free. **Location:** Simple. **Surface:** asphalted. 01/01-31/12
Distance: snack 500m 1,5km 200m.

Tourist information Zeebrugge:
Havenrondvaart. 01/07-30/09 11h, 14h, 16h, Easter, 01/05-30/06 Su.
Seafront maritiem museum, Albertdok, Vismijnstraat 7. Maritime museum.
10-18h.
Boudewijn Seapark, St. Michiels. Amusement park with dolphinarium.
01/05-31/08 10-18h.

Zonnebeke   7C5
Café De Dreve, Lange Dreef 16. **GPS:** n50,85410 e2,97924.

BE

🛏free. **Surface:** gravel. 🔲 01/01-31/12
Distance: 🚶Zonnebeke 2,7km 🚗 3,5km A19 ⊗snacks 🚲 on the spot 🧍on the spot.
Remarks: Passendalemuseum-Zonnebeke.

East Flanders

Aalst 🌀 8A5
Zwembadlaan 2. **GPS:** n50,93825 e4,05829.

2 🛏free 🚰100liter 🗑Ch 🔌included1h ⚡€5.
Surface: metalled.
Distance: 🚶city centre ± 1km 🚗 3,8km 🚂on the spot.
Remarks: Only 2 plots indicated, more plots permitted.

Tourist information Aalst:
🧍 🔲 Thu-morning.

Aalter 7D4
Vaart-Zuid, Bellem. **GPS:** n51,09821 e3,49365. ⬆.

25 🛏free. **Surface:** asphalted.
Distance: 🚢Canal.

Aalter 7D4
Vaart-Noord, Bellem. **GPS:** n51,09875 e3,49468. ⬆ .

25 🛏free. **Surface:** asphalted.
Distance: 🚂600m 🚲 500m.

Aalter 7D4
Bellemdorpweg, Bellem. **GPS:** n51,09323 e3,48308. ⬆.

2 🛏free. **Surface:** asphalted.
Distance: 🚶500m.
Remarks: At football ground.

Tourist information Aalter:
Kasteel Poeke, Kasteelstraat 26, Poeke. 🔲 weekend, holidays, 01/04-31/10 Su 14-17h.
🧍 🔲 Wed-morning.

Assenede 7D4
Kapelledreef. **GPS:** n51,23067 e3,74891. ⬆➡.

5 🛏€ 5/72h 🚰€1/60 🗑Ch ⚡ WCfree 🛢€1/1.🚰 **Location:** Urban, comfortable, quiet. **Surface:** grassy. 🔲 01/01-31/12 ◉ Service: winter
Distance: 🚶500m ⊗600m 🚲on the spot 🧍on the spot.
Remarks: Behind gymnasium, max. 72h, sanitary during opening hours gymnasium.

Bazel 🌀 8A4
Sporthal De Dulpop, Beekdam 1. **GPS:** n51,14778 e4,30583. ⬆ .

10 🛏free. **Location:** Rural, simple. **Surface:** asphalted.
Distance: 🚶200m 🚗6km 🚲3km 🚂500m 🚌500 m 🚲on the spot 🧍on the spot.
Remarks: Barn-museum 200m.

Berlare 🎶🍴 7D5
Donklaan, Berlare-Overmere. **GPS:** n51,04258 e3,98293. ⬆➡.

4 🛏free. **Surface:** grasstiles. 🔲 01/01-31/12
Distance: 🚗9km 🚢Donkmeer ⊗on the spot.

⚓S **Eeklo** 〰 **7D4**
Jachthaven Eeklo, Nijverheidskaai. GPS: n51,17884 e3,54959. ⬆ .

12 ⬛€ 10/24h ⌐€0,50/130liter ⬛Ch ⚡€5/24h,6Amp WC⬛.
Surface: grasstiles/metalled.
◻ 01/01-31/12
Distance: 🚶1,5km ⊗1,5km 🚉800m.
Remarks: Check in at harbourmaster, use sanitary only during opening hours.
Tourist information Eeklo:
👁 Provinciaal Domein "Het Leen", Gentsesteenweg 80. Nature reserve.
◻ 9-12h, 13-17h ◉ Mo.

🔲 **Gavere** 〰 **7D5**
Sportdreef. GPS: n50,92823 e3,65810. ⬆ .

12 ⬛free. **Surface:** asphalted. ◻ 01/01-31/12
Distance: 🚉on the spot.
Remarks: Behind sports complex.

🔲 **Gentbrugge** **7D5**
Sportcentrum Driebeek, Driebeekstraat 22. GPS: n51,03762 e3,76628.⬆➡

5 ⬛free ⬛Chfree. **Surface:** asphalted. ◻ 01/01-31/12
Distance: 🚶900m, Gent 4,5km ⚓1,5km 🚋Tram Ghent-centre.
Remarks: Ghent Festival the week of July 21.
Tourist information Gentbrugge:
🏛 Ledebergplein, Ledeberg. Su 7.30-13h.
🏛 Schooldreef. Mo 7.30-13h.
🏛 Lazy River, Arsenaal. Jazz festival and village fair. ◻ Whitsuntide.

🔲 **Geraardsbergen** 〰 **7D5**
Jeugherberg 't Schipken, Kampstraat 59, N460, dir Ninove.
GPS: n50,79500 e3,90412.⬆➡

4 ⬛free. **Surface:** grassy. ◻ 01/01-31/12
Distance: 🚶Geraardsbergen 3,7km ⊷on the spot.
Remarks: Max. 1 night.
Tourist information Geraardsbergen:
😊 Provinciaal Domein "de Gavers", Onkelzelestraat 280. Recreation area; swimming, watersports, fishing, boat trips and tennis.Free entrance, payment per attraction.

🔲 **Hamme** **8A4**
Camperplaats Hamme, Mirabrug, Hamveer. GPS: n51,10418 e4,14246.⬆

2 ⬛free. **Location:** Rural, simple, quiet. **Surface:** metalled.
Distance: 🚶1km ⊗400m 🚉500m 🚲on the spot 🏊on the spot.
Remarks: Max. 48h.

🔲 **Lokeren** 〰 **7D4**
Veerstraat. GPS: n51,11013 e3,97163.⬆.

5 ⬛free. **Location:** Urban, noisy. **Surface:** metalled.
◻ 01/01-31/12
Distance: 🚉1,5km, bakery 500m.
Remarks: Parking in front of church, max. 48h.

🔲 **Lokeren** 〰 **7D4**
Verloren Bos, Aardeken. GPS: n51,10981 e3,99525.⬆.

2 ⬛free.
Location: Rural, simple. **Surface:** unpaved.
◻ 01/01-31/12
Distance: 🚶500m 🚉600m.

BE

Tourist information Lokeren:
⚐ Stationsplein. Flea market. ◻ Su 7-12h.
⚘ Molsbroek. Protected European Nature Reserve, 80ha marsh area with many birds, asphalted hiking trail. ◻ Su 14-17h, 01/07-31/08 Wed-Su 14-17h.

⌂S	Maldegem ⚘	7D4

Zwembad St.Anna, Gidsenlaan. **GPS:** n51,21160 e3,44172. ⬆ .

⌂free ⚏. **Location:** Urban. **Surface:** asphalted/metalled.
Distance: ⊗700m ⚑700m.
Remarks: Check in at swimming pool, water on demand.

⍨	St.Laureins	7D4

Taverne 't Oud Gemeentehuis, Sint Margrietestraat 44, Sint-Margriete.
GPS: n51,28065 e3,54677.

4 ⌂free. **Surface:** grassy. ◻ Thu

⌂	Temse ⚘	8A4

De Zaat, Nagelheetmakerslaan1. **GPS:** n51,12466 e4,21007. ⬆ .

⌂free. **Location:** Urban. **Surface:** asphalted. ◻ 01/01-31/12
Distance: ⚐400m ⚑250m.
Remarks: Behind police station, temporary stopover.

⌂S	Temse ⚘	8A4

Camperbedrijf Alpha Motorhomes, Kapelanielaan 13a, N16.
GPS: n51,13699 e4,18017.⬆.

⌂free ⚏Chfree. **Surface:** metalled.
Distance: ⚐city centre 3km.
Tourist information Temse:
⚐ Grote Markt. ◻ Fri-morning.

158

BE

⌂S	Zulte ⚘⚏	7D5

Leihoekstraat, Machelen. **GPS:** n50,96095 e3,48305. ⬆ .

8 ⌂€8/72h ⚏€1 ⚏Ch ⚏ included. **Surface:** metalled.
◻ 01/01-31/12
Distance: ⚐150m ⊗50m ⚑150m ⚛on the spot.
Remarks: Max. 72h.

Antwerp

⌂S	Antwerpen ⚘⚏	8A4

Vogelzang, Vogelzanglaan 7-9, Antwerp (Antwerpen). **GPS:** n51,18983 e4,40074.⬆.

140 ⌂€ 8,50, July-Aug € 10,50 ⚏included ⚏Ch ⚏(30x)€1/kWh.
Location: Simple. **Surface:** grassy/metalled.
◻ 01/01-31/12 ◻ 31/10-11/11, 04/01-19/01
Distance: ⚐city centre 3km ⛵1km ⚑3km ⊗500m ⚑1km ◉3km ⛟150m.

Tourist information Antwerp (Antwerpen):
ℹ Antwerp City Card gives free City tour, entrance to museums, churches and many discounts on purchases. ⊤ € 19.
ℹ Toerisme Antwerpen, Grote Markt, 13, www.visitantwerpen.be. Large port city, worth seeing is the city centre.
⚐ Dageraadsplaats. ◻ Thu 8-13h.
⚐ Lijnwaadmarkt. Antiques market. ◻ Easter-Oct Sa 9-17h.
⚐ St. Andriesplaats. ◻ Tue 8-13h.
⚐ St. Jansplein. ◻ Wed, Fri 8-13h.
⚐ St. Jansvliet. Bric-a-brac market. ◻ Su 9-17h.
⚐ Theaterplein. Exotic market. ◻ Sa.
⚐ Vogelenmarkt, Theaterplein. Famous flea market. ◻ Su-morning.

⌂S	Arendonk	8B4

De Vloed. **GPS:** n51,32253 e5,08610. ⬆ .

⌂free ⚏.
Distance: ⚐400m ⊗on the spot ⛟100m.
Remarks: Parking in front of swimming pool, max. 24h, water during openinghours swimming pool.

⌂	Bornem	8A4

Kasteel d'Ursel, Koningin Astridlaan. **GPS:** n51,10294 e4,27261. ⬆ .

5 🛏free. **Location:** Rural. **Surface:** unpaved. 🅾 01/01-31/12
Remarks: Parking next to castle, open 8-21h.

🛏 S **Brasschaat** 8A4

P5b, Elshoutbaan 17. **GPS:** n51,28555 e4,50325.⬆.

15 🛏free ⛽€1/100liter 🚰 Chfree ⚡€0,50/kWh. **Location:** Rural.
Surface: metalled/sand. 🅾 01/01-31/12
Distance: 🛒1,7km 🚲6km ⊗500m 🚊500m 🚊on the spot 🏃on the spot.
Remarks: Parking sports and recreation centre, max. 72h.
Tourist information Brasschaat:
🏃 Armand Reusensplein. 🅾 Mo 8-13h.

🛏 S **Brecht** 8A4

Mudeausstraat. **GPS:** n51,34814 e4,64123.⬆.

2 🛏free 📶At townhall. **Location:** Urban. **Surface:** metalled.
🅾 01/01-31/12
Distance: 🛒on the spot 🚲1,2km ⊗150m 🚊150m.
Remarks: Max. 48h.

🛏 **Brecht** 8A4

Schoolstraat. **GPS:** n51,34992 e4,64577.
10 🛏free. **Surface:** grassy.
Distance: 🛒800m 🚲1,5km.

🛏 S **Essen** 8A3

Kerkeneind, N133. **GPS:** n51,47086 e4,46401.⬆.

2 🛏free ⛽🚰 Chfree. **Location:** Urban, simple, central, quiet.
Surface: metalled. 🅾 01/01-31/12
Distance: 🛒on the spot ⊗150m 🚌on the spot 🚴on the spot.

Remarks: Max. 24h.

🛏 S **Grobbendonk** 8B4

Vaartkom. **GPS:** n51,18954 e4,73638.⬆.

6 🛏free ⛽€1/5minutes 🚰free Ch€1 ⚡(6x)€1. **Surface:** asphalted.
Distance: 🛒200m 🚲3,6km ⊗frituur 200m.

🛏 S **Herentals** 〰 8B4

Herenhoutseweg. **GPS:** n51,16586 e4,82664.⬆.

🛏⛽.
Surface: asphalted.
Distance: 🛒1,5km 🚲2,8km 🥖bakery 200m.
Remarks: Parking multipurpose area, next to footballstadium VC Herentals.

🛏 **Herentals** 〰 8B4

BLOSO centrum Netepark, Vorselaarsebaan. **GPS:** n51,18937 e4,82899.
15 🛏free. **Surface:** asphalted.
Tourist information Herentals:
🏃 Augustijnenlaan. 🅾 Su-morning.
🏃 Grote Markt. 🅾 Fri-morning.

🍴S **Herselt** 〰💐 8B4

Taverne Herberg Mie Maan, Diestsebaan 28. **GPS:** n51,06025 e4,92897.⬆.

6 🛏free ⛽. **Surface:** gravel.
🅾 01/01-31/12
Distance: 🛒3km ⊗on the spot 🚊3km.
Remarks: Restaurant visit appreciated, intersection hiking and biking trails.

🛏 **Kalmthout** 〰💐 8A4

Kalmthoutse Heide, Heibloemlaan. **GPS:** n51,37688 e4,44911.⬆.

BE

BE

2 ⚏free. **Location:** Rural, simple, isolated, quiet. **Surface:** grasstiles.
🅿 01/01-31/12
Distance: 🚶city centre 2km ⊗50m 🚲on the spot 🚶on the spot.
Remarks: Parking nature reserve, max. 24h.

| 🍴S | Kasterlee 🌳 | 8B4 |

Sint Hubertushoeve, Vinkendreef. **GPS:** n51,20560 e4,89714.⬆️

10 ⚏free 🔌 Chfree. **Location:** Rural, simple, quiet. **Surface:** grassy.
🅿 01/01-31/12
Distance: 🚶Kasterlee 6km, Herentals 6km ⊗on the spot.
Remarks: Caution key service € 5, bobbejaanland 1km.

| ⚏ | Koningshooikt | 8A4 |

Donderheide. **GPS:** n51,08439 e4,56541.⬆️➡️

⚏free. **Surface:** unpaved.
Distance: 🚶on the spot.
Remarks: In front of 'Het Fort'.

| ⚏S | Koningshooikt | 8A4 |

Motorhomes Konings, Sander de Vosstraat 141. **GPS:** n51,08774 e4,62816.⬆️

⚏€ 2,50 🔌€2 💧€2,50. **Surface:** asphalted.
Remarks: Apply during openinghours.

| ⚏S | Lier 🌿 | 8A4 |

Parking Mol Poort, Aarschotsesteenweg. **GPS:** n51,12525 e4,57332.

3 ⚏ 🔌€1 ⚏Ch 💧. 🅿 01/01-31/12

| ⚏ | Lier 🌿 | 8A4 |

Zaat, Leuvense Poort. **GPS:** n51,13020 e4,58212.⬆️

2 ⚏free. **Surface:** metalled.
🅿 01/01-31/12

Tourist information Lier:
ℹ️ Dienst Toerisme, Grote Markt 57. City with old centre worth a visit.
👁 City walls, prison tower and Zimmertoren. 🅿 10-12h, 14-17/18h.
⚓ Grote Markt/Eikelstraat. 🅿 Sa 8-13h.
✳️ Kerststallentocht. 🅿 Dec.

| ⚏S | Putte | 8A5 |

Ixenheuvel, Heuvel. **GPS:** n51,04678 e4,62564.⬆️

2 ⚏free 🔌 ⚏Chfree. **Location:** Simple. **Surface:** asphalted.
🅿 01/01-31/12
Distance: 🚶1,5km.
Remarks: Max. 48h.

| ⚏S | Puurs | 8A4 |

Eeuwfeeststraat/ Kerkhofstraat. GPS: n51,07476 e4,28337.⬆️➡️

2 ⚏free 🔌 ⚏Chfree. **Surface:** metalled. 🅿 01/01-31/12
Distance: 🚲5,3km.
Remarks: Max. 48h, intersection hiking and biking trails.

| ⚏S | St.Amands | 8A4 |

Parking Noord, Emile Verhaerenstraat. **GPS:** n51,05906 e4,20206.⬆️

2 free ⛽ 🔧 Ch free. **Surface:** metalled. 🅿 01/01-31/12
Distance: ⊗200m 🚰200m 🚲on the spot 🚶on the spot.

| 📷 | St.Job-in-'t-Goor | 8A4 |

Vaartlaan. **GPS:** n51,30151 e4,56888. ⬆.

2 free. **Location:** Urban. **Surface:** metalled. 🅿 01/01-31/12
Distance: 🚶on the spot ⊗50m 🚰50m.
Remarks: Max. 48h.

| ⚠ S | Turnhout 🌿 | 8B4 |

Baalse Hei, Roodhuisstraat. **GPS:** n51,35385 e4,95591.
7 🍴 € 19 - € 25 🔧 Ch 🔧 WC 🧺 🧼. 🅿 15/01-15/12
Distance: 🚶3km 🏊on the spot 🎣on the spot ⊗on the spot.
Tourist information Turnhout:
👁 Begijnhof. Beguine convent. 🅿 Tue-Sa 14-17h, Su 11-17h 🔘 Christmas.

| 📷 S | Willebroek | 8A4 |

Dijlelaan. **GPS:** n51,06028 e4,34472. ⬆.

3 free ⛽€1 🔧€1 Ch. **Surface:** metalled. 🅿 01/01-31/12
Distance: 🚶300m.
Remarks: Max. 2 nights.

Flemish Brabant

| 📷 S | Diest 🌿 | 8B5 |

De Halve Maan, Omer Vanaudenhovelaan 48. **GPS:** n50,98607 e5,06373. ⬆⬆.

4 🍴 € 15 ⛽ 🔧 Ch 🔧 (4x)included. **Location:** Comfortable, quiet.
Surface: grassy/gravel. 🔘 01/11-28/02
Distance: 🚶1,2km, beguine convent 350m 🎣 ⊗200m 🚲100m 🚶100m.

Remarks: Check in at pay desk recreation centre, max. 72h.
Tourist information Diest:
👁 Begijnhof. Beguine convent. Art studios open: sa/so afternoon and in july/aug each afternoon. 🅿 Beguine convent daily, Angel convent Sa/Su 14.30-17h, church Easter-Oct Su 14-17h.

| 📷 | Grimbergen 🌿 | 8A5 |

K.S.C. Grimbergen, Brusselsesteenweg. **GPS:** n50,92787 e4,36610. ⬆.
10 🍴free. **Location:** Simple. **Surface:** asphalted. 🅿 01/01-31/12
Distance: 🚶1km 🚲1km 🚌> Brussels.
Tourist information Grimbergen:
ℹ Gemeentelijke Dienst voor Toerisme, Prinsenstraat 22. Well-known for the Abbey beer, info at the beer museum.
👁 Abdijkerk. Abbey-church. 🅿 10-12h, 13-17h.
🎪 Jaarmarkt. Village festival with among other things fair, cattle market.
🅿 1st weekend Sep.

| 📷 S | Merchtem | 8A5 |

Brusselsesteenweg. **GPS:** n50,95553 e4,24011. ⬆.

4 🍴free 🔧 free. **Surface:** metalled.
Distance: 🚶300m 🚌Good bus connection for Brussels.
Remarks: Next to cemetery and sports fields, no camping activities.

| 📷 S | Rotselaar | 8B5 |

Recreatiedomein Sportoase Ter Heide, Vakenstraat 18.
GPS: n50,96217 e4,72288.

4 🍴free ⛽€1 🔧 Ch free 🔧€1 WC 🧺. **Surface:** gravel.
🅿 01/01-31/12
Distance: 🚶2km 🏊100m 🎣100m ⊗500m 🚰2km 🚌200m 🚲on the spot 🚶on the spot.

Limburg

| 📷 S | Bilzen 🌿 🏰 | 8C5 |

Parking Lanakerdij, Lanakerdij. **GPS:** n50,86985 e5,52215. ⬆.

7 🍴free ⛽€2 🔧 Ch (5x). **Surface:** asphalted. 🅿 01/01-31/12
Distance: 🚶300m 🚲3km ⊗300m 🚰300m 🚲on the spot 🚶on the spot.
Remarks: Max. 24h.

Tourist information Bilzen:
👁 Landcommanderij Alden Biesen, Rijkhoven. 🅿 10-17h. 🎟 free.

BE

👁 Zuivelhoeve 't Wanthof. Dairy farm. ⬛ Tue-Fri 10-22h, Sa-Su 9-23h.
🅿 Markt. ⬛ Wed.

🏕	Bocholt 🌿	8C4

Heuvelzicht, Schipperstraat 1. **GPS**: n51,17722 e5,58500.

7 🏕 € 6,50/24h 🔌 🛢 Ch 🔧 WC included 🚿 €1. **Surface:** asphalted.
⬛ 01/01-31/12
Distance: 🚶on the spot ⊗50m 🛒100m 🏊50m 🚲50m.
Remarks: Parking marina at Zuidwillemsvaart, max. 48h.

🏕 S	Bolderberg	8B5

Domein Bovy, Galgeneinde. **GPS**: n50,98690 e5,27048. ⬆.

3 🏕 free 🔌€2 Ch 🔋€2/1h.
Location: Rural. **Surface:** metalled.
Distance: 🚶500m ⊗150m 🛒500m 🚲 bike junction 🚶on the spot.
Remarks: Estate with i.e. restaurant, bar, brasserie, marked hiking trails,
herb garden, petting zoo, old tools.

🏕	Bree 🌿	8C4

N721, Opitter. **GPS**: n51,11788 e5,64524. ⬆.

5 🏕 free. ⬛ 01/01-31/12
Remarks: Parking next to church, in front of petrol station, max. 48h.
Tourist information Bree:
🅿 Vrijthof. ⬛ Fri.
☀ Sint-Antoniuskapel, Opitter.

🏕 S	Diepenbeek	8C5

Demerstrand, Stationsstraat. **GPS**: n50,91392 e5,42209. ⬆.

4 🏕 free 🔌€2/100liter 🛢 Ch 🔧€2/8h. **Surface:** asphalted.

⬛ 01/01-31/12
Distance: 🚶500m ⊗250m 🛒1km.
Remarks: At gymnasium, video surveillance.

🏕	Dilsen-Stokkem	8C5

De Wissen, Maaspark 3. **GPS**: n51,02361 e5,74945. ⬆.

4 🏕 free. **Surface:** metalled.
⬛ 01/01-31/12
Distance: 🚶500m 🚣on the spot 🚲on the spot ⊗Taverne Maascentrum
🛒500m 🚲on the spot.
Remarks: Parking at tourist office De Wissen, starting point of cycle routes.

🏕 S	Genk 🌿	8C5

Parking Kattevennen, Kattevennen. **GPS**: n50,95728 e5,53337.

8 🏕 € 5 🔌 🛢 Ch 🔧 included.
Surface: asphalted.
Distance: 🚶3km ⊗taverne 🚲on the spot 🚲on the spot 🚶on the spot.
Remarks: Max. 24h, mountainbike and hiking trails, national park Hoge
Kempen.

Tourist information Genk:
🅿 Zondagsmarkten. Flea market. ⬛ 01/06-31/08 9-13h.

🏕	Hamont	8C4

Kerkplein. **GPS**: n51,25152 e5,54612. ⬆ .

5 🏕 free. **Surface:** metalled. ⬛ 01/01-31/12
Distance: 🚶on the spot ⊗50m 🛒50m 🚲50m.
Remarks: Behind church, max. 24h.

🏕	Hamont	8C4

Michielsplein, Achel. **GPS**: n51,25423 e5,47985.

⑤free.
Distance: 🚲on the spot ⊗on the spot 🍴on the spot.
Remarks: At bicycle trail Limburgse Kempen, behind church of Achel, max. 24h, market Tuesday 8-13h.

	Hamont	8C4

Stadpark. GPS: n51,25085 e5,55200.

⑤free.
Surface: unpaved.
Remarks: Large parking in the centre behind tennis-courts, max. 24h.
Tourist information Hamont:
ℹ️ VVV, Generaal Dempseylaan 1, www.hamontachel.com. Historical little town.
🕐 Mo-Fri 9-12h, 13-16h, Sa 9-12h.

⑤S	Hasselt	8C5

Sporthal Alverberg, Herkenrodesingel. **GPS:** n50,93998 e5,32072.⬆️.

>5 ⑤free 🔌€2 🚰Ch. **Surface:** metalled. 🕐 01/01-31/12
Distance: 🚲city centre 3km 🍴Carrefour 🚗on the spot.

	Hasselt	8C5

Bakkerslaan. GPS: n50,92141 e5,32562.⬆️.

3 ⑤free. **Location:** Urban, simple. **Surface:** grasstiles/grassy.
🕐 01/01-31/12
Distance: 🚲2km 🚴600m ⊗500m 🍴500m 🚗on the spot.

🍴	Hasselt	8C5

Restaurant Myosotis, Overdemerstraat 20, Kuringen. **GPS:** n50,94663 e5,30877.
⬆️.

8 ⑤guests free.
Distance: ⊗on the spot 🍴bakery 50m.

	Hechtel/Eksel	8C4

In den Brand. **GPS:** n51,12673 e5,35090. ⬆️ .

⑤free. **Surface:** sand.
Distance: 🚲1,5km.

	Hechtel/Eksel	8C4

Parking CC De Schans, Rode Kruisplein 10, Hechtel. **GPS:** n51,12391 e5,36271.
⬆️ .

⑤free. **Surface:** asphalted.
Distance: 🚲400m.

	Hechtel/Eksel	8C4

Pijnven, Bosmuseum, Kiefhoekstraat. **GPS:** n51,16133 e5,31091. ⬆️ .

⑤free. **Surface:** asphalted.
Distance: 🚲4km.
Remarks: Parking forest.

	Helchteren 🚻	8C4

Parking de Dool, Sportstraat. **GPS:** n51,06087 e5,38650.⬆️.

BE

10 🛏free. **Surface:** asphalted. ⬛ 01/01-31/12
Distance: 🚶1km ⊗500m 🚌500m.
Remarks: Next to castle.

6 🛏free. **Surface:** metalled. ⬛ 01/01-31/12
Distance: 🚶6km ⊗on the spot.
Remarks: In front of abbey farm.

🛏 S	Herk-de-Stad	8B5

Park Olmenhof, Pikkeleerstraat. **GPS:** n50,93361 e5,16654.

🛏 S	Kortessem 🌿	8C5

Kapittelstraat. **GPS:** n50,85724 e5,39126.⬆➡.

7 🛏free ⛽€1/100liter 🗑Ch 💧€0,60/kWh WC. **Location:** Rural, simple.
Surface: asphalted. ⬛ 01/01-31/12
Distance: 🚶400m 🚲7km ⊗50m 🚇300m.
Remarks: Max. 48h.

5 🛏free ⛽. **Surface:** asphalted. ⬛ 01/01-31/12
Distance: 🚶200m ⊗200m 🥖bakery 200m 🚴on the spot.
Remarks: At gymnasium, max. 2 nights.

Tourist information Kortessem:
🏛 't Rood Kasteel, Guigoven. Former medieval water castle.

🍴 S	Hoepertingen 🚶	8B5

De Verborgen Parel, Hoenshovenstraat 5. **GPS:** n50,80170 e5,28944.⬆.

🍴 S	Leopoldsburg 🌿⛵🚶	8B4

De Lido, Lidostraat 171. **GPS:** n51,13633 e5,24179.

6 🛏€7,50 ⛽🗑Ch 💧. **Location:** Simple. **Surface:** gravel.
⬛ 01/01-31/12
Distance: 🚶1,5km 🚇1,5km 🚴on the spot 🚶on the spot.

🛏	Houthalen 🌿🚶	8C5

De Dool, Sportstraat. **GPS:** n51,06143 e5,38670.⬆.

35 🛏€9 ⛽🗑Ch 💧🚿🚽included. 🚴 **Location:** Rural, comfortable, isolated, quiet. **Surface:** gravel. ⬛ 01/01-31/12
Distance: 🚶3km 🎣fish pond ⊗on the spot.

⚓ S	Leopoldsburg 🌿⛵🚶	8B4

Jachthaven, Antwerpsesteenweg 129. **GPS:** n51,12892 e5,25028.⬆.

5 🛏free. **Surface:** asphalted. ⬛ 01/01-31/12
Distance: 🚶Helchteren 800m 🚲5,6km ⊗800m.

🛏	Houthalen 🌿🚶	8C5

Parking Kelchterhoef, Kelchterhoefstraat. **GPS:** n51,03015 e5,44063.⬆.

22 🛏€8 ⛽💧included WC 🗑€1. **Surface:** asphalted. ⬛ 01/01-31/12
Distance: 🚶2km 🏊on the spot ⊗on the spot 🚇2km.
Remarks: Check in at harbourmaster.

⚓ S	Lommel	8C4

Taverne Haven de Meerpaal, Boskantstraat 60. **GPS:** n51,24266 e5,36891.⬆.

BE

15 ⛲€ 10 🚰€0,50 💧Ch ⚡(6x)€1 WC 🚽€1. **Surface:** asphalted.
Distance: ⊗on the spot.
Remarks: Near marina.

| 📷 | Maaseik 🌿 | 8C4 |

Sportlaan P4. **GPS:** n51,10108 e5,78964. ⬆.

20 ⛲free. **Surface:** asphalted. ⏺ 01/01-31/12
Distance: 🚶historical centre 200m.

Tourist information Maaseik:
🏛 Marktplein. ⏺ Wed 9-12h.

| 📷 | Meeuwen-Gruitrode | 8C4 |

CC Gruitrode, Royerplein 1, Gruitrode. **GPS:** n51,08939 e5,58949. ⬆ ⬆.

8 ⛲free. **Surface:** metalled. ⏺ 01/01-31/12
Distance: 🚶200m ⊗on the spot 🚰200m 🚮200m.
Remarks: Max. 24h.

| 📷 S | Neeroeteren 🌿 | 8C4 |

Komweg. **GPS:** n51,08375 e5,70284.
10 ⛲€5 🚰💧Ch⚡. **Surface:** asphalted.
Remarks: At football ground.

| 📷 S | Neerpelt | 8C4 |

De Welvaart, Jaak Tassetstraat. **GPS:** n51,23333 e5,43164. ⬆.

10 ⛲€6/24h 🚰💧Ch ⚡free. 🚰 ♻ **Surface:** metalled. ⏺ 01/01-31/12
Distance: 🚶500m.
Remarks: At the canal, parking marina, max. 48h, checked, coin waste dump € 1.

| P | Peer | 8C4 |

P1 Aan den Boogaard. GPS: n51,13193 e5,45741.
⛲free.
Distance: 🚶100m.
Remarks: Max. 24h.

| P | Peer | 8C4 |

P2 Noordervest. GPS: n51,13422 e5,45511.
⛲free.
Distance: 🚶150m.
Remarks: Max. 24h.

| 📷 | Rekem 🌿 | 8C5 |

Kanaalstraat. **GPS:** n50,92297 e5,70622. 🏕.

⛲free. **Surface:** unpaved.
Distance: 🚶1km 🏊on the spot 🚲on the spot ⊗500m 🛒1km 🚌100m
🚴on the spot.
Remarks: Max. 48h, walking and bicycle area.

Tourist information Rekem:
ℹ Oud-Rekem with museum-church, city walls and castle, marked walking route 2km.

| 📷 S | Rummen | 8B5 |

Ketelstraat. **GPS:** n50,89280 e5,16140.

2 ⛲free 💧Chfree. ⏺ 01/01-31/12
Distance: 🚶on the spot ⊗300m 🛒250m 🚴on the spot 🚶on the spot.

| 📷 S | Schalkhoven | 8C5 |

Nollekes Winning, Schalkhovenstraat 79. **GPS:** n50,84531 e5,44687.

4 ⛲ 🚰WC 🚽. **Surface:** gravel. ⏺ 01/01-31/12
Distance: 🚶200m ⊗on the spot.

| 📷 S | Tongeren 🌿 | 8C5 |

Pliniuspark, Fonteindreef. **GPS:** n50,78626 e5,45256. ⬆ ➡.
24 ⛲€ 10/24h 🚰€0,50/100liter 💧free Ch ⚡€0,50/kWh. 🚰 ♻
Surface: metalled. ⏺ 01/01-31/12
Distance: 🚶2 km 🚴on the spot 🚶on the spot.

Tourist information Tongeren:
ℹ Dienst Toerisme, Stadhuisplein 9, www.tongeren.be. Oldest city of Belgium with numerous historico-cultural heritage.
🏛 Maastrichterstraat, Schiervelstraat, Clarissenstraat. Biggest antique market in

the Benelux, also all antique stores open. ☐ Su 6-13h.

🚐 S   Tongerlo   8C4
De Kieper, Keyartstraat. **GPS**: n51,12397 e5,65449.

5 🚐free ⛽€1/100liter 💧€1. **Surface**: metalled.
Distance: 🚶10 min walking 🛒on the spot 🐟on the spot.

🚐   Veldwezelt 🌿   8C5
Omstraat 20. **GPS**: n50,86195 e5,62696. ⬆.

2 🚐free. **Surface**: metalled. ☐ 01/01-31/12
Distance: 🚶800m ⊗200m 🛒500m.
Remarks: Parking gymnasium.

Brussels

Ⓟ   Bruxelles/Brussel 🌿🍽🧁   8A5
Bruparck, Wemmel/Heizel, Brussels (Bruxelles/Brussel). **GPS**: n50,89745 e4,33826. 🚐.
Remarks: Ring road Brussels exit 8.

🚐 S   Bruxelles/Brussel 🌿🍽🧁   8A5
Jeugdherberg Génération Europe, Rue de l'Eléphant 4, Brussels (Bruxelles/Brussel). **GPS**: n50,85317 e4,33479.
5 🚐€30 ⛽💧 Ch ⬛ 💧 WC 🚿📶. ☐ 01/01-31/12
Distance: 🚶on the spot.

Ⓟ   Bruxelles/Brussel 🌿🍽🧁   8A5
Heizel/Heysel Metro, Brussels (Bruxelles/Brussel). **GPS**: n50,89736 e4,33827. 🚐.
Remarks: Nearby Bruparck.

Tourist information Brussels (Bruxelles/Brussel):
ℹ Brussels City Card gives for free entrance on public transport and museums and many discounts on purchases. 🎫 € 24.
ℹ Bureau van Toerisme, Office de Tourisme, Grote Markt 1, Grand Place, www.brucity.be. Capital of Belgium, with a history of more than 1000 years. A lot of buildings worth seeing and historical places.
👁 Koninklijke Serres van Laken, Les serres royales à Laeken. Park, garden, nature area.
Ⓜ Autoworld, Jubelpark, Parc du Cinquantenaire. Motorcar history from 1886 up to 1970s. ☐ 01/04-30/09 10-18h, 01/10-31/03 10-17h.
Ⓜ Museum van de stad Brussel Broodhuis, Musée de la ville Bruxelles, Grote Markt 44, Grand Place. History of the city. ☐ Tue-Su 10-17h.
✝ Basiliek van Koekelberg, basilique de Koekelberg. The fifth largest church of the world. ☐ 01/10-18/10 Su 14-17.45h, 01/07-31/08 Sa-Su. 🎫 € 2,50.
🌳 Grote Markt, Grand place. Flowers and plant market. ☐ 8-18h.
🌳 Grote Zavel, Place du Grand Sablon. Antiques and book market. ☐ Sa 9-17h, Su 9-13h.
🌳 Vossenplein. ☐ 7-14h.
🌳 Kunstmarkt, marché d'art, Boterstraat, rue au Beurre. Painters and portraitists. ☐ 11-18h.
😊 Atomium, Bruparck, Boulevard du Centenaire, Laeken. Built for the occasion of the 1958 Brussels World Fair, symbolising a crystallised iron molecule to the scale of its atoms enlarged 160 thousand million times. ☐ 10-18h, 01/04-31/08

9-20h. 🎫 € 5.
😊 Bruparck, Boulevard du Centenaire 20, Laeken. Family park with among other things Mini-Europe, paradise pool and The Village with restaurants, cafés and shops. ☐ 01/01-31/12.
😊 Mini-Europe, Bruparck, Boulevard du Centenaire, Laeken. Europe in miniature, 300 monuments. ☐ 30/03-03/01.
😊 Oceade, Bruparck, Boulevard du Centenaire, Laeken. Subtropical leisure pool park. ☐ holidays, Sa-Su 10-22h.

Liège

🚐 S   Aywaille 🚲🍽   8C6
Esplanade du Fair-Play, Rue de la Heid. **GPS**: n50,47583 e5,67809. ⬆➡.

8 🚐€8/48h, incl. 1 coin (water or 2h electricity) ⛽€2 💧Ch 💧(4x)€1/h.
Surface: metalled. ☐ 01/01-31/12
Distance: 🚶300m 🛒200m.
Remarks: At recreation area.

😊 S   Blégny-Mine   8C5
Domaine de Blégny-Mine, Rue Lambert Marlet. **GPS**: n50,68617 e5,72367. ⬆.

8 🚐free ⛽💧Ch free 💧(8x)€2/12h. **Location**: Rural, comfortable, isolated, quiet. **Surface**: gravel. ☐ 01/01-31/12
Distance: 🚴4,6km ⊗on the spot 🐟on the spot 🏃on the spot.
Remarks: At former coalmine, UNESCO World Heritage, access € 9,30, 1 day all inclusive € 29,50, coins electricity at reception park.

🚐   Eupen 🌿   8D6
Langesthal 164. **GPS**: n50,62180 e6,09148.

🚐free. **Surface**: asphalted. ☐ 18-10h.
Distance: 🚶Eupen 4km 🛒150m Taverne.
Remarks: At weir, isolated.

Tourist information Eupen:
🌳 Benedenstad. ☐ Wed 7-12.30h.
🌳 Eupen/Keltenis. Flea market. ☐ Su 7-16h.

🚐 S   Hamoir 🏘🍽🏖   8C6
Complexe Sportif, Quai du Batty. **GPS**: n50,42463 e5,53522. ➡.

10 ⬛€ 8/24h ⛽ ⬛ Ch free. ⬛ ♻ **Location:** Urban, comfortable.
Surface: grassy/gravel. ⬛ 01/01-31/12
Distance: 🚲200m ⛱on the spot 🛒on the spot ⊗200m 🍴200m.
Remarks: Along the Ourthe river.

| ⬛ | Huy ❀ | 8B6 |

Avenue Godin Parnajon. **GPS:** n50,52379 e5,24310.⬆.

2 ⬛ free. **Location:** Urban, central, noisy. **Surface:** asphalted.
⬛ 01/01-31/12
Distance: 🚲500m ⊗on the spot 🍴500m.
Remarks: Parking in front of restaurant Quick.

| ⬛ | Huy ❀ | 8B6 |

Quai de Namur. **GPS:** n50,51673 e5,23453.⬆.

2 ⬛ free. **Location:** Urban, central, noisy. **Surface:** asphalted.
⬛ 01/01-31/12
Distance: 🚲500m 🚶on the spot ⊗on the spot 🍴500m.
Remarks: Under the citadel, along the Meuse River, in front of Hôtel du Fort to the right to the quay.

Tourist information Huy:
ℹ Office du Tourisme, Quai de Namur,1, www.huy.be. Tourist town, citadel above the city.
Ⓜ✖ Fort en museum. ⬛ Easter-Sep 10-17/18/19h.

| ⬛ S | Malmedy ❀❄ | 8D6 |

Avenue de la Gare, N62. **GPS:** n50,42282 e6,03080.⬆➡.

30 ⬛€ 5/24h ⛽ ⬛ Ch 🔌 (8x)included. ⬛ **Surface:** gravel/metalled.
⬛ 01/01-31/12

Distance: 🚲300m ⊗300m 🍴bakery 100m, supermarket 800m 🚂on the spot 🚲on the spot 🚶on the spot 🎿 Waimes 5km.
Remarks: At cycle route (former railroad).

Tourist information Malmedy:
⛪ Place St. Géréon. ⬛ Fri 7-13h.
♨ 🚴 🎿 Hautes Fagnes. Nature reserve Hautes Fagnes.

| ⬛ | Sourbrodt ❝❞ ❄ | 8D6 |

Signal de Botrange, Rue de Botrange. **GPS:** n50,50148 e6,09312.⬆.

20 ⬛ free. **Location:** Rural, simple, noisy. **Surface:** gravel.
⬛ 01/01-31/12
Distance: 🚲 on the spot ⊗on the spot 🚶on the spot 🎿 on the spot.

| ⬛ S | St.Vith | 8D6 |

An den Weyern, Rodter Strasse 9a. **GPS:** n50,28091 e6,12240.⬆➡.

20 ⬛ free ⛽€1/4minutes ⬛. **Location:** Urban, simple. **Surface:** asphalted.
⬛ 01/01-31/12
Distance: 🚲500m ⊗on the spot 🍴on the spot.
Remarks: At sports centre.

| 🍴🍴 S | Waimes ❝❞ | 8D6 |

La Faitafondue, Rue de Merkem 4. **GPS:** n50,39532 e6,07024.⬆.

10 ⬛€ 9, free with a meal ⛽ ⬛ 🔌 WC 📶. **Location:** Rural, comfortable.
Surface: gravel. ⬛ 01/01-31/12 ⬛ Wed
Distance: 🚲4km 🚴 6km 🚲on the spot 🚶on the spot 🎿200m.

Hainaut

| ⬛ | Aubechies | 7D6 |

Parking Archéosite, Rue de l'Abbaye 1Y. **GPS:** n50,57419 e3,67546.
⬛.

Tourist information Aubechies:
ℹ Archéosite d'Aubechies. Archeological open air museum. ⬛ Easter-01/11 Mo-Fri 9-17h, Sa, Su 14-18h.

| ⬛ | Beloeil ❀ | 7D6 |

Château Beloeil. GPS: n50,55000 e3,73242.
⬛free. ⬛ 01/01-31/12
Remarks: Parking castle.

| △ S | Beloeil ❀ | 7D6 |

Camping à la Ferme, Rue de la Hunelle 16. **GPS:** n50,55165 e3,73275.

BE

12 🛏6 + € 2/pp 🚐🚰Ch🔌€1 WC🚿. ⬛ 15/03-15/11

Tourist information Beloeil:
🏰 Château de Beloeil, www.beloeil.be/. ⬛ 01/06-30/09 10-19h, 01/04-31/05 Sa,Su 10-19h.

| | Bernissart 〰 | 7D6 |

Musée de l'Iguanodon, Ruelle des Médecins. **GPS:** n50,47530 e3,64958.

🛏free.
Distance: ✈6km.
Remarks: Parking 100m of dinosaur museum.

| S | Binche 〰 | 8A6 |

Pastures, Rue des Pastures. **GPS:** n50,41413 e4,17070.
50 🛏free 🚰Ch🔌. **Surface:** asphalted. ⬛ 01/01-31/12
Distance: 🚶on the spot.
Remarks: Parking just outside centre.

Tourist information Binche:
ℹ Office du Tourisme, Parc communal, rue des Promenades, 2, www.binche.be. Medieval city with ramparts.

| | Blaton | 7D6 |

Place de Feignies. **GPS:** n50,50179 e3,66135.

🛏free.
Distance: 🚶200m.
Remarks: Nearby Romanesque church.

| S | Bouffioulx | 8A6 |

Rue du Général Jacques. **GPS:** n50,39024 e4,51406.
🛏🚐🚰Ch🔌against payment. **Surface:** metalled.
Remarks: Next to Centre d'Interprétation de la Poterie, coins at Maison de la Poterie.

| S | Boussu-lez-Walcourt ⛵ | 15C1 |

Les Lacs de l'Eau d'Heure, Route de la Plate Taille. **GPS:** n50,19265 e4,37958.
⬆.

20 🛏free 🚐🚰Chfree. **Surface:** asphalted. ⬛ 01/01-31/12
Distance: ⌀on the spot ⚓on the spot ⊗on the spot ⚓on the spot.

| P | Chimay | 15C1 |

Place Froissart. **GPS:** n50,04728 e4,31307.
🛏.

| P | Chimay | 15C1 |

Place Léopold. **GPS:** n50,04747 e4,31784.
🛏. ⬛ Fri

| S | Dottignies | 7C5 |

Rue des Écoles 75b. **GPS:** n50,72821 e3,30011.
🛏🚐🛏free. ⬛ 01/01-31/12
Distance: 🚶500m ✈1,3km.
Remarks: Square behind fire-station.

| | Ecaussines | 8A6 |

Château de la Folie, Rue de la Folie. **GPS:** n50,57443 e4,17851.
🛏free.
Distance: 🚶800m.

| | Ecaussines | 8A6 |

Eglise Sainte Aldegonde, Rue Jacquemart Boulle 28, Ecaussines-Lalaing.
GPS: n50,57085 e4,18107.
🛏free.
Distance: 🚶500m.

| | Fleurus | 8A6 |

Parking Gare, Avenue de la Gare. **GPS:** n50,48215 e4,54433.

| | Fleurus | 8A6 |

Stade Communal, Rue de Fleurjoux. **GPS:** n50,47852 e4,55237.
🛏free.

| | Harchies | 7D6 |

Place du Rivage. **GPS:** n50,47106 e3,69619.
🛏.

| | Hornu | 7D6 |

Le Site du Grand Hornu, Rue Sainte-Louise 82. **GPS:** n50,43488 e3,83707.⬆.

🛏free.
Distance: 🚶1km.

Tourist information Hornu:
👁 Grand-Hornu. Old industrial mining complex, a remarkable reminder of the Industrial Revolution. ⬛ Tue-Fri 10-18h. 🎫 € 6.

| | Houdeng Aimeries | 8A6 |

Musée de la Mine de Bois-du-Luc, Rue Saint-Patrice. **GPS:** n50,47081 e4,14952.
🛏free.

| | La Louvière 〰 | 8A6 |

Boulevard de Roi Baudouin. **GPS:** n50,46619 e4,19055.
🛏free.
Remarks: P Station Sud.

Tourist information La Louvière:
Ⓜ Ascenseur Funiculaire de Strépy-Thieu, Strépy-Bracquegnies. Drawworks, 19th century. ⬛ 01/02-27/11 9.30-18.30.
🎪 Rue du Marché. ⬛ Sa 8-13h.

| | Lahamaide | 7D5 |

Place Plada. **GPS:** n50,69465 e3,72202.

Remarks: At Ecomuseum.

| | Le Roeulx | 8A6 |

Grand Place. **GPS:** n50,50019 e4,10919.
🛏.

| | Le Roeulx | 8A6 |

Place de la Chapelle. **GPS:** n50,50294 e4,10874.
🛏.

Distance: 🚶100m.
Remarks: Next to church.

| | Le Roeulx | 8A6 |

Place de la Tannée. **GPS:** n50,50339 e4,10819.

BE

🚐.

| 🚐 | **Le Roeulx** | 8A6 |

Place du Château. **GPS**: n50,50406 e4,11024.

🚐 **Remarks:** Parking at castle.

| 🚐 S | **Leers Noord** | 7C5 |

La Maison du Canal, Rue du Canal 6. **GPS**: n50,69089 e3,25728.➡️

3 🚐free 🚰 🍴Chfree. **Location:** Rural, quiet. **Surface:** gravel.
🚪 01/01-31/12
Distance: 🚶on the spot ⊗on the spot 🚲on the spot 🎿on the spot.
Remarks: Tarerne closed on Monday.

| 🚐 | **Lessines** | 7D5 |

Rue des 4 fils Aymon. **GPS**: n50,71280 e3,83403.
🚐free.
Distance: 🚶400m.

| 🚐 | **Leuze-en-Hainaut** | 7D6 |

Rue du Pont de la Cure. **GPS**: n50,59924 e3,61347.
🚐free.

| 🚐 | **Marchienne-au-Pont** | 8A6 |

Musée d'Histoire et d'Archéologie Industrielle, 134 rue de la Providence.
GPS: n50,41301 e4,40450.
🚐free.
Remarks: In front of museum.

| 🚐 | **Mons/Bergen** 🌿 | 7D6 |

Maison Van Gogh, Rue de Pavillon 3, Cuesmes, Mons (Mons/Bergen).
GPS: n50,44174 e3,92630.
🚐free.
Remarks: In case of city-visit use parking nearby station or bypass.

Tourist information Mons (Mons/Bergen):
Ⓜ Maison Van Gogh, Rue du Pavillon 3, Cuesmes. Former place of residence of
painter Van Gogh 1879/80, exhibition of reproductions.
🚪 10-18h 🔲 Mo.
🏰 Château Havré, Havré. Castle, 12-13th century.

| 👁 | **Morlanwelz-Mariemont** | 8A6 |

Musée Alex Louis Martin, Place de Carnières, 52, Carnières.
GPS: n50,44402 e4,25416.
10 🚐free.

| 👁 | **Mouscron** | 7C5 |

Musée du Folklore, Rue des Brasseurs, 3.
GPS: n50,74217 e3,21795.
🚐free.
Remarks: Possibility make a reservation tel 02.56.33.23.36.

| 👁 | **Nimy** | 7D6 |

Musée de la Pipe et du Vieux Nimy, Rue Mouzin. **GPS**: n50,47499 e3,95853.
🚐free. **Surface:** metalled.
Remarks: Museum closed: Nov-Mar.

| 🚐 | **Quaregnon** | 7D6 |

La Grand Place. **GPS**: n50,44369 e3,86428.
2 🚐.

| 👁 | **Quevaucamps** | 7D6 |

Musée de la Bonneterie, Rue Paul Pastur. **GPS**: n50,52671 e3,68776.⬆️➡️

2 🚐free. 🚪 01/01-31/12
Remarks: Parking in front of museum, via N527.

| 🚐 | **Ronquières** 🌿 | 8A6 |

Grande tour et promenade en Bateau Mouche, Route de Baccara.
GPS: n50,59121 e4,22115.
🚐free.
Distance: 🚶on the spot 🚲on the spot.

| 🚐 | **Sivry** | 15C1 |

Observatoire de Sivry, Route de Mons 52. **GPS**: n50,17897 e4,22646.
2 🚐.
Remarks: Centre for nature studies.

| 🚐 | **Soignies** | 8A6 |

Collégiale et vieux cimentière, La Grand Place, la Place Vert, la Place Van
Zeeland. **GPS**: n50,57832 e4,06869.
🚐free. **Surface:** gravel/sand. 🔲 Tue market
Distance: 🚶on the spot ⊗on the spot 🛒on the spot.

| 🚐 | **Solre-Sur-Sambre** | 8A6 |

Château-Fort, Rue du Chateau Fort. **GPS**: n50,30918 e4,15585.
🚐free.
Remarks: At castle.

| 🚐 | **Thuin** | 8A6 |

Drève des Alliés. **GPS**: n50,33951 e4,29860.
🚐.
Remarks: Max. 24h.

| 🚐 | **Thuin** | 8A6 |

L'Abbaye d'Aulnes, Rue Vandervelde. **GPS**: n50,36592 e4,33324.
🚐free.
Remarks: Near abbey, max. 24h.

| 🚐 | **Thuin** | 8A6 |

Place du Chapitre. **GPS**: n50,33980 e4,28724.
🚐.
Remarks: Max. 24h.

| 🚐 S | **Tournai/Doornik** 🌿 | 7C6 |

Maison de la Culture, Boulevard Frère Rimbaud, Tournai (Tournai/Doornik).
GPS: n50,60432 e3,38199.⬆️.

15-20 🚐free 🚰 🍴Chfree. **Surface:** metalled.
🚪 01/01-31/12
Distance: 🚶5 min walking ⊗5 min walking 🛒5 min walking 🚌on the spot.

| 🚐 | **Trazegnies** | 8A6 |

Place Albert I 32. **GPS**: n50,46248 e4,33025.
🚐.
Distance: 🚲1,5km.
Remarks: Parking at castle.

Namur

| 🍴 | **Alle-sur-Semois** 🌿 ⛲ 👥 🏊 | 15D2 |

Recreatiecentrum Recrealle, restaurant les Pierres du Diable, Rue Léon
Henrard 16. **GPS**: n49,84648 e4,97579.⬆️.

10 🚐 free. **Location:** Rural, simple. **Surface:** unpaved.
📅 01/01-31/12
Distance: 🏙 700m 🏊 on the spot 🎣 fishing permit obligatory 🍴 on the spot 🛒 700m.

Tourist information Alle-sur-Semois:
☺ Recrealle. Canoe rent; departures for canoe and kayaks, fishing and swimming possibilities, bowling, tennis, play ground, restaurant.

[S] Ave-et-Auffe 16A1

Le Roptai, Rue du Roptai 34. **GPS**: n50,11144 e5,13373. ➡.

10 🚐 € 16-19 🚰 Ch 🔌 (10x)€3/24h WC included 🚿 €1 🧺 €4 📶 €1/3h.
Location: Rural, comfortable, quiet. **Surface:** grassy/gravel.
📅 08/01-31/12
Distance: 🏙 4km 🏊 2km 🍴 1km 🛒 .5km 🚌 1km 🚶 on the spot.
Remarks: Bread-service, Han 5km.

🚐 [S] Han-Sur-Lesse 16A1

Rue de la Lesse. **GPS**: n50,12751 e5,18819. ⬆.

40 🚐 € 7,50, Jul/Aug € 10 🚰 Ch 🔌 WC included. **Location:** Urban.
Surface: asphalted. 📅 01/01-31/12
Distance: 🏙 200m 🍴 200m 🛒 200m 🚌 on the spot.
Remarks: Parking nearby caves and centre.

Tourist information Han-Sur-Lesse:
[i] Tourist centre around the caves.
👁 Grottes de Han. Caves, son-et-lumière and boat trip on underground river.
📅 01/04-31/10 10-16/18h, 01/11-31/03 11.30-16h.
☺ Réserve d'Animaux. European animals alive today and those which lived previously in this area. 📅 01/03-31/12 10-17h, 01/07-31/08 9.30-18h.

🚐 [S] Namur 8B6

Tabora, Place André Ryckmans. **GPS**: n50,46770 e4,85056. ⬆.

8 🚐 free 🚰 Ch €7,50. **Surface:** asphalted. 📅 01/01-31/12
Distance: 🏙 1km 🍴 1km 🛒 1km 🚌 200m.
Remarks: Behind gymnasium.

🚐 [S] Nismes 15D1

Rue Longue. **GPS**: n50,07387 e4,54863. ⬆.

± 8 🚐 free 🚰 €2/100liter Ch 🔌 €2/h. **Surface:** asphalted.
📅 01/01-31/12
Distance: 🏙 on the spot 🍴 100m 🛒 bakery 100m 🚲 on the spot 🚶 on the spot.
Remarks: Coins at tourist info.

🚐 Profondeville 8B6

Chaussée de Namur. **GPS**: n50,37644 e4,87106. ⬆.

4 🚐 free. **Surface:** asphalted. 📅 01/01-31/12
Distance: 🏙 50m 🎣 150m 🛒 50m.
Remarks: Max. 24h.

🚐 Rochefort 16A1

Route de Marche. **GPS**: n50,15800 e5,22639. ➡.

10 🚐 free. **Location:** Urban, simple. **Surface:** metalled.
📅 01/01-31/12
Distance: 🏙 200m 🍴 200m 🛒 200m.

🚐 [S] Saint-Hubert 16A1

Chemin des Etangs/ Rue de Lavaux. **GPS**: n50,02689 e5,38088. ⬆➡.

BE

3 ⬛free ⬛⬛ ⬛free.
Location: Urban, simple. **Surface:** gravel.
⬛ 01/01-31/12
Distance: ⬛500m ⊗500m ⬛500m ⬛on the spot ⬛on the spot.
Remarks: Max. 48h, 10 parking places tolerated, european capital of hunting, events: 1st weekend September and November 1st Saint Hubert.

⬛S **Saint-Hubert** ⬛⬛ **16A1**
Fourneau Saint Michel, Rue Saint Hubert. **GPS:** n50,08480 e5,33902.⬛

10 ⬛free ⬛⬛ Ch free ⬛(4x)€1/h. **Location:** Rural, simple.
Surface: asphalted/grassy. ⬛ 01/01-31/12
Distance: ⬛St Hubert 9km ⊗200m ⬛on the spot.
Remarks: At open air museum from Fourneau Saint-Michel.

⬛S **Treignes** ⬛⬛ **15D1**
Rue de la Gare. **GPS:** n50,09085 e4,68182.⬛

3 ⬛free ⬛€2 ⬛Ch ⬛€2. **Surface:** gravel.
⬛ 01/01-31/12
Distance: ⬛900m.
Remarks: At former station, coins at tourist info Nismes, steam train museum.

Luxembourg

⬛S **Arlon** ⬛⬛ **16B2**
Casserne Callemeyn, Drève des Espagnols, N882. **GPS:** n49,68990 e5,81929.⬛

5 ⬛free ⬛⬛ ⬛free. **Location:** Urban, simple. **Surface:** asphalted.
⬛ 01/01-31/12
Distance: ⬛600m ⬛5,8km.

Remarks: At fire-station.
Tourist information Arlon:
⬛ Parc Archéologique, Rue des Thermes. Archeological site. ⬛ 9-12h, 14-17h.
⬛ Flea market. ⬛ 01/03-31/10 1st Su of the month 7-19h.

⬛S **Barvaux** ⬛ **8C6**
Petit Barvaux. **GPS:** n50,35223 e5,49501.⬛

20 ⬛€ 10/24h ⬛€2 ⬛Ch. ⬛ **Surface:** grasstiles.
⬛ 01/01-31/12
Distance: ⬛300m ⬛Delhaize 50m ⬛Ravel-route ⬛on the spot.
Remarks: Along the Ourthe river, max. 24h, coins at tourist info.

Tourist information Barvaux:
⬛ Labyrinthus, Rue Basse Commene. Labyrinth park. ⬛ 01/07-31/08 10.30-19.30h. ⬛ € 7,50.
⬛ Domaine de Hottemme. Nature reserve with visitor centre. ⬛ 10.30-17h, summer 10.30-18h.

⬛S **Bastogne** ⬛⬛ **16A1**
Avenue Albert I. **GPS:** n49,99825 e5,71526.⬛

10 ⬛free ⬛⬛ ⬛free. **Location:** Urban, simple, central. **Surface:** asphalted.
⬛ 01/01-31/12
Distance: ⬛300m ⬛3km ⊗300m ⬛300m.

⬛S **Bouillon** ⬛ **15D2**
Parking du stade, Rue de la Poulie. **GPS:** n49,79106 e5,05767.

10 ⬛free ⬛⬛ Ch. **Surface:** gravel. ⬛ 01/01-31/12
Distance: ⬛1,3km ⊗1,3km ⬛1,5km.

⬛S **Durbuy** ⬛⬛⬛⬛ **8C6**
P Mobilhome Le Vedeur, Rue Fond de Vedeur. **GPS:** n50,35780 e5,45672.⬛⬛

BE

50 🔲 € 21, 2 pers.incl 🔌 🍴 Ch 🔧 WC 📶 included. **Location:** Comfortable. **Surface:** gravel. 🔲 01/01-31/12
Distance: 🚲750m 🚤on the spot 🎣fishing permit obligatory ⊗750m 🚉750m 🏊on the spot.

Tourist information Durbuy:
👁 Confiturerie Saint Amour, Rue St Amour 13. Production of traditional products. 🔲 10-18h ◐ 01/10-31/03 Mo. 🎫 free.
👁 Diamour, Rue de la Prevoté. Centre of diamonds and goldsmithing. 🔲 10.30-19.30h ◐ Tue-Wed. 🎫 free.
👁 Parc des Topiaires, Rue Haie Himbe. Model garden. 🔲 10-18h ◐ 01/01-31/01. 🎫 € 4,50.
🎪 Antiques and flea market. 🔲 01/03-30/09, 9-17h, 2nd Sa of the month.

| 🏕 S | Herbeumont 🔆🌳 | 16A2 |

Avenue de Combattants. **GPS:** n49,77729 e5,23700. 🔼.

50 🔲free 🔌 Ch free.
Location: Rural. **Surface:** asphalted/grassy.
Distance: 🚲500m 🚉500m.
Remarks: Parking of old station.

Tourist information Herbeumont:
ℹ Royal Syndicat d'Initiative, Avenue des Combattants, 7, www.herbeumont.be. Beautiful position in the Ardennes landscape. Ruins of medieval castle, free entry.
👁 Grottes, 7 km di Bertrix. Caves. 🔲 01/04-30/09 daily, 01/11-31/03 Sa-Su. 🎫 € 7.

| 🏕 S | Hotton 🔆 | 8C6 |

Rue du Batty. **GPS:** n50,26873 e5,44417. 🔼.

3 🔲free 🍴 Ch. **Location:** Urban, simple.
🔲 01/01-31/12
Distance: 🚲300m 🎣on the spot ⊗300m 🚉300m.

Tourist information Hotton:
👁 Grottes de Hotton. Caves. 🔲 01/04-31/10 10-17h, 01/07-31/08 10-18h.

| 🏕 | La Roche 🔆🏔 | 16A1 |

Rue du Harzé. **GPS:** n50,19075 e5,57432. 🔼.

5 🔲free. **Location:** Urban, simple. **Surface:** asphalted.
🔲 01/01-31/12
Distance: 🚲500m ⊗500m 🚉500m 🚌on the spot.
Remarks: Parking at sports park.

Tourist information La Roche:
ℹ Syndicat d'Initiative, Place du Marché, 15, www.la-roche-tourisme.com. Small town totally destroyed during the battle of the Ardennes, 1944/45.

| 🏕 | Nisramont 🔆🌊 | 16A1 |

Barrage de Nisramont, Rue de barrage. **GPS:** n50,14089 e5,67118. 🔼.

10 🔲free. **Location:** Simple, isolated, quiet. **Surface:** metalled.
🔲 01/01-31/12
Distance: 🚲3,7km 🚣15km 🚤on the spot 🎣on the spot ⊗on the spot 🏊on the spot.
Remarks: At artificial lake.

| 🏕 S | Poupehan 🔆🌳🔆🌊 | 15D2 |

Rue du Pont. **GPS:** n49,80886 e5,00418. 🔼.

20 🔲free 🔌 🍴 Ch free.
Location: Rural, simple, quiet. **Surface:** gravel.
🔲 01/01-31/12
Distance: 🚤on the spot 🎣on the spot ⊗200m 🚉300m.
Remarks: Along the Semois river, next to sports fields, max. 24h, canoe rental.

| 🏕 | Redu | 16A1 |

Rue de Saint Hubert. **GPS:** n50,00877 e5,16348. 🔼.

10 🔲free. **Location:** Rural, simple. **Surface:** gravel. 🔲 01/01-31/12
Distance: 🚲on the spot.

BE

LUXEMBOURG

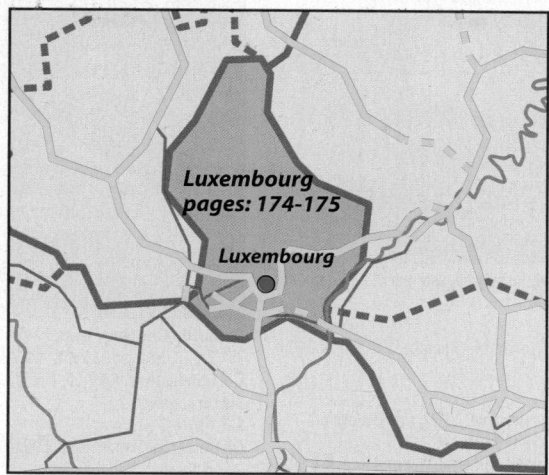

Luxembourg
pages: 174-175

Luxembourg

Capital: Luxembourg
Government: Grand duchy
Official Language: French, German, Luxembourgish
Population: 525,000 (2014)
Area: 2,586 km²

General information
Calling code: 00352
General emergency: 112
Currency: Euro

Regulations for overnight stays
Parking overnight and camping by public road is
forbidden. Motorhome-service only on campsites.

Additional public holidays 2015
May 1 Labor day
June 6 National Holiday
August 15 Assumption of the Virgin Mary
November 1 All Saints' Day

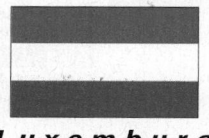

Luxemburg

Luxembourg

ⒸⓈ Bleesbrück 16B1
Camping Bleesbrück, 1, Bleesbreck. **GPS**: n49,87270 e6,18940.
2+2 ⛺ € 12 🔌🍽 Ch.
🅿 01/04-15/10
Remarks: Arrival >18h departure <9h, if not camping tariff.

ⒸⓈ Diekirch 🌿 16B1
Camping de la Sûre, Route de Gilsdorf. **GPS**: n49,86597 e6,16489. ⬆➡.

8 ⛺ € 12 🔌🍽 Ch. 🚿 WC included, sanitary only summer ▣ €3 📶 free 🚿.
Surface: grasstiles.
🅿 01/01-31/12
Distance: 🏖100m 🏊100m ⛵100m (permit € 4/month) 🎣100m 🚆100m.
Remarks: Max. 2 days.
Tourist information Diekirch:
Ⓜ Conservatoire National de véhicules historique, 20-22, rue de Stavelot.
Exhibition of historical vehicles. 🅿 10-18h ▣ Mo.
Ⓜ Musée National de l'histoire militaire, 10, Bamertal. War museum. 🅿 01/04-31/10 10-18h, 01/11-31/03 14-18h.
🍴 Rue de Marché. 🅿 Tue 8-12h.
☀ Al Dikkirch. Folk festival. 🅿 2nd week Jul.

⛺Ⓢ Dudelange 16B2
Parking Gare-Usines. **GPS**: n49,47176 e6,07772. ⬆.

6 ⛺ free 🔌🍽 Ch free. **Surface:** grasstiles/grassy.
🅿 01/01-31/12
Distance: 🏖1km 🚲4,1km 🚉near train station.
Remarks: Well situated for visiting Luxembourg city, 20min by train, max. 48h.
Tourist information Dudelange:
Ⓜ Musée National des Mines de Fer, carreau de la Mine, Rumelange. History of the mines. 🅿 14-17h. 🎫 € 7,50.

🅴 Echternach 🌿🚿 16C2
Villa Romaine, Route de Luxembourg. **GPS**: n49,80500 e6,40750. ⬆.

⛺free. **Surface:** asphalted/metalled. 🅿 01/01-31/12
Distance: 🏖1,5km 🏊350m ⊗500m 🎣on the spot.
Tourist information Echternach:
☀ Sprangprossessioun. Dancing procession. 🅿 Tue after Whitsuntide.

Ⓒ Ermsdorf 16B2
Neumühle. **GPS**: n49,83917 e6,22503.
2 ⛺. 🅿 01/01-31/12

ⒸⓈ Heiderscheid 16B1

Camping Fuussekaul - Heiderscheid

info@fuussekaul.lu - www.fuussekaul.lu
Electricity at each pitch
Open all year
Restaurant on the spot

Quickstop Camping Fuussekaul, Fuussekaul 4. **GPS**: n49,87806 e5,99278.
35 ⛺ € 10, Jul/Aug € 15 🔌🍽 Ch 🔲 🚿 (35x),16Amp WC included
⎕€1/5minutes ▣€4/2,50 📶€1/30minutes 🚿.
Surface: gravel.
🅿 01/01-31/12
Distance: 🏖1km 🚲8km 🏊8km ⛵5km ⊗on the spot 🎣on the spot
🚐on the spot 🧍on the spot.
Remarks: Arrival >16h departure <11h, max. 1 night.
Tourist information Heiderscheid:
☀ Heischter Mart. Traditional market. 🅿 end Jul.

🛏Ⓢ Hoscheid 🏔 16B1
Hotel-Restaurant Des Ardennes, Haaptstrooss. **GPS**: n49,94676 e6,08036.

4 ⛺ free with a meal 🔌🚿 WC 📶 included 🚿. **Surface:** asphalted.
🅿 01/02-15/12
Distance: ⊗on the spot 🚐on the spot.
Remarks: Parking behind hotel.

ⒸⓈ Larochette 🌿🏔🌳 16B2
Camping Birkelt, Um Birkelt 1. **GPS**: n49,78483 e6,21068. ⬆➡.

8 ⛺ € 11,75-16,75 excl. tourist tax 🔌🍽 Ch 🚿 WC included ▣€5 📶 🚿.
Surface: grasstiles. 🅿 01/03-31/10 ▣ 12/07-09/08
Distance: 🏖1km ⊗on the spot 🚐1km.
Remarks: Quick-Stop: >17h - <9h, max. 1 night.

△Ⓢ Larochette 🌿🏔🌳 16B2
Camping Auf Kengert. **GPS**: n49,80021 e6,19788.
6 ⛺from € 18,50 🔌🍽 Ch. 🅿 01/04-08/11

LU

Remarks: Quick-Stop: >19h - <9h.

Tourist information Larochette:

👁 Schiessentümpel. Waterfall with three cascades.

⚔ Château. 🔳 Easter-Oct, 10-18h, daily.

🔺	Maulusmühle	16B1

Woltzdal. GPS: n50,09266 e6,02869.

2 🍴. 🔳 01/01-31/12

🔺	Mersch	16B2

Um Krounebierg. GPS: n49,74403 e6,09075.

5 🍴 € 15-19,80. 🔳 15/03-31/10

🔺	Obereisenbach	16B1

Kohnenhof. GPS: n50,01630 e6,13682.

🍴. 🔳 11/04-26/10

🅿S	Redange/Attert	16B2

Rue de la Piscine 24. **GPS:** n49,76918 e5,89459.⬆.

12 🍴free 🚰🔌Ch ⚡ (5x)free. **Surface:** asphalted. 🔳 01/01-31/12

Distance: 🛒800m 🍽on the spot.

Remarks: Max. 48h.

🅿S	Schwebsange	16B2

Camport, Rue du Port. **GPS:** n49,51163 e6,36249.⬆.

18 🍴€ 10, 2 pers.incl 🚰🔌Chincluded ⚡€2,50 WC 🔲€2,50 🚿at restaurant 🍴. **Surface:** grasstiles. 🔳 01/04-15/10

Distance: 🛒500m 🎣fishing permit obligatory ⊗on the spot 🍽on the spot 🚌500m.

Tourist information Schwebsange:

Ⓜ A Possen, 1 rue Aloyse Sandt, Bech-Kleinmacher. Folkore and wine museum.

🔳 01/05-31/10 14-19h, 01/03-30/04, 01/11-31/12 Fri-Su 14-19h 🔳 Mo.

🏞	Vianden ⚓🍴🎣🎿🎭	16B1

39, rue du Sanatorium. **GPS:** n49,93717 e6,20556.⬆.

🍴free. **Surface:** asphalted. 🔳 01/01-31/12

Distance: ⊗500m 🍽500m.

Remarks: At the chair-lifts (télesiege).

Tourist information Vianden:

👁 SEO. Large hydro-electric power-station. 🔳 Easter-Sep 10-20h. 🎫 free.

Ⓜ Bakkerij museum, Grand rue 96-98. 🔳 Easter-Oct 11-17h 🔳 Mo.

⚔ Château de Vianden. 🔳 01/04-30/09 10-18h, 01/10-31/03 10-16h

🔳 02/11, 25/12, 01/01.

🎄 Nessmoort. Nuts market. 🔳 2nd Su Oct.

😊 Télesiège. Chair-lift. 🔳 Easter-Oct.

LU

FRANCE

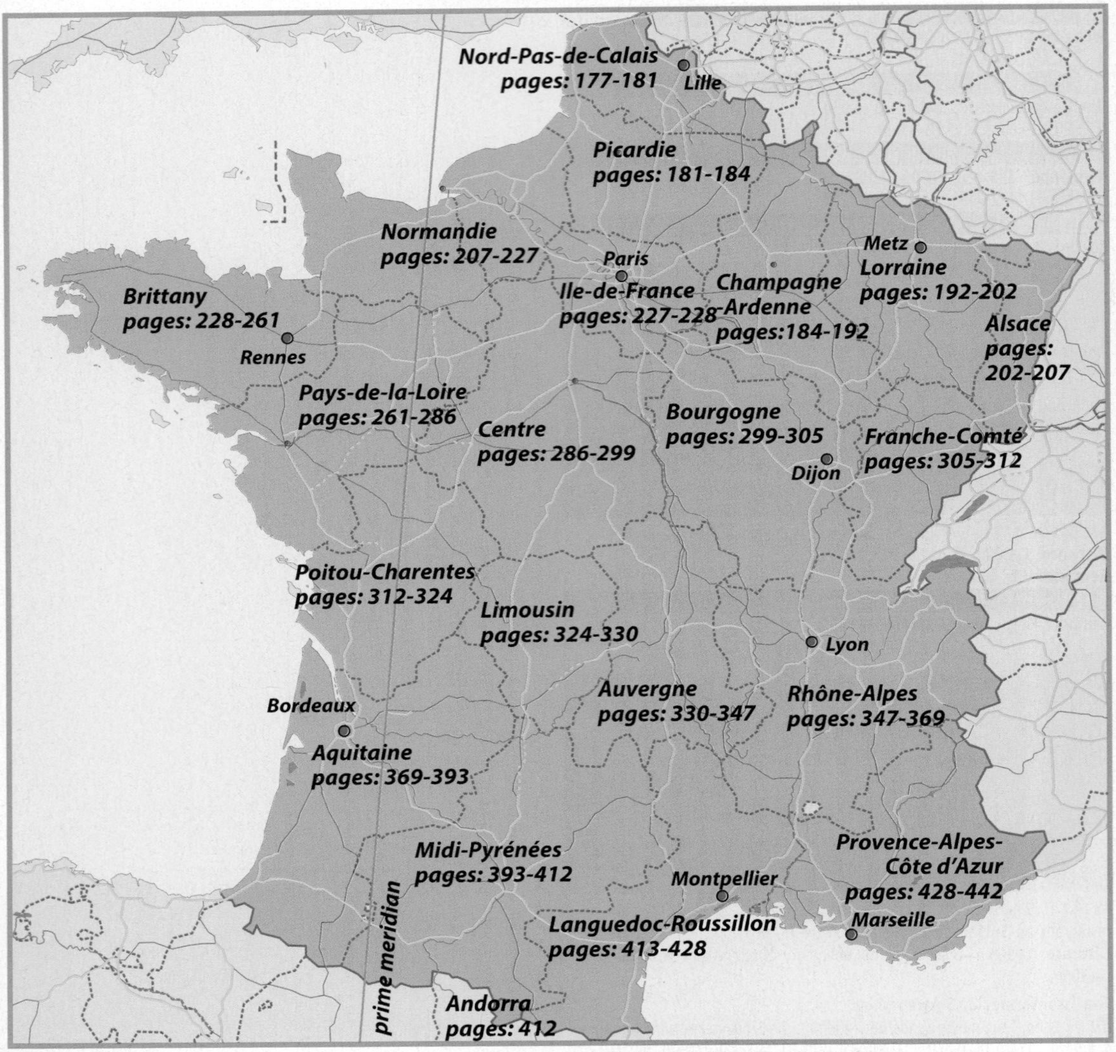

Nord-Pas-de-Calais
pages: 177-181
Lille

Picardie
pages: 181-184

Normandie
pages: 207-227

Paris

Metz
Lorraine
pages: 192-202

Ile-de-France
pages: 227-228

Champagne
Ardenne
pages:184-192

Alsace
pages:
202-207

Brittany
pages: 228-261

Rennes

Pays-de-la-Loire
pages: 261-286

Centre
pages: 286-299

Bourgogne
pages: 299-305

Franche-Comté
pages: 305-312

Dijon

Poitou-Charentes
pages: 312-324

Limousin
pages: 324-330

Lyon

Bordeaux

Auvergne
pages: 330-347

Rhône-Alpes
pages: 347-369

Aquitaine
pages: 369-393

Midi-Pyrénées
pages: 393-412

Montpellier

Provence-Alpes-
Côte d'Azur
pages: 428-442

Marseille

Languedoc-Roussillon
pages: 413-428

Andorra
pages: 412

prime meridian

Capital: Paris
Government: Unitary republic
Official Language: French
Population: 65,800,000 (2013)
Area: 543,965 km²

General information
Dialling code: 0033
General emergency: 112
Currency: Euro
Payments by credit card are accepted almost
everywhere, however chip and pin systems are non-
compatible with British cards and fuel for example can
only be bought at supermarkets during opening
hours.

Regulations for overnight stays
Wild camping is accepted almost everywhere
throughout inland France. Special regulations for
motor homes you can find on signs by entering
the town. It is permitted to stopover at motorway
services, be aware that toll roads often issue time-
constrained tickets.

Additional public holidays 2015
April 3 Good Friday
May 1 Labor Day
May 8 Liberation Day
July14 National Holiday
August15 Assumption of the Virgin Mary
November 1 All Saints Day
November 11 Armistice Day 1918

FR

Nord-Pas de Calais

Ambleteuse 7A5
D940 > Wimereux. **GPS**: n50,80638 e1,61484.⬆.

7 ⬛€3. **Location**: Rural. **Surface**: grassy.
Distance: 750m 1,2km.

Arques 7B5
Rue Michelet. **GPS**: n50,74551 e2,30459.⬆➡.

20 ⬛€3,50 €1,50 Ch. **Surface**: gravel. 01/04-31/10
Distance: 2km 100m.
Remarks: Behind camp site Beauséjour.

Arras 7C6
Rue des Rosati. **GPS**: n50,29463 e2,78812.⬆.

10 ⬛free €2/100liter Ch €2/1h. **Surface**: asphalted.
01/01-31/12
Distance: 700m 500m.
Tourist information Arras:
Hôtel de Ville. Town hall in Gothic style. Also guided tours of the subterranean passages of Arras.
Wed, Sa.

Bailleul 7B5
Rue du collège. **GPS**: n50,74010 e2,73170.

20 ⬛free. **Surface**: asphalted. 01/01-31/12
Distance: 700m 2,8km.
Remarks: At commemorative monument.

Banteux 15A1
GPS: n50,06259 e3,20106.⬆.

5 ⬛€4 Chfree. **Location**: Rural, simple. **Surface**: grassy/gravel.
01/01-31/12 service 01/11-31/03
Distance: 500m 2,5km on the spot on the spot.

Bavay 7D6
Chemin de Ronde. **GPS**: n50,30004 e3,79551.⬆.
10 ⬛free Chfree. **Surface**: gravel. 01/01-31/12
Distance: 200m 200m.

Berck-sur-Mer 7A6
Baie d'Authie, Chemin aux Raisins. **GPS**: n50,39701 e1,56431.⬆➡.

80 ⬛€10 Chincluded. **Surface**: gravel. 01/01-31/12
Distance: 1,5km 100m frituur 100m.
Remarks: Baker every morning.

Berck-sur-Mer 7A6
Parking Terminus, Rue Dr. Calot, Berck-Nord. **GPS**: n50,42361 e1,56750.⬆.

40 ⬛€10 Chincluded. **Location**: Simple. **Surface**: gravel.
01/01-31/12
Distance: beach 200m.
Remarks: Beach parking.

Berck-sur-Mer 7A6
Chez Mireille, Chemin Genty. **GPS**: n50,41654 e1,57696.
80 ⬛€7 Ch (4x)€2/kWh free. **Surface**: grassy.
01/04-31/10
Distance: 600m 800m on the spot.

Remarks: To be paid at bar.

Tourist information Berck-sur-Mer:
☺ Bagatelle, CD 940. Amusement park. ☐ Easter-Sep 10-18.30h.

| | Bergues 〰⛱ | 7B5 |

Rue Maurice Cornette. **GPS**: n50,96543 e2,43596. ⬆➡.

50 🛏free. **Surface:** gravel. ☐ 01/01-31/12
Distance: ⚓500m 🚲2,2km.
Remarks: Behind football ground, max. 48h.

| | Boulogne-sur-Mer ⛲🍦🌊 | 7A5 |

Parking Moulin Wibert, Boulevard Sainte Beuve, D940.
GPS: n50,74308 e1,59688. ⬆.

40 🛏€ 5,25/24h 🚰€3/10minutes 🗑Ch ♻. **Surface:** metalled.
Distance: ⚓centre 2,5km 🚲5,5km 🏊on the spot 🚌on the spot.

| | Boulogne-sur-Mer ⛲🍦🌊 | 7A5 |

Boulevard Chanzy. **GPS**: n50,72194 e1,60027. ⬆.

🛏free. **Surface:** asphalted.
Distance: ⚓500m 🚲4,5km.
Remarks: Nearby casino.

Tourist information Boulogne-sur-Mer:
🚏 Boulevard Clocheville. ☐ Wed-morning.
🚏 place Dalton, centre. ☐ Wed + Sa morning.
🚏 place Vignon. ☐ Su-morning.

| | Boussois | 7D6 |

Rue du Rivage. **GPS**: n50,28845 e4,04544. ⬆.
4 🛏 🚰🗑Ch. **Surface:** gravel. ☐ 01/01-31/12
Distance: ⚓1km.

| | Calais | 7A5 |

Digue Gaston Berthe. **GPS**: n50,96688 e1,84406.

60 🛏free, 01/04-31/10 € 7/24h 🚰🗑Ch 🚽WC included.
Surface: asphalted.
Distance: 🏊500m 🏊100m ⊗100m 🍺100m.

| | Calais | 7A5 |

Quai Edmond Pagniez. **GPS**: n50,96050 e1,84466. ⬆.

100 🛏free, 01/04-31/10 € 7/24h 🚰🗑Ch 🚽included. **Surface:** asphalted.
☐ 01/01-31/12
Distance: ⚓300m ⊗350m.
Remarks: Service: Digue Gaston Berthe.

Tourist information Calais:
Ⓜ Centre d'Information Eurotunnel. Exhibition about the Channel tunnel.
🚏 ☐ Wed, Thu, Sa.

| | Cambrai | 15A1 |

Grand Carré. **GPS**: n50,18515 e3,22587. ⬆.
6 🛏€ 8 🚰🗑Ch ♻ included. 🛏**Location:** Comfortable, quiet.
Surface: asphalted. ☐ 01/01-31/12
Distance: ⚓1,5km ⊗750m.

| | Cassel 〰 | 7B5 |

Route d'Oxelaere, C301. **GPS**: n50,79328 e2,48852. ⬆➡.

5 🛏free 🚰€2 🗑Ch 🚽€2. **Location:** Isolated, quiet. **Surface:** gravel.
☐ 01/01-31/12
Distance: ⚓1km.
Remarks: At sports park, coins at tourist info.

| | Catillon-sur-Sambre | 15B1 |

Avenue de la Groise, N43. **GPS**: n50,07624 e3,64615. ⬆.

FR

5 🚐 €5 🚰 Ch 🔌 included. **Surface:** asphalted. 🗓 01/01-31/12
Distance: 🏘200m 🚌 on the spot.
Remarks: At the canal, max. 72h.

🚐 Catillon-sur-Sambre 15B1

Rue de la Gare. **GPS**: n50,07699 e3,64404. ⬆➡.

20 🚐 free. **Surface:** gravel. 🗓 01/01-31/12
Distance: 🏘500m 🚌 on the spot.
Remarks: At the canal.

🚐 [S] Embry 7A6

Les Salons de l'Embryenne, D108. **GPS**: n50,49534 e1,96610. ⬆.

8 🚐 €6 🚰 €2,50 Ch 🔌 €2,50/4h WC 🚿 €2,50 💳. 🍴 **Location:** Isolated, quiet. **Surface:** gravel. 🗓 01/01-31/12

🚐 [S] Equihen-Plage 7A5

Plage de la Crevasse, Rue du Beurre Fondu. **GPS**: n50,67993 e1,56830. ⬆➡.

20 🚐 €5 🚰 €3/10minutes Ch 🔌 (6x)€3/12h. **Surface:** grassy/gravel.
🗓 01/01-31/12
Distance: 🏘100m 🏖100m 🍷100m.

🚐 Grand-Fort-Philippe 7B5

Bd François Lévêque. **GPS**: n51,00142 e2,10851. ⬆.
8 🚐 free. **Surface:** asphalted. 🗓 01/01-31/12
Distance: 🏘 on the spot 🏖600m.
Remarks: At the canal, >3,5t not allowed.

[S] Gravelines 7B5

Rue de la Gendarmerie. **GPS**: n50,99342 e2,13177. ⬆➡.
🚰 €2 Ch 💳.

⚓ Gravelines 7B5

Parking des Miaules, Rue des Islandais/Rue du Port. **GPS**: n50,98766 e2,12232. ⬆.

20 🚐 € 3, 01/04-01/10 € 6. 🚌 💳 **Location:** Rural, simple, quiet.
Surface: gravel.
Distance: 🏘500m 🚌 nearby 🍴300m.

🚐 Hardelot 7A5

Place R.L. Peeters. **GPS**: n50,63500 e1,59888. ⬆.

🚐 free. **Surface:** asphalted. 🗓 01/01-31/12
Distance: 🏖1,7km.

🚐 [S] Hondschoote 7B5

Impasse Spinnewyn. **GPS**: n50,97628 e2,58033. ⬆➡.

8 🚐 free 🚰 €2/100liter Ch 🔌 €2/1h. **Surface:** asphalted.
Distance: 🏘800m 🍷 nearby.
Remarks: Behind Moulin de la Victoire, coins available, addresses indicated on the spot.

🚐 Landrecies 15B1

Avenue Dumey. **GPS**: n50,12715 e3,69007.
4 🚐. 🗓 01/01-31/12

🚐 [S] Le Portel 7A5

Rue des Champs. **GPS**: n50,71188 e1,57485. ⬆➡.

40 🚐 € 3, 01/06-30/09 € 4 🚰 €2/100liter Ch 🔌 €2/4h 💳. 🚌 💳
Surface: metalled. 🗓 01/01-31/12
Distance: 🏘200m 🏖300m 🍴300m 🍷300m.
Remarks: Next to sports fields, 300m from beach (stairs).

🚐 [S] Le Touquet-Paris Plage 7A6

Parc International de la Canoke, Boulevard de la Canche.
GPS: n50,52648 e1,59869. ⬆.

FR

100 🛏€9 ⛽€2/100liter 🗑Ch 🚿€2/55minutes 🗑. **Surface:** grassy/gravel.
⏹ 01/01-31/12
Distance: 🚶10 min walking 🏊on the spot ⊗on the spot 🍴on the spot
🚌on the spot.

Centre Nautique du Touquet Base Nord, Avenue Jean Ruet.
GPS: n50,53588 e1,59285. ⬆➡.

60 🛏€13 ⛽€2/100liter 🗑Ch 🚿€2/55minutes. **Surface:** asphalted.
⏹ 01/01-31/12
Distance: 🚶10 min walking 🏊on the spot ⊗on the spot 🍴on the spot
🚌on the spot.
Tourist information Le Touquet-Paris Plage:
😊 Aqualud. Leisure pool park. ⏹ 15/02-30/11 10-18h.

Avenue du Maréchal Leclerc, N43. **GPS:** n50,10197 e3,55491. ⬆.

5 🛏free ⛽🗑Ch 🚿free. **Surface:** asphalted. ⏹ 01/01-31/12
Distance: 🚶1km.

Stade Bollaert-Delelis P6, Rue Maurice Fréchet. **GPS:** n50,43192 e2,82057.

6 🛏free ⛽🗑Ch free 🚿against payment 🗑. **Surface:** asphalted.
⏹ 01/01-31/12
Distance: 🚶500m ⊗on the spot 🍴1km 🚌on the spot.
Remarks: Max. 24h.

Ferme du Louvet, 5, Route de Wierre, D52 Desvres > Samer.
GPS: n50,64667 e1,79062. ⬆➡.

8 🛏€6 ⛽€3 🗑Ch 🚿included. **Location:** Rural, isolated, quiet.
Surface: gravel.
Remarks: Narrow entrance.

Place de la Gare. **GPS:** n50,46026 e1,58053. ⬆.

12 🛏free. **Surface:** gravel. ⏹ 01/01-31/12

Avenue des Garennes. **GPS:** n50,45944 e1,75939.
8 🛏free ⛽€2/100liter 🗑Ch free 🚿(2x)against payment.
Surface: asphalted. ⏹ 01/01-31/12
Distance: 🚶500m ⊗300m 🍴450m.

La Pommeraie, 13, route nationale. **GPS:** n50,30516 e2,29375. ⬆➡.

5 🛏€5 ⛽€2 🗑Ch 🚿€5 📶free. **Location:** Rural, comfortable, quiet.
Surface: gravel. ⏹ 01/01-31/12
Distance: ⊗50m.
Remarks: Covered pool € 3.

Les Huttes d'Oye Plage. **GPS:** n50,99703 e2,04228. ⬆.

10 🛏free. **Surface:** gravel. ⏹ 01/01-31/12
Distance: 🏊on the spot ⊗100m.
Remarks: Beach parking, service Oye-Plage: 50,97713 2,03966.

Richebourg 7B6
Rue de la Briqueterie. **GPS:** n50,58028 e2,74639. ⬆➡

6 🚐free 🚰€2/100liter 🔋€2/55minutes 📶included. **Location:** Rural, comfortable. **Surface:** grassy. ⬤ 01/01-31/12
Distance: 🚶500m 🚲 on the spot 🧍on the spot.
Remarks: Max. 48h.

Stella-plage 7A6
Cours des Champs Elysées. **GPS:** n50,47470 e1,57726. ⬆

30 🚐free. **Location:** Simple, isolated. **Surface:** asphalted.
Distance: 🚶1km 🏖on the spot ⊗650m.
Remarks: Parking at dune.

Tardinghen 7A5
Le site des 2 caps, La Ferme d'Horloge, 1615 Route d'Ausques, D249. **GPS:** n50,86250 e1,64890. ⬆➡

30 🚐€5/24h 🚰€3 🍽Ch 🚿€3/24h 📶. **Surface:** metalled. ⬤ 01/01-31/12
Distance: 🚶1,6km.
Remarks: Swin-golf € 5.

Tardinghen 7A5
Le site des 2 caps, La Fleur des Champs. **GPS:** n50,85639 e1,65139. ⬆

50 🚐€5/24h. **Surface:** grassy. ⬤ 01/01-31/12
Distance: 🚶2km 🏖2km.

Tardinghen 7A5
Le site des 2 caps, Le Fond de Sombre, Hervelinghen > Wissant. **GPS:** n50,89361 e1,68972. ⬆

10 🚐€5/24h. **Surface:** grassy. ⬤ 01/01-31/12
Distance: 🏖1km.

Wissant 7A5
Parking Wissant, Avenue Georges Clémenceau. **GPS:** n50,88684 e1,67064. ⬆➡

30 🚐free 🍽Chfree. **Surface:** metalled. ⬤ 01/01-31/12
Distance: 🚶700m 🏖1,1km.

Picardie

Ault 14C1
Rue Gest. **GPS:** n50,10333 e1,45083. ⬆➡

10 🚐free 🚰€2 🍽Ch 🔋€2. **Surface:** asphalted. ⬤ 01/01-31/12
Distance: 🚶200m 🏖250m ⊗200m 🚮200m.
Remarks: >3,5t not allowed, coins at tourist info.

Bellicourt 15A1
Hameau de Riqueval, D1044. **GPS:** n49,95156 e3,23519. ⬆

2 🚐free 🚰🍽Ch 🔋Service €4. **Surface:** asphalted. ⬤ 01/01-31/12
⬤ service: 01/10-31/03
Distance: 🚶300m ⊗on the spot 🚌on the spot.
Remarks: Coins at tourist info.

Bourseville 14C1
Lotissement le Village. **GPS:** n50,10350 e1,52702. ⬆➡

FR

35 🛏€5 ⚡€2 🚰Ch 💧€3. 🚐 **Location:** Isolated, quiet.
Surface: asphalted. 🅿 01/01-31/12
Distance: 🚶500m 🏊3km ⊗500m 🛒500m.

13 🛏€6,50 ⚡Ch 💧€1,50/12h WC included. 🚐 🗺 **Location:** Urban, comfortable. **Surface:** asphalted. 🅿 01/01-31/12
Distance: 🚶centre 1,8km 🏊on the spot 🚲on the spot ⊗on the spot 🛒on the spot 🎣on the spot 🚶on the spot.
Remarks: Along the Marne river.

Bruyères-et-Montberault — 15B2
Avenue de Verdun. **GPS:** n49,52538 e3,66080. ⬆➡

4 🛏free. **Surface:** asphalted. 🅿 01/01-31/12
Distance: 🚶100m ⊗100m 🛒200m.

Cayeux-sur-Mer — 14C1
Rue Faidherbe. **GPS:** n50,20300 e1,52612. ⬆➡

Conty — 14D2
Rue du Marais. **GPS:** n49,74333 e2,15583. ⬆

30 🛏free ⚡€2/100liter 🚰Ch WC. **Surface:** grassy. 🅿 01/01-31/12
Distance: 🚶200m 🚲6,5km 🚲300m ⊗300m 🛒300m.
Remarks: Coins at tourist info, town hall and bakery.

Coucy-le-Château-Auffrique — 15B2
Chemin du Val Serain. **GPS:** n49,52037 e3,31150. ⬆

30 🛏€5 ⚡€3 🚰Ch. **Surface:** gravel. 🅿 01/01-31/12
Distance: 🚶2km 🏊At the sea, no beach ⊗2km 🛒2km.
Remarks: To be paid at campsite.

Cayeux-sur-Mer — 14C1
Route blanche, Le Hourdel, D102. **GPS:** n50,21448 e1,55208. ➡

6 🛏€5 ⚡Ch 💧included. 🚐 🗺 **Location:** Rural, comfortable.
Surface: gravel. 🅿 01/01-31/12
Distance: 🚶500m ⊗on the spot 🛒500m.
Remarks: Castle 1km.

Doullens — 14D1
Rue du Pont à l'Avoine, N25-Arras-Amiens. **GPS:** n50,15390 e2,34260. ⬆

30 🛏free. **Location:** Simple, isolated, quiet. **Surface:** gravel.
🅿 01/01-31/12
Distance: 🚶500m, Cayeux 6km 🏊sea 50m ⊗500m 🛒3km.

Château-Thierry — 15B4
Aire de Château. **GPS:** n49,03657 e3,38365. ⬆➡

4 🛏free ⚡🚰free. **Surface:** asphalted.

Fort Mahon Plage — 7A6
Plage Parking de la Dune, Rue de la Bistouille. **GPS:** n50,33833 e1,55611. ⬆

60 ⌰€9 ⌂Ch WC free. 🅿 **Surface:** gravel. ⬛ 01-01-31/12
Distance: 200m 600m 200m.

⬛S **La Pérouille** 21B3
Étang de la Roche, Le Champ Perrot. **GPS:** n46,70507 e1,52259.
⌰free €2 ⌂Ch WC. **Location:** Rural, isolated, quiet.
Surface: grassy/gravel.
Distance: 750m 5km A20 750m.
Remarks: At small lake, coins at town hall and restaurant (750m).

⬛ **Laôn** 15B2
Promenade de la Couloire. **GPS:** n49,56313 e3,62967.

6 ⌰free. **Surface:** metalled.
Distance: 300m 500m.
Remarks: Near city wall.

⬛S **Le Crotoy** 7A6
Camping-Car Park le Tarteron, Route de Rue. **GPS:** n50,22972 e1,64128.
24 ⌰€12 ⌂Ch included. **Location:** Quiet. **Surface:** gravel.
⬛ 01-01-31/12
Distance: 2km 2km 2km.

⬛S **Le Crotoy** 7A6
Aire Camping-car, Bassin des Chasses. **GPS:** n50,21800 e1,63300.

50 ⌰€5/24h €2/100liter ⌂Ch €2/1h. 🅿 **Surface:** sand.
⬛ 01-01-31/12
Distance: 5 min walking 15 min walking Laverie Crotelloise, 20, avenue
du Gal de Gaulle.

⬛S **Le Crotoy** 7A6
Aire Camping-car, Chemin du Marais. **GPS:** n50,22886 e1,61253.

35 ⌰€5/24h €2/10minutes ⌂Ch €2/1h. **Surface:** sand.
⬛ 01-01-31/12
Distance: 1,5km on the spot 1,5km Laverie Crotelloise, 20, avenue
du Gal de Gaulle.

⬛S **Le Nouvion-en-Thiérache** 15B1
Allée du S/l François d'Orléans. **GPS:** n50,00542 e3,78078.
5 ⌰€3 ⌂Ch. **Location:** Rural. **Surface:** asphalted.
⬛ 01-01-31/12
Distance: 2km.
Remarks: Coins at campsite.

⬛S **Long** 14D1
Camping Municipal La Peupleraie, Rue de la Chasse à Vaches.
GPS: n50,03457 e1,98313.

8 ⌰€5 €2 ⌂Ch free €2/h WC ⬛. **Surface:** grassy/gravel.
⬛ 01-01-31/12 ⬛ service: 16/10-30/04
Distance: on the spot on the spot.

⬛S **Longpont** 15A3
Rue Saint-Louis, D17. **GPS:** n49,27395 e3,22129.

3 ⌰free €2 ⌂Ch against payment. **Location:** Rural. **Surface:** gravel.
⬛ 01-01-31/12
Distance: 100m.
Remarks: Max. 72h, abbey 150m.

⬛S **Mers-les-Bains** 14C1
Chemin de la Petite Allée. **GPS:** n50,06175 e1,40150.

50 ⌰€5,50 €2 ⌂Ch. **Location:** Comfortable. **Surface:** gravel.

FR

🅾 01/01-31/12
Distance: ⬛1,3km ⬜sandy beach 1,5km ⬛Auchan 600m.

| 🅂 | **Morienval** | 15A3 |

Route de Pierrefonds 32. **GPS:** n49,30352 e2,92309. ⬆➡.

21+9 ⬛€8 ⬛€2/100liter ⬛Ch ⬛stay ⬛(21x)€2/day. 🚹 **Location:**
Rural, comfortable, quiet. **Surface:** grassy/gravel. 🅾 22/03-16/11
Distance: ⬛500m ⊗500m ⬛500m.
Remarks: In case of absence, money in an envelope in mail box.

| 🅂 | **Neuilly-Saint-Front** | 15A3 |

Chemin de la Chantraine. **GPS:** n49,16713 e3,26003.
20 ⬛free ⬛€3 ⬛Ch ⬛€3/55minutes. **Surface:** grassy.
Distance: ⬛600m.

| 🅂 | **Picquigny** | 14D1 |

Rue de la Cavée d'Airaines. **GPS:** n49,94388 e2,13496. ⬆.

8 ⬛€5 ⬛Ch ⬛€2 WC included. 🚹
Location: Rural. **Surface:** grassy.
Distance: ⬛500m ⬛500m.

| 🅂 | **Quend** | 7A6 |

Ferme de la Grande Retz. **GPS:** n50,32893 e1,61811. ⬆➡.

10 ⬛€7 ⬛Ch ⬛€3 included. **Surface:** grassy. 🅾 01/01-31/12
Distance: ⬛3km ⊗9km ⬛9km ⬛2km.

| 🅂 | **Quend-plage-les-Pins** | 7A6 |

Plage des Pins. **GPS:** n50,32410 e1,55545. ⬆.

100 ⬛€7/24h ⬛€3/10minutes ⬛Ch ⬛€3/1h. **Surface:** gravel.
🅾 01/01-31/12

Distance: ⬛800m ⬜beach 900m 🐾 on the spot.

| 🅂 | **St.Valery-sur-Somme** | 14C1 |

Rue de la Croix l'Abbé. **GPS:** n50,18220 e1,62881. ⬆➡.

180 ⬛€9/24h ⬛⬛Chincluded. 🚹 **Location:** Rural. **Surface:** gravel.
🅾 01/01-31/12
Distance: ⬛1km ⊗nearby ⬛nearby.
Remarks: Market on Sunday.

| 🅂 | **Villers-Côtterets** | 15A3 |

Rue Alfred Juneaux. **GPS:** n49,26052 e3,08713. ⬆➡.

6 ⬛free ⬛€3/10minutes ⬛Chfree ⬛€3/1h. **Location:** Urban,
comfortable, quiet. **Surface:** gravel/metalled. 🅾 01/01-31/12
Distance: ⬛on the spot ⊗600m ⬛600m.
Remarks: Max. 72h, service 50m.

| | **Villers-Côtterets** | 15A3 |

Grand Bosquet Parc du Château, Place Aristide Briand.
GPS: n49,25483 e3,09400. ⬆.

6 ⬛free. **Location:** Urban, simple, central, noisy. **Surface:** grassy/metalled.
🅾 01/01-31/12
Distance: ⬛on the spot ⬛20km ⊗200m ⬛500m ⬛100m.

Champagne Ardenne

| 🅂 | **Arc-en-Barrois** | 15D6 |

Camping municipal, D3/D159. **GPS:** n47,95056 e5,00528. ⬆➡.

25 ⬛€5 ⬛Ch WC included, on camp site. 🚹 **Location:** Simple.
Surface: gravel. 🅾 01/01-31/12 🔘 Whitsuntide

Distance: 🚶500m ⊗500m 🚰500m.

🛁S **Attigny** 15D2
D987. **GPS:** n49,48583 e4,58077.⬆️.

4 🅿free 🚰🔌Ch free. **Location:** Rural, simple.
Distance: 🚶800m ⊗800m 🚰900m.

🛁S **Avize** 15C4
Place du Bourg Joli. **GPS:** n48,97175 e4,00999.⬆️.

5 🅿free 🚰🔌Ch free. **Location:** Urban, simple, central, quiet.
Surface: asphalted. ◻ 01/01-31/12
Distance: 🚶on the spot ⊗200m 🚰bakery 50m.
Remarks: Next to town hall.

🛁S **Bar-sur-Aube** 15D6
7, Rue des Varennes. **GPS:** n48,23491 e4,70065.⬆️➡️.

1 🅿free 🚰€3,50/100liter 🔌Ch €3,50/1h. **Location:** Simple.
Surface: asphalted. ◻ 01/01-31/12
Distance: 🚶on the spot ⊗on the spot 🚰on the spot.

🛁S **Beaunay** 15B4
Ferme Du Bel Air, Rue Principale. **GPS:** n48,88177 e3,87475.⬆️.

12 🅿€6 🚰🔌Ch 🔪(6x)included 🗑️💧 **Location:** Rural, simple, isolated, quiet. **Surface:** gravel. ◻ 01/01-31/12
Distance: 🚶2km ⊗2km 🚰2km.

🛁S **Bogny-sur-Meuse** 15D2
Rue de la Meuse. **GPS:** n49,85780 e4,74225.⬆️.

6 🅿free 🚰€2/100liter 🔌Ch €2/2h, only 2-euro coins. **Location:** Rural, simple, quiet. **Surface:** asphalted. ◻ 01/01-31/12
Distance: 🚶on the spot ⊗on the spot ⊗250m 🚰400m 🚗500m.
Remarks: Along the Meuse river, service 75m.

🛁S **Brienne-le-Château** 🌿 15D5
Rue de la Gare. **GPS:** n48,39617 e4,53130.⬆️➡️.

10 🅿free 🚰€3/10minutes 🔌Ch €3/55minutes.
Location: Simple, noisy. **Surface:** asphalted.
◻ 01/01-31/12 water disconnected in winter
Distance: 🚶300m ⊗400m 🚰300m.
Remarks: At former station, coins at tourist info, supermarket Champion.

🛁S **Cerisières** 15D5
D186, Froideau. **GPS:** n48,29921 e5,06339.⬆️➡️.

20 🅿free 🚰🔌Ch free. **Location:** Rural, simple, isolated, quiet.
Surface: gravel. ◻ 01/01-31/12
Distance: 🚶2km.

🛁S **Chamery** 15C3
Salle Polyvalente, Rue du Château Rouge. **GPS:** n49,17475 e3,95446.⬆️.

5 🅿free 🚰€2/100liter 🔌Ch €2/2h. **Location:** Rural, simple, quiet.
Surface: gravel. ◻ 01/01-31/12
Distance: 🚶300m ⊗400m.
Remarks: In front of community centre.

🛁S **Champigny-lès-Langres** 16A6
Rue du Port, D74. **GPS:** n47,88167 e5,33861.⬆️.

6 free WC. **Location:** Simple, noisy. **Surface:** gravel.
01/01-31/12
Distance: ⊗400m 800m.

| | | Chaource 🌿 | 15C6 |

Chemin de Ronde/Rue des Roises. **GPS:** n48,05944 e4,13861. ⬆➡.

10 free €2/100liter Ch €2/1h.
Location: Comfortable, quiet.
Surface: grassy.
Distance: 100m ⊗on the spot on the spot on the spot on the spot.
Remarks: Coins at tourist info, 2, Grande rue, monday-morning market.

| | | Charleville-Mézières | 15D2 |

Rue des Pâquis. **GPS:** n49,78056 e4,72056. ⬆.

8 free €2/100liter Ch €2/55minutes €5,40, ask at camp site.
Surface: asphalted.
01/01-31/12 electricity: 01/11-31/03
Distance: 800m on the spot ⊗500m 2km 600m Nearby campsite Nearby campsite.
Remarks: Service only with 2-euro coins, ask for electricity at campsite.

Tourist information Charleville-Mézières:
Musée Ardennes, Place Ducale. Regional museum. 10-12, 14-18 Mo.
place Ducale. Regional products. Tue, Thu, Sa.

| | | Chaumont 🌊 | 16A6 |

Port de la Maladière, RN74 Neufchâteau > Chaumont. **GPS:** n48,11815 e5,15437. ⬆.

12 € 6,50, € 0,20/pp tourist tax Ch included WC €2,40

€2,20/3,20 free. **Location:** Quiet. **Surface:** metalled.
01/04-31/10
Distance: 4km Canal de la Marne ⊗100m nearby.
Remarks: Baker every morning.

| | | Chavanges 🌿 | 15D5 |

Ruelle du Fief Berthaux. **GPS:** n48,50691 e4,57627. ⬆➡.

8 free €3 Ch. **Location:** Simple, quiet. **Surface:** asphalted/gravel.
01/01-31/12
Distance: 300m 400m.
Remarks: Coins at the shops.

| | | Colombey-les-deux-Eglises 🌿 | 15D6 |

Rue de Général de Gaulle. **GPS:** n48,22316 e4,88619. ⬆.

10 free Ch WC free. **Location:** Simple, quiet.
Surface: asphalted/gravel. 01/04-30/11
Distance: on the spot ⊗50m 50m.
Remarks: Museum and Memorial Général De Gaulle 800m.

| | | Corgirnon 👥 | 23A1 |

Allée du Parc. **GPS:** n47,80681 e5,50308. ⬆➡.

8 €4 Ch included. **Location:** Rural, comfortable, isolated, quiet. **Surface:** gravel. 01/01-31/12 water disconnected in winter
Distance: 500m 10km 500m, baker on site (Tue-Su).
Remarks: Bread-service.

| | | Dolancourt ⬆ | 15D6 |

Nigloland, RN19. **GPS:** n48,26086 e4,60945. ⬆.

28 € 6/24h, free with a meal Ch included. **Location:** Simple,

isolated. **Surface:** asphalted. ◻ 03/04-03/11
Distance: ⊗on the spot.
Remarks: Parking amusement park, max. 24h.

| 🏕S | Donjeux | 16A5 |

Halte Nautique, D67a. **GPS:** n48,36586 e5,14891.⬆️

4 🏕free ⌁ Ch ⚓ (4x)free. **Location:** Comfortable, quiet.
Surface: gravel/metalled. ◻ 01/01-31/12
Distance: ⚓1km ⚓Canal de la Marne ⚓on the spot ⊗1km ⚓800m
⚓ on the spot.
Remarks: Baker every morning.

| 🏕S | Épernay 🍴 | 15C4 |

Rue Dom Pérignon. **GPS:** n49,03602 e3,95130.⬆️

3 🏕free ⌁€2/100liter 🏕 Ch 🔲€2/1h WC€0,50/time.
Location: Urban, simple, central, noisy. **Surface:** asphalted.
Distance: ⚓within walking distance ⚓Avenue Jean Jaurès.
Remarks: Behind church St.Pierre-St.Paul, coins at tourist info.

Tourist information Épernay:
👁 Cave de Catellane, 154, avenue de Verdun.
👁 Mercier, 70, avenue de Champagne. ◻ Mo-Sa 9.30-11.30h, 14-16.30h, Su/
holidays 9.30-11.30h, 14-17.30h.

| 🏕S | Esternay | 15B4 |

Place des Tilleuls, D48, Rue de la Paix. **GPS:** n48,73196 e3,55719.⬆️

8 🏕free ⌁🏕free. **Location:** Urban, simple, central, quiet. **Surface:** gravel.
◻ water: 15/03-15/11
Distance: ⚓within walking distance ⊗200m ⚓400m.
Remarks: Behind church.

| 🏕S | Froncles | 16A5 |

Halte Nautique. GPS: n48,29954 e5,15246.⬆️

10 🏕€1,50 ⌁€1,50/day 🏕 Ch ⚓ (8x)€1,50/1day 🔲€2/2time ⚓€3/3.🚿
Location: Comfortable. **Surface:** gravel. ◻ 01/01-31/12
Distance: ⚓500m ⚓river-beach ⚓on the spot ⊗on the spot ⚓1km
⚓on the spot.
Remarks: Baker on site (Tue-Su).

| 🏕 | Fumay | 15D1 |

Quai des Carmélites. **GPS:** n49,99736 e4,70986.⬆️

+10 🏕free. **Surface:** unpaved. ◻ 01/01-31/12
Distance: ⚓400m.
Remarks: Along the Meuse river.

| 🏕S | Giffaumont-Champaubert ⚓ | 15D5 |

Site de Chantecoq, Rue du grand Der. **GPS:** n48,56880 e4,70294.⬆️

50 🏕free ⌁€3,80/80liter 🏕 Ch 🔲€3,80/45minutes WC.
Location: Rural, simple. **Surface:** metalled. ◻ 01/01-31/12
Distance: ⚓on the spot ⊗900m.
Remarks: At lake Der de Chantecoq, coins at tourist info.

| 🏕S | Giffaumont-Champaubert ⚓ | 15D5 |

Station Nautique, Rue du Port. **GPS:** n48,55354 e4,76715.⬆️

50 🏕€7,50 20-8h, parking free ⌁🏕 Ch 🔲 📶included ⚓.🚐⚓
Location: Rural. ◻ 01/01-31/12
Distance: ⚓on the spot ⊗200m ⚓8km Montier-en-Der ⚓on the spot
⚓on the spot.

| 🏕 | Givet | 15D1 |

Rue Jean Jaurès. **GPS:** n50,13593 e4,82138.⬆️

12 ⬛free. **Location:** Urban, simple, central, quiet. **Surface:** asphalted.
☐ 01/01-31/12

Ⓖ Ⓢ | Givet | 15D1
Camping Municipal, Rue Berthelot. **GPS:** n50,14291 e4,82611.⬆.

5 ⬛free 🚰€3/100liter ⬛ Ch ⬛€3/h. **Location:** Rural, simple.
Surface: asphalted. ☐ 01/01-31/12
Distance: 🚶750m ⊗750m ⚓1km.
Remarks: Coins at campsite.

⬛ Ⓢ | Goncourt | 16A6
Rue des Lottes, D74. **GPS:** n48,23685 e5,60998.⬆.

30 ⬛€2 🚰€2 ⬛ Ch. **Location:** Rural, comfortable.
Surface: asphalted/gravel. ☐ 01/01-31/12
Distance: 🚶100m ⊘on the spot ⊗100m ⚓100m.
Remarks: Along the Meuse river, max. 48h, baker at 8am.

⬛ Ⓢ | Haybes | 15D1
Halte Fluviale, Quai du Docteur Adolphe Hamai. **GPS:** n50,01093 e4,70762.⬆.

4 ⬛free 🚰 ⬛ Ch€2,05 ⬛⬛€3,30/3,30.
Surface: metalled. ☐ 01/01-31/12
Distance: 🚶200m ⊗50m ⚓bakery 200m.
Remarks: Along the Meuse river, service at camping municipal.

⬛ Ⓢ | Javernant | 15C6
Le Cheminot, N77. **GPS:** n48,14789 e4,01046.⬆.

5 ⬛free 🚰⬛Chfree. **Location:** Simple. **Surface:** asphalted.
☐ 01/01-31/12
Remarks: 2013: during inspection service out of order.

⬛ Ⓢ | Joinville 〰️⛵ | 16A5
Halte Nautique, Rue des Jardins. **GPS:** n48,44583 e5,15000.⬆.

12 ⬛free 🚰€2 ⬛ Ch ⬛€2 🗑.⬛🛒 **Location:** Simple, quiet.
Surface: gravel/metalled. ☐ 01/01-31/12
Distance: 🚶500m ⊘on the spot 🍴on the spot ⊗800m ⚓100m
☗on the spot.

⬛ Ⓢ | Juzennecourt | 15D6
Place de la Mairie. **GPS:** n48,18429 e4,97890.⬆.

4 ⬛free 🚰 Ch ⚡WC. **Location:** Simple, quiet. **Surface:** metalled.
☐ 01/01-31/12
Distance: 🚶on the spot ⚓bakery in the village ☗on the spot.
Remarks: Parking townhall.

⬛ Ⓢ | La Cheppe | 15C4
Champ d'Attila, Rue de Champo d'Attila. **GPS:** n49,04892 e4,49377.⬆.

5 ⬛free 🚰€2/100liter ⬛ Ch ⬛€2/2h WC 🗑.
Location: Rural, simple, quiet. **Surface:** asphalted. ☐ 01/01-31/12
Distance: 🚶500m.

⬛ Ⓢ | La Gault-Soigny | 15B4
Rue de la Liberté, D373. **GPS:** n48,81758 e3,59072.⬆.

8 ⬛free 🚰⬛Chfree. **Location:** Rural, simple, quiet. **Surface:** asphalted.
⬛ 01/01-31/12
Distance: on the spot.
Remarks: Near Salle des Fêtes, service 50m.

Langres 23A1
Ruelle de la Poterne. **GPS:** n47,85795 e5,32989. ⬆➡.

15 ⬛free 🚰Chfree. **Location:** Simple, quiet. **Surface:** asphalted.
⬛ 01/01-31/12
Distance: 800m.

Langres 23A1
Parking Panorama, Allée des Marronniers. **GPS:** n47,86104 e5,33674. ⬆.

⬛free. **Location:** Simple, quiet. **Surface:** asphalted. ⬛ 01/01-31/12
Distance: on the spot on the spot.
Remarks: Inclining pitches, free elevator to old town.

Langres 23A1
Place de Bel Air. **GPS:** n47,85885 e5,33225. ⬆.

⬛free WC. **Location:** Urban, simple, noisy. **Surface:** asphalted.
⬛ 01/01-31/12
Distance: on the spot on the spot.
Tourist information Langres:
⬛ Fri.

Launois-sur-Vence 15D2
Avenue Louis Jolly. **GPS:** n49,65467 e4,54005. ⬆.

10 ⬛free. **Location:** Rural, simple, quiet. **Surface:** unpaved.
⬛ 01/01-31/12
Distance: on the spot ⊗50m.
Remarks: In front of tourist office, max. 48h.

Launois-sur-Vence 15D2
Rue du Thin. **GPS:** n49,65810 e4,53987. ⬆➡.
🚰€2/100liter Ch€2/1h. ⬛ water: frost
Remarks: Coins at tourist info.

Tourist information Launois-sur-Vence:
⬛ Relais de Poste. Monthly antiques and flea market. ⬛ 3rd Su of the month 9-18h.

Les Riceys 15C6
D452. **GPS:** n47,99222 e4,36458. ⬆➡.

40 ⬛free 🚰€2 Ch€2. **Location:** Simple, isolated, quiet.
Surface: asphalted. ⬛ 01/01-31/12
Distance: 500m ⊗500m 500m.

Mareuil-sur-Ay 15C4
Relais nautique, Place Charles de Gaulle. **GPS:** n49,04522 e4,03490. ⬆.

8 ⬛free 🚰Ch€5/3h. **Location:** Urban, comfortable, central, quiet.
Surface: asphalted. ⬛ 01/01-31/12 ⬛ water disconnected in winter
Distance: on the spot on the spot ⊗on the spot on the spot on the spot.
Remarks: On the canal, in village, coins at supermarket.

Mesnil-St.Père 15C6
Rue du Lac. **GPS:** n48,25524 e4,34090.

50 ⚏free. **Location:** Simple. **Surface:** asphalted. ⬛ 01/01-31/12
Distance: ⚓beach 400m.
Remarks: Nearby lake Orient.

⚏S Monthermé 15D1
Etape fluviale, Quai A. Briand. **GPS:** n49,88608 e4,73593.⬆

± 20 ⚏€ 3 + € 0,20/pp tourist tax 🚰⚏Ch ⚡€2,90/day ⏳€1,50
⚏€4,50/4,50. **Surface:** grasstiles.
Distance: ⚏300m.
Remarks: Along the Meuse river, check in at harbourmaster.

⚏S Monthermé 15D1
Rue du Général de Gaulle, D989. **GPS:** n49,88136 e4,72979.⬆

6 ⚏free. **Location:** Rural, simple, quiet. **Surface:** grassy.
⬛ 01/01-31/12
Distance: ⚏900m ⚏on the spot.
Remarks: Along the Meuse river, max. 24h.

⚏S Montier-en-Der 🌿 15D5
Rue de l'Isle. **GPS:** n48,47861 e4,76861.⬆

6 ⚏free 🚰€2,60/8minutes ⚏Ch ⚏€2,60/55minutes WC.
Location: Simple. **Surface:** gravel.
Distance: ⚏on the spot ⊗500m ⚏500m.
Remarks: Coins at tourist info.

⚏S Mouzon 15D2
Halte fluviale. **GPS:** n49,60687 e5,07710.
8 ⚏€ 7,80, 01/11-31/03 free 🚰⚏Ch ⚡WC ⏳⚏ ≋included.
Surface: asphalted. ⬛ 01/01-31/12 ⬤ Service: winter
Distance: ⚏100m.
Remarks: Along the Meuse river, sanitary and wifi code at harbour master, felt museum 100m (May-Sep).

⚏S Mutigny 15C3
Aire de l'étang, Route de Montflambert. **GPS:** n49,06894 e4,02669.⬆➡

8 ⚏free 🚰€5/100liter ⚏€5/3h ⚡. **Location:** Rural, simple, isolated, quiet.
Surface: asphalted. ⬛ 01/01-31/12
Distance: ⚏1km ⊗3km ⚏3km.

ⓒS Nogent-sur-Seine 15B5
Parking camping/piscine, Rue du camping. **GPS:** n48,50388 e3,50888.⬆

5 ⚏€ 6,58/night, € 2,99/3h 🚰⚏Chfree ⚡(2x)included3h.⚏
Location: Urban, simple, quiet. **Surface:** asphalted. ⬛ 01/01-31/12
Distance: ⚏1,5km ⚓2km ⊗1,5km ⚏1,5km ⚏2km.
Remarks: Max. 48h.

ⓒS Peigney 23A1
Lac de la Liez, D284, rue Côté de Recey. **GPS:** n47,87272 e5,38077.⬆➡

8 ⚏€ 10,50 🚰⚏Ch ⚡≋€2.⚏⚏
Location: Simple. **Surface:** asphalted.
⬛ 01/01-31/12
Distance: ⚏500m ⚓on the spot ⚏on the spot ⊗on the spot ⚏on the spot.

⚏S Piney 15C5
Place des Anciens Combattants, Rue du Général de Gaulle.
GPS: n48,35878 e4,33442.⬆➡

3 ⚏free 🚰€3/10minutes ⚏Ch ⚏€3/1h.
Location: Simple. **Surface:** metalled.
⬛ 01/01-31/12 ⬤ water: frost
Distance: ⚏500m ⊗500m ⚏500m.
Remarks: Coins at Office de Tourisme Mesnil-Plage and restaurant le Tadorne.

FR

Reims 15C3

Parc du CIS de la Comédie, Esplanade André Malraux, chaussée Bocquaine. **GPS**: n49,24881 e4,02110.

7 free Ch free. **Location:** Urban, simple, central, noisy. **Surface:** metalled.
Distance: 15 min walking 1,4km 350m 100m.
Remarks: Max. 48h, call for entrance code, noisy place.

Sainte-Marie-du-Lac-Nuisement 15D5

Port de Nuisement, D13A. **GPS**: n48,60285 e4,74922.
6 free Ch . **Surface:** asphalted. 01/01-31/12
Distance: 4km on the spot.

Sapignicourt 15D5

Rue Deperthes à Larzicourt. **GPS**: n48,65111 e4,80583.

4 €2,50/10minutes Ch €2,50/55minutes. **Location:** Rural, simple, isolated, quiet. **Surface:** grassy.
Distance: 500m.
Remarks: Coins at town hall and Mr. Bauer, 14, grande rue.

Sedan 15D2

Rue Hue Tanton. **GPS**: n49,70145 e4,95092.
free. 01/01-31/12
Remarks: Parking places around the castle of Sedan.

Sézanne 15B4

Place du Champ Benoist. **GPS**: n48,72222 e3,72125.

7 free €2/100liter Ch €2/1h WC free.
Location: Urban, simple, central, noisy. **Surface:** asphalted.
01/01-31/12 Sa market
Distance: on the spot 50m 300m 50m.

St.Dizier 15D5

Centre Loisirs Caravanning, Route de Villiers en lieu. **GPS**: n48,64255 e4,91035.

6 free Ch WC free. **Location:** Simple. **Surface:** asphalted.
01/01-31/12
Distance: 1,5km 400m.
Remarks: At motorhome dealer, coins during opening hours.

Suippes 15D3

Rue de l'Abreuvoir. **GPS**: n49,13074 e4,53419.

10 free €2/liter Ch €2/1h . **Location:** Urban, simple.
Surface: asphalted. 01/01-31/12
Distance: on the spot 200m 200m.

Vendeuvre-sur-Barse 15C6

Place du 8 mai 1945, Rue du Pont Chevalier. **GPS**: n48,23727 e4,46646.

5 free €3 Ch €3. **Location:** Urban, simple, simple.
Surface: asphalted. tue-evening, wed-morning (market)
Distance: 100m on the spot ATAC on the spot.

Viéville 16A6

Halte Nautique La Licorne. **GPS**: n48,23825 e5,12988.

6 € 1,50 €1,50/day (6x)€1,50/day. **Location:** Rural, simple, quiet. **Surface:** gravel.
Distance: on the spot 3km 500m on the spot on the spot.

Villeneuve-Renneville-Chevigny 15C4

Champagne Leclère-Massard, 12, rue du Plessis. **GPS**: n48,91488 e4,05959.

6 🛏€5 🚰🔌Ch ⚡ included 📶€2/day. 🅿️ **Location:** Comfortable.
Surface: asphalted.
Distance: 🛒3km 🍽2km 🛍3km ⊗3km 🚶on the spot.
Remarks: Tu-Su fresh bread, champagne tastery.

| 🛏S | Villers-sous-Châtillon | 15B3 |

Halte camping-cars, Rue du Parc. **GPS:** n49,09642 e3,80078. ⬆️➡️.

5 🛏free 🚰€3/100liter 🔌Ch 🔌€3/1h. **Location:** Rural, simple, quiet.
Surface: asphalted. 🅿️ 01/01-31/12
Distance: 🛒1,2km 🍽50m ⊗1,2km 🛍2km.
Remarks: Coins at town hall and restaurant du Commerce.

Lorraine

| 🛏S | Allarmont | 16D5 |

Le Meix du Haut Regard, 21, rue du Haut Regard. **GPS:** n48,48070 e7,01381.
2 🛏 🚰🔌Ch ⚡€5/24h 🔌€4 📶free. **Location:** Comfortable, luxurious.
Surface: gravel.
Distance: 🛒400m ⊗400m 🛍400m.
Remarks: Swimming pool available.

| 🛏S | Amnéville | 16B3 |

Rue de l'Europe. **GPS:** n49,24780 e6,13842.
15 🛏free 🚰€3 🔌Ch. **Surface:** grassy.
Distance: 🛒1,8km.
Remarks: Behind tourist info, max. 48h.

| 🛏 | Ancerville | 15D5 |

Impasse des Pransons. **GPS:** n48,63641 e5,01582. ⬆️.

2 🛏free. **Location:** Urban, simple, quiet. **Surface:** metalled.
🅿️ 01/01-31/12
Distance: 🛒on the spot ⊗400m 🛍400m.

| 🍴 | Avocourt | 16A3 |

Restaurant La Terrasse, Rue du Moulin. **GPS:** n49,20417 e5,14227. ⬆️.
4 🛏free. **Location:** Rural, simple. **Surface:** unpaved.
🅿️ 01/01-31/12
Distance: 🛒on the spot ⊗on the spot.

| 🛏S | Baccarat | 16C5 |

Place du General Le'Clerc. **GPS:** n48,44667 e6,74000. ⬆️.

15 🛏€5/night 🚰€2/100liter 🔌Ch 🔌€2/3minutes WC.
Surface: asphalted. 🅿️ 01/01-31/12 🔵 Fri-morning market
Distance: 🛒300m 🍽on the spot 🛍on the spot ⊗300m 🛍300m.
Remarks: Along river, max. 24h.

Tourist information Baccarat:
Ⓜ️ Musée du Cristal. Crystal museum. 🅿️ Mo-Sa 10-18h. 🎫 € 2,50.

| ⚓S | Bar-le-Duc | 16A4 |

Halte du port fluvial, Rue du débarcadère. **GPS:** n48,77536 e5,16654. ⬆️➡️.

8 🛏free 🚰€2/100liter 🔌Ch 🔌€2/55minutes. **Location:** Urban, simple,
noisy. **Surface:** asphalted. 🅿️ 01/01-31/12
Distance: 🍽on the spot 🛍on the spot ⊗150m 🛍150m 🚌150m
🚴on the spot.
Remarks: At the canal, coins at tourist info, 7 rue Jeanne d'Arc.

| 🛏 | Beaulieu-en-Argonne | 15D4 |

Parking Mairie, Grande Rue, D2B. **GPS:** n49,03183 e5,06665. ⬆️.

6 🛏free. **Location:** Urban, simple, central, quiet. **Surface:** asphalted.
🅿️ 01/01-31/12
Distance: 🛒on the spot ⊗50m 🚴on the spot 🚶on the spot.
Remarks: In front of police station.

| 🛏 | Beaulieu-en-Argonne | 15D4 |

Parking St. Rouin, D2. **GPS:** n49,03554 e5,02975. ⬆️.

4 🛏free. **Location:** Isolated. **Surface:** gravel.
Distance: 🛒Beaulieu 6km.
Remarks: Isolated parking.

FR

🏕️S **Bitche** 16D3
Rue Bombelles. **GPS**: n49,05431 e7,43446. ⬆️.
5 🛏️free 🚰€2 Ch ➕€2. **Location**: Comfortable, isolated, quiet.
Surface: gravel.
Distance: 🚶750m ⊗750m 🚊750m.

🏕️S **Bruley** 16B4
D118, rue Saint-Martin. **GPS**: n48,70640 e5,85554. ⬆️.

10 🛏️free 🚰€3/10minutes Ch ➤ (2x)€3/8h. **Surface**: gravel.
⏺️ 01/01-31/12
Distance: 🚶200m ⊗300m 🚊300m.
Remarks: Max. 48h.

🏕️S **Bulgnéville** 16B6
Étang des Récollets, Rue des Récollets. **GPS**: n48,20733 e5,83899. ⬆️➡️.

10 🛏️€ 3/24h 🚰 Ch WC included.
Location: Rural, luxurious, quiet. **Surface**: asphalted.
⏺️ 15/04-31/12
Distance: 🚶700m ⬧ 1,8km ⊿on the spot ➤on the spot ⊗100m 🚊700m.

🏕️S **Certilleux** 16A5
Rue de l'Église. **GPS**: n48,31193 e5,72679. ⬆️.

8 🛏️free 🚰free. **Location**: Urban, simple. **Surface**: asphalted.
⏺️ 01/01-31/12
Distance: 🚶on the spot.
Remarks: Beautiful view.

🏕️ **Champougny** 16A5
D145f. **GPS**: n48,54410 e5,69277. ⬆️.

3 🛏️free. **Location**: Rural, simple, quiet. **Surface**: grassy.
⏺️ 01/01-31/12
Distance: 🚶200m ➤25m.

⛵S **Charmes** 16B5
Port de plaisance. **GPS**: n48,37334 e6,29542. ⬆️.

100 🛏️€ 7 🚰included Ch ➤ (80x)€2 WC €1,50 ⚡€3/day.
Surface: gravel/metalled. ⏺️ 01/01-31/12
Distance: 🚶1km ⬧ 1,5km ⊿on the spot 🚊on the spot ⊙walking distance.
Tourist information Charmes:
⛺ ⏺️ Fri-morning.

🏕️S **Commercy** 16A4
Rue du Docteur Boyer. **GPS**: n48,76374 e5,59616. ⬆️.

4 🛏️free 🚰€3/15minutes Ch ➤ (4x)€3/4h ⚡free.
Location: Comfortable. **Surface**: asphalted. ⏺️ 01/01-31/12
Distance: 🚶800m ⊿on the spot ➤on the spot ⊗600m 🚊100m.
Remarks: On the canal.

🏕️S **Contrisson** 15D4
Ballastière. **GPS**: n48,80530 e4,94714. ⬆️.

10 🛏️free WC. **Location**: Rural, simple, isolated, quiet. **Surface**: unpaved.
⏺️ 01/01-31/12
Distance: 🚶800m ⊿on the spot ➤on the spot ⊗1km 🚊1km.
Remarks: At small lake.

🏕️S **Damvillers** 16A3
Rue de L'Ile d'Envie, D905. **GPS**: n49,33790 e5,39752. ⬆️.

4 🛏️free 🚰€2/100liter Ch ➕€2. **Location**: Urban, simple, central.

FR

Surface: asphalted. ▯ 01/01-31/12
Distance: 🚶on the spot ⊗on the spot 🚰 on the spot.

🅂 Damvillers 16A3
Etang, D905. **GPS:** n49,34978 e5,39970.⬆.
10 🛏free. **Location:** Isolated. **Surface:** grassy. ▯ 01/01-31/12
Distance: 🚶Damvillers 1km.

⚓🅂 Dieue-sur-Meuse 16A3
Port de plaisance, Route des Dames. **GPS:** n49,07110 e5,42634. ⬆.

15 🛏free 🚰free. **Location:** Rural, simple, quiet. **Surface:** gravel.
▯ 01/01-31/12
Distance: 🚶200m ⚓on the spot 🚲on the spot ⊗200m 🚰200m.
Remarks: At the canal.

🅂 Dun-sur-Meuse 🌼 16A3
Rue du Vieux Port. **GPS:** n49,38919 e5,17787.⬆.

16 🛏€7 🚰🔌Ch 🛁 (8x) WC 🚽included 🚻.🚿
Location: Rural, comfortable, central, quiet. **Surface:** gravel.
▯ 01/01-31/12 🚰 sanitary building: 01/11-01/04
Distance: 🚶600m ⚓on the spot 🚲on the spot ⊗400m 🚰600m.

🅂 Épinal 16C6
Camping-Car Park, Chemin du Petit Chaperon Rouge. **GPS:** n48,17969 e6,46865.
⬆.
50 🛏€12 🚰🔌Ch 🛁 (20x) 📶included. 🛒 🏧 ▯ 01/01-31/12
Distance: 🚶1,5km.

⚓🅂 Épinal 16C6
Port d'Épinal, Quai de Dogneville, D12. **GPS:** n48,18671 e6,44493.⬆.

5 🛏summer € 5, winter € 8 🚰🔌Ch 🛁Service€3/15min 🛒.
Surface: asphalted.
Distance: 🚶1km 🚲3,5km.
Remarks: Max. 48h.

🅂 Etain 16A3
Allée du champ de foire, D631. **GPS:** n49,20942 e5,63755.
6 🛏free. **Location:** Simple, noisy. **Surface:** metalled.
▯ 01/01-31/12
Distance: 🚶on the spot ⊗500m 🚰500m.

🅂🅂 Etival-Clairefontaine 16C5
Rue du Vivier. **GPS:** n48,36355 e6,86504.⬆.

20 🛏free 🚰🔌Chfree. **Surface:** gravel. ▯ 01/01-31/12 🚰 water
disconnected in winter
Distance: 🚶on the spot.
Remarks: Behind town hall.

🅂 Fains-Veel 🚤 15D4
Halte Fluviale, Rue du Stade. **GPS:** n48,79298 e5,12503.⬆.

2 🛏free.
Location: Simple, quiet. **Surface:** metalled.
▯ 01/01-31/12
Distance: 🚶450m ⚓on the spot 🚲on the spot ⊗on the spot 🚰on the spot.

🅂 Favières 16B5
Base de Loisirs. **GPS:** n48,46660 e5,96124.⬆.

8 🛏free 🚰€2 🔌Ch 🛁€2 WC 📶.
Location: Rural, comfortable, central, quiet. **Surface:** gravel/metalled.
Distance: 🚶200m 🚲13km ⚓on the spot 🚲on the spot ⊗on the spot
🚰bakery 300m 🛒 on the spot 🎣 on the spot.

🅂 Fénétrange 16D4
Wally Services, Route de Sarre Union. **GPS:** n48,85365 e7,02723.⬆.
5 🛏free 🚰€2 🔌Ch 🛁€2. **Surface:** grassy/metalled.
Remarks: Max. 48h.

🅂🅂 Fraize 16D6
Impasse de la Gare/ Place Jean Sonrel. **GPS:** n48,18188 e7,00360.

6 🛏free 🚰€3 🔌Ch 🛁€3 WC. **Surface:** asphalted. ▯ 01/01-31/12
Distance: 🚶100m ⊗100m 🚰100m.
Remarks: Behind tourist info.

🅢 Gérardmer ☂ ◢ ❄ 16C6
Chemin de la Rayée, La Mauselaine. **GPS**: n48,05846 e6,88862. ⬆

100 🚽 € 4,50/24h ⟶€2/100liter 🗑 Ch. **Surface**: asphalted.
⭕ 01/01-31/12
Distance: 🚶Gérardmer 1,7km.
Remarks: Parking at skipistes, coins at tourist info.

🅢 Gérardmer ☂ ❄ 16C6
Parking de la Prairie, Boulevard d'Alsace. **GPS**: n48,07199 e6,87333. ⬆

100 🚽 € 4,50 ⟶€2/100liter 🗑 Ch WC ◢. **Surface**: asphalted/gravel.
⭕ 01/01-31/12
Distance: 🚶on the spot.
Remarks: Coins at tourist info.

Tourist information Gérardmer:
⛺ ⭕ Thu, Sa.

Gondrecourt-le-Château 🍲 16A5
Parking Musée du Cheval, Rue Saint Blaise. **GPS**: n48,51390 e5,50975.
2 🚽free. **Surface**: metalled.
Distance: 🚶on the spot ⊗50m 🛒50m.

Gondrecourt-le-Château 🍲 16A5
Rue du Général Leclerc. **GPS**: n48,51373 e5,50386.
3 🚽free. **Location**: Urban. **Surface**: unpaved. ⭕ 01/01-31/12
Distance: 🚶on the spot ⊗on the spot 🛒on the spot.

🅢 Haironville 🌿 ◢ 15D4
GPS: n48,68438 e5,08586. ⬆

5 🚽free ⟶€2/10minutes 🗑Ch 📦€2/50minutes.
Location: Rural, simple, central, quiet. **Surface**: gravel. ⭕ 01/01-31/12
Distance: 🚶200m 🛒200m.
Remarks: Coins at the shops in the village.

🅢 Heudicourt sous les Côtes ◢ 16A4
Ste Nautique de Madine. **GPS**: n48,93549 e5,71548. ⬆

50 🚽first night € 10, € 7 each additional night ⟶ 🗑 Ch WC 🚿. 👶
Location: Rural, comfortable, quiet. **Surface**: grassy/gravel. ⭕ 01/04-31/10
Distance: 🚶3km ⟲on the spot ⟶on the spot ⊗on the spot.
Remarks: View on Lac de Madine.

Heudicourt sous les Côtes ◢ 16A4
Entrée 2, D133. **GPS**: n48,94035 e5,71741. ⬆

50 🚽 € 7. 👶 **Location**: Rural, simple, quiet. **Surface**: grassy.
⭕ 01/04-31/10
Distance: 🚶3km ⟲100m ⟶100m.
Remarks: Next to campsite.

🅢 Hombourg-Haut 16C3
Rue des Suédois. **GPS**: n49,12448 e6,77888.
🚽free ⟶€2 🗑 Ch 📦€2. **Surface**: asphalted. ⭕ 01/01-31/12
Distance: 🚶400m ⊗200m 🛒on the spot.

Issoncourt 16A4
Parking Relais de la Voie Sacrée. **GPS**: n48,97070 e5,28776. ⬆ .

4 🚽free. **Location**: Rural, simple, quiet. **Surface**: gravel.
Distance: 🚶50m.

La Bresse 16D6
Route de Lispach. **GPS**: n48,04354 e6,93348.
🚽free. **Surface**: grassy/gravel. ⭕ 01/01-31/12
Remarks: At cross-country skiing circuit.

🅒🅢 La Bresse 16D6
Camping Belle Hutte. **GPS**: n48,03500 e6,96268.

20 🚽 € 12,50-22,50 ⟶ 🗑 Ch 🚿 WC 🗑against payment.

FR

Surface: grassy/gravel. ◻ 01/01-31/12
Distance: ⬛9km ✈100m ⚓500m.
Remarks: Summertime on campsite, wintertime in front of campsite.

[C][S] **La Bresse** 16D6

Camping du Haut Des Bluches, 5, route des Planches. **GPS:** n48,00005 e6,91718.

18 ◻€ 5 12.00-12.00h ⬛⬛Ch✎WC ◻included. ◻ 01/01-31/12
◻ 05/11-14/12
Remarks: Zone camping-car.

[S] **La Bresse** 16D6

Route de Niachamp. **GPS:** n47,99430 e6,85431.
⬛€2/100liter ⬛Ch. ◻ 01/01-31/12

[⬛][S] **La Croix-sur-Meuse** 16A4

Auberge de la Truite, Route de Seuzey. **GPS:** n48,98267 e5,53393.⬆

4 ◻free ⬛✎ (4x)€3/24h WC ⬛. **Location:** Rural, comfortable, quiet.
Surface: grassy. ◻ 01/01-31/12
Distance: ⬛2km ⬛on the spot ⊗on the spot.

[⬛] **Lachaussée** 16B4

Domaine du Vieux Moulin, Grande Rue. **GPS:** n49,03507 e5,81735.
4 ◻. **Location:** Rural, simple. **Surface:** gravel.
Distance: ⬛100m ⬛50m ⊗on the spot.
Remarks: Along Étang de Lachaussée.

[⬛] **Laheycourt** 15D4

Rue de la Gare. **GPS:** n48,88903 e5,02165.⬆

3 ◻free. **Location:** Rural, simple, quiet. **Surface:** grassy.
◻ 01/01-31/12
Distance: ⬛on the spot ⬛50m ⬛50m.
Remarks: Along the Chée river.

[⬛][S] **Les Islettes** 15D3

Route du Lochères. **GPS:** n49,12122 e5,03684.⬆➡

16 ◻€ 5/24h ⬛⬛Ch⬛WC ◻included. ⬛ **Location:** Rural, comfortable.
Surface: gravel. ◻ 01/01-31/12
Distance: ⬛3km ⬛10,5km ⊗3km ⬛3km.

[⬛][S] **Ligny-en-Barrois** 16A4

Relais Nautique, Rue Jean Willemert. **GPS:** n48,68787 e5,31943.⬆➡

8 ◻free ⬛€2/10minutes ⬛Ch €2/55minutes. **Location:** Comfortable,
central, quiet. **Surface:** asphalted.
Distance: ⬛200m ⬛on the spot ⊗200m ⬛200m ⬛on the spot
⬛on the spot.
Remarks: Along Canal de la Marne au Rhin.

[⬛] **Ligny-en-Barrois** 16A4

Aire de Pilvetus, Chemin des Pains de Seigle. **GPS:** n48,69262 e5,33621.⬆
10 ◻free. **Location:** Simple, isolated. **Surface:** gravel.
◻ 01/01-31/12
Distance: ⬛1,2km.

[⬛] **Loison** 16A3

Parking Camp Marguerre. **GPS:** n49,28962 e5,56737.⬆ .

6 ◻free. **Location:** Rural, simple, isolated.
Remarks: Isolated parking, Camp Marguerre: militair erfgoed '14-18.

[⬛] **Longeville-en-Barrois** 16A4

Gr Grande Rue. **GPS:** n48,74201 e5,20645.⬆

10 ◻free. **Location:** Urban, simple, quiet. **Surface:** gravel.
Distance: ⬛on the spot ⬛on the spot ⬛on the spot ⊗100m ⬛100m
⬛on the spot ⬛on the spot.
Remarks: Along the Ornain river.

FR

⌂S Longuyon △⊕ 16A3
Parking Salvador Allende, N18. **GPS**: n49,44802 e5,59973.⬆.

2 ⌁free 🚰🍽Ch🚽WC🧹.
Location: Urban, simple, central, noisy.
Surface: asphalted.
Distance: 🚶on the spot ⊗on the spot 🚉100m.
Remarks: Parking next to tourist info, not suitable for big motorhomes.

⌂S Longwy 16B2
Stade Municipal, Avenue du 8 Mai 1945. **GPS**: n49,52656 e5,76559.⬆.
7 ⌁free 🚰€2,50/20minutes 🍽Ch🚽€2,50/4h. **Location:** Urban, simple,
central, noisy. **Surface:** asphalted. ☐ 01/01-31/12
Distance: 🚶on the spot ⊗400m 🚉350m.

C S Lunéville 16C5
Les Bosquets, Quai des Petits Bosquets. **GPS**: n48,59652 e6,49865.⬆.

15 ⌁€ 5,50/24h 🚰🍽Ch🧹included 🚿free. 🚐🧹☐ 01/01-31/12
Distance: 🚶700m ⊗600m.
Tourist information Lunéville:
🏰 Château Petit Versailles. Castle, 18th century and museum. ☐ 10-12h,
14-18h ◉ Tue.

⌂S Marbotte 16A4
Parking de la Mairie, Rue Principale, D12. **GPS**: n48,83445 e5,58142.⬆.

2 ⌁free. **Location:** Simple, quiet. **Surface:** unpaved.
Distance: 🚶on the spot.

⌂S Maxey-sur-Meuse 16A5
GPS: n48,44861 e5,69500.⬆.

4 ⌁free 🧹(4x)free. **Location:** Simple. **Surface:** gravel.
☐ 14/05-31/12
Distance: 🚶2km 🚉2km 🚌500m.

⌂S Maxey-sur-Vaise 🌾 16A5
Grande Rue. **GPS**: n48,53836 e5,66705.⬆.

6 ⌁free. **Location:** Simple, central, quiet.
☐ 01/01-31/12
Distance: 🚶on the spot.

⌂S Metz 16B3
Allée Metz Plage. **GPS**: n49,12371 e6,16887.⬆.

8 ⌁free 🚰🍽Chfree. **Surface:** asphalted.
Distance: 🚶350m 🚲1,5km ⊗300m.
Remarks: At entrance campsite, max. 48h, inclining pitches.
Tourist information Metz:
👁 Place St Louis. Square surrounded by houses from the 14th century.
✝ Cathédrale St Etienne. Cathedral.

⌂S Millery 16B4
Avenue de la Moselle, D40. **GPS**: n48,81507 e6,12716.⬆.

5 ⌁free 🚰🍽Chfree. **Surface:** asphalted. ☐ 01/04-31/10 ◉ water:
01/11-31/03
Distance: 🚶on the spot 🚲3,5km.
Remarks: Along Mosel.

⌂S Mirecourt 16B5
Place Thierry. **GPS**: n48,29945 e6,13591.⬆.
20 ⌁€ 6 🚰🍽Ch🧹WCincluded. **Location:** Comfortable, central.
Surface: gravel.
Distance: 🚶on the spot.

⌂S Monthureux-sur-Saône 16B6
D460. GPS: n48,03199 e5,97390.⬆➡.

8 ⌕free ⟿ ⬛ Ch WC free ⤶€3/48h, Wifi-Stop. **Location:** Comfortable, quiet. ⬛ 01/01-31/12
Distance: ⚓on the spot ⤶on the spot ⊗200m ⚡75m.
Remarks: At football ground.

Montigny-lès-Vaucouleurs 🚻 16A5
Rue de la Côte. **GPS:** n48,58875 e5,63007.⬆.

10 ⌕free. **Location:** Rural, simple, quiet. **Surface:** gravel.
⬛ 01/01-31/12
Distance: ⚓700m.

Montplonne 🚻 16A4
Rue du Four. **GPS:** n48,68630 e5,16934.⬆.

4 ⌕free. **Location:** Rural, simple. **Surface:** gravel.
Distance: ⚓on the spot.
Remarks: Next to cemetery.

Morley 16A5
Parking Lavoir, D5A. **GPS:** n48,57848 e5,24878.⬆.

5 ⌕free.
Location: Rural, simple, central, quiet.
Distance: ⚓on the spot.

Nancy 16B4
Parking Faubourg les III Maisons, Rue Charles Keller. **GPS:** n48,70403 e6,17598.⬆.

⌕€ 0,50-3,50. **Surface:** asphalted. ⬛ 01/01-31/12
Distance: ⚓city centre ± 1km.

Nancy 16B4
Port Saint Georges, N57, boulevard du 21ème Régiment d'Aviation.
GPS: n48,69221 e6,19318.

6 ⌕€ 10/night ⟿ ⬛ Ch ⚡ WC ⤶ included.
Surface: asphalted.
⬛ 01/05-01/11
Distance: ⚓500m ⚊on the spot ⤶on the spot ⊗100m ⚡100m ⎯100m.
Remarks: Max. 5 nights, check in at harbourmaster.

Tourist information Nancy:
Ⓜ Musée Historique Lorraine, Palais Ducal. Regional museum.
⬛ 15/06-15/09 ⬛ Tue.
☺ Zoo Haye, Velaine-en-Haye. Zoo with centre for wild birds.

Nant-le-Grand 🚻 16A4
Grand Rue, D169A. **GPS:** n48,67530 e5,22382.⬆.

4 ⌕free. **Location:** Rural, simple, quiet. **Surface:** gravel.
Distance: ⚓on the spot.

Niderviller 16D4
Marina Niderviller, Avenue de Lorraine. **GPS:** n48,71748 e7,09901.
12 ⌕€ 10 ⟿€1/100liter ⬛ Ch ⤶€0,50/kWh WC ⤶.

Nonsard Lamarche 16B4
Base de Loisirs, Base de Loisirs de Madine. **GPS:** n48,93064 e5,74873.⬆.

30 ⌕€7 ⟿€3 ⬛ Ch. ⚓ **Location:** Rural, simple, isolated, quiet.
Surface: grassy/metalled. ⬛ 01/04-31/10

FR

Distance: 🛢700m ⚓on the spot ⛽on the spot ⊗on the spot.
Remarks: At lake Madine, coins at campsite.

🏕 **Nubécourt** 16A4

D151, Rue Raymond Poincaré. **GPS:** n48,99704 e5,17256.⬆➡.

10 🛏free. **Location:** Rural, simple, central, quiet. **Surface:** metalled.
◘ 01/01-31/12
Distance: 🛢on the spot ⛽200m 🎿on the spot 🏊on the spot.

🏕S **Phalsbourg** 16D4

Avia, ZAC Louvois, Route du Luxembourg. **GPS:** n48,77047 e7,24198.
🛏free 🚰€2 🚽Ch ⬛€2. **Surface:** asphalted. ◘ 01/01-31/12
Distance: ⊗on the spot.

🏕 **Pierre-Percée** 16C5

D182A. **GPS:** n48,46723 e6,92911.

± 8 🛏free. **Surface:** asphalted.
Distance: ⚓on the spot ⛽on the spot.
Remarks: Picnic area at artificial lake.

🏕S **Plombières-les-Bains** ⚓ 16C6

Avenue des Etats-Unis. **GPS:** n47,96208 e6,45411.⬆.

5 🛏€ 8/24h 🚰 ⚒ (5x)included. **Surface:** asphalted. ◘ 01/04-15/10

🏕S **Pompierre** 16A6

Chemin de la Corvée. **GPS:** n48,25691 e5,67188.⬆➡.

3 🛏free 🚰 ⚒ free. **Location:** Urban, simple, noisy. **Surface:** asphalted.
◘ 01/01-31/12
Distance: 🛢1km ⚓500m 🏊500m.

⚓S **Pont-à-Mousson** 🌿🏖⛵ 16B4

Port de plaisance, Avenue des Etas Unis, D910. **GPS:** n48,90296 e6,06088.⬆.

42 🛏€ 8 🚰⚒Ch ⚒ WC ▢included.
Location: Luxurious. **Surface:** asphalted.
◘ 01/04-31/10
Distance: 🛢400m 🚲 3,4km ⛽on the spot ⊗400m 🏊400m ⛴on the spot.
Remarks: Check in at reception.

🏕S **Rebeuville** 16A5

Rue du Cougnot. **GPS:** n48,33530 e5,70128.⬆➡.

3 🛏free 🚰⚒Ch ⚒ free. **Location:** Rural, comfortable, isolated.
Surface: asphalted. ◘ 01/01-31/12
Distance: 🛢5km ⛽on the spot ⊗5km 🏊5km ⛴500m.

🏕S **Remiremont** 16C6

Rue du Lit d'Eau. **GPS:** n48,01540 e6,60208.⬆.
30 🛏€ 6 🚰⚒Ch ⚒€3. ⛟ **Surface:** gravel.
Distance: 🛢1km.
Remarks: At small lake.

🏕S **Revigny-sur-Ornain** 🏺 15D4

Stade/Office de Tourisme, Rue de l'Abattoir. **GPS:** n48,82642 e4,98330.⬆➡.

2 🛏free 🚰€3 🚽Ch ⚒€3.
Location: Urban, simple, central, quiet. **Surface:** asphalted.
◘ 01/01-31/12
Distance: 🛢on the spot ⛽100m ⊗on the spot 🏊on the spot ⛴on the spot.
Remarks: Coins at tourist info.

⚓S **Rhodes** 16C4

Port Municipal, Rue Principale. **GPS:** n48,75784 e6,90053.
30 🛏€ 18/24h 🚰⚒Ch ⚒ WC ▢included. **Surface:** grassy.
◘ Easter-01/10
Distance: ⚓on the spot ⛽on the spot.
Remarks: Along Etang du Stock.

🏕S **Richardmenil** 16B5

Chemin de la Maize. **GPS:** n48,59457 e6,16078.⬆.

FR

5 🛏free 🚰💧Ch 🚿(4x)free. **Surface:** asphalted. ⬛ 01/01-31/12
Distance: 🚶1km 🛒on the spot 🍽on the spot 🏊500m 🚉1km 🚌1km.
♿🅂 | **Rollainville** | 16B5
Rue de la Cure. **GPS:** n48,36185 e5,73842.⬆➡

1 🛏free 🚰💧free. **Location:** Urban, simple, central. **Surface:** asphalted.
⬛ 01/01-31/12
Distance: 🚶on the spot.
Remarks: Baker at 8am.
♿🅂 | **Rupt-sur-Moselle** | 16C6
Quai de la Parelle. **GPS:** n47,92061 e6,66194.⬆

6 🛏free 🚰€3/10minutes 💧Ch 🚿(4x)€3/3h WC. **Surface:** asphalted.
Distance: 🏊350m 🚉250m 🚌on the spot 🥾Voie Verte.
Remarks: Coins at the shops and town hall.
♿🅂 | **Saint-Nicolas-de-Port** | 16B5
Rue du jeu de Paume. **GPS:** n48,63515 e6,30048.⬆➡

10 🛏free 🚰€4 💧Ch 🍽. **Location:** Urban, simple, central, quiet.
Surface: gravel. ⬛ 01/01-31/12
Distance: 🚶on the spot 🏊150m 🚉200m 🚌100m.
♿ | **Sarralbe** | 16D4
Rue de la Sarre. **GPS:** n49,00171 e7,03240.⬆
4 🛏free. **Surface:** asphalted. ⬛ 01/01-31/12
Distance: 🚶350m 🏊350m.
Remarks: At sports centre.
♿ | **Seuil-d'Argonne** | 15D4
Rue du Commandant Laflotte, D2/D20. **GPS:** n48,98294 e5,06215.⬆

5 🛏free. **Location:** Urban, simple, quiet. **Surface:** gravel.
⬛ 01/01-31/12
Distance: 🏊650m 🚉650m 🚲650m 🥾650m.
Remarks: In fron of sports fields.
♿ | **Sierck-les-Bains** | 16B3
Place de la Gro. **GPS:** n49,44424 e6,36217.⬆
8 🛏free. **Location:** Simple. **Surface:** asphalted. ⬛ 01/01-31/12
Distance: 🏊200m 🚉350m.
Remarks: Along ther Moselle river, nearby police station.
♿ | **Souilly** | 16A4
Route de St.André-en-Barrois, D159. **GPS:** n49,02730 e5,27985.⬆
6 🛏free. **Surface:** gravel. ⬛ 01/01-31/12
Distance: 🚶600m.
♿🅂 | **Soulosse-sous-Saint-Élophe** | 16B5
Square Guy Bellamy. **GPS:** n48,40953 e5,73886.⬆➡

3 🛏free 🚰💧Chfree. **Location:** Rural, simple. **Surface:** gravel.
⬛ 01/01-31/12
Distance: 🚶500m.
♿🅂 | **St.Mihiel** | 16A4
Chemin Gué Rapeau. **GPS:** n48,90227 e5,53960.⬆➡

4 🛏€3 🚰💧Chfree 🚿€3/24h. **Location:** Rural, simple, isolated, quiet.
Surface: asphalted. ⬛ 01/01-31/12
Distance: 🚶1,5km 🏊1km 🚉1,5km.
Remarks: Directly at the river, nearby sluices, next to camping municipal, max.
24h.
♿🅂 | **St.Nabord** | 16C6
Rue de la Croix Saint Jacques. **GPS:** n48,04527 e6,58175.⬆

3 free €3/80liter Ch €3. **Surface:** asphalted. 01/01-31/12
Distance: 300m 200m 50m.

Stenay 16A2
Aire Camping-car, D947. **GPS:** n49,48979 e5,18323.

47 €8 Ch WC €4/4 included. **Location:** Rural,
comfortable, quiet. **Surface:** metalled. 01/01-31/12
Distance: 150m 150m 800m, bakery 300m.
Remarks: Pay and entrance code at harbourmaster, musée Européen de la Bière,
beer museum.

Stenay 16A2
Port de plaisance, Rue du Port. **GPS:** n49,49096 e5,18312.

6 €8 Ch WC €4/4 included. **Location:** Comfortable, quiet.
Surface: asphalted. 01/01-31/12
Distance: on the spot 200m 500m.
Remarks: Pay at harbourmaster.

Tourist information Stenay:
M Musée de la Bière. Beer museum.
Château, Louppy-sur-Loison. Renaissance castle, 17th century.

Tannois 16A4
Parking du Belvédère, D169. **GPS:** n48,71917 e5,22967.

10 free. **Location:** Rural, simple, isolated, quiet. **Surface:** gravel.
01/01-31/12
Distance: 1,3km 1,5km on the spot on the spot.

Thaon-les-Vosges 16C6
Aire du Coignot, Rue du Coignot. **GPS:** n48,24889 e6,42611.

20 free Ch free. **Surface:** asphalted/gravel. 01/03-01/10
Distance: 1,5km 400m.
Remarks: Next to port fluvial.

Thierville-sur-Meuse 16A3
Thierville sur-meuse, Avenue de l,etangbleu. **GPS:** n49,17499 e5,36357.

20 free. **Location:** Rural, simple, central. **Surface:** gravel.
01/01-31/12
Distance: 100m 50m 50m on the spot on the spot.
Remarks: Along the Meuse river.

Tilleux 16A5
Grande Rue. **GPS:** n48,29300 e5,72250.

8 free free. **Location:** Simple. **Surface:** gravel.
01/01-31/12
Distance: 100m.
Remarks: Inclining pitches, entrance road max. 3,5t.

Toul 16B4
Avenue du Colonel Péchot. **GPS:** n48,67939 e5,88806.

9 €7 Ch (8x)included. **Surface:** asphalted. 01/01-31/12
Distance: 4km.
Remarks: In front of police station.

Val-et-Châtillon 16D5
Rue de Petitmont. **GPS:** n48,55704 e6,96566.
6 free €3 Ch €3. **Surface:** gravel. 01/01-31/12
Distance: 3,5km on the spot.
Remarks: Max. 4 days, bread-service.

Vaucouleurs 16A5

Rue du Cardinal Lépicier. **GPS:** n48,60179 e5,66737.

3 ⌂ € 5 ⛽€2/100liter Ch ■€2 WC. **Location:** Urban, simple, central. **Surface:** asphalted. 01/01-31/12
Distance: on the spot ⊗500m 500m.

Vauquois 15D3

Parking municipal, D212. **GPS:** n49,20405 e5,07398.

8 ⌂free. **Location:** Rural, simple. **Surface:** gravel.
Distance: on the spot.

Velaines 16A4

D120A. **GPS:** n48,70589 e5,29804.

4 ⌂free. **Location:** Simple, central. **Surface:** gravel.
Distance: on the spot on the spot.

Ventron 16C6

Chemin du Plain. **GPS:** n47,93906 e6,86900.
10 ⌂free ⛽€2/100liter Ch ■€2/55minutes. **Location:** Simple, central, quiet. **Surface:** asphalted. 01/01-31/12
Remarks: Coins at tourist info.

Ventron 16C6

Route de Frère Joseph. **GPS:** n47,92495 e6,86364.
⌂free. **Surface:** asphalted. 01/01-31/12
Distance: Ventron 3,2km on the spot.
Remarks: Parking at skipistes.

Verdun 16A3

Dragées Braquir, Rue du Fort de Vaux, D112. **GPS:** n49,15955 e5,39989.

10 ⌂free.
Location: Urban, simple, central. **Surface:** metalled.
Distance: on the spot.
Remarks: Max. 1 night.

Vigneulles-les-Hattonchat 16A4

Rue Miss Skinner. **GPS:** n48,99200 e5,70122.
5 ⌂free. **Location:** Isolated, quiet. **Surface:** gravel.
Distance: 2km.

Void-Vacon 16A4

Rue de la Gare. **GPS:** n48,68240 e5,61960.

20 ⌂free ⛽€2/100liter Ch ■€2. **Location:** Rural, simple, isolated, quiet.
Surface: grassy/gravel. 01/01-31/12
Distance: 700m 10m 10m.
Remarks: Coins at shop/town hall.

Alsace

Benfeld 17A5

Concessionnaire CLC Alsace, 9, Rue de Hollande, RN83 dir Strasbourg-Colmar.
GPS: n48,37772 e7,59778.
5 ⌂free ⛽ Ch free. **Surface:** gravel/metalled. 01/01-31/12
Distance: 2km ⊗2km 2km.
Remarks: At motorhome dealer.

Bourbach-le-Haut 23D1

Route Joffre. **GPS:** n47,79463 e7,02868.

5 ⌂€6 ⛽ Ch included. **Surface:** asphalted. 15/03-15/11
Distance: 50m ⊗100m 100m 5km.
Remarks: In front of fire-station.

Chavannes-sur-l'Etang 23D1

Aire pique-nique La Porte d'Alsace, RD419, Rue d'Alsace.
GPS: n47,63325 e7,01858.

15 ⌂€7 (19-9 h) ⛽ Ch WC free. **Surface:** asphalted.
01/01-31/12
Distance: 900m 1km.
Remarks: Parking picnic area.

Colmar 16D6

Rue de la Cavalerie. **GPS:** n48,08218 e7,35990.

FR

20 Ⓢ€ 3, overnight stay free.
Location: Central, noisy. **Surface:** asphalted.
Distance: 200m ⊗on the spot ⚲on the spot ▣on the spot.

| Ⓢ | Colmar 〜 ⬆ | 16D6 |

Rue Henry Wilhelm. **GPS:** n48,08366 e7,35527. ⬆.
16 Ⓢ€ 3, overnight stay free. **Location:** Urban, simple, central.
Surface: asphalted.
Distance: 400m ⊗400m ⚲400m.

| ⚓Ⓢ | Colmar 〜 ⬆ | 16D6 |

Port de Plaisance de Colmar, 6 rue du Canal. **GPS:** n48,08054 e7,37599.
25 Ⓢ€ 11-15 + € 0,22/pp tourist tax ⌁ ⚡Ch ✎ WC ▯▣€3/2 ⚟included.
Location: Comfortable, quiet. **Surface:** asphalted.
◯ 01/01-31/12
Distance: 1,3km ⚲Lidl 400m.

| ⚓ | Eguisheim ⬆ | 16D6 |

Bannwarth, Rue de Bruxelles 3. **GPS:** n48,04456 e7,30478.

6 Ⓢfree. **Surface:** metalled.
Distance: 100m.

| ⚓Ⓢ | Ferrette 〜 ⬆⬆ | 23D1 |

Rue de Lucelle. **GPS:** n47,48882 e7,31118. ⬆.

5 Ⓢfree ⌁€2/10minutes ⚡Ch ▣€2/55minutes. **Location:** Simple,
isolated, quiet. **Surface:** asphalted.
Distance: 700m ⊗2km ⚲2km.

| ⚓Ⓢ | Fessenheim | 16D6 |

Allée de la Guyane. **GPS:** n47,91833 e7,53139. ⬆.

30 Ⓢfree ⌁€2 ⚡Ch ▣€2. **Surface:** asphalted/gravel. ◯ 01/01-31/12
Distance: 700m ⊗700m ⚲200m.
Remarks: Coins available at swimming pool, supermarket.

| Ⓢ | Guebwiller ⬆ ⬆⬆ | 16D6 |

Avenue Maréchal Foch. **GPS:** n47,90554 e7,21869. ⬆.

Ⓢfree. **Surface:** gravel. ◯ 01/01-31/12
Distance: 300m ⌁on the spot ⊗300m ⚲300m ⟺300m ⚲5km.

| ©Ⓢ | Guewenheim ⬆⬆ ⬆⬆ | 23D1 |

Le Doller. **GPS:** n47,75612 e7,09855.

10 Ⓢfree ⌁€3,50 ⚡Ch ▣ WC ▯▣.
Surface: gravel. ◯ 01/01-31/12
Distance: 2km ⌁1km ⊗2km ⚲2km.

| ⚓Ⓢ | Harskirchen | 16D4 |

Port de Plaisance, Rue de Bissert. **GPS:** n48,93930 e7,02759. ⬆→.
2 Ⓢ€ 10 ⌁⚡Ch ✎▯⚟included. **Surface:** gravel. ◯ 15/03-11/11
Distance: ⚲on the spot.
Remarks: At canal Houillères de la Sarre, max. 24h.

| Ⓢ | Hartmannswiller | 16D6 |

Grand Rue. **GPS:** n47,86311 e7,21494. ⬆.
4 Ⓢfree ⌁€4,30 ⚡ ✎€4,30 ▱. **Surface:** asphalted.

| Ⓢ | Heiligenstein | 16D5 |

Lieu-dit Lindel, D35. **GPS:** n48,42780 e7,45147. ⬆.

3 Ⓢfree. **Surface:** gravel. ◯ 01/01-31/12
Distance: 800m ⊗300m ⚲500m.
Remarks: Hiking trails and wine tasting.

| Ⓢ | Hirtzbach | 23D1 |

Place de la Gare. **GPS:** n47,60061 e7,22542.
10 Ⓢfree ⌁⚡Chfree. ◯ 01/01-31/12

| Ⓢ | Kaysersberg 〜 ⬆ | 16D6 |

Aire Camping-car P1, Place de l'Erlenbad. **GPS:** n48,13565 e7,26325. ⬆→.

FR

80 ⌂€7/24h ⛽🚿Ch WC 🔌free. 🏠 **Surface:** asphalted.
◻ 01/01-31/12
Distance: 🛒300m ⊗300m 🚉300m.
Remarks: Wifi at Office de Tourisme.
Tourist information Kaysersberg:
Ⓜ Musée Albert Schweitzer. The life of Albert Schweitzer.

| | Le Bonhomme ❄ | 16D6 |

Col du Bonhomme, D148, route des Crètes. **GPS:** n48,16495 e7,07971.

🚿free. **Surface:** gravel.
Distance: ⊗on the spot.

| S | Linthal | 16D6 |

Rue du Markstein, D430. **GPS:** n47,94495 e7,12783. ⬆.
4 🚿free ⛽€4,30 🚻€4,30 ♻. **Location:** Simple, quiet.
Surface: asphalted.

| | Michelbach | 23D1 |

Salle des polyvalente, Rue Principale. **GPS:** n47,75800 e7,11000. ⬆.

5 🚿free. **Surface:** metalled. ◻ 01/01-31/12
Distance: 🛒250m 🚲2km ⊗2km 🚉1km 🚉1km.
Remarks: Behind community centre.

| | Mittelbergheim | 16D5 |

Parking Zotzenberg, Rue Ziegelscheuer. **GPS:** n48,39869 e7,44194. ⬆.

4 🚿free. **Surface:** asphalted.
Distance: 🛒300m 🚲3,1km ⊗300m 🚉300m 🚶on the spot.
Remarks: At cemetery, wine tasting.

| S | Munster 🌿🚉 | 16D6 |

Aire Aire de camping-cars Munster, Rue du Dr Heid. **GPS:** n48,03779 e7,13471. ⬆.
54 🚿€6 ⛽€3 🚻Ch ♻€3 WC 🚽€1,50 🔌. **Surface:** gravel.
◻ 01/01-31/12
Distance: 🛒on the spot ⊗on the spot 🚉on the spot 🚲on the spot.

| | Munster | 16D6 |

Place de la salle des Fêtes. **GPS:** n48,03944 e7,13944. ⬆.

8 🚿free. **Surface:** asphalted. ◻ 01/01-31/12
Distance: 🛒300m ⊗300m 🚉300m 🚌on the spot.

| S | Murbach 🌿🏕❄ | 16D6 |

Abbaye de Murbach, Rue de Guebwiller. **GPS:** n47,92321 e7,16059. ⬆.

20 🚿free ⛽Service€4,30 🚻Ch ♻ ♻. **Location:** Isolated, quiet.
Surface: gravel/metalled. ◻ 01/01-31/12
Distance: 🛒350m 🚉on the spot ⊗on the spot 🚉500m 🚲5km.

| | Obernai 🌿🚉 | 16D5 |

Parking de l'Altau, Route d'Ottrott. **GPS:** n48,46239 e7,47369. ⬆.
🚿free. **Location:** Urban, simple, central. **Surface:** asphalted.
◻ 01/01-31/12
Distance: 🛒600m ⊗600m 🚉600m.
Remarks: Video surveillance.

| | Obernai 🌿 | 16D5 |

Parking des Remparts, Rue Poincaré. **GPS:** n48,45972 e7,48667. ⬆➡.

50 🚿free. **Surface:** gravel. ◻ 01/01-31/12
Distance: 🛒300m 🚲2,7km ⊗300m 🚉300m 🚌200m.
Remarks: Large parking in centre, video surveillance.

| S | Obernai 🌿🚉 | 16D5 |

Camping municipal Le Vallon de l'Ehn, 1, rue de Berlin.
GPS: n48,46471 e7,46757. ⬆➡.
⛽€2 🚻Ch. ◻ 01/01-31/12

| S | Oltingue 🚉🏕 | 23D1 |

Place Saint Martin. **GPS:** n47,49158 e7,39068. ⬆.

3 ⬛free ⬛€2/10minutes ⬛Ch ⬛€2/55minutes. **Surface:** asphalted. ⬛ 01/01-31/12
Distance: ⬛100m ⬛200m.

15 ⬛€ 1,50/5h, € 1,50/night ⬛€2 ⬛Ch. ⬛ **Location:** Simple.
Surface: gravel. ⬛ 01/01-31/12
Distance: ⬛400m ⬛on the spot ⬛on the spot.
Remarks: Next to Cave de Ribeauvillé.
Tourist information Ribeauvillé:
⬛ Sa.

| ⬛⬛ | Orbey | 16D6 |

Hôtel Restaurant Les Terrasses du Lac Blanc, Lac Blanc.
GPS: n48,13540 e7,08957.⬛

| ⬛⬛ | Riquewihr ⬛⬛ | 16D6 |

Avenue Jacques Preiss. **GPS:** n48,16608 e7,30175.⬛

8 ⬛€ 5, free with a meal ⬛included ⬛Ch ⬛(8x)€2,50.
Surface: grassy/gravel.
Distance: ⬛500m ⬛500m ⬛on the spot.
Remarks: Guests free.

6 ⬛€ 2/5h, € 4/night ⬛€2 ⬛Ch ⬛€2. ⬛ **Surface:** asphalted.
⬛ 01/01-31/12
Distance: ⬛200m ⬛200m ⬛200m.
Remarks: Motorhomes <7m, video surveillance.
Tourist information Riquewihr:
⬛ Office de Tourisme, Rue de 1ère Armée. Picturesque street with houses of the 16th century.

| ⬛⬛ | Orschwihr ⬛⬛⬛ | 16D6 |

Rue de la Source. **GPS:** n47,93722 e7,23083.⬛⬛

| ⬛ | Saverne ⬛ | 16D4 |

Rue des Emouleurs. **GPS:** n48,74512 e7,36854.
⬛free. **Surface:** gravel/sand. ⬛ 01/01-31/12
Distance: ⬛centre 650m.

| ⬛⬛ | Saverne ⬛ | 16D4 |

Camping Les Portes d'Alsace, Rue du Père Liebermann.
GPS: n48,73131 e7,35504.⬛
15 ⬛€ 8, Jul/Aug € 10 ⬛⬛Ch ⬛WC ⬛⬛included. **Surface:** gravel.
⬛ 01/04-30/09
Remarks: Service passerby € 3.
Tourist information Saverne:
⬛⬛ Château de Rohan. Museum, former summer residence of the bishops of Strasbourg.

4 ⬛free ⬛⬛Ch ⬛€4,30 ⬛. **Surface:** asphalted. ⬛ 01/01-31/12
Distance: ⬛200m ⬛200m ⬛500m.
Remarks: Max. 48h.

| ⬛⬛ | Pfaffenheim | 16D6 |

Aire du Winzerhof, Rue de la Tuilerie. **GPS:** n47,98639 e7,29167.

| ⬛⬛ | Soufflenheim ⬛ | 17A4 |

Rue des Menuisiers. **GPS:** n48,82940 e7,95395.⬛⬛

5 ⬛free ⬛€3 ⬛Ch ⬛(5x)€2 WC ⬛. **Surface:** gravel/metalled.
⬛ 01/01-31/12
Distance: ⬛400m ⬛400m ⬛500m.

| ⬛⬛ | Ribeauvillé ⬛ | 16D6 |

Route de Guémar. **GPS:** n48,19231 e7,32867.⬛

3 ⬛free ⬛€2 ⬛Ch ⬛€2. **Surface:** asphalted. ⬛ 01/01-31/12
Distance: ⬛300m ⬛200m ⬛300m ⬛200m.

| ⬛⬛ | Soultz | 16D6 |

Rue de la Marne. **GPS:** n47,88806 e7,23139.⬛

FR

30 🛏free ⚡Service€4,10 🔌Ch 🚿. **Surface:** asphalted. ⬛ 01/01-31/12
Distance: 🚲500m ⊗500m ▣500m ▣500m 🚌500m.
Remarks: Payment only by bank card.

🛏🅂 **Ste.Marie-aux-Mines** 🌿🏕🎠❄ **16D6**
Place des Tisserands. **GPS**: n48,24700 e7,18322.⬆.

4 🛏free. **Surface:** asphalted. ⬛ 01/01-31/12
Distance: 🚲300m ⊗300m ▣300m.
Remarks: Max. 24h.

Tourist information Ste.Marie-aux-Mines:
ℹ Office de Tourisme, 86, rue Wilson, www.tourisme.fr/office-de-tourisme/
sainte-marie-aux-mines-68.htm. Mineral city with silvermine, Mine d'Argent
Sainte-Barthélemy.

🛏🅂 **Strasbourg** 🌿🏕🎠 **17A5**
Parking Auberge de Jeunesse des Deux Rives (Parc du Rhin), Rue des
Cavaliers. **GPS**: n48,56659 e7,79975.⬆.

20 🛏free ⚡€2,50/100liter 🔌Ch 🚿€2,50/1h ♻. **Surface:** grassy/sand.
⬛ 01/01-31/12
Distance: 🚲Strasbourg centre 5km 🚌bus 21 + tram.

Tourist information Strasbourg:
👁⊗ Maison Kammerzell. Restaurant, 1467-1589, one of the most beautyfull
half-timbered houses in the Alsace region.
Ⓜ Musée Alsacien. Folk art and handycrafts.
✝ Cathédrale de Nôtre-Dame.

🛏🅂 **Thann** 🌿🏕🎠🌿 **23D1**
Place du Bungert, Rue des Pélerins. **GPS**: n47,81159 e7,10450.

10 🛏free ⚡🔌Ch 🚿free. **Surface:** asphalted.
⬛ 01/01-31/12 🔲 Sa-morning market
Distance: 🚲600m 🏊on the spot ⊗500m ▣500m 🚌500m.

🛏🅂 **Thann** 🌿🏕🎠🌿 **23D1**
Rue du Général de Gaulle. N66. **GPS**: n47,80889 e7,10460.⬆.
30 🛏free ⚡🔌ChService€4 ♻. **Location:** Noisy. **Surface:** asphalted.
⬛ 01/01-31/12
Distance: 🚲250m ⊗50m ▣50m.

🛏🅂 **Trois Épis** 🌿🏕🎠🌿 **16D6**
Place des Antonins. **GPS**: n48,10101 e7,22948.⬆➡.

25 🛏free ⚡€2 🔌Ch ▦€3/55minutes WC ▯€1. **Surface:** asphalted.
⬛ 01/01-31/12
Distance: 🚲150m ⊗150m ▣150m.

🛏🅂 **Turckheim** 🏕🎠 **16D6**
Quai de la gare. **GPS**: n48,08555 e7,27739.

6 🛏free. **Location:** Noisy. **Surface:** metalled. ⬛ 01/01-31/12
Distance: 🚲historical centre 250m ⊗250m ▣300m 🚌on the spot.

🅂 **Turckheim** 🏕🎠 **16D6**
Camping municipal Les Cigognes, 4, quai de la Gare. **GPS**: n48,08539 e7,27535.
⚡€5,40 🔌Ch. ⬛ 15/03-31/10

🅂 **Ungersheim** **16D6**
Ecomusée. **GPS**: n47,85200 e7,28400.⬆➡.

20 🛏€6 ⚡🔌included. **Surface:** gravel/metalled. ⬛ 01/01-31/12
Distance: 🚲6km.
Remarks: Check in at hotel.

S **Villefranche-sur-Saône** 22D5
Camping-car Park, 2788 Route de Riottier. **GPS**: n45,97278 e4,75135.⬆
128 ⬛€12 ⚡nearby Ch ⚡included. 🏠 **Location**: Urban, luxurious.
◯ 15/05-15/09
Distance: A6 1,3km Station > Lyon 3,4km.
Remarks: Wifi code: 692712.

S **Westhalten** 16D6
Rue St Blaise, D18, Vallée Noble, dir Soultzmatt.. **GPS**: n47,95626 e7,25135.

6 ⬛free ⚡€2 Ch ⚡€2. **Location**: Noisy. **Surface**: asphalted.
◯ 01/03-30/11
Distance: nearby nearby on the spot.
Remarks: Max. 48h.

S **Willer-sur-Thur** 23D1
Place de l'Eglise. **GPS**: n47,84315 e7,07292.⬆➡

3 ⬛free ⚡ Ch free. **Surface**: asphalted. ◯ 01/01-31/12
Distance: 250m 500m 500m, bakery 50m 500m 500m.

Normandie

S **Agon-Coutainville** 13B3
Flot Bleu Park, Boulevard Louis Lebel-Jéhenne. **GPS**: n49,05176 w1,59123.⬆➡

25 ⬛€6,30/24h ⚡ Ch ⚡included 🏠 **Location**: Comfortable.
Surface: grassy. ◯ 01/01-31/12
Distance: 800m.
Remarks: Service passerby €2,70.

S **Angiens** 14B1
Aire de Château d'Iclon, Impasse des Roseaux. **GPS**: n49,84390 e0,81945.⬆➡

10 ⬛€5 + €1/pp ⚡€2,50 ⚡€2,50 Ch ⚡€3. **Surface**: grassy/gravel.
◯ 01/01-31/12
Distance: 3km.

S **Ardevon** 13B4
La Bidonnière - Ardevon

campingcar@ardevivre.fr - http://campingcar.ardevivre.fr
Paved and flat motorhome pitches
Beautiful view
Sanitary facilities

La Bidonnière, Route de la Rive 5. **GPS**: n48,60352 w1,47612.⬆
50 ⬛€10, 01/11-31/03 €6 ⚡ Ch ⚡ (40x)€3,70/24h WC €3/stay included.
Location: Rural, luxurious, quiet. **Surface**: grassy/gravel.
◯ 01/01-31/12
Distance: on the spot 3km 1km 3km 1,5km on the spot on the spot.
Remarks: Bread-service, free bicycles available, view on Mt.St.Michel.

S **Arromanches-les-Bains** 13C2
Rue François Carpentier. **GPS**: n49,33904 w0,62553.⬆

14 ⬛free ⚡€2/10minutes ⚡ Ch ⚡€2/1h free15minutes.
Surface: asphalted. ◯ 01/01-31/12
Distance: 150m 100m 100m 250m.
Remarks: Next to camping municipal.

S **Arromanches-les-Bains** 13C2
Arromanches 360, Cinéma Circulaire, Chemin du Calvaire / D514.
GPS: n49,33924 w0,61419.⬆

FR

20 🕭 € 6. 💈 **Location:** Rural, comfortable.
🅾 01/01-31/12
Distance: 🚶400m ⚓300m.
Remarks: Beautiful view.

| 🕭 S | Auderville | 13A1 |

D901. **GPS:** n49,71431 w1,93481. ⬆.

15 🕭 free. **Location:** Rural, simple. **Surface:** grassy/gravel.
🅾 01/01-31/12
Distance: 🚶300m ⚓700m 🏊600m.

| 🕭 S | Auffay 💈 | 14B2 |

Place de Bleckede. **GPS:** n49,71755 e1,10055. ⬆ ➡.

6 🕭 free 🚰€3/100liter 🗑 Ch. **Surface:** asphalted. 🅾 01/01-31/12
Distance: 🚶on the spot ⚔100m 🛒100m.

| 🕭 S | Avranches 💈🏕 | 13B4 |

Centre Culturel, Boulevard Jozeau Marigné. **GPS:** n48,68585 w1,367. ⬆ ➡.

8 🕭 free 🚰€2/10minutes 🗑 Ch.
Location: Urban, simple. **Surface:** gravel/metalled.
🅾 01/01-31/12
Distance: 🚶200m 🚲1,9km ⚔200m 🛒200m.
Remarks: Behind community centre, max. 1 night, attractive medieval centre.

Tourist information Avranches:
👁 Jardins des Plantes. Garden with exotic plants.
✝ Basilique St Germain. 🅾 9-12h, 14-16h.
🏕 place des Halles. 🅾 Sa + Tue-morning.

| 🕭 | Bagnoles-de-l'Orne 💈🏕🎣🌊⚓ | 13C4 |

D235. **GPS:** n48,55821 w0,4129. ⬆ ➡.

6 🕭 free. **Location:** Urban, simple. **Surface:** gravel.
🅾 01/01-31/12
Distance: 🚶on the spot ⚔400m 🏪400m 🏊on the spot.
Remarks: Behind tourist info, Place du Marché.

| 🕭 S | Barfleur | 13B2 |

Route Alfred Rossel, D1. **GPS:** n49,66998 w1,26355.

8 🕭 free 🚰 Ch WC. **Location:** Urban, simple. **Surface:** metalled.
Distance: 🚶200m.

| 🕭 | Barneville-Carteret | 13A2 |

Quai Émile Valmy, rue du port. **GPS:** n49,37300 w1,789.

12 🕭 free. **Location:** Urban, simple. **Surface:** asphalted.
Distance: 🚶600m 🏊on the spot 🛒on the spot ⚔600m.
Remarks: In front of the Gare Maritime.

| S | Barneville-Carteret | 13A2 |

Carrefour Market, Route du Pont Rose. **GPS:** n49,38553 w1,75239.
🚰€2 🗑 Ch 🚽€2/1h. **Location:** Simple.
🅾 01/01-31/12

| 🕭 S | Bayeux 💈🏕🛒 | 13C3 |

Place Gauquelin-Despallières. **GPS:** n49,28044 w0,70775. ⬆.

5 🕭 free 🚰 🗑 Ch WC free. **Location:** Urban. **Surface:** asphalted.
🅾 01/01-31/12
Distance: 🚶on the spot ⚔100m 🛒100m 🚌on the spot.
Remarks: Max. 12h.

FR

Tourist information Bayeux:
Ⓜ Musée Memorial 1944. Battle of Normandy, June 6 till August 22, 1944.
🕐 9.30-17h, 01/05-30/09 9-19h.
✝ Cathédrale Nôtre Dame. Gothic cathedral.

🚐S **Beauvoir** 13B4
Aire de camping-car du mont St Michel, Route de Mont St Michel.
GPS: n48,59426 w1,5122.⬆️.

122 💶€ 12,50 🚐🔌Ch ⚡(122x)included 📶free. 🚐 ✏ **Location:** Rural,
comfortable, luxurious, quiet. **Surface:** grassy/gravel. 🕐 01/01-31/12
Distance: 🚶500m ⊗500m.
Remarks: Service passerby € 4,50, le Mont Saint Michel 5km.

🚐S **Beauvoir** 13B4
Le Mont-St-Michel, Rue Au Bis. **GPS:** n48,60841 w1,50681.

220 💶€ 20/24h 🔌. **Surface:** asphalted. 🕐 01/01-31/12
Distance: ⊗on the spot 🚌on the spot.
Remarks: Free shuttle to Le Mont-Saint-Michel 07.30-00.30h.

🍴S **Beauvoir** 13B4
La Ferme Saint Michel, Route du Mont Saint Michel, D976.
GPS: n48,61112 w1,50978.➡️.

35 💶guests free 🚐🔌Ch WC 📶. **Location:** Simple. **Surface:** gravel.
🕐 01/01-31/12 🅾 Mo
Distance: 🚶600m ⊗on the spot 🛒600m 🚌on the spot.

🚐S **Beuvron-en-Auge** 🌿🏛 13D3
Parking de la Gare, Avenue de la Gare. **GPS:** n49,18560 w0,0495.⬆️.

16 💶€ 6 🚐🔌Ch included. 🚐 **Location:** Rural, comfortable, quiet.

Surface: gravel. 🕐 01/01-31/12
Distance: 🚶200m ⊗on the spot 🍽on the spot.
Remarks: Pay and coins at Tabac-Presse 200m.

🚐S **Bretteville-sur-Odon** 13D3
Camping-car service, 4-6 Avenue des Carrières. **GPS:** n49,18449 w0,41465. ⬆️.

6 💶free 🔌Ch free. **Location:** Urban, simple. **Surface:** metalled.
🕐 01/01-31/12
Distance: 🚶1km 🚌500m.

🚐S **Bréville-les-Monts** 13D3
Rue des Dentellières. **GPS:** n49,24167 w0,228.⬆️.

4 💶free 🚐€2/10minutes 🔌Ch. **Location:** Simple, comfortable.
Surface: asphalted. 🕐 01/03-15/11
Distance: 🚶on the spot.
Remarks: Max. 72h, (may-july-aug) 48h, coins at tourist info Merville and
harbour.

🚐S **Bricquebec** 🌿 13B2
Bas de Cattigny, D900, route de Cherbourg. **GPS:** n49,47402 w1,64674.⬆️.

6 💶free 🚐🔌Ch ⚡(2x)free.
Location: Comfortable, quiet. **Surface:** gravel.
Distance: 🚶1km 🛒on the spot.

🚐S **Broglie** 14A3
Parc de la bibliothèque. **GPS:** n49,00563 e0,52948.⬆️➡️.

8 💶€ 5/night 🚐€2,50/100liter 🔌Ch 🔵€2,50/1h. **Surface:** grassy/metalled.
🕐 01/03-31/10 7-22h, 01/11-28/02 7.30-19h
Distance: 🚶200m ⊗200m 🔵200m, 7.30-19h.

FR

Tourist information Broglie:
⛺ ▢ Fri 7-13h.

♿ S | **Buchy** | 14B2
D919, Route de Forges. **GPS:** n49,58538 e1,36417.⬆.

6 🅿free ⛽€2 ⚡Ch 🔋€2. **Surface:** asphalted. ▢ 01/01-31/12
Distance: 🛒500m ⊗500m 💧500m.

♿ S | **Cabourg** ⚓🌊 | 13D3
Avenue Michel d'Ornano. **GPS:** n49,28225 w0,11994.⬆.

6 🅿free ⛽€2/10minutes ⚡Ch 🧹. **Location:** Rural, comfortable, quiet.
Surface: asphalted. ▢ 01/01-31/12
Distance: 🛒centre 900m 🚲7,5km ⛴1,6km 🚉on the spot.
Remarks: Nearby Hippodrome.

♿ S | **Cambremer** | 13D3
Place de l'Europe/Avenue des Tilleuls. **GPS:** n49,14991 e0,04729.⬆.

7 🅿free ⛽€2/100liter ⚡Ch 🔋€2/1h. **Location:** Rural, simple, central,
quiet. **Surface:** gravel. ▢ 01/01-31/12
Distance: 🛒50m ⊗100m 💧bakery 100m.
Remarks: Coins at the shops and town hall.

♿ S | **Campigny** | 14A3
Chemin de la Motte. **GPS:** n49,31139 e0,55223.⬆.

3 🅿free ⛽⚡Chfree. **Surface:** grassy. ▢ 01/01-31/12
Remarks: On inner court of old presbytery, max. 24h.

♿ S | **Carentan** | 13B2
Camping-Car Park de Carentan, Chemin du Grand Bas Pays.
GPS: n49,30937 w1,2392.⬆.

12 🅿€12 ⛽⚡Ch 🧹 📶included. 🚲 **Location:** Comfortable, quiet.
Surface: gravel/metalled. ▢ 01/01-31/12
Distance: 🛒500m 🚉500m.
Remarks: Service passerby € 5.

♿ S | **Carolles** | 13B4
Rue du Mont Dol. **GPS:** n48,75931 w1,57062.⬆➡.

15 🅿€8 ⛽€3/100liter ⚡Ch 🔋€3/55minutes. 🚲 **Location:** Comfortable.
Surface: grassy/gravel. ▢ 01/01-31/12
Distance: 🏖150m ⊗on the spot 💧on the spot.
Remarks: Only exact change.

Ⓒ S | **Carolles** | 13B4
La Guérinière, Residence les Jaunets. **GPS:** n48,74989 w1,55695.⬆.
5 🅿€2 ⛽⚡Ch 🔋€2. **Surface:** asphalted. ▢ 01/01-31/12
Distance: 🛒on the spot 🚉2km.
Remarks: In front of town hall.

☺ S | **Caumont-l'Éventé** 🌿 | 13C3
Souterroscope des Ardoisières, Route de Saint Lô, D71.
GPS: n49,08868 w0,81645.➡.

3 🅿free ⛽€2/10minutes ⚡Ch 🔋€2/55minutes ᵂᶜ.
Location: Simple, isolated. **Surface:** asphalted.
▢ 01/01-31/12, service 15/02-15/11
Distance: ⊗on the spot 💧500m 🚶on the spot.

♿ S | **Cerisy-la-Forêt** | 13C3
GPS: n49,19806 w0,93389.⬆.

10 🅿free ⛽€2 ⚡Ch 🔋€2. **Location:** Rural, simple. **Surface:** gravel.

◻ 01/01-31/12
Distance: 🚶500m ⚓500m.
Remarks: Near abbey.

Cherbourg 🌿⚓🍴 13B2
Musée Cité de la Mer, Llée du President Menut. **GPS:** n49,64740 w1,61782.

40 🅿free. **Location:** Urban, simple. **Surface:** asphalted.
Distance: 🚶1km 🛒on the spot ✕1km ⚓on the spot.
Remarks: Max. 1 night.

Tourist information Cherbourg:
Ⓜ Musée Fort du Roule. War museum. ◻ 9.30-12h, 14-17.30h.

Clecy 👥 13C4
Rue du Stade. **GPS:** n48,91886 w0,48114. ⬆➡

5 🅿free 🔌€2/20minutes 🕳Ch 🛁. **Location:** Simple, quiet.
Surface: gravel. ◻ 01/01-31/12
Distance: 🚶100m 🚿100m ⚓300m 🚌200m.
Remarks: Coins at the shops in the village.

Clères 14B2
Rue Edmond Spalikowski, Côte du Mont Blanc. **GPS:** n49,60228 e1,11667. ⬆➡

10 🅿free 🔌€5/100liter 🕳Ch 🛁€5/6h. **Surface:** gravel.
◻ 01/01-31/12 ⦿ service: 01/11-28/02
Distance: 🚶500m 🚿500m ⚓500m.
Remarks: Nearby football ground, max. 72h, coins at bakery, butcher and Bar-Tabac.

Colleville-Montgomery 13D3
Rue de Saint-Aubin/Rue les Petites Rues. **GPS:** n49,27166 w0,29891. ⬆➡

9 🅿free 🔌🕳Chfree. **Location:** Rural, simple, quiet. **Surface:** grassy.
◻ 01/01-31/12
Distance: 🚶200m ⚓450m.

Tourist information Colleville-Montgomery:
Ⓜ Musée Omaha Beach, St.Laurent-sur-Mer. Collection of military vehicles, weapons and costumes.

Cormeilles 🌿 14A3
Route du Château de Malou, D810. **GPS:** n49,24926 e0,37371. ➡

8 🅿free 🔌🕳Chfree. **Surface:** asphalted. ◻ 01/01-31/12
Distance: 🚶400m ⚓river 400m.

Coudeville-sur-Mer 🌿⚓🍴 13B3
Avenue de la Mer D351. **GPS:** n48,88707 w1,56607. ⬆

10 🅿€5,65/24h 🔌🕳Ch ✏included 🚿🛁 **Location:** Rural.
Surface: grassy/gravel. ◻ 01/01-31/12
Distance: 🚶500m 🏊200m 🛒200m ✕500m ⚓500m.

Courseulles-sur-Mer 🌿⚓🍴 13D3
Avenue de la Libération. **GPS:** n49,33440 w0,44551. ⬆

13 🅿€6,20 🔌🕳Chincluded. **Location:** Urban, comfortable, central.
Surface: asphalted. ◻ 01/01-31/12
Distance: 🚶50m 🏊200m ✕pizzeria 50m.
Remarks: Nearby entrance campsite, max. 24h.

Courseulles-sur-Mer 🌿⚓🍴 13D3
Juno Beach, Voie des Français Libres. **GPS:** n49,33694 w0,46502. ⬆

25 🅿free. **Location:** Central, quiet. **Surface:** metalled. ◻ 01/01-31/12
Distance: 🚶100m 🏊50m.

FR

⌧S Couterne 13C5
Place de la Mairie. **GPS:** n48,51223 w0,41417.➡.

10 🛏free 🚿🔌 Ch WC free. **Location:** Urban, simple. **Surface:** asphalted.
🅿 01/01-31/12
Distance: 🚶on the spot ⊗nearby 🛒nearby 🚌on the spot.
Remarks: Max. 1 night, closed when frosty.

⌧ Criel-sur-Mer 14B1
Rue de la Plage, D222. **GPS:** n50,03241 e1,31000.⬆.

75 🛏free. **Surface:** grassy/gravel. 🅿 01/01-31/12
Distance: 🚶500m 🏖on the spot 🛒on the spot ⊗500m 🛒1km.

⌧S Deauville 13D3
Boulevard des Sports. **GPS:** n49,35727 e0,08417.⬆.

8 🛏free 🚿🔌Ch 🧹(6x)free. **Location:** Urban, simple, quiet.
Surface: gravel. 🅿 01/01-31/12
Distance: 🚶on the spot 🏖800m 🛒500m.
Remarks: Behind stadium, max. 24h.

⌧S Dieppe 14B1
Quai de la Marne. **GPS:** n49,93014 e1,08667.⬆.

45 🛏€7/24h 🚿🔌Ch free 📶.📠 **Surface:** metalled.
🅿 01/01-31/12
Distance: 🚶500m 🏖on the spot 🛒on the spot ⊗500m 🛒500m.
Remarks: Max. 48h, wifi card available at harbour master.

Tourist information Dieppe:
🏰 Château Dieppe. Castle, 15th century, with maritime museum. 🅿 10-12h,

14-18h 🅿 01/10-31/05 Tue.
🍴 🅿 Tue, Thu 8-14h.
🍴 Normandic market. 🅿 Sa 8-14h.

⌧S Dives-sur-Mer 13D3
Rue de l'avenir. **GPS:** n49,29028 w0,10345.⬆➡.

10 🛏free 🚿€2/10minutes 🔌Ch 🧹. **Location:** Rural, comfortable, quiet.
Surface: asphalted. 🅿 01/01-31/12
Distance: 🚶500m 🏖900m.
Remarks: Nearby Port Guillaume.

⌧S Doudeville 14B2
Place du Mont Criquet, centre-ville. **GPS:** n49,72000 e0,78750.⬆.

25 🛏free 🚿€3,50/100liter 🔌Ch. **Surface:** asphalted. 🅿 01/01-31/12
Distance: 🚶100m 🏖100m 🛒100m.

⌧S Dragey-Ronthon 13B4
Route de la Plage. **GPS:** n48,70945 w1,5139.⬆.

8 🛏free. **Location:** Simple, simple, isolated. **Surface:** grassy/sand.
🅿 01/01-31/12
Distance: 🚶2km 🏖on the spot 🛒on the spot 🚶on the spot.
Remarks: Max. 24h.

⌧S Ducey 13B4
P du Domaine, Rue St Quentin. **GPS:** n48,62513 w1,294.⬆➡.

30 🛏free 🚿€2/100liter 🔌Ch 🚽€2 WC. **Location:** Simple, noisy.
Surface: gravel/metalled. 🅿 01/01-31/12
Distance: 🚶500m ⊗500m 🛒500m 🚶on the spot.
Remarks: Only exact change.

FR

⚐S Englesqueville-la-Percée 13C2

Ferme de la Rouge Fossé, D514. **GPS:** n49,38781 w0,94829. ⬆️

6 🍽€5 ⚡🔌 Ch€3/time 🚿 (6x)included24h. ♿ **Location:** Comfortable, isolated, quiet. **Surface:** grassy/gravel. 🅿️ 01/01-31/12
Distance: 🏖500m.

Equeurdreville 13B2

Rue Jean Bart. **GPS:** n49,65465 w1,65044. ⬆️

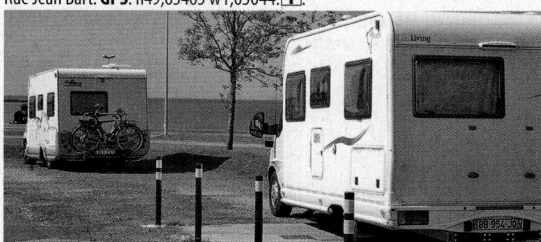

6 🍽free ⚡🔌 Chfree.
Location: Urban, simple. **Surface:** gravel/sand.
Distance: 🚶1km ⊗1km 🛒on the spot.

⚐S Etretat 🚗 14A2

Aire de stationnement Maupassant, Rue Guy de Maupassant.
GPS: n49,70009 e0,21579. ⬆️➡️

30 🍽€8/24h ⚡€3/100liter 🔌 Ch 🔧€3/55minutes.
Surface: grassy/metalled. 🅿️ 01/10-31/12
Distance: 🚶1km 🏖1,2km ⊗1km 🛒1km.
Remarks: Next to camping municipal, max. 24h.

Etretat 🚗 14A2

Pl. de la Gare. **GPS:** n49,70843 e0,21524. ⬆️
10 🍽free. **Surface:** metalled. 🅿️ 01/01-31/12
Distance: 🚶900m 🏖1km.

Tourist information Etretat:
ℹ️ Office de Tourisme, Place Maurice Guillard, www.etretat.net. The cliffs which have the shape of an arch are a well-known tourist attraction.

⚐S Fécamp 14A2

Parking de la Mâture, Chaussée Gayant. **GPS:** n49,76024 e0,37412. ⬆️
+10 🍽free ⚡€3 🔌 Ch. **Location:** Urban. **Surface:** asphalted.
Distance: 🚶on the spot.

Fécamp 14A2

Quai Sadi Carnot. **GPS:** n49,76087 e0,37157. ⬆️

10 🍽free. **Surface:** asphalted. 🅿️ 01/01-31/12
Distance: 🚶200m 🏖on the spot 🛒on the spot ⊗200m 🛒500m.
Remarks: Between pier and marina.

Tourist information Fécamp:
ℹ️ Office de Tourisme, 113, rue Alexandre le Grand, www.fecamptourisme.com. City against the chalk-cliff of the Côte d'Albâtre, fishing-port is now mainly a marina.
Ⓜ️🍴 Palais Bénédictine. Museum with Bénédictine distillery and tasting-pub.
🅿️ 01/07-31/08 10-18h, 01/09-30/06 10.30-11.30h, 14-17h.

Fermanville 13B1

Le Cap Lévi. GPS: n49,69002 w1,4673. ⬆️⬆️➡️

6 🍽€3. ♿ **Location:** Rural, simple, quiet. **Surface:** grassy.
🅿️ 01/01-31/12

⚐S Fervaches 13B3

La Vallée. **GPS:** n48,99550 w1,0826. ⬆️
8 🍽€3 ⚡🔌 Ch WC included 📶free. **Location:** Rural, comfortable.
Surface: grassy/gravel.
Distance: 🚶150m 🛒150m.
Remarks: Wifi code at grocery.

Forges-les-Eaux 🏛 14C2

Aire de camping car de la Minière, Boulevard Nicolas Thiessé.
GPS: n49,60569 e1,54288. ⬆️

35 🍽€6,77, 01/11-15/03 free ⚡🔌 Ch 🚿 included. **Surface:** asphalted.
🅿️ 01/01-31/12
Distance: 🚶2km.
Remarks: Max. 48h.

⚐S Formigny 13C2

La Ferme du Lavoir, D517. **GPS:** n49,34041 w0,89654. ⬆️

FR

6 🍴 € 10/night 🚰 🔌 Ch 🚿 WC 🚮 📶 included. ♿ **Location:** Rural, comfortable, quiet. **Surface:** asphalted/grassy.
Distance: 🚶300m ⛰3km.
Remarks: Organic orchards, cider production.

| 🚐 S | Gacé 🌱 | 14A4 |

Rue du Marché aux Bestiaux. **GPS:** n48,79500 e0,29583. ⬆️.

30 🍴free 🚰€2 🔌Ch. **Surface:** asphalted. 📷 01/01-31/12
Distance: 🚶on the spot 🚲2,6km ⊗50m.
Remarks: In front of tourist office, max. 24h.

| 🚐 S | Gavray | 13B3 |

D38. **GPS:** n48,91113 w1,34641. ⬆️.

8 🍴free 🚰€4/10minutes 🔌Ch. **Location:** Urban, comfortable.
Surface: asphalted. 📷 01/01-31/12
Distance: 🚶400m ⛰200m 🛒600m 📮100m.
Remarks: In front of police station.

| 🚐 S | Gisay-la-Coudre | 14A4 |

D35. **GPS:** n48,95001 e0,62670. ➡️.

6 🍴free 🚰€2/100liter 🔌Ch 🏪. **Surface:** asphalted. 📷 01/01-31/12
Distance: 🚶on the spot ⊗300m.
Remarks: Coins available at restaurant La Tortue.

| 🚐 S | Gournay-en-Bray | 14C2 |

Avenue Sadi Carnot. **GPS:** n49,48055 e1,72640.
10 🍴free 🚰 🔌Ch free. **Surface:** asphalted. 📷 01/01-31/12
📷 Thu-morning closed because of market + 2nd weekend Sep
Distance: 🚶on the spot ⊗on the spot 🏧on the spot 📮on the spot.

Remarks: Max. 48h.

| 🚐 S | Gournay-en-Bray | 14C2 |

Route du Vieux Saint-Clair. **GPS:** n49,50106 e1,72245. ⬆️.
🍴€6 🚰€1 🚿€2.
Location: Rural, simple, isolated, quiet.
Distance: 🚶2,5km.

| 🚐 S | Gouvets | 13B3 |

Le Bourg D454. **GPS:** n48,93133 w1,09492. ⬆️.

20 🍴 🚰 🔌 🚿 WC free. **Location:** Rural, simple, isolated, quiet.
Surface: asphalted/metalled. 📷 01/01-31/12
Distance: 🚶on the spot ⊗6km 🚶on the spot.

| 🚐 S | Gouville-sur-Mer 🏖 | 13B3 |

Chemin du Beau Rivage. **GPS:** n49,09970 w1,60896. ⬆️➡️.

40 🍴€5/19-10h 🚰liter 🔌Ch 🏪minutes WC included. 🛒
Location: Urban. **Surface:** gravel. 📷 01/01-31/12
Distance: 🏊on the spot ⊗on the spot 🚍50m.

| 🚐 S | Grainville-Langannerie | 13D3 |

Rue de Lapford. **GPS:** n49,01438 w0,26805. ⬆️➡️.

6 🍴free 🚰€2/10minutes 🔌Ch 🏪€2/55minutes 🏪.
Location: Rural, comfortable. **Surface:** metalled. 📷 01/01-31/12
Distance: 🚶100m.
Remarks: Near Salle des Fêtes.

| 🚐 S | Grandcamp-Maisy | 13C2 |

Rue du Moulin Odo. **GPS:** n49,38620 w1,03782. ➡️.

14 🍴free 🚰€2 🔌Ch. **Location:** Rural, comfortable, quiet.

Surface: asphalted/gravel.
Distance: 500m 500m.
Remarks: Coins at tourist info, rue Aristide Briand.

| S | Granville | 13B4 |

Haute Ville, Rue du Roc. **GPS:** n48,83530 w1,6095.

20 €6 €2/10minutes Ch €2/55minutes .
Location: Simple. **Surface:** asphalted/gravel.
01/01-31/12
Distance: 500m 500m 500m on the spot.
Remarks: Motorhome parking behind sea aquarium, upper city, Atlantic Wall 50m, max. 24h.

Tourist information Granville:
Office de Tourisme, 4, Cours Jonville, www.ville-granville.fr. The old centre, Haute-Ville, is surrounded by ramparts. The lower city is a bathing resort.
Wed, Sa.

| S | Gréville-Hague | 13A1 |

D402. **GPS:** n49,67509 w1,80127.

10 free €2 Ch €2 WC. **Location:** Rural, comfortable.
Surface: metalled.
Distance: on the spot 100m.
Remarks: Next to sports fields.

| S | Grigneuseville | 14B2 |

La Plaine d'Hermesnil, 7 rue de la Plaine. **GPS:** n49,64427 e1,19900.

7 €6 Ch included. **Surface:** gravel.
Distance: 2,5km 2,5km 2,5km.

| S | Grossville | 13A2 |

Bar-Epicerie Caladjo, Rue des Touzés. **GPS:** n49,50659 w1,74311.

15 €6 €2 Ch free €2. **Location:** Rural, simple. **Surface:** gravel.
01/01-31/12
Distance: on the spot on the spot.

| S | Guilberville | 13C3 |

D159. **GPS:** n48,98871 w0,94844.

15 free €2/100liter Ch €2/1h. **Location:** Rural, simple, quiet.
Surface: gravel. 01/01-31/12 service: 01/11-01/03
Distance: 300m 1,5km 300m 300m.
Remarks: Coins at tourist info, Bistro and bakery.

| S | Hermanville-sur-Mer | 13D3 |

Rue Verte. **GPS:** n49,28592 w0,31243.

6 free Ch free. **Location:** Simple, central, quiet. **Surface:** asphalted.
01/01-31/12
Distance: on the spot 200m.
Remarks: Tuesday market.

Tourist information Hermanville-sur-Mer:
Tue morning.

| | Hérouvilette | 13D3 |

Place l'Aiguillon, Avenue de Caen, D 513A. **GPS:** n49,21983 w0,24497.

8 free Ch free. **Location:** Rural, comfortable. **Surface:** asphalted.
01/01-31/12
Distance: 250m 200m.

| S | Heurteauville | 14B2 |

Les Cerisiers, Rue de Village. **GPS:** n49,44777 e0,81333.

12 ⌁€8 ⛽🔌 Ch included 💧€2. **Surface:** grassy/gravel. ⬛ 01/04-31/10
Distance: 🚶3km 🏖20m 🚌20m ⊗3km 🚊3km.
Remarks: Along the Seine river.

🅂 **Honfleur** ⚓   **14A2**
Bassin de l'Est, Quai de la cale. **GPS:** n49,41916 e0,24166. ⬆

20 ⌁free ⛽€3/100liter 🔌 Ch. **Surface:** grassy/gravel. ⬛ 01/03-30/11
Distance: 🚶1km 🏖500m 🚌200m 🚊200m.
Remarks: Coins at Tourist Info and bakery.

🅲🅂 **La Ferrière-aux-Etangs**   **13C4**
Camping du Lac, Rue de l'Etang. **GPS:** n48,65931 w0,51706. ⬆➡

120 ⌁€10 ⛽🔌 Ch 💧(60x)included. 📷 ♻
Location: Urban, simple, central. **Surface:** gravel.
⬛ 01/01-31/12 ⬛ service in winter
Distance: 🚶500m 🚲2,7km ⊗300m 🚊500m.

🅂 **Isigny-sur-Mer**   **13B2**
Quai Neuf. GPS: n49,32150 w1,10456. ⬆

7 ⌁free ⛽€2/10minutes 🔌 Ch 💧€2/1h.
Location: Simple, quiet. **Surface:** metalled.
⬛ 01/01-31/12
Distance: 🚶400m ⊗400m 🚊400m 🚶on the spot.
Remarks: At lake, at tennis-court, only exact change.

🅂 **La Ferté-Macé**   **13D4**
Ruelle des Fournelles, D916. **GPS:** n48,59018 w0,35528. ⬆

6 ⌁free ⛽€2/100liter 🔌 Ch. **Location:** Rural. **Surface:** asphalted.
Distance: 🚶300m 🚌on the spot 🚊200m.

🅂 **Jobourg**   **13A1**
Nez de Jobourg, D202. **GPS:** n49,67722 w1,93806.

15 ⌁free ⛽🔌 Ch WC free. **Location:** Urban, simple. **Surface:** asphalted.
⬛ 01/01-31/12
Distance: 🚶on the spot ⊗on the spot 🚊on the spot.
Remarks: Parking at church.

🅂 **La Lucerne-d'Outremer**   **13B4**
D35. GPS: n48,78437 w1,42727. ⬆

10 ⌁free ⛽WC free. **Surface:** metalled. ⬛ 01/01-31/12
Distance: 🏖500m 🚌500m.

🅂 **Jumièges**   **14B2**
Rue Alphonse Callais. GPS: n49,43106 e0,81452. ⬆➡

6 ⌁free, voluntary contribution ⛽🔌 Ch 🚻voluntary contribution WC free.
Location: Urban, simple. **Surface:** asphalted. ⬛ 01/01-31/12
Distance: 🚶on the spot ⊗100m 🚊100m.
Remarks: Next to castle, max. 2 days.

🅂 **La Mailleraye-sur-Seine**   **14B2**
Quai Paul Girardeau. GPS: n49,48444 e0,77333. ⬆

FR

34 � € 5, 1/11-31/3 free ⚡€3/10minutes 🚰 Ch ➕.
Surface: grassy.
◻ 01/01-31/12 ◉ 2nd weekend April/May
Distance: 🚶200m ⚓on the spot ⊗on the spot 🚉200m.
Remarks: Along the Seine river, coins at town hall and shops.

La Poterie-Cap-d'Antifer 14A2
GPS: n49,68317 e0,16480.⬆➡

4 �37free. **Location:** Simple, quiet. **Surface:** grassy/gravel.
◻ 01/01-31/12
Distance: 🚶2km.

La Vespière 14A3
Chemin de la Grand Mare/Campaugé. **GPS**: n49,02763 e0,42221.⬆

2 �37free ⚡€2/100liter 🚰 Ch ➕€2/1h. **Location:** Simple, comfortable.
Surface: asphalted. ◻ 01/01-31/12
Distance: 🚶300m 🛣 A28 2,2km 🚉Carrefour 200m.

La-Rivière-Saint-Sauveur 14A2
Parking de l'Orange - Place Albert Harel, Chemin des Bancs, D580.
GPS: n49,40856 e0,26926.⬆

20 �37free ⚡€5/100liter 🚰 Ch ➕€5/30minutes. **Location:** Rural,
simple, central, quiet. **Surface:** asphalted. ◻ 01/01-31/12
Distance: 🚶on the spot 🛣700m 🚉supermarket + bakery 100m.
Remarks: Coins at the shops in the village.

Langrune-sur-Mer 13D3
Rue du Colonel Pierre Harivel. **GPS**: n49,32474 w0,36814.⬆➡

3 �37free. **Location:** Comfortable, central. **Surface:** asphalted/metalled.
◻ 01/01-31/12
Distance: 🚶on the spot ⚓beach 50m 🚉50m.

Le Billot 13D3
D39. **GPS**: n48,96948 e0,07217.⬆

4 �37free ⚡€2,50 🚰 Ch ➕€2,50 WC. **Location:** Rural, simple.
Surface: gravel/metalled. ◻ 01/01-31/12
Distance: ⊗200m.
Remarks: Coins at Relais du Billot 200m, beautiful view.

Le Havre 13D2
Chaussée John Kennedy. **GPS**: n49,48499 e0,10673.⬆➡

19 �€6 ⚡🚰 Ch 🧹€5 ♻.
Location: Simple, central. **Surface:** asphalted.
◻ 01/01-31/12
Distance: 🚶5 min walking ⚓on the spot ⊗200m 🚉200m.
Remarks: Max. 48h.

Tourist information Le Havre:
Ⓜ Musée de l'Ancienne Havre, rue Jerome Bellarmato. History of the city.
◻ Wed-Su 14-18h.
⊛ Canyon Parc, CD34, Epretot. Family park in western style.

Le Mesnil-Jumièges 14B2
Base de loisirs UCPA, Route de Mesnil. **GPS**: n49,41172 e0,84494.⬆.

10 �37free, July-Aug € 10 ⚡🚰 Ch ♻. **Surface:** asphalted. ◻ 01/01-31/12
Distance: 🚶1km ⚓200m 🛣200m ⊗1km 🚉1km.

⛰Ṡ Le Mont-Saint-Michel 🌿⚓ 13B4
Aire Camping-car du Mont-Saint-Michel. GPS: n48,61401 w1,50773.

Ṡ€ 12,50/24h ⛽🔧Ch🔌🔦📶. **Surface:** grassy. ⬛ 23-06h
Distance: ⊗La Rotisserie 🍽on the spot.

⛰Ṡ Le Mont-Saint-Michel 🌿⚓ 13B4
Parking Véolia, La Jacotière Ardevon. GPS: n48,61388 w1,5058.⬆

50 Ṡ€ 20,60/24h. 🚌 **Location:** Rural. **Surface:** metalled.
⬛ 01/01-31/12
Distance: ⊗100m.
Remarks: Free shuttle to Le Mont-Saint-Michel.

Tourist information Le Mont-Saint-Michel:
ℹ Office de Tourisme, Corps de Garde des Bourgeois, www.mont-saint-michel. net. Town with abbey on a cliff in the sea.

🏕Ṡ Le Noyer-en-Ouche 14A3
Ferme Lesur, La Godinière, D140. GPS: n49,01017 e0,72444.⬆

5 Ṡ€ 7,50 ⛽€3 🔋€3. **Surface:** grassy. ⬛ 01/01-31/12

⛰Ṡ Le Sap 14A4
Les Terriers, Rue Nicolas Lesieur, D12. GPS: n48,89525 e0,33249.⬆

4 Ṡfree ⛽🔧Ch🔧 free. **Surface:** gravel. ⬛ 01/01-31/12
Distance: 🛒500m 🍽on the spot ⊗500m 🍽500m.
Remarks: Next to fire-station.

⛰Ṡ Le Tréport ⚓ 14C1
Du Funiculaire, Route Touristique, D126E. GPS: n50,05777 e1,36222.⬆

25 Ṡ€ 6 ⛽€2,10/100liter 🔧Ch🔌€2,10/55minutes 🧺. 🚌
Location: Comfortable, isolated, quiet. **Surface:** grasstiles.
Distance: 🛒Le Tréport centre 2km 🏊2km ⊗100m.
Remarks: Free cableway to city centre, max. 48h.

⛰Ṡ Le Tréport ⚓ 14C1
Parc Sainte Croix, Rue Pierre Mendès France. GPS: n50,05954 e1,38919.⬆➡

61 Ṡ€ 9,50, tourist tax incl ⛽🔧Ch🔧 (61x)included. 🚌🧺
Location: Comfortable, isolated, quiet. **Surface:** asphalted. ⬛ 01/01-31/12
Distance: 🛒700m 🏊700m 🍽500m Mr.Ed.
Remarks: Industrial area, near camping municipal, max. 48h.

Tourist information Le Tréport:
🏰 Château d'Eu, Eu. Royal castle, 19th century. ⬛ 15/03-01/11 🔵 Sa.

⛰Ṡ Les Pieux 🌊 13A2
Plage Sciotot. GPS: n49,50722 w1,84731.
6 Ṡfree. **Location:** Simple. **Surface:** metalled. ⬛ 01/01-31/12
Distance: 🏊beach 50m.
Remarks: Large parking, 50m from beach.

⛰Ṡ Les Pieux 🌊 13A2
Intermarché, Route de Cherbourg. GPS: n49,51736 w1,79797.⬆

6 Ṡfree ⛽€2/100liter 🔧Ch. **Surface:** asphalted.
Distance: 🍽on the spot.

⛰Ṡ Lessay 13B3
Place Saint Cloud. GPS: n49,21850 w1,53548.⬆➡

4 Ṡfree ⛽🔧Ch🔧 WCfree. **Location:** Urban, simple. **Surface:** asphalted.
⬛ 01/01-31/12

Distance: 🚶on the spot ⊗150m. 🚰200m.
Remarks: Check in at town hall (service).

| Lion-sur-Mer 🏖 | 13D3 |

Rue du General Gallieni. **GPS:** n49,30174 w0,31316.⬆.

4 🛏free. **Location:** Urban, central, noisy. **Surface:** asphalted.
🅿 01/01-31/12
Distance: 🏊on the spot ⊗on the spot 🚰100m.
Remarks: At sea, parking townhall, only overnight stay allowed.

| 🛏♿ S | Lisieux | 14A3 |

Parking du Carmel, Rue d'Alençon. **GPS:** n49,14413 e0,22788.⬆➡.

🛏free 🚰€3/100liter ♨Ch ➕€3/1h WC. **Surface:** asphalted.
🅿 01/01-31/12
Distance: 🚶on the spot 🏊river ⊗on the spot 🚰on the spot.

| Luc-sur-Mer 🏖 | 13D3 |

Route de Lion-sur-Mer. **GPS:** n49,31430 w0,34346.⬆➡.

4 🛏free. **Location:** Rural, simple. **Surface:** asphalted.
🅿 01/01-31/12
Distance: 🏊200m.

| 📷 | Lyons-la-Fôret | 14C2 |

La Cuette. **GPS:** n49,39908 e1,47912.
🛏free.
Distance: 🚶100m ⊗100m 🚰100m.

| 🛏♿ S | Lyons-la-Fôret | 14C2 |

Les Grandes Molaises, Les Hogues. **GPS:** n49,41312 e1,42562.⬆.

20 🛏€8 + € 0,20/pp tourist tax 🚰📶included. **Location:** Rural, isolated.

Surface: grassy.

| 🛏♿ S | Marigny | 13B3 |

Rue Auguste Eudeline, D53. **GPS:** n49,09911 w1,24776.⬆➡.

10 🛏free 🚰€2/10minutes ♨Ch ➕€2/55minutes. **Location:** Urban, simple.
Surface: metalled. 🅿 01/01-31/12
Distance: 🚶700m 🚲200m ⊗700m 🚰700m 🚌on the spot.

| 🛏♿ S | Merville Franceville 🏖 | 13D3 |

Boulevard Wattier. **GPS:** n49,28483 w0,21071.⬆.

6 🛏free 🚰€2/10minutes ♨Ch. **Location:** Comfortable, quiet.
Surface: asphalted. 🅿 01/03-15/11
Distance: 🏊75m.

| 🛏♿ S | Montebourg | 13B2 |

Parking Louis Lecacheux. **GPS:** n49,48486 w1,37449.⬆.

10 🛏free 🚰 ♨Chfree. **Location:** Simple. **Surface:** metalled.
🅿 01/01-31/12

| 🏨 S | Montfiquet | 13C3 |

Hotel-Restaurant Relais de la Fôret, L'Embranchement, D572.
GPS: n49,19400 w0,863.⬆.

60 🛏€14 🚰 ♨Chincluded WC€2/time, use sanitary €2. **Surface:** asphalted.
🅿 01/01-31/12
Distance: 🚶1km ⊗1km.
Remarks: Pay at reception, picnic tables available.

| 🛏♿ S | Montville 🏞🚴👥 | 14B2 |

Place de l'Abbé Kerebel. **GPS:** n49,54710 e1,07304.⬆➡.

15 � free ⌐€4,50/100liter ⌐Ch ⌐€4,50/h ⌐free,(8-22.30).
Surface: gravel. ⌐01/01-31/12
Distance: 400m ⌐400m.
Remarks: Coins at mairie, restauration Hexagone, museum.
Tourist information Montville:
⌐ Mo-morning.

Mortain   13C4
Place du Château. **GPS:** n48,64887 w0,94489.↑→.

6 ⌐free ⌐⌐Ch⌐WC free. **Location:** Urban, simple. **Surface:** asphalted.
⌐01/01-31/12
Distance: on the spot ⌐on the spot ⌐on the spot ⌐on the spot.
Remarks: Max. 48h.
Tourist information Mortain:
⌐ Office de Tourisme, Rue du Bourglopin, www.ville-mortain.fr. Hiking trail to the Grande and Petite Cascade, waterfalls.

Nonancourt   14B4
D53, Rue Hippolyte Lozier. **GPS:** n48,77269 e1,19261.
4 ⌐free ⌐⌐Ch free ⌐. **Surface:** asphalted.
Distance: 200m.

Notre-Dame-de-Courson   14A3
D4. **GPS:** n48,99021 e0,25922.↑.

9 ⌐free ⌐€2/20minutes ⌐Ch ⌐€2/20minutes.
Location: Rural, comfortable, quiet. **Surface:** gravel. ⌐01/01-31/12
Distance: 200m ⌐Le Tournebroche 200m.
Remarks: Service only with 1-euro coins.

Oissel   14B3
Rue du Bras St.Martin. **GPS:** n49,33783 e1,09183.↑.

2 ⌐free ⌐€2/100liter ⌐Ch ⌐€2/55minutes.
Surface: gravel.
⌐01/01-31/12
Distance: 200m ⌐on the spot ⌐on the spot ⌐200m ⌐200m.
Remarks: <7m, coins at the bakery: 1, Rue du Maréchal Foch.

Ouistreham   13D3
Rue des Dunes/Boulevard Maritime. **GPS:** n49,28716 w0,24968.↑.

45 ⌐€8 ⌐⌐Ch ⌐included. ⌐⌐ **Location:** Urban, comfortable, noisy.
Surface: asphalted/gravel. ⌐01/01-31/12
Distance: 650m ⌐150m ⌐2km.
Remarks: Near car ferry.

Pirou-Plage   13B3
Rue des Hublots. **GPS:** n49,16522 w1,58937.↑→.

6 ⌐free ⌐€2/10minutes ⌐Ch ⌐€2/55minutes. **Location:** Simple.
Surface: asphalted. ⌐01/01-31/12
Distance: 500m ⌐500m ⌐500m ⌐500m.
Remarks: Coins at campsite Clos Marin and restaurant La Marée, market on Sunday.

Pont-d'Ouilly   13D4
Rue de la Libération. **GPS:** n48,87794 w0,41304.↑→.

43 ⌐€11/24h ⌐€2 ⌐Ch ⌐(43x)included ⌐.⌐⌐
Location: Rural, comfortable, quiet. **Surface:** gravel. ⌐01/01-31/12
Distance: 550m ⌐on the spot ⌐550m ⌐550m.
Remarks: Along the Orne river.

Pont-l'Évèque 14A3

Les Mouettes, Avenue de Verdun. **GPS:** n49,28563 e0,18769. 🚶.

6 🚐free. **Location:** Urban, simple, central.
📅 01/01-31/12
Distance: 🚶on the spot 🚲6km ✖100m 🛒150m.

Port-en-Bessin-Huppain 13C2

Rue du 11 Novembre. **GPS:** n49,34583 w0,75861. ⬆➡.

17 🚐€ 3,50/night. **Location:** Rural, simple. **Surface:** sand.
📅 01/01-31/12
Distance: 🚶300m 🏊400m ✖400m 🛒500m.

Port-en-Bessin-Huppain 13C2

Super U, Avenue du Général de Gaulle. **GPS:** n49,34307 w0,75212. ⬆.

12 🚐free 🚰€3/time 🗑 Ch 🔌€3/24h. **Location:** Simple.
Surface: gravel/metalled. 📅 01/01-31/12
Distance: 🚶200m 🏊400m ✖400m 🛒on the spot.

Portbail 13B2

Rue Gilles Poerier. **GPS:** n49,33776 w1,69273. ⬆.

10 🚐free 🚰🗑 Chfree.
Location: Comfortable, quiet. **Surface:** asphalted.
Distance: 🚶500m.

Réville 13B2

Ferme de la Froide Rue, 165, Rue des Monts. **GPS:** n49,62583 w1,25278. ⬆.

6 🚐€7 🚰🗑 Ch . **Location:** Rural, comfortable. **Surface:** grassy.
📅 01/01-31/12
Distance: 🚶1km.

Rots 13C3

Centre Commercial Cora, Chemin de la Croix Vautier, RN13.
GPS: n49,19985 w0,46027. ⬆.

🚐free 🚰🗑 Chfree 🔌. **Location:** Noisy. **Surface:** asphalted.
📅 01/01-31/12
Distance: 🚿1km ✖on the spot 🛒on the spot.
Remarks: Terrain with video surveillance.

Rugles 14A4

Place de la Liberté. **GPS:** n48,82230 e0,70846. ⬆.

4 🚐free 🚰🗑 Ch 🔌free. **Surface:** metalled. 📅 01/01-31/12
Distance: 🚶on the spot ✖200m 🛒200m.
Remarks: Max. 48h.

Saint Fromond 13B3

Rue des Gabariers, D8. **GPS:** n49,22202 w1,08956. ⬆.

Rauville-la-Bigot 13B2

D900. **GPS:** n49,51723 w1,68368.

FR

50 ⬛free 🚰€2 Ch 🚽€2. **Location:** Rural, simple.
Surface: asphalted/gravel. ⬛ 01/01-31/12
Distance: 🚶on the spot ⊗50m 🛒on the spot.

Tourist information Saint Fromond:
🛈 Office de Tourisme, Bd de Verdun, Carentan, www.ot-carentan.fr. Old bishop city with Gothic cathedral.

Saint-André-de-l'Eure 14B4
Boulevard Verdun. **GPS:** n48,90644 e1,26927.⬆.

10 ⬛free 🚰 Ch free. **Location:** Urban, comfortable, noisy.
Surface: metalled. ⬛ 01/01-31/12
Distance: 🚶1km 🚌on the spot 🛒1km 🛒on the spot.
Remarks: Along railwayline.

Saint-Martin de Bréhal 13B3
Av. de l'Hippodrome. **GPS:** n48,89829 w1,56583.⬆➡.

20 ⬛€3/24h 🚰 free. 🐾 **Location:** Urban. **Surface:** asphalted.
⬛ 01/01-31/12
Distance: 🚶300m 🏖beach 150m ⊗300m 🛒400m.

Saint-Pierre-sur-Dives 13D3
Aire Camping-Cars de la Halle Médiévale, Place du Marché.
GPS: n49,01713 w0,03047.⬆ .

12 ⬛€5/24h 🚰 Ch.🛒 🐾 **Location:** Urban, simple, central.
Surface: gravel. ⬛ 01/01-31/12 ⬤ Mo-morning market
Distance: 🚶on the spot ⊗50m 🛒150m.
Remarks: Service passerby € 3.

Saint-Saire 14C2
Rue de la Gare, D7. **GPS:** n49,69677 e1,49476.⬆.
⬛free 🚰 Ch 🐾. **Location:** Rural, comfortable, quiet.
Surface: asphalted/grassy. ⬛ 01/01-31/12
Distance: 🚶300m ⊗on the spot 🚲 Avenue Verte.

Saint-Sever-Calvados 13B4
Place de la Mairie. **GPS:** n48,84169 w1,04842.⬆➡.

15 ⬛free 🚰 Ch free. **Location:** Urban, simple, noisy. **Surface:** gravel.
⬛ 01/01-31/12
Distance: 🚶100m 🚲15km 🛒100m.

Saint-Vigor-le-Grand 13C3
Les Peupliers, Rue de Magny. **GPS:** n49,29949 w0,67436.⬆.

7 ⬛€ 6, € 9 service incl 🚰 Ch 🐾 included. 🐾 **Location:** Rural, comfortable, isolated, quiet. **Surface:** gravel. ⬛ 01/01-31/12
Distance: 🚶2km.
Remarks: Baker every morning, service passerby € 4, bayeux centre 3,5km, Arromanches beaches 6,5km.

Sallenelles 13D3
Boulevard Maritime D514. **GPS:** n49,26474 w0,22694.⬆.

2 ⬛free 🚰€2/10minutes Ch. **Location:** Rural, simple, quiet.
Surface: asphalted. ⬛ 01/01-31/12
Distance: 🚶100m 🏖on the spot 🛒300m.
Remarks: Max. 48h.

Sideville-Lorimier 13B2
Camping-car l'Orimier, Route du Pont Roger, D152. **GPS:** n49,58722 w1,69222.
⬆.

6 🛌 € 7 🚰🍴 Ch 🚿(6x)included. **Location:** Comfortable, quiet.
Surface: asphalted/grassy.
Remarks: Regional products.

🏕️S | **Siouville-Hague** | 13A2
Avenue des Peupliers. **GPS:** n49,56356 w1,8442.

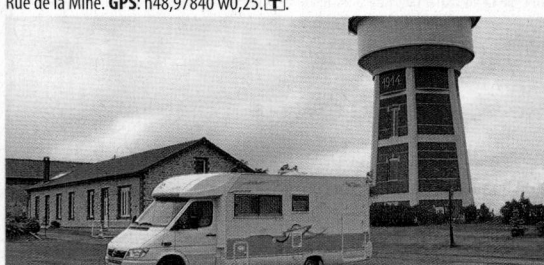

30 🛌free 🚰€2 🍴Ch. **Surface:** grassy.
Distance: 🏖️200m.

🏕️S | **Soumont-Saint-Quentin** | 13D3
Rue de la Mine. **GPS:** n48,97840 w0,25.⬆️.

20 🛌 € 6 + € 0,20/pp tourist tax 🚰🍴Ch🚽included. 🛒 **Location:** Simple.
Surface: grassy. 🅾️ 01/01-31/12
Distance: 🚶1km.
Remarks: Former iron mine.

🏕️S | **Sourdeval** | 13C4
Parc Saint-Lys, Rue Jean Baptiste Janin. **GPS:** n48,72603 w0,92308.⬆️➡️.

8 🛌free 🚰🍴Ch🚿free. **Location:** Urban, simple.
Surface: gravel/metalled. 🅾️ 01/01-31/12
Distance: 🚶100m ⊗400m 🚆400m.

🏕️S | **St.Hilaire-du-Harcouët** 〰️ | 13B4
Place de la Motte. **GPS:** n48,57602 w1,09086.⬆️➡️.

---

10 🛌free 🚰€2 🍴Ch🚽€2. **Location:** Urban, simple.
Surface: asphalted/metalled. 🅾️ 01/01-31/12
Distance: 🚶on the spot ⊗on the spot 🚆on the spot.
Remarks: Behind church.

🏕️S | **St.Jouin-Bruneval** | 14A2
Rue des Pruniers. **GPS:** n49,65099 e0,16322.⬆️.

20 🛌free 🚰€2 🍴Ch🚽€2. 🅾️ 01/01-31/12
Distance: 🚶1km 🏖️1km 🚆1km.

🏕️ | **St.Jouin-Bruneval** | 14A2
Plage de Bruneval. **GPS:** n49,64970 e0,15349.⬆️.

30 🛌free. **Surface:** gravel. 🅾️ 01/01-31/12
Distance: 🚶4km 🏖️pebbled beach 🚲on the spot ⊗100m 🚆4km.

🏕️S | **St.Lô** 🌿🍴 | 13B3
Place de la Vaucelle. **GPS:** n49,11351 w1,10309.⬆️➡️.

10 🛌free 🚰€2/10minutes 🍴Ch🚽€2/h 🚿. **Location:** Urban, comfortable.
Surface: asphalted. 🅾️ 01/01-31/12
Distance: 🚶100m ⊗100m 🚆100m 🚌on the spot.
Remarks: Along river.

Tourist information St.Lô:
👁️ Haras National, Rue du Maréchal Juin. National Stud farm established by Napoleon in 1806. 🅾️ 01/06-30/09 14-18.
Ⓜ️ Musée de la Libération, place du Champ de Mars. Invasion in 1944. 🅾️ 10-19h, winter 14-19h ⏹️ Tue. 🎫 free.
✝️ Nôtre Dame. Renovated church 13th century.

FR

⬛S St.Nicolas d'Aliermont 14B1
Place du 19 Mars 1962, Rue d'Arques. **GPS:** n49,88045 e1,22092. ⬆.

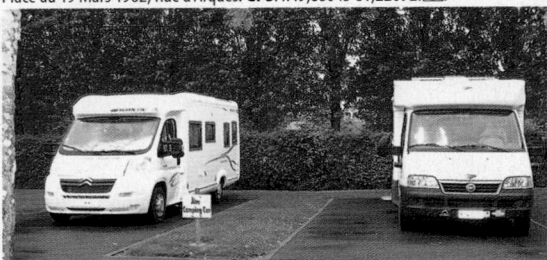

2 🛏free 🚰€2 ♻Ch 🔌€2. **Surface:** asphalted.
⬛ 01/01-31/12
Distance: 🚶200m 🚲12km ⊗200m 🚰200m.
Remarks: Behind town hall, max. 48h, coins at town hall and library.

⬛S St.Nicolas-de-Bliquetuit 14A2
Route du Bac. **GPS:** n49,52083 e0,72777. ⬆➡.

12 🛏free 🚰€2 ♻Ch 🔌€2. **Surface:** asphalted. ⬛ 01/01-31/12
Distance: 🚶1,4km ⚓on the spot 🛒on the spot ⊗2km 🚰2km
🏃on the spot.
Remarks: Along the Seine river, coins at town hall.

⬛S St.Pair-sur-Mer 13B4
Avenue Léon Jozeau-Marigné. **GPS:** n48,81711 w1,56988. ⬆➡.

30 🛏€5 🚰€2/10minutes ♻Ch 🔌€2/55minutes. 📷🚐 **Location:** Urban,
simple. **Surface:** asphalted/gravel. ⬛ 01/01-31/12
Distance: 🚶500m ⚓beach 500m ⊗500m 🚰on the spot.
Remarks: Parking at tennis-court, max. 48h.

⬛S St.Pierre-Eglise 13B2
Parking du 8 Mai 1945. **GPS:** n49,66897 w1,40387. ➡.

6 🛏free 🚰€2/100liter ♻Ch **Location:** Urban. **Surface:** metalled.
⬛ 01/01-31/12
Distance: 🚶300m 🚰on the spot.

⬛S St.Pierre-le-Vieux 🎑 14B1
Ferme du Moulin, D237. **GPS:** n49,85816 e0,88000. ⬆➡.

5 🛏€5 + €1/pp 🚰 ♻Ch 🔌€3. **Surface:** grassy/gravel. ⬛ 01/01-31/12
Distance: 🚶1km ⊗1km 🚰1km.

⬛S St.Sauveur-le-Vicomte 🌿 13B2
Place Auguste Cousin. **GPS:** n49,38678 w1,52947.

🛏free 🚰 ♻Ch free. **Surface:** asphalted.
Distance: 🚶on the spot.
Remarks: Next to town hall, max. 48h.

⬛S St.Vaast-la-Hougue 🏰🚢 13B2
Aire de la Gallouette, Rue Galouette. **GPS:** n49,58400 w1,267. ⬆.

27 🛏€7 🚰€2/10minutes ♻Ch 🔌€2/1h. **Location:** Comfortable.
Surface: metalled. ⬛ 01/01-31/12
Distance: 🚶300m 🚰300m.
Remarks: Near campsite Gallouette.

Tourist information St.Vaast-la-Hougue:
ℹ Office de Tourisme, 1, place Gen. de Gaulle, www.saint-vaast-reville.com.
Important port for allied forces in 1944. Now large marina.
👁 Île de Tatihou, Port. Island in front of the coast, maritime museum and bird
hide. ⬛ 01/04-30/09 10-18h.

⬛S St.Valery-en-Caux 🏰🚢 14A1
Quai d'Aval. **GPS:** n49,87220 e0,70898. ⬆.

40 🛏free, peak season €5/day + €0,20/pp 🚰€3 ♻Ch. **Surface:** asphalted.
⬛ 01/01-31/12
Distance: 🚶600m ⚓on the spot 🛒on the spot ⊗500m 🚰bakery 600m.
Remarks: Max. 48h, coins at tourist info.

☒S Ste.Honorine-des-Pertes 13C2
Garage Vally, Route d'Omaha Beach, D514, dir Colleville-sur-Mer.
GPS: n49,34868 w0,81635.⬆.

32 ⬛€6 ⛽€1,50/100liter ⬛Ch ⚡(32x)included. ♿ **Location**: Rural, comfortable, quiet. **Surface**: grassy. ⬛ 01/01-31/12
Distance: 🚶200m ⛱500m ⊗on the spot.
Remarks: Automatic bread distributor, service passerby € 2,50.

☒S Ste.Marie-du-Mont 13B2
Camping-car Park, La Madeleine, D913. **GPS**: n49,41417 w1,18643.⬆.

49 ⬛€12 ⛽⬛Ch ➕⬛€4/3,50 📶included. 📶 **Location**: Simple, quiet.
Surface: grassy/gravel. ⬛ 01/01-31/12
Distance: ⛱500m.
Remarks: Code wifi: f2d1941a5c.

Tourist information Ste.Marie-du-Mont:
Ⓜ Musée du Débarquement, Utah-Beach. Landing museum.

S Ste.Mère-Eglise 13B2
Super U, ZA les Crutelles. **GPS**: n49,40461 w1,32223.

⛽€2 ⬛Ch.
Surface: asphalted.
Distance: 🚶1km ⚓on the spot.
Remarks: Motorhome washing place max. ⌃3.80m.

Tourist information Ste.Mère-Eglise:
ⓘ Borne 0 de la voie de la Liberté. Marker 0, start of the Libery Road.
ⓘ Office de Tourisme, 2, Rue Eisenhower, www.sainte-mere-eglise.info. Village well-known for the paratrooper who landed on the church-tower.
Ⓜ Musée Airborne. Exhibition about the invasion at St.-Mère-Eglise.
⬛ 10-12h, 14-18h.

☒S Surtainville 13A2
Rue des mielles. **GPS**: n49,46373 w1,82871.

10 ⬛free ⛽€4,16/10minutes ⬛Ch ➕€4,16/55minutes ⚡.
Location: Urban. **Surface**: metalled.
Distance: 🚶on the spot ⛱100m.
Remarks: Coins at camping municipal.

☒S Tinchebray 13C4
Rue André Breton, D911. **GPS**: n48,76302 w0,73753.⬆➡.

3 ⬛free ⛽⬛Ch ⚡free. **Location**: Urban, simple. **Surface**: asphalted.
⬛ 01/01-31/12
Distance: 🚶on the spot ⊗300m.

☒S Tourlaville 13B2
Espace Loisirs Colignon, piscine-camping municipal, Rue des Algues.
GPS: n49,65398 w1,56606.

⬛free ⛽€2 ⬛Ch. **Location**: Simple. **Surface**: asphalted.
Remarks: Coins at campsite or swimming pool.

☒ Tourlaville 13B2
Quai Amiral Kniskern/Boulevard Maritime. **GPS**: n49,64549 w1,59976.

⬛free.
Remarks: Parking at ferry-boat.

☒S Tréauville 13A2
1, La Chaussee, D65. **GPS**: n49,54444 w1,83472.⬆.

FR

10 ☐€6,50 ⌁ Ch ⚡ included. **Surface:** grassy/metalled.
Distance: ⌁2,5km.

☐S | **Valognes** | 13B2
Place Félix Buhot. **GPS:** n49,51159 w1,47813. ⬆️

7 ☐free ⌁€2 Ch ⬛€2. **Location:** Simple. **Surface:** asphalted.
Distance: ⌁1km ⚡on the spot.
Remarks: Next to supermarket Champion.

☐S | **Valognes** | 13B2
Zone Artisanale d'Armanville, Chemin de la Brique. **GPS:** n49,51433 w1,50004. ⬆️

☐€5/24h ⌁€2 Ch ⬛€2 WC. **Location:** Simple. **Surface:** asphalted.
🅿️ 01/01-31/12
Distance: ⌁1km.
Remarks: Motorhome washing place.

☐ | **Veules-les-Roses** 🌊⚓🍦🥖 | 14B1
Parking des Falaises. GPS: n49,87555 e0,79269. ⬆️➡️

☐free. **Surface:** grassy. 🅿️ 01/01-31/12
Distance: ⌁500m ⚓on the spot ⛽on the spot ⊗500m ⚡500m.

☐S | **Veules-les-Roses** | 14B1
Camping des Mouettes, Avenue Jean Moulin. **GPS:** n49,87596 e0,80289. ⬆️➡️

15 ☐€10/24h ⌁€3 Ch. **Surface:** metalled. 🅿️ 01/01-31/12
Distance: ⚓300m ⌁500m ⛽500m ⊗300m ⚡300m ⛟on the spot.
Remarks: Max. 48h, coins at campsite, 12-14h closed.

☐S | **Veulettes-sur-Mer** | 14A1
Chemin des Courses. **GPS:** n49,85233 e0,60165. ⬆️

15 ☐€5 ⌁€3,50/100liter Ch ⬛€3,50/1h ⚡ (16x). 🚿
Surface: asphalted. 🅿️ 01/01-31/12
Distance: ⌁200m ⚓100m ⛽100m ⊗100m ⚡200m.
Remarks: Behind Syndicat d'Initiative, coins at tourist info, campsite and supermarket.

☐S | **Veulettes-sur-Mer** | 14A1
Parking de la Plage, D10. **GPS:** n49,85488 e0,60702. ⬆️

50 ☐€5 ⌁€3,50/10minutes ⬛€3,50/1h. 🚿 **Surface:** grassy.
🅿️ 01/01-31/12
Distance: ⌁200m ⚓50m ⛽50m.
Remarks: Beach parking, max. 24h.

☐ | **Villedieu-les-Poêles** 🌊⚓🍦🥖 | 13B4
Parc de la Commanderie, Rue Taillemarche. **GPS:** n48,83682 w1,22436. ⬆️

5 ☐free. **Location:** Urban, simple. **Surface:** asphalted.
🅿️ 01/01-31/12
Distance: ⌁on the spot ⚡2,4km ⊗100m ⚡100m.

☐S | **Villers-Bocage** | 13C3
Rue du Canada. **GPS:** n49,07973 w0,6609. ⬆️➡️

FR

Ile-de-France

5 🛏free ⚡€2/10minutes 🚰Ch🚰€2/55minutes ♻. **Location:** Urban, simple, quiet. **Surface:** asphalted. 🅾 01/01-31/12
Distance: ⚓1,5km ⊗on the spot 🚊400m ♨on the spot.
Remarks: Max. 48h.

Paleospace l'Odyssee, Rue des Martois. **GPS:** n49,32910 e0,01273. ⬆➡.

14 🛏€10 ⚡€4 🚰Ch ✎included 🔌€1 ♻.🗑♻ **Location:** Urban, comfortable, quiet. **Surface:** metalled. 🅾 01/01-31/12
Distance: 🚰1km 🏖beach 250m 🍞bakery 1,5km.
Remarks: Max. 48h.

D916, Avenue du Dr. Dentu. **GPS:** n48,93152 e0,19604. ⬆.

6 🛏free ⚡🚰Ch ✎(2x) WC free. **Location:** Urban, simple, central.
Surface: asphalted. 🅾 01/01-31/12
Distance: 🚰400m ⊗500m 🛒Carrefour 200m.
Remarks: Major centre in the Camembert-region, Camembert museum.

Place du champ de foire. **GPS:** n48,84084 w0,88862. ⬆➡.

25 🛏free ⚡🚰Chfree. **Location:** Urban, simple, noisy. **Surface:** asphalted.
🅾 01/01-31/12 🔵 Fri-Sa
Distance: 🚰on the spot ⊗on the spot 🔵on the spot.
Remarks: Water closed during wintertime, friday-Saturday market.

Quai de l'Ile. **GPS:** n48,41713 e3,23745.

20 🛏free ⚡🚰Chfree 🔵. **Surface:** asphalted.
Distance: 🚰100m ⊗100m.
Remarks: Max. 72h.

Tourist information Bray-sur-Seine:
🏹 🅾 Fri 8-13h.

Parking Disneyland Paris, Boulevard du Parc. **GPS:** n48,87500 e2,79700. ⬆.

🛏€ 30/day ⚡🚰Ch ✎WC included. **Surface:** asphalted.
🅾 01/01-31/12
Remarks: Motorhome area at amusement park, note: tariffs will be charged per day, even if you arrive in the evening.

Tourist information Coupvray:
🔵 Disneyland Paris, Marne-la-Vallée. Attractions and themepark.

Route de Nemours. **GPS:** n48,39798 e2,48021. ⬆.
6 🛏free ⚡🚰Chfree. **Location:** Rural. **Surface:** asphalted.
🅾 01/01-31/12
Distance: 🚰1km ⚓9,4km A6.
Remarks: In front of Conservatoire Nationale des Plantes, gate opens automatically.

Total, 49-51 Avenue de Ganay. **GPS:** n48,40720 e2,46782. ⬆.

🛏€ 3,50 ⚡🚰Ch. **Surface:** grassy. 🅾 01/01-31/12
Distance: 🚰centre 500m ⚓7,7km A6.
Remarks: Behind petrol station, gate open 6-21h.

Les Colverts de Kabaya, Route de Moret. **GPS:** n48,27866 e2,69893. ⬆.
6 🛏€6 ⚡€3. **Surface:** grassy. 🅾 01/01-31/12
Distance: 🚰1,6km ⚓2,3km ⊗200m 🚊200m.

Parking Office de Tourisme, Chemin de Villecran. **GPS:** n48,56189 e3,27993.
⬆➡.

FR

30 🛏 € 8 ⛲€3,50 🔌Ch ♦€3,50 ♦.🛢 🗑 **Surface:** gravel.
🅿 01/01-31/12 🔘 service: frost
Distance: 🚲500m ⊗500m.
Tourist information Provins:
⚓ 🅿 Sa 8-14h.

15 🛏free. **Surface:** asphalted. 🅿 01/01-31/12
Distance: 🚲1,5km ⛰50m ➝50m ⊗50m ⚓50m.

♿S **Arzon** 12D4
Aire d'accueil des Camping-cars de Kermor, Avenue de Kerlun, Kerjouanno.
GPS: n47,53886 w2,88028.⬆➝.

♿S **Souppes-sur-Loing** 15A6
GPS: n48,18083 e2,72343.⬆➝.

5 🛏 € 5 ⛲🔌Ch ♦included. 🚿 **Surface:** asphalted.
Remarks: Max. 72h.

♿S **St.Cyr-sur-Morin** 15A4
Avenue Daniel Simon. **GPS:** n48,90627 e3,18516.
4 🛏free ⛲🔌Chfree. **Surface:** grassy. 🅿 01/01-31/12
Distance: 🚰on the spot.
Remarks: Behind church.

♿S **St.Fargeau-Ponthierry** 14D5
Base de loisirs Seine-Ecole, Avenue Max Pierrou. **GPS:** n48,53610 e2,55065.⬆.
5 🛏 € 5,20 ⛲🔌Chincluded. **Surface:** grassy.
Distance: 🚲850m.
Remarks: Recreation park.

Britanny

♿S **Antrain** 13B5
Route de Pontorson. **GPS:** n48,46307 w1,47938.⬆.

2 🛏free ⛲🔌Ch🚽 WCfree. **Surface:** asphalted.

♿ **Arzal** 12D4
Barrage d'Arzal, D139. **GPS:** n47,50089 w2,38074.🔱.

49 🛏€ 7/24h ⛲🔌Ch ♦(16x)📶included. 🛢🗑 **Surface:** asphalted.
🅿 01/01-31/12
Remarks: Nearby Plage du Fageo, June/Sep max. 72h.

♿S **Audierne** 12B3
Rue Lamartine. **GPS:** n48,02733 w4,53721.⬆.

10 🛏free ⛲€2/10liter🔌Ch🚽. **Location:** Simple. **Surface:** unpaved.
🅿 01/01-31/12
Distance: 🚲1,5km ⊗500m.

♿S **Auray** 12C4
Chemin de Bellevue. **GPS:** n47,66365 w2,97393.⬆➝.

🛏free ⛲€3/20minutes🔌Ch🚽. **Surface:** asphalted.
Distance: 🚲200m.

♿S **Auray** 12C4
Place du Golhéres. **GPS:** n47,66524 w2,99036.⬆➝.

3 🛏free 🚰€2 🔵Ch 🔵€2. **Surface:** asphalted. **Distance:** 🚶500m 🔵on the spot.

Tourist information Auray:
⛺ 🔵 Mo.

🔵 **Baud** 12C3

Rue du Champ de Foire. **GPS:** n47,87375 w3,02008.⬆️.

20 🛏free. **Surface:** metalled. 🔵 01/01-31/12

🔵 **Baud** 12C3

Route de Locminé. **GPS:** n47,88112 w2,97465. 🚰🔵Ch🔵free. 🔵 01/01-31/12

🔵 **Bédée** 13A5

Rue de Dinan. **GPS:** n48,18099 w1,94416.⬆️.

6 🛏free 🚰🔵Ch free. **Surface:** asphalted. **Distance:** 🔵200m 🔵50m.
Remarks: Nearby cemetery.

🔵 **Belle-Isle-en-Terre** 12C2

Les Jardins du Guer, Rue Guerveur, D33. **GPS:** n48,54332 w3,39417.⬆️➡️.

10 🛏free 🚰🔵Ch ⚡free. **Surface:** gravel. 🔵 01/04-30/11
Distance: 🚶100m 🔵10m.

🔵 **Belz** 12C4

Parc de Loisirs, Rue des Sports. **GPS:** n47,66940 w3,17744.⬆️➡️.

10 🛏free. **Surface:** gravel/metalled. 🔵 01/01-31/12

🔵 **Berric** 12D4

Chemin de l'Étang. **GPS:** n47,63365 w2,52806.⬆️➡️.

6 🛏€5 🚰€2/10minutes 🔵Ch 🔵€2/55minutes. 🔵 **Surface:** asphalted.
Distance: 🚶500m 🔵on the spot 🔵on the spot 🔵500m 🔵500m.
Remarks: Along river, coins at the shops in the village, access via Rue du Grand Pont.

🔵 **Binic** 12D2

Aire camping-car de l'Ic, Rue de l'Ic. **GPS:** n48,60059 w2,83573.⬆️➡️.

50 🛏free 🚰🔵Ch free. **Location:** Urban, simple, central, quiet.
Surface: gravel. 🔵 01/01-31/12
Distance: 🚶500m 🔵700m 🔵500m 🔵500m.

Tourist information Binic:
⛺ 🔵 Thu.

🔵 **Bourg-Blanc** 12B2

Rue de Brest. **GPS:** n48,49188 w4,50312.⬆️.

6 🛏free 🚰🔵Ch free. **Surface:** sand. 🔵 01/01-31/12
Distance: 🔵fish pond 🔵100m.

🔵 **Brech** 12C4

Rue de Pont Douar/Avenue des Pins, D768. **GPS:** n47,71917 w3,00111.⬆️➡️.

FR

6 🛏free ⚡€3 🔌 Ch. **Surface:** grassy. 🌙 01/01-31/12
Distance: 💧100m ⛵Small lake ✖200m 🛒200m.
Remarks: Parking nearby small lake, plan d'eau, coins at the bakery.

| 😊 | **Brest** | 12B2 |

Parking Océanopolis, Rue du Cormoran. **GPS:** n48,38893 w4,43535.⬆.

24 🛏free. **Surface:** asphalted. 🌙 01/01-31/12
Distance: ⛱on the spot 🛒on the spot 🚌300m.
Remarks: Busy parking during the day, gate closes at 18h.

| Ⓢ | **Brest** | 12B2 |

Port du Moulin Blanc, Rue Eugène Berest. **GPS:** n48,39174 w4,43612.⬆.

⚡🔌 Ch 💳free.
🌙 01/01-31/12

Tourist information Brest:
👁 Tour Tanguy. Diorama old Brest. 🌙 daily, 01/10-31/05 Wed, Su afternoon.
🙂 Océanopolis. Sea-centre, penguin and seals. 🌙 01/04-31/08 9-18h, 01/09-31/03 10-17h 🌙 Mo.

| 🏕 | **Brillac** | 12D4 |

Rue Saint-Maur. **GPS:** n47,54143 w2,81748.⬆.

7 🛏free. **Surface:** asphalted. 🌙 01/01-31/12
Distance: ⛱400m ✖450m.

| 🏕Ⓢ | **Callac (22)** | 12C2 |

Av Ernest Renan. **GPS:** n48,40200 w3,43737.⬆.

8 🛏free ⚡€2 🔌 Ch 💳€2. **Surface:** gravel. 🌙 01/01-31/12
Distance: ⛵200m 🚌200m.
Remarks: Lac Verte Vallée.

| 🏕Ⓢ | **Camaret-sur-Mer** | 12B2 |

Rue Georges Ancey. **GPS:** n48,27513 w4,60793.⬆➡.

75 🛏01/04-31/10 € 6 ⚡€2/100liter 🔌 Ch 💳€2/55minutes. 🚐
Location: Rural, comfortable, quiet. **Surface:** gravel.
🌙 01/01-31/12
Distance: 💧1km ⛵500m ✖500m 🛒500m 🚲on the spot 🚶on the spot.
Remarks: Max. 72h.

| 🏕Ⓢ | **Campénéac** | 12D3 |

Rue de l'Étang. **GPS:** n47,95736 w2,29039.⬆➡.

30 🛏free 💧€2 WC. **Surface:** grassy. 🌙 01/01-31/12
Distance: 💧250m.
Remarks: Coins at Fauchoux, rue nationale 32.

| Ⓢ | **Campénéac** | 12D3 |

Rue de la Fontaine. **GPS:** n47,95674 w2,29364.⬆➡.
⚡€2 🔌Ch.
Remarks: Coins at town hall and supermarket.

| Ⓢ | **Cancale** | 13A4 |

Aire camping-car Ville Ballet, Rue des Français Libres.
GPS: n48,67004 w1,86583.⬆.

100 🛏free, 15/03-15/11 € 6/24h ⚡10minutes 🔌 Ch 💳55minutes,€3 🚿
🚐 **Surface:** grassy. 🌙 01/01-31/12
Distance: ⛱on the spot ✖1km 🛒800m 🚌100m.

Remarks: Bread-service.
Tourist information Cancale:
👁 La Ferme Marine. Guided tour oyster farm. ⬛ summer 11h,15h,17h Français, 14h English, 16h Deutsch.

⬛Ⓢ **Carantec** 🏖🏄 12B2
Aire du Meneyer, Rue Castel an Dour. **GPS:** n48,65967 w3,9138.

20 🚐free 🚰€3/15minutes 🧺Ch ➕€3/55minutes.
Surface: gravel/metalled. ⬛ 01/01-31/12
Distance: 🏊500m.
Remarks: Max. 48h.

⬛Ⓢ **Carantec** 🏖🏄 12B2
Chemin du Roch Glaz. **GPS:** n48,65235 w3,90308.

10 🚐free. **Surface:** asphalted. ⬛ 01/01-31/12
Distance: 🏊beach 300m 🚶on the spot.
Remarks: Max. 24h, seaview.

⬛Ⓢ **Carantec** 🏖🏄 12B2
Rue Pen Al Lann. **GPS:** n48,66861 w3,895.

15 🚐free. **Surface:** asphalted. ⬛ 01/01-31/12
Distance: 🏙500m 🏊150m 🛒150m ⊗1km 🍴1km.
Remarks: At tennis-courts, max. 48h.

⬛Ⓢ **Carantec** 🏄 12B2
Square du Grand Sacconex, Rue du Kélenn. **GPS:** n48,66892 w3,91085.

10 🚐free. **Surface:** unpaved.
Distance: 🏙300m 🏊on the spot 🛒on the spot ⊗on the spot 🍴300m
◉on the spot.

Remarks: At gymnasium.
Tourist information Carantec:
Ⓜ Musée Maritime. Navigation museum. ⬛ 15/05-15-09 ◉ Thu.

⬛Ⓢ **Carhaix-Plouguer** 12C3
Rue de Bazeilles/Rue des Augustins. **GPS:** n48,27829 w3,57257.⬆.

10 🚐free 🚰🧺Ch ➕free. **Surface:** metalled. ⬛ 01/01-31/12
Distance: 🏙200m 🏊200m 🍴200m.

⬛Ⓢ **Carnac** 🏖🏄 12C4
Square d'illertissen. **GPS:** n47,58505 w3,08242.⬆➡.

50 🚐free 🚰€2 🧺 🚿. **Surface:** asphalted. ⬛ 01/01-31/12
Distance: 🏙50m 🏊1,5km ⊗50m 🍴50m.
Remarks: Max. 1 night.
Tourist information Carnac:
ℹ Office de Tourisme, 74, avenue des Druides, www.carnac.fr. Seaside resort and important place of finding of 30.000 prehistoric menhirs.
Ⓜ Musée de la Préhistoire. Prehistoric museum. ⬛ 10-12.30h and 14-18h ◉ 01/12-01/04. 🎫 € 6.

⬛Ⓢ **Caulnes** 13A5
Lavoir Fontaine, Rue de Dinan. **GPS:** n48,28655 w2,15517.⬆.

10 🚐free 🚰€2/10minutes 🧺Ch ➕€2/1h WC. **Surface:** gravel.
⬛ 15/03-15/11
Distance: 🏙500m ⊗100m 🍴100m 🚌200m.
Remarks: Max. 24h.

⬛Ⓢ **Cesson-Sévigné** 13A5
Route de La Valette. **GPS:** n48,11802 w1,59121.⬆.

8 🛏free 🚰€2,30/10minutes 🚽 Ch 🔌€2,30/55minutes 🗑. **Surface:** metalled. 📷 01/01-31/12

| 🏕️🅂 | **Châteauneuf-du-Faou** | 12B3 |

Penn ar Pont. GPS: n48,18286 w3,81576.⬆️.
15 🛏free. **Surface:** gravel. 📷 01/01-31/12
Distance: 🚶1,3km.

| 🏕️🅂 | **Châtillon-en-Vendelais** | 13B5 |

D108. GPS: n48,23112 w1,17959.

10 🛏free 🚰 🚽Chfree. **Surface:** asphalted.
Distance: 🏊lake.
Remarks: At the lake, next to campsite.

| 🏕️🅂 | **Cléden-Cap-Sizun** | 12A3 |

Place du 19 mars 1962, Rue de la ville d'ys. **GPS:** n48,04803 w4,65008.⬆️.

20 🛏free 🚰€2/10minutes 🚽Ch WC. **Location:** Rural, simple, quiet. **Surface:** asphalted/metalled. 📷 01/01-31/12
Distance: 🚶on the spot.

| 🏕️🅂 | **Cléden-Cap-Sizun** | 12A3 |

Pointe du Van, D7. **GPS:** n48,05936 w4,70727. ⬆️ .

20 🛏free WC. **Surface:** gravel. 📷 01/01-31/12
Distance: 🚶Cléden-Cap-Sizun ± 5km 🏊on the spot 🎣on the spot.

| 🏕️ | **Cléden-Cap-Sizun** | 12A3 |

Route de Kastel Koz, Beuzec-Cap-Sizun. **GPS:** n48,08473 w4,51844.⬆️ .

10 🛏free. **Location:** Rural, simple, isolated. **Surface:** grassy/gravel.
📷 01/01-31/12
Distance: 🏊on the spot 🎣on the spot.

| 🏕️🅂 | **Cléden-Poher** | 12C3 |

Route du Stade. **GPS:** n48,23686 w3,67165.⬆️.
🛏free 🚰 🚽Ch 🚿 (4x)free. **Surface:** asphalted. 📷 01/01-31/12
Distance: ⊗50m 🥖bakery 200m.

| 🏕️🅂 | **Clohars-Carnoët** | 12C3 |

D16, Rue de Quimperlé. **GPS:** n47,79810 w3,58516.⬆️.
4 🛏free 🚰€2 🚽Ch 🔌€2. **Surface:** asphalted. 📷 01/01-31/12
Distance: 🚶200m 🚲10km 🏊beach 4,5km 🥖bakery 200m.

| 🏕️🅂 | **Clohars-Carnoët** | 12C3 |

Place de NAVA, Rue de Quimperlé. **GPS:** n47,79790 w3,585.

3 🛏free 🚰€2 🚽Ch 🔌€2. **Surface:** asphalted. 📷 01/01-31/12

| 🏕️🅂 | **Combrit** | 12B3 |

Place du 19 mars 1962, Hent Ty Plouz. **GPS:** n47,88755 w4,1546.

10 🛏free 🚰€2/10minutes 🚽 Ch 🔌€2. **Location:** Simple, quiet.
Surface: metalled. 📷 01/01-31/12
Distance: 🚶on the spot.
Remarks: Coins at the shops in the village.

| 🏕️🅂 | **Commana** 🏘️ | 12B2 |

Place du salles de Sports, D11. **GPS:** n48,41611 w3,96139.⬆️➡️.

5 🛏free 🚰 🚽free. **Location:** Rural, simple, isolated, quiet. **Surface:** grassy.
📷 01/01-31/12
Distance: 🚶200m ⊗300m 🥖bakery 300m 🚴on the spot 🎣on the spot.

FR

Concarneau 12B3

Le Porzou, Allée Jean Bouin. **GPS:** n47,86320 w3,9051.

40 free €4/10minutes Ch €4/55minutes WC. **Location:** Urban, simple. **Surface:** asphalted. 01/01-31/12
Distance: city centre 2km on the spot.
Remarks: Foot ferry to centre.

Concarneau 12B3

Parking de la Gare, Avenue de la Gare. **GPS:** n47,87864 w3,9202.

47 € 2/20-08h €4 Ch €4/55minutes. **Location:** Simple.
Surface: asphalted. 01/01-31/12
Distance: 500m beach 1,4km on the spot on the spot.
Remarks: Parking station.

Tourist information Concarneau:
Mo, Fri.

Crac'h 12C4

Intermarché, AC Les Alizés. **GPS:** n47,60421 w2,99669.

8 free €2/10minutes Ch. **Surface:** asphalted. 01/01-31/12
Distance: on the spot on the spot.

Crozon 12B2

Parking du Loc'h, Rue de l'Atlantique, Morgat. **GPS:** n48,22523 w4,50851.

30 € 4,08 €3,20/10minutes Ch €3,20/55minutes.
Location: Simple. **Surface:** asphalted. 01/01-31/12
Distance: 300m on the spot on the spot 100m.
Remarks: Max. 48h, market Wednesday.

Crozon 12B2

Le Fret, Le Sillon, D55. **GPS:** n48,28457 w4,50934.

6 free €2,08/10minutes Ch. **Location:** Rural, simple, quiet.
Surface: unpaved. 01/01-31/12
Distance: on the spot Resto 250m.

Crozon 12B2

Parking office de tourisme, Boulevard de Pralognan, D887.
GPS: n48,24770 w4,4934.

20 free €2 €2. **Location:** Urban, simple. **Surface:** asphalted.
01/01-31/12
Distance: on the spot.
Remarks: Nearby Office de Tourisme, max. 48h.

Damgan 12D4

Parking de Kervoyal, Boulevard de l'atalante. **GPS:** n47,51465 w2,56038.

76 € 6 Ch included. **Surface:** metalled/sand. 01/01-31/12
Distance: 600m Sandy beach.
Remarks: Parking at the beach, max. 48h.

Dinan 13A4

Rue du Port, D12. **GPS:** n48,45450 w2,0389.

30 € 0,30/30min 9-19h, overnight stay free. **Surface:** asphalted.
01/01-31/12
Distance: 800m 500m.

Dol-de-Bretagne 13A4

Place Jean Hamelin. **GPS:** n48,54736 w1,75442.

FR

16 🅿 free 🚰 €2 🅲 Ch 🚽 €2. **Location:** Urban, simple, noisy. **Surface:** asphalted.
Distance: 🚶 on the spot ⊗100m 🚰100m 🚌150m.

🅲🆂 **Elven** 12D4
Avenue des Martyrs de la Résistance, Le Guého. **GPS:** n47,73879 w2,58134. ⬆➡

7+25 🅿 €1 + €1,50/pp 🚰 €3 🅲 Ch 🧹 (12x)€2/4h. **Location:** Simple, quiet. **Surface:** grassy/gravel. 🅾 parking 01/01-31/12 service 01/07-31/08
Distance: 🚶1,5km ⊗950m 🚰950m.

🅲🆂 **Erdeven** 12C4
Boulevard d'Atlantique. **GPS:** n47,61429 w3,15958. ⬆➡

20 🅿 €6,50/24h 🚰 🅲 Ch 🚽 🧹 Surface: grassy.
Distance: ⚓500m 🚰200m 🚌200m.

🅲🆂 **Erdeven** 12C4
Chemin De Kerouriec. **GPS:** n47,62717 w3,17988. ⬆
12 🅿 €6 🚰 €2 🧹 €2. **Location:** Simple, isolated, quiet. **Surface:** grassy.
🅾 01/01-31/12
Distance: ⚓1,1km.

Erdeven 12C4
Place de St Margen. **GPS:** n47,64200 w3,157. ⬆

10 🅿 free. **Surface:** metalled. 🅾 01/01-31/12
Distance: 🚶50m ⊗50m 🚰50m.
Remarks: Parking in centre, behind city hall.

🍴🆂 **Erdeven** 12C4
Rue des Menhirs. **GPS:** n47,63750 w3,15156. ⬆➡

10 🅿 €7 🚰 €2 🅲 Ch 🧹 €2. **Surface:** grassy/metalled.
Distance: 🚶500m ⊗on the spot 🚰Lidl 300m.

🅲🆂 **Erquy** 12D2
Caroual Plage, Rue des Hirondelles. **GPS:** n48,62120 w2,4724. ⬆

47 🅿 €6/24h 🚰 €2 🅲 Ch 🚽 €2. **Surface:** metalled. 🅾 01/04-15/11
Remarks: Beach parking, max. 48h.

🅲🆂 **Etel** 12C4
Camping municipal, Rue de la Barre. **GPS:** n47,65100 w3,202. ⬆➡

25 🅿 €6,50/night 🚰 €2 🅲 Ch. **Surface:** grassy. 🅾 01/04-30/09
Remarks: Baker every morning (Jul/Aug).

🅲🆂 **Fouesnant** 12B3
Plage Mousterlin, Chemin de Kerneuc. **GPS:** n47,85144 w4,04662. ⬆

15 🅿 free. **Surface:** grassy/sand.
Distance: 🏊beach 50m.
Remarks: Beach parking, max. 48h.

🆂 **Fouesnant** 12B3
Leclerc, D45, Route de Quimper. **GPS:** n47,90234 w4,02938. ⬆

12free ⌨€2/10minutes 🔲Ch 🔲€2/55minutes. **Surface:** asphalted. ⚫ 01/01-31/12
Distance: 🛒on the spot.

🔲🅂 Fougères 🔷⚓ 13B5
Allée des Fêtes. **GPS:** n48,35660 w1,20242. ⬆.

🔳free ⌨🔲Ch WC free. **Surface:** asphalted. ⚫ 01/01-31/12
Distance: 🛒500m ⊗200m 🛒200m.

🔲🅂 Fougères 🔷⚓ 13B5
Parking de la Poterne, Boulevard de Rennes. **GPS:** n48,35524 w1,2113. ⬆.

16 🔳free ⌨🔲Ch free. **Surface:** metalled. ⚫ 01/01-31/12
Distance: 🛒on the spot ⊗250m.
Remarks: Castle of Fougères 500m.

🔲🅂 Fréhel 12D2
La Ville Oie, Rue des Sports, D117, Pléhérel-plage. **GPS:** n48,65032 w2,35241.
⬆➡.

40 🔳€6 ⌨Service €4 🔲Ch 🔲 ▧.🅵 ◈ **Surface:** unpaved. ⚫ 01/01-31/12
Distance: 🛒1,1km 🛒beach 1,2km.

🔲🅂 Gâvres 12C4
Rue des Filets Bleus. **GPS:** n47,69515 w3,35097. ⬆.
40 🔳€7 ⌨🔲Ch 🔲. **Surface:** grassy. ⚫ 01/01-31/12
Distance: 🛒100m 🛒100m.

🅒🅂 Glomel 12C3
Etang du Coronc, Rue du Lac. **GPS:** n48,22052 w3,38972. ⬆➡.

12 🔳free ⌨€2/100liter 🔲Ch 🔲€2/1h ▧.
Surface: asphalted. ⚫ 01/01-31/12
Distance: 🛒150m.
Remarks: At lake.

🔲🅂 Goulven 12B2
Aire Naturelle Ty Poas. **GPS:** n48,63109 w4,30833. ⬆➡.

15 🔳€5 + tourist tax ⌨€2 🔲Ch 🔲€2 WC 🔲.▧
Location: Comfortable, quiet. **Surface:** grassy/metalled. ⚫ 15/06-30/09
Distance: 🛒500m 🛒beach 200m 🛒500m.

🔲🅂 Gueltas 12D3
Boju, Keriffe. **GPS:** n48,10406 w2,79064. ⬆➡.

16 🔳 ⌨🔲Ch WC free. **Location:** Rural, simple, quiet. **Surface:** gravel.
⚫ 01/01-31/12
Distance: 🛒1km 🛒on the spot.
Remarks: At the Nantes-Brest Canal.

🔲🅂 Gueltas 12D3
Cité des Écureuils, D125. **GPS:** n48,09667 w2,80111. ⬆➡.

10 🔳free ⌨🔲Ch free. **Location:** Rural, simple, isolated, quiet.
Surface: gravel.
Distance: 🛒200m.
Remarks: Nearby sports park.

🔲🅂 Guern 12C3
Kervazo, Rue de la Vallée, D1. **GPS:** n48,02815 w3,09215. ⬆.

8 🛏free 🚰 ♻ Ch free. **Location:** Rural, simple, quiet. **Surface:** asphalted.
◻ 01/01-31/12
Distance: 🚶250m 🛒bakery 300m.

| 🅂 | Guern | 12C3 |

Etang du Ponterre, D1. **GPS:** n48,03472 w3,0975. ⬆.

6 🛏free. **Location:** Rural, simple. **Surface:** gravel.
◻ 01/01-31/12
Distance: 🚶700m 🚶on the spot 🛒700m bakery.

| 🅂 | Guichen | 13A6 |

Le Boel, Pont Réan. **GPS:** n48,00221 w1,77336. ⬆ ➡.

5 🛏€5 🚰 ♻ Ch WC free. **Surface:** metalled. ◻ 01/01-31/12
Distance: ⚓on the spot 🚶on the spot 🛒bakery 150m.
Remarks: Max. 48h.

| 🅂 | Guidel | 12C4 |

Guidel plage. **GPS:** n47,76640 w3,5258. ⬆.

20 🛏free. **Surface:** sand. ◻ 01/01-31/12
Distance: ⚓250m.
Remarks: Behind Résidence Maéva.

| 🅂 | Guidel | 12C4 |

Arc-en-Ciel, ZA de Pen Mané. **GPS:** n47,80980 w3,4633. ⬆ ➡.

🛏 🚰service €2, during opening hours ♻ Ch 🧹 WC. ◻ 01/01-31/12

| 🅂 | Guimiliau 🍽 | 12B2 |

Parking Salle Polyvalente, Rue des Bruyeres. **GPS:** n48,48676 w3,99665. ⬆ ➡.

15 🛏free 🚰 ♻ free. **Location:** Simple, central, noisy. **Surface:** metalled.
◻ 01/01-31/12
Distance: 🚶on the spot ⊗400m 🛒400m 🚲on the spot 🚶on the spot.
Remarks: Max. 2 nights.

| 🅂 | Guingamp | 12C2 |

Place du Vally. **GPS:** n48,56024 w3,1489. ⬆ ➡.

🛏free 🚰 ♻ Ch ➕free. **Surface:** asphalted. ◉ Fri market
Distance: 🚶on the spot.
Remarks: Max. 24h.

| 🅂 | Guiscriff | 12C3 |

La Gare de Guiscriff, Rue de la Gare. **GPS:** n48,05722 w3,65401. ⬆.

22 🛏free 🚰 ♻ Ch 🧹 free. **Location:** Simple. **Surface:** metalled.
◻ 01/01-31/12
Distance: ⚓on the spot.
Remarks: Behind yachting school, max. 24h.

| 🅂 | Guidel | 12C4 |

Plage du Loc'h, D152, Guidel-Plage > Fort-Bloqué. **GPS:** n47,75052 w3,50654.
⬆ ➡.

FR

4 ⌇free ⚡ Ch ✄ (4x)€5. **Location:** Rural. **Surface:** metalled. ⊙ 01/01-31/12
Distance: 🚶1km 🥖bakery 1km 🚴on the spot ⋏on the spot.

| | | Guissény | 12B2 |

Rue de Plouguerneau. **GPS:** n48,63299 w4,41127.⬆.

⌇free ⚡€2 Ch. **Location:** Comfortable. **Surface:** gravel. ⊙ 01/01-31/12
Distance: 🚶on the spot 🏖beach 550m 🥖250m bakery.
Remarks: Coins at the shops and town hall.

| | Hédé-Bazouges | 13A5 |

La Magdelaine. **GPS:** n48,30592 w1,79218.

50 ⌇free. **Location:** Simple. **Surface:** grassy/gravel. ⊙ 01/01-31/12
Distance: 🚶1km ⊗50m 🚴on the spot ⋏on the spot.

| | | Hillion | 12D2 |

Le Tertre Piquet, Lermot-plage. **GPS:** n48,53098 w2,66387.⬆→.

20 ⌇free ⚡ Ch WC free. **Surface:** grassy. ⊙ 01/01-31/12
Distance: 🏖sandy beach 100m.
Remarks: Beach parking.

| | | Hillion | 12D2 |

Rue Olivier Provost. **GPS:** n48,51743 w2,66772.⬆.

7 ⌇free ⚡ Ch free. **Surface:** gravel. ⊙ 01/01-31/12
Distance: 🚶500m 🥖100m.

| | | Hirel | 13A4 |

D155. **GPS:** n48,60841 w1,82032.⬆.

100 ⌇free, night € 6 ⚡€2/100liter Ch 🔌€2/55minutes. **Surface:** grassy. ⊙ 01/01-31/12
Distance: 🚶700m 🥖200m.

| | | Huelgoat | 12C2 |

Place du Camping-cars, Route du Fao, D769a. **GPS:** n48,36115 w3,75612.⬆→.

30 ⌇free ⚡€5/10minutes Ch 🔌 1h. **Location:** Rural, simple, quiet.
Surface: metalled. ⊙ 01/01-31/12
Distance: 🚶500m 🏖on the spot 🛒on the spot ⊗500m 🥖500m 📮500m 🚴500m ⋏500m.
Remarks: In front of campsite municipal, service 100m.

| | | Janzé | 13A6 |

Aire du Hardier, D41. **GPS:** n47,97258 w1,53825.⬆.

5 ⌇free ⚡€2 Ch. **Location:** Simple. **Surface:** asphalted.

| | | Josselin | 12D3 |

Josselin, Place St.Martin. **GPS:** n47,95639 w2,55056.

50 🛏free 🚰€2,50 🔌 Ch WC. **Surface:** metalled.
⭕ 01/01-31/12 🅿 Sa 9-14h
Distance: 🚶300m 🛣N24 900m ⊗300m 🛒bakery 300m.
Remarks: Castle of Josselin 400m.

Tourist information Josselin:
ℹ️ Office de Tourisme, Place de la Congregation, www.paysdejosselin.com. City is dominated by the castle of Rohan.

🅢	Kerlouan	12B2

Lestonquet. **GPS:** n48,66952 w4,36161.

🛏free 🚰€2 🔌Ch. **Surface:** grassy. ⭕ 01/01-31/12
Remarks: Former campsite.

🅢	Kerlouan	12B2

La Digue. **GPS:** n48,66195 w4,37879.⬆️

4 🛏free. **Location:** Isolated. **Surface:** gravel. ⭕ 01/01-31/12
Distance: 🏖100m 🚲on the spot 🎣on the spot.

🅢	Kernascléden	12C3

Domaine du Scroff, Canquisquelen. **GPS:** n47,99785 w3,31845.⬆️
2 🛏€10 🚰🔌Ch 🔧WC ≋included. **Location:** Comfortable.
⭕ 01/01-31/12
Distance: 🚶1km ⊗on the spot 🎣on the spot.
Remarks: Heated pool.

🅢	La Chèze	12D3

Chemin d'Aliénor, Allée du 19 Mars 1962. **GPS:** n48,13419 w2,65787.⬆️➡️

10 🛏free 🚰🔌Ch 🔧(6x) WC free. **Surface:** asphalted. ⭕ 01/01-31/12
Distance: 🚶200m 🛒200m.

Remarks: Parking at small lake.

🅢	La Martyre	12B2

Route de Ploudiry, D35. **GPS:** n48,44861 w4,15694.⬆️

10 🛏free 🚰🔌Ch 🔧WC free. **Surface:** gravel. ⭕ 01/01-31/12
Distance: 🚶100m ⊗100m 🛒100m.
Remarks: Nearby Maison du Plateau.

🅢	La Roche-Bernard	12D4

Place du Dôme. **GPS:** n47,51753 w2,29733.⬆️

>20 🛏free. **Surface:** asphalted. ⭕ 01/01-31/12
Distance: 🚶50m ⊗100m 🛒50m.

🅒🅢	La Roche-Bernard	12D4

Halte Camping-car, Rue du Patis. **GPS:** n47,52012 w2,30466.⬆️➡️

15 🛏€ 9,30, 01/07-25/08 € 10,90 🚰🔌Ch 🔧€4,50 WC 🔌. **Surface:** grassy.
⭕ 02/04-16/09
Distance: 🚶100m 🛒50m 🛒50m ⊗100m 🛒100m.
Remarks: Next to campsite du Patis.

Tourist information La Roche-Bernard:
ℹ️ Small town especially known for the beautiful hanging bridge over the Vilaine river, 50m high and over 400m long.

🅢	La Roche-Derrien	12C2

Rue du Jouet. **GPS:** n48,74696 w3,25976.⬆️

12 🛏€2 🚰€2 🔌Ch 🔧(6x) 🔌. 🚿 **Location:** Rural, simple, central, quiet.
Surface: gravel. ⭕ 01/01-31/12
Distance: 🚶100m ⊗100m 🎣100m.
Remarks: Coins at the shops and town hall.

Lampaul-Plouarzel 12A2

Aire de Porspaul, Rue de Beg ar Vir. **GPS:** n48,44667 w4,77722.⬆️➡️.

50 🍴free, 15/04-15/10 € 3,50, Jul/Aug + € 0,30/pp 🚰€2/20minutes 🗑️ Ch▥€2/55minutes WC▥€1,60 ▥€3/3,50. **Location:** Comfortable. **Surface:** grassy. 🅿️ 01/01-31/12
Distance: 🛒150m ⛵100m ⊗200m 🚏500m 🚌on the spot 🚶on the spot. **Remarks:** Shower and washing machine Jul/Aug.

Landerneau 12B2

Rue du Calvaire. **GPS:** n48,44694 w4,25667.⬆️.

25 🍴€ 5, incl. electricity 🚰€2 🗑️ Ch 🧹 included 🧺.🏪 **Location:** Comfortable. **Surface:** grassy/gravel. 🅿️ 01/01-31/12
Distance: 🛒500m ⛵river ⊗500m 🚌500m 🚶on the spot.

Landivisiau 12B2

P de Keravel, Rue du Manoir. **GPS:** n48,51015 w4,0758.

3 🍴free 🚰 🗑️Ch free. **Surface:** asphalted. 🅿️ 01/01-31/12
Distance: 🛒on the spot ⊗on the spot 🚌100m 🏙️centre.

Landudec 12B3

Super U, Rue des Écoles. **GPS:** n48,00143 w4,34088.⬆️.

5 🍴free 🚰€2/10minutes 🗑️ Ch▥€2/55minutes. **Location:** Rural, simple. **Surface:** asphalted. 🅿️ 01/01-31/12
Distance: 🛒1km ⊗on the spot 🚌on the spot.
Remarks: Motorhome washing place.

Lanfains 12D2

Étang du Pas, Le Pas, D7. **GPS:** n48,36466 w2,87938.⬆️.

6 🍴free 🗑️ Ch WC free. **Location:** Quiet. **Surface:** asphalted/grassy. 🅿️ 30/04-30/09
Distance: ⊗on the spot 🚏on the spot.
Remarks: Parking at small lake.

Languidic 12C3

Zone Lanveur, Place du Bouilleur de Cru. **GPS:** n47,83722 w3,16188.⬆️➡️.

20 🍴free 🚰 🗑️Ch free. **Location:** Simple, noisy. **Surface:** metalled. 🅿️ 01/01-31/12
Distance: 🛒700m ⊘N24 300m.

Lannilis 12B2

Aire Fontaine Rouge. GPS: n48,55667 w4,50528.⬆️➡️.

12 🍴free 🚰 🗑️Ch WC. **Surface:** metalled. 🅿️ 01/01-31/12
Distance: 🛒1km ⊗1,5km 🚌1,5km.

Lannilis 12B2

Rue Haie Blanche. **GPS:** n48,57125 w4,52151.

🍴free 🚰 🗑️Ch free. **Surface:** asphalted. 🅿️ 01/01-31/12
Distance: 🛒100m 🥖bakery 150m.
Remarks: In front of cemetery.

Lanvallay 13A4

Rue du terrain des sports. **GPS:** n48,45420 w2,03028.

FR

5 ⛺free 🚰€2/100liter 🗑 Ch 🔌€2. **Surface:** asphalted. ⬛ 01/01-31/12
Distance: 🛒50m.

🅿 **Larmor-Baden** 12C4
Route d'Auray. **GPS:** n47,58816 w2,89868. ⬆➡.

8 ⛺free 🚰€2 🗑 Ch 🔌€2/55minutes WC 🚻. **Location:** Comfortable, isolated, quiet. **Surface:** asphalted. ⬛ 01/01-31/12
Distance: 🚶1,5km 🏃on the spot.

🍴S **Le Faouët** 12C3
Restaurant Ty Blomen, Le Grand Pont. **GPS:** n48,03575 w3,48125. ⬆.

3 ⛺free. **Surface:** asphalted. ⬛ 01/01-31/12
Distance: 🛒50m ⊗100m 🚲100m.

🅿S **Larmor-Plage** 12C4
Parking les Pins, Rue des Pins. **GPS:** n47,70970 w3,3791.

15 ⛺free 🚰€2 🗑 Ch. **Location:** Rural, simple. **Surface:** asphalted.
⬛ 01/01-31/12
Distance: ⊗on the spot.

🅿S **Le Folgoët** 12B2
Parking Frepel, Route de Gorrékear. **GPS:** n48,56002 w4,33507. ⬆➡.

4 ⛺free 🚰 🗑 Ch WC free. **Surface:** asphalted. ⬛ 01/01-31/12
Distance: 🏖50m ⊗100m 🚲100m.
Remarks: Nearby plage de Toulhars, max. 72h.

♿S **Le Conquet** 12A2
Parking Parklec'H, Rue Général Leclerc. **GPS:** n48,36055 w4,7701. ⬆.

30 ⛺free 🚰 🗑 Ch 🎣free.
Surface: gravel/metalled. ⬛ 01/01-31/12
Distance: 🛒on the spot ⊗100m 🚲100m.
Remarks: Nearby basilica.

🅿S **Le Trévoux** 12C3
Rue des Sports. **GPS:** n47,89683 w3,64228.

+10 ⛺free 🚰€2/100liter 🗑 Ch 🔌€2/1h.
Surface: gravel.
⬛ 01/01-31/12
Distance: 🛒200m 🏖beach 800m ⊗400m 🚲bakery 300m 🚲on the spot.
Remarks: Coins at tourist info and town hall.

🅿S **Le Croisty** 12C3
Aire de pique-nique, D132, Kergoff. **GPS:** n48,06510 w3,38144.

⛺free 🚰 🗑 Ch 🔌free.
Location: Simple. **Surface:** gravel. ⬛ 01/01-31/12
Distance: 🛒on the spot.
Remarks: Nearby tennis-courts, max. 48h.

🅿S **Le Trévoux** 12C3
Plan d'Eau, Rue de Quimperlé. **GPS:** n47,89356 w3,6386.
10 ⛺free. **Surface:** gravel.
Distance: 🏊on the spot 🚲bakery.
Remarks: At lake.

⑤ 🅂 **Le Vivier-sur-Mer** 13A4
Camping-Car Park, Rue de l'Abri des Flots. GPS: n48,60291 w1,77255.⬆️.
49 ⌇€ 12 ⌁⌇Ch⚓ (49x) ⌁included. 🄿⌇ **Location:** Rural,
comfortable, quiet. **Surface:** asphalted. ⚫ 01/01-31/12
Distance: ⊗150m. ⚏150m.

⑤ 🅂 **Le Vivier-sur-Mer** 13A4
Rue de la Grève, D155. GPS: n48,60383 w1,7799.⬆️➡️.

10 ⌇€ 5 ⌁€2/100liter ⌇Ch ⬚€2/1h.
Surface: metalled. ⚫ 01/01-31/12
Distance: ⚏200m ⚏on the spot ⊗on the spot ⚏on the spot.

🅂 **Léhon** 13A5
Parking Club de Tennis. GPS: n48,44177 w2,04233.⬆️.

6 ⌇free ⌁⌇Chfree. **Surface:** asphalted. ⚫ 01/01-31/12
Distance: ⚏on the spot ⚏bakery 100m.

🅂 **Les Forges** 12D3
Place de l'Église, D117. GPS: n48,01820 w2,6482.⬆️.

5 ⌇free ⌁⌇ WCfree. **Surface:** metalled. ⚫ 01/01-31/12
Distance: ⚏100m ⚏100m.

🅂 **Lézardrieux** 12C2
Rue de l'Île à Bois. GPS: n48,83002 w3,08165.⬆️.

5 ⌇free. **Location:** Simple, isolated, quiet. **Surface:** gravel/sand.
⚫ 01/01-31/12
Distance: ⚏Lézardrieux 6km ⚏50m ⚏on the spot.
Remarks: Max. 24h.

Ⓒ 🅂 **Lézardrieux** 12C2
Camping Municipal, Cité des Gardiens de Phare. GPS: n48,78021 w3,1147. ⬆️➡️.

4 ⌇€ 3 ⌁€3,20 ⌇Ch⚓ WC ⬚€1,26.
Surface: asphalted. ⚫ 01/01-31/12
Distance: ⚏500m ⚏200m ⊗300m ⚏300m ⚏on the spot.

🅂 **Liffré** 13B5
Intermarché. GPS: n48,22459 w1,50165.⬆️➡️.

⌇free ⌁⌇Ch ⬚free. **Surface:** asphalted. ⚫ 01/01-31/12
Distance: ⚏300m ⚏on the spot.

🅂 **Locmaria-Plouzané** 12B2
Plage de Portez, Rue de Portez, Porsmilin. GPS: n48,35501 w4,67269. ⬆️➡️.

8 ⌇€ 4,40 ⌁⌇Chincluded. **Surface:** gravel. ⚫ 01/01-31/12
Distance: ⚏3,5km ⚏beach 50m ⚏on the spot ⚏on the spot.
Remarks: To be paid at campsite.

🅂 **Locmaria-Plouzané** 12B2
Zône détente Ty Izella, Rue de la Fontaine. GPS: n48,37306 w4,64306.⬆️.

12 ⌇free ⌁€2 ⌇Ch ⬚€2. **Location:** Quiet. **Surface:** gravel.
⚫ 01/01-31/12
Distance: ⚏100m ⊗250m ⚏250m.
Remarks: Coins at town hall.

🅂 **Locmariaquer** 12C4
Aire de Pierres Plates, > Route des Plages. GPS: n47,55720 w2,9486.⬆️➡️.

FR

±30 ⌇free. Surface: metalled. ⬛ 01/01-31/12
Distance: ⌇beach 500m 🚐on the spot.
Remarks: Max. 24h, 500m from 'Les Pierres Plates'.

| S | | Locmariaquer | | 12C4 |

Camping La Falaise. GPS: n47,55639 w2,94139.⬆➡.
🚰€2 🗑Ch.
Remarks: 6/6/11 during inspection service point out of order.

| S | | Locmariaquer | | 12C4 |

Résidence de Cresidui. GPS: n47,57204 w2,95328.
🚰€2/100liter 🗑Ch.

Tourist information Locmariaquer:
ℹ Office de Tourisme, Rue de la Victoire, www.ot-locmariaquer.com. Port city with many megalithics, signed dolmen.

| 📷S | | Locminé | | 12D3 |

Rue Laennec / rue du Pont Person. GPS: n47,88788 w2,83174.⬆.

10 ⌇free 🚰🗑Ch free. Location: Simple. Surface: gravel.
Distance: ✎N24 1,4km.
Remarks: Max. 48h.

| ⚓ | | Locmiquelic | | 12C4 |

Port de Ste. Catherine, Quai Rallier du Baty. GPS: n47,72364 w3,34958.

⌇free. Surface: asphalted.
Distance: ⌇on the spot.
Remarks: Max. 1 night.

| 📷S | | Locqueltas | | 12D4 |

Rue de la Fontaine. GPS: n47,75841 w2,76901.⬆.

6 ⌇free 🚰🗑Ch free ✎ (4x)€3,50.
Surface: grassy. ⬛ 01/01-31/12
Distance: ⌇100m ⌇600m 🍴100m 🛒100m.
Remarks: Max. 24h, coins at Bar-Tabac, 18 Place de la Mairie, town hall.

| 📷S | | Locronan 🌿🏛 | | 12B3 |

Parking de la Croix de Mission, Rue du Prieuré. GPS: n48,09811 w4,21245.

10 ⌇free, 01/06-15/10 € 5/24h 🚰€2 🗑Ch 🚽€2 WC.
Surface: grassy/sand. ⬛ 01/01-31/12
Distance: ⊗50m.

| | | Loctudy 🏖 | | 12B3 |

Plage des Sables Blancs, Rue du Beau Rivage. GPS: n47,79883 w4,19739.⬆.

6 ⌇free.
Location: Rural, simple. Surface: asphalted. ⬛ 01/01-31/12
Distance: ⌇4km ⌇beach 80m.
Remarks: Beach parking.

| 📷S | | Loudéac | | 12D3 |

Parking de la Gare, Boulevard de la Gare. GPS: n48,18058 w2,76277.⬆➡.

3 ⌇free 🚰🗑Ch free. Surface: metalled. ⬛ 01/01-31/12
Distance: ⌇600m ⊗50m 🛒200m 🍴200m.

| 📷S | | Maël-Carhaix | | 12C3 |

Place de l'école, Route de Rostrenen. GPS: n48,28344 w3,42148.⬆➡.

5 ⌇free ⟿€2 ⬛Ch WC. **Surface:** asphalted. ▯ 01/01-31/12
Distance: 📍100m ⊗100m 🚰100m.
Remarks: Coins at town hall.

12 ⌇free. **Surface:** metalled/sand. ▯ 01/01-31/12
Distance: 📍100m ⚓on the spot ⟿on the spot ⊗100m 🚰100m.
Remarks: Max. 48h.

Malansac 12D4
Rue Saint Fiacre. **GPS:** n47,67820 w2,29942. ⬆➡.

Marzan 12D4
Rue de la Source. **GPS:** n47,54023 w2,32383. ⬆.

5 ⌇free ⟿⬛Ch free. **Surface:** grassy.
Distance: 📍100m ⊗100m 🚰100m.

+20 ⌇free ⟿⬛Ch WC free. **Surface:** asphalted.
Distance: 📍50m 🚰20m.

Malestroit 12D4
Chemin des Tanneurs. **GPS:** n47,80772 w2,37885. ⬆➡.

Mauron 12D3
Rue de la Libération. **GPS:** n48,08472 w2,2833. ⬆.

12 ⌇free ⟿⬛Ch free. **Surface:** gravel/metalled. ▯ 01/01-31/12
Distance: 📍500m ⚓on the spot ⊗350m.
Remarks: Max. 48h.

⌇free ⟿⬛Ch free. **Surface:** asphalted.
Distance: 📍150m 🚰150m.

Malestroit 12D4
Rue de Narvik. **GPS:** n47,80896 w2,37591. ⬆➡.

Mellé 13B5
Rue Rouviel. **GPS:** n48,48919 w1,18814. ⬆.

⌇free ⟿⬛Ch free. **Surface:** asphalted.
Distance: 📍1,5km ⚓600m ⟿600m ⊗2km 🚰1km.

6 ⌇free ⟿⬛Ch WC free. **Surface:** metalled.
Distance: 📍200m 🚰200m.
Remarks: Nearby football ground, max. 48h.

Malestroit 12D4
Chemin de l'Écluse. **GPS:** n47,81250 w2,38197. ⬆➡.

Meslin 12D2
Allée des Loisirs, D28. **GPS:** n48,44363 w2,56994. ⬆.

10 ⌇free ⌁ Ch free. **Surface:** metalled.
Distance: ⊗bar/crêperie 50m 🚰50m.

| 📷 | Moëlan-sur-Mer | 12C3 |

Route de l'Île Percée. **GPS:** n47,79045 w3,70314.⬆.
4 ⌇free. **Location:** Rural. **Surface:** gravel. ☐ 01/01-31/12
Distance: ⊶300m.

| 📷 | Moëlan-sur-Mer | 12C3 |

Rue de Beg Tal Gward. **GPS:** n47,77749 w3,64404.⬆➡.

4 ⌇free.
Location: Rural, isolated, quiet. **Surface:** asphalted. ☐ 01/01-31/12
Distance: ⊶Moëlan 5km ⌇sea 50m.

| C S | Moncontour | 12D3 |

Camping la Tourelle, Rue François Lorant. **GPS:** n48,35271 w2,63719.⬆➡.

4 ⌇€2 ⌁€2 Ch 💶€2/55minutes 🧺. **Surface:** gravel.
☐ 01/01-31/12
Distance: ⊶1,5km ⊗1,5km 🚰1,5km.
Remarks: Max. 48h.

| 📷 S | Morlaix 🌳🌊 | 12C2 |

Rue de Brest. **GPS:** n48,57422 w3,8316.⬆.

5 ⌇free ⌁ Ch free. **Location:** Urban, simple, central, noisy.
Surface: asphalted. ☐ 01/01-31/12
Distance: ⊶on the spot ⊶on the spot ⊗200m 🚰100m 🚌200m 🚂on the
spot 🚶on the spot.

| 📷 S | Neulliac | 12C3 |

Rue des Deux Croix, D767. **GPS:** n48,12812 w2,98552.⬆➡.

4 ⌇free ⌁€2 Ch 💶€2. **Location:** Simple, isolated, quiet.
Surface: asphalted.
Distance: ⊶300m ⊗300m.

| 📷 S | Névez | 12B3 |

Rue de Port Manech, Impasse du Stade. **GPS:** n47,81560 w3,7894.⬆.

20 ⌇free ⌁€2/10minutes ⌁Ch 💶€2/55minutes WC.
Location: Simple. **Surface:** asphalted.
☐ 01/01-31/12
Remarks: Parking next to stadium, max. 24h, service only with 2-euro coins.

| 📷 | Névez | 12B3 |

Plage de Dourveil, Rue de Dourveil, D1. **GPS:** n47,79407 w3,8101.⬆.

5 ⌇free. **Surface:** sand.
Distance: ⌇on the spot.
Remarks: Max. 24h, no camping activities.

| 📷 | Névez | 12B3 |

Plage de Tahiti, Kerstalen. **GPS:** n47,79287 w3,79011.⬆.

± 11 ⌇free. **Location:** Simple. **Surface:** grassy/sand. ☐ 01/01-31/12
Distance: ⌇beach 150m.
Remarks: Beach parking, max. 24h.

| 📷 | Névez | 12B3 |

Rue de la Plage. **GPS:** n47,80499 w3,74261.⬆.

FR

5 🛏️ free. **Location:** Rural, simple. **Surface:** sand.
🅿️ 01/01-31/12
Distance: 🏖️ 50m.
Remarks: Max. 24h.

| 🛏️S | Névez | 12B3 |

Rue des Iles, Raguénez. **GPS:** n47,78908 w3,80174. ⬆️.

10 🛏️ free. **Location:** Simple. **Surface:** asphalted. 🅿️ 01/01-31/12
Distance: 🏖️ sea 10m, beach 150m ⊗100m.
Remarks: Max. 24h.

| 🛏️S | Noyal-Pontivy | 12D3 |

Le Valvert, Caudan. **GPS:** n48,07833 w2,91583. ⬆️➡️.

20 🛏️ free 🚰 🚻 WC free. **Location:** Rural, comfortable, isolated, quiet.
Surface: asphalted. 🅿️ 01/01-31/12
Distance: 🏘️ Noyal-Pontivy 4,5km 🏊 on the spot 🎣 on the spot ⊗50m.
Remarks: At small lake.

| 🛏️S | Paimpol | 12D2 |

Parking Pierre Loti, Rue Pierre Loti. **GPS:** n48,78404 w3,0463.

15 🛏️ free 🚰 €3,30/100liter 🚻 Ch 🚽 €3,30/55minutes. **Surface:** gravel/sand.
🅿️ 01/01-31/12
Distance: 🏘️ on the spot 🏊 1km 🚉 400m 🚌 100m 🚲 on the spot
🚶 on the spot.
Remarks: Service 100m.

| 🛏️ | Paimpol | 12D2 |

Parking de Goas Plat, Rue de Goas Plat. **GPS:** n48,77535 w3,04009. ⬆️.

37 🛏️ free.
Location: Urban, simple, central, quiet. **Surface:** asphalted.
Distance: 🏘️ centre 500m 🏊 2km ⊗500m 🛒 500m.
Remarks: Max. 24h.

| 🛏️S | Paimpont | 12D3 |

Rue de l'Enchanteur Merlin. **GPS:** n48,02286 w2,17128. ⬆️.

10 🛏️ free 🚰 €3,50/10minutes 🚻 ChWC. **Surface:** gravel.
Remarks: Coins at tourist info.

| 🛏️S | Pénestin | 12D4 |

Allée du Grand Pré. **GPS:** n47,48111 w2,47361. ⬆️➡️.

7 🛏️ free, € 6/night + € 0,20/pp 🚰 €2,50/100liter 🚻 Ch 🚽 €2,50/1h.
Surface: asphalted.
Distance: 🏘️ 500m 🏊 1,5km ⊗500m.
Remarks: Check in all aires in Pénestin: Office de tourisme; Bar-PMU Le Narval,
Rue Calvaire; Café O 20 100 O, Port de Tréhiguier, max. 48h, coins at tourist info.

| 🛏️ | Pénestin | 12D4 |

Aire camping-car de la Pointe du Bile, Route de l'Espernel.
GPS: n47,44524 w2,48029. ⬆️.

🛏️ free, € 6/night + € 0,20/pp. **Surface:** grassy/sand. 🅿️ 01/01-31/12
Distance: 🏖️ 100m.
Remarks: Max. 48h.

| 🛏️ | Pénestin | 12D4 |

Allée de Camaret. **GPS:** n47,49010 w2,49078. ⬆️.

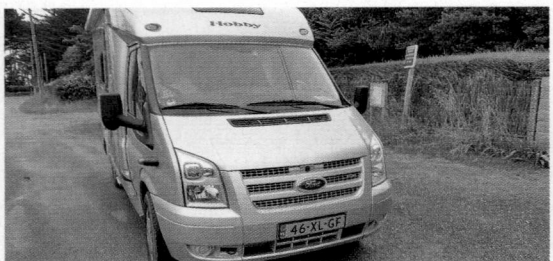

4 🛏 free, € 6/night + € 0,20/pp. **Surface:** gravel.
Distance: ⚓100m.
Remarks: Max. 48h.

| | Pénestin 🏖⛵⚓ | 12D4 |

Allée de Poudrantais. **GPS**: n47,46681 w2,48716.⬆.

4 🛏 free, € 6/night + € 0,20/pp. **Surface:** gravel/metalled.
Distance: ⚓50m.
Remarks: Max. 48h.

| | Pénestin 🏖⛵⚓ | 12D4 |

Plage de la Source, Allée du Maro. **GPS**: n47,48158 w2,49005.⬆.

10 🛏 free, € 6/night + € 0,20/pp. **Surface:** grassy/metalled.
Distance: ⚓300m.
Remarks: Max. 48h.

| | Pénestin 🏖⛵⚓ | 12D4 |

Plage du Palandrin, L'Isle du Clos Parc, Kerséguin. **GPS**: n47,45000 w2,46417.
⬆➡.

6 🛏 free, € 6/night + € 0,20/pp tourist tax. **Location:** Simple, isolated.
Surface: grassy/sand. 🅿 01/01-31/12
Distance: ⚓Sandy beach ⊗1km.
Remarks: Pay at tourist office.

| | Pénestin 🏖⛵⚓ | 12D4 |

Route du Loguy. **GPS**: n47,49050 w2,49667.⬆.

20 🛏 free, € 6/night + € 0,20/pp. **Surface:** grassy/metalled.
Distance: ⚓150m.
Remarks: Max. 48h.

| | Penmarch ⚓ | 12B3 |

Aire du Viben, Rue de la Plage. **GPS**: n47,82390 w4,3708.⬆.

30 🛏 9-19h free, 19-9h € 4. 🚿 **Location:** Rural, simple, quiet.
Surface: metalled. 🅿 01/01-31/12
Distance: 🍴bakery 1km 🛒900m 🚲on the spot 🚶on the spot.

| S | Penmarch | 12B3 |

Aire de Kerameil, Rue du Pont Nevez. **GPS**: n47,81369 w4,36077.⬆.

🚰€2/10minutes 🔌 Ch 🚻 WC.
Location: Rural, simple. 🅿 01/01-31/12
Distance: 🍴3km.
Remarks: Only overnight stays 19-9h.

| ⚓ | Penmarch ⚓ | 12B3 |

Aire de Port du Bouc, Route du Ster Kérity. **GPS**: n47,79981 w4,34794.⬆.

10 🛏 € 4/19-9h. 🚿 **Location:** Rural. **Surface:** grassy/gravel.
🅿 01/01-31/12
Distance: 🍴1,5km ⚓50m ⊗1km 🛒5km.

| | Penvins | 12D4 |

Camping La Gree Penvins, Chemin du Marais 20. **GPS**: n47,49746 w2,68606.

FR

20 ⌐€5. Surface: grassy. 01/01-31/12
Distance: on the spot ⊗350m.
Remarks: Max. 48h.

| ⌐S | Penzé | 12B2 |

Rue du Dossen. GPS: n48,59811 w3,93439.

5 free ⌐€2 Ch ⌐€2 WC. Location: Simple, quiet. Surface: asphalted.
01/01-31/12
Distance: 100m on the spot on the spot ⊗50m 250m
on the spot on the spot.
Remarks: Nearby port.

| ⌐S | Piré-sur-Seiche | 13B6 |

Rue de Boistrudan. GPS: n48,00719 w1,42871.

15 free ⌐ Ch free. Surface: metalled.
Distance: 300m 300m.
Remarks: At fish lake.

| ⌐S | Plabennec | 12B2 |

Rue de l'Aber. GPS: n48,50155 w4,43374.

5 free ⌐ Ch free. Location: Simple. Surface: metalled.
01/01-31/12 on the spot.
Remarks: Parking at small lake.

| ⌐S | Planguenoual | 12D2 |

Bien y Vient. GPS: n48,53447 w2,54506.
6 €5 ⌐. Location: Rural, isolated, quiet.
Surface: grassy. 01/01-31/12

| ⌐S | Planguenoual | 12D2 |

Ferme Gesbert, D786. GPS: n48,54883 w2,5556.

6 free ⌐€2 Ch ⌐€2. Location: Rural. Surface: grassy/gravel.
01/01-31/12
Distance: 1km ⊗1km 1km.

| ⌐S | Plémet | 12D3 |

Rue de l'Étang, D16. GPS: n48,17897 w2,58918.

15 free ⌐€2/100liter Ch ⌐€2/55minutes. Surface: gravel.
01/01-31/12
Remarks: Parking at small lake.

| ⌐S | Pléneuf-Val-André | 12D2 |

Avenue du Général Leclerc. GPS: n48,58355 w2,55669.
€6 ⌐€2 Ch. Surface: unpaved. 01/01-31/12
Distance: 450m.

| ⌐S | Pléneuf-Val-André | 12D2 |

Port de Plaisance de Dahouët, Bassin des Salines, Chemin du Bignon.
GPS: n48,57528 w2,56639.

45 €3,60/24h, tourist tax €0,20/pp ⌐€2 Ch ⌐€2 WC ⌐€2 €4/h.
Surface: gravel. 01/01-31/12
Distance: 300m.

| ⌐S | Plérin | 12D2 |

Sous la Tour, Rue de la Tour, D24. GPS: n48,53146 w2,72483.

20 free ⌐ Ch free. Location: Simple, quiet. Surface: gravel.
01/01-31/12
Distance: on the spot ⊗300m 1km.

FR

Pleslin-Trigavou   13A4
D28. **GPS**: n48,53631 w2,05009.

20 ⛺free ⛽ 🚰 Ch free. **Surface:** asphalted.
Distance: 🚲on the spot 🚴 on the spot 🚶 on the spot.
Remarks: Cycle and hiking routes: voie verte, Circuit des Mégalithes.

Plessala   12D3
Rue de l'Étang. **GPS**: n48,27394 w2,62427.

12 ⛺free ⛽ 🚰 Ch free. **Surface:** gravel. 📅 01/01-31/12
Distance: 🚲200m 🍴on the spot.
Remarks: At fish lake, fishing permit available.

Plestin-les-Grèves   12C2
Voie Communale de l'Armorique. **GPS**: n48,68157 w3,63411.

6 ⛺free. **Surface:** unpaved. 📅 01/01-31/12
Distance: 🚲3km 🏊50m 🛒2km 🚶 on the spot.
Remarks: Beach parking, max. 24h.

Plestin-les-Grèves   12C2
Du Grand Rocher, Avenue de la Lieue de Grève. **GPS**: n48,66968 w3,5858.
⛺free. **Location:** Simple, isolated, quiet.
Distance: 🚲1,3km 🏊100m 🛒1,3km.

Plestin-les-Grèves   12C2
Route de la Corniche. **GPS**: n48,67235 w3,63602.

6 ⛺free. **Location:** Rural, simple, quiet. **Surface:** grassy/sand.
📅 01/01-31/12
Distance: 🚲1km 🏊on the spot 🛒300m 🛒Lidl 2km.
Remarks: Max. 24h.

Plestin-les-Grèves   12C2
Rue de Guergay. **GPS**: n48,66232 w3,62562.
⛽€2/10minutes 🚰Ch 🚻€2/1h.
Remarks: Motorhome washing place.

Pleubian   12C2
Port Béni. **GPS**: n48,84834 w3,17053.

4 ⛺free. **Location:** Rural, simple, isolated, quiet. **Surface:** asphalted.
📅 01/01-31/12
Distance: 🚲Pleubian 2,5km 🏊on the spot 🛒2,5km 🚶 on the spot.
Remarks: Max. 24h.

Pleubian   12C2
Rue de Kermagen, Kermagen. **GPS**: n48,85667 w3,14194.

4 ⛺free. **Surface:** grassy. 📅 01/01-31/12
Distance: 🚲Pleubian 1,6km 🏊beach 100m 🚶 on the spot.
Remarks: Max. 24h.

Pleubian   12C2
Rue de Pen Lan, Lanéros. **GPS**: n48,85760 w3,07883.

4 ⛺free. **Surface:** asphalted.
Distance: 🚲Pleubian 5,5km 🏊on the spot 🚶 on the spot.
Remarks: Max. 24h.

Pleumeur-Bodou   12C2
Parking de Toul ar Stang, Rue de Toul ar Stang, Ile Grande.
GPS: n48,79868 w3,58342.

6 ⛺€6/night ⛽€2/10minutes 🚰Ch 🚻€2/1h. 🚿
Location: Rural, simple, quiet. **Surface:** grassy.

⬛ 01/01-31/12
Distance: 🚶Plemeur-Bodu 6km 🏊sandy beach 150m ⊗150m 🏃on the spot.

☺ S | **Pleumeur-Bodou** ⛱ | 12C2
Cosmopolis-Parc Scientifique, Route du Radome. **GPS:** n48,78472 w3,52694.
⬆.

20 🚐parking free, € 5/night 🚰🍽 Ch 🔌 WC 🗑. **Surface:** gravel/sand.
⬛ 01/01-31/12
Distance: 🚶1km 🏊1km ⊗on the spot 🏃on the spot.

P | **Plévenon** | 12D2
Parking Cap Fréhel. GPS: n48,68174 w2,31811.

40 🚐free, 01/06-30/09 € 4. **Surface:** metalled.
Distance: 🏊50m.

S | **Ploemeur** | 12C4
Rue Louis Lessart. **GPS:** n47,73790 w3,4314.⬆.

7 🚐free 🚰🍽Chfree. **Surface:** asphalted. ⬛ 01/01-31/12
Remarks: Parking centre, max. 24h.

🚐 | **Ploemeur** | 12C4
Aire du Courégant, D152, Boulevard de l'Atlantique. **GPS:** n47,71111 w3,47138.
7 🚐free. **Surface:** asphalted. ⬛ Easter-01/11
Distance: 🏊200m ⊗on the spot.
Remarks: Only overnight stays 20-10h.

🚐 | **Ploemeur** | 12C4
Golf Ploemeur, D152, Boulevard de l'Atlantique. **GPS:** n47,72316 w3,48156.⬆
10 🚐free. **Surface:** gravel. ⬛ 01/01-31/12
Distance: 🚶Ploemeur 5km 🛣N165 10km 🏊beach 300m 🛒1,8km.

🚐 S | **Plogoff** ⛱ | 12A3
Aire Naturelle Kerguidy Izella, Rue Guillaume Pennamen.
GPS: n48,03694 w4,68139.⬆.

30 🚐€ 12 🚰🍽 Ch 🔌🍽 WC 🍽 📶included. **Location:** Rural, comfortable.
Surface: grassy. ⬛ 01/01-31/12
Distance: 🚶2km.
Remarks: 9><20h.

🚐 S | **Plogoff** ⛱ | 12A3
Parking de l'Eglise, Rue Cleder cap Sizum. **GPS:** n48,03727 w4,6652.⬆➡.

4 🚐free 🚰€2/10minutes 🍽Ch. **Location:** Rural, comfortable.
Surface: asphalted. ⬛ 01/01-31/12
Distance: 🚶centre.

🚐 | **Plogoff** ⛱ | 12A3
Aire de la Pointe du Raz, Route des Langoustiers. **GPS:** n48,03651 w4,7173.⬆.

40 🚐€ 5 day/€ 5 night. **Location:** Rural, simple. **Surface:** metalled.
⬛ 01/01-31/12
Distance: 🚶3km ⊗50m.

🚐 | **Plogoff** ⛱ | 12A3
Parking du Stade, Rue du 19 Mars 1962. **GPS:** n48,03245 w4,66316.⬆.

50 🚐free. **Location:** Rural, simple, quiet. **Surface:** grassy/metalled.
⬛ 01/01-31/12
Distance: 🚶on the spot ⊗450m 🛒450m bakery.

🚐 S | **Plomelin** | 12B3
Plomelin, Rue Hent Keramer. **GPS:** n47,93410 w4,1515.⬆.

5 �free 🚰€2/10minutes 🔌Ch🚻€2. **Location:** Rural, simple, quiet.
Surface: asphalted. 🔲 01/01-31/12
Remarks: Parking sports park, max. 24h.

Plonévez-Porzay 12B3
Plonévez-Porzay, Rue des Eglantines. **GPS:** n48,12469 w4,22414.⬆️.

15 �free 🚰€2/10minutes 🔌Ch🚻. **Location:** Rural, comfortable.
Surface: grassy. 🔲 01/01-31/12
Distance: 600m 450m bakery + Spar.

Plonévez-Porzay 12B3
Kervel Izella. **GPS:** n48,11570 w4,28065.⬆️.

10 �free. **Location:** Rural, simple, simple. **Surface:** grassy/sand.
🔲 01/01-31/12
Distance: 5,5km 50m on the spot.
Remarks: Beach parking, max. 48h.

Plouarzel 12A2
Aire de camping-car de Ruscumunoc, Route de Ruscumunoc.
GPS: n48,42232 w4,78486.⬆️➡️.

�free, 15/05-15/09 € 4,60 🚰€2,50/10minutes 🔌Ch🚻€2,60/50minutes
€1 ⚡. **Location:** Comfortable, quiet. **Surface:** grassy.
🔲 01/01-31/12
Distance: 3km 100m.

Ploubalay 13A4
Rue des Ormelets. **GPS:** n48,58057 w2,14524.⬆️.

3 �free 🚰🔌Ch🚻free. **Surface:** asphalted. 🔲 01/01-31/12
Distance: 100m 500m.

Ploubazlanec 12D2
Park Nevez, Cité de Lan ar Mendy. **GPS:** n48,80085 w3,03054.⬆️.
3 �free. **Location:** Simple. 🔲 01/01-31/12
Distance: bakery.
Remarks: Max. 24h.

Ploubazlanec 12D2
Pointe de l'Arcouest, Route de l'Embarcadère. **GPS:** n48,82102 w3,01948.⬆️.

20 �free, 30/06-30/09 € 6/24h. **Location:** Simple, isolated, quiet.
Surface: grassy. 🔲 01/01-31/12
Distance: 2km 50m on the spot.

Ploubazlanec 12D2
Rue du Port Loguivy. **GPS:** n48,82011 w3,06279.
6 �free. **Surface:** asphalted.
Distance: 100m on the spot 100m 100m.

Plouescat 12B2
Rue de Pen an Théven. **GPS:** n48,65902 w4,21863.⬆️.

6 �free. **Surface:** metalled. 🔲 01/01-31/12
Distance: 3,5km 100m.

Plouescat 12B2
Intermarché, La Rocade-Kerchapalain. **GPS:** n48,65083 w4,18444.⬆️➡️.

4 �free 🚰€2 🔌Ch🚻€2 €5/1. **Location:** Comfortable.
Surface: asphalted. 🔲 01/01-31/12
Distance: 500m 600m on the spot on the spot.

Remarks: Parking supermarket.

🛉 ▦ **Plouézec** 12D2

Parking A. Le Calvez. GPS: n48,74980 w2,98409.
3 🅿️free. ◯ 01/01-31/12
Distance: 🚶on the spot ⊗on the spot 🛒on the spot.

🛉 ▦ **Plouézec** 12D2

Parking de la Corniche, Bréhec. **GPS:** n48,72662 w2,94849.
5 🅿️free. ◯ 01/01-31/12
Distance: 🏊on the spot ⊗on the spot.

🛉 ▦ **Plouézec** 12D2

Place du 19 mars 1962. **GPS:** n48,74788 w2,9853.⬆️.

3 🅿️free. **Surface:** asphalted. ◯ 01/01-31/12
Remarks: Service at camping municipal.

🛉 S **Plougasnou** 🌊⛱▦ 12C2

Parking de la Métairie, Rue Charles de Gaulle. **GPS:** n48,69404 w3,79209.⬆️.

7 🅿️free 🔌€2/10minutes 🚰 Ch ▦€2/1h WC. **Location:** Rural.
Surface: gravel. ◯ 01/01-31/12
Distance: 🚶on the spot 🏊sandy beach 1,4km ⊗200m 🛒250m bakery 🚲on the spot 🎣on the spot.
Remarks: Tuesday morning market.

🛉 S **Plougasnou** 🌊⛱▦ 12C2

Rue des Grands Viviers, Le Diben. **GPS:** n48,70811 w3,82731.⬆️.

7 🅿️free 🔌€2 🚰 Ch ▦. **Location:** Rural, simple, isolated, quiet.
Surface: asphalted. ◯ 01/01-31/12
Distance: 🚶300m 🏊on the spot 🚤on the spot ⊗300m 🎣on the spot.
Remarks: Max. 48h, coins at town hall.

🛉 ▦ **Plougasnou** 🌊⛱▦ 12C2

Parking de la Baie, Rue du Grand Large, Primel-Trégastel.
GPS: n48,71201 w3,81621.⬆️➡️.

7 🅿️free. **Location:** Rural, simple, central, quiet. **Surface:** gravel.
◯ 01/01-31/12
Distance: 🏊50m.
Remarks: Max. 48h.

🛉 S **Plougastel-Daoulas** 12B2

Rue de la Fontaine Blanche. **GPS:** n48,37111 w4,36428.

15 🅿️free 🚰 Ch 📶free. **Surface:** asphalted. ◯ 15/05-15/10
Distance: 🚶450m ⊗450m 🛒450m.
Remarks: Parking at sports grounds.

🛉 S **Plougonvelin** 12A2

Rue de Bertheaume. **GPS:** n48,33792 w4,70742.⬆️➡️.

50 🅿️€6 🔌 🚰 Ch 💧 WC 🚿included. 🛁 **Location:** Comfortable, quiet.
Surface: grassy/sand. ◯ 01/01-31/12
Distance: 🚶1km 🏊beach 650m.

🛉 S **Plougonvelin** 12A2

Intermarché, Rue du Stade. **GPS:** n48,34245 w4,72248.

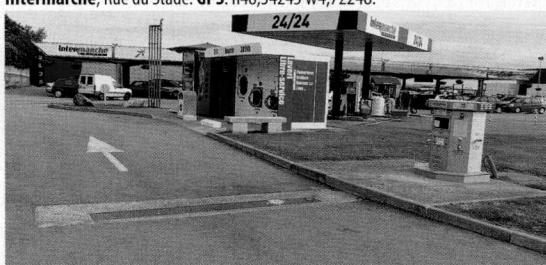

🅿️€7 🔌€2/100liter 🚰 Ch ▦€1/1h 💧€5. 🛁 ▦ **Surface:** asphalted.
Distance: 🛒on the spot.

🛉 S **Plouguerneau** ▦ 12B2

Lilia. **GPS:** n48,61891 w4,55341.⬆️➡️.

10 ⊠free ⌁€4/10minutes ⚏Ch⊟€4/55minutes. **Location:** Comfortable. **Surface:** asphalted. ◻ 01/01-31/12
Distance: ⛟400m ⛱850m ⛽450m.

| | | Plouha ⚓⛵ | 12D2 |

Plage de Palus, Route du Palus. **GPS:** n48,67667 w2,88556.⬆.

10 ⊠free. **Location:** Rural, simple, isolated, quiet. **Surface:** grassy. ◻ 01/03-31/10
Distance: ⛟3km ⛱sandy/pebbled beach 100m ⊗50m ⚹ on the spot.
Remarks: Max. 3 days.

| | | Plouhinec | 12C4 |

Kervelue. **GPS:** n47,68116 w3,23633.⬆➡.

45 ⊠€8 ⌁⚏Ch⚡(16x) WC. 🚽 📦 **Surface:** metalled. ◻ 01/01-31/12
Distance: ⛟Plouhinec 2,5km.

| | | Ploumoguer | 12A2 |

Rue Huon de Kermadec, D28. **GPS:** n48,40507 w4,72492.⬆➡.

15 ⊠free ⌁€2 ⚏Ch⊟€2 WC. **Location:** Simple, quiet. **Surface:** metalled. ◻ 01/01-31/12
Distance: ⛟500m ⛱100m 🛵100m ⊗500m ⛽500m.
Remarks: Parking at small lake.

| | ⓢ | Pluméliau | 12C3 |

Allée du vieux Blavet. **GPS:** n47,98229 w3,04209.⬆.

15 ⊠free ⌁⚏Chfree. **Location:** Rural, comfortable. **Surface:** gravel. ◻ 01/01-31/12
Distance: ⛟500m 🛵on the spot ⊗250m 🚲on the spot ⚹ on the spot.
Remarks: Along the Blavet river, attention: max. ^3.1m.

| | ⓢ | Pont-Aven | 12C3 |

Rue Louis Lomenech. **GPS:** n47,85401 w3,74333.➡.

30 ⊠free ⌁€2,45/10minutes ⚏Ch⊟€2,45/55minutes.
Location: Simple. **Surface:** asphalted. ◻ 01/01-31/12
Distance: ⛟450m ⊗450m.
Remarks: Parking near stadium Sinquin, coins at tourist info (D783).

| | | Pont-Aven ⚓ | 12C3 |

Rue des Abbès Tanguy. **GPS:** n47,85646 w3,75203.⬆.

30 ⊠free, July-Aug € 3 ⌁€2/80liter ⚏Ch⊟€2/45minutes WC 🚽€2 ⚡€4/2,30. **Surface:** metalled. ◻ 01/04-30/11
Distance: ⛟200m ⊗200m ⛽200m.
Remarks: Next to stadium, max. 48h, coins at town hall, supermarket, bakery and Tabac.

| | ⓢ | Plouvorn ⛵ | 12B2 |

Plan d'Eau de Lanorgant. **GPS:** n48,57722 w4,03056.⬆➡.

⊠free. **Location:** Simple. **Surface:** asphalted. ◻ 01/01-31/12
Distance: ⛟400m.

| | ⓢ | Pont-Croix | 12B3 |

Place de la Métairie. **GPS:** n48,04207 w4,48549.⬆.

FR

40 🛏free 🚰€2/10minutes 🗑 Ch 🛁 . 🚐 **Location:** Urban, simple.
Surface: metalled. 🕐 01/01-31/12
Distance: 🚶10min ⊗on the spot.
Remarks: Thursday market.

Tourist information Pont-Croix:
⚓ 🕐 Thu.

🚐S | **Pont-l'Abbé** | 12B3
Parking de la Gare, Rue de la Gare. **GPS:** n47,87070 w4,22506.⬆️.

5 🛏free 🚰🗑 Ch 🛁free. **Location:** Urban. **Surface:** asphalted.
🕐 01/01-31/12
Distance: 🚶on the spot.

🚐S | **Pont-l'Abbé** | 12B3
Leclerc, Route de Saint Jean Trolimont. **GPS:** n47,86414 w4,23646.⬆️.

13 🛏free 🚰€2 🗑 Ch 🛁€2 📶. **Location:** Urban, simple.
Surface: asphalted. 🕐 01/01-31/12
Distance: 🚶on the spot 🚻on the spot.
Remarks: At supermarket.

🚐S | **Pontivy** | 12C3
Rue de la Fontaine. **GPS:** n48,06758 w2,96941.⬆️.

6 🛏free 🗑free. **Location:** Urban, simple. **Surface:** asphalted.
🕐 01/01-31/12
Distance: 🚶800m 🛒on the spot 🥖bakery 300m 🚲on the spot.

🚐S | **Port-Louis** | 12C4
Aire de la Côte Rouge, D781 Port-Louis > Riantec. **GPS:** n47,70873 w3,34295.
⬆️.

18 🛏€ 5/24h, 01/06-15/09 € 10/24h 🚰🗑 Ch 🛁 included. 🚐 🏷
Surface: asphalted. 🕐 01/01-31/12
Distance: 🏖on the spot 🚻on the spot.

🚐S | **Port-Louis** | 12C4
Aire des Remparts, Promenade Henri François Buffet. **GPS:** n47,70496 w3,35602.
⬆️.

20 🛏€ 5/24h, 01/06-15/09 € 10/24h 🚰🗑Ch 🛁included. 🚐 🏷
🕐 01/01-31/12
Remarks: In front of campsite.

🚐S | **Portsall** | 12A2
Aire camping-cars Kerros, Rue de Porsguen. **GPS:** n48,56583 w4,69944.⬆️➡️.

37 🛏€ 5,20/24h 🚰🗑 Ch 🛁included 🚿. **Location:** Comfortable, quiet.
Surface: grassy. 🕐 01/01-31/12
Distance: 🚶on the spot 🏖350m ⊗200m 🚻200m.
Remarks: Max. 3 days.

🚐S | **Poullaouen** | 12C2
D236, Rue de Ty Meur. **GPS:** n48,33672 w3,64218.⬆️.
🛏free 🚰🗑Chfree. **Location:** Rural. **Surface:** metalled. 🕐 01/01-31/12
🚲 Véloroute Roscoff-Nantes 🚶on the spot.

©S | **Primelin** | 12A3
Camping Municipal de Kermaléro, Route de l'Océan.
GPS: n48,02550 w4,61821.

15 🛏free 🚰€2 🗑 Ch 🛁€2. **Location:** Simple. **Surface:** metalled.
🕐 01/01-31/12

FR

Ⓒ Ⓢ Priziac 12C3

Base de Loisirs du Lac du Bel Air, Etang du Bel Air. **GPS:** n48,06183 w3,41132. ⬆️.

⬙€ 5,50 🚰 ⬙ Ch included.
Distance: ⊗300m.

⬙ Ⓢ Quiberon ⚓ 🌊 12C4

Rue de Port Kerné. **GPS:** n47,49165 w3,13941. ⬆️➡️.

140 ⬙€ 6/24h 🚰€1/30liter ⬙ Ch 🛏️ 🧺, 📷 ⬍ **Surface:** asphalted.
⬛ 01/01-31/12 ⬤ service: 15/10-01/04
Distance: 2km ⛵sea 250m.
Remarks: Next to camping municipal, max. 3 days, seaview.

⬙ Ⓢ Quimperlé 12C3

Aire Saint Nicolas, Rue du Viaduc. **GPS:** n47,86640 w3,54334. ⬆️.

3 ⬙free 🚰 ⬙ Chfree. **Surface:** metalled. ⬛ 01/01-31/12

⬙ Ⓢ Quintin 12D2

Place du Champ de Foire. **GPS:** n48,40056 w2,90222. ⬆️➡️.

7 ⬙free 🚰 ⬙ Chfree. **Surface:** asphalted. ⬛ 01/01-31/12
Distance: on the spot ⛵on the spot.
Remarks: Near the lake.

Tourist information Quintin:
⛲ ⬛ Tue-morning.

⬙ Ⓢ Radenac 🌊 12D3

Sente Verte, Les Gambris. **GPS:** n47,95778 w2,71333. ⬆️.

5 ⬙free. **Location:** Rural, simple, quiet. **Surface:** gravel.
⬛ 01/01-31/12
Distance: 700m on the spot 🚲on the spot ⛲on the spot.
Remarks: At small lake.

⬙ Ⓢ Redon 20A1

Quai Surcouf. **GPS:** n47,64510 w2,0897. ⬆️➡️.

10 ⬙free 🚰 ⬙ Chfree. **Surface:** asphalted. ⬛ 01/01-31/12
Distance: 500m on the spot 100m ⊗200m ⚡200m.
Remarks: In front of Bureau du Port de Plaisance.

Tourist information Redon:
👁 Manoir de l'Automobile de Loheac. Car collection: Ferrari, Lamborghini, Porsche, Maserati.

⬙ Ⓢ Réguiny 🌊 12D3

Base de Loisirs, Rue de la Piscine. **GPS:** n47,96843 w2,73828. ⬆️.

10 ⬙free 🚰 ⬙ Chfree. **Location:** Rural, simple, quiet. **Surface:** unpaved.
⬛ 01/01-31/12
Distance: 1,3km ⚡bakery 1,3km 🚲 on the spot ⛲on the spot.

Ⓒ Ⓢ Rennes 13A5

Rue du Professeur Maurice Audin. **GPS:** n48,13531 w1,64542. ⬆️.

5 ⬙free 🚰€2/100liter ⬙ Ch 🛏️€2/1h ⚡€1/30minutes.
Surface: asphalted. ⬛ 01/01-31/12
Remarks: In park, max. 48h.

Tourist information Rennes:
Ⓜ Musée de Bretagne. Regional museum.

FR

⚲ ▢ Tue-Sa.

⚏Ⓢ Riantec 12C4
Leclerc, Rond-point de Kersabiec. **GPS:** n47,72611 w3,32137.
12 ⬛free ⟜€2 ⬛ ⬛€2/55minutes. **Surface:** asphalted. ▢ 01/01-31/12
Distance: ⬛on the spot.

⚏Ⓢ Riantec 12C4
Route de Plouhinec. **GPS:** n47,71111 w3,29889.⬆.

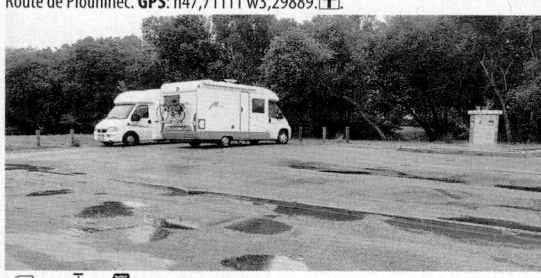

4 ⬛free ⟜€2 ⬛. **Surface:** metalled.
▢ 01/01-31/12
Distance: ⬛on the spot.
Remarks: Parking lake, max. 24h.

⚏ Rochefort-en-Terre 🌿⛵🏖🎭 12D4
Parking des Grées, Rue du Souvenir. **GPS:** n47,69975 w2,33384.⬆.

>100 ⬛€ 2/24h. **Surface:** gravel. ▢ 01/01-31/12
Distance: ⬛200m.

⚏Ⓢ Rohan ⛵ 12D3
Port de Plaisance, Rue Saint-Gouvry. **GPS:** n48,07187 w2,75559.⬆➡.

14 ⬛free ⟜ ⬛ Ch WC free. **Location:** Rural, comfortable, quiet.
Surface: asphalted. ▢ 01/01-31/12
Distance: ⬛500m ⬛on the spot ⬛on the spot ⊗500m ⬛on the spot.
Remarks: At the Nantes-Brest Canal.

⚏Ⓢ Romagné 13B5
Allée des Prunus, D812. **GPS:** n48,34409 w1,27415.⬆.

5 ⬛free ⟜ ⬛ Ch WC free. **Surface:** metalled. ▢ 01/01-31/12
Distance: ⬛100m ⬛1,7km ⬛200m ⬛50m.

⚏Ⓢ Roscoff ⚓ 🏖 12B2
Route du Laber. **GPS:** n48,71215 w3,99918.⬆.

30 ⬛free ⟜ ⬛ Ch free. **Location:** Isolated. **Surface:** asphalted.
▢ 01/01-31/12
Distance: ⬛2km.
Remarks: Service 200m.

Tourist information Roscoff:
ℹ Office de Tourisme, 46, rue Gambetta, www.roscoff-tourisme.com. Seaside resort and former pirates town.
⚲ ▢ Wed.

⚏Ⓢ Rostrenen 12C3
Rue Rosa l'Hénaff, D23. **GPS:** n48,23318 w3,32019.⬆.

6 ⬛free ⟜€2/100liter ⬛ Ch ⬛€2/1h.
Surface: asphalted.
▢ 01/01-31/12
Distance: ⬛100m.
Remarks: Coins at tourist info, town hall, maison de presse, tabac.

⚏Ⓢ Sains 13B4
Rue du Puits Rimoult. **GPS:** n48,55305 w1,58603.⬆➡.

10 ⬛€ 5 ⟜ ⬛ Ch free. ⬛ **Surface:** grassy/metalled. ▢ 01/01-31/12
Distance: ⬛100m ⊗150m ⬛150m.

⚏Ⓢ Saint Aignan 12C3
Place de l'Église. **GPS:** n48,18306 w3,01361.⬆➡.

20 ⬛free ⟜ ⬛ Ch WC free. **Location:** Comfortable, quiet.
Surface: asphalted. ▢ 01/01-31/12

Distance: 🚶100m 🚲 on the spot ⚲ on the spot.
Remarks: Square behind the church.

⚑S **Saint Gérand** 12D3
Keroret, D322. **GPS:** n48,11333 w2,89028.⬆.

12 ⚑free 🚰🗑Ch WC free. **Location:** Rural, comfortable, quiet.
Surface: gravel. ◻ 01/01-31/12
Distance: 🚶800m ⊗150m 🚲 on the spot ⚲ on the spot.
Remarks: At the Nantes-Brest Canal.

⚑S **Saint-Gelven** 12C3
Rue de l'Ecole, D95. **GPS:** n48,22442 w3,09589.⬆.

10 ⚑free 🚰🗑Ch free. **Surface:** concrete. ◻ 01/01-31/12

⚑S **Saint-Gelven** 12C3
Tregnanton, D117. **GPS:** n48,21153 w3,08457.⬆.
⚑free. **Location:** Isolated, quiet. **Surface:** metalled.
Distance: 🚶2,5km ⚓on the spot 🚤on the spot ⚲on the spot.

⚑S **Saint-Pierre-Quiberon** 12C4
Rue du Stade. **GPS:** n47,51160 w3,13903.⬆➡.

120 ⚑€6/24h 🚰€2/4minutes 🗑Ch 💧€2/55minutes 💳.🚐 ⚡
Surface: asphalted. ◻ 01/01-31/12
Distance: 🚶1km ⚓1,5km.
Remarks: Max. 48h.

⚑S **Saint-Rivoal** 12B2
D42. **GPS:** n48,34930 w3,99782.⬆.

6 ⚑free 🚰🗑Ch 🚿free1h. **Surface:** grassy/metalled. ◻ 01/01-31/12
Distance: 🚶200m.

🍴S **Santec** 12B2
Bistrot à Crèpes, Rue de Méchouroux. **GPS:** n48,70102 w4,03868.

15 ⚑€3 🚰€2 🗑Ch 🚿included WC 📶. **Location:** Quiet. **Surface:** grassy.
◻ 01/01-31/12
Distance: ⚓Beach Staol 50m ⊗on the spot 🚲800m.

⚑S **Sarzeau** 12D4
Aire du Rohaliguen, Rue du Raker/Rue du Pont Neui. **GPS:** n47,49769 w2,76748.
⬆➡.

10 ⚑€5/18-8h 🚰🗑Ch WC free. **Surface:** metalled.
◻ 01/01-31/12
Distance: ⚓on the spot.

⚑S **Sarzeau** 12D4
Banastère, Rue du Palud Bihan. **GPS:** n47,51444 w2,66778.⬆➡.

10 ⚑€5/18-8h 🚰€2 🗑💧€2. **Surface:** metalled. ◻ 01/01-31/12
Distance: ⚓on the spot.

⚑S **Sarzeau** 12D4
Rue de Brénudel. **GPS:** n47,52969 w2,7598.⬆.

20 ⚑€5/24h 🚰€2 🗑Ch 💧€2. **Surface:** asphalted. ◻ 01/01-31/12
◉ school hours (8-16h)

⚑S **Sarzeau** 12D4
Rue du Port St.Jacques, Kerbodo. **GPS:** n47,48906 w2,79297.⬆➡.

FR

15 🅿€ 5/18-8h 🚰🔌Ch🔲 free WC 🔲€2. **Surface:** asphalted.
📅 01/01-31/12
Distance: ⚓500m 🚲100m 🛒200m.
Remarks: Nearby port, max. 48h.

📷S | Sarzeau | 12D4

Rue du Stang, St.Colombier. **GPS:** n47,54665 w2,72151.⬆️➡️.

5 🅿€ 5/18-8h 🚰🔌Ch free. **Surface:** asphalted.
Distance: 🚲St.Colombier 100m ⊗50m 🛒50m.
Remarks: Max. 48h.

📷 | Sarzeau | 12D4

Pointe de Penvins, Route de la Chapelle. **GPS:** n47,49472 w2,68139.⬆️➡️.

15 🅿€ 5. **Surface:** asphalted. 📅 01/01-31/12
Distance: ⚓on the spot.
Remarks: Max. 48h.

📷S | Scaër 🌀 | 12C3

Rue Louis Pasteur. **GPS:** n48,02774 w3,6951.⬆️.

10 🅿free. **Surface:** asphalted. 📅 01/01-31/12
Distance: 🚲400m ⊗400m 🛒400m.

📷S | Silfiac | 12C3

P Salle Polyvalente, Rue du Résistant P. le Bourlay. **GPS:** n48,14816 w3,15668.
⬆️➡️.
🅿free 🚰🔌Ch free. **Location:** Simple. **Surface:** asphalted.
📅 01/01-31/12
Distance: 🚲150m 🛒150m 🚲on the spot 🚶on the spot.

📷 | Silfiac | 12C3

Etang de pont Samuel, Pont Samuel. **GPS:** n48,12847 w3,17109.⬆️➡️.

5 🅿. **Location:** Rural, simple, isolated. **Surface:** unpaved.
📅 01/01-31/12
Distance: 🚲300m ⊗200m 🚶200m.

📷S | St.Aubin d'Aubigné | 13A5

Rue de Rennes. **GPS:** n48,26147 w1,60621.⬆️.

5 🅿free 🚰🔌Ch WC free. **Surface:** asphalted. 📅 01/01-31/12
Distance: 🚲on the spot ⊗100m 🚲on the spot 🚃on the spot.

📷S | St.Barnabé | 12D3

Place du Vieux Chêne, Rue Pierre Loti. **GPS:** n48,13672 w2,70146.⬆️.

🅿free 🚰€2/10minutes 🔌Ch 🔲€2/55minutes WC. **Location:** Rural,
simple, quiet. **Surface:** asphalted. 📅 01/01-31/12
Distance: 🚲500m 🛒bakery 200m 🚲on the spot 🚶on the spot.
Remarks: Max. 72h, coins at camping municipal.

📷 | Sérent | 12D4

Du Pont Salmon, Rue du Général De Gaule,. **GPS:** n47,82445 w2,50194.⬆️➡️.

10 🅿free 🚰🔌Ch free. **Surface:** gravel. 📅 01/01-31/12
Distance: 🚲200m 🛒bakery 50m.

📷S | St.Benoit-des-Ondes | 13A4

Rue Bord de Mer. **GPS:** n48,61681 w1,84714.

FR

10 � free ⌖€3/50liter ⌘Ch ⌖€3/15minutes. **Surface:** asphalted.
🛇 S | St.Brice-en-Coglès | 13B5
Espace Jules Verne, Rue de Normandie, D102. **GPS:** n48,41126 w1,36252.⬆️

8 ⌘free ⌖€2/100liter ⌘Ch ⌖€2/55minutes WC.
Surface: asphalted/metalled. 🗓 01/01-31/12
Distance: 🚶300m ⊗500m ⛳400m ⌖300m.
🛇 S | St.Carreuc | 12D2
Rue de la Lande, D27. **GPS:** n48,40300 w2,73923.⬆️

12 ⌘free ⌖€2/10minutes ⌘Ch ⌖€2/55minutes ⌖.
Surface: grassy/gravel. 🗓 01/01-31/12
Distance: 🚶300m ⌖on the spot ⌖on the spot.
Remarks: At Etang-du-Plessis, max. 24h.
🛇 | St.Cast-le-Guildo | 12D2
Bois Bras. GPS: n48,61083 w2,26806.⬆️

⌘free. **Location:** Simple, isolated. 🗓 01/01-31/12
Distance: 🚶2,5km ⚓2,5km ⌖Intermarché 500m.
🛇 S | St.Derrien | 12B2
GPS: n48,54820 w4,1817.

20 ⌘free ⌖€3 ⌘Ch ⌖€3 WC. **Location:** Quiet. **Surface:** gravel/metalled.
🗓 01/05-31/10
Distance: 🚶100m ⌖on the spot ⌖on the spot ⊗300m ⌖300m.
Remarks: Nearby recreation area.
C S | St.Gildas-de Rhuys ⌖ | 12D4
Camping municipal de Kerver, Route du Rohu. **GPS:** n47,52238 w2,85803.⬆️
➡️

35 ⌘€ 6/24h ⌖€2 ⌘Ch ⌖.⌖⌖ ⌖ **Surface:** asphalted.
🗓 15/03-04/11
Distance: 🚶4km ⌖50m ⛳400m ⚓4km.
🛇 S | St.Guyomard ⌖ ⌖ | 12D4
Route de Malestroit, D112. **GPS:** n47,78166 w2,51188.⬆️➡️

20 ⌘€ 5/night ⌖€3 ⌘Ch ⌖€3. **Surface:** asphalted.
Distance: 🚶300m ⊗100m.
Remarks: Behind church, check in at town hall.
🛇 | St.Jacut-de-la-Mer | 13A4
Rue de la Manchette. **GPS:** n48,58969 w2,18947.⬆️

26 ⌘€ 6. **Surface:** grassy/gravel.
Distance: 🚶1km ⌖500m.
Remarks: Baker at 8am.
S | St.Jacut-de-la-Mer | 13A4
Rue de Dinan. **GPS:** n48,58727 w2,19027.
⌖€2 ⌘Ch ⌖€2.
🛇 S | St.Malo ⌖⌖ | 13A4
Les Iltots, Avenue de la Guimorais, Rothéneuf. **GPS:** n48,68109 w1,96348.

FR

50 🛏€ 5,30, Jul/Aug € 10,60 🚰€3 🔌 Ch ⚡included. **Surface:** grassy.
🅿 28/03-12/11
Distance: 🏖sandy beach 100m. 🚰200m.

St.Malo · 13A4

Parking Paul Féval, Rue Paul Féval. **GPS:** n48,64341 w1,99385.

200 🛏€ 7,50, overnight stay 19-9h free 🚰€2,50 🔌 Ch.
Surface: gravel.
🅿 holidays + 01/07-07/09
Distance: 🚰800m 🚍on the spot.
Remarks: Free bus to centre.

Tourist information St.Malo:
🏰🗡 Château. Castle, 14/15th century, historical museum. 🅿 10-12h, 14-18h.
🎫 € 4,50.
🗡 Fort National. Fort designed by Vauban. At ebb accessible by foot. 🎫 € 5.

St.Pol-de-Léon · 12B2
Quai de Pempoul. **GPS:** n48,68361 w3,97083.⬆

30 🛏free 🚰€2 🔌 Ch 🔌€2 WC. **Surface:** metalled. 🅿 01/01-31/12
Distance: 🚲800m 🏖on the spot 🛒on the spot ⊗800m 🚰800m.
Remarks: At sea.

St.Pol-de-Léon · 12B2
Rue Hervé Mesguen. **GPS:** n48,67919 w3,99749.⬆

8 🛏free 🚰€2/10minutes 🔌 Ch 🔌€2/55minutes. **Location:** Comfortable.
Surface: asphalted. 🅿 01/01-31/12
Distance: 🚰on the spot.
Remarks: In front of supermarket Leclerc.

St.Rénan · 12B2
Route de l'Aber. **GPS:** n48,43878 w4,63063.

10 🛏free 🚰€2 🔌 Ch 🔌€2 ♻. **Surface:** gravel. 🅿 01/01-31/12
Remarks: Jul/Aug max. 48h.

St.Servais · 12B2
Cité Yan d'Argent. **GPS:** n48,50984 w4,15434.

10 🛏free 🚰 🔌 Ch ⚡free WC. **Location:** Simple, quiet.
Surface: gravel/metalled. 🅿 01/01-31/12
Distance: 🚲200m ⊗200m 🚰200m.

St.Thégonnec · 12B2
Park an Iliz, D118. **GPS:** n48,52215 w3,94637.⬆

25 🛏free 🚰 🔌 Ch ⚡free. **Location:** Urban, comfortable, central, quiet.
Surface: gravel. 🅿 01/01-31/12
Distance: 🚲on the spot ⊗150m 🚰150m 🚴on the spot 🧗on the spot.
Remarks: Free coins available at shops.

Tourist information St.Thégonnec:
🎣 🅿 Fri.
⊗ Crêperie Steredenn, Rue de la Gare 6.

Sulniac · 12D4
Salle des Fêtes, Rue des Écoles. **GPS:** n47,67756 w2,56642.⬆➡

15 🛏free 🚰 🔌 Chfree. **Surface:** metalled. 🅿 01/01-31/12
Distance: 🚲400m 🚰bakery 500m.

Taden · 13A4
Salle Neuville, Rue de la Robardais. **GPS:** n48,47251 w2,02203.⬆

FR

20 ⌇free ⌁€2 ⌁Ch ⌁€2. **Surface:** gravel. ⬚ 01/01-31/12
Distance: ⌁700m ⊗100m ⌁100m ⌁500m.
Remarks: Service in front of campsite municipal.

| ⌁ S | **Theix** | 12D4 |

Allée de Noyalo. **GPS:** n47,62726 w2,66183.

4 ⌇free ⌁ ⌁Ch free. **Surface:** asphalted. ⬤ Service: winter
Distance: ⌁500m ⊗500m ⌁500m.

| ⌁ S | **Tinténiac** | 13A5 |

Quai de la Donac. **GPS:** n48,33168 w1,83202.⬆

10 ⌇€3 ⌁ ⌁Ch free. **Surface:** grassy/gravel. ⬚ 01/04-31/10
Distance: ⌁500m ⌁Along river ⊗100m ⌁550m.

| ⌁ S | **Trébeurden** ⌁ | 12C2 |

Route de Lannion, D65. **GPS:** n48,76711 w3,5514.⬆

5 ⌇parking free, € 5/night ⌁€4,20 ⌁Ch ⌁€4,20 ⌁. **Location:** Rural,
comfortable, central, quiet. **Surface:** asphalted.
Distance: ⌁on the spot ⌁1,4km ⊗1,5km ⌁1km bakery,
Intermarché 1,5km.

| ⌁ | **Trébeurden** ⌁ ⌁ | 12C2 |

Plage Goas-Treiz, Chemin de Crec'h Hellen. **GPS:** n48,78231 w3,57714.⬆➡

35 ⌇parking free, € 5/night. ⌁ **Location:** Rural, simple, isolated.
Surface: unpaved. ⬚ 01/01-31/12
Distance: ⌁Trébeurden 2km ⌁sandy beach 80m ⊗2km ⌁on the spot.
Remarks: Beach parking.

| ⌁ S | **Trégastel** ⌁ | 12C2 |

Rue de Poul-Palud. **GPS:** n48,82437 w3,49874.⬆

56 ⌇€ 4, 01/03-15/11 € 7,50 ⌁€2 ⌁Ch. ⌁ ⌁ **Location:** Rural,
comfortable, isolated, quiet. **Surface:** asphalted. ⬚ 01/01-31/12
Distance: ⌁1km ⊗1km ⌁Super U ⌁on the spot.
Remarks: Aug max. 3 nights, max. 5 nights.

| ⌁ S | **Tréquier** | 12C2 |

Boulevard Anatole le Braz. **GPS:** n48,78932 w3,23144.

20 ⌇free ⌁Ch free. **Surface:** asphalted. ⬚ 01/01-31/12
Distance: ⌁100m ⌁20m ⌁20m ⊗100m ⌁100m.

| S | **Tréguier** | 12C2 |

Super U, Boulevard Jean Guehenno. **GPS:** n48,77892 w3,23346.⬆
⌁€1/10minutes ⌁Ch ⌁€1/55minutes. ⬚ 01/01-31/12
Distance: ⊗200m ⌁on the spot.

| ⌁ S | **Trégunc** | 12B3 |

Parking Quentel, Place de la Mairie, Rue de Pont-Aven.
GPS: n47,85472 w3,85139.⬆

6 ⌇free ⌁€3 ⌁Ch ⌁€3 ⌁. **Surface:** metalled. ⬚ 01/01-31/12
Remarks: Behind town hall, max. 24h.

| ⌁ | **Trégunc** | 12B3 |

Parking de Pouldohan, Route de Pouldohan. **GPS:** n47,84435 w3,88832.⬆➡

5 🛏free. **Location:** Rural, simple, isolated. **Surface:** grassy.
🅾 01/01-31/12
Distance: ⚓400m ⛵400m.

Trégunc	12B3

Plage Ster Greich. GPS: n47,84918 w3,88656.⬆️
6 🛏free. **Surface:** sand. 🅾 01/01-31/12
Distance: ⚓on the spot.
Remarks: Max. 24h.

Trégunc	12B3

Route de Kerlaëron. **GPS:** n47,82964 w3,8872.⬆️

6 🛏free. **Location:** Rural, simple. **Surface:** grassy.
🅾 01/01-31/12
Distance: ⚓200m.
Remarks: Max. 24h.

Trégunc	12B3

Rue de Porzh Breign. **GPS:** n47,84079 w3,89736.⬆️➡️

5 🛏free. **Location:** Rural, simple, quiet. **Surface:** grassy.
🅾 01/01-31/12
Distance: ⚓200m.
Remarks: Max. 24h.

Trégunc	12B3

Supermarché Casino, Route de Concarneau, D783. **GPS:** n47,85633 w3,86343.⬆️.

4 🛏free 🚰€2 🍴Ch➕€2/55minutes 🧺. **Location:** Simple.
Surface: asphalted.

Distance: 🍴on the spot.

Tremblay	13B5

Route de Fougères. **GPS:** n48,42328 w1,47095.⬆️.

15 🛏free 🚰€2/10minutes ➕€2/55minutes. **Surface:** asphalted.
🅾 01/01-31/12
Distance: 🛒400m 🍴200m.

Trémuson	12D2

Aire du Buchon, Rue de Brest, D712. **GPS:** n48,52250 w2,85278.

5 🛏free 🚰🍴Chfree. **Surface:** asphalted. 🅾 01/01-31/12
Distance: ⊗50m 🍴500m.
Remarks: Max. 48h.

Vannes	12D4

Camping-car Parc, Avenue du Maréchal Juin. **GPS:** n47,63283 w2,77996.⬆️.

34 🛏€ 9,60, Jul/Aug € 12 🚰🍴Chincluded 🔌€4 📶. 📶 🧺
Surface: asphalted.
🅾 01/01-31/12
Distance: 🛒Vannes 4km ⚓200m 🚌on the spot.
Remarks: Note: access only after buying entrance (3 formulas) via www.campingcarpark.com (wifi available), free shuttle (summer).

Tourist information Vannes:
ℹ️ Office de Tourisme, 1, rue Thiers, www.tourisme-vannes.com. The old district is surrounded by ramparts with gates and parks with historical wash places.
✝ Cathédrale St Pierre.

Pays de la Loire

Angers	20C1

Boulevard Olivier-Couffon. **GPS:** n47,46616 w0,56549.⬆️.

FR

20 🎫 € 4/4h, € 7/10h 🚰 🔌 Ch free. 🐕 **Location:** Urban, noisy.
Surface: asphalted. 🅿 01/01-31/12
Distance: 🚶centre 950m 🚲 3km.
Remarks: Max. 36h, Château d'Angers 600m.
Tourist information Angers:
👁 Haras National du Lion d'Angers. National stud-farm. 🅿 15/04-11/09 daily,
12/09-14/04 Sa-Su 10.30h, 14.30h, 16h.
♟ Château d' Angers. Fortified castle, museum for contemporary art.
🅿 10-17.30h. 🎟 € 6.

| ♿ S | Angrie 👥 | 20B1 |

Route du Vieux Bourg. **GPS:** n47,57176 w0,97312. ⬆➡

10 🎫 free 🚰 🔌 Ch free. **Location:** Rural. **Surface:** gravel/metalled.
🅿 01/01-31/12
Distance: 🚶400m 🏪 on the spot.
Remarks: Max. 48h.

| ♿ S | Arnage 🚤 | 13D6 |

Rue du Port. **GPS:** n47,93035 e0,18418. ⬆

2 🎫 free 🚰 €2 🔌 Ch 🚿 €2/15minutes 🧺. **Location:** Urban, simple, quiet.
Surface: asphalted. 🅿 01/01-31/12
Distance: 🚶250m 🏪 on the spot 🏪 500m 🏊 on the spot.

| ♿ S | Assérac 🚤 | 12D4 |

Camping-Car Park de la Baie, Chemin du Bas Village. **GPS:** n47,42472 w2,44364.
⬆
10 🎫 € 12 🚰 🔌 Ch 🚿 WC 🔌 🛜 included. 🚌 🧺 **Location:** Rural,
comfortable, quiet. **Surface:** metalled. 🅿 01/01-31/12
Distance: 🚶Assérac 5km 🏖 sandy beach 350m.

| ♿ S | Assérac 🚤 | 12D4 |

Pen-Bé. **GPS:** n47,42556 w2,45528. ⬆

5 🎫 free WC. **Location:** Simple. **Surface:** grassy. 🅿 01/01-31/12
Distance: 🚶50m 🏊100m 🏪100m ⊗200m 🍴200m.

| ♿ S | Assérac | 12D4 |

Chemin de la Marché aux Bœufs. **GPS:** n47,43111 w2,45194.

🎫 free WC. **Surface:** metalled.
Distance: 🚶1km 🏊300m 🏪300m ⊗2km 🍴2km.

| ♿ S | Aubigné-sur-Layon | 20C2 |

Rue de 17 mars 1962. **GPS:** n47,21167 w0,46383. ⬆

3 🎫 free 🚰 🔌 Ch free. **Surface:** metalled. 🅿 01/01-31/12
Distance: 🚶100m.

| ♿ S | Averton 👥 | 13D5 |

Étang des Perles. **GPS:** n48,34744 w0,24468. ➡

10 🎫 free 🚰 €2,50 🔌 Ch 🚿 €2,50 WC. **Location:** Rural. **Surface:** gravel.
🅿 01/01-31/12
Distance: 🏊lake 🏪 on the spot 🚲 on the spot 🏊 on the spot.

| ♿ S | Batz-sur-Mer | 12D5 |

Route de la Govelle. **GPS:** n47,26747 w2,4537. ⬆➡

FR

8 🛏free 🚰€2 🔌 Ch 🚽€2 WC. **Location:** Simple. **Surface:** metalled.
🅿 01/01-31/12
Distance: 🚶1,5km 🏖100m ⊗100m 🚉1,5km 🚌50m.
Remarks: Max. 48h.

🏕 **Batz-sur-Mer** 🌊 **12D5**
Baie du Manéric, Route du Dervin. **GPS:** n47,27028 w2,46139.
± 10 🛏free. **Surface:** grassy. 🅿 summer
Distance: 🏖50m.

🏕 S **Baugé** 🍴 **20D1**
Chemin du Pont des Fées. **GPS:** n47,53886 w0,09637.⬆️.

10 🛏free 🚰€3/15minutes 🔌 Ch 🚽€3/15minutes. 📮 ✉ **Location:** Rural.
Surface: gravel.
Distance: 🚶2km ⊗400m.

🏕 S **Baugé** 🍴 **20D1**
Rue de la Croix de Mission, Le Vieil Baugé. **GPS:** n47,53066 e0,11899.

8 🛏free 🚰 🔌 Chfree. **Location:** Rural. **Surface:** gravel.
🅿 01/01-31/12
Distance: 🚶on the spot 🛒bakery 100m.
Remarks: Service 50m.

🏕 **Bazouges-sur-le-Loir** **20D1**
Voie de la Liberté. **GPS:** n47,68994 w0,16952.⬆️⬆️.

🛏free. **Location:** Rural, quiet. **Surface:** gravel. 🅿 01/01-31/12
Distance: 🚶200m ⊗200m.

🏕 S **Beauvoir-sur-Mer** **12D5**
Rue de Nantes. **GPS:** n46,91685 w2,0465.➡️.

24 🛏free, overnight stay € 5 🚰€2,50/3minutes 🔌 Ch 🚽€2,50/15minutes
WC ✉ 📮 ✉ **Location:** Urban, simple. **Surface:** asphalted.
🅿 01/01-31/12
Distance: 🚶400m ⊗800m 🚉800m.
Remarks: Max. 48h.

🏕 **Belleville-sur-Vie** **20A3**
Rue des Écoliers. **GPS:** n46,78160 w1,42875.⬆️➡️.

15 🛏free. **Surface:** grassy/gravel. 🅿 01/01-31/12
Distance: 🚶500m ⊗500m 🚉200m.
Remarks: Near Salle des Fêtes.

🏕 S **Benet** **20C4**
Rue de la Gare. **GPS:** n46,36896 w0,59482.

10 🛏free 🚰 🔌 Ch WC free.
Location: Rural, simple. **Surface:** asphalted.
Distance: 🚶300m ⊗300m 🚉on the spot 🚌50m.

🏕 S **Blain** **20A1**
Place Jollan de Clerville, Rue Victor Schoelcher. **GPS:** n47,47444 w1,76139.⬆️.

30 🛏free 🚰 🔌 Chfree. **Surface:** gravel. 🅿 01/01-31/12
Distance: ⊗100m 🚉100m.

🏕 S **Blaison-Gohier** **21A1**
Rue de Thibaut de Blaison. **GPS:** n47,39923 e0,37515.⬆️➡️.

FR

5 🛏free 🚰 🗑 Ch free. **Surface:** asphalted. ◯ 01/01-31/12
Distance: 🛒on the spot ⊗200m 🍴200m.

Rue Chevrière. **GPS:** n47,41913 w0,61117. ⬆➡.

40 🛏free, 01/03-30/11 € 10 🚰€0,50/50liter 🗑Ch 🧹WC 🚿€1 📶included.
🗑 ✎ **Surface:** grassy/gravel.
◯ 01/01-31/12 ◉ service: 01/12-28/02
Distance: 🚌50m.
Remarks: Along the river Maine, former campsite, baker every morning (Jul/
Aug).

GPS: n47,00918 w2,02782. ⬆ .

10 🛏free. **Location:** Rural, simple. **Surface:** grassy/gravel.
◯ 01/01-31/12
Distance: 🏊on the spot.

GPS: n46,99821 w2,03314. ⬆ .

🛏free. **Surface:** gravel. ◯ 01/01-31/12

D758. **GPS:** n47,04028 w1,95704. ⬆.

10 🛏free 🚰 🗑 Ch WC free. **Location:** Simple. **Surface:** asphalted.
◯ 01/01-31/12 ◉ Service: winter
Distance: 🛒300m 🚌200m ⊗300m 🍴300m.
Remarks: Parking tourist info, max. 48h.

Place des Marronniers. **GPS:** n47,04240 w1,18648. ⬆➡.

4 🛏free 🚰€2/100liter 🗑Ch 🚿€2/60minutes. **Location:** Simple.
Surface: asphalted. ◯ 01/01-31/12
Distance: 🛒200m ⊗200m 🍴200m 🚲on the spot.
Remarks: Max. 48h, coins at town hall, poste.

Parking de la Normandelière, Rue de la Source. **GPS:** n46,61664 w1,85974. ⬆.

25 🛏free. **Location:** Simple. **Surface:** metalled. ◯ 01/01-31/12
Distance: 🛒1,5km 🏊sandy beach 500m 🍴1,5km 🚲on the spot
🚶on the spot.
Remarks: Service: Super U D38, GPS 46,62537 -1,85787.
Tourist information Brétignolles-sur-Mer:
🚶 ◯ Thu, Su.

Plage de Briollay. GPS: n47,56766 w0,50733. ⬆.
10 🛏free 🚰€2 🗑Ch. **Surface:** grassy/gravel. ◯ 01/01-31/12
Remarks: Along Sarthe River, closed when frosty and high water.

FR

ⓈⓈ **Brissac-Quincé** 20C1
Rue de l'Aubance. **GPS**: n47,35465 w0,4463. ⬆➡

2 🛏free 🚰🪑 Ch. **Surface**: asphalted. ◻ 01/01-31/12
Distance: 🚶300m ⊗300m 🛒300m.

ⓈⓈ **Chailland** 13C5
Coccimarket. **GPS**: n48,22139 w0,86583. ⬆➡

4 🛏free 🚰🪑Ch free. **Location**: Rural, simple. **Surface**: asphalted.
◻ 01/01-31/12
Distance: 🚶300m ⊗300m 🛒on the spot.
Remarks: Max. 24h.

ⓈⓈ **Chaille-les-Marais** 20B4
Rue du 8 Mai 1945. **GPS**: n46,39228 w1,02127. ⬆

20 🛏free 🚰€3 WC free. **Location**: Simple, quiet. **Surface**: grassy.
◻ 01/01-31/12 ◓ Thu-morning
Distance: 🚶100m 🛒100m 🛒300m 🚌50m.
Remarks: At fire-station and sports park.

ⓈⓈ **Challans** 20A3
Parking du Viaud Marais. **GPS**: n46,85027 w1,8742. ⬆➡

15 🛏free 🚰🪑Ch free. **Location**: Urban. **Surface**: asphalted.
◻ 01/01-31/12
Distance: 🚶1km ⊗500m 🛒500m 🚌100m.
Remarks: Max. 3 days.

ⓈⓈ **Chalonnes-sur-Loire** 20C1
Avenue de la Gare. **GPS**: n47,34961 w0,74847. ⬆

15 🛏free 🚰🪑Ch free. **Surface**: forest soil. ◻ 01/01-31/12
Distance: 🚶1km ⊗1km 🛒on the spot.
Remarks: Parking nearby caveau the dégustation and swimming pool.

ⓈⓈ **Chambretaud** 20B2
Aire des Diamants, Rue Notre Dame. **GPS**: n46,92300 w0,9717. ⬆➡

5 🛏free 🚰€2/150liter 🪑Ch WC. **Location**: Rural, simple.
Surface: asphalted. ◻ 01/01-31/12
Distance: 🚶1km ⛵5km ⊗on the spot 🛒1km.

ⓈⓈ **Champtocé-sur-Loire** 20B1
Rue de la Hutte. **GPS**: n47,41143 w0,86958. ⬆➡

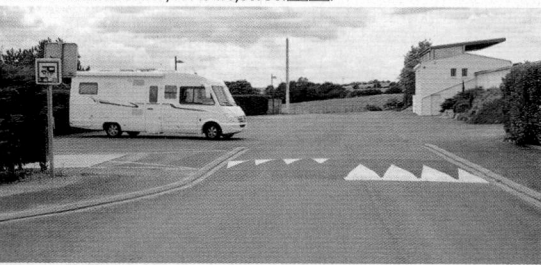

8 🛏free 🚰🪑Ch free. **Location**: Rural, simple. **Surface**: asphalted.
◻ 01/01-31/12
Distance: 🚶300m ⛵5,7km ⊗400m 🛒400m.
Remarks: At stadium.

ⓈⓈ **Champtoceaux** 20B1
Parking Champalud, Place de Niederheimbach. **GPS**: n47,33816 w1,2649. ⬆➡

5 🛏free 🚰🪑Ch €3/24h WC. **Surface**: asphalted. ◻ 01/01-31/12
Distance: 🚶150m ⛵23km.
Remarks: Square behind the church, max. 48h.

ⓈⓈ **Champtoceaux** 20B1
Le Port du Moulin, Le Cul du Moulin, D751. **GPS**: n47,33913 w1,27445. ⬆

FR

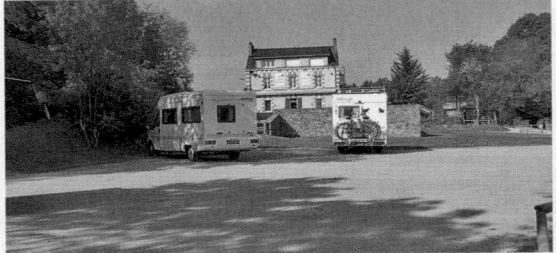

3 🍴free WCfree. **Surface:** metalled. 🔲 01/01-31/12
Distance: 🚶1,5km ⚓on the spot 🛒on the spot ⊗on the spot 🛒1,5km.
Remarks: Along Loire river, max. 48h.

🚐S　　　　　　　　**Changé** 🏕🚽🌳🛶　　　　　　13C6
Parking du plan d'eau du Port, Rue du Bac. **GPS:** n48,10047 w0,78584. ⬆.

10 🍴free 🚰🗑Chfree. **Location:** Urban, simple. **Surface:** gravel/sand.
🔲 01/01-31/12
Distance: 🚲5km 🛒800m.
Remarks: Along the Mayenne river.

🚐S　　　　　　　　**Chantonnay**　　　　　　20B3
Rue de l'Arc en Ciel. **GPS:** n46,68754 w1,04104. ⬆➡.

5 🍴free 🚰€2/100liter 🗑Ch 🚽€2/60minutes. **Location:** Rural, simple,
noisy. **Surface:** asphalted. 🔲 01/01-31/12
Distance: 🚶1km ⊗500m 🛒1km.
Remarks: Next to sports fields, coins at tourist info.

🚐S　　　　　　　　**Chanzeaux**　　　　　　20C2
Aire de Ploizeau, D121. **GPS:** n47,25548 w0,63848. ⬆.

6 🍴free 🚰€2/100liter 🗑Ch. **Surface:** metalled. 🔲 01/01-31/12
Distance: 🚶1km 🛒on the spot ⊗1km 🛒1km.

🚐S　　　　　　　**Château-d'Olonne**　　　　20A3
Rue des Plesses. **GPS:** n46,49132 w1,74293. ⬆➡.

20 🍴€ 6,10/night, € 10,20/2 nights 🚰€2/6minutes 🗑Ch 🚽€3/10minutes.
🚐🧼**Location:** Simple. **Surface:** asphalted.
🔲 01/01-31/12
Distance: 🛒500m.

🚐S　　　　　　**Château-Gontier** 🌿🏛🧁🛶　　13C6
Quai-du-Docteur Lefevre. **GPS:** n47,82450 w0,70206. 🔼.

30 🍴free. **Location:** Urban, simple, central. **Surface:** asphalted.
🔲 01/01-31/12
Distance: 🚶200m 🛒on the spot ⊗50m.
Remarks: Along the Mayenne river.

🚐S　　　　**Chavagne-en-Paillers**　　　20B3
Place des Arcades. **GPS:** n46,89083 w1,24917. ⬆➡.

3 🍴free 🚰€2/10minutes 🗑Ch 🚽€2/55minutes. **Location:** Simple, central,
quiet. **Surface:** asphalted. 🔲 01/01-31/12
Distance: 🚶300m ⊗50m 🛒100m 🚐300m.
Remarks: Coins at tourist office/Rest. Le petit Marmiton/Boulanger de Quartier,
8 rue G de Gaulle/ Carrefour Express, 197 rue G de Gaulle.

🚐S　　　　　**Chavagnes les Eaux**　　　20C2
Place de la Mairie. **GPS:** n47,27024 w0,45437. ⬆➡.

3 🍴free 🚰🗑Chfree. **Surface:** metalled. 🔲 01/01-31/12
Distance: 🚶on the spot 🛒150m.
Remarks: Behind church.

🚐S　　　**Chênehutte-Trèves-Cunault** 🛶　20D2
Rue Beauregard, D751, Cunault. **GPS:** n47,32685 e0,19459. ⬆➡.

40 🛏free ⛽€3/100liter 🚰 Ch ⚡€3/6h 🗑. **Surface:** grassy.
📅 01/01-31/12
Distance: 🏪500m ⊗500m 🛒500m.

📖 S		
	Chenillé-Changé 〰	20C1

Le Pin, D78. **GPS:** n47,69919 w0,66693. ⬆️➡️.

8 🛏€ 2,80-4 ⛽€2,80 🚰 Ch. **Location:** Simple. **Surface:** gravel.
📅 01/01-31/12
Distance: 🏪on the spot ⊗100m.
Remarks: Along the Mayenne river, coins at cafe.

📖 S		
	Coëx	21C3

Rue des Goélettes. **GPS:** n46,69717 e1,76410. ⬆️.

4 🛏free ⛽€2/10minutes 🚰 Ch ⚡€2/55minutes. **Location:** Rural.
Surface: asphalted. 📅 01/01-31/12
Distance: 🏪200m ⊗500m 🛒500m.
Remarks: Max. 48h, coins at town hall.

📖 S		
	Combrée 〰	20B1

Rue de Bretagne, Bel-Air. **GPS:** n47,71281 w0,9989. ➡️.

3 🛏free ⛽🚰 Ch WC free. **Location:** Rural. **Surface:** unpaved.
📅 01/01-31/12
Distance: 🏪100m.

📖		
	Combrée 〰	20B1

D203. **GPS:** n47,70321 w1,02755. ⬆️.

3 🛏free. **Location:** Rural, quiet. **Surface:** asphalted. 📅 01/01-31/12
Distance: 🏪200m ⊗50m.
Remarks: Behind tennis-court.

📖 S		
	Concourson-sur-Layon	20C2

Aire de Repos, D960. **GPS:** n47,17405 w0,34317. ➡️.

10 🛏free ⛽€2 🚰 Ch WC. **Surface:** asphalted. 📅 01/01-31/12
Distance: 🏪400m ⊗400m 🛒400m.

📖 S		
	Dampierre-sur-Loire	20D2

L'Aigrette, Route de Montsoreau. **GPS:** n47,24157 w0,0232. ⬆️.

40 🛏€ 5 ⛽🚰 Ch WC. 🚿 **Surface:** forest soil. 📅 01/04-02/11
Distance: 🏪on the spot ⊗on the spot 🛒on the spot.
Remarks: On the river Loire.

📖 S		
	Deux-Evailles	13C5

Site de la Fenderie, Champ de Vigne, D129. **GPS:** n48,20203 w0,52018. ➡️.

20 🛏free ⛽€2 🚰 Ch ⚡€2 WC. **Location:** Rural, comfortable, quiet.
Surface: grassy/gravel. 📅 01/01-31/12
Distance: 🏪1km ⛰20m 🎣20m ⊗20m 🛒5km Montsurs 🚶on the spot.
Remarks: Coins at Auberge.

📖 S		
	Doué-la-Fontaine	20C2

Rue Jean Gaschet. **GPS:** n47,18280 w0,25742.
3 🛏free ⛽🚰 Ch free.

📖		
	Durtal	20D1

Rue du Petit Port. **GPS:** n47,66842 w0,24172. ⬆️.

FR

5 🛏free. **Location:** Rural, quiet. **Surface:** asphalted.
Distance: 🚶300m 🚲 2,4km.

Ⓒ Ⓢ   **Durtal**   **20D1**
Rue Beausite. **GPS:** n47,67139 w0,2406. ⬆.

2 🛏free ⛽€2/10minutes 🍽Ch 💧€2/60minutes. **Location:** Simple.
Surface: asphalted. ⬛ 01/01-31/12
Distance: 🚶300m 🚲 2,4km.
Remarks: Inclining pitches.

Ⓛ Ⓢ   **Ernée**   **13C5**
Plan d'eau d'Ernée, Plan d'eau d'Ernée. **GPS:** n48,29670 w0,93997.

2 🛏free ⛽WC free. **Location:** Urban, simple, quiet. **Surface:** asphalted.
⬛ 01/01-31/12
Distance: 🚶500m 🚲on the spot ⊗500m 🍴500m.
Remarks: Parking at small lake.

Ⓢ   **Faye d'Anjou**   **20C2**
Chateau du Fresne, D55, Rue des Monts. **GPS:** n47,29923 w0,53806. ⬆➡.

10 🛏free ⛽🍽Ch free. **Surface:** gravel. ⬛ 01/01-31/12
Distance: 🚶2km ⊗3km.

Ⓢ   **Feneu**   **20C1**
Port Albert. **GPS:** n47,56560 w0,60994. ⬆.

6 🛏free ⛽€2 🍽Ch. **Location:** Rural, quiet. **Surface:** gravel.
⬛ 01/01-31/12
Distance: 🚶1,5km.
Remarks: Along the Mayenne river.

Ⓢ   **Fontaines**   **20B4**
Place du Champ de Foire. **GPS:** n46,42291 w0,81952.

20 🛏free ⛽🍽Ch WC free.
Location: Rural, simple. **Surface:** gravel.
Distance: 🚲2km.

Ⓢ   **Fontenay-le-Comte** 🌿   **20B4**
Avenue du Général de Gaulle. **GPS:** n46,46203 w0,80544. ➡.

10 🛏€5 ⛽€2/4minutes 🍽Ch 🔧included. **Location:** Simple, isolated,
noisy. **Surface:** asphalted. ⬛ 01/01-31/12
Distance: 🚶500m ⊗500m 🍴500m.
Remarks: In front of police station, max. 24h, centre.

Ⓢ   **Fontevraud l'Abbaye**   **20D2**
Allée des Bruyères. **GPS:** n47,18444 e0,04917. ⬆➡.

9 🛏free ⛽🍽Ch WC free. **Surface:** asphalted.
Distance: 🚶400m ⊗400m 🍴400m.

Ⓢ   **Foussais-Payré**   **20C4**
Place du Prieuré. **GPS:** n46,53000 w0,68275. ⬆➡.

FR

20 ⬛free 🚰 ♨Chfree. **Location:** Rural, simple. **Surface:** gravel.
⭕ 01/01-31/12
Distance: 🚶500m ⊗500m 🚆200m.

⬛Ⓢ **Fresnay-sur-Sarthe** **13D5**
Rue de la Gare. **GPS:** n48,28171 e0,02978.➡.

8 ⬛free 🚰 ♨Chfree. **Location:** Simple. **Surface:** gravel.
⭕ 01/01-31/12
Distance: 🚶600m ⊗600m 🚆50m.

⬛Ⓢ **Gené** **20C1**
Escale du Haut Anjou, La Petite Fenouillère. **GPS:** n47,63770 w0,79641.⬆➡.

7 ⬛€ 12 🚰♨Ch🖌 included. 🐾 **Location:** Rural, simple. **Surface:** gravel.
⭕ 01/01-31/12
Distance: 🚶1,2km ➙fish pond.
Remarks: Cheese farm.

⬛Ⓢ **Grez-en-Bouère** **13C6**
Place A. Peigné. **GPS:** n47,87306 w0,52306.➡.

6 ⬛free 🚰♨Ch 🖌 free WC. **Location:** Rural, simple. **Surface:** asphalted.
⭕ 01/01-31/12, service: 01/04-30/11
Distance: 🚶50m ⊗50m 🚆100m.
Remarks: Max. 48h.

⬛Ⓢ **Grez-Neuville** **21A1**
Rue du Port, D291. **GPS:** n47,60119 e0,68504.⬆➡.

8 ⬛free 🚰♨Chfree. **Location:** Rural, simple. **Surface:** grassy.
⭕ 01/01-31/12
Remarks: Former campsite.

⬛Ⓢ **Guenrouet** **20A1**
Rue des Hauts du Port. **GPS:** n47,52198 w1,94978.⬆.

2 ⬛free 🚰€2 ♨Ch ⚄€2. **Surface:** asphalted.
⭕ 01/04-31/10
Distance: 🚶200m ➙50m ⊗200m 🚆200m.
Remarks: Along canal of Nantes/Brest, next to campsite Saint Clair, max. 24h.

⬛Ⓢ **Guérande** 🌿🚲🏕 **12D4**
Avenue de la Brière, D99E. **GPS:** n47,33389 w2,42083.⬆➡.

20 ⬛free 🚰€5/100liter ♨Ch ⚄€5/1h 🧽. **Location:** Simple, noisy.
Surface: asphalted/grassy. ⭕ 01/01-31/12
Distance: 🚶1km.
Remarks: Max. 48h.

⬛Ⓢ **Jans** **20A1**
Place de l'Église. **GPS:** n47,62222 w1,61222.⬆.

6 ⬛free 🚰♨ChWCfree. **Surface:** gravel. ⭕ 01/01-31/12
Remarks: Behind town hall.

⬛Ⓢ **Jard-sur-Mer** 🏕📶 **20A4**
Route des Goffineaux. **GPS:** n46,41074 w1,59358.⬆➡.

FR

16 🛏 € 6,20/24h, € 10,40/48h 🔌 €2,10/10minutes 🔲 Ch 🔲.🔲 🔲
Location: Rural, simple. **Surface:** asphalted. 🔲 01/01-31/12
Distance: 🚶1km 🏖50m ⊗1,5km 🛒1,5km.

🔲 S | Juvigné | 13B5
Plan d'Eau de Saint Martin, Rue de la Croixille, D29. **GPS:** n48,22806 w1,03806. ⬆.

20 🛏 free 🔌 🔲 Ch WC free. **Location:** Urban, simple. **Surface:** gravel.
🔲 01/01-31/12
Distance: 🚶200m 🛒20m ⊗200m 🛒100m 🏊 on the spot.
Remarks: Max. 72h.

🔲 S | La Baconnière | 13C5
Place de l'Eglise. **GPS:** n48,18361 w0,89139. ➡.

5 🛏 free 🔌 🔲 Ch 🔲 free.
Location: Urban, simple. **Surface:** asphalted.
🔲 01/01-31/12
Distance: 🚶on the spot 🛒100m.
Remarks: Behind church, service (winter) on demand (town hall).

🔲 S | La Baule | 12D5
Boulevard Guy de Champsavin, La Baule-Escoublac. **GPS:** n47,28196 w2,42509.
⬆➡.

20 🛏 free 🔌 €3 🔲 Ch 🔲 (20x)€3/55minutes 🔲. **Location:** Comfortable,
quiet. **Surface:** metalled.
Distance: 🏖beach 700m.

🔲 S | La Bernerie-en-Retz | 12D5
Parking Wilson, Avenue de Jean d Arc. **GPS:** n47,07871 w2,03399. ⬆.

37 🛏 € 5,33-6,56 🔌 €3,30 🔲 Ch 🔲 €3,30 WC 🔲.🔲 🔲
Surface: asphalted. 🔲 01/01-31/12
Distance: 🚶300m 🏖100m ⊗300m 🛒300m 🚐on the spot.
Remarks: Max. 48h.

🔲 S | La Chapelle-Saint-Florent | 20B1
Aire du Stade, Rue de l'Evre. **GPS:** n47,33411 w1,05178. ⬆➡.

6 🛏 free 🔌 🔲 Ch. **Surface:** gravel/metalled. 🔲 01/01-31/12
Distance: 🚶300m 🏖300m 🛒50m.

🔲 S | La Daguenière | 20C1
Chemin de Beausse, Rue de Stade. **GPS:** n47,42222 w0,43936. ⬆.

12 🛏 free 🔌 🔲 Ch free. **Location:** Rural. **Surface:** asphalted.
🔲 01/01-31/12
Distance: 🚶200m 🏖300m 🛒300m.
Remarks: Next to sports fields.

🔲 S | La Daguenière | 20C1
Port Maillard. GPS: n47,41743 w0,43781. ⬆.

6 🛏 free WC. **Location:** Rural. **Surface:** unpaved. 🔲 01/01-31/12
Remarks: Along Loire river.

🔲 S | La Flèche | 20D1
Promenade du Maréchal Foch. **GPS:** n47,69767 w0,07875. ⬆ .

10 ⅏free ⚱free. **Location:** Urban. **Surface:** asphalted. ▢ 01/01-31/12
◉ Wed, market
Distance: ⚓100m ⊗100m ⚑100m.

⟦S⟧ La Fresnaye-sur-Chédouet ⛲ 14A5
La forêt de Perseigne, Les Ventes du Four, D236. **GPS:** n48,43469 e0,25972.⬆.

20 ⅏free ⚱ ⚏Chfree. **Location:** Rural, quiet. **Surface:** gravel.
▢ 01/01-31/12
Distance: ⚓La Fresnaye 1,5km ⚘on the spot.

⟦S⟧ La Meilleraie-Tillay 20B3
Rue des Ombrages. **GPS:** n46,73923 w0,84578.⬆➡.

6 ⅏free ⚱€2/5minutes ⚏ChWC⚏€1. **Location:** Simple, isolated, quiet.
Surface: asphalted. ▢ 01/04-31/10
Distance: ⚓700m ⊗700m ⚑700m.

⟦S⟧ La Plaine-sur-Mer 12D5
Boulevard des Nations Unies. **GPS:** n47,13994 w2,19057.⬆➡.

8 ⅏free ⚱⚏Chfree. **Location:** Simple, isolated. **Surface:** asphalted.
▢ 01/01-31/12
Distance: ⚓300m ⊗800m ⚑500m.
Remarks: Max. 24h.

⟦S⟧ La Poitevinière 20B2
Place de la Fontaine, D15. **GPS:** n47,22750 w0,897.⬆.

4 ⅏free ⚱⚏Ch⚏WC free. **Surface:** asphalted. ▢ 01/01-31/12
Distance: ⚓50m ⊗on the spot ⚑50m.
Remarks: Coins available at bar.

⟦S⟧ La Roche-sur-Yon 20A3
Boulevard Italie. **GPS:** n46,66833 w1,41861.⬆.

20 ⅏free ⚱⚏Ch ⚲free. **Location:** Urban. **Surface:** metalled.
▢ 01/01-31/12
Distance: ⚓500m ⊗500m ⚑500m.
Remarks: Max. 36h.

⟦S⟧ La Séguinière 20B2
Avenue de Nantes. **GPS:** n47,06005 w0,93668.⬆➡.

10 ⅏free ⚱€2/100liter ⚏Ch⚏€2/1h WC. **Location:** Simple.
Surface: asphalted.
Distance: ⚓100m ⊗on the spot ⚑50m.

⟦S⟧ La Suze-sur-Sarthe 13D6
Rue du Camping. **GPS:** n47,88917 e0,03040.⬆➡.

10 ⅏€3 ⚱⚏Ch⚏free WC. **Location:** Urban, simple.
Surface: grassy/gravel. ▢ 01/01-31/12
Distance: ⚓300m ⊗300m ⛴on the spot ⚘on the spot.
Remarks: Along Sarthe River, in harbour.

⟦S⟧ La Tranche-sur-Mer ⚓⛵ 20A4
Boulevard de la Petite Hollande. **GPS:** n46,34965 w1,44769.⬆➡.

FR

20 ⌚free, 14/06-14/09 € 10 🚰€3,50/10minutes 📺Ch📶 🧺 🚿 **Location:** Simple, quiet. ⬛ 01/01-31/12
Remarks: Max. 7 days.

La Tranche-sur-Mer 20A4
Parking du Stade, Avenue du Général de Gaulle. **GPS:** n46,35028 w1,43688.⬆️➡️.

30 ⌚free, 14/06-14/09 € 10 🚰€3,50 📺Chfree. **Location:** Rural.
Surface: asphalted.
Distance: 🚶1km.
Remarks: Max. 7 days.

La Tranche-sur-Mer 20A4
Parking de la Baleine, Place des Baleines. **GPS:** n46,34340 w1,46222.⬆️.

10 ⌚free, 14/06-14/09 € 10 🚰stay. **Location:** Rural, quiet. **Surface:** gravel.
⬛ 01/01-31/12
Distance: 🏖️200m ⊗on the spot 🍴on the spot.
Remarks: Max. 7 days.

La Turballe 12D4
Boulevard de la Grande Falaise. **GPS:** n47,33106 w2,49919.⬆️.
6 ⌚free, June-Sep € 3 🚰📺Ch 🚿included.
Location: Simple. **Surface:** gravel. ⬛ 01/01-31/12
Distance: 🚶2km.
Remarks: Max. 5 nights.

La Turballe 12D4
Rue Alphonse Daudet. **GPS:** n47,34870 w2,50804.⬆️.

15 ⌚free, June-Sep € 3 🚰📺Chfree. **Location:** Simple, quiet.

Surface: gravel. ⬛ 01/01-31/12
Distance: 🚶800m 🏖️500m ⊗100m 🍴100m.
Remarks: Max. 5 days.

Lassay-les-Châteaux 13C5
Allée du Haut Perrin. **GPS:** n48,43777 w0,49822.⬆️.

⌚free 🚰€2 📺Ch. **Location:** Urban, simple, central. **Surface:** asphalted.
⬛ 01/01-31/12
Distance: 🚶100m.
Remarks: Coins at Tourist Info and bakery.

Laval 13C6
Parking de la Halte Fluviale, Rue du Vieux Saint-Louis.
GPS: n48,07589 w0,77142.⬆️➡️.

10 ⌚free 🚰📺Chfree. **Location:** Urban, simple. **Surface:** asphalted.
⬛ 01/01-31/12
Distance: 🚶300m ▸on the spot ⊗on the spot 🍴on the spot.
Remarks: Parking nearby viaduct.

Tourist information Laval:
Ⓜ️🏛️ Vieux Château. Medieval castle, museum with collection of naive art.
⬛ 10-12h, 14-18h.

Le Coudray Macouard 20D2
Route de Bron. **GPS:** n47,18806 w0,11722.⬆️➡️.

5 ⌚free 🚰📺. **Location:** Rural, isolated, quiet. **Surface:** grassy.
⬛ 01/01-31/12
Distance: 🚶800m 🍴800m.

Le Croisic 12D5
Le Lin Gorzé, Rue du Lin Gorzé. **GPS:** n47,29917 w2,52194.⬆️➡️.

9 🛏 € 5,30 🚰 €2 🗑 Ch 🧺. **Location:** Simple, quiet. **Surface:** asphalted.
🔲 01/01-31/12
Distance: 🚶500m ⛱500m ⊗500m 🛒800m.
Remarks: Max. 48h.

🅂 **Le Croisic** 🏖⚓🍴 12D5
Les Courlis, Rue des Courlis. **GPS:** n47,29000 w2,505. ⬆➡.

15 🛏 € 5,45 🚰 €2 🗑 Ch 🧺. **Location:** Simple. **Surface:** gravel.
🔲 01/04-31/10
Distance: 🚶500m ⛱500m ⊗500m 🛒500m.
Remarks: Max. 48h.

🅂 **Le Croisic** 🏖⚓🍴 12D5
La Vigie, Avenue de Pierre Longue, D45. **GPS:** n47,28917 w2,53667. ⬆.

9 🛏 € 5,30. 🚐 🧺 **Location:** Simple. **Surface:** asphalted. 🔲 01/01-31/12
Distance: 🚶3km ⛱50m ⊗3km 🛒3km.
Remarks: Max. 48h.

🅂 **Le Croisic** 🏖⚓🍴 12D5
Les Bassins, Rue du Bassin. **GPS:** n47,29194 w2,50741. ⬆➡.

9 🛏 € 5,45/night. **Location:** Urban, simple, quiet. **Surface:** asphalted.
🔲 01/01-31/12
Distance: 🚶200m ⛱20m ⊗200m 🛒200m.
Remarks: Max. 48h.

🅂 **Le Croisic** 🏖⚓🍴 12D5
P1 Kerdavid, Rue Kerclavid 1. **GPS:** n47,29835 w2,51995. ⬆.

8 🛏 € 5,30. 🚐 🧺 **Location:** Urban, simple, quiet. **Surface:** asphalted.
🔲 01/01-31/12
Distance: 🚶500m ⛱500m ⊶500m 🛒800m.
Tourist information Le Croisic:
☻ Océarium du Croisic. Sea aquarium. 🔲 01/06-31/08 10-19h, 01/05-31/05, 01/09-30/09 10-12h, 14-18h, 01/10-30/04 14-18h.

🅂 **Le Guédéniau** 20D1
Rue du Lavoir. **GPS:** n47,49405 w0,04488. ⬆➡.

15 🛏 free 🚰 🗑 Ch free. **Location:** Rural. **Surface:** metalled.
🔲 01/01-31/12
Distance: 🚶on the spot.
Remarks: Recreation area at lake.

🅂 **Le Mans** 🏖⚓🍴 13D6
Quai de l'Amiral Lalande. **GPS:** n48,00233 e0,18915. ⬆.

7 🛏 free 🚰 🗑 Ch free. **Location:** Urban, simple. **Surface:** asphalted.
🔲 01/01-31/12
Distance: 🚶centre 1km 🏊8km.
Remarks: Along Sarthe River.

Le Mans 🏖⚓🍴 13D6
Rue Denfert Rochereau. **GPS:** n48,01111 e0,19750. ⬆.

🛏 free. **Location:** Urban, simple, noisy. **Surface:** asphalted.
🔲 01/01-31/12
Distance: 🚶500m ⊗500m 🛒500m.
Remarks: Max. 24h, sunday morning market.

FR

Tourist information Le Mans:
Ⓜ Circuit Le Mans. Motorcar museum.
⌂ Place des Jacobins. ◼ Wed + Su-morning, Fri.

| | Le Pallet | | 20B2 |

Rue Pierre Abelard. **GPS:** n47,13494 w1,3305.⬆.

20 free ⚡€1 Ch. **Location:** Rural, simple. **Surface:** asphalted.
◼ 01/01-31/12
Distance: 500m 500m 500m on the spot on the spot.
Remarks: Wine museum, coins at the shops in the village.

| | Le Poiré-sur-Vie | | 20A3 |

Rue de Roc. **GPS:** n46,76773 w1,51162.⬆➡.

5 free ⚡ Ch free. **Location:** Central, quiet. **Surface:** gravel.
◼ 01/01-31/12
Distance: 500m 500m 500m.

| | Le Puy-Notre-Dame | | 20D2 |

Place du Gâte Argent. **GPS:** n47,12390 w0,23155.⬆.
15 free ⚡ Ch free. **Surface:** metalled. ◼ 01/01-31/12
Distance: 100m 200m 200m.
Remarks: Next to cemetery.

| | Le Puy-Notre-Dame | | 20D2 |

Cave-Champignonnière St.Maur, 1, Rue du Chateau, Sanziers.
GPS: n47,11755 w0,20526.⬆➡.

8 free ⚡ WC free. **Surface:** metalled. ◼ 01/03-30/10
Distance: 2km.
Remarks: At mushroom grower.

| | Le Puy-Notre-Dame | | 20D2 |

Domaine de la Renière, Les Caves. **GPS:** n47,13429 w0,24256.⬆.

5 €5 ⚡ included. **Surface:** metalled. ◼ 01/03-01/11
Distance: 700m.

| | Le Puy-Notre-Dame | | 20D2 |

Domaine du Vieux Tuffeau, Les Caves. **GPS:** n47,13498 w0,24704.➡.

6 free ⚡. **Surface:** metalled. ◼ 01/01-31/12
Distance: 1km.

| | Le Puy-Notre-Dame | | 20D2 |

Domaine de la Girardrie, Rue Fontaine de Cix. **GPS:** n47,11616 w0,24127.⬆.

5 free. **Surface:** gravel. ◼ 01/01-31/12
Distance: 1km 1km 1km.

| | Le Vaudelnay | | 20C2 |

Domaine du Vieux Pressoir, 235, Rue Château d'Oiré. **GPS:** n47,14669 w0,25239.
➡.

4 free. **Surface:** metalled. ◼ 01/01-31/12
Distance: 3km 3km 3km.

| | Les Epesses | | 20B3 |

Le Puy du Fou, D27. **GPS:** n46,89425 w0,92506.⬆➡.
100 €5 ⚡€2/100liter Ch (36x)€2/12h. Location: Simple,
isolated, noisy. **Surface:** grassy.
Remarks: Baker at 8am, free shuttle to Puy du Fou.

| | Les Essarts | | 20B3 |

Rue de la piscine. **GPS:** n46,77380 w1,23499.⬆➡.

10 🆓free 🔌€2/10minutes 🗑 Ch 💧 (2x)€2/55minutes. **Location:** Rural, simple. **Surface:** asphalted. ⬛ 01/01-31/12
Distance: 🚶600m 🚲5,6km ⊗600m 🚉600m.
Remarks: At swimmingpool and campsite.

Les Herbiers 20B3
Rue Saint Exupéry. **GPS:** n46,87410 w1,01765. ⬆➡.

8 🆓free 🔌🗑 Ch free. **Location:** Simple. **Surface:** asphalted.
⬛ 01/01-31/12
Distance: 🚶600m ⊗600m 🚉600m.
Remarks: Max. 24h.

Les Sables-d'Olonne 20A3
Les Salines, 120 route de l'Aubraie. **GPS:** n46,51635 w1,80533. ⬆➡.

20 🆓€5 🔌🗑 Ch included 💧€4 📶free. 🚿
Location: Rural. **Surface:** sand.
⬛ 01/04-30/09
Distance: 🏊600m 🛝on the spot.
Remarks: Baker every morning, july/Aug only overnight stays (18-11h).

Les Sables-d'Olonne 20A3
Parking Vinci Parc, Rue Printanière. **GPS:** n46,49646 w1,77493. ➡.

150 🆓€12, winter free 🔌🗑 Ch 💧 WC included. 🖥 📖 **Location:** Simple.
Surface: metalled. ⬛ 01/01-31/12 ⬤ service 06/11-31/03
Distance: 🏊beach 400m.

Les Sables-d'Olonne 20A3
Parking de la Sablière. **GPS:** n46,50585 w1,78796.
🆓free. **Surface:** asphalted.

Tourist information Les Sables-d'Olonne:
🛈 Cours Dupont. ⬛ Wed + Sa morning.
🦁 Zoo d'Olonne. Zoo.

Liré 20B1
Le Haut Fief, Square Espéranto. **GPS:** n47,34130 w1,16751. ⬆.

5 🆓free 🔌🗑 Ch 💧 WC free. **Surface:** asphalted. ⬛ 01/01-31/12
Distance: 🚶500m ⊗250m 🚉50m.
Remarks: Max. 48h.

Longué-Jumelles 20D1
Boulevard Victor Hugo. **GPS:** n47,38119 w0,11254. ⬆➡.

10 🆓free 🔌🗑 Ch WC free.
Location: Simple, quiet. **Surface:** gravel. ⬛ 01/01-31/12
Distance: 🚶100m 🚲3,3km ⊗on the spot 🚉on the spot.
Remarks: Service 300m: N 47,38046 W -0,11488, attention: follow the signs.

Luçon 20B4
Domaine des Guifettes. **GPS:** n46,43339 w1,18189. ⬆➡.

🆓€10,50, dog €2,60 🔌🗑 Ch 💧included 📶.
Location: Rural, comfortable, isolated, quiet.
Surface: gravel/metalled.
Distance: 🏊on the spot 🛝on the spot ⊗on the spot 🚉on the spot
🛒on the spot 🚿on the spot.
Remarks: Free entrance swimming pool, jacuzzi, sauna, midget golf.

Tourist information Luçon:
🛈 Centre Ville. ⬛ Wed + Sa morning.

L'Aiguillon-sur-Mer 20B4
Centre de Voile, Avenue Amiral Coubert. **GPS:** n46,33238 w1,30726. ⬆➡.

FR

50 € 5 €2/100liter Ch WC. **Location:** Rural, simple.
Surface: asphalted. 01/01-31/12
Distance: 300m 300m on the spot 300m 300m.
Remarks: At lake, yachting school.

S Maillé 20B4

La Petite Cabane. **GPS**: n46,34082 w0,79349.

€ 8 Ch included.
Location: Rural, simple, quiet.
Surface: grassy.
Distance: 500m 200m.
Remarks: Check in at harbourmaster, service passerby € 3, bicycle rental 500m.

S Maillezais 20C4

Rue de l'Ecole. **GPS**: n46,37081 w0,74123.

20 free €2/100liter Ch. **Location:** Simple. **Surface:** asphalted.
01/01-31/12
Distance: 500m 500m 200m.

S Maisdon-sur-Sèvre 20B2

Domaine des Croix, Les Croix. **GPS**: n47,10710 w1,38757.
12 free Ch €4/24h WC €1.
Location: Rural. **Surface:** gravel. 01/01-31/12
Distance: 1km.
Remarks: Max. 72h, wine tasting.

S Mamers 14A5

Rue de la Piscine. **GPS**: n48,35523 e0,37187.

8 € 7/night, € 18/3 nights Ch included. **Location:** Rural, comfortable. **Surface:** grassy/gravel. 01/01-31/12
Distance: 1km 500m 500m 1km 1km.
Remarks: Entrance code available at campsite.

S Martigné-Briand 20C2

Jardin des Vieux Pressoirs, Rue d'Anjou. **GPS**: n47,23584 w0,42851.

4 free Ch free. **Surface:** metalled. 01/01-31/12
Distance: 200m 200m 100m.
Remarks: Closed when frosty.

S Mayenne 13C5

Quai Carnot. **GPS**: n48,30000 w0,62.

4 free €1,50 Ch. **Location:** Urban, simple, noisy. **Surface:** asphalted.
01/01-31/12
Distance: 1km 10m.
Remarks: Max. 24h, coins at tourist info.

S Mervent 20C4

Chemin du Chêne Tord. **GPS**: n46,52385 w0,76432.

free €2/100liter Ch. **Location:** Rural, simple, isolated, quiet.
Surface: gravel.
Distance: 1km.
Remarks: At cemetery, coins at tourist info.

S Mesnard-la-Barotière 20B3

Base de Loisirs de la Tricherie. **GPS**: n46,85280 w1,11764.

free €3 Ch. **Location:** Rural, simple. **Surface:** grassy.
Distance: 2km beach on the spot on the spot on the spot.
Remarks: At lake of Tricherie.

FR

☒S **Mezeray** 13D6
Rue de la Vezanne. **GPS:** n47,82300 w0,01485. ↑→.

8 ⌇free ⚡€2 ⚐Ch ⊞€2. **Location:** Rural, simple. **Surface:** gravel.
◻ 01/01-31/12
Distance: ⚲300m.

☒S **Montfort-le-Gesnois** 14A6
Parc des Sittelles. **GPS:** n48,03763 e0,41375. ↑→.

16 ⌇€10 ⚡⚐Ch ⚘included. **Location:** Rural, simple, quiet.
Surface: forest soil. ◻ 01/01-31/12
Distance: ⊗50m.

☒S **Montreuil-Bellay** 20D2
Rue Georges Girouy. **GPS:** n47,13272 w0,15835. ↑.

20 ⌇free ⚡€2 ⚐Ch. **Surface:** gravel/metalled. ◻ 01/01-31/12
◻ 15/06-15/09 10-19h
Distance: ⚲150m ⊗150m ⚑150m.
Remarks: Along river, nearby campsite Les Nobis.

☒S **Montreuil-Bellay** 20D2
Caveau de la Prévoté, Rue du Cohu 55, Méron. **GPS:** n47,13522 w0,11121. ↑.

3 ⌇free ⚡⚐Ch ⚘⌇free. **Surface:** metalled. ◻ 01/01-31/12
Distance: ⚲50m ⊗3km ⚑3km.

Tourist information Montreuil-Bellay:
ℹ Office de Tourisme, Place du Concorde, www.ville-montreuil-bellay.fr. City
with a fortress from 1025.

☒S **Montreuil-Juigné** 20C1
Rue Saint Jean Baptiste. **GPS:** n47,54132 w0,61526. ↑→.

8 ⌇free ⚡⚐Chfree. **Location:** Rural, simple. **Surface:** gravel/metalled.
◻ 01/01-31/12
Distance: ⚲1km ⊗50m ⚑800m.
Remarks: Along the Mayenne river.

☒S **Montsoreau** 20D2
Domaine de la Perruche, 29, Rue de la Maumenière. **GPS:** n47,21828 e0,05079.
↑.
⚐.
Distance: ⚲500m ⊗500m.
Remarks: 10.30><18.30h.

☒S **Moutiers-sur-le-Lay** 20B3
Palias. **GPS:** n46,55375 w1,15483. →.

6 ⌇free ⚡⚐Ch WCfree. **Location:** Simple. **Surface:** grassy.
◻ 01/01-31/12
Distance: ⚲400m ⊗400m ⚑400m ⎚200m.
Remarks: At gymnasium.

☒S **Mouzillon** 20B2
Route de la Vendée. **GPS:** n47,13944 w1,28194. ↑→.

12 ⌇free ⚡€2 ⚐Ch. **Location:** Simple. **Surface:** asphalted.
Distance: ⚲200m ⊗200m ⚑200m ⚙on the spot.

☒S **Nantes** 20A2
Camping-car park du Petit Port, Boulevard du Petit Port.
GPS: n47,24252 w1,5568. ↑→.

15 ⌇€12/24h ⚡⚐Ch ⚘included.
Location: Urban, simple, central. **Surface:** grassy/metalled.

FR

FR

⬜ 01/01-31/12
Distance: 🚶on the spot 🚲3,5km ⊗on the spot 🍴300m 🚋tram 150m.
Remarks: Wifi code: 44-2207, entrance code 2207A.
Tourist information Nantes:
Ⓜ Musée Jules Verne.

| 📷S | Noirmoutier-en-l'Ile ⚓🌊 | 12D5 |

Place des Ormeaux, L'Epine. **GPS:** n46,98060 w2,26404.⬆️.

40 🔲€ 7/24h, € 13/48h, € 19/72h ⛽100liter 🔲Ch 🔌included50minutes
WC.🚿♻ **Surface:** metalled. ⬜ 01/01-31/12
Distance: 🚶100m 🏖1,3km 🛒on the spot ⊗200m 🍴3km.
Remarks: Max. 72h.

| 📷S | Noirmoutier-en-l'Ile ⚓🌊 | 12D5 |

Place Florent Caillaud, Noirmoutierr-en-l'Ile. **GPS:** n47,00139 w2,25167.⬆️.

182 🔲€ 5, 01/04-30/09 € 8, parking free ⛽€2/100liter 🔲Ch 🔌€2/2h
📶free.🚿 **Surface:** asphalted. ⬜ 01/01-31/12
Distance: 🚶750m 🏖sandy beach 2,5km 🍴750m.
Remarks: Max. 7 days.

| 📷S | Noirmoutier-en-l'Ile ⚓🌊 | 12D5 |

Place R. Ganachaud, l'Herbaudière. **GPS:** n46,83058 w2,12996.⬆️.

18 🔲€ 5, 01/04-30/09 € 8, parking free ⛽€2/100liter 🔲Ch 🔌€2/1h. 🚿
Surface: asphalted. ⬜ 01/01-31/12
Distance: 🏖on the spot ⊗350m.
Remarks: Parking behind town hall.

| 📷S | Noirmoutier-en-l'Ile ⚓🌊 | 12D5 |

Rue de la Tresson, La Guérinière. **GPS:** n46,96588 w2,21451.⬆️.

20 🔲€ 5, 01/04-30/09 € 8, parking free ⛽🔲Chfree 🔌4.🚿♻
Surface: gravel. ⬜ 01/01-31/12
Distance: 🏖sandy beach 450m ⊗200m 🍴100m.
Remarks: Max. 48h.
Tourist information Noirmoutier-en-l'Ile:
🌳 Place de la République. ⬜ Fri.
😊 Sealand Aquarium, Le Vieux Port.

| 📷S | Nort-sur-Erdre 🌊 | 20A1 |

13 Place du Bassin. **GPS:** n47,43746 w1,49546.⬆️.

15 🔲free ⛽€2 🔲Ch WC 🔲free. **Location:** Simple, quiet.
Surface: asphalted. ⬜ 01/01-31/12
Distance: 🚶300m 🛒100m 🍴300m 📶300m.
Remarks: Max. 24h.

| 📷S | Notre-Dame-de-Monts | 12D5 |

Aire de la Clairière, Rue de la Clairière. **GPS:** n46,83460 w2,14282.⬆️➡️.

35 🔲€ 5/20-8h ⛽🔲Chfree. 🚿♻ **Location:** Rural, simple.
Surface: gravel. ⬜ 01/01-31/12
Distance: 🚶800m 🛒200m ⊗800m 🍴800m.
Remarks: Motorhome parking at the beach.

| 📷S | Notre-Dame-de-Monts | 12D5 |

Aire Place de Gaulle, Rue des Maraichins. **GPS:** n46,83058 w2,12994.⬆️.

20 🔲€ 5/20-8h ⛽🔲Ch WC free. 🚿♻ **Surface:** asphalted.
⬜ 01/01-31/12
Distance: 🚶300m ⊗500m 🍴300m.

| 📷S | Nozay | 20A1 |

Étang de Nozay. GPS: n47,57500 w1,62528.⬆️.

16 ⬧€5 🚰🝙Ch ✎ (16x)WC included.
Surface: gravel. ⬛ 01/01-31/12 ⬛ service: frost
Distance: 🚶200m ✗2km 🚲10m ⊗200m 🛒200m.

12 ⬧€6 🚰€2/100liter 🝙Ch WC.
Location: Comfortable. **Surface:** metalled. ⬛ 01/01-31/12
Distance: 🚶2km ⛵50m ⊗2km 🛒2km.
Remarks: Parking to sea.

| 🏕S | **Olonne-sur-Mer** 🔊 | 20A3 |

| 🏕S | **Piriac-sur-Mer** 🔊 | 12D4 |

Aire de Camping-car Olonne Escale, Rue des Anciens Combattants d'Afrique du Nord. **GPS:** n46,53814 w1,77517. ⬆➡.

Parking de Lérat, Route de Mesquène, D99, Lieu-dit Lérat.
GPS: n47,36807 w2,53273. ⬆.

21 ⬧€8/24h 🚰🝙Ch ✎ included. 🚐🗑
Location: Simple.
Distance: 🚶300m 🛒600m.
Remarks: Jul/Aug max. 48h, max. 72h.

25 ⬧€6 🚰€2/100liter 🝙Ch. **Location:** Simple. **Surface:** metalled.
⬛ 01/01-31/12
Distance: 🚶2,5km ⛵600m ✗600m ⊗500m 🛒500m.

| 🏕S | **Parnay** | 20D2 |

| 🏕S | **Piriac-sur-Mer** 🔊 | 12D4 |

D947. **GPS:** n47,23146 e0,01098. ⬆.

Port de Piriac, Rue de la Tranchée. **GPS:** n47,37861 w2,5422. ⬆.
10 ⬧€6 🚰€2/100liter 🝙Ch. 🚐 ⬛ 01/01-31/12
Distance: 🚶500m ⊗500m 🛒500m.

Tourist information Piriac-sur-Mer:
⛺ ⬛ 01/06-30/09 Mo + Wed + Sa-morning, 01/10-30/05 Tue.
⛺ Arts market. ⬛ 01/07-31/08 Thu-evening.

| 🏕S | **Pornic** | 12D5 |

Le Val Saint-Martin. **GPS:** n47,12053 w2,09162. ⬆➡.

5 ⬧free 🚰€2 🝙Ch. **Surface:** asphalted. ⬛ 01/01-31/12
Distance: 🚶200m.

| 🏕S | **Pellouailles-les-Vignes** | 20C1 |

Rue Nationale, D323. **GPS:** n47,52141 w0,43698. ⬆.

7 ⬧free 🚰€2/100liter 🝙Ch ✎. **Location:** Comfortable, isolated.
Surface: asphalted. ⬛ 01/01-31/12
Distance: 🚶city centre 1,5km.
Remarks: Next to swimming pool.

| 🏕S | **Pouancé** 🔊 | 13B6 |

Rue de l'hippodrôme, Aubin. **GPS:** n47,75223 w1,18007. ⬆➡.

3 ⬧free 🚰🝙Ch free.
Location: Rural. **Surface:** asphalted. ⬛ 01/01-31/12
Distance: 🚶on the spot ✗1,4km ⊗100m 🛒bakery 50m.

| 🏕S | **Piriac-sur-Mer** 🔊 | 12D4 |

Parking de Brambel, Avenue du Général de Gaulle, D452.
GPS: n47,39647 w2,51292. ⬆.

FR

10 🗐 € 2,75 🚰 🗑 Ch 🧹 (4x) WC free. **Location:** Rural, simple, quiet.
Surface: grassy. 🅿 01/01-31/12
Distance: 🚶500m 🏖small beach 20m 🚣20m ⊗1km 🍴1km.
Remarks: Along étang de Saint-Aubin.

🅂 Pouzauges 20B3
Parking de la Vallée, D49/D203. **GPS:** n46,77639 w0,82861. ⬆️➡️.

10 🗐 free 🚰 🗑 Ch free. **Location:** Simple. **Surface:** asphalted.
🅿 01/01-31/12
Distance: 🚶1km ⊗1km 🍴1km.

🅂 Préfailles 12D5
Camping-Car Park de La Pointe, Chemin du Port aux Anes.
GPS: n47,13872 w2,22213. ⬆️.

49 🗐 € 12/24h 🚰 🗑 Ch 🔌 included 📶.📶🧺 ✏️ **Location:** Comfortable.
Surface: grassy/gravel. 🅿 01/01-31/12

🅂 Préfailles 12D5
Aire de Biochon, Chemin de Levertrie. **GPS:** n47,12973 e2,19028.

75 🗐 € 3. 🚿 **Location:** Rural, simple, quiet. **Surface:** gravel/sand.
🅿 01/01-31/12
Distance: 🚶3km 🏖500m 🚣500m ⊗3km 🍴3km.
Remarks: Max. 48h, baker every morning.

🅂 Préfailles 12D5
Aire de la Pointe St-Gildas, D313, chemin des Pinettes.
GPS: n47,13663 w2,23843.

45 🗐 € 5. 🚿 **Location:** Rural, simple, quiet. **Surface:** grassy/gravel.
🅿 01/01-31/12

Distance: 🚶3km 🏖50m ⊗200m 🍴3km.
Remarks: Max. 48h, baker every morning.

🅂 Préfailles 12D5
Rue de la Prée. **GPS:** n47,13439 w2,2117.
🚰 €2,50/100liter 🗑 Ch.
Location: Simple. 🅿 01/01-31/12
Remarks: Coins at tourist info.

🅂 Rablay sur Layon 20C2
D54. **GPS:** n47,29772 w0,57767. ⬆️➡️.
10 🗐 free 🚰 🗑 Ch WC free.
Location: Rural, simple. **Surface:** gravel/sand.
Distance: 🚶300m.

🅂 Riaille 20B1
Rue de la Benate. **GPS:** n47,51412 w1,28803. ⬆️➡️.

5 🗐 free 🚰 🗑 Ch WC 🧺 free. **Location:** Rural, simple, quiet. **Surface:** gravel.
🅿 01/01-31/12
Distance: 🚶700m ⊗700m 🍴700m.
Remarks: Max. 48h.

🅂 Rouans 20A2
Aire naturelle de Messan, Route des Marais. **GPS:** n47,19272 w1,85419. ⬆️➡️.

8 🗐 € 3 🚰 🗑 Ch WC free. **Location:** Rural, simple. **Surface:** grassy/metalled.
🅿 01/01-31/12
Distance: 🚶1km 🚣on the spot ⊗on the spot 🍴1km.
Remarks: To be paid at town hall.

🅂 Saint-Léonard-des-Bois 13D5
Aire Municipale, Le Gué Plard. **GPS:** n48,35318 w0,08127. ⬆️.

10 🗐 free 🚰 🗑 Ch WC free.
Location: Simple, quiet. 🅿 01/01-31/12
Distance: 🚶500m 🏖on the spot 🚣on the spot ⊗500m 🚌on the spot
🎣on the spot 🎯on the spot.

🅂 Saint-Loup-du-Gast 13C5
Zone d'Activité du Creusot. **GPS:** n48,38750 w0,58548. ⬆️➡️.

6 🛏free 🚽🍽Chfree. **Location:** Rural, simple. **Surface:** asphalted/grassy. ◯ 01/01-31/12
Distance: 🚲350m.
Remarks: Departure Vélorail, € 15 per bike for 4 pers.

5 🛏free. **Location:** Simple, central. **Surface:** gravel.
◯ 01/01-31/12
Distance: 🚲500m ⛵10m 🚲10m 🏍on the spot 🚶on the spot.

	Saint-Michel-en-l'Herm	20B4
Route de la Mer D60. **GPS:** n46,36155, w1,24929.
6 🛏free 🚽€2 🍽Ch.
Distance: 🚶200m 🚰200m.
Remarks: Coins at the shops.

	Saulgé l'Hôpital	20C2
Terrain de Loisirs, Chemin de la Planche. **GPS:** n47,29853 w0,38344. ⬆

	Saint-Nazaire	12D5
Route de l'Océan, D292, Saint-Marc-sur-Mer. **GPS:** n47,23700 w2,30033. ⬆.

15 🛏free 🚽€3/100liter 🍽Ch🚿€3/1h 🧹. **Location:** Rural, simple, quiet.
Surface: gravel. ◯ 01/01-31/12
Distance: 🚲2km ⛵100m 🚌100m.

15 🛏free 🚽🍽Chfree. **Surface:** gravel. ◯ 01/01-31/12
Distance: 🚲100m 🚶100m 🚰100m.

	Saint-Nazaire	12D5
Bois-Joalland, Route de Quelmer. **GPS:** n47,27669 w2,25771.
3 🛏free. **Location:** Rural, simple, quiet. **Surface:** unpaved.
◯ 01/01-31/12
Distance: 🚲1km ⛵5m 🏍on the spot 🚶on the spot.
Remarks: Nearby base nautique.

	Segré	20C1
Aire de l'Europe, D775. **GPS:** n47,68497 w0,85719. ⬆➡.

	Saint-Nazaire	12D5
Parking du Théâtre, Boulevard Paul Leferme. **GPS:** n47,27760 w2,20362.

🛏free 🚽🍽Ch WC free. **Location:** Rural. **Surface:** asphalted.
◯ 01/01-31/12
Distance: 🚲1km.

	Segré	20C1
Place du Moulin sous la Tour, Rue Emile Zola. **GPS:** n47,68409 w0,87436.➡.

8 🛏free. **Location:** Urban, simple, isolated. **Surface:** asphalted.
◯ 01/01-31/12
Distance: 🚲on the spot 🚰500m 🚌50m.

	Saint-Nazaire	12D5
Quai du Port de Méan. **GPS:** n47,29937 w2,18333.
6 🛏free. **Surface:** metalled.
Distance: 🚲4km 🚰1km 🚌150m.

	Saint-Nazaire	12D5
Route du Bois Joalland. **GPS:** n47,27954 w2,26229. ⬆.

10 🛏free 🚽🍽Chfree. **Location:** Rural, simple. **Surface:** gravel.
◯ 01/01-31/12 ◉ Service: winter
Distance: 🚲300m 🚶on the spot 🚶100m 🚶on the spot.

	Sillé-le-Guillaume	13D5
2, Place de la Gare. **GPS:** n48,18167 w0,13111. ⬆➡.

8 🚐 free 🚰 €2 ⬇ Ch 🔌 €2. **Location:** Urban, simple. **Surface:** asphalted.
📅 01/01-31/12
Distance: 🏙 300m 🍴 300m 🛒 400m 🚆 train 50m.
Remarks: May 2012 during inspection service out of order.

[S] St.Aubin-de-Luigné 20C2

Domaine La Biquerie, D17. **GPS**: n47,30843 w0,70211.[↑].

30 🚐 free 🚰 ⬇ Ch free. **Surface:** grassy. 📅 01/01-31/12
Distance: 🏙 5km.

[S] St.Calais 14A6

Boulevard du Docteur Gigon. **GPS**: n47,92416 e0,74459.[↑→].

4 🚐 free 🚰 ⬇ Ch WC free. **Location:** Rural, simple. **Surface:** asphalted.
📅 01/01-31/12
Distance: 🏙 400m 🚶 on the spot.

[S] St.Calais 14A6

Le Champ Long, D249. **GPS**: n47,93375 e0,74568.[↑] .

15 🚐 free WC. **Location:** Rural. **Surface:** asphalted. 📅 01/01-31/12
Distance: 🏙 1,6km 🏖 lake 🎣 on the spot 🚶 on the spot.

[S] St.Clément-des-Levées 20D2

Rue de la Laiterie. **GPS**: n47,33064 w0,18042.[↑→].

10 🚐 free 🚰 €2 ⬇ Ch. **Surface:** metalled. 📅 01/01-31/12
Distance: 🏙 300m.
Remarks: Coins at the shops and town hall.

[S] St.Cyr-en-Bourg 20D2

Cave de Saumur, Route du Mureau. **GPS**: n47,19642 w0,07266.[↑→].

15 🚐 free 🚰 ⬇ Ch WC free. **Surface:** asphalted. 📅 15/03-15/09
Distance: 🏙 3km.
Remarks: Max. 48h, wine tasting 300m.

[S] St.Georges-sur-Loire 20C1

Rue de la Villette. **GPS**: n47,40610 w0,76301.

20 🚐 free 🚰 ⬇ Ch free. **Location:** Rural, simple. **Surface:** asphalted.
📅 01/01-31/12
Distance: 🏙 300m 🏖 100m 🍴 300m 🛒 300m.
Remarks: Next to the old abbey, max. 24h.

[S] St.Gilles-Croix-de-Vie 20A3

La Rabalette, Rue de la Rabalette. **GPS**: n46,70302 w1,94728.[↑].

35 🚐 15/03-15/11 € 5/night 🚰 €2,60/10minutes ⬇ Ch. **Location:** Urban, simple. **Surface:** asphalted. 📅 01/01-31/12
Distance: 🏙 500m 🏖 1km 🍴 500m 🛒 500m.
Remarks: Nearby lake Soudinière, coins at tourist info.

[S] St.Gilles-Croix-de-Vie 20A3

Stade de la Chapelle, Rue du Bois. **GPS**: n46,69449 w1,92716.
🚐 € 5 🚰 €2,60 ⬇ Ch.
Surface: asphalted.
📅 01/04-30/09 weekend and school holidays

Distance: 🚶centre 500m.
Remarks: Coins at tourist info, 2013: during inspection service out of order.
Tourist information St.Gilles-Croix-de-Vie:
🏠 ⬛ St.Gilles: Tue, Thu, Su; Croix de Vie: Wed, Sa.

| 🗺️ S | St.Hilaire de Riez 🚐🌊 | 12D6 |

Base des vallées, Chemin des Vallées. **GPS:** n46,73154 w1,91132.⬆️

10 🛏free 🚰€2,60/10minutes 🔌Ch ♻️. **Location:** Rural, simple.
Surface: asphalted. ⬛ 01/01-31/12
Distance: 🚶St.Hilaire 3,7km 🏖️7km.

| 🗺️ S | St.Hilaire de Riez 🚐🌊 | 12D6 |

Parking des Becs, Avenue des Becs. **GPS:** n46,76040 w2,02656.⬆️
20 🛏€ 5/24h 🚰€2,60/10minutes 🔌Ch. 🚽 ♻️ **Location:** Rural.
Surface: asphalted. ⬛ 01/01-31/12
Distance: 🏖️sandy beach 750m ⊗200m.
Remarks: Max. 3 nights.

| 🗺️ S | St.Hilaire de Riez 🚐🌊 | 12D6 |

Allée de la Plage de la Parée Préneau. **GPS:** n46,72865 w1,99167.⬆️

48 🛏free, night € 5. 🚽
Location: Rural. **Surface:** metalled. ⬛ 01/01-31/12
Distance: 🏖️on the spot.
Remarks: Beach parking.

| 🗺️ S | St.Hilaire de Riez 🚐🌊 | 12D6 |

Champ Gaillard, Avenue de Baisse. **GPS:** n46,76903 w2,03337.⬆️

28 🛏free.
Location: Rural, isolated. **Surface:** gravel. ⬛ 01/01-31/12
Distance: 🏖️sandy beach 1km.

| Ⓒ S | St.Hilaire-de-Chaléons | 20A2 |

Rue Eloi Guitteny, D61. **GPS:** n47,10389 w1,86639.⬆️

2 🛏free 🚰🔌Ch WC free. **Surface:** asphalted. ⬛ 01/01-31/12
Distance: 🚶100m ⊗500m 🛒100m.
Remarks: Next to campsite de l'Etoile, max. 24h.

| 🗺️ S | St.Jean-de-Monts | 12D6 |

Le Repos des Tortues, Route de Notre Dame de Monts 38.
GPS: n46,79879 w2,07344.⬆️

98 🛏€ 8, 01/07-31/08 € 12 🚰🔌Ch 🔌(49x),4Amp WC ⬛€5/stay
⬛€4 📶included. 🚽♻️ **Location:** Rural, luxurious. **Surface:** grassy/gravel.
⬛ 01/01-31/12
Distance: 🚶800m 🏖️1,5km ⊗50m 🛒2km.
Remarks: Video surveillance.

| 🗺️ S | St.Jean-de-Monts | 12D6 |

Aire de stationnement des Pimprenelles, Rue des Pimprenelles.
GPS: n46,78882 w2,07939.
20 🛏€ 8 🚰🔌Ch 🔌 included. 🚽
Location: Comfortable. ⬛ 01/01-31/12
Distance: 🏖️sandy beach 200m.
Tourist information St.Jean-de-Monts:
🏠 ⬛ Wed, Sa.

| 🗺️ S | St.Jean-sur-Mayenne 🌊 | 13C5 |

Les Marchanderies. **GPS:** n48,12793 w0,75244.⬆️➡️

25 🛏€ 7,60 🚰🔌Ch 🔌 WC ⬛included. **Location:** Rural, luxurious, quiet.
Surface: grassy/gravel. ⬛ 01/01-31/12
Distance: 🚶500m 🔌on the spot ⊗300m 🛒400m bakery 🍴on the spot.
Remarks: Along the Mayenne river.

| 🗺️ S | St.Mars-La-Jaille 🌊 | 20B1 |

Rue Neuve. **GPS:** n47,52327 w1,18357.

FR

12 ⬛ free ⛽ ⬛ Ch WC free. **Location:** Rural. **Surface:** asphalted. ⬛ 01/01-31/12
Distance: 🚉 200m 🚌 on the spot.
Remarks: Parking at small lake.

♿ S | **St.Michel-Chef-Chef** | 12D5

Camping-Car Park Le Thar-Cor La Plaine sur Mer, Avenue Cormier. **GPS:** n47,16017 w2,16881. ⬆️.

24 ⬛ € 12/24h ⛽ ⬛ Ch 🔌 📶 included. **Location:** Simple, isolated, quiet. ⬛ 01/01-31/12
Distance: 🏖️ sandy beach 400m 🚌 400m 🚰 400m.

♿ S | **St.Michel-Chef-Chef** | 12D5

Rue du Chevecier. **GPS:** n47,18209 w2,14664. ⬆️.

30 ⬛ free, 20-8h € 6 ⛽ €2,95/100liter ⬛ Ch.
Location: Simple. **Surface:** asphalted.
⬛ 01/01-31/12
Distance: 🚉 300m ⊗300m 🚰 300m.
Remarks: Parking townhall, coins at tourist info and town hall.

© S | **St.Michel-Chef-Chef** | 12D5

Camping Clos Mer et Nature, Route de Tharon. **GPS:** n47,17309 w2,15779. ⬆️.

⬛ € 6 ⛽ €2/100liter ⬛ Ch ⬛ €2. **Location:** Simple, quiet. **Surface:** grassy.
⬛ 01/01-31/12
Distance: 🚉 500m 🏖️ sandy beach 400m 🚰 300m.
Remarks: Check in at reception campsite.

♿ S | **St.Michel-Mont-Mercure** | 20B3

Place du Sommet. **GPS:** n46,83222 w0,88222. ⬆️➡️.

50 ⬛ free ⛽ €2/150liter ⬛ Ch. **Location:** Simple, isolated. **Surface:** gravel/sand. ⬛ 01/01-31/12
Distance: 🚉 500m ⊗on the spot 🚰 500m.

♿ S | **St.Philbert-de-Grandlieu** | 20A2

Chemin de la Plage. **GPS:** n47,04500 w1,64172. ⬆️➡️.

10 ⬛ free ⛽ ⬛ Ch free. **Surface:** gravel. ⬛ 01/01-31/12
Distance: 🚉 1km 🏖️ on the spot 🚌 on the spot ⊗550m 🚰 1km.

♿ S | **St.Rémy-la-Varenne** | 20C1

Rue St Aubin-D132. **GPS:** n47,39805 w0,31612. ⬆️➡️.

3 ⬛ free ⛽ ⬛ Ch WC free. **Surface:** asphalted. ⬛ 01/01-31/12
Distance: 🚉 on the spot ⊗100m 🚰 100m.

♿ S | **St.Saturnin-sur-Loire** | 20C1

Route de Saumur, D751. **GPS:** n47,39267 w0,43285. ⬆️➡️.

3 ⬛ free ⛽ ⬛ Ch free. **Surface:** metalled. ⬛ 01/01-31/12
Distance: 🚉 on the spot ⊗100m 🚰 100m.

♿ S | **St.Viaud** | 20A1

Rue du Parc des Sports. **GPS:** n47,25917 w2,015. ⬆️.

FR

10 ⬛free 🚰⬛Ch 🧹(2x). **Location:** Rural, comfortable, quiet.
Surface: metalled. ⬛ 01/01-31/12
Distance: 🛒500m 🏊100m ⊗500m ⚓500m.
Remarks: At recreational lake, max. 8 days.

Chemin des Roulettes, Le Goulet. **GPS:** n46,41038 w1,5413.⬆️➡️.

43 ⬛€ 0,35/h 🚰€2/10minutes ⬛Ch ▦€2/55minutes 🧹.🚐🧹
Location: Rural, simple. **Surface:** metalled.
⬛ 01/01-31/12 ⬤ Service: winter
Distance: 🛒1km 🏊100m ⚓400m.

Parking des Gâtines, Rue des Gâtines. **GPS:** n46,46761 w1,61718.⬆️.

16 ⬛€ 5/24h 🚰€3/100liter ⬛Ch ▦€3/50minutes.🚐🧹
Location: Rural, simple. **Surface:** asphalted. ⬛ 01/01-31/12
Distance: 🛒500m 🏊Small lake (100m) ⚓100m.

Parking du Château Guibert, Avenue de la Plage. **GPS:** n46,44098 w1,66351.
⬆️➡️.

16 ⬛€ 5/24h 🚰€3 ⬛Ch WC 🧹.🚐🧹 **Location:** Rural, simple.
Surface: metalled. ⬛ 01/04-31/10
Distance: 🏊1km.
Remarks: Max. 48h.

Rue des Ducs d'Anjou. **GPS:** n47,22393 e0,02858.⬆️.

20 ⬛free 🚰€2,50 ⬛Ch. **Surface:** metalled. ⬛ 01/01-31/12
Distance: 🛒100m ⊗50m ⚓50m 🚌on the spot.
Remarks: Behind church, coins at the shops in the village.

Rue Robert Gletron, D57. **GPS:** n48,04189 w0,48285.✈️.

5 ⬛free 🚰€2 ⬛Ch. **Location:** Urban, simple, noisy. **Surface:** gravel.
⬛ 01/01-31/12
Distance: 🛒500m 🏌1,7km 🚲20m ⚓700m bakery.

Aire de Plaisance, Rue de la Mairie. **GPS:** n47,21658 w0,60326.⬆️.

6 ⬛free 🚰⬛Ch WC free. **Surface:** metalled. ⬛ 01/01-31/12
Distance: 🛒200m.
Remarks: Nearby town hall.

Rue Pierre Nicolas Loué. **GPS:** n46,68250 w1,51472.

5 ⬛free. **Surface:** sand. ⬛ 01/01-31/12
Distance: 🛒500m 🏊100m ⊗300m ⚓500m.

Route de l'Océan. **GPS:** n46,82690 w1,1217.⬆️.

FR

Centre

5 🛏 free 💧 €3/150liter ⚱ Ch free. **Location:** Rural, simple, quiet. **Surface:** metalled/sand. ⬛ 01/01-31/12
Distance: 🚶200m.
Remarks: Coins at the bakery.

Vihiers 20C2
Rue Champ de Foire des Champs. **GPS:** n47,14355 w0,5358. ⬆️➡️.

5 🛏 free 💧⚱ Ch WC. **Location:** Urban. **Surface:** asphalted.
⬛ 01/01-31/12
Distance: 🚶50m ⊗100m 🛒100m.

Villeveque 20C1
Rue du Port. **GPS:** n47,56222 w0,42257. ⬆️.
6 🛏 free 💧 €1 ⚱ Ch WC. ⬛ 01/01-31/12
Distance: 🚶100m ⊗50m 🛒bakery 200m.

Villiers-Charlemagne 13C6
Village Vacances et Pêche, Rue des Haies. **GPS:** n47,92083 w0,68167. ⬆️➡️.

25 🛏 € 8,10, first night free 💧 €2 ⚱ Ch 🖼️.
Location: Rural, comfortable, quiet. **Surface:** grassy.
⬛ 01/01-31/12
Distance: ⊘on the spot 🎣day pass available 🛒500m 🧍on the spot.

Vouvant 20B3
Rue de Château Neuf. **GPS:** n46,57462 w0,77462. ⬆️➡️.

20 🛏 free 💧⚱ Ch free. **Surface:** gravel. ⬛ 01/01-31/12
Distance: 🚶500m ⊗500m 🛒500m.

Allogny 21D2
D944. **GPS:** n47,21913 e2,32329. ⬆️➡️.

10 🛏 free 💧 free. **Surface:** asphalted. ⬛ 01/01-31/12
Distance: 🚶800m ⊘50m 🎣50m.

Amboise 21B1
Vinci Park, Allée de la Chapelle Saint-Jean. **GPS:** n47,41761 e0,98742. ⬆️.

20 🛏 € 12/24h 💧⚱ Ch included ⚡ (20x)€2 🚿 🖼️ 📷
Location: Rural, comfortable, central, quiet. **Surface:** asphalted/grassy.
⬛ 01/01-31/12
Distance: 🚶200m ⊘200m ⊗200m 🛒200m 🚲on the spot 🧍on the spot.
Remarks: Next to campsite, castle 500m.

Amboise 21B1
Parking St. Jean, Avenue Leonardo da Vinci 43 , D61. **GPS:** n47,40814 e0,98986. ⬆️➡️.

11 🛏 free. **Location:** Urban, simple, isolated, quiet. **Surface:** asphalted.
⬛ 01/01-31/12
Distance: 🚶on the spot ⊗1,5km 🛒1,5km 🚲on the spot.

Angé 21B2
Place de la Mairie. **GPS:** n47,33239 e1,24450. ⬆️➡️.

20 🛏 free 💧 €3/100liter ⚱Ch 🎣. **Location:** Simple, isolated, quiet.
Surface: sand. ⬛ 01/01-31/12
Remarks: Coins at town hall and supermarket.

FR

🅢 **Ardentes** 21C3
Avenue de Verdun. **GPS:** n46,74682 e1,82826.⬆️.
🛁🚰📧Ch🧹🗑.
Distance: 🛒on the spot 🍴on the spot.

🅢 **Argent-sur-Sauldre** 21D1
Super U, D940. **GPS:** n47,54916 e2,44797.⬆️.

2 🚰free 🚰€2 📧Ch 🔌€2. **Surface:** asphalted. 🅾️ 01/01-31/12
Distance: 🛒1,1km.

Argenton-sur-Creuse 21B4
Rue de la Grenouille. **GPS:** n46,58715 e1,52497.⬆️➡️.

50 🚰free. **Surface:** gravel. 🅾️ 01/01-31/12
Distance: 🛒50m 🚴3,4km ⊗50m 🍴50m.

🅢 **Argenton-sur-Creuse** 21B4
Alleé du Champ de Foire. **GPS:** n46,58501 e1,52283.⬆️.
🚰📧Ch WC free. 🅾️ 01/01-31/12
Distance: 🛒on the spot.

🅢 **Athée-sur-Cher** 21A2
Aire d'Athée-sur-Cher, D83, Rue de Cigogné. **GPS:** n47,31439 e0,91756.⬆️➡️.

3 🚰free 🚰📧Ch free. **Location:** Rural, simple, isolated, quiet.
Surface: metalled. 🅾️ 01/01-31/12
Distance: 🛒800m 🚴11km ⊗1,5km 🍴1km 🚴on the spot.
Remarks: Max. 24h.

🅢 **Aubigny-sur-Nère** 🌿⛲ 21D1
Parc des Sports, D7. **GPS:** n47,48201 e2,44995.⬆️➡️.

12 🚰free 🚰📧Ch free. **Location:** Isolated, quiet. **Surface:** asphalted.

🅾️ 01/01-31/12
Distance: 🛒1km ⛵1km 🍴2km.
Remarks: Playground.

🅢 **Aubigny-sur-Nère** 🌿⛲ 21D1
Parking du Pré qui Danse, Mail Guichard. **GPS:** n47,49140 e2,43830.⬆️.

40 🚰free 🚰📧Ch WC free. **Surface:** asphalted. 🅾️ 01/01-31/12
Distance: 🛒200m ⊗200m 🍴200m.

🅢 **Avoine** ⛲👥 20D2
Avenue de la République. **GPS:** n47,21287 e0,17706.⬆️.

11 🚰€4 🚰€2/10minutes 📧Ch 🧹(11x)€4/24h 🗑.🚐 **Location:**
Rural, comfortable, luxurious, isolated, quiet. **Surface:** asphalted/metalled.
🅾️ 01/01-31/12
Distance: 🛒1km ⛵Lac Mousseau 300m ⊗300m.
Remarks: Max. 3 nights.

🅢 **Azay-le-Rideau** 🌿⛲🧁👥 21A2
Camping municipal Le Sabot, Rue du Stade. **GPS:** n47,25925 e0,46992.⬆️➡️.

8 🚰free 🚰€3/100liter 📧Ch 🗑€1,70, on camp site. **Location:** Urban,
comfortable, central, quiet. **Surface:** asphalted. 🅾️ 01/04-01/10
Distance: 🛒200m ⊗300m 🚴on the spot 🍴on the spot.
Remarks: Max. 24h, coins at camping (9/16h), castle 300m.

🅢 **Azé** 14B6
M et Mme Hersant, Les Places, D957 Épuisay-Galette. **GPS:** n47,86451 e0,97659.
⬆️➡️.

6 🚰€10 🚰📧Ch 🧹included. 🚴 **Location:** Rural, comfortable, isolated,
quiet. **Surface:** grassy/gravel. 🅾️ 01/01-31/12

Barlieu 21D1
ı. **GPS**: n47,47918 e2,63168.⬆️.

15 🛌first night € 3,50, € 2,50 each additional night 🚰🔲Ch ⚡€2,50 WC 🗑️free. **Surface:** grassy/gravel. 🔲 Easter-01/11
Distance: 🚶1km 🛒nearby.

Beaugency 21C1
Quai Dunois. **GPS**: n47,77949 e1,63646.⬆️.

20 🛌free 🚰€2/10minutes 🔲Ch 🔲€2/55minutes WC 🗑️.
Surface: metalled. 🔲 01/01-31/12
Distance: 🚶100m 🏊8,8km ⛵100m 🛒50m ✖️100m 🍴100m.
Remarks: Quay along the Loire river, max. 24h.

Bessais-le-Fromental 22A3
Base de loisirs de l'Étang de Goule, Champ de la Croix.
GPS: n46,73402 e2,80034.⬆️➡️.

50 🛌free 🚰€2 🔲Ch. **Surface:** asphalted/grassy. 🔘 service: frost
Distance: 🚶4km ⛵on the spot 🛒on the spot ✖️on camp site 🍴on camp site.

Blois 21B1
P2, Rue Jean Moulin. **GPS**: n47,58653 e1,32641.⬆️.

20 🛌€ 5/24h 🚰🔲Ch free. **Surface:** asphalted. 🔲 01/05-30/09
Distance: 🚶on the spot 🏊6,9km ✖️100m 🍴100m 🚌on the spot.
Tourist information Blois:
🏰 Château de Blois.
✝️ Cathédrale St Louis.

🪝 Quatier Coty. 🔲 Wed 7-13h.

Bonny-sur-Loire 22A1
Chemin de la Cheuille. **GPS**: n47,55925 e2,83967.⬆️.
6 🛌free 🚰🔲Ch free. **Location:** Rural. **Surface:** gravel.
Distance: 🚶150m ✖️50m 🍴on the spot 🚴on the spot 🪝on the spot.
Remarks: Along La Cheuille river.

Boulleret 22A2
Place des Charmes. **GPS**: n47,42304 e2,87244.⬆️➡️.

5 🛌free 🚰€2/100liter 🔲Ch ⚡(2x)€2/6h WC. **Surface:** asphalted.
🔲 01/01-31/12
Distance: 🚶on the spot ✖️on the spot 🍴on the spot 🚴on the spot 🪝on the spot.
Remarks: Coins at the shops and restaurant.

Bourges 21D2
Boulevard de l'Industrie. **GPS**: n47,07224 e2,39337.⬆️➡️.

5 🛌free 🚰🔲Ch free. **Surface:** metalled. 🔲 01/01-31/12
Distance: 🚶500m ✖️500m 🍴500m.
Remarks: 100m from campsite.

Bourges 21D2
Rue Jean Bouin. **GPS**: n47,07597 e2,39897.⬆️.

50 🛌free 🚰🔲Ch free. **Surface:** asphalted. 🔲 01/01-31/12
Distance: 🚶50m ✖️500m 🍴500m. **Remarks:** Max. 48h.
Tourist information Bourges:
🌸 Ballades de Bourges. Festivities and market in the city centre. 🔲 01/07-31/08.

Brézolles 14B4
Rue de Verneuil, D939. **GPS**: n48,69083 e1,06972.⬆️.

FR

10 ⌇free ⌂ ⌇Chfree. **Surface:** gravel. ◘ 01/01-31/12
Distance: ⌇200m ⊗200m.

🗺S **Briare-le-Canal** 22A1
Flot Bleu Park. GPS: n47,64304 e2,72270.⬆.

12 ⌇€7/24h ⌂⌇Ch ⌇included.⌇ ⌇ **Surface:** grassy.
◘ 01/01-31/12
Distance: ⌇on the spot ⌇on the spot ⌇on the spot ⊗800m ⌇800m.
Remarks: Max. 72h.

🗺S **Briare-le-Canal** 22A1
Rue des Vignes. **GPS:** n47,63215 e2,73981.⬆.

40 ⌇free ⌂€2 ⌇Ch ⌇ ⌇. **Surface:** gravel. ◘ 01/01-31/12
Distance: ⌇300m ⌇50m ⊗on the spot.

⛪S **Briare-le-Canal** 22A1
Port du Commerce, Quai de Mazoyer. **GPS:** n47,63470 e2,74030.⬆.

10 ⌇free ⌂WCfree. **Surface:** asphalted. ◘ 01/01-31/12
Distance: ⌇200m ⌇4,5km ⌇on the spot ⊗on the spot.

🗺S **Brou** 👥 14B5
Madison Cars 28. GPS: n48,21379 e1,14681.⬆➡.

15 ⌇€5 ⌂€1/100liter ⌇€1 Ch€1 ⌇(4x)€3/24h ⊙€1.⌇ **Location:**
Rural, comfortable, isolated, quiet. **Surface:** gravel. ◘ 01/01-31/12
Distance: ⌇1km ⌇1km ⊗on the spot.
Remarks: In front of Swin de Brou, bread-service.

🗺S **Chabris** 21C2
Place du Champ de Foire. **GPS:** n47,25317 e1,65211.
⌇free ⌂€2 ⌇Ch ⌇€2. **Location:** Rural.
Distance: ⌇on the spot ⊗250m ⌇250m.
Remarks: Coins at Tourist Info and Maison de la Presse (250m).

🗺S **Chambord** 21B1
Château de Chambord, Place St.Louis. **GPS:** n47,61608 e1,51057.

100 ⌇<7.90m € 7/day + € 10/night, >7.90m € 45/day + € 45/night.
Surface: asphalted.
Distance: ⊗100m ⌇100m.
Remarks: Parking castle, max. 1 night.

🗺S **Champigny-sur-Veude** 20D2
Place du Chapeau Rouge, Rue de la Bonne Dame. **GPS:** n47,06499 e0,31773.⬆.
8 ⌇free ⌂⌇Ch. **Surface:** asphalted. ◘ 01/01-31/12
Remarks: At small lake.

🗺S **Chaon** 21D1
Rue des Genêts, D129. **GPS:** n47,60942 e2,16611.⬆➡.

10 ⌇free ⌂⌇Chfree. **Location:** Isolated, quiet. **Surface:** grassy/metalled.
◘ 01/01-31/12
Distance: ⌇200m.

🗺S **Châteaudun** 14B6
Aire de Châteaudun, Rue des Fouleries. **GPS:** n48,07172 e1,32421.⬆➡.

FR

15 🛏free 🚰€2/100liter 🔌Ch 🚻€2/20minutes WC. **Location:** Urban, comfortable, central, quiet. **Surface:** asphalted. 📷 01/01-31/12
Distance: 🚶400m 🛶Canoe rental 🛒on the spot ⊗on the spot.
Remarks: Along Loir river, castel of Châteaudun 300m.

| | | **Châteauroux** | 21C3 |

17, Avenue de Parc des Loisirs. **GPS:** n46,82278 e1,69507.⬆️

5 🛏free 🚰€2,50 🔌Ch 🚻€2,50/1h. **Surface:** asphalted.
📷 01/05-31/10
Distance: 🚶3,6km ⊗2km 🛒2km.
Remarks: Parking at wave pool.

| | | **Châtillon-sur-Loire** 〰️ | 22A1 |

Rue du Port. **GPS:** n47,59128 e2,76044.⬆️
± 6 🛏free 🚰🔌Ch. **Location:** Rural, comfortable, quiet.
Surface: asphalted/gravel.
Distance: 🚶800m 🚄9km A77 ⊗400m 🛒bakery 500m.
Remarks: At the canal.

| | | **Chenonceaux** 🌿🏕️ | 21B2 |

Aire de Chenonceaux, Chemin de la Varenne. **GPS:** n47,33053 e1,06824.⬆️

10 🛏free. **Location:** Rural, simple, isolated, noisy. **Surface:** grassy.
📷 01/01-31/12
Distance: 🚶500m ⊗500m 🚃on the spot 🚲on the spot.
Remarks: Along railwayline.

| P | | **Chenonceaux** 🌿🏕️ | 21B2 |

Rue du Château. **GPS:** n47,33020 e1,06648.⬆️

20 🛏free. **Location:** Rural, simple, isolated. **Surface:** metalled.

📷 01/01-31/12
Distance: 🚶500m ⊗500m 🚲on the spot.
Remarks: Parking at castle of Chenonceaux.
Tourist information Chenonceaux:
⚔️ Castle.

| | | **Cheverny** | 21B1 |

Château Cheverny P3, D102. **GPS:** n47,49762 e1,46097.

20 🛏free. **Surface:** metalled.
📷 9.30-12h, 14.15-17h, Apr-Sep 9.30-18.15h
Distance: 🚶100m ⊗100m.

Tourist information Cheverny:
⚔️ Château Cheverny. Castle. 📷 9.30-12h, 14.15-17h, Apr-Sep 9.30-18.15h.

| | | **Chouzé-sur-Loire** | 20D2 |

Aire de Chouzé-sur-Loire, Rue de l'Église. **GPS:** n47,23809 e0,12649.⬆️➡️

6 🛏free 🚰€2 🔌Ch. **Location:** Rural, comfortable, central, quiet.
Surface: gravel. 📷 01/01-31/12
Distance: 🚶on the spot ⊗250m 🛒on the spot 🚲on the spot ⛺on the spot.
Remarks: Coins at the shops and town hall.

| | | **Courville-sur-Eure** | 14B5 |

Avenue Thiers. **GPS:** n48,44600 e1,24166.⬆️
6 🛏free 🚰€2,50/100liter 🔌Ch🚻€2,50/55minutes. **Surface:** asphalted.
📷 01/01-31/12
Remarks: Coins at campsite and shops.

| | | **Culan** | 21D4 |

Place du Champ de Foire. **GPS:** n46,54727 e2,34630.⬆️

20 🛏free 🚰€1,50 🔌Ch 🚻€1,50 WC. **Surface:** asphalted.
📷 01/01-31/12
Distance: 🚶50m ⊗50m 🛒50m.
Remarks: Near office de tourisme.

| | | **Cuzion** 🌿🏕️ | 21C4 |

Base de Loisirs Pont des Piles, Rue des Petites Côtes. **GPS:** n46,45639 e1,61167.
⬆️➡️

6 🛏free. **Location:** Isolated, quiet. **Surface:** grassy/metalled.
◻ 01/01-31/12
Remarks: Max. 1 night.

Dry 21C1
Rue de Meung. **GPS:** n47,79824 e1,71419.⬆➡

10 🛏free ⛽€2/10minutes 🚰Ch ☒€2/55minutes. **Location:** Simple.
Surface: metalled. ◻ 01/01-31/12
Distance: 🚶on the spot ⛰1km ⊗50m.
Remarks: Coins at town hall.

Épineuil-le-Fleuriel 21D4
Le Bourg. **GPS:** n46,55690 e2,58265.⬆
5 🛏free ⛽🚰Chfree. **Location:** Rural. **Surface:** gravel.
◻ 01/01-31/12

Esvres-sur-Indre 21A2
Salle des Fêtes, Impasse Auguste Noyant. **GPS:** n47,28291 e0,78418.⬆

7 🛏free ⛽🚰free. **Location:** Urban, simple, central, quiet. **Surface:** gravel.
◻ 01/01-31/12 ◉ water disconnected in winter
Distance: 🚶on the spot ⊗100m ☒250m 🚌on the spot 🚲on the spot
🏃on the spot.

Genillé 21B2
Ferme Jouvin, La Galerie, D 764 Loches> Montrichard. **GPS:** n47,21409 e1,10871.⬆

🛏€2 ⛽service€3 🚰Ch ✂included. 📶 **Location:** Rural, simple, isolated, quiet. **Surface:** grassy. ◻ 01/01-31/12
Distance: 🚶2,7km 🚲on the spot.

Gien 21D1
Quai de Nice. **GPS:** n47,67985 e2,64308.⬆

8 🛏free ⛽€2,10 🚰Ch ☒€2,10. **Surface:** asphalted. ◻ 01/01-31/12
Distance: 🚶2km 🚲on the spot.
Remarks: Max. 48h, coins at swimming pool.

Gizeux 20D1
Aire de Gizeux, Route du Lavoir. **GPS:** n47,39275 e0,19689.⬆➡

20 🛏free ⛽€3/100liter 🚰Ch ☒€3/1h. **Location:** Rural, comfortable, central, quiet. **Surface:** gravel.
Distance: 🚶200m 🚲500m ⊗In village 🚲on the spot 🏃on the spot.
Remarks: Coins at the shops and town hall, Château de Gizeux 400m.

Guilly 21C2
Le Prieuré Chambres d'Hôtes, Rue du Prieuré. **GPS:** n47,07920 e1,72100.⬆

10 🛏€5 ⛽€3 🚰Ch ☒. **Surface:** grassy/metalled.
Distance: 🚶150m ⊗10m ☒150m.

Humbligny 21D2
D44. **GPS:** n47,25451 e2,65850.⬆

10 🛏free ⛽€2/100liter 🚰Ch ☒€2/10minutes. **Location:** Rural.
Surface: gravel. ◻ 01/01-31/12
Distance: 🚶on the spot.
Remarks: Coins at town hall.

La Chapelle-Saint-Mesmin 14C6
Aire camping-cars, Chemin de Fourneaux. **GPS:** n47,88550 e1,83990.⬆➡

23 🛏€ 5/24h, € 9/48h, € 12/72h ⚡🔌 Ch 🧹 included. 📶🚾 ♻
Location: Urban, comfortable, quiet. **Surface:** grassy. ⬛ 01/04-31/12
Distance: 🚶500m, Orléans 5km ⚓2,7km 🏊50m 🚲50m ⊗500m 🛒500m
🚉 on the spot 🚶 on the spot.
Remarks: Along Loire river.

| 🅂 | La Châtre | 21C4 |

Rue du Champ de Foire. **GPS:** n46,58250 e1,98250.

10 🛏€ 2. **Surface:** asphalted.
Distance: 🚶50m ⊗50m 🛒50m.

| 🅂 | La Châtre | 21C4 |

Supermarché Super U, Avenue d'Auvergne, D943. **GPS:** n46,58278 e2,00139.
10 🛏free ⚡€2/10minutes 🔌 Ch 🔋€2/1h. **Surface:** asphalted.
⬛ 01/01-31/12
Distance: 🚶800m 🛒50m.

| 🅂 | La Ferte-Beauharnais | 21C1 |

D922. **GPS:** n47,54455 e1,84882. ⬆

12 🛏free ⚡€2/10minutes 🔌 Ch 🔋€2/55minutes 🚾.
Location: Simple, noisy. **Surface:** grassy/metalled. ⬛ 01/01-31/12
Distance: 🚶300m ⊗on the spot 🚲on the spot ⊗250m 🛒100m.
Remarks: At small lake.

| | La Ferté-Saint-Cyr | 21C1 |

D925, Rue Faubourg de Bretagne. **GPS:** n47,65623 e1,67249. ⬆
4 🛏. **Surface:** metalled.

| 🅂 | Lailly-en-Val | 21C1 |

Place de l'Église. **GPS:** n47,77023 e1,68544. ⬆

30 🛏free ⚡🔌 Ch 🚾 free. **Surface:** gravel. ⬛ 01/01-31/12
Distance: 🚶100m 🚲50m ⊗300m 🛒200m.

| 🅂 | Lamotte-Beuvron ⚓ | 21C1 |

Chemin de Maisonfort. **GPS:** n47,59795 e2,02524. ⬆

6 🛏free ⚡🔌 Ch 🚾 WC 📶free.
Surface: metalled.
⬛ 01/01-31/12 ⬤ Fri-morning, water disconnected in winter
Distance: 🚶200m ⚓4,5km ⊗on the spot 🚲on the spot ⊗200m 🛒300m.
Remarks: At the canal.

Tourist information Lamotte-Beuvron:
🛈 Avenue de la Republique. Market. ⬛ Fri-morning.

| 🅂 | Langon (Loir-et-Cher) | 21C2 |

Parking Canal du Berry, D976. **GPS:** n47,28253 e1,82862. ⬆

7 🛏free ⚡€2/10minutes 🔌 Ch 🔋€2/1h. **Surface:** asphalted.
⬛ 01/01-31/12 ⬤ Service: winter
Distance: 🚶50m 🚲20m ⊗100m 🛒100m.
Remarks: Coins at the shops and town hall.

| 🅂 | Le Blanc 〰⚓ | 21B3 |

Place du Général de Gaulle. **GPS:** n46,63154 e1,06164. ⬆
🛏free ⚡€2/100liter 🔌 Ch 🔋€2/1h. **Location:** Central, noisy.
Surface: asphalted. ⬛ 01/01-31/12 ⬤ service: 01/11-01/04
Distance: 🚶on the spot ⊗250m.

| 🅂 | Le Châtelet 〰 | 21D4 |

Le Tivoli, Avenue de la Gare. **GPS:** n46,64502 e2,27863. ⬆

5 🛏free ⚡€2 🔌 Ch 🧹. **Surface:** asphalted. ⬛ 01/01-31/12
Distance: 🚶50m ⊗50m 🛒300m.

| ⚓🅂 | Léré | 22A1 |

Le Port, Rue du Champ des Noyers. **GPS:** n47,47485 e2,87477. ⬆
4 🛏free ⚡🔌 Ch. **Location:** Rural. **Surface:** asphalted.
⬛ 01/01-31/12
Remarks: At the canal.

| 🅂 | Les Montils | 21B1 |

Camping-Car Park des Montils, Route de Seur. **GPS:** n47,49308 e1,30571. ⬆
45 🛏€ 12 ⚡🔌 Ch 🧹 (36x) 📶 included. 📶🚾 ♻
Location: Rural. **Surface:** grassy.
Distance: 🚶500m.

Remarks: Along river, former campsite.

🗺️Ⓢ **Levet** 21D3
Chemin du Crot A Thibault. **GPS:** n46,92306 e2,40639. ⬆️ .

3 🛏️free 🚰🗑️ Ch free 🚿 (3x). **Surface:** gravel. ⬛ 01/03-31/10
Distance: 🛒250m ⊗250m ⚕️250m.
Remarks: Max. 24h.

🗺️ **Loches** 🌿⛵🍵 21B2
Allée du Maquis Césario. **GPS:** n47,12656 e1,00221.
4 🛏️free. ⬛ 01/01-31/12
Distance: 🛒700m⚕️700m.

🗺️ **Loches** 🌿⛵🍵 21B2
Avenue Louis XI. **GPS:** n47,13315 e1,00023.⬆️.
5 🛏️free. **Surface:** gravel. ⬛ 01/01-31/12
Distance: 🛒centre 250m.
Remarks: Max. 24h.

🗺️ **Loches** 🌿⛵🍵 21B2
Rue de l'Amiral de Pointis. **GPS:** n47,13744 e1,00115.⬆️.
4 🛏️free. **Location:** Simple, noisy. **Surface:** asphalted.
⬛ 01/01-31/12
Distance: 🛒1,4km ⊗1,4km.

Ⓢ **Loches** 🌿⛵🍵 21B2
Avenue Aristide Briand. **GPS:** n47,12240 e1,00164.⬆️.

🚰🗑️ Ch 🚽free. ⬛ 01/01-31/12

🏕️Ⓢ **Louzouer** 15A6
Cidre Chivet, 323 Les Mussereaux. **GPS:** n48,02833 e2,87062.

5 🛏️€5 🚰€3 🗑️ Ch. **Location:** Comfortable. **Surface:** asphalted/metalled.
⬛ 15/03-31/12
Distance: 🛒1,5km.
Remarks: Max. 24h.

🗺️Ⓢ **Luant** 21B3
L'Étang Duris. **GPS:** n46,72222 e1,57338.⬆️.
10 🛏️free 🚰€2 🗑️ Ch 🚽€2. **Location:** Isolated, quiet. **Surface:** gravel.
⬛ 01/01-31/12
Distance: 🛒3km 🚗3,3km A20 🚤lake ⊗bar/brasserie 🎣on the spot.

🗺️Ⓢ **Marboué** ♨️ 14B6
L'Espace Loisirs des Fontaines, Rue du Croc Marbot. **GPS:** n48,11240 e1,32870.
⬆️➡️.

13+5 🛏️free 🚰€2/10minutes 🗑️ Ch 🚽€2/50minutes. **Location:** Rural,
comfortable, central, quiet. **Surface:** grassy/metalled.
⬛ 01/01-31/12
Distance: 🛒on the spot 🚲500m ⊗150m 🚌on the spot 🎣on the spot.

🗺️Ⓢ **Marcilly-en-Villette** 21C1
Rue du Lavoir. **GPS:** n47,76197 e2,02448.
6 🛏️free 🚰🗑️ Ch free. **Location:** Rural, quiet. **Surface:** gravel.
Distance: 🛒200m ⊗400m 🎣on the spot.

🗺️Ⓢ **Martizay** 21B3
Aire de Loisirs, Rue des Afrique du Nord. **GPS:** n46,80528 e1,03806.⬆️.

9 🛏️free 🚰🗑️ Ch 🚿 (4x) WC free. **Location:** Quiet. **Surface:** metalled/sand.
⬛ 01/01-31/12
Distance: 🚲on the spot ⚕️bakery 500m.

🗺️Ⓢ **Mehun-sur-Yèvre** 21D2
Quai du Canal. **GPS:** n47,14409 e2,21010.⬆️.
6 🛏️€2 🚰🗑️ Ch. **Surface:** asphalted. ⬛ 01/01-31/12 .
Distance: 🛒500m ⊗400m.
Remarks: At the canal.

🗺️Ⓢ **Menetou-Salon** 21D2
Rue de la Mairie. **GPS:** n47,23162 e2,49002.⬆️➡️.

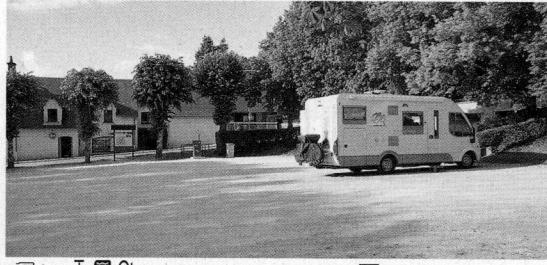

6 🛏️free 🚰🗑️ Ch free. **Surface:** gravel/metalled. ⬛ 01/04-31/10
Distance: 🛒on the spot ⊗50m ⚕️100m.

🗺️Ⓢ **Mennetou-sur-Cher** 🌿 21C2
Place du 11 Novembre, N76. **GPS:** n47,26861 e1,86472.⬆️➡️.

FR

8 ☞free ⚡€2/10minutes ⚐ Ch ▣€2/1h. **Surface:** sand.
🅾 01/01-31/12
Distance: ⚘150m ⛟100m ⊗150m ⚓150m.
Remarks: Coins at shops and tourist office, small fortified town.

⚐S Méry-sur-Cher 21C2
Chemin Lucien Bonneau/N76. **GPS:** n47,24586 e1,98989.⬆️

6 ☞€5/24h ⚡ Ch ⚒ WC included. ♿ **Surface:** metalled.
🅾 01/01-31/12
Distance: ⚘150m ⚓100m.

⚐S Meung-sur-Loire 21C1
Chemin des Grêves. **GPS:** n47,82327 e1,69814.⬆️
8 ☞free ⚡€2 ⚐ Ch. **Location:** Rural. **Surface:** gravel.
🅾 01/01-31/12
Distance: ⚘250m ⊗300m ⚓250m bakery.
Remarks: At swimming pool.

⚐S Montoire-sur-le-Loir 🅦⛵ 21A1
Avenue de la République. **GPS:** n47,75750 e0,86928.⬆️

15 ☞free ⚡ ⚐ Ch free ▣€1. **Location:** Urban, comfortable, quiet.
Surface: asphalted. 🅾 01/01-31/12
Distance: ⚘on the spot ⊗500m ⚓500m ⛟on the spot.
Remarks: At former station.

⚐S Montoire-sur-le-Loir 🅦⛵ 21A1
Aire de Montoire-sur-le-Loir, Boulevard des Alliés, Quartier Marescot.
GPS: n47,74990 e0,86317.⬆️➡️

8 ☞free. **Location:** Urban, simple, central, quiet. **Surface:** asphalted.

🅾 01/01-31/12
Distance: ⚘50m ⚓on the spot ⛟on the spot ⊗500m ⚓500m ⛟on the spot ⚹ on the spot.

⚐S Montrésor 🅦 21B2
Rue du 8 Mai. **GPS:** n47,15750 e1,20169.⬆️
10 ☞free ⚡ ⚐ Ch free. **Surface:** asphalted. 🅾 01/01-31/12
Distance: ⚘200m.

⚐S Neuillay-les-Bois 21B3
Route de Buzançais, D1. **GPS:** n46,76917 e1,47333.

5 ☞free ⚡ Ch ⚒ WC free. **Surface:** metalled. 🅾 01/05-31/10
Distance: ⚘50m ⛟50m ⊗50m ⚓50m.
Remarks: Max. 24h.

⚐S Neuillé-Pont-Pierre 21A1
Parc Chauvin, Rue De Gaulle, D766. **GPS:** n47,54756 e0,55209.⬆️⬆️

10 ☞free ⚡ ⚐ Ch ⚒ (12x)free WC. **Location:** Urban, simple, noisy.
Surface: asphalted. 🅾 01/01-31/12
Distance: ⚘on the spot ⛵3,5km ⊗on the spot ⚓on the spot.

⚐S Neuvy-Le-Barrois 22A3
La Prairie, Le Pénisson, D45. **GPS:** n46,86159 e3,03930.⬆️➡️

6 ☞€6 ⚡ ⚐ Ch ▣€4 ⬡€2. **Location:** Rural, comfortable, isolated, quiet.
Surface: gravel/metalled. 🅾 01/01-31/12
Distance: ⚘200m ⊗200m.

⚐S Neuvy-Pailloux 21C3
Les Gloux, RN151. **GPS:** n46,88278 e1,83682.⬆️
15 ☞free ⚡ ⚐ Ch WC free. **Location:** Simple, isolated. **Surface:** asphalted.
🅾 01/01-31/12

⚐S Nogent-le-Roi 14C4
Rue du Pont des Demoiselles. **GPS:** n48,65059 e1,52894.⬆️
4 ☞free ⚡ ⚐ Ch ▣free. **Surface:** asphalted.
Distance: ⚘400m ⊗400m ⚓400m.
Remarks: Next to sports fields.

⚐ Nogent-sur-Vernisson 22A1
Rue du Gué Mulet. **GPS:** n47,84055 e2,73996.⬆️➡️

6 ☐free. **Location:** Simple, quiet. **Surface:** gravel. ☐ 01/01-31/12
Distance: 1km on the spot on the spot 1km.

☒ **Nogent-sur-Vernisson** 22A1
Rue Georges Bannery. **GPS:** n47,85363 e2,74014.
€2 Ch€2.
Remarks: Coins at tourist info, PMU Rue Bannery or bar in Rue A. Briand.

☒ **Nouan-le-Fuzelier** 21C1
Rue Gauchoix. **GPS:** n47,53324 e2,03437.

6 ☐free. **Surface:** grasstiles/metalled. ☐ 01/01-31/12
Distance: 300m 300m 300m.

☒ **Oulches** 21B4
Impasse de l'Étang. **GPS:** n46,61339 e1,29547.
☐free €2 Ch€2. **Location:** Rural. **Surface:** gravel.
Distance: on the spot 100m.

☒ **Ouzouer-sur-Trézée** 22A1
Parking halte nautique, Rue Saint-Roche. **GPS:** n47,67000 e2,80888.

5 ☐free. **Surface:** asphalted. ☐ 01/04-31/10
Distance: 500m on the spot 500m.
Remarks: At canal 'de Briare', max. 48h.

☒ **Ouzouer-sur-Trézée** 22A1
Camping municipal, Chemin du Rochoir. **GPS:** n47,66819 e2,80611.

6 ☐ € 4,50 Ch €2,60 WC included. **Surface:** grassy/gravel.
☐ 01/04-31/10

☒ **Paucourt** 15A6
Rue de l'Église. **GPS:** n48,03441 e2,79179.

☐free Chfree. **Location:** Rural. **Surface:** asphalted.
☐ 01/01-31/12
Distance: on the spot 4,5km.

☒ **Pont-de-Ruan** 21A2
D17. **GPS:** n47,26373 e0,57632.
☐free €2 Ch €2.
Location: Simple, isolated. **Surface:** gravel/sand.
Distance: 300m.

☒ **Pouligny-Saint-Pierre** 21B3
Route du Blanc, D950, Bénavent. **GPS:** n46,65591 e1,02054.
10 ☐free €2 Ch€2 €2.
Location: Rural, quiet. **Surface:** gravel.
Distance: bakery 50m.
Remarks: Coins at the bakery.

☒ **Reignac-sur-Indre** 21A2
Rue Louis de Barberin, D58. **GPS:** n47,22922 e0,91585.

5 ☐free €2/100liter Ch. **Location:** Rural, simple, central, noisy.
Surface: asphalted. ☐ 01/01-31/12
Distance: 300m 20km on the spot on the spot on the spot.
Remarks: Max. 24h, coins at the shops in the village.

☒ **Restigné** 20D2
Rue Basse. **GPS:** n47,28041 e0,22614.

10 ☐free €2/100liter Ch. **Location:** Rural, simple, central, quiet.
Surface: gravel. ☐ 01/01-31/12
Distance: on the spot on the spot on the spot on the spot.
Remarks: Coins at town hall.

☒ **Saint-Benoît-du-Sault** 21B4
Place du Champ de Foire. **GPS:** n46,44117 e1,39249.
☐ Ch. ☐ 01/01-31/12
Distance: 300m 300m.

☒ **Saint-Claude-de-Diray** 21B1
Rue du Moulin D98. **GPS:** n47,61356 e1,41402.
4 ☐free Chfree. **Location:** Simple, quiet. **Surface:** gravel.
Distance: 500m.

FR

Remarks: Next to cemetery.

🛁S **Saint-Denis-les-Ponts** 🍴 14B6

Aire de Saint Denis-les-Ponts, Rue Jean Moulin. **GPS:** n48,06643 e1,28950.⬆️➡️.

+10 🗑free ⚓€2/100liter 🔌 Ch.
Location: Urban, comfortable, central, quiet. **Surface:** gravel.
⬛ 01/01-31/12 🔲 Service: winter
Distance: 🚂Châteaudun 3km 🏊on the spot 🛒on the spot ⊗100m 🚌on the spot 🎣on the spot.
Remarks: Coins at the shops in the village, Châteaudun (city and castle) 4km.

🛁S **Saint-Genouph** 21A2

Rue de l'Auberdière. **GPS:** n47,37702 e0,60200.⬆️.
🗑free ⚓🔌Ch. **Surface:** metalled. ⬛ 01/01-31/12
Distance: 🚂350m ⊗350m.

🛁S **Saint-Jean-le-Blanc** 14C6

Base de loisirs de l'Ile Charlemagne, Levée de la Chevauchée.
GPS: n47,89437 e1,93870.
🗑free ⚓€2 🔌Ch. **Surface:** sand.
Distance: 🚂Orléans 3km.

🛁S **Saint-Saturnin** 21D4

Route de Perassay. **GPS:** n46,50565 e2,23585.⬆️.
🗑free ⚓€2 🔌Ch 🧺. **Surface:** grassy. ⬛ 01/01-31/12
Distance: 🚂300m.

🛁S **Sainte-Maure-de-Touraine** 🍲 🍴 21A2

Aire du Bois Chaudron, D910, Le Bois Caudron. **GPS:** n47,09315 e0,61275.⬆️➡️.

40 🗑€ 2,50, 2 pers.incl ⚓€2 🔌€1 Ch€3 🧺 (4x)€2/12h WC]€2 🔲€4/3 📶 🚿 **Location:** Rural, comfortable, isolated, quiet. **Surface:** grassy.
⬛ 01/01-31/12
Distance: 🚂1,5km 🏊4,4km ⊗1,5km 🛒1,5km 🎣on the spot.
Remarks: Bread-service.

🛁S **Sainte-Maure-de-Touraine** 🍲 🍴 21A2

Parking Ronsard, Rue de la Métairie. **GPS:** n47,11096 e0,61640.⬆️➡️.

15 🗑free ⚓🔌Chfree WC. **Location:** Urban, simple, central, quiet.
Surface: asphalted. ⬛ 01/01-31/12
Distance: 🚂200m 🏊3km ⊗200m 🛒200m 🚌on the spot.

🛁S **Sainte-Sévère-sur-Indre** 🚤 21C4

Place du Champ de Foire, rue de Verdun. **GPS:** n46,48724 e2,07167.⬆️.
🗑free ⚓€2 🔌Ch. **Location:** Rural. **Surface:** gravel/sand.
Distance: 🚂100m 🛒180m.

🛁S **Sancoins** 22A3

Quai du Canal. **GPS:** n46,83356 e2,91568.⬆️➡️.

20 🗑free ⚓€2,50 🔌Ch WC. **Location:** Quiet. **Surface:** gravel/metalled.
⬛ 01/01-31/12
Distance: 🚂200m 🏊on the spot 🛒on the spot 🛒200m.

🛁S **Saran** 14C6

Allée Claude Bernard. **GPS:** n47,95106 e1,87315.⬆️.
10 🗑free ⚓🔌Chfree. **Surface:** gravel. ⬛ 01/01-31/12
Distance: 🚂on the spot 🚲on the spot 🎣on the spot.

©S **Selles-sur-Cher** 21C2

Avenue Kleber-Loustau, D856. **GPS:** n47,27639 e1,55889.⬆️.

15 🗑€ 5 ⚓€4,50 🔌Ch 🧺€4,50 WC]. **Surface:** asphalted/grassy.
⬛ 01/01-31/12
Distance: 🚂500m 🛒200m ⊗500m 🛒500m.
Remarks: Coins at camping, tourist info and town hall.

🛁S **St.Amand-Montrond** 21D3

Base de Loisirs Virlay. GPS: n46,73362 e2,48851.⬆️➡️.

21 🗑free ⚓🔌Chfree. **Location:** Rural. **Surface:** asphalted/grassy.
⬛ 01/01-31/12
Distance: 🚂1km 🏊5km ⊗500m 🛒500m.

🛁S **St.Amand-Montrond** 21D3

Quai Lutin, via Avenue Maréchal Foch. **GPS:** n46,71818 e2,50480.⬆️➡️.

FR

4 🛏free ⛽ 🅰 Ch free. **Surface:** asphalted/gravel. ⬜ 01/01-31/12
Distance: 🚲200m ⬛on the spot 🛒on the spot ⊗200m 🛁200m.

Rue des Ruets, route d'Autry, D52. **GPS:** n47,64680 e2,68028.⬆️.

6 🛏free ⛽€3 🅰 Ch 🚻€3. **Surface:** asphalted. ⬜ 01/01-31/12
Distance: 🚲100m ⊗100m 🛁100m 🚌50m.
Remarks: Parking nearby town hall.

Allée de la Presle. **GPS:** n46,99999 e2,09884.
10 🛏free ⛽ 🅰 Ch free. **Location:** Rural, isolated, quiet. **Surface:** gravel.
⬜ 01/01-31/12
Distance: ⬛on the spot 🛒on the spot.
Remarks: At small lake, former campsite, max 3,5t.

N151. **GPS:** n46,97740 e2,06908.

10 🛏free ⛽ 🅰 Ch WC free.
Location: Simple, isolated. **Surface:** asphalted.

Rue de Sully. **GPS:** n47,69808 e2,53876.⬆️.

3 🛏free ⛽ 🅰 Ch free. **Surface:** asphalted. ⬜ 01/01-31/12
Distance: 🚲300m 🛁300m.
Remarks: Max. 48h.

Rue du Petit Clou. **GPS:** n47,69995 e2,54356.⬆️.
10 🛏free ⛽ 🅰 Ch free. **Location:** Rural. **Surface:** metalled.

⬜ 01/01-31/12
Remarks: In front of cemetery.

Chemin de la Salle Verte. **GPS:** n47,77139 e2,38451.⬆️➡️.

16 🛏free ⛽ 🅰 Ch 🚻 free. **Surface:** gravel/metalled. ⬜ 01/01-31/12
Distance: 🚲800m ⬛on the spot 🛒on the spot ⊗800m 🛁800m.
Remarks: Nearby castle of Sully, narrow entrance.

Plan d'eau, Rue Saint Père. **GPS:** n47,73114 e0,77617.🔼.

10 🛏free ⛽ Ch free WC. **Location:** Rural, simple, central, quiet.
Surface: gravel. ⬜ 01/01-31/12
Distance: 🚲on the spot ⬛on the spot 🛒on the spot.

Chemin du Ronaire. **GPS:** n47,31849 e2,03775.⬆️.

10 🛏free ⛽ 🅰 Ch free. **Surface:** gravel/metalled. ⬜ 01/01-31/12
Distance: 🚲250m 🛁250m.

Rue de la Paix, D48. **GPS:** n46,63199 e1,43096.
🛏free ⛽€2 🅰 Ch 🚻€2. **Surface:** metalled.
Distance: 🚲200m.
Remarks: Coins at the shops and town hall.

Aire de Thiron-Gardais, Avenue de la Gare. **GPS:** n48,31194 e0,99583.⬆️➡️.

10 🛏free ⛽ 🅰 Ch free.
Location: Urban, simple. **Surface:** asphalted.

FR

Distance: 🛒100m 🚰300m ⊗300m ⚡300m 🚿on the spot 🚶100m.

🚐S Tour-en-Sologne   21B1

Rue de la Mairie. **GPS:** n47,53786 e1,49973.

10 🚐free 🚰€2,50/100liter 🔵Ch 💧€2,50/h WC. **Surface:** gravel.
Distance: 🛒50m 🚰200m 🛒bakery 100m.
Remarks: Coins at townhall and bakery.

🚐S Tours   21A2

Parking relais du Lac, Avenue du Général Niessel. **GPS:** n47,36700 e0,70007.⬆️
6 🚐€2,60 🚰€2/100liter 🔵Ch 🔸.🔵🔸 **Surface:** asphalted.
Distance: 🛒2,5km.

🚐S Vailly-sur-Sauldre   21D1

Rue du Pont. **GPS:** n47,45727 e2,64665.⬆️

5 🚐free. **Location:** Urban, simple, central. **Surface:** asphalted.
🔲 01/01-31/12
Distance: 🛒500m.

🚐S Villaines les Rochers 🌳   21A2

Aire de Villaines-les-Rochers, Place de la Mairie/ Rue des Ecoles.
GPS: n47,22083 e0,49583.⬆️➡️

6 🚐free 🚰🔵Ch WC free. **Location:** Urban, comfortable, central, quiet.
Surface: asphalted. 🔲 01/01-31/12
Distance: 🛒on the spot ⊗100m ⚡100m 🚿on the spot 🚶on the spot.
Remarks: Max. 24h.

🚐S Villandry 🌳🚿🌳   21A2

Aire de Villandry, Rue Principale. **GPS:** n47,34100 e0,51127.⬆️

20 🚐€3,50 🚰🔵Ch free 🔸€2,50 WC 🔵€0,80. 🚿
Surface: gravel/metalled. 🔲 01/04-31/10
Distance: 🛒300m 🚿on the spot ⊗nearby ⚡nearby.
Remarks: Along the Sauldre river.

Tourist information Vailly-sur-Sauldre:
🏕️ 🔲 Fri.

🚐S Valençay 🌳🚿   21C2

Avenue de la Résistance. **GPS:** n47,16080 e1,56163.⬆️

25 🚐free 🚰€2/100liter 🔵Ch WC 🔸.
Location: Rural, comfortable, central, quiet. **Surface:** grasstiles.
🔲 01/01-31/12
Distance: 🛒50m ⛵3,1km 🏊300m ⊗90m ⚡90m 🚿on the spot
🚿on the spot 🚶on the spot.
Remarks: Coins at tourist info(100m), Château de Villandry 200m.

🚐S Villedômer 🌳🔸   21A1

Aire de Loisirs de Lavoir, Rue du Lavoir. **GPS:** n47,54465 e0,88727.⬆️➡️

10 🚐free 🚰€2 🔵Ch 🔸. **Surface:** metalled. 🔲 01/01-31/12
Distance: 🛒100m ⊗100m ⚡100m.
Remarks: Nearby entrance castle.

Tourist information Valençay:
🏰 Château. Castle, 15th-18th century. 🔲 01/03-30/11.

🚐S Veigné 🌳🚿🌳🍴   21A2

Camping de la Plage, 'D50. **GPS:** n47,28921 e0,73436.
3 🚐free 🚰€2/100liter 🔵Ch 💧€2/10minutes. **Location:** Comfortable, noisy.
Surface: metalled.
Distance: 🛒on the spot 🏊on the spot 🚰on the spot ⊗100m ⚡100m.

🚐S Vendôme 🌳🚿🍴🌳   21B1

Aie de Vendôme, Rue Geoffroy Martel. **GPS:** n47,79111 e1,07528.⬆️

5 🚐free, 15/06-15/09 €5 🚰€2/100liter 🔵Ch 🔵€4/1h.
Location: Rural, simple, central, quiet. **Surface:** metalled.
🔲 01/01-31/12
Distance: 🛒100m ⛵8,1km 🏊100m ⊗200m ⚡200m 🚿on the spot
🚶on the spot.

FR

Remarks: Max. 24h, coins at town hall (200m), bakery (200m) and supermarket (50m).

Villequiers 22A2

L'Étappe Berrichonne, Le Petit Azillon. **GPS:** n47,08828 e2,77429. ⬆️➡️

6 🅂€6 ⛽🔧 Ch ➕ included. **Location:** Isolated, quiet. **Surface:** gravel/metalled. 🅳 01/01-31/12 **Distance:** 🛒3km.

Vitry-aux-Loges 14D6

Rue des Érables. **GPS:** n47,93915 e2,27078. 🅂free ⛽🔧 Ch free. **Location:** Rural. **Surface:** asphalted. 🅳 01/01-31/12 **Distance:** 🛒100m 🔧100m 🚿 on the spot 🏊 on the spot. **Remarks:** At canal of Orléans.

Vouvray 21A1

Parking Bec de Cisse, Rue Bec de Cisse. **GPS:** n47,40929 e0,79735. ⬆️➡️

3 🅂free ⛽€2/100liter 🔧 Ch ➕€2/1h WC. **Location:** Rural, comfortable, central, quiet. **Surface:** asphalted. 🅳 01/01-31/12 🔘 Service: winter **Distance:** 🛒on the spot 🚴8,5km 🏊500m 🔧150m 🚿150m 🚌on the spot 🏊 on the spot. **Remarks:** Max. 48h, coins at campsite and tourist info.

Bourgogne

Anost 22C2

Place Centrale. **GPS:** n47,07778 e4,09869. ⬆️

10 🅂free ⛽🔧 Ch free. **Location:** Rural, simple, quiet. **Surface:** metalled. 🅳 01/01-31/12 **Distance:** 🛒on the spot.

Autun 22C3

Route de Chalon. **GPS:** n46,95548 e4,31667. ⬆️➡️

18 🅂free ⛽€3,50 🔧 Ch. **Location:** Urban, simple. **Surface:** asphalted. 🅳 01/01-31/12 **Distance:** 🛒city centre 2km 🍞100m ⊗100m 🚿supermarket 900m 🏊 on the spot 🎣 on the spot. **Remarks:** Parking at small lake Le Vallon at N80, in front of McDonalds.

Tourist information Autun: 🎭 Musée Rolin. Roman and Medieval excavations. 🏛️ 🅳 Wed, Fri, Su.

Auxerre 22B1

Quai de l'Ancienne Abbaye. **GPS:** n47,79742 e3,57738. ⬆️.

10 🅂free. **Surface:** asphalted. 🅳 01/01-31/12 **Distance:** 🛒300m ⊗300m 🚿300m. **Remarks:** Along the Yonne river.

Tourist information Auxerre: 🏛️ 🅳 Tue, Fri.

Beaune 22D3

Parking Charles de Gaulle. **GPS:** n47,01731 e4,83628. ⬆️.

5 🅂free ⛽€3,50 🔧 Ch ➕€3,50/2h. **Location:** Urban, simple, central. **Surface:** asphalted. **Distance:** 🛒500m 🚴2,6km ⊗200m 🚿centre commercial 300m. **Remarks:** 5 special pitches, all parking places permitted.

Tourist information Beaune: 👁️M Hôtel Dieu et Musée. Former hospital, 15th century, museum. 🍷 Château de Meursault, Meursault. Castle with vineyard and wine tastery.

Beaurepaire-en-Bresse 23A4

Le Bourg. **GPS:** n46,66966 e5,38985. ⬆️. 5 🅂free ⛽🔧 Ch. **Location:** Simple, quiet. **Surface:** asphalted. 🅳 01/01-31/12 🔘 Service: winter **Distance:** 🚿bakery.

Chablis 22B1

Route d'Auxerre, D235. **GPS:** n47,81711 e3,78425. ⬆️.

5 ⏚free ⟋⏛free. **Location:** Simple, quiet. **Surface:** asphalted.
Distance: ⬈centre 500m ⊗on the spot.

5 ⏚free ⟋⏛Ch. **Surface:** metalled. ◻ 01/04-31/10
Distance: ⚲50m.

⌖S Chalon-sur-Saône 🍲	22D3

P Ville Historique, Promenade Sainte Marie. **GPS:** n46,78365 e4,86046.⬆.

⌖S Chiddes	22C3

Le Bourg. **GPS:** n46,86108 e3,94091.⬆→.

2 ⏚free ⟋⏛Chfree. **Location:** Simple. **Surface:** asphalted.
◻ 01/01-31/12
Distance: ⬈500m ⊗50m.
Remarks: Free shuttle to centre.

4 ⏚free ⟋⏛Chfree WC. **Location:** Simple. **Surface:** gravel.
◻ 01/01-31/12
Distance: ⬈on the spot ⊗on the spot.
Remarks: Max. 48h, free coins available at restaurant.

⌖S Charolles ⚓	22C4

Route de Viry. **GPS:** n46,43956 e4,28203.⬆.

⌖ Clamecy 🌿	22B2

Rue de l'Abattoir. **GPS:** n47,46222 e3,52250.⬆.

8 ⏚€3 ⟋⏛Ch▦€3. **Location:** Simple. **Surface:** gravel.
◻ 01/04-01/10
Distance: ⬈300m.
Remarks: Max. 48h.

6 ⏚free. **Location:** Simple. **Surface:** gravel. ◻ 01/01-31/12
Distance: ⬈350m ⊗150m.

⌖S Décize ⚓	22B3

Esplanade des Halles, Allée Marcel Merle. **GPS:** n46,83223 e3,46133.⬆.

⌖S Château-Chinon	22C3

Rue Jean Sallonnyer. **GPS:** n47,06304 e3,93627.⬆.

± 15 ⏚free ⟋€3⏛Ch 🛶. **Location:** Simple. **Surface:** gravel.
◻ 01/01-31/12
Distance: ⬈200m ⌇on the spot ⬈on the spot.
Remarks: On the river Loire, nearby tennis-courts.

10 ⏚free ⟋⏛Chfree WC. **Location:** Simple. **Surface:** metalled.
◻ 01/01-31/12
Distance: ⬈200m ⊗250m ⚲250m.
Remarks: Max. 24h.

⌖S Châtillon-en-Bazois	22B3

Place Pierre Saury. **GPS:** n47,05310 e3,65511.⬆.

⌖S Digoin	22C4

Place de la Grève, Route de Vichy. **GPS:** n46,48102 e3,97288.⬆→.

± 15 🅢free ✎ (4x) WC. **Location:** Simple, central. **Surface:** asphalted.
🅾 01/01-31/12
Distance: 📍on the spot ⊗on the spot 🍽on the spot ▣on the spot.
Remarks: Next to office de tourisme.

🇨🇪🅢 **Dijon** 🏺 22D2
Aire de Dijon, 3, Boulevard Chainoine Kir. **GPS:** n47,32125 e5,01090.⬆.

16 🅢€ 10/24h ⛽🍽 Ch ✎ (17x)included. 🚾
Location: Urban, comfortable, noisy. **Surface:** asphalted.
🅾 01/01-31/12 ◉ water: frost
Distance: 📍centre Dijon 1,5km 🚲10km ⛰300m ➤300m ⊗500m 🍽500m
➤>Dijon 150m 🏊10m.
Remarks: Attention: motorhomes ∧3m take access road from southerly
direction.

Tourist information Dijon:
ℹ Office de Tourisme, Place Darcy, www.dijon-tourism.com. City worth a visit
with a number of large mansions and streets with half-timbered houses.
Ⓜ Musée de Moutarde Amora, 48, quai Nicolas-Rolin. History of mustard and
the Amora factory. Ⓣ free.

🅢 **Ecuisses** 22C3
Place Marcel Pagnol, Route du Bourg. **GPS:** n46,76019 e4,52283.⬆.

20 🅢free ⛽🍽free. **Location:** Simple. **Surface:** metalled.
🅾 01/01-31/12
Remarks: Max. 48h.

🅢 **Étang-sur-Arroux** 22C3
Place du Mousseau. GPS: n46,86631 e4,18946.⬆➡.

🅢free ⛽🍽Chfree. **Location:** Simple. **Surface:** asphalted.
🅾 01/01-31/12
Distance: 📍100m 🍽100m.

🅢 **Fontaine-Française** 23A1
Rue Berthault. GPS: n47,52487 e5,36768.⬆➡.

5 🅢free ⛽€3 🍽 Ch.
Location: Rural, simple. **Surface:** asphalted/grassy.
🅾 01/01-31/12
Distance: 📍100m 🚲16km ➤on the spot 🍽250m bakery.
Remarks: Along river and betwee 2 lakes, coins at shops in the village 08-21h.

🅢 **Fours** 22B3
Rue des Saules, D981. **GPS:** n46,81720 e3,71806.⬆.

10 🅢free ⛽🍽 Ch🚻free. **Location:** Simple. **Surface:** gravel.
🅾 01/01-31/12
Distance: 📍200m ⊗200m 🍽200m.

🅢 **Génelard** 🌿 22C4
Place du Bassin, D974. **GPS:** n46,57750 e4,23500.⬆➡.

2 🅢free ⛽🍽 Ch ✎ free. **Location:** Simple. **Surface:** asphalted
🅾 01/01-31/12
Distance: 📍on the spot.

🅢 **Gilly-sur-Loire** 22B4
Le Gatefer. GPS: n46,53768 e3,78218.⬆.
10 🅢free ⛽🍽Chfree. **Surface:** metalled. 🅾 01/01-31/12

🅢 **Givry** 22D3
Relais camping-car, Rue de la Gare. **GPS:** n46,78000 e4,74830.⬆.

FR

15 ⌂ free ⚡€2/100liter ⚑ Ch ▣ €2/1h. **Location:** Comfortable.
Surface: asphalted. ◻ 01/01-31/12
Distance: ⚐ on the spot ⊗300m 🍞 bakery 300m ⚶ on the spot
🚶 on the spot.
Remarks: Coins at restaurant.
Tourist information Givry:
🌳 Marché. Market. ◻ Thu.
🚲 La Voie Verte de Givry à Cluny. Cycle route on former railway,.

| ⚐ S | Gron | 15A6 |
Rue des Petits Prés. **GPS:** n48,16011 e3,25636.⬆
5 ⌂ free ⚡ ⚑ Ch WC. **Location:** Simple, quiet. **Surface:** asphalted.
◻ 01/01-31/12

| ⚐ S | Gurgy | 22B1 |
Quai des Fontaines. **GPS:** n47,86348 e3,55376.⬆➡

20 ⌂ free ⚡€4/10minutes ⚑ Ch ▣ €4/1h. **Surface:** grassy/gravel.
◻ 01/04-31/10
Distance: ⚐50m 🚲7km ⚓on the spot ⊗500m 🍷300m.
Remarks: Along the Yonne river, coins at supermarket.

| ⚐ S | Heuilley-sur-Saône | 23A2 |
Rue Condé. **GPS:** n47,32800 e5,45471.⬆

20 ⌂ free ⚡€3 ⚑ Ch WC. **Location:** Rural, quiet. **Surface:** gravel/sand.
◻ 01/01-31/12
Distance: ⚐on the spot 🍞100m ⊗100m.
Remarks: Coins at town hall.

| ⚐ S | La Chapelle-de-Guinchay | 22D5 |
Le Clos Meziat. **GPS:** n46,21017 e4,76720.⬆

± 10 ⌂ free ⚡ ⚑ Ch WC free. **Location:** Rural, comfortable, quiet.
Surface: gravel/metalled. ◻ 01/01-31/12
Distance: ⚐centre 1,2km 🚲 A6 10km ⊗1,2km 🍷1,2km.

| ⚐ S | La Charité-sur-Loire | 22A2 |
Quai Romain Mollot. **GPS:** n47,17483 e3,01123.

5 ⌂ free ⚡€4 ⚑ Ch ▣ €4/55minutes 🧺. **Surface:** asphalted.
◻ 01/01-31/12
Distance: ⚐250m ⚓on the spot 🍞on the spot ⊗on the spot 🍷on the spot
🛒on the spot.
Remarks: Parking at the river, max. 24h.

| ⚐ | La Charité-sur-Loire | 22A2 |
Quai de la Tête de l'Ourth. **GPS:** n47,17577 e3,01254.
3 ⌂free. **Surface:** asphalted. ◻ 01/01-31/12
Remarks: Parking at river.

| ⚐ | Laignes | 22C1 |
Chemin du Moulin Neuf, D965. **GPS:** n47,84850 e4,36132.⬆➡

6 ⌂free. **Location:** Simple, quiet. **Surface:** grassy. ◻ 01/01-31/12
Distance: ⚐1km ⚓on the spot.
Remarks: Parking at river, max. 24h.

| ⚐ S | Louhans | 23A4 |
Halte nautique, Rue du Port. **GPS:** n46,62952 e5,21302.⬆

15 ⌂free, 01/05-30/09 € 5 + € 0,20/pp tourist tax ⚡ ⚑ Ch WC ⅃included.
Location: Comfortable, quiet. **Surface:** gravel.
Distance: ⚐400m.
Remarks: To be paid at Halte Nautique, sanitary building: 01/05-30/09.

| ⚐ S | Louhans | 23A4 |
Boivin Claude, Rue de la Griffonnière. **GPS:** n46,63070 e5,24857.⬆
12 ⌂€5 ⚡ ⚑ Ch included 🚿 €5. **Surface:** gravel. ◻ 01/01-31/12

| ⚐ S | Luzy | 22C3 |
Place du champ De Foire. **GPS:** n46,79028 e3,96840.⬆➡

4 ⌧free ⚡ ⚑ Ch WC free. **Location:** Simple. **Surface:** metalled.
⬛ 01/01-31/12
Distance: ⌧centre 300m ⊗100m ⚱200m 🚂500m.
Remarks: Max. 48h, coins at the shops and restaurant.

| ⌧ S | **Mailly-le-Château** | 22B1 |

L'espace naturel du Beauvais, Rue de Beauvais. **GPS:** n47,59308 e3,63059. ⬆
⌧free ⚡€3 ⚑ Ch ✂€3 📶. **Location:** Isolated, quiet. **Surface:** grassy.
⬛ 01/01-31/12
Distance: ⌧650m.
Remarks: Coins at the shops.

| ⌧ S | **Marsannay-la-Côte** | 22D2 |

Espace du Rocher, Rue du Rocher. **GPS:** n47,27099 e4,99224. ⬆➡

5 ⌧free ⚡ ⚑ Ch free. **Location:** Urban, simple, quiet. **Surface:** asphalted.
⬛ 01/01-31/12
Distance: ⌧500m ⚓3,5km 🚂750m.

| ⌧ | **Marsannay-la-Côte** | 22D2 |

Rue de Mazy, D122. **GPS:** n47,27027 e4,98761.
⌧free. **Surface:** asphalted. ⬛ 01/01-31/12
Distance: ⌧on the spot ⚓5km.
Remarks: Parking next to Office du Tourisme.

| ⌧ S | **Nolay** | 22D3 |

Avenue de la Liberté. **GPS:** n46,95016 e4,62828. ⬆

± 10 ⌧free ⚡ ⚑ Ch 🚽service€2. **Location:** Urban, simple. **Surface:** gravel.
⬛ 01/01-31/12
Distance: ⌧100m ⊗300m 🚂300m.
Remarks: Coins at town hall.

Tourist information Nolay:
🖐 Site Champetre du Bout du Monde, Vauchignon. Water falls.

| ⌧ S | **Nuits-Saint-Georges** | 22D2 |

Rue de Cussigny. **GPS:** n47,13178 e4,95189. ⬆➡

10 ⌧free ⚡ ⚑ Ch free. **Location:** Urban, simple. **Surface:** asphalted.
⬛ 01/01-31/12
Distance: ⌧400m ⚓2,1km ⊗500m 🚂Intermarché 300m.
Tourist information Nuits-Saint-Georges:
🎪 ⬛ Fri.

| ⌧ S | **Pouges-les-Eaux** | 22A2 |

D907. **GPS:** n47,08315 e3,09382. ⬆

5 ⌧free ⚡€2/10minutes ⚑ Ch 🚽€2/10minutes 🗑. **Surface:** asphalted.
⬛ 01/01-31/12
Distance: ⌧250m ⚓1,4km ⊗100m.
Remarks: Coins at campsite and tourist info.

| ⚒ S | **Prissé** | 22D4 |

Cave de Prissé. **GPS:** n46,32226 e4,75257. ⬆

5 ⌧free ⚡ ⚑ Ch WC free. **Location:** Rural, simple. **Surface:** asphalted.
⬛ 01/01-31/12
Distance: ⌧500m ⚓3km.
Remarks: Max. 24h.

| ⌧ S | **Pruzilly** | 22D5 |

La Croix Blanche, salle des Fêtes. **GPS:** n46,25708 e4,69792. ⬆

6 ⌧free ⚡ ⚑ Ch WC free. **Location:** Rural, simple, quiet. **Surface:** asphalted.
⬛ 01/01-31/12
Distance: ⌧on the spot ⊗on the spot.
Remarks: Max. 48h, vins de Côte de Beaujolais.

| ⚒ S | **Quarre-les-Tombes** | 22C2 |

Rue des Ecoles. **GPS:** n47,36853 e3,99936.
6 ⌧ ⚡ free. **Surface:** metalled. ⬛ 01/04-31/10
Distance: ⌧100m ⊗100m 🚂100m.

| ⌧ S | **Rogny-les-Sept-Écluses** | 22A1 |

Quai Sully. **GPS:** n47,74673 e2,88104. ⬆
4 ⌧free ⚡ ⚑ Ch free. **Location:** Simple, quiet. **Surface:** grassy.
⬛ 01/01-31/12
Distance: ⌧on the spot ⊗350m.
Remarks: At the canal.

| ⌧ S | **Rouvray** | 22C2 |

Place du Champs de foire, D906. **GPS:** n47,42271 e4,10412. ⬆➡

FR

4 🗑free ⛽🚰 Ch free. **Surface:** metalled.
Distance: 🚶on the spot.
Remarks: Max. 48h.

♿S   **Saint-Fargeau** 🌿   22A1
Rue de Laveau, D18. **GPS:** n47,63968 e3,06999.⬆.

10 🗑free ⛽🚰 Ch WC free. ⬜ 01/01-31/12
Distance: 🚶50m ⊗50m.

♿S   **Saint-Julien-du-Sault**   15A6
Stade Jean Sax, Rue du Stade. **GPS:** n48,02906 e3,30116.
13 🗑free ⛽🚰 Ch free. ⬜ 01/01-31/12

♿S   **Saint-Léger-sur-Dheune** 🚤   22D3
Route de Saint-Bérain. **GPS:** n46,84648 e4,63248.⬆.

12 🗑€7/24h ⛽🚰 Ch 🧹 included. 🚐 ♻ ⬜ 01/01-31/12
Distance: 🚶on the spot.

♿S   **Savigny-le-Sec**   22D2
Rue de la Mare. **GPS:** n47,43365 e5,04607.⬆.

10 🗑€3,50 ⛽€2 🚰 Ch WC. 🚐 **Location:** Rural, simple, isolated, quiet.
Surface: asphalted/gravel. ⬜ 01/01-31/12
Distance: 🚶1,3km 🛒bakery 1,3km.

♿S   **Semur-en-Auxois**   22C1
Avenue Pasteur. **GPS:** n47,49529 e4,38810.⬆.

30 🗑free ⛽🚰 Ch free.
Location: Simple, quiet. **Surface:** asphalted.
⬜ 01/01-31/12 🚰 water: Nov-March
Distance: 🚶historical centre 1,3km 🚲10km ⊗800m 🛒800m.
Remarks: Behind stadium, nearby police station.
Tourist information Semur-en-Auxois:
⌂ Alise-Ste-Reine. Findings of Gallo-Roman city. ⬜ 01/04-31/10 daily.

♿S   **Seurre**   23A3
Rue de la Perche à l'Oiseau. **GPS:** n47,00405 e5,14318.⬆➡.

15 🗑free ⛽🚰 Ch 🧹 Service €4/20min ♻. **Location:** Rural, simple, quiet.
Surface: asphalted. ⬜ 01/01-31/12
Distance: 🚶800m 🏊100m 🚲100m ⊗700m 🛒700m.

♿S   **St.Gengoux-le-National**   22D4
GPS: n46,60624 e4,66844.⬆.

16 🗑free ⛽€3/15minutes 🚰 Ch 🔌€3/50minutes WC ♻.
Location: Simple, quiet. **Surface:** gravel. ⬜ 01/01-31/12
Distance: 🚶500m.
Remarks: At former station.
Tourist information St.Gengoux-le-National:
🚲 La Voie Verte. Cycle route on former railway,.

♿S   **St.Honoré-les-Bains** 🌿⛲🌳🍃   22B3
Allée de la Cressonnière. **GPS:** n46,90471 e3,84059.⬆➡.

4 🗑free ⛽€2 🚰 Ch 🔌€2. **Location:** Simple. **Surface:** gravel.
⬜ 01/01-31/12

Distance: 300m 300m 50m.
Remarks: Max. 48h, coins at town hall and supermarket.

S Treigny 22A1

Rue du Champ de Foire. **GPS**: n47,54982 e3,18159.
2 free Ch. **Location:** Simple, quiet. **Surface:** asphalted.
01/01-31/12
Distance: 200m 200m 200m.

S Vinzelles 22D5

Clos Bonin. **GPS**: n46,27145 e4,77008.

10 free Chfree. **Location:** Rural, simple. **Surface:** asphalted.
01/01-31/12
Distance: 200m A6 2,8km on the spot on the spot on the spot.

Franche Comté

S Arc-et-Senans 23B3

Grande rue. **GPS**: n47,03343 e5,78120.

10 free €2 Ch. **Location:** Simple. **Surface:** gravel.
01/01-31/12
Distance: 500m 500m.
Remarks: Coints at mairie, supermarket and campsite.

S Arinthod 23A4

Rue de la Prélette. **GPS**: n46,39654 e5,57013.

5 €6 Ch included. **Location:** Rural. **Surface:** gravel.
01/01-31/12
Distance: 100m.
Remarks: Near sports fields.

S Arsure-Arsurette 23B3

Châlet des Arches, Route de l'Aliance de vie blanc. **GPS**: n46,72168 e6,08402.

10 free €2 WC. **Location:** Isolated. **Surface:** asphalted.
01/01-31/12

S Baume-les-Dames 23C2

Quai du Canal. **GPS**: n47,34023 e6,35778.

44 € 8,80 + € 0,20/pp tourist tax Ch WCincluded €1,70.
Location: Rural, comfortable. **Surface:** asphalted/grassy. 01/01-31/12
Distance: on the spot 5,3km on the spot on the spot on the spot.
Remarks: Bread-service.

Tourist information Baume-les-Dames:
Abbaye Nôtre Dame. Historical monument, 18th century.

Baume-les-Messieurs 23A3

Cascade des Tufs, Rue des Moulins. **GPS**: n46,69124 e5,63946.

10 free. **Location:** Simple.

Belvoir 23C2

Chateaux Belvoir. **GPS**: n47,32139 e6,61097.

3 free. **Location:** Rural, simple. **Surface:** asphalted/gravel.
01/01-31/12

S Besançon 23B2

Parking du Crous, Cité Carnot, Quai Veil Picard. **GPS**: n47,23702 e6,01644.

FR

12 ⌀ € 5/24h ⌁ 🗑 Ch free. 🚻 ♻ **Location:** Urban, simple.
Surface: asphalted. ☐ 01/01-31/12
Distance: 🚶on the spot ⊗500m 🚰500m 🏊on the spot.
Tourist information Besançon:
👁 Jardin Botanique, avenue de la Paix. Botanical gardens.
🏰 Château, Vaire-le-Grand. ☐ 15/08-18/09, 19/09-14/08 by agreement.
⛲ 🚻 Tue, Fri, Su.
😊 Parc Zoologique de la Citadelle, Citadelle. Zoo. ☐ 10-17/19h. 🎫 € 7.

🖥 S | **Bois-d'Amont** 🌿 ⚓ | 23B4
Impasse de l'Eglantine. **GPS:** n46,53771 e6,13934. ⬆➡.

10 ⌀ free ⌁€2 🗑 Ch 🔌 €2. **Location:** Rural, comfortable, quiet.
Surface: asphalted. ☐ 01/01-31/12
Distance: ⊗on the spot 🏊on the spot 🚴on the spot 🛶on the spot.

🖥 S | **Brognard** | 23C1
Base de Loisirs de la Savoureuse, Rue de Paquis. **GPS:** n47,52834 e6,85652. ⬆.

3 ⌀ free ⌁ 🗑 Ch free. **Location:** Rural, noisy. **Surface:** asphalted.
☐ 01/01-31/12
Distance: 🏊50m 🚰1,3km.
Remarks: Max. 48h.

🖥 S | **Champagnole** | 23B3
20, Rue Georges Vallerey. **GPS:** n46,74633 e5,89918. ⬆.

5 ⌀ free, 1/6-15/9 € 6 ⌁ 🗑 Ch 🔌€3,80. **Location:** Simple.
Surface: gravel/sand. ☐ 01/01-31/12
Distance: 🚶500m 🚰250m.
Remarks: Max. 1 night, coins at campsite.

🖥 S | **Clairvaux-les-Lacs** | 23B4
Route de Lons-le-Saunier, D678. **GPS:** n46,58246 e5,74660. ⬆.

6 ⌀ free ⌁ 🗑 Ch free. **Location:** Urban, simple.
☐ 01/01-31/12
Distance: 🚰nearby.
Remarks: On entering village, nearby police station.

🖥 S | **Conliège** 🌿 ⚓ 🏛 | 23A4
Rue du Saugeois. **GPS:** n46,65270 e5,59981. ⬆➡.

2 ⌀ free ⌁ 🗑 Ch WC free.
Location: Urban, simple. **Surface:** asphalted.
Distance: ⊗100m.

🖥 S | **Consolation-Maisonnettes** 🏛 | 23C2
Parc du Seminaire du Cirque de Consolation., D377.
GPS: n47,15848 e6,60600. ⬆.

10 ⌀ € 10/24h ⌁ 🗑 Ch 🚿 WC included 🚻.
Location: Rural, simple. **Surface:** asphalted.
Distance: 🛶on the spot.
Remarks: Check in at shop.

🖥 S | **Corravillers** | 16C6
Rue de la Mairie. **GPS:** n47,89431 e6,62162. ⬆⬆➡.

2 ⌀ free ⌁€2/23minutes 🗑 Ch free 🚿€2/23minutes.
Location: Rural, simple. **Surface:** grassy/gravel. ☐ 01/01-31/12
Distance: ⊗500m 🚰500m.

🖥 S | **Corre** | 16B6
Fluvial Loisirs, Pré le Saônier. **GPS:** n47,91402 e5,99308. ⬆➡.

32 ⌁ € 6 01/11-31/03, € 8 01/04-31/10 ⛽🚰 Ch 🛁 included 🛗€1,50 📷€4 ⚡€3/2day 🗑. **Location:** Rural, comfortable, quiet. **Surface:** gravel. ⊙ 01/01-31/12
Distance: 🚶200m ⛱50m ⊗50m 🚍 bakery 300m, supermarket 500m 🚏100m.

Cousance 23A4
Grande rue, Champs de foire. **GPS:** n46,52929 e5,39154.⬆.

4 ⌁free ⛽🚰 Ch WC free. **Surface:** asphalted. ⊙ 01/01-31/12
Distance: 🚶100m 🚲6,6km 🚍100m.

Crosey-le-Petit 23C2
Rue de begin. **GPS:** n47,35039 e6,48913.⬆➡.

1 ⌁free. **Location:** Rural, simple. **Surface:** asphalted/gravel. ⊙ 01/01-31/12 🚴 on the spot 🚶 on the spot.

Dôle 23A2
Parking de Lahr, Avenue de Lahr. **GPS:** n47,08983 e5,49641.⬆➡.
20 ⌁free. **Location:** Simple, central, noisy. **Surface:** asphalted.
⊙ Village fair: mid-May
Distance: 🚶on the spot 🚶 on the spot.

Tourist information Dôle:
Ⓜ Maison natale de Louis Pasteur, 43 de la rue Pasteur. Birth house Pasteur, museum. ⊙ 1/4-31/10 10-12h, 14-18h, 01/11-31/03 Sa-Su 14-18h
⊙ Su-morning. Ⓣ free.

Esmoulières 23C1
D236. **GPS:** n47,85243 e6,61502.⬆.

Faucogney-et-la-Mer 23C1
Rue des Chars. **GPS:** n47,83735 e6,56003.⬆➡.

6 ⌁free ⛽€2/23minutes 🚰 Ch free 🛁€2/20minutes. **Location:** Rural, simple. **Surface:** grassy/gravel. ⊙ 01/01-31/12
Distance: 🚶800m.

Gray 23A2
Rue de la Plage. **GPS:** n47,46045 e5,61874.⬆➡.

12 ⌁free ⛽🚰Ch free. **Location:** Comfortable. **Surface:** grassy/gravel. ⊙ 01/01-31/12
Remarks: Near camping municipal.

Jeurre 23A4
35, Rue Principale. **GPS:** n46,36662 e5,70769.⬆➡.

40 ⌁€ 5 ⛽€2 🚰 Ch 💶€2 🛁€3/day. **Location:** Rural, simple. **Surface:** grassy. ⊙ 01/05-31/10

La Chapelle des Bois ❄ 23B4
Station de ski, Chemin du Marais Blanc. **GPS:** n46,60307 e6,11317.⬆.

⌁free. **Surface:** unpaved.
Distance: ⛷ on the spot.

La Montagne 16C6
D136. **GPS:** n47,92581 e6,58710.

2 ⌁free. **Location:** Rural, simple. **Surface:** asphalted. ⊙ 01/01-31/12

FR

2 ⏚free. **Location:** Rural, simple. **Surface:** asphalted.
🅾 01/01-31/12
Remarks: Parking at skipistes.

| 🄢 S | La Pesse | 23B4 |

Rue de l'Epicéa, D25. **GPS:** n46,28400 e5,84764. ⬆.

15 ⏚free ⛽€2 🍽 Ch WC. **Location:** Rural, simple. **Surface:** unpaved.
🅾 01/01-31/12
Distance: ⚡on the spot ☎on the spot.
Remarks: At start of langlauf circuit.

| 🍴 S | La Pesse | 23B4 |

Ferme Auberge de La Combe aux Bisons, Lieu-dit Pré Reverchon.
GPS: n46,29278 e5,86011.

3 ⏚guests free ⛽. **Location:** Simple, isolated.
🅾 01/01-31/12 🅾 Mon, Tue
Distance: ⊗on the spot.

| 🄢 S | Lamoura ❄ | 23B4 |

Route de Prémanon, D25. **GPS:** n46,41107 e5,99458. ⬆.

20 ⏚free ⛽🍽 Chfree WC.
Location: Rural, simple. **Surface:** asphalted.
Distance: ⊗winter ⚡on the spot ☎on the spot.
Remarks: Service sportcentre La Serra, only in winter time.

| 🄢 S | Lamoura ❄ | 23B4 |

Route de Prémanon, D25. **GPS:** n46,40139 e5,98561.

6 ⏚free ⛽.
Distance: ⚡on the spot ☎on the spot.

| 🄢 S | Le Vernois | 23A3 |

Caveau des Byards. GPS: n46,73342 e5,59405. ⬆.

2 ⏚ ⛽free. **Location:** Urban, simple. **Surface:** grassy/gravel.

| 🄢 S | Les Rousses 🎿⛷❄ | 23B4 |

Parking l'Aube, Route du Lac. **GPS:** n46,48779 e6,06690. ⬆➡.

30 ⏚free, € 4/Winter ⛽€3,60/100liter 🍽 Ch 🔲€3,60/1h ✏.
Location: Simple. **Surface:** asphalted. 🅾 01/01-31/12
Distance: ⚡500m ⊗500m ☎200m.

| 🄢 S | Les Rousses 🎿⛷❄ | 23B4 |

Porte du Balanciers, Route Blanche, N5. **GPS:** n46,44852 e6,07591. ⬆.

30 ⏚free, € 4/Winter ⛽€3,50 🍽 Ch 🔲 WC. **Surface:** asphalted.
🅾 01/01-31/12
Distance: ⊗Restaurant ⚡5km.
Remarks: Coins at tourist info, ski station, ski rental, ski school.

| 🄢 S | Luxeuil-les-Bains 🎿⛷♨ | 23C1 |

Place de l'Etang de la Poche, Rue Gambetta. **GPS:** n47,81679 e6,38659. ⬆.

20 ⌷free 🚰€2/100liter 🗑Ch💧€2/1h. **Location:** Simple, quiet.
Surface: gravel. ⭘ 01/01-31/12
Distance: 🚶1km ⚓100m ⊗1km 🛒Auchan/Aldi 500m ⊗1km.
Tourist information Luxeuil-les-Bains:
ℹ️ Fougerolles. Since the 16th century the small town is the centre of distilleries (Kirsch and cherry brandy).

| 🅿️S | Maisod 🌿⛲ | 23A4 |

La Mercantine. **GPS**: n46,46500 e5,68864.

40 ⌷€6 🚰€2 🗑Ch. **Location:** Rural, simple. **Surface:** gravel.
Distance: ⚓100m ⊗200m.
Remarks: At lake Vouglans, max. 24h.

| 🅿️S | Mesnay ⛲ | 23B3 |

Rue Vermot. **GPS**: n46,89834 e5,80036. ⬆️➡️

5 ⌷free 🚰€2/10minutes 🗑Chfree ⚡€2/55minutes 🗑.
Location: Simple. ⭘ 01/01-31/12
Distance: 🚶500m, 2,5km Arbois.

| 🅿️S | Montbéliard 🌿 | 23C1 |

Parking du Champ de Foire. **GPS**: n47,50663 e6,79128. ⬆️

4 ⌷free 🚰€1,60 🗑Ch💧€1,60. **Location:** Urban. **Surface:** asphalted.
Remarks: Max. 48h.

| 🅿️S | Montreux-Château ⛵ | 23D1 |

D11. **GPS**: n47,60283 e7,00252. ⬆️

8 ⌷€5/24h 🚰€5/10minutes 🗑Ch⚡(8x) WCincluded. 🚐**Location:**
Simple. **Surface:** gravel.

| 🅿️S | Moussières 🌿⛲ | 23B4 |

GPS: n46,32111 e5,89778. ⬆️

6 ⌷free 🚰€2 🗑Ch💧€2. **Location:** Rural, simple. **Surface:** gravel.
⭘ 01/01-31/12
Distance: 🛒on the spot.
Remarks: In front of cheese farm.

| 🅿️S | Mouthe 🏔 | 23B3 |

Place de l'Eglise. GPS: n46,71042 e6,19570. ⬆️➡️

20 ⌷free 🚰€3 🗑Ch💧.
Location: Rural, simple. **Surface:** asphalted.
Remarks: Coins at the bakery, supermarket, tourist office.

| 🅿️S | Nozeroy | 23B3 |

Rue des Remparts. **GPS**: n46,77249 e6,03516. ⬆️➡️

10 ⌷free 🚰🗑Ch⚡,2Amp WC⌷included. **Location:** Rural, comfortable.
Surface: grassy/gravel. ⭘ 01/01-31/12
Distance: 🚶200m.

| 🅿️S | Orgelet | 23A4 |

Place Ancien Champ de Foire, Rue du Faubourg de l'Orme.
GPS: n46,52232 e5,60860. ⬆️

FR

20 ⌆free ⌕ ⌁ Ch WC free. **Location:** Simple. **Surface:** grassy/metalled. ◌ 01/01-31/12
Distance: ⌓300m.
Remarks: Closed when frosty.

5 ⌆free. **Location:** Rural, simple. **Surface:** asphalted.

⌆S **Salins-les-Bains** ⌂ ⌣ 23B3
Rue de la République, D472. **GPS:** n46,93254 e5,87899.⬆

⌆S **Raddon-et-Chapendu** 23C1
GPS: n47,84899 e6,47427.

6 ⌆free ⌕€2/23minutes ⚡€2/23minutes. **Location:** Rural, simple.
Surface: gravel.
Remarks: Near sports fields.

⌆ **Randevillers** 23C2
Rue de la Cote. **GPS:** n47,30944 e6,52707.⬆➡.

8 ⌆free ⌕ ⌁ Ch ⊟ free. **Location:** Simple. **Surface:** asphalted. ◌ 01/01-31/12
Distance: ⌓50m.
Remarks: Permitted to park/stay overnight on all parkings.

⌆ **Sancey-le-Grand** 23C2
D-31. **GPS:** n47,29040 e6,57742.⬆.

3 ⌆free. **Location:** Rural. **Surface:** asphalted/gravel.

⌆ **Saint-Bresson** 16C6
La Rue Saint Bresson. **GPS:** n47,86999 e6,50226.⬆➡.

2 ⌆free. **Location:** Rural, simple. **Surface:** gravel. ◌ 01/01-31/12
Distance: ⌓500m.

⌆S **Sancey-le-Long** 23C2
D31/D464. **GPS:** n47,30513 e6,59477.⬆.

2 ⌆. **Location:** Rural, simple. **Surface:** asphalted.

⌆ **Sainte-Marie-en-Chanois** 23C1
Rue de la Lolonge. **GPS:** n47,83663 e6,51216.⬆➡.

2 ⌆free ⌕€2 ⌁ Ch ⊟€2.
Location: Rural, simple. **Surface:** gravel.
Remarks: Coins at supermarket, cafe, centre commercial.

⌆S **Saulx** 23B1
Place de l'Eglise. **GPS:** n47,69620 e6,28030.⬆➡.

FR

4 🛁free 🚰€2/100liter 🔌€2/2h WC free. **Location:** Simple, quiet. **Surface:** metalled. **Distance:** ⊗on the spot 🍴baker on site.

| 🏞️ | Sermamagny | 23C1 |

Rue Alfred Lallemand. **GPS:** n47,68351 e6,81416. ⬆️ .

40 🛁€6 🚰10minutes 🧺Ch 🧺 55minutes WC free. 🚽 🗑️ **Surface:** gravel/sand. 🅿️ 01/03-30/11 **Distance:** 💧on the spot. **Remarks:** Max. 3 nights, no camping activities.

| 🏞️S | Thoirette 🛶 | 23A5 |

Grande Rue. **GPS:** n46,26924 e5,53529. ⬆️ .

30 🛁free. **Surface:** grassy.

| 🏞️S | St.Claude | 23B4 |

Avenue de la Libération, D436. **GPS:** n46,38049 e5,85209. ⬆️➡️ .

5 🛁€6 🚰 🧺Ch 🔌 🧹 included. **Location:** Simple. **Surface:** gravel. **Distance:** 🛒25m 🏊50m 🍴25m.

| 🏞️S | Vaivre-et-Montoille ⚓🏞️ | 23B1 |

Avenue des Rives du Lac. **GPS:** n47,62938 e6,12701. ⬆️ .

3 🛁free 🚰 🧺Ch 🗑️free. **Location:** Urban, simple, noisy. **Surface:** asphalted. 🅿️ 01/01-31/12 **Distance:** 🛒1km.

Tourist information St.Claude:

ℹ️ Tourist town, production of pipes.

👁️ Musée du Pipe et Diamant. Pipes and diamond exhibition.

🅿️ 01/06-30/09 9.30-12h, 14-18.30h, 01/10-31/05 14-18h 🔵 Su.

| 🏞️S | St.Loup-sur-Semouse | 16B6 |

Rue de Champ de Tir. **GPS:** n47,88643 e6,27051.

7 🛁free 🚰€2,50 🧺Ch. **Location:** Rural, simple, quiet. **Surface:** sand. 🅿️ 01/01-31/12 **Distance:** 🛒1,5km 🏊beach 100m 🚶100m ⊗25m 🚴 on the spot 🏇on the spot. **Remarks:** Swimming pool complex, lake.

| 🏞️S | Vaivre-et-Montoille ⚓🏞️ | 23B1 |

Avenue du Lac. **GPS:** n47,63718 e6,10752. ⬆️ .

4 🛁free 🚰€3 🧺Ch 🔌. **Surface:** asphalted. 🅿️ 01/03-30/11 **Distance:** 🛒on the spot 🏊500m ⊗on the spot 🍴on the spot 🚌on the spot. **Remarks:** Behind church, max. 24h.

| 🏞️S | St.Point-Lac | 23B3 |

Aire d'acceuil pour camping-cars, Rue du lac. **GPS:** n46,81268 e6,30375.

5 🛁free. **Location:** Rural. **Surface:** asphalted. 🅿️ 01/01-31/12 **Distance:** 🛒on the spot 🚴on the spot 🏇on the spot. **Remarks:** Directly at lake.

| 🏞️ | Vellevans | 23C2 |

D464. **GPS:** n47,31042 e6,49139. ⬆️ .

FR

2 ⌇ free. **Location:** Rural. **Surface:** grassy/gravel.

| | | Villers-le-Lac ☀☂⚓ | 23C3 |

Vedettes Panoramiques, Rue du Clos Rondot. **GPS:** n47,05948 e6,67195. ⬆.

8 ⌇ free ⚡€2 🚰 Ch 🔧 free 🗑. **Location:** Simple. **Surface:** concrete.
◻ 01/01-31/12
Distance: 🚶50m.
Remarks: Small pitches.

| | | Villers-le-Lac ☀☂⚓ | 23C3 |

Bateaux du Saut du Doubs. **GPS:** n47,05500 e6,67000. ⬆.

50 ⌇ € 8, free with boat trip ⚡€3,50/time 🚰 Ch 📶 at office/shop. 🚻
Location: Simple, central. **Surface:** grassy/gravel.
◻ 01/04-31/10
Distance: 🚶100m.
Remarks: Check in at Bateaux.

Poitou Charentes

| | | Agris 🌳 | 20D6 |

Le Pont d'Agris, D6. **GPS:** n45,78619 e0,33944. ⬆.

6 ⌇ free ⚡€2 🚰 Ch 📷€2. **Surface:** asphalted. ◻ 01/01-31/12
Distance: 🚶 on the spot 🚻 on the spot 🚌 on the spot.

| | | Aigre | 20D5 |

Parc Les Charmilles, Rue des Charrières. **GPS:** n45,89341 e0,00578. ⬆.

10 ⌇ € 5,50 ⚡ 🚰 Ch 🔧 (4x) WC included 🗑. **Surface:** metalled.
◻ 01/04-31/10
Distance: 🚶 on the spot 🛒 on the spot 🚻 on the spot.
Remarks: 4th night free.

| | | Angliers | 20D3 |

Aire de repos de la Briande, D347. **GPS:** n46,95861 e0,10472. ⬆➡.

8 ⌇ free ⚡€2 🚰 Ch 🔧 free WC. **Surface:** asphalted. ◻ 01/01-31/12
Distance: 🚶 Angliers 1km 🛒 50m.

| | | Angoulins | 20B5 |

Rue du Chay. **GPS:** n46,10623 w1,13565. ⬆.

17 ⌇ free. **Location:** Rural, simple. **Surface:** asphalted.
Distance: 🚶1km 🏖20m.

| | | Arçais | 20C4 |

Aire camping-cars du Coursault, Rue de Coursault. **GPS:** n46,29583 w0,69. ⬆.

20 ⌇ free, 01/04-30/09 € 7 ⚡ 🚰 Ch WC free. 🚻 **Location:** Simple, quiet.
Surface: grassy. ◻ 01/01-31/12
Distance: 🚶400m 🛒 on the spot 🛒 nearby 🚻 nearby.

| | | Aubeterre-sur-Dronne ☀☂ | 28C1 |

D2, Route de Ribérac. **GPS:** n45,26980 e0,17570. ⬆.

FR

10 ⛺free ⛽🚿 Ch free. **Surface:** grassy/metalled. 🅿 01/01-31/12
Distance: 🚶500m ⛵on the spot ⊗300m 🚇500m.
Remarks: At tennis-courts.

Tourist information Aubeterre-sur-Dronne:
⛺ Place de Village. 🅿 Thu, Su.

♿S	Aulnay	20C5

Rue de Salles. **GPS:** n46,02239 w0,34528.⬆.

10 ⛺free ⛽🚿 Ch free. **Surface:** gravel.
Distance: 🚶200m ⊗200m 🚇200m.
Remarks: Max. 24h.

♿	Aulnay	20C5

Place Charles de Gaulle, Rue Haute de l'Eglise. **GPS:** n46,02306 w0,35444.⬆.

10 ⛺free. **Surface:** metalled. 🅿 01/01-31/12
Distance: 🚶200m ⊗200m 🚇200m.

♿S	Aytré	20B5

Route de la Plage. **GPS:** n46,11311 w1,12331.⬆➡.

30 ⛺free ⛽🚿 Ch free. **Location:** Rural, simple. **Surface:** asphalted. 🅿 01/01-31/12
Distance: ⛵on the spot.
Remarks: Max 3,5t, max. 48h.

♿S	Bougon 🌿🌻	20D4

Musée des Tumulus, La Chapelle. **GPS:** n46,37845 w0,06825.⬆.

10 ⛺free ⛽🚿 Ch free. **Location:** Simple, isolated. **Surface:** asphalted.
🅿 01/01-31/12
Distance: 🚶3km.
Remarks: Parking museum.

♿	Bourcefranc-le-Chapus	20B5

Bois de Pin, Prise du Portail Rouge. **GPS:** n45,82611 w1,14278.⬆.

20 ⛺€ 6. 🚐 **Location:** Isolated, quiet. **Surface:** gravel.
🅿 01/01-31/12
Distance: 🚶4km ⛵on the spot 🚲on the spot 🚇3km.

♿	Bourcefranc-le-Chapus	20B5

Rue Kennedy. **GPS:** n45,84546 w1,14929.⬆.
⛺free. **Location:** Simple, central. **Surface:** asphalted.
🅿 01/01-31/12
Distance: 🚶250m ⛵750m ⊗250m 🚇250m.

©S	Bourcefranc-le-Chapus	20B5

Fief de Bonnemort. **GPS:** n45,83112 w1,15073.⬆.
⛺free, night € 6 ⛽€2,60/100liter 🚿 Ch. **Surface:** gravel.
🅿 01/01-31/12
Distance: 🚶2,5km ⛵on the spot.
Remarks: Coins at tourist info and town hall.

♿S	Bressuire	20C3

Place Labâte. **GPS:** n46,84417 w0,49086.⬆.
⛺free ⛽🚿 Ch. **Location:** Urban, simple, noisy. **Surface:** sand.
🅿 01/01-31/12
Distance: 🚶400m ⊗400m.

♿S	Cellefrouin 🐑	20D5

D739. **GPS:** n45,89361 e0,38639.⬆➡.

50 ⛺free ⛽🚿 Ch WC free. **Location:** Simple, isolated, quiet. **Surface:** gravel.
🅿 01/01-31/12
Distance: 🚶300m.

♿S	Celles-sur-Belle 🌿⛪	20C4

Place de l'Aumônerie, Rue des Halles. **GPS:** n46,26278 w0,20806.⬆.

FR

10 ⬛free 🚰 🔌 Ch free. **Surface:** gravel. 🅿 01/01-31/12
Distance: 🚶100m ⊗on the spot 🛒on the spot.

📷 Ⓢ   **Chabanais**   21A5
Chemin des Tanneries, N141. **GPS:** n45,87447 e0,72008.⬆

4 ⬛free. **Location:** Rural, simple. **Surface:** asphalted.
🅿 01/01-31/12 ⭘ Thu
Distance: 🚶on the spot ⊗100m 🛒100m.
Remarks: Along the river Vienne.

📷 Ⓢ   **Château-Larcher**   20D4
Val de Clouère. **GPS:** n46,41444 e0,31556.⬆

10 ⬛€4 🚰 🔌 Ch 🚽 WC included. ♿ **Location:** Rural, comfortable, isolated, quiet. **Surface:** grassy/gravel. 🅿 01/03-31/11
Distance: 🚶1km ⊿on the spot.
Remarks: At small lake, former campsite.

📷 Ⓢ   **Châtelaillon-Plage**   20B5
Avenue de l'Hippodrome. **GPS:** n46,07253 w1,07886.⬆

54 ⬛€12 🚰 🔌 Ch included ⚡ 📶 free. 🧺 **Location:** Rural, simple. **Surface:** asphalted/grassy. 🅿 01/01-31/12
Distance: 🚶700m ⊿800m ⊗700m.

📷 Ⓢ   **Châtelaillon-Plage**   20B5
Parking de l'Office du Tourisme, Avenue de Strasbourg. **GPS:** n46,07679 w1,08859.➡

5 ⬛free 📶. **Location:** Urban, simple. **Surface:** metalled.
🅿 01/01-31/12
Distance: 🚶on the spot ⊿500m ⊗on the spot 🛒on the spot.

📷 Ⓢ   **Chef-Boutonne**   20D5
Aire camping-cars, Chemin du Parc. **GPS:** n46,10982 w0,07869.⬆➡

20 ⬛free 🚰 🔌 Ch WC free. **Surface:** grassy/gravel. 🅿 01/04-31/10
Distance: 🚶800m ⊿300m ⊗800m 🚌on the spot.

📷 Ⓢ   **Cherves-Richemont**   20C6
Allee des Coquelicots. **GPS:** n45,74030 w0,35607.⬆➡

6 ⬛free 🚰 🔌 Ch free. **Surface:** asphalted.
🅿 01/01-31/12 ⭘ service 01/11-15/04
Distance: 🚶500m ⊗100m 🛒500m.

📷 Ⓢ   **Chey**   20D4
Place de la Liberté. **GPS:** n46,30412 w0,05002.⬆

3 ⬛free 🚰 🔌 Ch WC free. **Surface:** gravel. 🅿 01/01-31/12
Distance: 🚶on the spot ⊗on the spot 🛒on the spot.

📷 Ⓢ   **Clérac**   28C1
D261E1. **GPS:** n45,17906 w0,228.⬆

🛏free 🚰🔧Ch free. **Surface:** gravel.
Distance: 🚶200m ⛵on the spot ⊗100m 🛒100m 🏊on the spot
🧍on the spot.
Remarks: Behind bakery, at small lake.

| 📷S | Cognac | 20C6 |

Place de la Levade, Quartier Saint-Jacques. **GPS:** n45,69847 w0,33265.⬆.

4 🛏free 🚰€2 🔧Ch. **Location:** Urban, simple, central. **Surface:** asphalted.
⬛ 01/01-31/12
Distance: 🚶100m ⊗on the spot 🛒100m 🖥500m 🚃on the spot.

Tourist information Cognac:
👁 Otard. Cognac distillery in 16th century castle. Guided tour and tasting.
⬛ daily ⬤ 01/10-31/03 weekend.
Ⓜ Cognac-musée. Culture around the Cognac. ⬛ 01/10-31/05 14-17.30h,
01/06-30/09 10-12h, 14-18h.

| ©S | Confolens 🌊👥🏖 | 21A5 |

Camping les Ribières, Avenue de Sainte-Germain. **GPS:** n46,01894 e0,67570.⬆.

🛏free, May-Sep € 5 🚰🔧Ch 🚾WC ⬛included. **Surface:** metalled.
⬛ 01/01-31/12 ⬤ service: 16/09-14/05
Distance: 🚶750m.

Tourist information Confolens:
⛩ ⬛ Wed, Sa.

| 📷S | Couhé | 20D4 |

Place du Marché. **GPS:** n46,29906 e0,17882.⬆➡.
🛏free 🚰WC free. **Location:** Simple, central, quiet. **Surface:** asphalted.
⬛ 01/01-31/12
Distance: 🚶50m ⊗50m 🛒100m.

| 📷S | Coulon 🌊🏖🌾 | 20C4 |

Parking d'Autremont, Rue André Cramois. **GPS:** n46,32102 w0,59063.⬆.

80 🛏€7,50 🚰🔧Ch 🚾WC. **Surface:** grassy/gravel. ⬛ 01/04-30/11
Distance: 🚶350m ⊗350m 🛒350m 🏊on the spot 🧍on the spot.

| 📷S | Criteuil la Magdeleine | 20C6 |

GPS: n45,53778 w0,21556.⬆➡.

5 🛏free 🚰🔧Ch 🚾WC free. **Location:** Simple, quiet. **Surface:** asphalted.
⬛ 01/01-31/12
Distance: 🚶on the spot.
Remarks: In the village.

| 📷S | Dolus-d'Oléron | 20B5 |

Route du Stade. **GPS:** n45,91137 w1,25255.⬆.

40 🛏free 🚰€2/100liter 🔌€2/1h. **Location:** Rural, simple. **Surface:** grassy.
⬛ 01/01-31/12
Distance: 🚶500m 🛒1,2km Hypermarché.
Remarks: Coins at tourist info.

| 📷S | Echillais | 20B5 |

Place de la Carrière. **GPS:** n45,89753 w0,95545.⬆.

15 🛏€ 5,10 🚰€3 🔧Ch.🚿
Location: Rural, simple. **Surface:** asphalted.
Remarks: Access via rue de l'église.

| 📷S | Fouras | 20B5 |

Plage Nord, Avenue du Cadoret. **GPS:** n45,99194 w1,08694.

15 ⛆ € 7 ⛲ €1/50liter. 🚐 **Location:** Urban, simple. **Surface:** metalled. 🅿 01/01-31/12
Distance: 🔧on the spot ⊗on the spot 🚰on the spot.
Remarks: In front of campsite Cadoret, Fun golf, max. 48h, coins at campsite and tourist info.

| 🅂 | Fouras | 20B5 |

Prairie du Casino, Dir pointe de la Fumée. **GPS:** n45,99583 w1,10611.

30 ⛆ € 6 ⛲liter. **Location:** Rural, simple. **Surface:** metalled. 🅿 01/01-31/12
Distance: 🔧on the spot ⊗on the spot 🚰on the spot.
Remarks: Max. 48h.

| 🅂 | Gencay | 20D4 |

Place du Champs de Foire. **GPS:** n46,37315 e0,40638. ⬆➡.

10 ⛆free ⛲€2 🔧 Ch ⛲€2 WC. **Surface:** grassy/metalled. 🅿 01/01-31/12
Distance: 🔧on the spot ⊗on the spot 🚰on the spot.
Remarks: Coins at the shops.

| 🅂 | Genté | 20C6 |

Rue de l'Eglise. **GPS:** n45,62861 w0,315. ⬆➡.

6 ⛆free ⛲🔧 Ch 🧹(6x) WC free. **Surface:** asphalted. 🅿 01/01-31/12
Distance: 🔧on the spot ⊗350m 🚰on the spot.

| 🅂 | Hiers-Brouage | 20B5 |

D3. **GPS:** n45,86250 w1,07667.

20 ⛆free. **Location:** Rural. **Surface:** grassy/gravel. 🅿 01/01-31/12
Distance: 🔧250m ⊗250m 🚰250m.
Remarks: Arrival >20h, departure <9h.

| 🅂 | Hiers-Brouage | 20B5 |

Rue Palissy, D3. **GPS:** n45,85284 w1,07745.
⛲€4 🔧 Ch 🚰. **Surface:** metalled. 🅿 01/01-31/12

| 🅂 | Jonzac 〰🏖☕🍽 | 20C6 |

Place du 8 Mai 1945. **GPS:** n45,44800 w0,433. ⬆.

18 ⛆free ⛲€4,10/100liter 🔧 Ch 🚰€4,10/1h. **Location:** Urban.
Surface: asphalted. 🅿 01/01-31/12
Distance: 🔧200m ⊗200m 🚰200m 🚌on the spot.
Remarks: Max. 24h, coins at tourist info.

| 🅂 | Jonzac 〰🏖☕🍽 | 20C6 |

Chez M. Alex Beurg, Chez Marchand. **GPS:** n45,44121 w0,40427.
3 ⛆free. **Location:** Simple, isolated, quiet.
Remarks: Max. 24h.

| 🅂 | La Brée-les-Bains | 20A5 |

Rue de la Baudette. **GPS:** n46,00810 w1,35764. ⬆.

50 ⛆free ⛲🔧Ch. **Location:** Rural, simple, quiet. **Surface:** asphalted. 🅿 01/01-31/12
Remarks: Coins at tourist info.

| 🅂 | La Couronne | 20D6 |

Rue du Champs de Foire. **GPS:** n45,60619 e0,10015. ⬆.

⛆free ⛲🔧Ch WC free.
Location: Simple, central. **Surface:** asphalted.

◨ 01/01-31/12 ◉ Wed-morning, Sa-morning market
Distance: 🛒on the spot ⊗on the spot 🍴on the spot 🚰on the spot.

🏕️ S	La Roche-Posay	21A3

Super U, ZA Les Chaumettes. **GPS:** n46,79361 e0,79750.

🚐free 🚰🔌 Ch free. **Surface:** asphalted. ◨ 01/01-31/12
Distance: 🛒1,5km.

🏕️ S	La Rochefoucauld 🌸 🏵️	20D6

Aire camping-car, Rue des Flots, Rivières. **GPS:** n45,74505 e0,38085.⬆️

+20 🚐 🚰🔌 Ch ✍️ WC ⬜.🍴🚐 📖 ◨ 01/01-31/12
Distance: 🛒1km.
Remarks: Beside river Tardoire, next to campsite, Château de La Rochefoucauld 1,3km.

🏕️	La Rochelle 🌸🏵️🍨🏖️	20B4

Esplanade des Parc, Chemin des Remparts. **GPS:** n46,16620 w1,1544.⬆️

24 🚐free. **Location:** Urban. **Surface:** asphalted. ◨ 01/01-31/12
Distance: 🛒250m ⊗100m 🍴250m 🚌50m.

🏕️ S	La Rochelle 🌸🏵️🍨🏖️	20B4

Vieux Port, Avenue Jean Moulin. **GPS:** n46,15250 w1,13944.⬆️

50 🚐€ 10,50/24h 🚰🔌 Ch. **Surface:** asphalted. ◨ 01/01-31/12
Distance: 🛒1,5km 🚌free.
Remarks: Pay at reception, shuttle bus to city centre.

🏕️	La Rochelle 🌸🏵️🍨🏖️	20B4

Quai du Lazaret. GPS: n46,14213 w1,16773.⬆️

40 🚐free. **Location:** Urban, simple. **Surface:** asphalted.
◨ 01/10-30-06

Tourist information La Rochelle:
Ⓜ La Maison Henri II, Rue de Augustins. Archeological museum. ◨ 15/5-30/9 Sa-Fr 10-19h Sa-Su 14-19h.
🐟 Aquarium, Port des Minimes. Sea aquarium. ◨ 01/07-31/08 9-23h, 01/09-30/06 10-19/20h.

🏕️ S	La-Mothe-St.Héray	20D4

Rue du Pont l'Abbé. **GPS:** n46,35971 w0,11775.⬆️

4 🚐free 🚰€1/50liter 🔌 Ch WC. **Surface:** gravel. ◨ 01/01-31/12
Distance: 🛒500m ⊗200m 🍴200m.

🏕️	Le Bois-Plage-en-Ré 🏖️	20A4

Parking Municipal, Avenue du Pas des Boeufs. **GPS:** n46,17708 w1,38613.⬆️
15 🚐free. **Location:** Simple. **Surface:** gravel/sand.
Distance: 🏖️150m.

Ⓒ S	Le Bois-Plage-en-Ré 🏖️	20A4

Aire Camping-Car Campéole, Avenue du Pas des Boeufs.
GPS: n46,17741 w1,38674.⬆️

35 🚐€ 8,60-€ 12,80 🚰€3/time 🔌 Ch ✍️€2/12h. 🍴
Location: Rural, simple. **Surface:** gravel/metalled. ◨ 01/01-31/12
Distance: 🏖️150m.
Remarks: Payment also possible at campsite.

🏕️ S	Le Château d'Oléron	20B5

Boulevard Philippe Daste. GPS: n45,89641 w1,20236.⬆️➡️

90 🚐€ 10 🚰🔌 Ch 📦 ✍️ WC ⬜included. 🍴 📖

FR

Location: Rural, comfortable. **Surface:** grassy.
Distance: ⚓ on the spot.
Remarks: Former campsite.

[S] **Le Grand Village Plage** ⚐ 20B5
Allée des Pins. **GPS:** n45,86222 w1,24111. ⬆️ ➡️

8 ⛺ € 6 ⛽ € 4/100liter 🔧 Ch 🚿 € 4. 🚐 **Location:** Rural, simple.
Surface: asphalted. 🚽 01/01-31/12
Remarks: 01/04-30/09 max. 24h.

[S] **Les Mathes/La Palmyre** ⚐⚐ 20B6
Parking du Corsaire, Avenue de l'Atlantique. **GPS:** n45,69153 w1,18906. ⬆️

90 ⛺ € 8/24h ⛽ € 4/100liter 🔧 Ch 🚽 € 2/1h 🚿 . **Surface:** asphalted.
🚽 01/01-31/12
Distance: 🏖️ 1km ⚓ 200m ⬅️ 200m.
Remarks: Coins at tourist info.

[S] **Les Mathes/La Palmyre** ⚐⚐ 20B6
Rue de la Garenne, Les Mathes. **GPS:** n45,71444 w1,1475. ⬆️
⛺ € 8 ⛽ € 4/100liter 🔧 Ch WC . 🚐 **Surface:** metalled. 🚽 01/01-31/12
Distance: ⚓ 400m.
Remarks: Coins at town hall Mo-Fri 9-18h and tourist info La Palmyre daily
9-19h in July/Aug.

[S] **Les Mathes/La Palmyre** ⚐⚐ 20B6
Boulevard de la Plage, La Palmyre. **GPS:** n45,68287 w1,17942.
⛺ € 8. 🚐 **Surface:** asphalted. 🚽 01/01-31/12 ⬤ 01/07-31/08
Distance: 🏖️ 1,2km ⚓ 100m ⬅️ 200m.

Tourist information Les Mathes/La Palmyre:
☺ Zoo de la Palmyre. Zoo, 1600 animals, 14Ha. 🚽 01/04-30/09 9-20.30h,
01/10-31/03 9-12h, 14-18h.

[S] **Les Portes-en-Ré** 20A4
Parking de la Patache, Route du Fier. **GPS:** n46,22925 w1,48315. ⬆️

10 ⛺ € 10/24h ⛽ 🔧 Ch WC free. 🚐 **Location:** Rural, simple.
Surface: metalled. 🚽 01/01-31/12
Distance: ⚓ on the spot ⬅️ on the spot 🍴 3,5km.
Remarks: Max. 24h, payment only with coins.

[S] **Lezay** 20D4
Rue de Gâte Bourse. **GPS:** n46,26500 w0,01139. ⬆️

15 ⛺ free ⛽ 🔧 Ch free. **Surface:** asphalted. 🚽 01/01-31/12
Remarks: Coins at tourist info.

[S] **Londigny** 20D5
Place de l'Eglise. **GPS:** n46,08333 e0,13472.

5 ⛺ free ⛽ 🔧 Ch 🚿 WC free. **Location:** Isolated, quiet. **Surface:** gravel.
🚽 01/01-31/12
Remarks: Max. 48h.

[S] **Loudun** 20D2
Place de la Porte Saint Nicolas. **GPS:** n47,01357 e0,07833. ⬆️
3 ⛺ free ⛽ 🔧 Ch. **Surface:** asphalted.
Distance: 🏖️ 500m ⬅️ 500m 🍴 500m.

[S] **Lussac-les-Châteaux** 21A4
Place l' Amitié entre les Peuples. **GPS:** n46,40250 e0,72583. ⬆️

20 ⛺ free ⛽ 🔧 Ch WC free. **Surface:** metalled.
🚽 01/01-31/12 ⬤ Fri
Distance: 🏖️ 200m ⬅️ 200m 🍴 400m.

Magné 🌊 20C4
Embarcadére Cardinaud, Avenue de la Repentie. **GPS:** n46,32130 w0,5803.

30 ⛺ free. **Surface:** grassy/gravel. 🚽 01/01-31/12
Distance: 🏖️ 900m ⬅️ on the spot 🍴 on the spot.

[S] **Magné** 🌊 20C4
Super U, Avenue du Marais Poitevin. **GPS:** n46,31632 w0,55656.
⛽ € 2 🔧 Ch 🚽 € 2. 🚽 01/01-31/12

[S] **Marennes** 20B5
1 Avenue William Bertrand. **GPS:** n45,82140 w1,13828. ⬆️ .

FR

5 🛏free. **Location:** Rural, simple. **Surface:** metalled.
⬛ 01/01-31/12
Distance: ⚓on the spot.

🛏🅂 **Mauzé-sur-le-Mignon** 20C4
Le Port, Rue du Port. **GPS:** n46,19989 w0,67952.⬆.

10 🛏free 🔧€4 🄲Ch 🚻 WC. **Location:** Rural. **Surface:** gravel.
⬛ 01/01-31/12
Distance: 🛒1km ⚓on the spot.
Remarks: Coins at campsite and shops.

🛏🅂 **Meschers-sur-Gironde** 20B6
Port de plaisance, Route des Salines. **GPS:** n45,55614 w0,9451.⬆.

10 🛏€7,50 🔧 🄲Ch 🛁 (4x)€1,50 💡€2/2 🔌. **Location:** Comfortable,
quiet. **Surface:** asphalted. ⬛ 01/01-31/12
Distance: 🛒1km ⚓100m 🚰1km.

🛏🅂 **Montguyon** 28C1
Rue de Vassiac. **GPS:** n45,21796 w0,18368.⬆.

15 🛏free 🔧 🄲Ch WC free. **Surface:** gravel. ⬛ 01/01-31/12
Distance: 🛒500m ⊗500m 🚰500m.

🛏🅂 **Montmorillon** 21A4
Rue Léon Dardant. **GPS:** n46,42326 e0,86788.⬆.
🛏free 🔧 🄲Ch. **Location:** Urban, simple, central. **Surface:** asphalted.
⬛ 01/01-31/12
Distance: 🛒500m ⊗500m 🚰2km.
Remarks: Along the Gartempe river.

🏔🅂 **Montmorillon** 21A4
Leclerc, 2, Avenue de Provence. **GPS:** n46,41903 e0,85358.⬆.
10 🛏free 🔧 🄲Ch free. **Surface:** asphalted. ⬛ 01/01-31/12
Distance: 🚰on the spot.
Remarks: Parking supermarket.

⬆🅂 **Mortagne-sur-Gironde** 20B6
Le Port de Mortagne, Quai des Pêcheurs. **GPS:** n45,47472 w0,79778.⬆.

50 🛏€7,50 🔧 🄲Ch 🛁included WC 🔌. 🛒 **Surface:** grassy.
⬛ 01/01-31/12
Distance: 🛒750m ⊗200m 🚰750m.
Remarks: In front of Capitainerie.

🛏🅂 **Moulismes** 🌳 21A4
RN147. **GPS:** n46,33306 e0,81000.⬆.

50 🛏free 🔧€3 🄲Ch 🚻 WC. **Surface:** grassy/metalled. ⬛ 01/01-31/12
Distance: ⚓on the spot 🛍on the spot.
Remarks: At small lake (plan d'eau).

🛏🅂 **Nersac** 🌿 20D6
Rue d'Epagnac. **GPS:** n45,62599 e0,05015.⬆➡.

7 🛏free 🔧 🄲Ch 🛁(4x)free. **Surface:** asphalted. ⬛ 01/01-31/12
Distance: 🛒on the spot ⊗100m 🚰100m 🚌100m.
Remarks: Max. 48h.

🛏🅂 **Nieuil-l'Espoir** 🌿 21A4
Allée du champ de foire. **GPS:** n46,48505 e0,45417.⬆➡.

10 🛏free 🔧€2 🄲Ch 🚻€2. **Surface:** grassy/metalled. ⬛ 01/01-31/12
Distance: 🛒200m 🚰150m.

FR

Remarks: At Base de Loisirs, coins at the shops.

Nieulle-sur-Seudre 20B5

Place de la Mairie. **GPS:** n45,75275 w1,00209.⬆.

4 ⬛free ⚡€4 🚰 Ch 📷. **Location:** Simple, central. **Surface:** asphalted.
◻ 01/01-31/12
Distance: on the spot.

Niort 20C4

Aire des camping-cars du Pré Leroy, Rue de Bessac. **GPS:** n46,32917 w0,46444. ⬆➡.

14 ⬛€7,70 ⚡🚰 Ch📷 included. **Location:** Urban. **Surface:** metalled.
◻ 01/01-31/12
Distance: 1,2km 150m 300m.
Tourist information Niort:
🅿 ◻ Tue, Sa.
🌿 Marais Poitevin. Swamp area, possibility of making boat trips.

Oriolles 28C1

Ferme Auberge chez Baron, D131. **GPS:** n45,36180 w0,11784.⬆.

8 ⬛€9,10, guests free ⚡🚰 Ch included €1,50 €3.
◻ 01/07-31/08

Pamproux 20D4

Rue de la Cueille. **GPS:** n46,39625 w0,05874.⬆.

3 ⬛free ⚡€2/20minutes 🚰Ch 📷€2/20minutes. **Surface:** asphalted.
◻ 01/01-31/12
Distance: 100m 5,2km 100m.

Parthenay 20C3

Aire base de loisirs Bois Vert, Rue de Boisseau 14. **GPS:** n46,64088 w0,26689. ⬆➡.

10 ⬛€6, 1/7-31/8 €8, 2 pers.incl ⚡🚰 Ch included €3 €4/1,50 €7/day. **Surface:** gravel.
◻ 22/03-31/10
Distance: 2,5km on the spot nearby 2km 100m.
Remarks: Along the Thouet river, car rental €5/day + €0,19/km.

Pons 20C6

Avenue du Poitou. **GPS:** n45,57765 w0,55536.⬆.
4 ⬛free ⚡🚰 Ch 📷€6. **Surface:** asphalted.

Port-des-Barques 20B5

Pré des Mays, Avenue des Sports. **GPS:** n45,94722 w1,09.⬆➡.

30 ⬛€6,20/24h ⚡€2/10minutes 🚰Chfree €2/55minutes.
Location: Rural, simple. **Surface:** metalled. ◻ 15/03-15/11
Remarks: In front of stadium.

Rivedoux-Plage 20B4

125, Av Gustave Perreau. **GPS:** n46,15889 w1,27139.⬆.

17 ⬛€14-€17 ⚡€4 🚰 Ch. **Location:** Urban, simple. **Surface:** asphalted.
◻ 01/01-31/12
Distance: 100m Plage Nord.
Remarks: Next to campsite Le Platin, to be paid at campsite.

Rochefort 20B5

Rue de la Fosse aux Mâts. **GPS:** n45,92735 w0,95467.⬆➡.

25 🛏 € 6/24h ⛽ 🔌 Ch included. 🚿 ♻ **Location:** Urban, simple.
Surface: asphalted. ⭕ 01/01-31/112

Rochefort 20B5
Avenue Marcel Dassault. **GPS:** n45,94661 w0,96002. ⬆️

15 🛏 € 6. 🚿 ♻ **Location:** Urban, simple. **Surface:** asphalted.
⭕ 01/01-31/12
Distance: 🛒1km.

Rochefort 20B5
Pont Transbordeur, Chemin de Charente. **GPS:** n45,91792 w0,96388. ⬆️

5 🛏 free. **Location:** Urban, simple. **Surface:** grassy/gravel.
⭕ 01/01-31/12

Rochefort 20B5
Rue de la Vieille Forme. **GPS:** n45,94448 w0,95554. ⬆️
10 🛏 € 6. 🚿 ♻ **Location:** Simple. **Surface:** gravel.
Remarks: Near marina.

S **Rochefort** 20B5
Port de Plaisance, Quai Lemoigne de Sérigny. **GPS:** n45,94444 w0,95556. ⬆️
⛽ 🔌 Ch free.
⭕ 01/01-31/12

Tourist information Rochefort:
👁 Corderie Royale. Old royal rope-walk.
⛺ ⭕ Tue, Thu, Sa.

S **Rouillac** 20D5
Super U, Rue de Genac. **GPS:** n45,77650 w0,06133. ⬆️➡️

8 🛏 free ⛽€3 🔌 Ch 🚽. **Surface:** gravel. ⭕ 01/01-31/12
Distance: 🛒500m ⊗500m 🍴50m.
Remarks: Coins available at supermarket.

S **Roumazières-Loubert** 21A5
Aire de Détente de Ronmatiéres, RN141. **GPS:** n45,88275 e0,57287. ⬆️➡️

3 🛏 free ⛽ 🔌 Ch ♻ WC free. **Surface:** asphalted. ⭕ 01/01-31/12
Distance: 🛒500m ⊗100m 🍴300m.

S **Ruffec** 20D5
SARL Remy Frères Camping-Cars, D26. **GPS:** n46,03316 e0,18366.

10 🛏 free ⛽ 🔌 Ch free. **Surface:** asphalted.
Distance: 🛒1km.
Remarks: At motorhome dealer.

S **Saint Césaire** 20C5
Parking Paléosite, Rue de Groies. **GPS:** n45,75370 w0,50744. ⬆️➡️
20 🛏 free ⛽ 🔌 Ch free. **Surface:** asphalted/metalled. ⭕ 01/01-31/12
Distance: 🛒on the spot ⊗500m 🍴100m.

Tourist information Saint Césaire:
👁 Paléosite, Route de la Montée Verte. Interactive park, in the footsteps of the
Neanderthals. ⭕ 10.30-18.30, Jul-Aug 10-20 ⭕ January.

S **Saint Laurant de la Prée** 20B5
La Cabane, Route de l'Océan. **GPS:** n45,99043 w1,04942. ⬆️

10 🛏 € 7 ⛽ 🔌 Ch included. **Location:** Rural, simple. **Surface:** gravel.
⭕ 01/01-31/12

S **Saint-Martin-de-Ré** 20A4
Rue de Rempart. **GPS:** n46,19925 w1,36514. ⬆️➡️

17 🛏 € 11 ⛽ 🔌 Ch included. 🚿 ♻ **Location:** Rural. **Surface:** gravel.
⭕ 01/01-31/12
Distance: 🛒500m ⛰700m ⊗500m 🍴500m.
Remarks: 01/04-30/09 max. 72h.

FR

Saint-Pierre-d'Oléron 20A5
Avenue des Pins, La Cotinière. **GPS:** n45,92393 w1,3427. ⬆️.

10 🛏️ € 9 🚰 €4/time 🔧 Ch.
Location: Rural, simple. **Surface:** grassy/gravel.
Remarks: In front of campsite municipal, pay at reception.

Saintes 20C6
Aire camping-cars, Avenue de Saintonge. **GPS:** n45,73973 w0,62779. ⬆️.
12 🛏️ € 5 🚰 €5 🔧 Ch 🔋 ⛽ **Location:** Urban. **Surface:** asphalted.
⬛ 01/01-31/12
Distance: 🛒 1km ⚓ Leclerc 100m.
Remarks: Max. 7 days.

Tourist information Saintes:
👁️ Les Arènes. Roman anfiteatro.
🎪 Place 11 November. ⬛ Tue + Fri morning.
🎪 Grande Foire. Large regional market. ⬛ 1st Mon of the month.

Saujon 20B6
Route de Ecluses. **GPS:** n45,67503 w0,932. ⬆️.

10 🛏️ € 4 🚰 €2/100liter 🔧 Ch 🔋 €2/1h 🗑️. **Surface:** asphalted.
⬛ 01/01-31/12
Distance: 🛒 900m.
Remarks: Max. 6 days.

Sauzé-Vaussais 20D5
Place des Halles. **GPS:** n46,13540 e0,10660.

🛏️free 🚰 🔧 Ch 🔋 WC free. **Surface:** asphalted.
⬛ 01/01-31/12 💧 water: Nov-March
Distance: 🛒 on the spot ⊗ on the spot ⚓ on the spot.

Segonzac 20C6
Place Blanche. **GPS:** n45,61456 w0,22113. ⬆️➡️.

4 🛏️free 🚰 🔧 Ch 🧹 (4x) WC free. **Surface:** gravel. ⬛ 01/01-31/12
Distance: 🛒 500m, Cognac 8km ⊗500m ⚓500m.

Segonzac 20C6
Cognac Forgeron, Chez Richon. **GPS:** n45,62545 w0,17514. ⬆️.
20 🛏️free 🚰 🔧 Ch 🧹. **Location:** Rural. **Surface:** grassy.
⬛ 01/01-31/12
Distance: 🛒 500m.

Soubise 20B5
Aire camping-car, Le Port/rue Colbert. **GPS:** n45,92833 w1,00666. ⬆️.

17 🛏️ € 7 🚰 🔧 Ch 🧹 WC ⬜ included. **Location:** Rural, simple.
Surface: grassy/metalled. ⬛ 01/01-31/12
Distance: 🛒 on the spot ⊗50m.
Remarks: Along river, max. 24h, incl. showers and warm water.

St.Agnant 20B5
Place de Verdun. **GPS:** n45,86635 w0,9641. ⬆️.

10 🛏️free 🚰 🔧 Ch free. **Location:** Rural, simple. **Surface:** asphalted.
⬛ 01/01-31/12
Remarks: Next to town hall.

St.Amand-sur-Sèvre 20B3
Boulevard de Maumusson. **GPS:** n46,86903 w0,8. ⬆️.
5 🛏️free 🚰 🔧 Ch free. **Location:** Simple, quiet. **Surface:** grassy.
⬛ 01/01-31/12
Distance: 🛒 500m ⊗500m ⚓500m.

St.Amand-sur-Sèvre 20B3
Le Moulin Chaligny. **GPS:** n46,88493 w0,82342. ⬆️.
7 🛏️ € 10 🚰 🔧 Ch 🧹 WC included. **Location:** Rural, isolated, quiet.
Surface: grassy. ⬛ 01/01-31/12
Distance: 🛒 3km ⊗on the spot ⚓3km.

St.Clément-des-Baleines 20A4
Rue de la Forêt. **GPS:** n46,22756 w1,54644. ⬆️.

30 🛏 € 11/night, € 18/2 nights ⚓stay 🗑 Ch ⊞ € 4/1h ✦ free. 🚐
Location: Rural, simple. **Surface:** metalled. ⬛ 01/01-31/12
Distance: ⛱250m 🚻500m.
Remarks: Next to campsite, payment only with coins.

🏕 S | **St.Denis-d'Oléron** | 20A5
Aire du Moulin, Route des Huttes. **GPS:** n46,02750 w1,38306. ⬆

150 🛏 € 9 ⚓ 🗑 Ch ✦ WC 🗑 included 🃏. **Location:** Rural, simple.
Surface: grassy. ⬛ 01/01-31/12
Distance: 🚶1km.
Remarks: Max. 4 nights.

🏕 S | **St.Génis-de-Saintonge** | 20C6
Place Alcide Beauvais, N137. **GPS:** n45,47985 w0,56844. ⬆ ➡

6 🛏 free ⚓ 🗑 Ch ✦ (3x) WC 🗑 free. **Surface:** asphalted.
⬛ 01/01-31/12
Distance: 🚶200m ⛱300m 🚻300m.
Remarks: Max. 48h.

🏕 S | **St.Génis-de-Saintonge** | 20C6
Rue Fanny. **GPS:** n45,48330 w0,56569. ⬆
20 🛏 € 6 ⚓ 🗑 Ch ⊞ included. **Surface:** asphalted. ⬛ 01/01-31/12
Distance: 🚶on the spot.
Remarks: Behind cinema, max. 72h.

🏕 S | **St.Germain-de-Marencennes** | 20B5
Rue du Moulin Neuf. **GPS:** n46,07882 w0,78283. ⬆
10 🛏 € 6 ⚓ 🗑 Ch ⊞ WC included. 🚐 **Location:** Simple, quiet.
Surface: asphalted. ⬛ 15/03-15/11
Distance: 🚶500m.

🏕 | **St.Hilaire-la-Palud** | 20C4
Place de la Marie. **GPS:** n46,26444 w0,71306. ⬆ .

10 🛏 free. **Surface:** asphalted. ⬛ 01/01-31/12
Distance: 🚶on the spot ⊗on the spot 🚻on the spot.
Remarks: Parking in front of town hall, max. 2 nights.

🏕 S | **St.Jean-d'Angély** | 20C5
Base de Plein Air, Avenue de Marennes, D18. **GPS:** n45,94537 w0,53735. ⬆

10 🛏 free ⚓ 🗑 Ch free. **Surface:** gravel. ⬛ 01/01-31/12
Distance: 🚶1km ⛱100m 🍽100m ⊗200m 🚻1km.
Remarks: Max. 2 nights.

🏕 S | **St.Pochaire** | 20B5
Place du Champ de Foire. **GPS:** n45,82063 w0,78215. ⬆

10 🛏 free ⚓ 🗑 Ch WC free. **Surface:** gravel. ⬛ 01/01-31/12
Distance: 🚶400m ⛱200m.
Remarks: Max. 48h.

🏕 S | **St.Trojan-les-Bains** | 20B5
Parking de la Liberté, Rue Marie Curie. **GPS:** n45,84371 w1,20899. ⬆

9 🛏 free ⚓ € 4. **Location:** Urban, simple. **Surface:** asphalted.
⬛ 01/01-31/12
Distance: 🚶200m ⊗on the spot.
Remarks: Max. 72h.

🏕 | **St.Trojan-les-Bains** | 20B5
Parking Patoizeau, Boulevard de la plage. **GPS:** n45,84100 w1,20491.

FR

10 ⬛free. **Location:** Rural, simple. **Surface:** asphalted. ⬛ 01/01-31/12
Distance: 600m 100m.
Remarks: In front of fire-station, max. 72h.

Tourist information St.Trojan-les-Bains:
ℹ️ Bureau Municipal de Tourisme, Carrefour du Port, www.st-trojan-les-bains.fr. Seaside resort on the island of Oléron, well-known for the mimosa and oyster culture.
🛒 place de Filles de la Sagesse. Food and drugs market. ⬛ Thu + Sa-morning, summer daily.
🛒 Marche Nocturne, rue de la République. Evening market. ⬛ Thu from 17h.

△S | St.Yrieix-sur-Charente | 20D6
Camping du Plan d'eau, Rue du Plan d'Eau, Impasse des Ooyères.
GPS: n45,69176 e0,14517. ⬆️➡️.

14 ⬛ € 7,20, Jul/Aug € 9,25 Chfree €3,65. **Location:** Comfortable, luxurious. **Surface:** asphalted. ⬛ 01/04-31/10
Distance: 2km 1km 1km 1km 3km 1km.

♿S | Thouars | 20D2
Rue Felix Gellusseau. **GPS:** n46,97614 w0,21151. ⬆️➡️.

⬛free Ch WC free. **Surface:** sand. ⬛ 01/01-31/12
Distance: 100m 100m 100m.

Tourist information Thouars:
🛒 ⬛ Tue, Fri.

♿S | Thurageau | 20D3
Fam. Turpeau, Agressais. **GPS:** n46,78388 e0,25644. ⬆️.

5 ⬛free Chfree. **Location:** Rural. **Surface:** gravel.
⬛ 01/01-31/12
Distance: 2,5km.
Remarks: Goat farm, farm products.

♿S | Tonnay-Charente | 20B5
Quai des Capucins. **GPS:** n45,93921 w0,88171. ➡️.

15 ⬛free Chfree. **Location:** Urban, simple. **Surface:** gravel.
⬛ 01/01-31/12
Distance: 1km 500m.

♿S | Vasles | 20D3
Mouton Village, Rue de la Cité. **GPS:** n46,57329 w0,02309. ⬆️➡️.

10 ⬛free Ch WC free. **Location:** Simple, quiet. **Surface:** gravel.
⬛ 01/01-31/12
Distance: 400m 400m.

♿S | Vicq-sur-Gartempe | 21A3
25, Route de la Roche Posay. **GPS:** n46,72414 e0,86189. ⬆️.

10 ⬛free Ch WC free. **Surface:** gravel. ⬛ 01/01-31/12
Distance: 500m.

Limousin

♿S | Allassac | 29A1
Avenue du Saillant. **GPS:** n45,25897 e1,47358. ⬆️.

4 ⬛free Ch (2x)free. **Surface:** gravel/sand. ⬛ 01/01-31/12
Distance: 500m 5km 500m 500m.
Remarks: Parking station.

Aubusson 21C5

Parking Champ de Foire, Rue des Fusilles, D988. **GPS**: n45,95694 e2,17528.

10 free Ch free WC. **Surface**: asphalted. 01/01-31/12
Distance: 500m 500m 500m.

Auriat 21C5

Etang d'Auriat. GPS: n45,87790 e1,64277.
free Ch free. **Location:** Rural, simple, isolated, quiet.
Surface: metalled. 01/01-31/12
Distance: on the spot on the spot.
Remarks: At small lake.

Ayen 29A1

Route de la Noix, Ayen Bas. **GPS**: n45,24964 e1,32343.

20 free Ch free. **Surface:** grassy/gravel. 01/01-31/12
Distance: 300m.
Remarks: Nearby D39, campsite and sports grounds.

Beaumont du Lac 21C6

GPS: n45,78640 e1,87077.

20 free. **Surface:** gravel. 01/01-31/12
Distance: 5km on the spot on the spot 100m.
Remarks: At lake Vassivière.

Bellac 21B5

Aire d'accueil camping-car rives du Vincou, Rue des Tanneries.
GPS: n46,11513 e1,05242.
3 free Ch free. **Surface:** asphalted. 01/01-31/12
Distance: 1km.
Remarks: Service 100m.

Bellac 21B5

Le Champ de foire, Rue des Doctrinaires. **GPS**: n46,12085 e1,05018.
free. **Surface:** asphalted.
Distance: on the spot on the spot on the spot.
Remarks: >3,5t not allowed.

Bellac 21B5

Parking de la Mairie, Place de la République. **GPS**: n46,12155 e1,04604.
4 free. **Surface:** asphalted. 01/01-31/12
Distance: 300m.

Bessines-sur-Gartempe 21B5

Rue d'Ingolsheim. **GPS**: n46,10979 e1,37008.

10 free €2 Ch €2. **Surface:** asphalted. 01/01-31/12
Distance: on the spot 900m 100m.

Bort-les-Orgues 29B1

Rue de la Fontaine Grande. **GPS**: n45,39913 e2,49710.

10 free Ch free. **Surface:** asphalted. 01/01-31/12
Distance: 200m river 200m 200m.

Bosmoreau-les-Mines 21C5

Le bourg. **GPS**: n46,00068 e1,75882.
3 free Ch free. **Location:** Rural. **Surface:** gravel.
01/01-31/12
Distance: 500m.

Bourganeuf 21C5

Place de l'Etang, Avenue du Dr Butaud. **GPS**: n45,95444 e1,75750.

10 free Ch free. **Surface:** gravel.
01/01-31/12 tue-evening, wed-morning (market)
Distance: on the spot on the spot on the spot.
Remarks: Max. 48h.

Bujaleuf 21B6

Route du Champ de Foire. **GPS**: n45,79747 e1,63141.

5 free Ch free. **Surface:** gravel. 01/01-31/12
Distance: 500m 500m.
Remarks: Max. 24h.

FR

🚐Ⓢ **Bussière-Poitevine** 21A4

Croix de l'Hosanne, Rue du Quatriéme Zouave. **GPS**: n46,23670 e0,90173.
🚿➡️🗑️Ch WC. **Surface**: gravel. ⬛ 01/01-31/12
Distance: 🚶450m.
Remarks: Coins at the shops.

🚐Ⓢ **Chalus** 21A6

Aire des Energies, Avenue Jean Jaurès. **GPS**: n45,66095 e0,98798.⬆️
🚿free ➡️€2🗑️Ch ⬛€2. **Surface**: asphalted.
Distance: 🚶1,2km 🛒on the spot.
Remarks: Behind petrol station.

🚐Ⓢ **Chamberet** 21C6

Route de St Dulcet. **GPS**: n45,57961 e1,72051.⬆️
6 🚿free ➡️🗑️Ch 🔌free. **Surface**: gravel. ⬛ 01/01-31/12
Distance: 🚶900m.
Remarks: Next to football ground.

🚐Ⓢ **Chambon-sur-Voueize** 〰️🏛️🅿️ 21D5

Rue du Stade. **GPS**: n46,18579 e2,43426.⬆️➡️

4 🚿free ➡️€2 🗑️Ch ⬛€2. **Surface**: asphalted.
⬛ 01/01-31/12 🔵 service 01/11-31/03
Distance: 🚶500m ⊗500m 🛒200m.
Remarks: Near camping municipal.

🚐Ⓢ **Châtelus-le-Marcheix** 🏛️🅿️ 21B5

Rue du Tursaud. **GPS**: n45,99894 e1,60339.⬆️➡️

8 🚿free ➡️€2 🗑️Ch ⬛€2. **Surface**: asphalted. ⬛ 01/01-31/12
Distance: 🚶300m ⊗300m 🛒300m.
Remarks: Next to camping municipal.

🚐Ⓢ **Chénérailles** 21C5

Route d'Aubusson, lotissement Marlaud, D990. **GPS**: n46,11058 e2,17753.⬆️➡️

5 🚿free ➡️€2 🗑️Ch ⬛€2. **Surface**: asphalted. ⬛ 01/01-31/12
Distance: 🚶200m ⊗50m.
Remarks: Coins available at restaurant le Coq d'Or (50m).

🚐Ⓢ **Collonges-la-Rouge** 〰️🏛️🅿️ 29A1

Parking le Marchadial. **GPS**: n45,05833 e1,65889.⬆️➡️

20 🚿€5/24h ➡️🗑️Ch 🔌WC included. **Surface**: gravel.
⬛ 01/01-31/12
Distance: 🚶500m ⊗500m 🛒500m.

🚐Ⓢ **Concèze** 🅿️ 29A1

D56E. **GPS**: n45,35472 e1,34583.⬆️➡️

3 🚿free ➡️🗑️Chfree. **Surface**: gravel. ⬛ 01/01-31/12
Distance: 🚶on the spot.

🚐Ⓢ **Cressat** 21C5

D990, rue de Laprade. **GPS**: n46,13956 e2,11015.⬆️➡️

5 🚿free ➡️€3 🗑️Ch ⬛€3. **Surface**: asphalted.
⬛ 01/01-31/12
Distance: 🚶100m 🛒500m.
Remarks: At fish lake, coins at superette 'la Montagne' (500m) and town hall.

🚐Ⓢ **Cussac** 21A6

Jardin de la Palène, Rue du 8 Mai 1945. **GPS**: n45,70519 e0,84936.⬆️
4 🚿➡️🗑️Ch 🔌. **Surface**: grassy/gravel. ⬛ 01/04-31/10
Distance: 🚶200m ⊗200m 🛒100m.
Remarks: Coins at town hall, bar and restaurant.

🚐Ⓢ **Dampniat** 29A1

Stade, Le Mas. **GPS**: n45,16262 e1,63728.⬆️
🚿free ➡️€2/10minutes 🗑️Ch 🔌€2/55minutes. **Location**: Rural, simple.
Surface: gravel.
Distance: 🚶850m.
Remarks: At sports centre.

🚐Ⓢ **Donzenac** 29A1

Village de Vacance La Rivière, Rue de la Riviere. **GPS**: n45,21897 e1,51829.⬆️➡️

FR

10 🛏free ⊞ 🔌 Ch ✈ €4/night, peak season WC free. **Surface:** gravel. ◻ 01/01-31/12
Distance: 💧4km ✈ 1,3km ⊗4m 🛒4km.
Remarks: Max. 48h.

🅢🅢 **Egletons** 29A1
Parking Espace Ventadour, Rue Henri Dignac. **GPS:** n45,40406 e2,04791. ⬆.

20 🛏free ⊞ 🔌 Ch free. **Surface:** gravel. ◻ 01/01-31/12 ◉ Service: winter
Distance: 💧300m ✈ 3,5km ⊗300m 🛒300m.

🅢🅢 **Felletin** 21C5
Parking Lagrange, Avenue Joffre. **GPS:** n45,88308 e2,17667. ⬆➡.

10 🛏free ⊞ 🔌 Ch WC free. **Surface:** gravel. ◻ 01/01-31/12
Distance: 💧on the spot.

🅢🅢 **Gouzon** 🔆 21D5
Place du champ de foire, Rue d'Alcantera. **GPS:** n46,19139 e2,24028. ⬆➡.

6 🛏free ⊞ 🔌 Ch free. **Surface:** sand. ◻ 01/01-31/12
Distance: 💧300m ⊗300m 🛒300m.

🅢🅢 **Jarnages** 21C5
Route des Promenctes, D65. **GPS:** n46,18417 e2,08098. ⬆➡.

6 🛏free ⊞ €2 🔌 Ch ⊞ €2. **Surface:** asphalted. ◻ 01/01-31/12
Distance: 💧500m ✈ 500m 🛒500m.
Remarks: At tennis-courts.

🅢🅢 **Javerdat** 21A5
Le Bourg. **GPS:** n45,95249 e0,98582. ⬆.

4 🛏free ⊞ €2 🔌 Ch ⊞ €2 WC. **Surface:** gravel. ◻ 01/01-31/12
Distance: ⊗100m.
Remarks: Coins at Auberge Limousine (100m).

🅢🅢 **La Courtine** 21D6
Rue Impasse J Bayle. **GPS:** n45,70591 e2,25890. ⬆.
10 🛏free ⊞ 🔌 Ch ⊞. **Surface:** asphalted. ◻ 01/01-31/12
Distance: 💧1km ⛰100m.

🅢🅢 **Les Salles-Lavaugyon** 21A6
Le Tilleul, Route de St Mathieu. **GPS:** n45,73998 e0,70100. ⬆➡.

6 🛏€4 ⊞ 🔌 ✈ included. **Surface:** grassy. ◻ 01/01-31/12

🅒🅢 **Liginiac** 29B1
Le Maury-Liginiac. **GPS:** n45,39158 e2,30387. ➡.

🛏free ⊞ 🔌 Ch free. **Surface:** gravel. ◻ 01/01-31/12
Distance: 💧Liginiac 4,5km ⛰Sandy beach ⊗on the spot.
Remarks: At lake Neuvic. Follow restaurant Le Maury.

🅢🅢 **Meuzac** 21B6
Étang de la Roche, D243. **GPS:** n45,54933 e1,43869. ⬆➡.

FR

15 🛏free 🚰 ⬛Ch WC free. **Location:** Rural. **Surface:** gravel.
🔲 01/01-31/12
Distance: 🚶100m 🚲5km 🏊on the spot ⊗on the spot 🍴100m.

20 🛏€5 🚰€2/50liter ⬛Ch 🔌included WC ⬛€2 🗑.🛒 🧺
Surface: grassy/metalled. 🔲 01/01-31/12
Distance: 🚶500m 🏪500m.
Remarks: Max. 7 days, baker on site: Tue-Sa, free electricity 72h, swimming pool 200m, entrance code available at tourist info.

🛁S | **Meymac** | 21C6
Parking Lac de Sechemailles, Le Montbazet. **GPS:** n45,52500 e2,12761. ⬆➡

🛁S | **Oradour-sur-Glane** | 21A5
Aire camping-car, Rue du Stade. **GPS:** n45,93570 e1,02471. ⬆

20 🛏free 🚰€2,60 ⬛Ch 🚽€2,60. **Surface:** gravel. 🔲 01/01-31/12
Distance: 🚶2km 🏊500m ⊗500m.
Remarks: Coins available at Office du Tourisme and bar.

©S | **Meymac** | 21C6
Boulevard de la Garenne. **GPS:** n45,53973 e2,15381. ⬆
30 🛏free 🚰€2 ⬛Ch 🔌€2. **Surface:** gravel. 🔲 20/04-02/11
Remarks: Coins at campsite and tourist info.

🛁S | **Montboucher** | 21C5
GPS: n45,95152 e1,68069. ⬆➡

20 🛏free 🚰€2 ⬛Ch 🚽€2 WC. **Surface:** grassy/metalled.
🔲 01/01-31/12
Distance: 🍴nearby.
Remarks: Playground.

Tourist information Oradour-sur-Glane:
ℹ️ Office de Tourisme, Place du Champ de Foire. Martyre town, was attacked by 200 SS-soldiers on 10 June 1944. They assassinated the population. Afterwards the village was burned down. In commemoration a wall was built round the the city after the war. 🎫 free.

🛁S | **Pageas** | 21A6
GPS: n45,67758 e1,00224. ⬆➡

5 🛏free 🚰 ⬛Ch WC free. **Surface:** grassy/gravel. 🔲 01/01-31/12

🛁S | **Nieul** | 21B5
19 Mars 1962, D28. **GPS:** n45,92564 e1,17236. ⬆

20 🛏free 🚰€3 ⬛Ch 🚽 WC. **Surface:** grassy/gravel. 🔲 01/01-31/12
Distance: 🚶100m 🏊on the spot ⊗on the spot 🍴on the spot.
Remarks: Near N21.

🛁S | **Peyrat-le-Château** | 21C6
Auphelle. **GPS:** n45,80750 e1,84111. ⬆➡

15 🛏free 🚰 ⬛Ch WC free. **Surface:** asphalted. 🔲 01/04-31/10
Distance: 🚶400m ⊗400m 🍴400m.

🛁S | **Objat** | 29A1
Parc Aquatique Espace Loisirs, Avenue Jules Ferry. **GPS:** n45,27110 e1,41147. ⬆➡

100 🛏€4,20, Jul/Aug €5,20 🚰€2,50/100liter 🔌€6,80/4h. **Surface:** grassy.
🔲 12/04-07/11

FR

Distance: 🏊Lac de Vassivière 300m.
Remarks: In front of campsite, bread-service in summer period.

🏕️ⓢ **Peyrat-le-Château** 21C6
Parking Pré de l'Age. GPS: n45,81468 e1,77085.⬆️

20 🏕️free 🚰€2 🗑️ Ch. **Surface:** gravel. 🅾️ 01/04-31/10
Distance: 🚿on the spot 🚤on the spot 🎿 Terra Aventura.
Remarks: Coins at tourist info and town hall.

Tourist information Peyrat-le-Château:
ℹ️ Office de Tourisme, 1, Rue du Lac, www.peyrat-tourisme.com. Tourist town close water sports lake, Lac de Vassivière, marked cycle and hiking routes. 🅾️ Sa-Su 15-17h. ⓣ free.

🏕️ⓢ **Sadroc** 29A1
Place du Château. **GPS:** n45,28325 e1,54854.⬆️➡️

6 🏕️free 🚰 🗑️ Ch 🔌 free. **Surface:** asphalted. 🅾️ 01/01-31/12
Distance: 🚿on the spot 🚲5,2km 🛒50m.
Remarks: Max. 24h.

🏕️ⓢ **Saint-Privat** 29B1
Rue des Chanaux. **GPS:** n45,14544 e2,09891.⬆️
10 🏕️ 🚰€2 🗑️ Ch. **Surface:** grassy/metalled. 🅾️ 01/01-31/12
Distance: 🚿200m 🛒200m.

🏕️ⓢ **Servières-le-Château** 29A1
Centre touristique du lac de Feyt. GPS: n45,14415 e2,03665.⬆️➡️

15 🏕️free, 29/03-27/09 € 5 🚰€2/100liter 🗑️ Ch 🔌€2/1h. **Location:** Rural, isolated, quiet. **Surface:** grassy/metalled. 🅾️ 01/01-31/12
Distance: 🏊Sandy beach 🚻on the spot.

🏕️ⓢ **Soubrebost** 21C5
La Martinèche, D13. **GPS:** n45,98489 e1,85317.⬆️
3 🏕️free 🚰 Ch free. **Location:** Isolated, quiet. **Surface:** asphalted.
🅾️ 01/01-31/12

🏕️ⓢ **St.Junien-la-Bregère** 21C5
Rue du Chevalier de Châteauneuf. **GPS:** n45,88236 e1,75282.⬆️

3 🏕️free 🚰 🗑️ Ch free. **Surface:** asphalted. 🅾️ 01/01-31/12

🏕️ⓢ **St.Laurent** 21C5
Rue des Cerisiers. **GPS:** n46,16639 e1,96167.⬆️➡️

4 🏕️free 🚰 🗑️ Ch 🔌 free. **Surface:** metalled. 🅾️ 01/01-31/12
Distance: 🚿on the spot 🚻on the spot.

🏕️ⓢ **St.Laurent-sur-Gorre** 21A6
Les Chênes, Allée des Primevères. **GPS:** n45,76528 e0,95639.⬆️➡️

20 🏕️€6 🚰 🗑️ Ch 🔌€2/24h WC 🗑️ 📶 included. **Surface:** grassy.
🅾️ 01/01-31/12
Distance: 🚿300m 🚲20m 🛒20m 🚻300m 🛒300m.
Remarks: Motorhome washing place.

🏕️ⓢ **St.Merd-les-Oussines** 21C6
D109 > Tarnac. **GPS:** n45,63500 e2,03719.⬆️

6 🏕️free 🚰€2 🗑️ Ch. **Location:** Rural, simple, isolated, quiet.
Surface: grassy/gravel. 🅾️ 01/01-31/12
Distance: 🚿400m.
Remarks: Coins at Auberge du Mont-Chauvet.

🏕️ⓢ **St.Yrieix-la-Perche** 🚴 ⛵ 21B6
Parking J.P Fabrègue, Avenue de Lattre de Tassigny, D901.
GPS: n45,51271 e1,20646.⬆️

5 ⏚free ⚡€3,50 🔧Ch. **Surface:** asphalted. 🅾 01/01-31/12
Distance: 🚶300m ⊗300m 🛒300m.
Remarks: Coins at tourist info, bar and maison de la presse.

St.Yrieix-la-Perche 21B6
Ferme du Poumier, Lieu-dit Poumier, Marcognac. **GPS:** n45,52065 e1,26853.⬆
➡.

4 ⏚€3 ⚡€3 🔧Ch 🚲. **Location:** Rural, isolated, quiet. **Surface:** gravel.
🅾 01/01-31/12
Distance: 🚶St.Yrieix 5km.

Treignac 21C6
Les rivières, Route du lac, D940. **GPS:** n45,54341 e1,79950.⬆➡.

25 ⏚free ⚡🔧Ch WC free. **Surface:** grassy/gravel. 🅾 01/04-31/10
🔘 service: frost.
Distance: 🚶2km ∠on the spot.
Remarks: Along river.

Tourist information Treignac:
ℹ Office de Tourisme, 1, Place de la République. Free itinerary city tour along all
curiosities, available at OT.

Turenne 29A1
Aire camping-cars, Avenue du Sénateur Labrousse, D8. **GPS:** n45,05391 e1,57988.
⬆➡.

10 ⏚free ⚡€2 🔧Ch 🚽€2 WC. **Surface:** gravel. 🅾 01/01-31/12
Distance: 🚶on the spot ⊗100m 🛒100m.
Remarks: Behind tourist info, coins at tourist info and supermarket, narrow road,
not suitable for motorhomes +7m.

Tourist information Turenne:
◠ Tour de Cesar. 🕐 Easter-Oct daily, winter Su.

Ussel 21D6
Aire du lac de Ponty. **GPS:** n45,54762 e2,28330. ⬆ .

15 ⏚free ⚡€2 🔧Ch 🚽€2 WC. **Surface:** grassy/gravel. 🅾 01/01-31/12
Distance: 🚶Ussel 3km 🚲8,5km.
Remarks: At lake, in front of entrance campsite.

Uzerche 29A1
Place de la Petite Gare, Rue Paul Langevin. **GPS:** n45,42477 e1,56696.⬆➡.

20 ⏚free ⚡🔧Ch 🚽WC free. **Surface:** asphalted. 🅾 01/01-31/12
Distance: 🚶300m 🚲4,4km ∠little stream.

Vigeois 29A1
D7, route de Brive. **GPS:** n45,36717 e1,53392.⬆➡.

12 ⏚free ⚡€3 🔧Ch 🚽€3. **Surface:** grassy/gravel. 🅾 01/04-31/10
Distance: 🚶2km 🚲7,2km ∠beach 150m.
Remarks: Coins at town hall and bars in the village.

Auvergne

Aigueperse 22A5
Place du Foirail, Rue de la Porte aux Boeufs. **GPS:** n46,02634 e3,20313.⬆.

15 ⏚free ⚡€2/10minutes 🔧Ch 🚽€2/1h. **Location:** Urban, simple, central,
quiet. **Surface:** asphalted. 🅾 01/01-31/12 🔘 17/08-28/08
Distance: 🚶on the spot ⊗nearby 🛒nearby.
Remarks: Market square.

Aiguilhe   29D1

Avenue de Bonneville. **GPS:** n45,05077 e3,88318. 🔼.
6 🚐 free. **Surface:** asphalted. 🔲 01/01-31/12
Distance: 🚆350m.
Remarks: Max. 24h.

Allanche   29C1

Aire de la Gare, Chemin de la Roche Marchal. **GPS:** n45,23000 e2,93139. 🔼.

25 🚐 free 🚰€2 Ch. **Location:** Rural, simple, quiet. **Surface:** gravel/sand.
🔲 01/05-30/09, parking 01/01-31/12
Distance: 🚆300m ⊗300m 🚆300m.
Remarks: Altitude 1000m, coins at camping, tourist info and town hall, accessed via Allanche centre.

Archignat   21D4

Rue des Chalets. **GPS:** n46,37336 e2,42408. 🔼.
5 🚐€5 + € 0,20/pp tourist tax 🚰€2 Ch ✎€3 WC. **Location:** Quiet.
Surface: grassy/gravel.
Distance: 🚆on the spot.

Arlanc   29D1

Loumans. **GPS:** n45,41233 e3,71782. 🔼➡️.

+10 🚐 free 🚰🚰 Ch free 🚿. **Location:** Rural, simple, quiet.
Surface: asphalted/grassy. 🔲 01/04-31/10
Distance: 🚆500m ⊠on the spot 🛒on the spot ⊗100m 🚆1km
🏃on the spot.
Remarks: At swimming pool and small lake.

Arnac (Cantal)   29B1

Aire camping-cars, RD61. **GPS:** n45,06056 e2,23389. 🔼.

2 🚐 free 🚰€2/100liter 🚰 Ch 🚽€2/1h. **Location:** Rural, simple, quiet.
Surface: grassy/gravel. 🔲 01/01-31/12
Distance: 🚆50m ⊗150m 🚆150m.

Aubusson-d'Auvergne   22B6

Base de Loisirs-lac d'Aubusson. **GPS:** n45,75377 e3,61079. 🔼.

50 🚐€6 🚰 🚰 Ch WC 🚿 free. **Location:** Rural, simple, isolated, quiet.
Surface: metalled. 🔲 01/01-31/12
Distance: ⊠on the spot 🛒on the spot ⊗200m 🚆8km 🏃on the spot.

Aurec-sur-Loire   29D1

Rue des Cheminots. **GPS:** n45,37164 e4,19919. 🔼.
🚐 free 🚰 🚰 Ch. **Surface:** asphalted. 🔲 01/01-31/12
Distance: 🚆450m ⊗450m.
Remarks: At station.

Aurillac   29B2

Place du Champ de Foire, Cours d'Angoulême. **GPS:** n44,92944 e2,44963. 🔼➡️.

10 🚐 free 🚰€3,50 🚰 Ch 🚽€3,50. **Location:** Urban, simple, noisy.
Surface: asphalted. 🔲 01/01-31/12 ⬛ service: 31/10-01/05
Distance: 🚆on the spot ⊗100m 🚆100m.
Remarks: Max. 24h, coins at tourist info.

Tourist information Aurillac:
🎭 European street theatre and festival. 🔲 3rd week Aug.

Aydat   22A6

Aire camping-cars. **GPS:** n45,66025 e2,97778. 🔼➡️.

41 🚐€ 9/24h 🚰 🚰 Ch 🚿 (28x) WC 🗑 included. 📷🧺
Location: Rural, comfortable, quiet. **Surface:** grassy. 🔲 01/01-31/12
Distance: 🚆200m ⊠on the spot 🛒on the spot ⊗on the spot 🚆250m.
Remarks: Former campsite, max. 8,20m.

Beaulieu   29D1

Zone d'Activité la Gerle. **GPS:** n45,12597 e3,94608. 🔼➡️.

15 🚐 free 🚰 🚰 Ch 🚿 (2x)free. **Location:** Rural, simple, quiet.

FR

Surface: gravel. ⬛ 01/04-31/10
Distance: 🚶400m.

| 🚐S | Beaulon 🚣 | 22B4 |

Écluse de Beaulon, La Curesse. **GPS:** n46,60443 e3,65840. ⬆➡.

+10 🛏free 🚰🔌Ch🚿(4x)free. **Location:** Rural, simple, isolated, quiet.
Surface: gravel. ⬛ 01/01-31/12
Distance: 🚶1,2km 🛶Canal 🛒on the spot ⊗1,2km 🏪1,2km 🚲on the spot
🏊on the spot.

| 🚐S | Bellerive-sur-Allier | 22B5 |

Riv'Air Camp, Rue Claude Decloitre. **GPS:** n46,11514 e3,43114. ⬆.

50 🛏€ 10 🚰🔌Ch🚿(50x)WC🎫included 🔲.🚿 **Location:** Urban,
comfortable, isolated, quiet. **Surface:** metalled. ⬛ 01/01-31/12
Distance: 🚶2,5km 🚲17km 🏊on the spot 🛒on the spot ⊗on the spot
🏪800m.
Remarks: Along the Allier river.

| 🚐S | Billy | 22B5 |

Rue de la Fontaine. **GPS:** n46,23586 e3,43044. ⬆🔼.

🛏free 🚰🔌Chfree. **Surface:** asphalted. ⬛ 01/01-31/12
Distance: 🚶on the spot.
Remarks: Max. 48h.

| 🚐S | Blesle 🏞 | 29C1 |

Route du Babory, D8. **GPS:** n45,31716 e3,17583. ⬆.
6 🛏free. **Surface:** gravel. ⬛ 01/01-31/12
Distance: 🚶300m ⊗300m 🏪300m.

| 🍴🛏S | Blesle 🏞 | 29C1 |

Hôtel-Restaurant Le Scorpion, D909. **GPS:** n45,31219 e3,18677. ⬆.

25 🛏€ 12,50 🚰🔌Ch🚿(8x)WC🎫included. **Location:** Rural, comfortable,
quiet. **Surface:** grassy. ⬛ 01/01-31/12
Distance: 🚲5,8km ⊗on the spot.

| 🚐S | Brioude 🏞⚓ | 29C1 |

Parking des Remparts, Avenue de Lamothe, D588. **GPS:** n45,29444 e3,38778.
⬆➡.

30 🛏free 🚰€2 🔌Ch🔋€2. **Location:** Urban, simple, central, quiet.
Surface: asphalted. ⬛ 01/01-31/12
Distance: 🚶100m ⊗100m 🏪100m.
Remarks: Coins at tourist info(100m).

Tourist information Brioude:
👁 L'aquarium-la Maison du Saumon et de la Rivière, Place de la Résistance.
Museum about the salmon. ⬛ 01/04-30/11.

| 🚐S | Buxières-les-Mines | 22A4 |

| Le Boucher - Buxières-les-Mines |

margabolmer@orange.fr - www.camping-leboucher.com

Electricity at each pitch
Sanitary facilities
Baker every morning

Le Boucher. GPS: n46,45464 e2,96791. ⬆➡.
6 🛏€ 13,10 🚰🔌Ch🔋🚿(6x),12Amp WC🎫🔲€5/3,50 📶included.🚿
Location: Rural, comfortable, isolated. **Surface:** grassy.
⬛ 01/01-31/12
Distance: 🚶2km 🚲12km 🛶5km 🛒2km ⊗5km 🏪2km.

| 🚐S | Calvinet | 29B2 |

Aire de Calvinet, Terrain de sport. **GPS:** n44,71023 e2,35914. ⬆➡.

6 🛏free 🚰€2 ᕲCh 🔌€2. **Location:** Rural, simple, quiet. **Surface:** gravel.
⬛ 01/01-31/12 🔘 service 01/11-31/03
Distance: 🚶1,5km ⊗1,5km 🍴1,5km.
Remarks: Nearby sports ground.

20 🛏free 🚰€2 ᕲCh. **Location:** Rural, simple, isolated, quiet.
Surface: grassy/gravel. ⬛ 01/04-31/10
Distance: 🚶1,3km ⊗1,3km 🍴500m.

🏕S	**Cassaniouze**	29B2

Aire camping-cars, Le Bourg. **GPS:** n44,69347 e2,38233. ⬆➡.

🏕S	**Chanaleilles** ⛰	29C2

Le Bourg. **GPS:** n44,85971 e3,49083. ⬆.

6 🛏free 🚰€2/80liter ᕲCh 🔌€2/1h 💡€1.
Location: Rural, simple, quiet. **Surface:** gravel.
⬛ 01/01-31/12 🔘 service 01/11-31/03
Distance: 🚶600m ⊗600m 🍴600m.

5 🛏free 🚰ᕲCh. **Location:** Rural, comfortable, isolated, quiet.
Surface: grassy/gravel.
Distance: 🚶500m ⊗375m.

🏕S	**Cayrols**	29B2

Aire camping-cars, La Devèze, D51. **GPS:** n44,83000 e2,23278. ⬆➡.

🏕S	**Charbonnières-les-Varennes**	22A5

Route de Saint-Georges, Paugnat. **GPS:** n45,88457 e2,97993. ⬆.

10 🛏free 🚰€3,80 ᕲCh 🔌€3,80 WC. **Location:** Rural, comfortable, quiet.
Surface: metalled. ⬛ 01/01-31/12 🔘 service 01/11-31/03
Distance: 🚶100m 🍴200m.
Remarks: Max. 1 week, coins at the shops in the village and petrol station.

10 🛏free 🚰€2/10minutes ᕲCh 🔌€2/55minutes.
Location: Rural, comfortable, quiet. **Surface:** grassy.
⬛ 01/01-31/12
Distance: 🚶500m 🍴bakery 500m 🥾on the spot.
Remarks: Coins at the shops in the village, trail to volcano crater.

🏕S	**Chambon-sur-Lac** ✈ ⛰ ❄	22A6

Camping Les Bombes, La Vergne. **GPS:** n45,56991 e2,90176. ⬆➡.

🏕S	**Chaspuzac**	29D1

Rue du Vol à Voile. **GPS:** n45,07491 e3,76131. ➡.

30 🛏€7 🚰€3 ᕲCh. 🛁 **Location:** Rural, simple, quiet.
Surface: grassy/gravel. ⬛ 01/01-31/12 🔘 service: 15/09-01/05
Distance: 🚶500m 🏊200m 🚲1km ⊗500m 🍴500m bakery 🐴on the spot
🥾on the spot.
Remarks: Pay and coins at campsite.

6 🛏free 🚰€2 ᕲCh.
Location: Rural, simple, quiet. **Surface:** asphalted.
Distance: ⊗50m.
Remarks: View on airport.

🏕S	**Champeix**	22A6

Champeix, Route de Montaigut, D996. **GPS:** n45,58845 e3,11568. ⬆➡.

🏕S	**Chastreix** ⛰ ❄	21D6

Parking Station de Ski, Chastreix Sancy. **GPS:** n45,53507 e2,77695. ⬆.

FR

14 ⌇free ⌁⌁Ch ⌇€9,(winter) WC⌇€2,(winter).
Location: Rural, simple, quiet. **Surface:** metalled. ◻ 01/01-31/12
Distance: ⌁Chastreix 6km ⌁on the spot.
Remarks: Check in between 9-17h.

⌇S **Château-sur-Allier** 22A3
Domaine Fessebois. **GPS:** n46,76379 e3,02714.⬆.
4 ⌇free ⌁€3 ⌇Ch ⌇. **Location:** Rural, simple, isolated, quiet.
Surface: gravel. ◻ 01/01-31/12
Remarks: Picnic area.

⌇S **Châtel-Guyon** ♨ 22A5
Place de la Musique Nationale. **GPS:** n45,92324 e3,06590.⬆➡.

7 ⌇€ 5/day ⌁€2 ⌇Ch WC. **Location:** Urban, comfortable, central, quiet.
Surface: asphalted. ◻ 01/01-31/12
Distance: ⌁nearby ⊗400m ⌁400m ⌁on the spot.
Remarks: Check in at police station, coins at tourist info.

⌇ **Châtel-Guyon** ♨ 22A5
Parking des Roches, Chemin de Bussane. **GPS:** n45,91789 e3,06545.⬆ .

10 ⌇free. **Location:** Urban, simple, quiet. **Surface:** asphalted.
◻ 01/01-31/12
Distance: ⌁500m ⊗600m ⌁600m.

⌇ **Châtel-Guyon** ♨ 22A5
Pré Morand, Avenue de Russie. **GPS:** n45,91713 e3,05724.
⌇free. **Surface:** gravel. ◻ 01/01-31/12
Remarks: Next to spa resort.

⌇S **Chaudes-Aigues** ♨ 29C2
Parking Beauredon, Avenue Georges Pompidou, D921.
GPS: n44,84972 e3,00306.⬆➡.

10 ⌇free ⌁€2 ⌇Ch ⊞€2/55minutes. **Location:** Urban, simple.
Surface: gravel. ◻ 15/04-15/10
Distance: ⌁100m ⊗300m ⌁300m.

Tourist information Chaudes-Aigues:
ℹ Office de Tourisme, 1, avenue Georges Pompidou, www.chaudesaigues.com.
Small town with warm thermal sources (82°C).

⌇S **Chevagnes** 22B4
Route Nationale. **GPS:** n46,61028 e3,55219.⬆.
4 ⌇free ⌁€2 ⌇Ch ⌇€2. **Location:** Comfortable, isolated, quiet.
Surface: gravel. ◻ 01/01-31/12
Distance: ⌁on the spot ⊗200m.

⌇S **Chomelix** ⛺ 29D1
Centre Multi Activités Les Marches d'Auvergne, Route d'Estables, D135.
GPS: n45,26219 e3,82573.⬆ .

6 ⌇free ⌁€4 ⌇Ch. **Location:** Rural, simple, quiet. **Surface:** gravel.
◻ 01/01-31/12
Distance: ⌁on the spot ⊗on the spot ⌁mountainbike trail ⌁on the spot.

⌇S **Clermont Ferrand** 22A6
P&R Les Pistes, Rue de la Fontaine de la Ratte. **GPS:** n45,79810 e3,11222.⬆.

6 ⌇€ 5 ⌁⌁Chfree. ⌇ **Location:** Urban. **Surface:** asphalted.
◻ 01/01-31/12
Distance: ⌁historical centre 3km ⌁50m.
Remarks: Nearby Michelin museum, check in at parking attendant.

⌇S **Coltines** 29C1
D40. **GPS:** n45,09612 e2,98555.➡.

FR

5 �📷free ⛽€2/100liter 🚿Ch 🚰€2. **Location:** Rural, simple. **Surface:** gravel. 💧 water: 15/10-15/04
Distance: 🛒400m ⊗400m 🗑400m.
Remarks: Coins at Epicerie-Presse, Centre Chantarisa and town hall.

Condat 29B1
Parking au Pont, D678. **GPS:** n45,33889 e2,76250. ⬆️.

4 📷free ⛽Service€2,50 🚿Ch 🚰. **Location:** Simple. **Surface:** asphalted.
◻ 01/01-31/12 💧 service: 01/10-01/05
Distance: 🛒50m 🚲10m 🗑50m.
Remarks: Coins at campsite La Borie Basse (500m).

Coubon 29D1
Route du Plan d'Eau. **GPS:** n44,99735 e3,91742. ⬆️.

5 📷free ⛽€2,50 🚿ChWC. **Surface:** metalled. ◻ 01/01-31/12
Remarks: Along river.

Crandelles 29B1
Aire camping-cars, Lac des Genevrières. **GPS:** n44,95877 e2,34289.

10 📷free ⛽€3,50 🚿Ch. **Location:** Comfortable, central, quiet.
Surface: gravel. ◻ 01/01-31/12 💧 service: 01/11-01/04
Distance: 🛒300m 🏊50m 🚲50m ⊗50m 🗑300m.

Craponne-sur-Arzon 29D1
Avenue de la Gare. **GPS:** n45,33360 e3,85057. ⬆️.

+20 📷free ⛽€2 🚿Ch 🚰€2/1h. **Location:** Urban, simple, quiet.
Surface: asphalted/gravel. ◻ 01/01-31/12
Distance: 🛒150m ⊗150m 🗑on the spot.

Diou 22B4
Camping du Gué de Loire, Chemin de la Procession. **GPS:** n46,53523 e3,74401. ⬆️.
6 📷free, 15/06-30/09 €5 ⛽🚿Ch 🦮. **Surface:** grassy. ◻ 01/01-31/12

Drugeac 29B1
Aire de campingcars, La Gare SNCF. **GPS:** n45,16694 e2,38667. ⬆️➡️.

4 📷free ⛽€2/100liter 🚿Ch 🚰€2/1h. **Location:** Rural, simple, quiet.
Surface: asphalted. ◻ 01/01-31/12 💧 service: 01/11-01/05
Distance: 🛒100m ⊗100m 🗑100m.
Remarks: At former station, now start Vélorail.

Ebreuil 22A5
Parking du Stade, D915. **GPS:** n46,10954 e3,07606. ⬆️.

10 📷free. **Location:** Simple. **Surface:** gravel. ◻ 01/01-31/12
Distance: 🚲6,5km.
Remarks: In front of campsite municipal, service 500m.

Ebreuil 22A5
Chemin des Nières. **GPS:** n46,11083 e3,08111. ⬆️.
⛽🚿Chfree. ◻ 01/01-31/12
Remarks: Overnight stay on Parking du Stade.

Estivareilles 21D4
Salle Polyvalente, Rue de la République. **GPS:** n46,42471 e2,61529. ⬆️➡️.

20 📷free ⛽🚿Chfree. **Location:** Urban, simple. **Surface:** gravel.
◻ 01/01-31/12
Distance: 🛒on the spot 🚲9km ⊗200m 🗑bakery 200m.

Jaligny-sur-Besbre 22B4
Rue de la Chaume. **GPS:** n46,38155 e3,59147. ⬆️➡️.

FR

5 ⌇free 🚰 Ch 🚿 (5x)free. **Location:** Rural, simple, quiet.
Surface: gravel. ⬛ 01/01-31/12
Distance: 🛒200m 🏊on the spot 🍴on the spot ⊗250m 🛒250m.
Remarks: Along the Besbre river.

| | La Bourboule | 21D6 |

Plateau de Charlannes. **GPS:** n45,57811 e2,73513.⬆ .

10 ⌇free. **Location:** Rural, simple, quiet. **Surface:** asphalted.
⬛ 01/01-31/12
Distance: 🛒6,5km ⊗Snackbar 🚶on the spot 🏃on the spot.
Remarks: Parking at funicular railway.

| | La Chapelle-Laurent ❄ | 29C1 |

Aire camping-cars, D10. **GPS:** n45,18028 e3,24389.⬆

5 ⌇free 🚰 Chfree. **Location:** Rural, simple. **Surface:** grassy.
⬛ parking 01/01-31/12, service 01/04-15/11
Distance: 🛒50m 🛒nearby ⊗100m 🛒100m.

| | La Roche-Blanche | 22A6 |

Les Trolières, La Pigné Sud, Route des Fours à Chaux. **GPS:** n45,71567 e3,14790.
⬆ .

100 ⌇€6 🚰€2/100liter 🚰 Ch 🚿 (4x)€6/6h.
Location: Rural, simple, isolated, quiet. **Surface:** grassy. ⬛ 01/03-30/11
Distance: 🚲1,1km.
Remarks: Max. 48h.

| | La Tour-d'Auvergne | 21D6 |

Route de Bagnols. **GPS:** n45,53290 e2,68213.⬆ .

25 ⌇free 🚰€2/100liter 🚰 Ch 🚐€2. **Location:** Simple, quiet.
Surface: metalled. ⬛ 01/01-31/12
Distance: 🛒on the spot ⊗650m 🛒650m bakery.

| | Lacapelle-Viescamp | 29B2 |

Aire camping-cars, D18. **GPS:** n44,92167 e2,26361.⬆ .

5 ⌇free 🚰€3/100liter 🚰 Ch 🚐€3/1h. **Location:** Rural, simple.
Surface: metalled. ⬛ 01/01-31/12
Distance: 🛒100m ⊗100m 🛒on the spot.
Remarks: Coins available at the shop.

| | Lapalisse | 22B5 |

Place Jean Moulin, RN7 dir Roanne. **GPS:** n46,25000 e3,63500.➡ .

50 ⌇free 🚰€2 🚰 Ch 🚿€2 WC. **Location:** Urban, simple, central, quiet.
Surface: asphalted. ⬛ 01/01-31/12
Distance: 🛒300m 🛒on the spot ⊗on the spot 🛒on the spot.

| | Laprugne | 22B5 |

Domaine La Bourbonnaise, D477. **GPS:** n45,98661 e3,74569.
⌇€8 🚰 Ch 🚿. **Surface:** asphalted. ⬛ 01/01-31/12
Distance: ⊗on the spot.

| | Lavaudieu | 29C1 |

Le Bourg. **GPS:** n45,26297 e3,45606.⬆ .

+10 ⌇free. **Location:** Simple, isolated, quiet. **Surface:** grassy/gravel.
⬛ 01/01-31/12
Distance: 🛒200m 🛒on the spot ⊗on the spot 🏃on the spot.

| | Le Breuil-sur-Couze | 29C1 |

Allée de Treize Vents. **GPS:** n45,46867 e3,26121.⬆➡ .

8 ⛺free 🚰 ♻Chfree. **Location:** Urban, simple. **Surface:** gravel.
📅 01/01-31/12
Distance: 🚂 900m 🚶700m bakery, supermarket.
Remarks: Along railwayline.

📷 S | **Le Cheix-sur-Morge** | 22A5
D425. **GPS:** n45,95138 e3,17812. ⬆➡.

6 ⛺free 🚰 ♻Chfree. **Location:** Rural, simple, isolated, quiet.
Surface: gravel. 📅 01/01-31/12
Distance: 🚶500m.
Remarks: Max. 48h.

| | **Le Donjon** | 22B4 |

Place du Champ de Foire, Rue Georges Gallay. **GPS:** n46,34940 e3,79473. ⬆ .

⛺free. **Location:** Simple, central, quiet. **Surface:** gravel.
📅 01/01-31/12
Distance: 🚶100m 🚶50m.
Remarks: Tuesday market.

📷 | **Le Monastier-sur-Gazeille** | 29D2
Rue Augustin Ollier. **GPS:** n44,93720 e3,99250. ⬆➡.

10 ⛺free. **Location:** Rural, simple. **Surface:** grassy.
📅 01/03-31/10
Distance: 🚶300m ⊗300m 🚶300m.

S | **Le Monastier-sur-Gazeille** | 29D2
Le Moulin de Savin. **GPS:** n44,93680 e3,98600. ⬆➡.
🚰♻Ch.
Remarks: Next to campsite.

📷 | **Le Puy-en-Velay** | 29D1
Avenue Charles Dupuy. **GPS:** n45,04358 e3,89240. ⬆➡.

12 ⛺€ 8, € 2/3h. 🅿 **Location:** Urban, simple, central, noisy.
Surface: asphalted. 📅 01/01-31/12
Distance: 🚶500m.
Remarks: Behind bus terminal, max. 24h.

S | **Le Puy-en-Velay** | 29D1
Boulevard de Cluny. **GPS:** n45,04963 e3,88976. ⬆ .
🚰€2 ♻Ch.

S | **Le Vernet** ♨ | 29D1
Le Bourg. **GPS:** n45,03560 e3,66952. ⬆.

10 ⛺€ 2 🚰€2/80liter ♻Ch 🔌€2/10minutes. 🚿 **Location:** Rural, simple,
isolated, quiet. **Surface:** grassy/sand. 📅 01/01-31/12
Distance: 🚶50m 🚶 on the spot.

📷 S | **Les Ancizes-Comps** | 22A5
Camping de Comps les Fads, Le Moulin. **GPS:** n45,93986 e2,79985. ⬆.
⛺€ 8,40, 2 pers.incl 🚰 ♻Ch 🔌€2. **Surface:** grassy. 📅 01/01-31/12

📷 | **Les Estables** ⛱⛰❄ | 29D2
Le Bourg. **GPS:** n44,90231 e4,15679. ⬆ .

8 ⛺free 🚰 ♻Chfree 📶. **Location:** Rural, simple. **Surface:** asphalted.
📅 01/01-31/12
Distance: 🚶50m ⊗50m 🚶 on the spot.
Remarks: Free wifi, code at tourist info.

📷 S | **Lezoux** | 22B6
Parking Musée départemental de la Céramique, Rue de la République.
GPS: n45,82686 e3,38459. ⬆➡.

FR

30 🗄free ⌐ 🗄 Ch WC free. **Location:** Comfortable, central, quiet.
Surface: gravel. 🔲 01/01-31/12 🔘 water: 01/11-31/03
Distance: 🚶500m 🚲 3,5km ⊗500m 🚰500m.

🗄S **Lurcy-Lévis** 🔹 **22A3**
Plan d'eau des Sézeaux, Rue de Fontgroix. **GPS:** n46,73797 e2,93863. ⬆️➡️

6 🗄free ⌐€3/100liter 🗄 Ch 🔌€3/55minutes WC. **Location:** Rural,
comfortable, quiet. **Surface:** grassy/gravel. 🔲 01/01-31/12
Distance: 🚶800m 🏊Small lake 🎣on the spot ⊗800m 🚰800m.
Remarks: Coins at cafe, in front of the church.

🗄S **Mandailles-Saint-Julien** 🏔 **29B1**
Aire de camping-cars, Le Mas, D17. **GPS:** n45,06916 e2,65611. ➡️

5 🗄free ⌐€3,50 🗄 Ch. **Location:** Rural, simple, quiet. **Surface:** metalled.
🔲 01/01-31/12 🔘 service: 30/09-01/05
Distance: 🚶200m ⊗200m 🚰200m 🏃on the spot.
Remarks: Max. 24h, coins at restaurants.

🗄S **Manzat** **22A5**
Place du 14 Juillet. **GPS:** n45,96180 e2,93883. ⬆️

20 🗄free ⌐ 🗄 Ch free. **Location:** Rural, simple, quiet. **Surface:** unpaved.
🔲 01/01-31/12
Distance: 🚶on the spot 🚲5,6km ⊗250m 🚰200m.
Remarks: In front of police station.

🗄S **Marcolès** **29B2**
Aire camping-cars, Terrain de sport. **GPS:** n44,78028 e2,35389. ⬆️

5 🗄€2 ⌐ 🗄 Ch free 🎣. **Location:** Rural, simple, quiet. **Surface:** gravel.
🔲 01/01-31/12 🔘 service 01/11-31/03
Distance: 🚶100m ⊗100m 🚰100m.
Remarks: Artists village.

🗄 **Massiac** **29C1**
Rue Jacques Chaban Delmas. **GPS:** n45,25360 e3,19395. ⬆️

5 🗄free ⌐ 🗄 Ch free. **Surface:** asphalted.
Distance: 🚶350m ⊗400m 🚰400m.

🗄 **Massiac** **29C1**
Rue Jacques Chaban Delmas. **GPS:** n45,25267 e3,19433. ⬆️➡️

🗄free. **Location:** Rural. **Surface:** grassy. 🔲 01/01-31/12
Distance: 🚶400m 🚲 1,4km 🏊on the spot ⊗400m 🚰400m 🚌200m.

🗄S **Mauriac** 🔹 **29B1**
Aire de campingcars, Rue du Val Saint Jean. **GPS:** n45,21863 e2,32183. ⬆️➡️

10 🗄free ⌐€2/100liter 🗄 Ch 🔌€2/1h 🎣. **Location:** Rural, simple, quiet.
Surface: metalled. 🔲 01/01-31/12
Distance: 🚶1km 🏊beach 300m ⊗1,2km 🚰1,2km.

🗄S **Maurs** **29B2**
Maurs La Jolie, Route de Quezac. **GPS:** n44,71442 e2,19615. ⬆️➡️

FR

5 🛏free ⛽€2/100liter ♨ Ch 🚿€2/1h. **Location:** Urban, simple, central, quiet. **Surface:** asphalted. 📅 01/01-31/12
Distance: 🛒300m ⊗300m 🛍300m ⬆300m.
Remarks: Coins at Papetterie and tourist office.

🅿S **Messeix** 21D6
Place des Pins. **GPS:** n45,61576 e2,55621. ⬆➡.

6 🛏free ⛽€2/10minutes ♨ Ch 🚿€2/55minutes. **Location:** Urban, simple, quiet. **Surface:** asphalted. 📅 01/01-31/12
Distance: 🛒500m ⚓18km 🚉1,7km 🚌on the spot.
Remarks: Coins at the shops.

🅿S **Montluçon** 21D4
Route de l'Etang de Sault, Prémilhat. **GPS:** n46,33469 e2,55855. ⬆➡.

8 🛏free ⛽€6/150liter ♨ Ch 🧹(6x)€2,50/10h 🗑. **Location:** Rural, comfortable. **Surface:** gravel. 📅 01/01-31/12
Distance: 🛒5km Montluçon ⚓2,6km ⛱150m 🏊150m ⊗500m.
Remarks: Max. 72h.

🅿S **Montluçon** 21D4
Place de la Fraternité, Rue des Marais. **GPS:** n46,35535 e2,58686. ⬆.

15 🛏free ⛽€5/150liter ♨ Ch 🚿€2,50/10minutes WC 🗑.
Location: Urban, simple, noisy. **Surface:** asphalted.
📅 01/01-31/12 🚰 water: Nov-March
Distance: 🛒on the spot ⚡A71 16km ⊗on the spot 🛒on the spot 🚌on the spot.
Remarks: Thu-morning closed because of market (6-15h).

🅿S **Montmurat** 29B2
Aire camping-cars, Le Bourg, D345. **GPS:** n44,62811 e2,19804. ⬆.

10 🛏free ⛽€1 ♨ Ch. **Location:** Rural, simple, isolated, quiet.
Surface: gravel. 📅 01/01-31/12
Distance: 🛒on the spot.

🅿S **Montoldre** 22B4
D21. **GPS:** n46,33272 e3,44727. ⬆➡.

+10 🛏free ⛽€2/100liter ♨ Ch. **Location:** Rural, simple, quiet.
Surface: asphalted. 📅 01/01-31/12
Distance: 🛒centre ⊗on the spot.
Remarks: In front of town hall.

🅿S **Montpeyroux** 22A6
D797C, Rue De l'Hume. **GPS:** n45,62373 e3,19911. ⬆.

+10 🛏free ⛽€2,50 ♨ Ch 🚿€2,50/1h. **Location:** Rural, simple, quiet.
Surface: gravel. 📅 01/01-31/12
Distance: 🛒100m ⚓200m ⊗200m.
Remarks: Coins at the shops in the village.

Tourist information Montpeyroux:
ℹ Small town with wine-cellar Cave de Montpeyroux. 📅 Mo/Sa 8.30-12.30h, 14-18/19h, Su 10.30-12h, 16-19h.

🅿S **Montsalvy** 29B2
Aire camping-cars, Route de Junhac. **GPS:** n44,70778 e2,49667. ⬆➡.

21 🛏free ⛽€2 ♨ Ch 🧹€2 WC 🛏€1. **Location:** Rural, comfortable, quiet.
Surface: asphalted. 📅 01/01-31/12
Distance: 🛒400m ⊗400m 🚉400m.

FR

⚏S Moulins ⚏⚏⚏ **22A4**

Flot Bleu Park, Chemin de Halage. **GPS:** n46,55852 e3,32491. ⬆️➡️

92 ⟁€ 0,10/h ⟁€2 ⚏Ch€2 ⚏€2/20minutes ⚏(12x)€2/4h .⚏
⚏ **Location:** Urban, comfortable, central, quiet. **Surface:** grassy/metalled.
⚏ 01/01-31/12
Distance: ⚏city centre 1km ⚏100m ⚏300m ⚏on the spot.

⚏S Murat **29C1**

Place du 19 mars. **GPS:** n45,10917 e2,86917. ⬆️

8 ⟁free ⟁€2 ⚏Ch⚏€2 WC. **Surface:** asphalted. ⚏ 01/05-31/10
Remarks: Marked pitches in the back of de parking.

⚏ Murat **29C1**

Avenue d'Olonne-sur-mer. **GPS:** n45,10757 e2,85975. ⬆️ .

⟁free. **Location:** Urban, simple. **Surface:** concrete.
⚏ 01/01-31/12
Remarks: At sports park.

⚏ Murat **29C1**

Parking du Stade, Rue du Stade. **GPS:** n45,10861 e2,87027.

⟁free. **Surface:** asphalted. ⚏ 01/01-31/12
Tourist information Murat:
⚏ ⚏ Fri-morning.

⚏S Murat-le-Quaire ⚏ **21D6**

Les Rives du Lac, Route de la Banne d'Ordanche. **GPS:** n45,60274 e2,73797. ⬆️
➡️

---

37 ⟁€ 9/24h ⟁⚏Ch ⚏(8x) WC included ⚏€1. **Location:** Rural,
comfortable, quiet. **Surface:** grassy/metalled. ⚏ 01/01-31/12
Distance: ⚏1,2km ⚏12km ⚏100m ⚏100m day pass available
⚏on the spot ⚏on the spot ⚏100m ⚏5km.
Remarks: Bread-service.

⚏S Murol ⚏⚏⚏ **22A6**

Rue du Tartaret, D5. **GPS:** n45,57288 e2,94101. ⬆️.

20 ⟁free ⟁service€2 ⚏Ch⚏. **Location:** Urban, simple.
Surface: asphalted. ⚏ 15/06-31/08
Distance: ⚏450m ⚏300m.
Remarks: Pay at tourist office, service 100m.

⚏S Naucelles **29B1**

Aire camping-cars, Rue du Terrou. **GPS:** n44,95694 e2,41757. ⬆️ .

5 ⟁free ⟁€3,50/100liter ⚏Ch⚏€3,50/1h. **Location:** Urban, simple, quiet.
Surface: asphalted. ⚏ 01/01-31/12
Distance: ⚏Spar 300m.
Remarks: Coins at supermarket in the village.

⚏S Néris-les-Bains ⚏ **21D4**

Camping du Lac, Avenue Marrx Dormoy, D155. **GPS:** n46,28673 e2,65235. ⬆️➡️

6 ⟁€7 ⟁⚏Ch ⚏(6x) WC included ⚏€1,50/h. ⚏ **Location:** Urban,
comfortable. **Surface:** gravel. ⚏ 01/03-31/10
Distance: ⚏500m ⚏12km ⚏bakery 500m.
Remarks: Max. 3 nights, to be paid at campsite.

⚏S Neussargues-Moissac **29C1**

Allée des Peupliers. **GPS:** n45,13438 e2,98130. ⬆️➡️.

5 🛏free ⛽€2/100liter 🧺 Ch 🚽€2/2h 📶. **Location:** Rural, comfortable, quiet. **Surface:** gravel. 🔌 01/01-31/12 ⦿ water disconnected in winter **Distance:** 🚶300m ⊗50m 🛒300m.

| 🏕S | Orcines | 22A6 |

Route du Puy de Dôme, D68. **GPS:** n45,76958 e2,98624.
🛏free ⛽ 🧺 Ch free. **Location:** Rural, isolated. **Surface:** asphalted.
🔌 01/01-31/12 ⦿ Service: winter

| 🏕 | Orcines | 22A6 |

D941. **GPS:** n45,80394 e2,98726.

10 🛏free. **Location:** Simple, noisy. **Surface:** metalled. 🔌 01/01-31/12 🚶on the spot.

| 🏕S | Orcines | 22A6 |

D941B dir Orcines Vulcania. **GPS:** n45,78765 e3,00947. ⬆.

⛽€2/100liter 🧺 Ch 🚽€2/1h. **Location:** Simple, noisy.
🔌 01/01-31/12

| 🏕S | Paray-le-Frésil | 22B4 |

Le Bourg. **GPS:** n46,65472 e3,61294. ⬆.
3 🛏free ⛽€2 🧺 Ch 🚽€2/55minutes. **Location:** Quiet. **Surface:** sand.
🔌 01/01-31/12 🛒on the spot 🚶on the spot.
Remarks: Service only by credit card.

| 🏕S | Périgny | 22B5 |

Rue de l'Église. **GPS:** n46,25306 e3,55307.
8 🛏free 🧺 Ch WC. **Location:** Rural, simple, isolated, quiet. **Surface:** gravel.
🔌 01/01-31/12

| 🏕S | Pierrefort | 29C2 |

Côte de Chabridet. **GPS:** n44,92172 e2,84199. ⬆➡.

20 🛏free ⛽€2/100liter 🧺 Ch 🚽€2. **Location:** Simple. **Surface:** gravel.
🔌 01/01-31/12
Distance: 🚶100m ⊗200m 🛒200m.

| 🏕S | Pleaux | 29B1 |

Parc des Auzerals, Place d'Empeyssine. **GPS:** n45,13556 e2,22833. ⬆➡.

30 🛏free ⛽ 🧺 Ch WC free. **Location:** Urban, simple, central, quiet.
Surface: asphalted/gravel. 🔌 01/01-31/12
Distance: 🚶on the spot ⊗100m 🛒100m.

| 🏕S | Pradelles | 29D2 |

Aire de la Salaison, N88. **GPS:** n44,77540 e3,88752. ⬆➡.

20 🛏free ⛽ 🧺 Ch 🛒(8x)€2 📶free. **Location:** Rural, comfortable, noisy.
Surface: grassy. 🔌 01/01-31/12
Distance: 🚶1km 🛒on the spot.
Remarks: Regional products and bread.

| 🏕S | Prunet | 29B2 |

Aire camping-cars, Le Bourg. **GPS:** n44,82049 e2,46398. ➡.

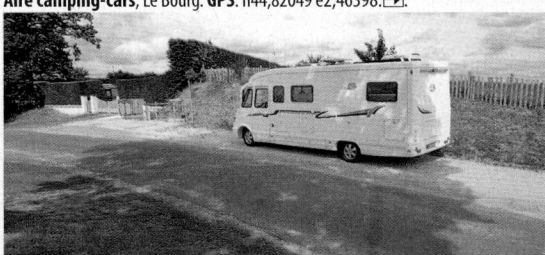

3 🛏free ⛽ 🧺 Ch 🚽free. **Location:** Rural, simple, quiet. **Surface:** gravel.
🔌 01/01-31/12 ⦿ service 01/11-31/03
Distance: 🚶300m ⊗300m.

| 🏕S | Randan | 22A5 |

Rue du Puy de Dôme. **GPS:** n46,01630 e3,35075. ⬆➡.

FR

5 ⌂free ⌐€2/15minutes ⚑Ch ⊞€2/15minutes. **Location:** Urban, simple, quiet. **Surface:** gravel. ◻ 01/01-31/12
Distance: ⌂500m ⊗500m ⛴200m.
Remarks: Coins at Maison de la Presse, Rue de Commerce.

♿S Raucoules 29D1
Raucoules, Le Bourg. **GPS:** n45,18640 e4,29750.⬆➡

4 ⌂free ⌐€2 ⚑Ch ⚓(4x)€2. **Location:** Rural, comfortable, central, quiet. **Surface:** asphalted. ◻ 01/01-31/12
Distance: ⌂200m ⊗300m.
Remarks: Coins available at the shops.

♿S Retournac 29D1
Rue de la Loire. **GPS:** n45,20328 e4,04501.⬆➡

20 ⌂free ⌐ ⚑Chfree. **Location:** Rural, simple, isolated, quiet. **Surface:** gravel. ◻ 01/01-31/12 ◉ Service: winter
Distance: ⌂city centre 1km ⊿on the spot ⌐on the spot ⊗650m ⛷on the spot.
Remarks: Along Loire river.

♿S Riom 22A5
Route d'Ennezat, D224. **GPS:** n45,89455 e3,12477.⬆➡

4 ⌂free ⌐€2/15minutes ⚑Ch ⊞€2/15minutes. **Location:** Urban, simple, central, noisy. **Surface:** gravel. ◻ 01/01-31/12
Distance: ⌂700m ✈2,5km ⊗nearby ⛴nearby.

S Riom-es-Montagnes 29B1
Rue du Champ de Foire. **GPS:** n45,28444 e2,65389.⬆➡

⌐€2/100liter ⚑Ch ⊞€2/1h.
Location: Simple. **Surface:** metalled.
◻ 01/01-31/12
Distance: ⌂on the spot ⊗100m ⛴100m.
Remarks: Overnight stay on Parking de la Piscine, GPS N 45,27902 E 2,66403.

♿S Ruynes-en-Margeride 29C1
GPS: n45,00111 e3,22389.➡

6 ⌂free ⌐€2/10minutes ⚑Ch ⊞€2/55minutes. **Surface:** asphalted.
◻ 01/01-31/12
Distance: ⌂50m ⊗50m ⛴50m.

♿S Saint-Flour 29C1
Cours Chazerat. **GPS:** n45,03389 e3,08750.⬆

20 ⌂free ⌐€2 ⚑Ch. **Location:** Urban, simple. **Surface:** metalled.
◻ 01/01-31/12
Distance: ⌂on the spot ✈4,6km ⊗50m ⛴50m.
Remarks: Higher part of the city.

♿S Saint-Flour 29C1
Place de l'Ander, ville basse. **GPS:** n45,03556 e3,09750.⬆

8 ⌂free ⌐€2 ⚑Ch ⊞€4. **Location:** Urban, simple. **Surface:** asphalted.
◻ 01/01-31/12
Distance: ⌂300m ✈4km ⊗300m ⛴300m.
Remarks: Near campsite, lower part of the city.

Tourist information Saint-Flour:
ℹ Office de Tourisme, 17bis, place d'Armes, www.saint-flour.com. City with car-free historical centre, Vieux Saint Flour.

🚐 [S] Saint-Georges 29C1

GPS: n45,03167 e3,13500. ⬆.

20 🚐 free 🚰 €2 Ch 🔌 €2 WC. **Location:** Highway. **Surface:** asphalted.
☐ 01/01-31/12
Distance: 🏘 3km 🛣 1km 🍴 200m 🥖 on the spot.
Remarks: At petrol station Esso.

🚐 [S] Saint-Gérand-de-Vaux 22B4

Etang du Moulin, Les Gaillards. **GPS**: n46,38416 e3,39972.

30 🚐 free 🚰 €2/100liter Ch 🔌 €2/1h. **Location:** Quiet. **Surface:** grassy.
☐ 01/01-31/12
Distance: 🍴 on the spot.

⛺ [S] Saint-Just 29C2

GPS: n44,88972 e3,20889. ⬆.

10 🚐 € 8 🚰 €2/100liter Ch 🔌 €2/55minutes WC 🚿. **Location:** Comfortable, quiet. **Surface:** grassy. ☐ 01/01-31/12
Distance: 🏘 50m 🛣 6,2km 🍴 100m 🥖 100m.
Remarks: Incl. use camp-site facilities.

🚐 [S] Salers 🐚 29B1

Le Mouriol, Route du Puy Mary. **GPS**: n45,14718 e2,49900. ⬆.

15 🚐 € 3,70 + € 0,50 tourist tax 🚰 €2,10 Ch 🚿 €1,50,on campsite.
Location: Rural.
Surface: gravel.
Distance: 🏘 1,2km 🍴 50m.
Remarks: Next to camping municipal, coins at campsite and tourist info.

🚐 Salers 🐚 29B1

D680. **GPS**: n45,14010 e2,49478.
12 🚐 € 3. 🚌 **Location:** Rural. **Surface:** asphalted/metalled.
Distance: 🏘 500m.
Remarks: Max. 24h, no camping activities.

🚐 Salers 🐚 29B1

Rue Notre-Dame. **GPS**: n45,13898 e2,49583.
6 🚐 € 3. 🚌 **Surface:** asphalted. ☐ 01/01-31/12
Distance: 🏘 250m.
Remarks: Max. 24h, no camping activities.

🚐 [S] Sansac-de-Marmiesse 29B2

Aire camping-cars, Rue de la Vidalie. **GPS**: n44,88389 e2,34639. ⬆➡.

3 🚐 free 🚰 €3,50 Ch 🔌 €3,50. **Location:** Urban, simple, central.
Surface: asphalted. ☐ 01/01-31/12 ■ service: 01/10-30/04
Distance: 🏘 on the spot 🍴 200m 🥖 on the spot.
Remarks: Coins at the bakery.

🚐 [S] Saugues 29C1

Place du Brieul. **GPS**: n44,95940 e3,54395. ⬆.

10 🚐 free 🚰 Ch free. **Location:** Simple. **Surface:** asphalted.
Distance: 🏘 on the spot 🥖 bakery 200m.

🚐 [S] Sauret-Besserve 22A5

D523. **GPS**: n45,99389 e2,81001.

4 🚐 free 🚰 €2 Ch €2. **Location:** Rural, simple, isolated.
☐ 01/01-31/12
Remarks: Near church, june 2012 during inspection service out of order.

🚐 [S] Ségur-les-Villas 29B1

Aire de camping-cars, Le Bourg. **GPS**: n45,22311 e2,81818. ⬆➡.

FR

10 🛏free 🚰€3/100liter 🔲 Ch 🔌€3/1h. **Location:** Rural, simple, quiet.
Surface: grassy. 🔲 01/05-31/10
Distance: 🏊200m ⊗300m 🛒200m.
Remarks: Nearby football ground, coins at the shops in the village.

| 🅂 | | Solignat | 22A6 |

Route des Dauphins d'Auvergne, D32. **GPS:** n45,51701 e3,17074. 🔼.

+50 🛏free 🚰€2/100liter 🔲Ch 🔌€2/1h. **Location:** Rural, simple, quiet.
Surface: grassy. 🔲 01/01-31/12
Distance: 🏊100m.

| 🅂 | | St Anthème 🏔 | 22B6 |

Rambaud. **GPS:** n45,52354 e3,91464. 🔼➡.

30 🛏€3 🚰 🔲Chincluded. **Location:** Rural, simple, central, quiet.
Surface: grassy/gravel. 🔲 01/01-31/12 ◉ Water when frosty
Distance: 🏊200m 🏖beach 250m ⊗200m ✈on the spot.
Remarks: Next to campsite Rambaud, water disconnected.

| 🅂 | | St.Bonnet-le-Froid | 30A1 |

Chemin de Brard. **GPS:** n45,14136 e4,43454. 🔼.
6 🛏€5 🚰 🔲Ch 🔧included. **Surface:** gravel. 🔲 01/03-15/11
Distance: 🏊150m ⊗150m 🛒150m.
Remarks: Access via D105.

| 🅂 | | St.Bonnet-Tronçais ⚓ | 21D3 |

Parking du Stade, Route de Tronçais, D39. **GPS:** n46,66001 e2,69717. 🔼.
10 🛏free 🚰€5 🔲Ch. **Surface:** gravel. 🔲 01/01-31/12 ◉ water
disconnected in winter
Distance: 🏊300m.
Remarks: Coins at the bakery and campsite.

| 🅂 | | St.Bonnet-Tronçais ⚓ | 21D3 |

Rue de l'Étang. **GPS:** n46,65896 e2,69228. 🔼➡.
10 🛏free. **Location:** Simple, central. **Surface:** gravel.
🔲 01/01-31/12
Distance: 🏊on the spot 🚲27km 🏖Lake 450m 🛒bakery 200m.

| 🅂 | | St.Christophe-sur-Dolaison | 29D1 |

Le Bourg. **GPS:** n44,99811 e3,82147. 🔼.

6 🛏free 🚰€2 🔲Ch 🔌€2.
Location: Rural, simple. **Surface:** asphalted.
Distance: 🏊100m ⊗150m.

| 🅂 | | St.Eloy-les-Mines | 22A5 |

Rue du Puy-de-Dôme, RN144. **GPS:** n46,15559 e2,83615. 🔼➡.

30 🛏free 🚰€2 🔲Ch 🔌€2. **Location:** Rural, simple. **Surface:** metalled.
🔲 01/01-31/12
Distance: 🏊on the spot ⊗700m 🛒400m Carrefour Market.
Remarks: Max. 48h.

| 🅂 | | St.Mamet-la-Salvetat | 29B2 |

Aire camping-cars, D20. **GPS:** n44,85714 e2,30981. 🔼➡.

3 🛏free 🚰€2/100liter 🔲Ch 🔌€2/1h WC. **Location:** Rural, simple, quiet.
Surface: asphalted. 🔲 01/01-31/12
Distance: ⊗500m 🛒350m.
Remarks: Coins at the shops and town hall.

| 🅂 | | St.Marcel-en-Murat | 22A4 |

D243. **GPS:** n46,32184 e3,00837. 🔼.

10 🛏free 🚰€2/100liter 🔲Ch 🔌€2/1h. **Location:** Rural, simple.
Surface: gravel. 🔲 01/01-31/12
Distance: 🚲3,5km exit 11 A71 ⊗nearby.
Remarks: Coins at town hall and restaurant.

| 🅂 | | St.Paul-des-Landes | 29B1 |

Aire camping-cars, Rue du Moinac. **GPS:** n44,94250 e2,31694. 🔼➡.

FR

3 ⛺free 🚰€3,50 ⚡Ch 🔌€3,50. **Location:** Rural, simple, central, quiet.
Surface: asphalted. 📅 01/01-31/12
Distance: 🛒50m ⊗200m 🚉50m.
Remarks: Coins at petrol station.

🅿🆂 St.Pourçain-sur-Sioule 🌊⚓🌿 22A4
Aire Camping-car de la Moutte, Rue de la Moutte. **GPS:** n46,31262 e3,29656.
⬆➡.

73 ⛺free 🚰€2 ⚡Ch 🧹(8x)€2/4h. **Location:** Urban, comfortable, central,
quiet. **Surface:** grassy. 📅 01/01-31/12
Distance: 🛒800m ⚓on the spot ⊗on the spot 🚉on the spot.
Remarks: Along the Sioule river.

🅿🆂 St.Rémy-de-Blot 22A5
Place du Bourg. **GPS:** n46,07722 e2,93139.⬆.

7 ⛺free WC. **Location:** Rural, simple, isolated, quiet. **Surface:** grasstiles.
📅 01/01-31/12
Distance: ⊗on the spot.

🅿🆂 St.Romain-Lachalm 29D1
Rulière. **GPS:** n45,26399 e4,33576.⬆.
4 ⛺free 🚰⚡Ch 🧹(4x)€2/4h. **Surface:** asphalted.
Distance: 🛒100m 🚉bakery 200m.
Remarks: Coins at the shops and town hall.

🅿🆂 St.Sauves d'Auvergne 🏔 21D6
Domaine de Lavaux, D82. **GPS:** n45,61688 e2,68975.⬆➡.

50 ⛺€8 🚰⚡Ch 🧹(10x)€4/day WC included 🚿€1,25 ◻€5. 🛁 **Location:**
Rural, comfortable, isolated, quiet. **Surface:** grassy. 📅 15/05-30/09

Distance: 🛒1km 🚶on the spot.

🅿🆂 Super Besse 🏕🏔❄ 22A6
Ronde de Vassivière. **GPS:** n45,50644 e2,85342.⬆➡.

172 ⛺€ 5,60/24h, € 37,80/8 days 🚰€1/20minutes ⚡Ch 🧹(100x)€2,40/4h
🛁.🚐🚾
Location: Comfortable, quiet. **Surface:** asphalted.
📅 01/01-31/12
Distance: 🛒300m ⊗300m 🎿on the spot 🚠300m.
Remarks: On ring-road around the lake, P5, P7 and P10, no camping activities.

🅿🆂 Super Lioran 🏔❄ 29B1
Aire de Laveissière, Parking Font d'Alagnon. **GPS:** n45,08856 e2,73819.🏃.

25 ⛺free. **Location:** Rural, simple, quiet. **Surface:** asphalted.
📅 01/01-31/12
Distance: ⊗200m 🚶200m 🚶50m 🎿30m 🚠30m.

🅿🆂 Talizat 29C1
Place du 19 mars 1962. **GPS:** n45,11417 e3,04583.

3 ⛺free 🚰€2 ⚡Ch 🔌€2. **Location:** Rural, simple, quiet.
Surface: asphalted. 📅 01/01-31/12
Distance: 🛒on the spot ⊗100m 🚉100m.
Remarks: Behind town hall.

🅿🆂 Thiel-sur-Acolin 22B4
Rue de la Motte. **GPS:** n46,52269 e3,58776.⬆.
11 ⛺free 🚰€2 ⚡Ch 🧹€2. **Location:** Rural, isolated, quiet.
Surface: gravel. 📅 01/01-31/12
Distance: 🛒650m.
Remarks: Service only by credit card.

🅿🆂 Thiers 22B6
Base de loisirs Iloa, D44 > Dorat. **GPS:** n45,87070 e3,48311.⬆.

FR

50 free free. **Location:** Rural, simple, isolated, quiet. **Surface:** metalled. ▢ 01/01-31/12 **Distance:** 2,6km.

⬛S **Thiézac** 29B1
Aire de camping-car "La Sapiniere", D59. **GPS:** n45,01583 e2,66278. ⬆➡

8 free €2 Ch €2. **Location:** Rural, simple, quiet. **Surface:** asphalted. ▢ 01/01-31/12 **Distance:** 50m ⊗100m 100m. **Remarks:** Max. 24h, coins at petrol station.

⬛S **Tiranges** 29D1
Accueil Camping Car, La Nerceyre. **GPS:** n45,30702 e3,99107. ⬆➡

10 free €2 Ch. **Location:** Rural, simple, quiet. **Surface:** asphalted. ▢ 01/01-31/12 **Distance:** 400m.

⬛S **Tourzel-Ronzières** 22A6
Aire camping-car, Chemin du Clos, D23. **GPS:** n45,52989 e3,13504. ⬆

15 free Ch WC free. **Location:** Rural, simple, isolated, quiet. **Surface:** grassy/gravel. ▢ 01/01-31/12 **Distance:** 500m ⊗500m.

⬛S **Treteau** 22B4
Rue du Rosier, D21. **GPS:** n46,36800 e3,51758. ⬆➡

+10 € 3,50/night €2 Ch €2 WC. **Location:** Rural, simple, quiet. **Surface:** grassy/metalled. ▢ 01/03-31/10 **Distance:** 500m on the spot day pass available ⊗100m on the spot. **Remarks:** At small lake.

⬛S **Valette** 29B1
Aire camping-cars, D678. **GPS:** n45,27000 e2,60222. ⬆➡

5 free €2 Ch €2. **Location:** Rural, comfortable, quiet. **Surface:** gravel. ▢ 01/01-31/12 ⦿ service: 01/11-01/05 **Distance:** 50m 100m ⊗150m.

⬛S **Valuéjols** 29C1
Place de 19 Mars 1962, D34. **GPS:** n45,05333 e2,92944.

12 free €3 Ch WC. **Location:** Rural, simple. **Surface:** asphalted. ▢ 01/01-31/12 **Distance:** 400m ⊗400m 400m on the spot.

⬛S **Varennes-sur-Allier** 22B4
Place Hôtel de Ville, Rue de Beaupuy. **GPS:** n46,31288 e3,40476. ⬆➡

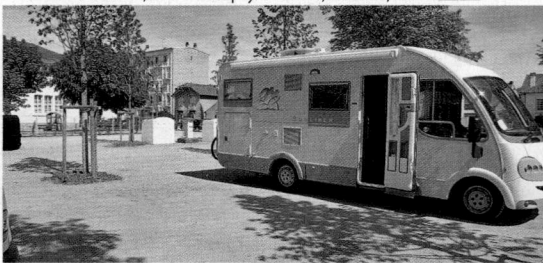

30 free €2/100liter Ch €2/h WC. **Location:** Urban, simple, central, noisy. **Surface:** metalled. ▢ 01/01-31/12 **Distance:** on the spot ⊗on the spot on the spot. **Remarks:** Coins at town hall.

⬛S **Velzic** 29B1
Lavernière, Rue de Fracort. **GPS:** n45,00166 e2,54638. ⬆➡

5 ⌂free ⚡€3,50 ☐Ch. **Location:** Rural, simple, isolated.
Surface: asphalted. ☐ 01/01-31/12 ☐ service: 31/10-01/04
Distance: ⛽1km ⊗1km ⚑1km ⚘on the spot.
Remarks: Coins at épicerie Pas de Peyrols.

4 ⌂free ⚡€2/10minutes ☐Ch ✎(4x)€2/2h. **Surface:** asphalted.
☐ 01/01-31/12
Distance: ⛽150m ✎12km ⊗150m ⚑150m.
Remarks: Coins available at the shops.

☐S	**Vézac**	29B2

Aire de camping-cars, Route de Cavanière. **GPS:** n44,89059 e2,51779. ⬆➡.

☐S	**Viverols**	29D1

Camping Le Pradoux, Le Ruisseau. **GPS:** n45,43123 e3,88279.

8 ⌂free ⚡€3,50 ☐Ch. **Location:** Rural, simple. **Surface:** asphalted.
☐ 01/01-31/12
Distance: ⛽100m ⊗50m ⚑700m.
Remarks: At golf court, coins at bar/tabac, 50m.

6 ⌂free ⚡€2 ☐Ch ⊟€2. **Surface:** gravel. ☐ 01/04-31/10

☐S	**Vorey-sur-Arzon**	29D1

Chemin de Félines. **GPS:** n45,18667 e3,90489. ⬆.

☐S	**Vic-sur-Cère**	29B1

Aire de camping-cars, Avenue des Tilleuls. **GPS:** n44,98194 e2,63111. ⬆➡.

10 ⌂free ⚡€2 ☐Ch ⊟€2. **Location:** Rural, comfortable, quiet.
Surface: asphalted. ☐ 01/01-31/12
Distance: ⛽200m ⊗200m ⚑150m.
Remarks: Coins at tourist info, Avenue Mercier.

5 ⌂€2 ⚡€3 ☐Ch ⊟. **Surface:** gravel. ☐ service: 01/04-31/10
Distance: ⛽200m ⛵on the spot ⊗200m ⚑200m ⚘on the spot
⚘on the spot.
Remarks: Along river Arzon, coins and code wifi available at campsite.

☐S	**Ytrac**	29B2

Aire camping-cars, Impasse Jean de la Fontaine. **GPS:** n44,91510 e2,36368. ⬆
➡.

☐S	**Vieillevie** 🌊	29B2

Aire de Vieillevie, Le Bourg. **GPS:** n44,64432 e2,41773. ⬆➡.

5 ⌂free ⚡€2 ☐Ch ⊟€2. **Location:** Rural, comfortable, quiet.
Surface: gravel. ☐ 01/01-31/12
Distance: ⛽50m ⛵100m ⚑50m.

3 ⌂free ⚡€3,50 ☐Ch ⊟€3,50. **Location:** Rural, simple, central.
Surface: asphalted. ☐ 01/01-31/12
Distance: ⛽150m ⊗100m ⚑150m.
Remarks: Coins at shops and tourist office.

Rhône Alpes

☐S	**Villefranche-d'Allier**	22A4

Avenue du 8 Mai 1945. **GPS:** n46,39565 e2,85672. ⬆.

☐S	**Aiguebelle**	23C6

Pré de foire. **GPS:** n45,54289 e6,30635. ⬆.

FR

18 ⌂free ⚡€2/100liter 🔲Ch. **Surface:** asphalted/grassy. ◼ 01/01-31/12 ◉ Thu-morning closed because of market
Distance: 🚶on the spot ⚓6,1km.
Tourist information Aiguebelle:
⚓ ◼ Tue-morning.

Aix-les-Bains 23B6
Avenue du Grand Port. **GPS:** n45,70504 e5,88810.⬆.

16 ⌂free ⚡free WC. **Location:** Urban, simple, noisy. **Surface:** gravel.
◼ 01/01-31/12
Distance: 🚶city centre 2km ⚓2km ⌂Lake 100m ⊗150m
🍞bread service 500m 🚌on the spot.
Remarks: Max. 48h, market Wednesday and Saturday.

Alba-la-Romaine 30A2
Bragigous. **GPS:** n44,55329 e4,59741.⬆.

⌂free ⚡€2 🔲Ch. **Location:** Rural, quiet. **Surface:** grassy/gravel.
◼ 01/01-31/12
Distance: 🚶on the spot ⊗200m 🍞200m.
Remarks: Service to be paid at retirement home.

Albertville 23C6
Parking Conflans, Montée Adolphe Hugues, Conflans. **GPS:** n45,67389 e6,39694.⬆.

6 ⌂free ⚡€3,50 🔲Ch 🗑. **Surface:** asphalted.
Distance: 🚶10 min walking.
Tourist information Albertville:
⚓ Quai des Allobroges. ◼ Thu 6-18h.

Allevard 30C1
Place du David. **GPS:** n45,38838 e6,07110.⬆➡.
+10 ⌂€4 ⚡🔲Ch WCfree. 🐕 **Location:** Rural. **Surface:** unpaved.
◼ 01/01-31/12
Distance: 🚶500m ⊗300m.
Remarks: Max. 48h.

Alpe d'Huez 30C1
Parking de Brandes. **GPS:** n45,08654 e6,07916.⬆➡.

75 ⌂€ 10/day + € 0,40/pp tourist tax ⚡🔲Ch 🚻WC.🚌🗑
Surface: asphalted.
Distance: 🚶1km 🐾on the spot.
Remarks: First buy a parking ticket at Palais des Sports et des Congrès.

Alpe d'Huez 30C1
Parking l'Eclose, Rue du 93me Ram. **GPS:** n45,08796 e6,07019.⬆➡.
25 ⌂€ 10/day + € 0,20/pp tourist tax ⚡🔲Ch 🚻WCincluded.
Surface: asphalted. ◼ 01/12-01/04, 11/07-31/08
Distance: 🚶200m ⊗200m 🍞200m 🐾on the spot.
Remarks: First buy a parking ticket at Palais des Sports et des Congrès.

Ambierle 22B5
Complexe sportif, Rue Sainte Claude. **GPS:** n46,10663 e3,89384.⬆➡.

3 ⌂free ⚡🔲Chfree.
Location: Rural, simple, quiet. **Surface:** asphalted.
Distance: 🚶on the spot ⊗200m 🍞300m.
Remarks: At sports park.

Amplepuis 22C5
Rue Paul de la Goutte. **GPS:** n45,97027 e4,33085.⬆.
⌂free ⚡🔲Chfree. **Surface:** asphalted.
Distance: 🚶on the spot ⊗50m 🍞100m 🚌on the spot.
Remarks: Behind gymnasium.

Annecy 23B5
Parking de Colmyr, Rue des Marquisats, N1508. **GPS:** n45,89070 e6,13915.⬆➡.

14 ⌂free ⚡🔲Chfree. **Location:** Urban, simple, central, quiet.
Surface: asphalted. ◼ 01/01-31/12
Distance: 🚶700m ⌂100m 🚐on the spot ⊗700m 🍞700m.
Remarks: Max. 24h, market days Tuesday, Friday, Sunday.

Tourist information Annecy:
🛈 Office de Tourisme, Bonlieu, 1 rue Jean Jaurès, www.lac-annecy.com. Located on lake of the same name and surrounded by mountain peaks. The old city centre exists of covered lanes, canals and bridges.
⚓ Place de Romains. ◼ Tue 7-19h.

Anthy-sur-Léman 23C4
Rue du Lac. **GPS:** n46,35889 e6,42192.

FR

5 free. **Surface:** gravel.
Distance: 700m 50m on the spot.
Remarks: Max. 48h, max. 7m.

| | Arçon | 22B5 |

Le Bourg. **GPS:** n46,00977 e3,88793.

3 free Ch free. **Location:** Rural, simple, quiet.
01/01-31/12
Distance: on the spot 50m.

| | Arlebosc | 30A1 |

Place du Marché aux Fruits. **GPS:** n45,03683 e4,65238.

10 free Ch free. **Location:** Rural, simple. **Surface:** gravel.
01/01-31/12
Distance: on the spot bakery 150m on the spot.

| | Aubignas | 30A2 |

Aire camping-cars. **GPS:** n44,58732 e4,63177.

10 voluntary contribution €2 €2/100liter Ch WC. **Surface:** gravel.
Distance: 300m.
Remarks: Beautiful view.

| | Balazuc | 30A2 |

Parking Champsgelly, La Croisette. **GPS:** n44,50601 e4,37366.

free. **Location:** Rural. **Surface:** gravel. 01/01-31/12
Distance: 1km.

| | Banne | 29D3 |

Quartier l'Eglise, D251. **GPS:** n44,36539 e4,15691.

25 free €2/60liter Ch €2/1h 2. **Surface:** gravel/metalled.
01/01-31/12
Distance: 500m.
Remarks: Behind church, beautiful view.

| | Barjac | 29D3 |

Rue Pierre Andre Benoit. **GPS:** n44,30589 e4,34343.

20 free Ch €3, water 10 min + electricity 55min. **Location:** Simple.
01/01-31/12
Distance: 100m 100m on the spot.
Remarks: Coins at tourist info and town hall, friday market.

| | Beausemblant | 30A1 |

Aire camping-cars, D122. **GPS:** n45,21826 e4,83282.

6 free Ch free. **Location:** Simple. **Surface:** gravel.
Distance: 100m 100m on the spot.
Remarks: Max. 48h.

| | Belleville | 22D5 |

Ancienne Avenue du Port. **GPS:** n46,10626 e4,75470.

FR

8 ☕free ⚰🔲🅒Chfree. **Surface:** asphalted. 🔲 01/01-31/12
Distance: 🚶centre 500m 🛣A6 900m ⊗500m 🚊500m.

🅶🆂 | Belley 🍽 | 23A6
Route de Saint-Germain, D41. **GPS:** n45,75535 e5,67790.⬆.

☕free ⚰🔲🅒Chfree. **Surface:** gravel. 🔲 01/01-31/12
Distance: 🚶200m ⊗200m 🚊300m.

🅶🆂 | Boulieu-lès-Annonay 🌿 | 30A1
Chemin du Lavoir. **GPS:** n45,26928 e4,66963.⬆➡.

20 ☕free ⚰€2 🔲🅒Ch🔲€2. **Location:** Urban, simple, central, quiet.
Surface: asphalted. 🔲 01/01-31/12
Distance: 🚶city centre 1km ⊗1km 🚊1km 🚌1km.
Remarks: Near sports park, service only with 1-euro coins.

🅶🆂 | Belmont-de-la-Loire | 22C5
Place de l'Église. **GPS:** n46,16543 e4,34634.⬆.

6 ☕free ⚰🔲🅒Ch WC free. **Location:** Rural, comfortable, quiet.
Surface: gravel.
Distance: 🚶400m ⊗400m 🚊400m.
Remarks: Voluntary contribution, market on Sunday.

🅶🆂 | Bourg-en-Bresse 🌿🍽 | 23A5
Parking V.L./Bus, Boulevard de Brou. **GPS:** n46,19854 e5,23766.⬆.

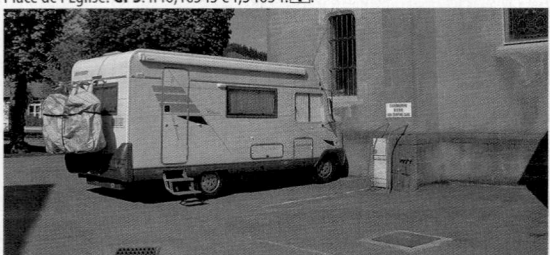

2 ☕free ⚰🔲🅒Ch🔲2 WC free. **Location:** Rural, simple, quiet.
Surface: metalled. 🔲 03/03-19/07, 01/08-31/10
Distance: 🚶50m ⊗100m 🚊100m 🚌on the spot.

🅶🆂 | Berrias-et-Casteljau 🏔📷 | 29D3
Place du 7 juillet, Les Borels. **GPS:** n44,39956 e4,21332.⬆.

10 ☕free WC 100m. **Location:** Urban, simple, central, noisy.
Surface: asphalted. 🔲 Wed, Sa
Distance: 🚶on the spot 🛣6km ⊗100m 🚊200m 🚌on the spot
🚲on the spot.

🅶🆂 | Bourg-St.Andéol | 30A3
Chemin de la Barrière. **GPS:** n44,37520 e4,64327.⬆.

☕free ⚰🔲🅒Ch🔲€3. **Surface:** gravel. 🔲 01/01-31/12
Distance: 🚶Berias-et-Casteljau 3,5km.

🅶🆂 | Bibost | 22D6
D91. **GPS:** n45,79500 e4,55144.⬆.
☕free ⚰🔲🅒Ch⚒free. **Location:** Rural, quiet. **Surface:** gravel.
🔲 01/01-31/12
Remarks: Beautiful view.

🅶🆂 | Boën | 22C6
Boulevard Moizieux. **GPS:** n45,74401 e4,00263.⬆⬆.

30 ☕free ⚰🔲🅒Ch⚒free. **Surface:** asphalted. 🔲 01/01-31/12
Distance: 🚶750m 🚊50m Lidl.
Remarks: Along railwayline, max. 48h.

🅶🆂 | Bourg-St.Maurice 🏔❄ | 23C6
Arc1600. **GPS:** n45,59523 e6,78951.
20 ☕free ⚰🔲€2. 🔲 01/01-31/12
Distance: 🚶Bourg St.Maurice 15km.

🅶🆂 | Bourget-du-Lac 🏔 | 23B6
International au l'Lle de Cygnes. GPS: n45,65250 e5,86378.⬆➡.

FR

32 ⛟€ 5,90-10,65 ⛽🔌 Ch WC 🛢 📶included. 🛒 🧺
Location: Rural, comfortable, quiet. **Surface:** metalled.
🅿 01/01-31/12 ⚪ service: 01/12-01/03
Distance: 🚶500m 🚲500m ⚓beach 300m 🚆100m ⊗on the spot 🍴on the spot 🚌100m 🚴on the spot 🎿on the spot.

Bourgneuf 23B6
Aire camping-cars, D925. **GPS**: n45,55257 e6,21091. ⬆️.

30 ⛟free ⛽€2 🔌Ch. 🅿 01/01-31/12
Distance: 🚲5km ⊗Brasserie/Pizzeria 🛒bakery.
Remarks: Coins available at Pizzeria/Tabac.

Bouvante 30B2
Font d'Urle, Font d'Urle. **GPS**: n44,89789 e5,32195. ⬆️.

10 ⛟free ⛽€2/100liter 🔌Ch 🚿(5x)€7/24h WC 🛢€2/time. **Location:** Simple, quiet. **Surface:** gravel. 🅿 01/01-31/12, service: 01/06-31/08
Distance: ⊗on the spot 🚶nordic walking 🎿on the spot.
Remarks: Altitude 1550m, coins at riding school.

Chalmazel 22B6
Le Bourg Le Pont d'Ouest. **GPS**: n45,70149 e3,85459. ⬆️.

8 ⛟free ⛽€2 🔌Ch 🚿€2/4h. **Location:** Comfortable. **Surface:** metalled.
🅿 01/01-31/12
Distance: 🚶50m ⚓on the spot ⊗50m 🛒50m 🚌on the spot 🚶on the spot 🎿2km.
Remarks: Along river.

Chambéry 23B6
Rue Costa de Beauregard. **GPS**: n45,56289 e5,93302. ⬆️.

6 ⛟free ⛽🔌Chfree. **Location:** Urban. **Surface:** asphalted.
Distance: 🚶500m 🚲1,2km ⊗500m 🚆500m.
Remarks: Water closed during wintertime.
Tourist information Chambéry:
👁 Vieux Cité. Historical centre with old mansions.
🏰 Château des Ducs de Savoie. Complex of buildings, 13-14th century.

Chamonix-Mont-Blanc 23D5
Parking Grépon, Aiguille du Midi, D1506. **GPS**: n45,91578 e6,86970. ⬆️.

50 ⛟€ 12,50/24h ⛽🔌Ch WCfree. **Surface:** asphalted.
🅿 01/01-31/12, service only during summer period
Distance: 🚶1km ⊗350m 🚆600m.
Tourist information Chamonix-Mont-Blanc:
☺ Aiguille du Midi. Telpher carrier from Chamonix (1036 m.) To Aiguille de Midi (3842m).
☺ Montenvers et mer de Glace. Tramline from Montenvers to the ice lake, a glacier of 7 km long and 1.2 km broad.

Chamrousse 30B1
Place des Niverolles, Rue de la Cembraie. **GPS**: n45,12666 e5,87356.

12 ⛟€ 8 ⛽🔌Ch 🚿 included. **Surface:** asphalted. 🅿 01/01-31/12
Distance: 🚶400m ⊗400m 🎿400m.
Remarks: Max. 24h.

Charix 23A5
Auberge du Lac Genin. **GPS**: n46,21981 e5,69556. ⬆️.

20 ⛟€ 5 + € 0,20/pp tourist tax, guests free ⛽🔌Chfree. 🛵
Location: Rural, simple, isolated, quiet. **Surface:** gravel.
Distance: 🚶4,7km ⚓lake 🛒on the spot ⊗on the spot 🚴on the spot 🚶on the spot.

Charlieu 22C5
Place d'Eningen. **GPS**: n46,16031 e4,17813. ⬆️.

FR

5 🛏free 🚰 Ch WC free. **Location:** Rural. **Surface:** gravel/metalled.
⬛ 01/01-31/12
Distance: 🚶historical centre 500m ⊗500m 🚊500m.
Remarks: In front of police station.

🛏🅢 **Charols** 30A2
Aire municipale, D9. **GPS:** n44,59160 e4,95441.

10 🛏free 🚰 🛢free. **Surface:** asphalted. ⬛ 01/01-31/12
Distance: 🚶200m ⊗200m 🚊50m.

🛏🅢 **Chichilianne** 30B2
Passière. **GPS:** n44,81226 e5,57532.⬆.

🛏free 🚰€3 🛢 Ch. **Surface:** grassy. ⬛ 01/01-31/12 ⚫ water
disconnected in winter. **Distance:** 🚶on the spot ⊗on the spot.
Remarks: Coins at town hall or Maison du Parc.

🛏🅢 **Clansayes** 🌼♿ 30A3
Aire de Toronne, Quartier Toronne RD133. **GPS:** n44,36975 e4,79901.⬆.

25 🛏€ 10, Jul/Aug € 13 🚰🛢 Ch ⚡€4/day WC 🛢€4/time 📶.♿
Location: Rural, comfortable, luxurious, isolated, quiet. **Surface:** grassy/gravel.
⬛ 01/01-31/12
Distance: 🚶2km 🚲10km ⊗buvette-menu rapide-restauration 🚊3km.
Remarks: Bread-service.

🛏🅢 **Colombier-le-Jeune** 30A1
Place de la Marie, Le Bourg. **GPS:** n45,01106 e4,70132.⬆.

🛏free 🚰🛢 Ch free. **Location:** Rural. **Surface:** metalled. ⬛ 01/01-31/12
⚫ water disconnected in winter
Distance: 🚶on the spot ⊗on the spot 🚊on the spot 🚶on the spot.

🛏🅢 **Cornas** 30A2
Impasse de Iris, Grande Rue, D86. **GPS:** n44,96024 e4,84722.⬆.

5 🛏free 🚰🛢 Ch free. **Location:** Simple. **Surface:** gravel.
⬛ 01/01-31/12
Distance: 🚶200m ⊗200m 🛒bakery 200m.
Remarks: Max. 48h, several 'Caves' with wine tasting.

🛏🅢 **Coucouron** 🛶 29D2
Les Eygades. **GPS:** n44,80168 e3,96148.⬆.

30 🛏01/05-30/09 € 7/day 🚰🛢 Ch 🔌included. ♿ **Location:** Rural, simple.
Surface: gravel. ⬛ 01/01-31/12
Distance: 🚶1km 🚲on the spot ⊗on the spot 🚊1km 🚶on the spot.
Remarks: At Lac de Coucouron, max. 7 days, outside season free stay on
campsite municipal (no facilities).

🛏🅢 **Cours-la-Ville** 22C5
La Rivière. **GPS:** n46,10399 e4,32315.⬆.

10 🛏free 🚰🛢 Ch free. **Location:** Rural, simple. **Surface:** grassy/gravel.
⬛ 01/01-31/12
Distance: 🚶300m ⊗on the spot 🚐on the spot 🚶on the spot.
Remarks: Along the river Trambouze, to be reached from northern direction,
Boulevard Pierre de Coubertin.

🛏🅢 **Courtenay** 🛶 23A6
Etang de Salette. **GPS:** n45,72417 e5,37124.⬆.

7 🅿free. **Location:** Rural, isolated, quiet. **Surface:** gravel.
Distance: 🚲1km ⊗Pizzeria 🥖bread service 1,2km 🚶on the spot.

🅿S | **Crémieu** 🏊🎣🛒 | 23A6
Rue du 19 mars 1962. **GPS:** n45,72549 e5,24670.⬆.

12 🅿free ⚡🔌Ch free. **Location:** Urban, simple, central. **Surface:** asphalted.
◻ 01/01-31/12
Distance: 🚲300m ⊗250m 🍽300m 🚌100m.

🅿S | **Crest** 🎣🏊 | 30A2
Place du Champ de Mars, Avenue Agirond. **GPS:** n44,72600 e5,02100.⬆.

17 🅿free ⚡🔌Ch ⚡€5,10min. water +1h electricity 📶free.
Location: Urban, simple. **Surface:** asphalted. ◻ 01/01-31/12
Distance: 🚲200m ⊗pizzeria 🍽bakery 50m.

🅿S | **Die** 🏊🎣🏔 | 30B2
Aire de Meyrosse, Avenue du Maréchal Leclerc, D238. **GPS:** n44,75103 e5,37385.
⬆.

30 🅿€5/24h ⚡🔌Ch WC free.
Surface: grassy/gravel. ◻ 01/01-31/12
Distance: 🚲300m ⊗300m 🍽1km.
Remarks: Max. 1 night, pay at Police Municpale.

🅿S | **Donzère** | 30A2
Aire de respos. GPS: n44,44060 e4,71899.⬆➡.

🅿free ⚡🔌Ch WC free. **Surface:** asphalted. ◻ 01/01-31/12
Distance: 🚲500m 🚤7km.
Remarks: Near RN7.

🅿S | **Eyzin-Pinet** | 30A1
Rue du Stade. **GPS:** n45,47463 e4,99965.⬆.

6 🅿free ⚡🔌Ch free. **Location:** Rural, simple, central, quiet. **Surface:** gravel.
◻ 01/01-31/12
Distance: 🚲50m ⊗50m 🗑20m 🚴on the spot 🚶on the spot.

🅿S | **Faverges** 🏊🎣🏔 | 23C6
Route d'Annecy, D2508. **GPS:** n45,74943 e6,28626.⬆➡.

20 🅿free ⚡🔌Ch free. **Location:** Rural, simple, noisy. **Surface:** gravel.
◻ 01/01-31/12 ⊙ Service: winter
Distance: 🚲800m ⊗800m 🍽on the spot 🎿100m ⛷100m.
Remarks: Max. 48h, market Wednesday.

🅿S | **Flaine** | 23C5
Parking P1. **GPS:** n46,00377 e6,69083.

25 🅿€5. **Surface:** gravel. ◻ 01/01-31/12
Distance: 🎿on the spot.
Remarks: Parking at skipistes.

🅿S | **Fontanes** | 22C6
Hameau Chantemerle. **GPS:** n45,54681 e4,44027.⬆.

3 ᗧfree 🚰🧺 Ch free. **Location:** Rural, simple, quiet. **Surface:** asphalted.
📷 01/01-31/12
Distance: 🚶500m 🚲 13km 🥾400m.
Remarks: At tennis-courts, inclining pitches.

♿S   **Gervans**   30A1
Place des Amandiers, Rue de l'école. **GPS:** n45,10932 e4,83031. ⬆️➡️.

4 ᗧfree 🚰🧺 Ch free. **Location:** Simple. **Surface:** gravel.
Distance: 🚶on the spot 🛒on the spot 🥾on the spot.
Remarks: Max. 24h, no camping activities.

♿S   **Grane**   30A2
Domaine Distaise, D104. **GPS:** n44,75564 e4,86768. ⬆️➡️.

15 ᗧ€2/pp 🚰📶. **Surface:** grassy. 📷 01/01-31/12

♿S   **Gresse-en-Vercors**   30B2
D8D, La Ville. **GPS:** n44,89184 e5,54766.

ᗧfree 🚰🧺 Ch. **Surface:** gravel.
Distance: 🚶on the spot.
Remarks: Max. 24h, service on campsite.

♿S   **Hauteluce**   23C6
Parking de la Fôret, Tetras, D123. **GPS:** n45,74633 e6,53441.

5 ᗧfree 🚰€2 🧺 Ch 📷€2. **Surface:** gravel. 📷 01/01-31/12
Distance: 🚶3km 🛒3km 🛒3km.

♿S   **Hauteluce** 🚵🏔️❄️   23C6
Parking Du Col des Saisies, D218b. **GPS:** n45,76297 e6,53382. ⬆️➡️.

40 ᗧ€8 🚰€2 🧺 Ch 📷€2 WC. **Surface:** asphalted. 📷 01/01-31/12
Distance: 🚶500m 🛒on the spot 🛒500m 🚴200m 200m.

♿S   **Hauterives** 🚵   30A1
D538. **GPS:** n45,25497 e5,03022.

ᗧfree, 01/04-31/10 €5/24h 🚰€2/50liter 🧺Ch included WC free.
Location: Rural, simple. **Surface:** gravel.
Distance: 🚶250m 🛒250m.

Tourist information Hauterives:
👁 Palais Idéal du Facteur Cheval.

♿S   **Illiat** 🌾   22D5
GPS: n46,18495 e4,88802. ⬆️.

4 ᗧfree 🚰🧺 Ch WC free. **Location:** Rural, simple, quiet. **Surface:** gravel.
📷 01/01-31/12
Distance: 🚶650m 🏊on the spot 🚣on the spot 🛒650m 🚵on the spot 🥾on the spot.
Remarks: At small lake.

♿S   **Izernore** 🌿🚵   23A5
Rue de l'Oignin. **GPS:** n46,21847 e5,55041. 🚫.

FR

15 ⬛free ⌐ 🔄 Ch free. **Location:** Rural, simple, central, quiet.
🔲 01/01-31/12
Distance: 🚰on the spot 🛒6km ⊗500m 🚮500m ♨500m ⚓500m.
Remarks: On the foot of the Monts Berthiand.

🔲S **Joux** 🚶 🌊 **22C5**
Salle des Fêtes, La Noirie, D79. **GPS:** n45,88869 e4,37587.⬆️.

10 ⬛free ⌐ 🔄 Ch free. **Location:** Rural. **Surface:** asphalted.
🔲 01/01-31/12 ⦿ water disconnected in winter
Distance: 🚰200m 🛒3,2km ⊗200m 🚮200m.
Remarks: Nearby castle garden.

🔲S **La Balme de Sillingy** 🚶🚶 **23B5**
Aire de Camping-cars Domaine du Tornet, D508. **GPS:** n45,97124 e6,03135.
⬆️⬆️.

30 ⬛€5 ⌐ 🔄 Ch free. 🚲 **Location:** Rural, simple, central, quiet.
Surface: gravel. 🔲 01/04-31/10
Distance: 🚰100m (fishing permit available) ⊗100m ♨on the spot.
Remarks: Recreation park, max. 48h.

🔲 **La Clusaz** **23C5**
Route des Confins. **GPS:** n45,92298 e6,48380.
⬛free. **Surface:** asphalted. 🔲 01/01-31/12
Remarks: Parking at pistes.

🔲S **La Féclaz** ⛷️ 🚶🚶 ❄️ **23B6**
Aire Camping-cars de la Féclaz, D206a. **GPS:** n45,64210 e5,98411.⬆️.

40 ⬛€4 ⌐€1,50 🔄 Ch 🔲€1,50 🧺. **Surface:** asphalted. 🔲 01/01-31/12
Distance: 🚰on the spot ⊗on the spot 🚮on the spot ▣300m.

🔲S **Lablachère** **29D2**
La Ferme Théâtre, D104, Notre Dame. **GPS:** n44,45481 e4,22004.⬆️.

20 ⬛€5/24h, guests free ⌐€2 🧺€3/12h.
Location: Rural. **Surface:** gravel.
🔲 01/01-31/12
Distance: 🚰1km ⊗150m.
Remarks: Max. 24h, theater, regional products.

🔲S **Lachamp-Raphaël** 🚶🚶 **29D2**
D122, Le Village. **GPS:** n44,81133 e4,28860.⬆️.

5 ⬛free ⌐€2 🔄 Ch. **Location:** Rural, simple, quiet. **Surface:** gravel.
🔲 01/01-31/12
Distance: 🚰300m ⊗300m 🚮Bread 300m ♨departure Nordic.
Remarks: Altitude 1330m, 2013: during inspection service out of order, coins at bar/hotel, beautiful view.

🔲S **Lalouvesc** 🚶🚶 **30A1**
Vallon d'Or, Sainte Agathe. **GPS:** n45,11947 e4,53384.⬆️.

3 ⬛free WC. **Location:** Simple, central. **Surface:** asphalted.
🔲 01/01-31/12
Distance: 🚰on the spot ⊗100m 🚮100m.

🔲S **Lalouvesc** 🚶🚶 **30A1**
La Fontaine. **GPS:** n45,12149 e4,53393.⬆️.

⌐€2/15minutes 🔄Ch🔲€2. 🔲 15/05-15/10
Remarks: Coins at petrol station and camping municipal.

🔲S **Lamastre** **30A1**
Parking Pont de Tain, Place Pradon. **GPS:** n44,98672 e4,58001.⬆️.

20 🅢 free ⛽€4,40/100liter 🅢 Ch ➕€2,20/1h 🗑. **Location:** Simple.
Surface: asphalted. ☐ 01/01-31/12
Distance: 🔵on the spot ⊗on the spot ⚡on the spot.

🅢🅢 **Lamure-sur-Azergues** 22C5
Place de la gare. **GPS:** n46,06120 e4,49185. ⬆️➡️

10 🅢 free ⛽€2 🅢 Ch ➕€2 WC. **Location:** Rural, simple.
Surface: asphalted. ☐ 01/01-31/12
Distance: 🔵on the spot ⊗100m ⚡100m 🚂train/bus 🔵on the spot.
Remarks: Near train station.

🅢🅢 **Lans-en-Vercors** 30B1
Route de l'Aigle. **GPS:** n45,12570 e5,59002. ⬆️➡️

30 🅢 free ⛽🅢 Ch WC free. **Location:** Rural, simple. **Surface:** gravel.
☐ 01/01-31/12
Distance: 🔵500m 🏊on the spot.
Remarks: Large parking, tuesday and Saturday market.

🅢🅢 **Lathuile** 23B6
Les Jardin du Tailleter, 190 route de la Porte, Bout du lac, N 508.
GPS: n45,79480 e6,20796. ⬆️➡️

4 🅢 free ⛽€2,50/20minutes 🅢 Ch ⚡(4x)€2,50/6h.
Location: Rural.
Surface: asphalted.
☐ 01/01-31/12
Distance: 🔵1km ⊗100m 🚵mountainbike trail 🔵on the spot 🏊on the spot.
Remarks: Altitude 1200m, coins at Chalet des Alpes and the shops.

🅢🅢 **Le Cheylard** 30A2
Super U, Chemin du pre-jalla, ZI la Palisse. **GPS:** n44,91143 e4,44162. ⬆️

20 🅢 free ⛽€2 🅢 Ch ➕€2. **Location:** Simple, noisy. **Surface:** asphalted.
☐ 01/01-31/12
Distance: ⊗on the spot ⚡on the spot.
Remarks: Max. 24h.

🅢🅢 **Le Cheylas** 30C1
Avenue de la Libération. **GPS:** n45,37170 e5,99014.
🅢 free ⛽🅢 Ch WC free. **Surface:** asphalted/metalled.
Distance: 🔵on the spot ⚡nearby.

🅢 **Le Grand Bornand** 23C5
Route de La Broderie. **GPS:** n45,94144 e6,43636.

10 🅢 free. **Surface:** metalled. ☐ 01/01-31/12
Distance: 🔵600m 🏊on the spot.
Remarks: Max. 48h.

🅢 **Le Lac d'Issarlès** 29D2
D16. **GPS:** n44,81948 e4,06156. ⬆️

24 🅢 €8 ⛽🅢 Ch included ⚡(24x)€2 🗑. 🛁 **Location:** Rural, simple.
Surface: grassy. ☐ 01/06-31/08
Distance: 🏞Lake of Annecy 750m.
Remarks: Max. 24h.

🅢🅢 **Le Bessat** 30A1
Croix de Chaubouret. **GPS:** n45,36812 e4,52768. ⬆️

16 🅢 €8,50 + €0,25/pp tourist tax ⛽🅢 Ch ⚡ WC included. 🛁
Location: Central. **Surface:** metalled. ☐ 01/05-31/10

Distance: 🚶100m ⊗100m 🚲100m.
Remarks: Attention: this town is not Issarlès!.

🏕🅂 **Le Reposoir** 23C5
Route Departementale D204. **GPS:** n46,01010 e6,53648.

10 💤free 🚰🔌 Ch free WC. **Surface:** metalled.
Distance: 🚶150m 🏃on the spot.

💤🅂 **Le Teil** 30A2
Alleé Paul Avon. **GPS:** n44,55138 e4,68972.⬆.

6 💤free 🚰🔌 Ch free. **Location:** Noisy. **Surface:** grassy/metalled.
Distance: 🏊on the spot ⊗on the spot 🚲500m.
Remarks: Nearby D86.

Tourist information Le Teil:
🎪 ⬤ Thu morning.

💤🅂 **Les Carroz-Arâches** 🏕🏔❄ 23C5
Télécabine Les Cluses. **GPS:** n46,02500 e6,64361.

💤free 🚰🔌 Ch 🔧 free. ⬤ 01/06-30/11
Distance: 🚶500m ⊗500m.
Remarks: Parking funicular railway.

💤🅂 **Les Deux-Alpes** 30C1
Avenue de la Muzelle, D213. **GPS:** n45,02394 e6,12120.⬆.
💤€7 🚰🔌Ch🔧included. **Surface:** asphalted. ⬤ winter
Remarks: Beautiful view.

💤🅂 **Les Gets** 🏕🏔❄ 23C5
Route du Front de Neige. **GPS:** n46,14992 e6,65673.⬆.

25 💤€ 0,90/pp tourist tax, winter € 17 🚰🔌Ch🍴 🔧. **Surface:** gravel.
⬤ 01/01-31/12
Distance: 🚶1km 🏃on the spot.
Remarks: Max. 7 days, bus to centre every 30 minutes.

Tourist information Les Gets:
🎪 Week market. ⬤ Thu-morning.

💤🅂 **Les Granges-Gontardes** 30A3
Domaine de la Tour d'Elyssas, Quartier Combe d'Elissas.
GPS: n44,41811 e4,75465.

15 💤free 🚰🔌 Ch 🔧 free. **Surface:** gravel. ⬤ 01/01-31/12
Distance: 🚲9km.
Remarks: At wine-grower.

💤🅂 **Les Houches** 23C5
Aire d'accueil camping-car Mont Blanc, 500 route du Pont.
GPS: n45,89257 e6,81706.⬆➡.
22 💤€15 🚰🔌Ch 🔧📶included. **Location:** Comfortable, isolated, quiet.
Surface: gravel. ⬤ 01/04-30/11
Distance: 🚶2,5km ⊗1km 🚲1km 🚌500m.

🅂 **Les Karellis** 30C1
GPS: n45,22778 e6,40639.
💤free. ⬤ 01/01-31/12
Remarks: Mountain station nearby St.Jean-de-Maurienne.

💤🅂 **Les Menuires** 🏔❄ 30C1
Les Bruyères, Dir Val Thorens. **GPS:** n45,32557 e6,53414.⬆➡.
70 💤€ 10/24h + € 0,20/pp tourist tax 🚰🔌 Ch 🔧 (7x)€2/4h WC 🔧.
Surface: asphalted. ⬤ 01/01-31/12
Distance: 🚶on the spot ⊗on the spot 🚲on the spot.
Remarks: Near the pistes.

💤🅂 **Les Noës** 22B5
Le Bourg, D47. **GPS:** n46,04083 e3,85206.⬆.

3 💤free 🚰🔌 Ch free. **Location:** Rural, simple, quiet. **Surface:** gravel.
⬤ 01/01-31/12
Distance: 🚶on the spot ⊗50m.

💤🅂 **Les Sauvages** 22C5
D121. **GPS:** n45,92083 e4,37711.⬆➡.

💤free 🚰🔌 Ch free. **Location:** Rural, simple, quiet. **Surface:** gravel.

🅿 01/01-31/12
Distance: 🚰on the spot ⊗100m 🛒100m 🚶on the spot.

🅂 ――――――― **Mâcot-la-Plagne** 🏔 ❄ ――――― 23C6
GPS: n45,50677 e6,68652.⬆.
46 🅿free, Winter € 10 ⌁€2 🚰 Ch 🔌 €4/8h. **Surface:** asphalted.
🅿 01/01-31/12
Distance: 🎿on the spot.

🅂 ――――――― **Marsanne** 🌿 ――――――― 30A2
Avenue de Bailliencourt, D57. **GPS:** n44,64568 e4,87175.⬆.

10 🅿free ⌁ 🚰Chfree. **Location:** Rural, quiet. **Surface:** grassy.
Distance: 🚰300m 🛒300m 🚶nearby.
Remarks: Max. 48h, medieval village.

――――――――― **Megève** ――――――――― 23C6
Chemin des Ânes. **GPS:** n45,86401 e6,62010.
🅿free. 🅿 01/01-31/12
Remarks: In front of parking Télécabine du Jaillet.

🅂 ――――――――― **Meyras** ――――――――― 29D2
Aire camping-cars, Grande rue, D26. **GPS:** n44,67939 e4,26847.⬆.

15 🅿€4 ⌁€3 🚰 Ch 🔧€3. 🛁 **Surface:** asphalted. 🅿 01/04-31/10
Distance: 🚰200m ⊗200m 🛒nearby.
Remarks: Max. 48h, coins at the shops in the village.

🅂 ――――――――― **Mijoux** 🌿 ⛷ 🏔 ❄ ――――――― 23B4
D50, Route de la Combe-en-Haut. **GPS:** n46,36963 e6,00247.⬆➡.

20 🅿free ⌁€3,50 🚰 Ch 🔧€3,50. **Surface:** gravel. ⏺ Service: winter
Distance: 🚰500m ⊗500m 🛒500m 🎿on the spot ⛷on the spot.
Remarks: Coins at town hall and supermarket.

🅂 ――――――― **Mirabel-aux-Baronnies** ――――――― 30A3
Aire camping-cars, Chemin des Grottes. **GPS:** n44,31260 e5,09968.⬆.

6+10 🅿voluntary contribution ⌁ 🚰Chfree. **Location:** Rural.
Surface: grassy/metalled. 🅿 01/01-31/12
Distance: 🚰200m.

🅲🅂 ――――――― **Montalieu-Vercieu** ――――――― 23A6
Chamboud. **GPS:** n45,82776 e5,42100.⬆.

6 🅿free ⌁ 🚰Ch WC campsite.
Location: Rural, simple, isolated, quiet.
Surface: asphalted.
Distance: 🚰2km ⊗2km 🛒2km 🚗1,5km.
Remarks: Next to campsite/Base de Loisirs de la Vallée Bleue, max. 2 nights.

🅂 ――――――― **Montbrison-sur-Lez** ――――――― 30A2
Place Publique. GPS: n44,43663 e5,01779.⬆.

6 🅿free 🔌 free. **Surface:** metalled. 🅿 01/01-31/12
Distance: 🚰100m ⊗100m 🛒100m.

🅂 ――――――― **Montbrison-sur-Lez** ――――――― 30A2
GPS: n44,42751 e5,02438.⬆.

⌁€2/60liter 🚰Ch 🔧€2. **Location:** Isolated.
Remarks: Coins at bar and garage.

🅂 ――――――― **Montbrun-les-Bains** 🌿 🍷 ――――――― 30B3
Toscan. **GPS:** n44,17247 e5,43881.⬆➡.

10 ⌃free. **Location:** Rural, quiet. **Surface:** grassy. ☐ 01/01-31/12
Distance: 🚶500m ⊗300m ⛲400m 🚲on the spot
🚶400m Tour de la Citadelle.

S | **Montbrun-les-Bains** 🌿♨ | **30B3**
Condamine. **GPS:** n44,17413 e5,44071.⬆.
🚰€2 🚽Ch➕€2.

🚐S | **Montélimar** | **30A2**
Domaine du Bois de Laud, Chemin du Bois de Laud. **GPS:** n44,56522 e4,75691.
⬆➡.

17 ⌃€ 4,30 🚰🚽Chincluded.🏠 📦 **Location:** Urban.
Surface: grassy/metalled. ☐ 01/01-31/12
Distance: 🚶500m ⛲100m.
Remarks: Near centre commercial Leclerc, max. 48h.

🚐S | **Morillon** 🌿♨🏔❄ | **23C5**
GPS: n46,08289 e6,67968.⬆➡.
10 ⌃free 🚰Ch WCfree. **Surface:** asphalted.
Distance: 🚶200m ⊗100m ⛲300m 🚴100m.

🚐S | **Nantua** 🍴🏔 | **23A5**
D74. **GPS:** n46,15497 e5,59656.⬆➡.

13 ⌃€ 7 + € 0,20/pp tourist tax 🚰🚽Chfree WC. 👣 **Location:** Urban,
comfortable, central. **Surface:** gravel. ☐ 01/04-30/09
Distance: 🚶700m 🚲7km ⛱on the spot 🛒on the spot ⊗150m ⛲150m
🚲on the spot 🚶on the spot.
Remarks: At Nantua lake.

🚐S | **Noirétable** ⛲🏔🍴📦 | **22B6**
Aire d'accueil de camping-cars, Lieu-dit La Roche. **GPS:** n45,80674 e3,77133.
⬆➡.

7 ⌃free 🚰€3 🚽Ch➕ 🚿€1/2h 📦. **Location:** Simple, quiet.
Surface: metalled. ☐ 01/01-31/12
Distance: 🚶800m 🏊100m 🚴100m ⊗100m ⛲800m 🚌on the spot
🚲on the spot 🚶on the spot.
Remarks: Next to campsite (50m), coins at campsite.

🚐S | **Nyons** | **30B3**
Promenade la Digue. **GPS:** n44,35778 e5,13861.⬆.

20 ⌃€ 9/24h 🚰🚽Ch WCincluded 🚿.🏠 📦 **Surface:** gravel.
☐ 01/01-31/12
Distance: 🚶250m ⊗250m ⛲250m 🗑250m.
Remarks: Next to Parc loisirs aquatique, max. 48h.

🚐S | **Nyons** | **30B3**
Domaine Rocheville, D 538. **GPS:** n44,36850 e5,11775.⬆.

6 ⌃€ 6, 2 pers.incl 🚰€4/100liter 🚽Ch 🚿€3,50 WC 🗑included,summer
📶free. **Surface:** grassy.

Tourist information Nyons:
ℹ️ Pavillon du Tourisme, Place de la Libération. Important Olive-city in the
Provence.
Ⓜ Musée de l'Olivier. Museum about the olive-tree and production of olive oil.
☐ daily ☐ 01/11-28/02 Su.
🚶 Centre-ville. Regional market. ☐ Thu-morning.

🚐S | **Orgnac l'Aven** | **30A3**
Le Fez, D217. **GPS:** n44,30419 e4,43240.⬆.

5 ⌃free 🚰🚽Chfree.
Location: Rural. **Surface:** gravel. ☐ 01/01-31/12

FR

Distance: 🚆200m ⊗10m 🛒300m.
Remarks: Caves of Aven d'Orgnac 2km.

🏕️S **Panissières** 22C6
Aire camping-cars, Allée des Acacias. **GPS:** n45,78835 e4,34355.⬆️.

4 🍴 € 6,50 🚐🔌 Ch 🚿 included4 WC 🗑️use sanitary € 3,30/pp 🧺.
Location: Rural, simple, quiet. **Surface:** metalled.
📷 01/01-31/12 ◉ Service: winter
Distance: 🚆300m ⊗300m 🛒300m.
Remarks: Use sanitary € 2,40/pp per day.

🏕️S **Planfoy** ⛲ 30A1
Chemin du Vignolet. **GPS:** n45,37445 e4,44910.⬆️➡️.

10 🍴free 🚐€2,50/15minutes 🔌 Ch 🚿 (8x)€2,50/6h.
Location: Rural, comfortable, quiet. **Surface:** asphalted. 📷 01/01-31/12
Distance: 🚆1,3km 🚲7km 🛒1,3km 🥾on the spot.
Remarks: Coins at the shops in the village.

🏕️S **Poncin** 🌿 🏞️ 🏖️ 23A5
Rue de la Verchère. **GPS:** n46,08710 e5,40396.⬆️➡️.

5 🍴free 🚐🔌 Ch free. **Location:** Urban, simple, central, quiet.
Surface: gravel/metalled.
Distance: 🚆on the spot 🚲1km 🛒200m ♿on the spot 🥾on the spot.
Remarks: Nearby Stade Guy Drut.

🏠 **Pont-de-Veyle** 22D5
D933, Rue de la Poste. **GPS:** n46,26437 e4,88697.⬆️.

20 🍴free 🚐🔌.
Location: Urban, simple, central, noisy. **Surface:** gravel.

Distance: 🚆on the spot 🚲3,5km 🏊on the spot 🎣on the spot ⊗50m 🛒150m.

🏕️S **Pontcharra-sur-Turdine** 22C6
Place A. Schweitzer. **GPS:** n45,87405 e4,49133.⬆️.

4 🍴free 🚐🔌 Ch WC free. **Location:** Urban.
📷 01/01-31/12
Distance: 🚆50m 🏊on the spot ⊗50m 🛒50m 🚌on the spot.

🏕️S **Pouilly-sous-Charlieu** 22C5
Place du Marché, Rue de la République. **GPS:** n46,14335 e4,10832.⬆️.
🍴free 🚐🔌 Ch WC free. **Surface:** asphalted. ◉ Su-morning (market)
Distance: 🚆on the spot.

🏕️S **Pouilly-sous-Charlieu** 22C5
Rue de la Berge. **GPS:** n46,14699 e4,10075.
4 🍴free. **Surface:** gravel. 📷 01/01-31/12
Remarks: Parking at the Loire river.

🏕️S **Prapoutel-les-Sept-Laux** 30C1
D281. **GPS:** n45,25769 e5,99785.

🍴free 🚐 WC. **Surface:** metalled. 📷 01/01-31/12
Distance: 🎿50m.
Remarks: Parking at pistes.

🏕️S **Privas** 30A2
Avenue de la gare. **GPS:** n44,73134 e4,59309.⬆️.

10 🍴free 🚐🔌 Ch. **Location:** Urban. **Surface:** gravel/metalled.
📷 01/01-31/12
Distance: 🚆centre 750m.

🏕️S **Puy-Saint-Martin** 30A2
Aire de camping-car. **GPS:** n44,62753 e4,97492.⬆️➡️.

13 ⛺free 🚰🚽Ch. **Location:** Rural, comfortable. **Surface:** grassy.
Distance: 🛒on the spot ⊗50m 🥖bakery 300m.
Remarks: Former campsite, max. 48h, voluntary contribution.

		Renaison 🌳🏕️	22B5

GPS: n46,04757 e3,92124. ⬆️➡️.

10 ⛺€6 🚰€2/15minutes 🔌€2 Ch€2 🔋€2,10 ⚡€2/8kWh WC ♻️.🚿🚗
Location: Urban, comfortable, quiet. **Surface:** metalled.
🅿️ 01/01-31/12
Distance: 🛒500m 🏊on the spot 🚆500m ⊗2km 🥖2km 🚌on the spot
🚴on the spot 🚶on the spot
Remarks: Max. 72h.

		Romans-sur-Isère 🍲	30A1

Avenue Gambetta. **GPS:** n45,04521 e5,05879. ⬆️.

5 ⛺free 🚰🚽Chfree. **Location:** Rural, simple, quiet. **Surface:** grassy/gravel.
🅿️ 01/01-31/12
Distance: 🛒400m 🏊on the spot 🥖700m.
Remarks: Along river.

🍴S		**Renaison** 🌳🏕️	22B5

Auberge du Barrage, La Tâche, D41 dir les Barrages. **GPS:** n46,04519 e3,87272.

4 ⛺free. **Location:** Urban, simple. **Surface:** metalled.
🅿️ 01/01-31/12
Distance: 🛒centre 700m.
Remarks: Parking in front of Marques Avenue, max. 48h.

		Saillans	30B2

Parking Gite Rural, Montmartel. **GPS:** n44,69549 e5,19350. ⬆️➡️.

12 ⛺€4, free with a meal 🚰🚽Ch 🔋€4,guestsfree ♻️. **Surface:** grassy.
🅿️ 15/03-01/11 🅿️ Mon, Tue (except Jul/Aug)
Distance: 🛒Renaison ± 4km 🏊100m ⊗on the spot 🥖4km.
Remarks: Construction work during inspection June 2013.

		Reventin-Vaugris	30A1

Rue Mouret. **GPS:** n45,46821 e4,84239. ⬆️.

20 ⛺free 🚰€2 🚽Ch. **Location:** Rural, simple. **Surface:** gravel.
Distance: 🛒300m.
Remarks: Along the Drôme river, closed when high water.

		Saint-Agrève 🍴	30A1

Coussac. **GPS:** n45,01042 e4,39339. ⬆️.

10 ⛺free 🚰WC. **Location:** Rural, simple, central, quiet.
Surface: gravel/metalled. 🅿️ 01/01-31/12
Distance: 🛒on the spot 🚲6km ⊗20m 🥖bakery 10m.

		Roanne 🌳🍲	22C5

Port de Plaisance, Allée Amiral Vermeilleux du Vignaux.
GPS: n46,03750 e4,08306. ⬆️➡️.

⛺free 🚰€3 🚽Ch 🔋€3,water 10 min + electricity 50min WC.
Location: Simple. **Surface:** asphalted. 🅿️ 01/01-31/12
Distance: 🛒500m 🏊500m 🥖500m.
Remarks: Coins at tourist info.

🍴S		**Saint-Agrève** 🍴	30A1

Le Lac de Véron, Pré de Gardy, D120. **GPS:** n44,99981 e4,40164. ⬆️.

5 ⌷ € 5/24h ✎ on demand 📶 free.
Location: Rural, comfortable, quiet. **Surface:** unpaved. ◻ 01/04-31/10
Distance: 🚶 village 1km 🛒 on the spot ⊗ on the spot 🏍 on the spot 🏃 on the spot.
Remarks: At fish lake.

Saint-André-d'Apchon   22B5
La Prébande. **GPS:** n46,03385 e3,92705. ⬆️

3 ⌷ free 🚰 🪑 Ch free. **Location:** Rural, simple, quiet. **Surface:** gravel.
◻ 01/01-31/12
Distance: 🚶 300m ⊗ 100m.

Saint-Étienne-la-Varenne   22D5
Le Bourg. **GPS:** n46,07731 e4,63024. ⬆️

4 ⌷ free 🚰 🪑 Ch ✎ free. **Location:** Rural, simple, quiet.
Surface: gravel/metalled. ◻ 01/01-31/12
Distance: 🚶 on the spot ⊗ 50m 🏍 on the spot 🏃 on the spot.
Remarks: Next to church.

Saint-Forgeux   22C6
Le Tram. **GPS:** n45,85733 e4,47566.

⌷ free 🚰 🪑 Ch ✎ free WC. **Location:** Rural, simple, quiet.
Surface: metalled. ◻ 01/01-31/12
Distance: 🚶 300m ⊗ 300m 🛥 300m 🏃 on the spot.

Saint-Genest-de-Beauzon   29D2
Domaine la Pize, La Pize. **GPS:** n44,43759 e4,19431.

⌷ € 10 🚰 🪑 Ch WC included 📶. **Location:** Rural, isolated, quiet.
Surface: unpaved. ◻ 01/01-31/12
Distance: 🚶 1,6km.

Saint-Germain-Lespinasse   22C5
Place du 8 mai 1945. **GPS:** n46,10510 e3,96229. ⬆️ ➡️

2 ⌷ free 🚰 🪑 Ch free.
Location: Rural, simple, quiet. **Surface:** gravel.
Distance: 🚶 200m ⊗ 50m 🚲 50m.

Saint-Haon-le-Châtel ☘   22B5
Fondanges, Route de la Croix du Sud, D39. **GPS:** n46,06362 e3,91313. ⬆️ ➡️

3 ⌷ free 🚰 🪑 Ch free.
Location: Rural, quiet. **Surface:** metalled. ◻ 01/01-31/12
Distance: 🚶 400m ⊗ 400m 🛥 400m 🔭 400m.

Saint-Martin-en-Haut 🎠   22C6
Etang du Kaiser, Lieu-dit-Jeangouttière. **GPS:** n45,64206 e4,53511. ⬆️

4 ⌷ free 🚰 🪑 Ch WC. **Location:** Rural, comfortable, quiet. **Surface:** gravel.
◻ 01/01-31/12
Distance: 🚶 St.Martin 4km 🛒 on the spot 🏍 on the spot 🏃 on the spot.
Remarks: At small lake, max. 72h.

Saint-Paul-le-Jeune   29D3
Rue Louis Roux, D901. **GPS:** n44,33999 e4,15322.

🛏free 🚰€2 ♨Ch 🔌€2. **Location:** Rural. **Surface:** grassy.
⬛ 01/01-31/12
Distance: 🚶on the spot 🚉100m.
Remarks: Coins at the shops in the village.

S **Saint-Restitut** 30A3
Le Village. **GPS:** n44,33144 e4,79093. ⬆

🛏free 🚰♨ Chfree. **Surface:** asphalted. ⬛ 01/01-31/12
Distance: 🚶on the spot.

S **Saint-Romain-d'Ay** 👥 30A1
Praperier, D6. **GPS:** n45,16430 e4,66339. ⬆

4 🛏free 🚰€2/20minutes ♨Ch 🚿 (4x)€2/4h WC. **Location:** Simple.
Surface: asphalted. ⬛ 01/01-31/12
Distance: 🚶550m ⊗100m.
Remarks: Coins at town hall and superette.

S **Saint-Symphorien-sur-Coise** 22C6
Bois des Pinasses. **GPS:** n45,62578 e4,45837. ⬆.

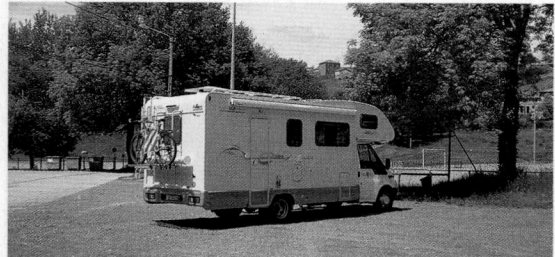

🛏free. **Location:** Rural, simple. **Surface:** gravel.
⬛ 01/01-31/12
Distance: 🚶1km 🏊50m.
Remarks: Next to sports fields.

S **Saint-Symphorien-sur-Coise** 22C6
Rue des Rameaux. **GPS:** n45,63378 e4,45883. ⬆.

🚰♨Chfree. **Location:** Simple. ⬛ 01/01-31/12
Remarks: Free coins at Bar-Tabac and town hall.

C S **Saint-Théoffrey** 30B1
Camping Ser-Sirant, Chemin du Lavoir. **GPS:** n45,00034 e5,77819. ⬆.
4 🛏€8-9,50 🚰€1,50 ♨Ch. **Location:** Rural. **Surface:** grassy.
Distance: 🏖beach Saint Théoffrey.
Remarks: At lake Laffrey, pay at reception campsite.

S **Samoëns** 🌊🚣🏖🏡👥❄ 23C5
Aire d'accueil camping-car de Vercland, Hameau de Vercland.
GPS: n46,07283 e6,69957. ⬆➡

10 🛏free 🚰♨Ch 🔌€5. **Surface:** metalled.
⬛ 01/01-31/12 ⬤ Service: winter
Distance: 🚶2km ⊗100m 🚉2km.

C S **Samoëns** 🌊🏖🏡🌳❄ 23C5
Parking du Giffre. GPS: n46,07666 e6,71899. ⬆.

5 🛏€10 🚰♨Ch 🚿 🧺. **Surface:** asphalted.
⬛ 01/01-31/12 ⬤ Service: winter
Distance: 🚶100m ⊗100m 🚉100m 🚌Skibus to Samoëns 1600 🎿100m
⛷on the spot.
Remarks: Near campsite du Giffre, parking 150m.

S **Sassenage** 30B1
Rue Pierre de Coubertin. **GPS:** n45,21346 e5,66858. ⬆.
9 🛏free 🚰♨Chfree. **Surface:** asphalted. ⬛ 01/01-31/12 🚲on the spot
🚶on the spot.
Remarks: At sports grounds, max. 48h.

S **Serrières-en-Chautagne** 🚶 23B6
GPS: n45,87964 e5,84230. ⬆.

FR

15 ⌖free 🅿️☕ Ch WC free. **Location:** Rural, central, quiet.
Surface: metalled. 🅿️ 01/01-31/12 ⬤ Service: winter
Distance: 🚲on the spot 🎣1km ⛱beach 50m 🛒on the spot ⊗200m
🛒100m 🚏100m.
Remarks: At little mountain stream.

	Seyssel		23B5

Parking Base de Loisirs, Quai du Rhône. **GPS:** n45,95146 e5,83343.

4 ⌖free 🅿️☕ Ch free. **Location:** Rural, simple, central, quiet. **Surface:** gravel.
🅿️ 01/01-31/12
Distance: 🚲800m 🏊on the spot 🛒on the spot ⊗500m 🚏800m
🚶on the spot.
Remarks: At recreational lake and Rhone river.

	Seyssel		23B5

Quai du Rhône. **GPS:** n45,95001 e5,83406.⬆.

12 ⌖free. **Location:** Rural, simple, central, quiet. **Surface:** gravel.
🅿️ 01/10-01/06
Distance: 🚲400m 🏊on the spot 🛒on the spot ⊗400m 🚏400m 🚌400m
🚶on the spot.

	Sixt-Fer-à-Cheval		23C5

Route du Cirque du Fer à Cheval. **GPS:** n46,05698 e6,78048.⬆.

20 ⌖free 🅿️☕Ch 🚿€4/12h. **Surface:** asphalted. 🅿️ 01/01-31/12
Distance: 🚲500m 🏊on the spot 🚏500m.

	St.Alban-Auriolles		29D3

Rue Marius Perbost. **GPS:** n44,42693 e4,30096.⬆.

⌖free 🅿️☕€3 Ch 🚽€3. **Surface:** gravel.
Distance: 🚲300m 🚏200m.

	St.Bonnet-le-Château		29D1

Esplanade de la Boule. **GPS:** n45,42514 e4,06436.⬆.

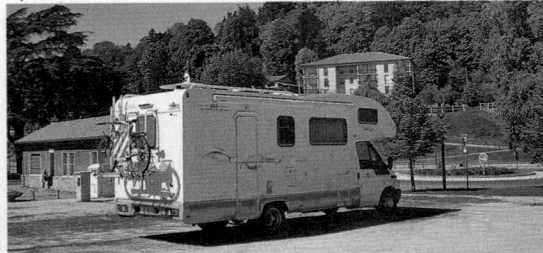

50 ⌖free 🅿️☕Ch WC free. **Location:** Simple. **Surface:** metalled. ⬤ Fri
Distance: 🚲200m 🛒1km ⊗200m 🚏200m.
Tourist information St.Bonnet-le-Château:
Ⓜ Musée de la Pétanque et des Boules, Esplanade de la Boule. All about the
beloved French national sport. 🅿️ 01/04-31/10.
Ⓜ Musée International Pétanque et Boules, Boulevard des Chauchères.
🎭 🅿️ Fri.

	St.Désirat		30A1

Musée de l'Alambic ,Distillerie Jean Gauthier, D291.
GPS: n45,25856 e4,79261.⬆.

⌖free 🅿️ 🚿 WC free. **Location:** Simple. **Surface:** asphalted.
Distance: 🚲300m 🚏300m.
Remarks: Max. 1 night.

	St.Donat-sur-l'Herbasse		30A1

Route de St.Bardoux. **GPS:** n45,11902 e4,98284.➡.

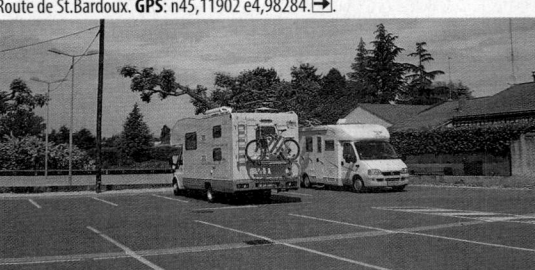

⌖free 🅿️☕Ch free. **Location:** Simple.
🅿️ 01/01-31/12
Distance: 🚲400m ⊗400m 🚏1km.
Remarks: In front of gymnasium, max. 1 night.

	St.Félicien		30A1

Place du Pré Lacour. **GPS:** n45,08453 e4,62848.

6 ⌖free ⌁€2 ⌁Ch.
Location: Urban, simple. **Surface:** asphalted/gravel. ◯ 01/01-31/12
Distance: ⌁on the spot ⊗on the spot ⌁on the spot.
Remarks: Max. 24h.

| ⌖S | St.Georges d'Espéranche | 22D6 |

Chemin des Platières. **GPS:** n45,55560 e5,07478. ⬆ ➡

14 ⌖free ⌁ ⌁Chfree. **Location:** Rural, simple, central, quiet.
Surface: metalled. ◯ 01/01-31/12
Distance: ⌁on the spot ⊗100m ⌁500m.
Remarks: Max. 48h.

| ⌖S | St.Gervais-les-Bains ⌁ | 23C5 |

77, impasse Cascade. **GPS:** n45,88864 e6,71287. ⬆

20 ⌖free ⌁€2 ⌁Ch ⌁€2. **Surface:** asphalted.
Distance: ⌁200m ⊗200m ⌁200m ⌁300m.
Remarks: Parking skating rink.

| ⌖S | St.Jean d'Ardières | 22D5 |

Domaine de Grande Ferrière, 831 route des Rochons. **GPS:** n46,12954 e4,71581.

5 ⌖free ⌁ ⌁Chfree ⌁€5/4night WC. **Location:** Rural, simple, quiet.
Surface: gravel.
Distance: ⌁3km ⌁6km ⌁5km ⌁500m ⊗3km ⌁3km.

| ⌖S | St.Jean-de-Bournay | 23A6 |

Place du Marche. **GPS:** n45,50130 e5,13845. ⬆

10 ⌖free ⌁ ⌁free Ch. **Location:** Rural, simple, central, quiet.
Surface: asphalted. ◯ 01/01-31/12
Distance: ⌁on the spot ⊗100m ⌁100m.

| ⌖S | St.Jean-de-Maurienne ⛱ ⛰ ❄ | 30C1 |

Rue Louis Sibue. **GPS:** n45,27995 e6,34776. ⬆
10 ⌖free ⌁€2 ⌁Ch ⌁€2 WC. **Surface:** asphalted. ◯ 01/01-31/12
Distance: ⌁2,5km ⊗100m.

| ⌖S | St.Jean-en-Royans ⛰ ⌂ | 30B1 |

Rue de la Gare. **GPS:** n45,02028 e5,29032. ⬆ ➡

3 ⌖free ⌁ ⌁Chfree. **Location:** Simple. **Surface:** gravel.
Distance: ⌁200m ⊗200m ⌁200m.

| ⌖S | St.Just-d'Ardèche | 30A3 |

Domaine La Favette, D86, route des Gorges d'Ardèche. **GPS:** n44,30134 e4,60649.

6 ⌖€5 ⌁€2 ⌁Ch ⌁€2. ◯ 01/01-31/12
Remarks: At wine-grower, max. 24h.
Tourist information St.Just-d'Ardèche:
⌂ ◯ Good starting point to discover the Ardèche gorges.
⛺ ◯ Thu.

| ⌖S | St.Just-en-Chevalet | 22B5 |

Boulevard de l'Astrée. **GPS:** n45,91411 e3,84727.

5 ⌖free ⌁ ⌁Chfree. ⌁ **Location:** Rural, simple.
◯ 01/01-31/12 ◯ Thu-morning
Distance: ⌁on the spot ⊗on the spot ⌁on the spot ⌁on the spot.

St.Paul-Trois-Châteaux 30A3

Parking Office de Tourisme, Le Courreau, Place Chausy.
GPS: n44,34786 e4,76995.

free Ch free WC. **Location:** Urban. **Surface:** asphalted.
Distance: 50m 50m.
Remarks: Max. 24h.

Tourist information St.Paul-Trois-Châteaux:
- Marché. Tue-morning.
- Marché aux truffes du Tricastin. Dec-Mar Su-morning.

St.Pierre-en-Faucigny 23C5

Avenue de la Gare. **GPS:** n46,05884 e6,37450.

4 free Ch free. **Surface:** asphalted. 01/04-30/11
Distance: on the spot 60m on the spot.
Remarks: Nearby railway station.

St.Rémèze 30A3

Les Chais du Vivarais, D362. **GPS:** n44,39536 e4,50576.

free Ch free. **Surface:** asphalted. 01/03-15/11
Distance: 500m 200m.
Remarks: Max. 48h.

Tourist information St.Rémèze:
- Grotte de la Madelaine. Caves. Apr-Oct 10-18h.
- Grotte de Marzal. Caves. Sa/Su/Holidays, 01/04-30/09 10.30-18h.
- Musée de la lavande. Museum and distillery with lavender fields. 01/05-30/09 10-17h, Apr + Oct Sa-Su-holiday 10-17h.

St.Romain-de-Lerps 30A1

Le Village, D287. **GPS:** n44,98029 e4,79596.

10 free Ch €4,100 liter water + 1h electricity WC.
Location: Rural, simple, quiet.
Surface: gravel.
01/01-31/12 01/10 en 01/04
Distance: 100m 100m bakery 100m.
Remarks: Less suitable for motorhomes >6,5m, coins at bakery, bar/resto 3duPic and town hall, panoramic view over the Rhône-valley 200m.

St.Thomé 30A2

N107, Les Crottes. **GPS:** n44,50059 e4,63445.

1 free Ch free. **Surface:** asphalted.

St.Victor-sur-Loire 29D1

Base Nautique du lac de Grangent. **GPS:** n45,44787 e4,25626.

10 free Ch free (4x) €2,60/4h WC. **Location:** Rural, comfortable.
Surface: asphalted. 01/01-31/12
Distance: on the spot on the spot on the spot.
Remarks: Max. 72h, coins at the shops in the village.

Suze-la-Rousse 30A3

Route de Bollène, D94. **GPS:** n44,28598 e4,83185.

free free. **Surface:** grassy/gravel. 01/01-31/12
Distance: 850m on the spot on the spot.
Remarks: At sports grounds.

Suze-la-Rousse 30A3

50 Impasse de la Zone Artisanale. **GPS:** n44,28965 e4,84783.

🚰🗑️Chfree. ⬛ 01/01-31/12
Distance: 🚶1,5km.
🅿️Ⓢ **Thueyts** ❄️🎿⛰️🌳🌊 **29D2**
Chemin d'Echelle du Roi, via N102. **GPS:** n44,67274 e4,21917.⬆️➡️

10 🚐free 🚰€2 🗑️Ch🔌€2/10minutes. **Location:** Rural, simple, quiet.
Surface: grassy/gravel. ⬛ 01/01-31/12
Distance: 🚶200m 🚰200m 🏊on the spot.
Remarks: Near the Ardèche river and Pont du Diable, max. 24h.
🅿️Ⓢ **Tournon-sur-Rhône** ⚓🌊 **30A1**
Chemin de la Beaume/D86. **GPS:** n45,07337 e4,82150.⬆️➡️

25 🚐€5 🚰🗑️Chfree. **Location:** Urban, simple. **Surface:** asphalted.
⬛ 01/01-31/12
Distance: 🚶1km 🚲5km 🏊1km 🚰1km.
Tourist information Tournon-sur-Rhône:
🎋 ⬛ Wed, Sa.
🚲 Route Panoramique, place Jean Jaurès. Starting point touristic route.
🅿️Ⓢ **Treffort** ⛰️🌳🏕️ **30B2**
Plage de la Salette, D110b. **GPS:** n44,90732 e5,67208.⬆️

12 🚐€10/24h 🚰€2 🗑️Ch🔌€2 WC.🚐
Surface: gravel.
⬛ 01/05-31/10
Distance: 🚶3km 🚤lake 🎣lake 🏊on the spot 🚴on the spot 🚶on the spot.
Remarks: At lake Monteynard.
🅿️Ⓢ **Trévoux** ❄️⛰️🏕️🏗️ **22D5**
Chemin du Camping. **GPS:** n45,94017 e4,76694.⬆️

4 🚐€5 🚰€2 🗑️Ch.🚐 **Location:** Urban, simple, central, quiet.
Surface: grassy/metalled.
⬛ 01/01-31/12
Distance: 🚶on the spot 🚲7km 🚤100m 🏊1km 🚰1km 🚌1km.
Remarks: Along river, at entrance campsite, pay at campsite or town hall.
🅿️Ⓢ **Ugine** **23C6**
Place du 8 Mai 1945. **GPS:** n45,74634 e6,41774.⬆️
🚐free 🚰€2 🗑️🔌€2. **Surface:** asphalted. ⬛ 01/01-31/12
Distance: 🚶50m 🏊50m 🚰50m.
Tourist information Ugine:
🎋 ⬛ Wed, Sa-morning.
🅿️Ⓢ **Val d'Isère** **30D1**
Le Pont Saint-Charles, Route du Col de l'Iseran, D902. **GPS:** n45,45432 e6,97005.

50 🚐free 🚰🗑️free. **Surface:** gravel. ⬛ 01/01-31/12
Distance: 🎿on the spot.
Remarks: Parking at skipistes.
🅿️Ⓢ **Valloire** **30C1**
Camping-Car Park Les Verneys, Route du Galibier. **GPS:** n45,14591 e6,42011.
⬆️
30 🚐€12 🚰🗑️Ch ⚡ WC 📶included. **Surface:** asphalted.
⬛ 01/01-31/12
Distance: 🏊on the spot 🎿250m.
Remarks: Free shuttle.
🅿️Ⓢ **Vallon-Pont-d'Arc** ⚓⛰️🌊 **30A3**
Chemin du Chastelas. **GPS:** n44,40537 e4,39683.⬆️

20 🚐€6/24h 🚰€2 🗑️Ch🔌€2 WC.🚐 ⬛ 01/01-31/12
Distance: 🚶100m 🏊100m 🚰100m.
Remarks: Free shuttle to the Pont d'Arc, 2x per hour.
🅿️Ⓢ **Vallon-Pont-d'Arc** ⚓⛰️🌊 **30A3**
Domaine de l'Esquiras, Chemin du Fez. **GPS:** n44,41583 e4,37738.⬆️

FR

5 �})€ 8, peak season € 10 + € 0,60/pp tourist tax ⛽ 🍽 Ch 🚿 €3 WC 🗑 ⚡free. **Surface:** gravel.
🅿 12/04-21/09
Distance: 🚶800m.
Remarks: Use sanitary facilities + swimming pool € 4/pp.

Tourist information Vallon-Pont-d'Arc:
ℹ️ Office de Tourisme, 1, place de l'ancienne gare, www.vallon-pont-darc.com. Small tourist town with the well-known Pont d'Arc, a natural arc over the Ardèche river.
👁 Grotte des Huguenots. Former shelter of the Huguenots. 🅿 15/06-31/08.
✈ 🅿 Thu-morning.

🏕S | **Valvignères** | 30A2
Le Colombier. GPS: n44,49904 e4,57672.

⌐)€ 7,70, 2 pers.incl. ⛽ 🍽 Ch free. 🅿 27/03-30/09 🔘 Service: winter
🏕S | **Vassieux-en-Vercors** 🌳🏕❄ | 30B2
Avenue du Mémorial, D76. **GPS:** n44,89703 e5,36927.⬆.

30 ⌐)free ⛽ 🍽 Ch free. **Location:** Rural, simple. **Surface:** metalled.
🔘 service in winter
Distance: 🚶200m ⊗200m 🚆200m 🚶 on the spot 🚲7km Font D'Urle ⛷on the spot.
Remarks: Next to football ground.

🏕S | **Vaujany** 🏕🏕❄ | 30C1
Télécabine. GPS: n45,15694 e6,08011.⬆➡.

15 ⌐)free ⛽ 🍽 Ch free 🚿 €5. **Surface:** gravel. 🅿 01/01-31/12
Distance: 🚶300m ⊗300m 🚆300m 🚲300m.

Remarks: Max. 24h, coins at tourist info (electricity).
🏕S | **Vienne** 🌿🍽 | 22D6
Place Joseph Muray et Jean Tardy, N7. **GPS:** n45,53860 e4,87271.⬆➡.

10 ⌐)free ⛽ 🍽 Ch free. **Location:** Urban, simple, central, noisy.
Surface: asphalted. 🔘 Wed-afternoon (market)
Distance: 🚶50m 🚲2km ⊗50m 🚆50m 🚌50m.
| **Villards-de-Lans** | 30B1
Chemin des Bartavelles. **GPS:** n45,06619 e5,55609.⬆.

15 ⌐)free. **Surface:** asphalted.
Distance: 🚶600m ⊗600m 🚆600m.
Remarks: Max. 48h.

| **Villars-les-Dombes** 🌿🍃 | 22D5
Parc des Oiseaux, RN83. **GPS:** n45,99126 e5,02582.⬆➡.

100 ⌐)free. **Location:** Simple, quiet. **Surface:** asphalted/grassy.
🅿 01/01-31/12 🔘 sundays, holidays, winter
Distance: 🚶2km 🏊1km 🚲1km ⊗2km 🚆2km 🚶on the spot.
Remarks: Parking bird park, max. 1 night, gate closed from 21-8h.

Tourist information Villars-les-Dombes:
☺ Parc des Oiseaux. Bird park, 23ha. 🅿 8.30-19h, winter 8.30-17.30h. 🅣 € 10.

🏕S | **Villerest** 🍃 | 22C5
Aire camping-car du Grezelon, D18, Route de Seigne. **GPS:** n45,98610 e4,04300.

15 ⌐)€ 5 ⛽€4 🍽 Ch. 🧺 **Surface:** gravel.
🅿 01/01-31/12 🔘 service: 01/10-30/04
Distance: ⊗on the spot 🚆1km 🚶on the spot.
Remarks: At Lac du Villerest and barrage, max. 48h.

Violay 22C6

Place Giroud. **GPS**: n45,85268 e4,35564.

2 free free Ch. **Location:** Rural, simple, quiet. **Surface:** metalled.
01/01-31/12
Distance: 100m A89 9km 200m 150m.
Remarks: Beautiful view.

Virieu 30B1

Rue du May, D17. **GPS**: n45,48166 e5,47746.

4 free Ch WC free. **Location:** Rural, simple, central, quiet.
Surface: gravel.
Distance: on the spot 200m 200m on the spot.
Remarks: Picnic area at edge of the village.

Viviers 30A2

Rue Valpeyrousse. **GPS**: n44,48225 e4,67999.

26 €6,50 Ch WC included. **Location:** Rural, luxurious,
quiet. **Surface:** metalled. 15/04-29/09
Distance: 1km 1km.
Remarks: Former campsite.

Tourist information Viviers:
Tue.

Vogüé 30A2

Chemin de Setras. **GPS**: n44,55163 e4,41308.

20 free. **Surface:** asphalted. 01/01-31/12
Distance: 50m Ardèche 200m.
Remarks: At cemetery.

Aquitaine

Accous 28B5

La Nabe, D339. **GPS**: n42,91028 w0,61939.

20 €12 Ch WC included. **Location:** Rural, comfortable, isolated, quiet. **Surface:** gravel.
Distance: 7km 100m on the spot.

Aire-sur-l'Adour 28B4

Rue des Graviers. **GPS**: n43,70333 w0,25535.

50 €3 €1 Ch. **Location:** Simple, quiet. **Surface:** gravel.
01/01-31/12 3rd week Jun
Distance: 200m on the spot on the spot.
Remarks: Near campsite, max. 72h.

Amou 28B4

Stade de Sport, Promenade pour Piétons. **GPS**: n43,58917 w0,74083.

10 free Ch free. **Surface:** asphalted. 01/01-31/12
Distance: 1km on the spot on the spot 1km 1km.

Andernos-les-Bains 28A2

Port Ostréicole, Avenue du Commandant Allègre. **GPS**: n44,74477 w1,10969.

60 €8,10 €2,10/10liter Ch €2,10. **Surface:** grassy.
01/01-31/12
Distance: on the spot on the spot 50m.
Remarks: In harbour, max. 48h.

FR

🚐 [S] Anglet 28A4

Aire de camping-car de La Barre, Avenue de l'Adour, D405.
GPS: n43,52608 w1,51488.[↑].

50 🚐€ 6, Jul/Aug € 10 🚰€3 🚽 Ch. 🚿 ✂ **Surface:** grassy/metalled.
☐ 13/04-11/11
Distance: 🏙1km 🏖300m 🐟50m 🍴500m 🥖500m 🚌100m.
Remarks: Private property.

🚐 [S] Anglet 28A4

Aire de camping-car des Corsaires, Boulevard des Plages.
GPS: n43,50696 w1,53373.[↑][→].

80 🚐€ 6, Jul/Aug € 10 🚰 🚽 Chincluded. 🚿 ✂ **Surface:** asphalted.
◉ 01/01-31/12 **Distance:** 🏙500m, Biarritz 2km 🏖500m 🍴500m 🥖500m.
Remarks: Max. 24h, baker every morning.

🚐 [S] Angoisse 21B6

Le Pont du Jour, L'Hépital, D704. **GPS**: n45,43296 e1,14413.[↑].
8 🚐€5 🚰 🚽 🔌€3 📶€3. **Location:** Rural. **Surface:** grassy.

🚐 [S] Arcachon 28A2

Boulevard Mestrézat, D650. **GPS**: n44,65142 w1,14864.[↑].

20 🚐free 🚰 🚽 Chfree. **Location:** Urban, simple, noisy. **Surface:** gravel.
☐ 01/01-31/12
Distance: 🏙1km 🥖50m.
Remarks: Max. 24h.

🚐 Arcachon 28A2

Avenue du Parc. **GPS**: n44,64868 w1,19672.
🚐free. **Surface:** gravel.
☐ 01/01-31/12
Distance: 🏖on the spot 🐟on the spot.

Tourist information Arcachon:
⛱ place du XI Novembre. Covered market. ☐ 01/06-31/08 daily 7-13h.

🚐 [S] Arette 28B5

Aire de camping car d'Arette, Place de la Mairie. **GPS**: n43,09477 w0,71511.
10 🚐free 🚰 🚽 Ch. **Location:** Simple. **Surface:** asphalted.
☐ 01/01-31/12

🚐 [S] Arzacq-Arraziguet 28B4

Aire de camping cars, Place du Marcadieu. **GPS**: n43,53481 w0,41035.[↑].

10 🚐free 🚰 🚽 Ch WCfree. **Surface:** asphalted. ☐ 01/01-31/12
Distance: 🏙on the spot 🏖500m 🐟500m 🍴100m 🥖100m.

🚐 [S] Azerat 28D1

Le Bourg. **GPS**: n45,14954 e1,12496.[↑][→].

6 🚐€ 2 🚰€3 🚽 Ch. **Location:** Simple, quiet. **Surface:** gravel.
☐ 01/01-31/12
Distance: 🏙50m.
Remarks: Pay at town hall.

🚐 [S] Azur 28A3

Camping-Car Park, Route du Lac. **GPS**: n43,78842 w1,3119.[↑].
31 🚐€ 12 🚰 🚽 Ch 🔌 📶included. 🚿 **Location:** Rural, quiet.
Surface: gravel. ☐ 01/01-31/12
Distance: 🏙1,5km 🏖150m 🐟150m 🍴200m 🚲on the spot 🚶on the spot.
Remarks: Wifi code: 403105.

🚐 [S] Badefols-sur-Dordogne 28D2

Le Bourg. **GPS**: n44,84254 e0,79160.[↑].

10 🚐free 🚰€2/100liter 🚽 Ch WCfree. **Location:** Rural, simple.
Surface: asphalted. ☐ 01/01-31/12 ◉ Sa market
Distance: 🏙on the spot 🥖bakery 50m.
Remarks: Coins at town hall.

🚐 [S] Beaumont du Périgord 28D2

Avenue Rhinau, D660. **GPS**: n44,77469 e0,76559.[↑][→].

20 🚐free 🚰 🚽 Chfree. **Surface:** asphalted. ☐ 01/01-31/12
Distance: 🏙800m.

Tourist information Beaumont du Périgord:

FR

👁 Bastide de Beaumont.

Bergerac 🚿🏖🍴 28C1
Parc Public de Pombonne, Avenue Marceau Feyry. **GPS**: n44,87104 e0,50408.
⬆➡

6 free €2/100liter Ch.
Location: Simple. **Surface:** metalled.
Distance: city centre 3km 1km.
Remarks: Max. 24h.
Tourist information Bergerac:
Ⓜ Musée du Tabac, Maison Peyrarède, Place du Feu. History of tobacco. Mo-Fri 10-12h, 14-18, Sa 10-12h, 14-17h, Su 14.30-17.30h, Nov-Mar Mo-Fr.
⛪ Église Notre Dame, Rue Saint Esprit. Wed, Sa 7-13h.

Bernos-Beaulac 28B2
La Grande Route, N524. **GPS**: n44,36949 w0,24257.⬆

10 free €2 Ch. **Location:** Simple, quiet. **Surface:** metalled.
01/01-31/12 water: frost
Distance: river on the spot bakery 100m.
Remarks: Coins at petrol station.

Beynac-et-Cazenac 🚿🏖🍴 28D2
Le Parc, D703. **GPS**: n44,84466 e1,14560.➡

20 free. **Location:** Rural, simple. **Surface:** gravel.
01/01-31/12
Distance: historical centre 500m 500m.

Biarritz 37D4
Parking Milady, Avenue de la Milady, Biarritz-sud, D911dir Bidart.
GPS: n43,46536 w1,57162.⬆

50 €12 Ch included. **Surface:** asphalted. 01/01-31/12
Distance: 500m 300m 500m 500m.
Remarks: Baker every morning.
Tourist information Biarritz:
⛪ Rue des Halles. daily.

Biron 28D2
Route de Vergt de Biron. **GPS**: n44,63080 e0,87055.⬆

10 free €2/100liter Ch €2/1h. **Location:** Simple.
Surface: grassy/metalled. 01/01-31/12 service 01/11-31/03
Distance: 250m 250m.
Remarks: Coins at grocery.

Biscarrosse 28A2
Aire camping-cars, Rue des Viviers, Biscarrosse-plage. **GPS**: n44,46027 w1,24627.⬆

180 €8, Jul/Aug €15 Ch WC. **Location:** Simple, quiet.
Surface: forest soil. 01/05-31/10
Distance: 2,5km 400m Superette 100m 50m on the spot.
Remarks: Video surveillance.

Biscarrosse 28A2
Biscarrosse Plage Sud, Chemin de Navarosse. **GPS**: n44,43223 w1,16566.⬆

30 €8, Jul/Aug €15 Ch free WC.
Location: Simple. **Surface:** metalled. 01/01-31/12
Distance: 4km 50m 100m 50m on the spot.
Remarks: Video surveillance.

Blanquefort 28B1
Château Saint Ahon, Rue de Saint-Ahon. **GPS:** n44,92663 w0,63217.
4 🚐 € 3. **Location:** Quiet. **Surface:** grassy.
Remarks: Arrival < 19h, max. 48h.

Blasimon 28C2
Rue Abbé Greciet. **GPS:** n44,74836 w0,07537.
4 🚐 free 🚰 🗑 Ch. **Location:** Simple, quiet. **Surface:** gravel.
📅 01/01-31/12
Distance: 🚶100m ⊗100m 🍷100m.

Blasimon 28C2
Château la Peyraude, Bleurette. **GPS:** n44,73463 w0,09942.⬆
10 🚐 free 🚰 ✦ WC 🚿free. **Location:** Simple. **Surface:** grassy.
Distance: 🚶3km.
Remarks: Arrival <22h.

Blaye 28B1
Parking de la Citadelle. GPS: n45,12521 w0,66623.
🚐free. **Surface:** metalled. 📅 01/01-31/12
Distance: 🚶250m ⊗300m.

Blaye 28B1
Château le Cône, Route des Cônes. **GPS:** n45,13742 w0,66507.⬆➡
12 🚐 🚰 🗑 Ch.

Bouglon 28C2
Le Clavier. **GPS:** n44,38599 e0,10271.

4 🚐free 🚰 WC. **Location:** Simple, quiet. **Surface:** asphalted.
📅 01/01-31/12
Distance: 🚶500m ⊗500m 🍷500m.
Remarks: Picnic area.

Bourdeilles 28D1
Plaine de loisirs, Le Bourg. **GPS:** n45,32270 e0,58260.⬆

20+ 🚐 € 4 🚰€2/100liter 🗑 Ch. 🛁 **Location:** Comfortable, quiet.
Surface: grassy. 📅 01/01-31/12
Distance: 🚶500m 🛒on the spot 🍞on the spot ⊗200m 🍷200m.
Remarks: Coins at the shops.

Bourg-sur-Gironde 28B1
Quai Jean Bart. **GPS:** n45,03794 w0,55762.⬆
20 🚐free, night € 5. **Surface:** asphalted. 📅 01/01-31/12
Distance: 🚶on the spot ⚓On the river Gironde.

Brantôme 28D1
Chemin de Vert Galant. **GPS:** n45,36134 e0,64842.⬆

50 🚐 € 4 🚰€2 Ch. **Location:** Simple, quiet. **Surface:** grassy.
📅 01/01-31/12
Distance: 🚶200m ⊗100m 🍷300m.

Brantôme 28D1
Aire Camping-cars Font Vendôme, Route de Nontron.
GPS: n45,37924 e0,64588.⬆➡

4 🚐 € 5 🚰 🗑 Ch ✦ included. **Surface:** asphalted. 📅 01/01-31/12
Distance: ⊗1km 🍷1km.
Tourist information Brantôme:
🏛 📅 Fri-morning.

Buzet-sur-Baïse 28C3
Port de Buzet-Val d'Albret. GPS: n44,25799 e0,30569.

20 🚐free 🚰€2 🗑 Ch ✦€2 WC 🚿€2/24h. **Surface:** grassy.
Distance: 🚲6,5km 🛒on the spot ⊗350m 🍷350m.

Cadillac 28B2
Avenue du Parc. **GPS:** n44,63871 w0,31721.⬆

10 🚐free 🚰 🗑 Chfree ✦€2/3h. **Surface:** asphalted.
📅 01/01-31/12
Distance: 🚶on the spot ⊗on the spot 🍷on the spot 🏧on the spot.
Remarks: Max. 3 nights, closed when frosty.

Cancon 28D2
Rue des Écoles. **GPS:** n44,53638 e0,62562.⬆➡

10 🛏free ⚡🚰♻Ch 🚿 WCfree. **Location:** Simple. **Surface:** metalled.
⬛ 01/01-31/12
Distance: 🏊100m ⊗100m 🛒100m.

📷S | **Capbreton** | 28A4
Plage l'Océanide, Parking des Ortolans, Allée des Ortolans.
GPS: n43,63578 w1,44681.➡️

135 🛏€ 7-€ 11 ⚡🚰♻Ch 🚿(120x) WCincluded. 🚮 **Surface:** asphalted.
⬛ 15/11-31/03 **Distance:** 🏊1,5km ⚓on the spot ⚓on the spot ⊗1,5km
🛒1,5km. **Remarks:** Beach parking, 14/07-20/08: max. 2 nights.

📷S | **Capian** | 28B2
D13/Chemin de Lavergne. **GPS:** n44,71177 w0,33093.⬆️

25 🛏 ⚡🚰♻Ch. **Surface:** gravel.

📷S | **Carcans** | 28A1
Route de Bombannes, Maubuisson. **GPS:** n45,08545 w1,14866.

20 🛏€ 5,80/20-9h ⚡🚰♻Chfree 🚿€2. 🚮 **Surface:** asphalted/metalled.
⬛ 01/06-30/09
Distance: ⚓on the spot 🎣on the spot.

Tourist information Carcans:
ℹ️ Office de Tourisme, Maison de la Station, www.carcans-maubuisson.com.
Touristic town between the ocean and a wine region, 120km signposted cycle routes.

📷S | **Casseneuil** 🌿 | 28D2
Rue Grande, D225. **GPS:** n44,44667 e0,61861.⬆️➡️

20 🛏free ⚡🚰♻Chfree. **Surface:** gravel. ⬛ 01/01-31/12
Distance: 🏊100m ⚓on the spot ⚓on the spot ⊗100m 🛒800m.

📷S | **Castelculier** | 28D3
GPS: n44,17475 e0,69452.⬆️

5 🛏free ⚡€2 ♻Ch. **Surface:** metalled. ⬛ 01/01-31/12
Distance: 🏊200m.

📷S | **Casteljaloux** ♨️ | 28C3
Ste Cast Chalets, D933. **GPS:** n44,29230 e0,07361.⬆️

20 🛏€ 10, Jul/Aug € 15, dog € 3 ⚡🚰♻Ch 🚿 WC 📶included.
Location: Comfortable, quiet. **Surface:** gravel/sand. ⬛ 01/10-31/10
Distance: 🏊2km ⚓Lac de Clarens.

📷S | **Casteljaloux** ♨️ | 28C3
Impasse de la Fôret. **GPS:** n44,31068 e0,07933.⬆️➡️

4 🛏free ⚡🚰♻Chfree. **Location:** Simple, quiet. **Surface:** asphalted.
⬛ 01/01-31/12
Distance: 🏊250m 🛒250m.
Remarks: Parking at swimming pool, max. 48h.

📷S | **Casteljaloux** ♨️ | 28C3
La Taillade, Route de la Forge, La Réunion. **GPS:** n44,26998 e0,08004.⬆️
3 🛏€ 10 ⚡🚰♻Ch 🚿 📶. **Location:** Rural, isolated, quiet.
Surface: forest soil.

📷S | **Caumont-sur-Garonne** 〰️ | 28C2
Bourg de Caumont. **GPS:** n44,44202 e0,17887.⬆️

9 ⌂free ⚡€1 🚰Ch 🚽€1/2h. **Surface:** gravel. ⬛ 01/01-31/12
Distance: 🏊8km ⚓on the spot.

Château-l'Evêque 28D1

Place de la Fontaine. **GPS:** n45,24472 e0,68743.⬆.

8 ⌂free ⚡€2 🚰Ch 🚽€2. **Surface:** gravel.
⬛ 01/03-31/10 ◉ summer: Su (flea market)
Distance: 🏊50m 🛒100m ⚓on the spot.
Remarks: Max. 12h, coins at shops in the village 08-21h.

Contis-Plage 28A3

Avenue du Phare. **GPS:** n44,09333 w1,31861.⬆.

76 ⌂€ 7, 01/06-01/09 € 11/24h, 01/12-28/02 free ⚡€2 🚰Ch 🚽WC .🚐
🧺 **Location:** Simple. **Surface:** gravel. ⬛ 01/01-31/12
Distance: 🏖200m ⚓on the spot.
Remarks: Max. 72h.

Créon 28B2

Vélo-centre, Boulevard Victor Hugo, D20. **GPS:** n44,77663 w0,34815.⬆.

5 ⌂free ⚡€3 🚰Ch 🚽€3/4h. **Surface:** asphalted.
⬛ 01/01-31/12 ◉ tue-evening, wed-morning (market)
Distance: 🏊500m ⚓500m.

Damazan 28C3

Chambre D'Hôtes Constantine, Route Cap de Bosc. **GPS:** n44,28130 e0,26285.
6 ⌂€ 10 🚰Ch ⚡WC 🔌. ⬛ 01/01-31/12
Distance: 🏊500m ⚓1km.

Dax 28A4

Parking du Pont des Arènes, Boulevard des Sports. **GPS:** n43,71427 w1,04931.⬆.

8 ⌂free ⚡🚰free. **Location:** Simple, noisy. **Surface:** asphalted.
⬛ 01/01-31/12
Distance: 🏊on the spot.
Remarks: Max. 72h, saturday market in the halls.

Tourist information Dax:
ℹ Office de Tourisme, 11, cours Foch, www.dax.fr. Health resort with warm water sources and medicinal mud.

Domme 28D2

Le Pradal. **GPS:** n44,80053 e1,22156.⬆➡.

20 ⌂free, overnight stay € 5 ⚡€2/100liter 🚰Ch 🚽€2/1h. 🚐🧺
Location: Simple, quiet. **Surface:** asphalted.
⬛ 01/01-31/12 ◉ Service: winter
Distance: 🏊500m ⊗500m.

Tourist information Domme:
ℹ Office de Tourisme, Place de la Halle, www.ot-domme.com. Fortified city worth seeing, parking for motorhomes outside of the town, being indicated.

Douchapt 28C1

Beauclair. **GPS:** n45,25145 e0,44335.⬆➡.

⌂€ 5 ⚡€2/100liter 🚰Ch 🚽€2/1h. **Location:** Rural, simple, isolated.
Surface: metalled. ⬛ 01/01-31/12
Distance: 🏊1,5km 🌊Dronne river ⊗1,5km.
Remarks: Pay and coins at Village Vacances Beauclair.

Duras 28C2

Municipal du château de Duras, Le Bourg. **GPS:** n44,67755 e0,17854.⬆.
5 ⌂free, July-Aug € 2,60 + € 3,15 pp ⚡🚰Ch 🚽€2,10.
Surface: unpaved.
Distance: 🏊350m ⊗350m. ⚡350m.

Eaux-Bonnes 28C5

Parking du Ley. **GPS:** n42,96304 e0,33933.⬆.

FR

20 🛏free. **Surface:** asphalted. 🅾 01/01-31/12
Distance: 🚶1,4km 🚲1,4km ⊗1,4km 🍴1,4km.
🅂 **Espés Undurein** 28A4
Etche Gochoki, D11. **GPS:** n43,26388 w0,88083.⬆.

6 🛏€8 💧€2 🚽Ch ♻€2. **Surface:** grassy/metalled. 🅾 01/01-31/12
Distance: 🚶500m ⊗500m 🍴400m.
🅂 **Excideuil** 28D1
Rue Léon Barreau. **GPS:** n45,33605 e1,05239.⬆.

4 🛏free 💧€3 🚽🔌. **Location:** Noisy. **Surface:** asphalted.
🅂 **Fontet** 28C2
Base de Loisirs Fontet. **GPS:** n44,56118 w0,02282.⬆➡.

25 🛏€9 💧🚽Ch ♻WC included 🔌€1. **Location:** Comfortable.
Surface: grassy/gravel. 🅾 01/01-31/12
Distance: 🚲on the spot 🍴bakery 500m, supermarket 4km.
Remarks: At lake.
🅂 **Fourques-sur-Garonne** 28C2
Halte Nautique d Pont des Sables, Pont des Sables, D933.
GPS: n44,46081 e0,13932.⬆.
4 🛏free 💧🚽Ch 🔌. **Surface:** metalled. 🅾 01/03-31/10
Distance: 🚶Fourques 2,5km 🚴3km.
🅂 **Frontenac** 28C2
D236. **GPS:** n44,73781 w0,16308.⬆➡.

10 🛏free 💧🔌free. **Surface:** grassy/gravel. 🅾 01/01-31/12
Distance: 🚶200m ⊗200m 🍴bakery 200m.
Remarks: Behind town hall, max. 48h.
🅂 **Fumel** 28D2
Place Du Saulou, rue Massenet, D911. **GPS:** n44,49809 e0,97165.⬆➡.

10 🛏free 💧🔌Ch WC free. **Location:** Urban, simple. **Surface:** asphalted.
🅾 01/01-31/12
Distance: 🚶200m ⊗200m.
Remarks: Château de Bonaguil 7km.
🅂 **Gastes** 28A2
Port de Gastes, Avenue du lac. **GPS:** n44,32880 w1,15068.⬆.

100 🛏€2-4,50, 16/05-15/09 €7 💧🔌Ch ♻WC 🔌included. 🚐🧹
Location: Comfortable. **Surface:** grassy.
🅾 01/01-31/12 🔘 service in winter
Distance: 🚶Parentis-en-Born 7km 🚲on the spot 🍴on the spot ⊗800m
🍴800m.
Remarks: Along lake, baker every morning.
🅲🅂 **Gastes** 28A2
Camping Les Echasses, 193 rue de Bernadon. **GPS:** n44,31871 w1,13879.⬆.

10 🛏€5-8 💧🔌€3 🚽Ch ♻ included. **Location:** Simple. **Surface:** grassy.
🅾 01/01-31/12
Distance: 🚲Gastes Lac 2km 🎣on the spot.
Remarks: Max. 1 night, no camping activities.
🅂 **Gornac** 28C2
Aire Municipale, Esplanade Fongave. **GPS:** n44,66061 w0,18145.⬆➡.

20 🦆free ⛽🦆Ch free. **Location:** Simple. **Surface:** gravel.
Distance: ⊗200m 🚿200m.

🦆Ⓢ | **Grenade-sur-l'Adour** | 28B3

Place du 19 mars 1962. **GPS:** n43,77500 w0,43472. ⬆.

10 🦆free ⛽🦆Ch WC free.
Location: Simple. **Surface:** asphalted/gravel.
Distance: 🚰100m ⊗100m 🚿100m.
Remarks: Next to cemetery, max. 24h.

🦆Ⓢ | **Hautefort** | 28D1

Route de Boisseuil. **GPS:** n45,26017 e1,14907. ⬆.

3 🦆free ⛽€2 🦆Ch ⚡€2 WC. **Surface:** asphalted. ◗ 01/01-31/12
Distance: 🚰50m ⊗100m 🚿Intermarché 1km.
Tourist information Hautefort:
⚔ Château Hautefort. Classified castle. ◗ 01/04-30/09 daily, 01/10-31/03
afternoons.
⚖ ◗ Wed-morning.

🦆Ⓢ | **Hendaye** | 37D4

Gare des deux Jumeaux, Rue d'Ansoenia. **GPS:** n43,37019 w1,7648. ⬆➡.

25 🦆€ 10 ⛽€2/100liter 🦆Ch ⚡€2/1h. **Surface:** asphalted.
◗ 01/01-31/12
Distance: 🚰on the spot 🏊800m ⊗450m 🚿450m 🛒on the spot.
Remarks: Railway-station Hendaye-plage, max. 72h.

🦆Ⓢ | **Hostens** 〽 | 28B2

Rue Chantegrue. **GPS:** n44,49321 w0,62898.

4 🦆free ⛽service €3 🦆Ch ⚡ ♻.

Location: Simple, quiet. ◗ 01/01-31/12
Distance: 🚰1km 🏊on the spot 🛒on the spot ⊗on camp site 🚿on camp
site.
Remarks: Next to campsite Ariales, june 2012 during inspection service out of
order.

🦆Ⓢ | **Houeillès** | 28C3

Aire de Repos, Rue du 19 Mars 1962. **GPS:** n44,19611 e0,03250.

🦆free ⛽WC. **Location:** Simple, quiet. **Surface:** grassy/gravel.
◗ 01/01-31/12
Distance: 🚰100m 🚿250m.
Remarks: Max. 24h.

🦆Ⓢ | **Hourtin** | 28A1

Mombet, Hourtin-Port. **GPS:** n45,18083 w1,08056. ⬆.

90 🦆€ 10 ⛽🦆Ch ✂€2 WC. 🎣 **Surface:** forest soil. ◗ 01/01-31/12
Distance: 🚰50m 🏊50m ⊗50m.

🦆Ⓢ | **Jumilhac-le-Grand** | 21A6

Boulevard du Pigeonnier, D78. **GPS:** n45,49219 e1,06092. ⬆.
🦆free ⛽🦆Ch free. **Surface:** asphalted. ◗ 01/01-31/12
Distance: ⊗200m 🚿bakery 200m.
Remarks: Near Château de Jumilhac.

🦆Ⓢ | **La Chapelle-Faucher** | 28D1

Champignonnière de Rochevideau, D78. **GPS:** n45,36195 e0,74112. ⬆.

6 🦆€3 ⛽🦆Ch ◻free. **Location:** Simple, quiet. **Surface:** concrete.
◗ 01/01-31/12
Distance: ⊗4km 🚿4km.

🦆Ⓢ | **La Coquille** | 21A6

N21, Place de l'église. **GPS:** n45,54245 e0,97702. ⬆.

5 🛏 free 🚰 ➰ Ch WC free. **Location:** Simple, central. **Surface:** asphalted. 🅾 01/01-31/12
Distance: 🚶100m ⊗200m 🛒200m.

🛁 S | **La Pierre-Saint-Martin** 🏔️ ❄️ | 28B5

Aire de campingcar de la Pierre-Saint-Martin, Braça de Guilhers.
GPS: n42,97918 w0,7487. ⬆️.

40 🛏 € 10 🚰 ➰ Ch 🔧 (winter). **Surface:** asphalted. 🅾 01/01-31/12
Distance: 🚶300m ⊗300m 🎿150m.

🛁 S | **La Réole** | 28C2

Les Justices, Avenue Gabriel-Chaigne. **GPS:** n44,58059 w0,03036. ⬆️.
10 🛏 € 4 🚰 ➰ Ch free. 🐕 **Surface:** grassy. 🅾 15/04-01/10
Distance: 🚶800m 🛒700m.
Remarks: Nearby Musée Automobile et Militaire.

🛁 S | **La Roche-Chalais** 🚣 | 28C1

Halte Nautique, D730. **GPS:** n45,15701 e0,00419. ⬆️.

4 🛏 free 🚰 ➰ Ch WC free. **Location:** Rural, simple. **Surface:** metalled. 🅾 01/01-31/12
Distance: 🚶400m 🏊100m ➰100m.
Remarks: Service at Intermarché, Av.d'Aquitaine, n45,14633 o0,00569.

🛁 S | **La Roque-Gageac** 🌿 ⚓ | 28D2

D703. **GPS:** n44,82428 e1,18376. ⬆️.

20 🛏 € 7 🚰 €2/10minutes ➰ Ch 🔌 €2/1h.
Location: Simple. **Surface:** metalled. 🅾 01/01-31/12
Distance: 🚶200m 🏊100m ➰100m ⊗200m 🛒200m.
Remarks: Along the Dordogne river, canoe rental.

Tourist information La Roque-Gageac:
ℹ️ www.cc-perigord-noir.fr. Small town worth seeing, in the Dordogne valley.

🛁 S | **La Teste-de-Buch** | 28A2

Aire de Camping Car du Lac de Cazaux, Rue Guynemer.
GPS: n44,53158 w1,16025. ⬆️.
30 🛏 € 12/24h 🚰 ➰ Ch 🔧 included. 🚐 **Location:** Comfortable, quiet.
Surface: gravel/metalled. 🅾 01/01-31/12
Distance: 🏊450m ➰450m ⊗on the spot.

🛁 S | **Labastide-d'Armagnac** 🌿 | 28B3

Les Embarrats. GPS: n43,97205 w0,18602. ⬆️.

20 🛏 free 🚰 ➰ Ch free.
Location: Rural, simple, quiet. **Surface:** grassy.
Distance: 🚶300m.

🛁 S | **Labenne** | 28A4

Route Océane. GPS: n43,59616 w1,45492. ⬆️.

50 🛏 € 8 🚰 ➰ Ch 🔧 included. 🐕 **Surface:** metalled. 🅾 10/04-01/10
Distance: 🚶1km 🏊2km ➰2km ⊗1km 🛒1km.
Remarks: Max. 48h, no camping activities.

🛁 S | **Lacanau** | 28A1

Le Huga, Rue des Sauviels. **GPS:** n45,00583 w1,16528. ⬆️➡️.

125 🛏 € 13,80/24h 🚰 ➰ Ch 🔌 included. 🚐 💳 🅾 01/01-31/12
Remarks: In front of heliport, max. 48h.

🛁 S | **Ladaux** | 28B2

Vignobles Lobre & Fils, Le Bos. **GPS:** n44,69677 w0,24393.

5 free WC. **Surface:** grassy/metalled. 01/01-31/12
Distance: 300m.

Lalinde — 28D2

Avenue Général Leclerc. **GPS:** n44,83938 e0,74302.

2 free Ch free. **Location:** Simple. **Surface:** unpaved.
01/01-31/12
Distance: 500m 500m 500m on the spot.
Remarks: Near train station.

Lanouaille — 28D1

Rue du Chemin Neuf. **GPS:** n45,39248 e1,14002.

6 free Ch WC free. **Location:** Comfortable, central, quiet.
Surface: asphalted. 01/01-31/12
Distance: 50m 100m 100m on the spot.
Remarks: Max. 48h.

Lanton — 28A2

Allée Albert Pitres, Taussat. **GPS:** n44,71710 w1,06991.

12 free Ch free. **Surface:** asphalted. 01/01-31/12
Distance: sandy beach 100m.

Laruns — 28B5

Artouste Fabrèges. **GPS:** n42,87914 w0,39693.

80 free €5/100liter Ch €5/1h WC. **Surface:** asphalted/grassy.
01/01-31/12
Distance: 200m on the spot on the spot on the spot on the spot 1km.
Remarks: Coins at tourist info.

Laruns — 28B5

Avenue de la Gare. **GPS:** n42,98919 w0,42481.

30 € 6 Ch WC. **Surface:** asphalted. 01/01-31/12
Distance: 450m 450m 450m 400m.
Remarks: Max. 24h, coins at tourist info.

Lavardac — 28C3

Rue de la Victoire - Place du Foirail. **GPS:** n44,17883 e0,29928.

3 free Ch free. **Location:** Simple. **Surface:** asphalted.
Distance: on the spot 22km bakery 150m.

Layrac — 28D3

Aire de Layrac, Rue du 19 Mars 1962. **GPS:** n44,13233 e0,65946.
6 free Ch WC free. **Surface:** asphalted.

Layrac — 28D3

Le Moulin, D129. **GPS:** n44,13640 e0,66441.

max. 4 € 10/24h Ch WC €3. **Surface:** grassy.
01/01-31/12
Distance: on the spot.
Remarks: Call if no one is present, video surveillance.

Le Bugue — 28D1

Place Léopold Salme. **GPS:** n44,91679 e0,92775.

50 € 7,00 Ch WC free. **Location:** Simple. **Surface:** grassy.
01/01-31/12 Service: winter
Distance: 200m 20m 100m Intermarché 100m.
Remarks: Along the river Vézère, tuesday and Saturday market.

FR

| | Le Porge | 28A1 |

Avenue de l'Océan. **GPS:** n44,89437 w1,2131.

🛒free. **Surface:** forest soil. 🅿 01/01-31/12
Distance: Le Porge 10km on the spot on the spot.
Remarks: Max. 24h.

| S | Le Porge | 28A1 |

Intermarché. **GPS:** n44,87574 w1,07883.
€2 Ch.

| S | Le Temple-sur-Lot | 28C2 |

Avenue de Verdun. **GPS:** n44,38000 e0,52639.

4 🛒free Ch WC free. **Surface:** asphalted. 🅿 01/01-31/12
Distance: 50m 100km 100m.

| S | Le Verdon-sur-Mer | 20B6 |

Plage fluviale, Allée des Baïnes. **GPS:** n45,54582 w1,05433.

30+20 🛒€ 5/24h, 01/06-30/09 € 8/24h €2/100liter Ch.
Surface: gravel.
🅿 01/01-31/12
Distance: 50m 500m 2km on the spot.
Remarks: Coins at town hall, tourist info and the shops at the beach.

| S | Lège-Cap-Ferret | 28A2 |

Route des Pastourelles, Avenue Charles de Gaulle, D106, Claouey.
GPS: n44,75127 w1,18033.

± 15 🛒free Ch Service €3,30/15min. **Surface:** forest soil.
🅿 01/01-31/12
Remarks: Coins at camping municipal, day parking also allowed,

overnight stay on motorhome stopovers.

| | Lège-Cap-Ferret | 28A2 |

Avenue Edouard Branly. **GPS:** n44,75203 w1,18809.

15 🛒free. **Surface:** forest soil.
Remarks: Near campsite Les Embruns.

| | Lège-Cap-Ferret | 28A2 |

D106, Avenue de Bordeaux, L'Herbe. **GPS:** n44,68655 w1,2451.

15 🛒free. **Surface:** unpaved.

| S | Léguillac-de-l'Auche | 28D1 |

Glenon. **GPS:** n45,20319 e0,55876.
6 🛒free €2 €3/24h. **Location:** Rural, isolated, quiet.
Surface: grassy.
Distance: 2km 2km 2km.

| S | Lembras | 28C1 |

Aire de Caudeau, Impasse de l'Anguillère. **GPS:** n44,88300 e0,52522.

🛒free Ch free (10x)€4/12h. **Location:** Rural, comfortable, central.
Surface: gravel. 🅿 01/01-31/12
Distance: 200m 200m 200m 2,5km.

| S | Léon | 28A3 |

Aire camping-cars, Route de Puntaou. **GPS:** n43,88444 w1,31861.

80 🛒€ 10 Ch included. **Location:** Simple.
Surface: grassy/gravel. 🅿 01/01-31/12
Distance: 1km 250m 50m 50m 50m.
Remarks: Nearby lake.

Les Eyzies 28D1

Parking de la Vézère, Promenade de la Vézère. **GPS:** n44,93863 e1,00907.

25 €4/night €2/100liter Ch. **Location:** Comfortable, quiet.
Surface: grassy. 01/01-31/12
Distance: 100m 100m 100m.
Remarks: Along the river Vézère, summer max. 48h, parking fee being collected at 9AM.

Tourist information Les Eyzies:
Le Village Troglodytique de la Madeleine, Turzac. Troglodyte-village.
Le Village du Bournat, Le Bugue. Open air museum. 01/04-31/10 10-17/18h.

Lescar 28B4

Parking Jacques Monod, Chemin de Beneharnum. **GPS:** n43,33062 w0,43458.
5 free. **Surface:** asphalted. 01/01-31/12
Distance: on the spot on the spot on the spot on the spot.
Remarks: Max. 48h.

Lescar 28B4

Place de l'Evêché. **GPS:** n43,33348 w0,43401.
3 free. **Surface:** metalled. 01/01-31/12
Distance: on the spot 150m on the spot.
Remarks: Near office de tourisme, max. 48h.

Limeuil 28D1

GPS: n44,88238 e0,89128.
free. **Location:** Rural, isolated, quiet. **Surface:** grassy/gravel.
01/01-31/12
Distance: on the spot on the spot 600m.
Remarks: Along the Dordogne river.

Limeuil 28D1

D31. **GPS:** n44,88564 e0,89151.
free. **Location:** Rural, simple, isolated. **Surface:** gravel.
01/01-31/12
Distance: 400m 400m 750m.

Lit-et-Mixe 28A3

Cap de l'Homy, 600, avenue Océan. **GPS:** n44,03730 w1,33419.

36 € 10-18, 2 pers.incl Ch WC. **Location:** Simple, quiet.
Surface: forest soil. 01/05-30/09
Distance: 400m 200m 200m on the spot.
Remarks: Next to camping municipal.

L'Hôpital-St.Blaise 28B4

Parking l'Église. GPS: n43,25088 w0,76925.

5 free WC. **Surface:** asphalted. 01/01-31/12
Distance: on the spot on the spot on the spot on the spot.

Macau 28B1

Domaine du Prat, 51, Avenue de la Coste. **GPS:** n45,00380 w0,60508.

5 free. **Location:** Simple. 01/01-31/12
Distance: 800m.

Macau 28B1

Chemin du Mahoura. **GPS:** n45,00722 w0,61278.

Ch free. 01/01-31/12

Marmande 28C2

La Filhole, Rue de la Filhole. **GPS:** n44,49667 e0,16412.

30 € 8 Ch included. **Surface:** grassy. 07/04-02/11

Marmande 28C2

Place du Moulin. **GPS:** n44,49833 e0,16028.

2 🛏free ⚡🚰 Ch free. **Surface:** asphalted. 🔲 15/09-15/05
Distance: 🏖150m ⚓on the spot.
Remarks: Max. 48h.

Mensignac 28D1
Combecouyere-Sud. **GPS:** n45,22309 e0,56553.
3 🛏free ⚡€2 Ch. **Location:** Rural. **Surface:** metalled.
🔲 01/03-31/10

Messanges 28A3
Plage principale, Avenue de la Plage. **GPS:** n43,81549 w1,40088. ⬆

10 🛏free. **Location:** Simple. **Surface:** metalled/sand.
Distance: 🏖1,5km ⚓200m.
Remarks: Max. 48h.

Mimizan 28A3
Hélistation Plage Sud, Rue des Lacs, Mimizan-Plage. **GPS:** n44,20517 w1,29675.
⬆➡.

85 🛏€ 8, 01/06-30/09 € 13 ⚡🚰Ch ✎ included. 🚗 ⚒
Location: Comfortable. **Surface:** asphalted. 🔲 01/01-31/12
Distance: 🏖500m ⚓on the spot ⊗500m ⚓200m.
Remarks: Parking at dune, no trailers allowed.

Mimizan 28A3
Route du C.E.L.. **GPS:** n44,21375 w1,28239. ⬆.

150 🛏€ 6 ⚡€3 🚰Ch. **Location:** Simple. **Surface:** grassy/gravel.
🔲 01/06-31/09
Distance: ⚓beach 1,5km 🚲on the spot.

Mimizan 28A3
Camping du Lac, Avenue de Woolsack, Mimizan-lac. **GPS:** n44,21956 w1,22972. ⬆.

21 🛏€ 11,20-17,80 + € 0,22/pp tourist tax, dog € 1,10-1,90 ⚡€2 🚰 Ch ✎ WC 🗑 📷.
Location: Comfortable. **Surface:** gravel. 🔲 30/04-30/09

Moliets-et-Maa 28A3
Avenue de l'Océan, Moliets-Plage. **GPS:** n43,85091 w1,38188. ⬆.

120 🛏€ 5, 01/04-31/08 € 11 ⚡🚰Ch ✎ WC. 🚗 ⚒ **Location:**
Comfortable, noisy. **Surface:** grassy/gravel.
Distance: 🏖200m ⚓750m ⊗200m ⚓200m.
Remarks: Shady.

Monbahus 28C2
Rue du Moulin, Le Bourg. **GPS:** n44,54738 e0,53517. ⬆➡.

3 🛏free ⚡🚰Ch ✎ (2x)free. **Location:** Rural, simple. **Surface:** asphalted.
🔲 01/01-31/12 📷 Service: winter
Distance: 🏖300m ⊗200m ⚓300m.
Remarks: Beautiful view, steep entrance road.

Monbazillac 28C2
Château du Haut Pezaud, Les Pezauds. **GPS:** n44,78471 e0,48687. ⬆.

10 🛏free ⚡€1 ✎ €1/night,winter€2 WC free 🗑€1/pppd 📡€1/day.
Location: Rural, simple. **Surface:** grassy. 🔲 01/01-31/12
Distance: ⊗table d'hôtes 🚶through the vineyards.
Remarks: Baker every morning, tasting of regional products.

FR

Monbazillac 28C2

Domaine La Lande, Route de Ribagnac, D13. **GPS**: n44,78822 e0,49587.⬆️

10 free 🚰 🔌 Ch WC free. **Location**: Rural, simple. **Surface**: grassy.
⬛ 01/01-31/12
Distance: 🚶800m ⊗200m 🛒on the spot.
Remarks: Baker every morning, sale of wines.

Monflanquin 28D2

Chemin de la Source, 3, Allée des Érables. **GPS**: n44,52812 e0,75537.⬆️

free 🚰 🔌 Ch free. **Location**: Simple. **Surface**: gravel.
⬛ 01/01-31/12
Distance: 🚶1,5km Lac de Coulon 150m ⊗1,3km 🛒250m.
Remarks: Service 500m n44,52477 o0,75642.

Tourist information Monflanquin:
ℹ️ Office de Tourisme, Place des Arcades, www.monflanquin-tourisme.com.
Medieval town.

Monpazier 28D2

La Duelle-nord. **GPS**: n44,68499 e0,89362.⬆️➡️

10 free 🚰 🔌 Ch free. **Surface**: gravel. ⬛ 01/01-31/12
Distance: 🚶300m ⊗400m 🛒500m.

Monségur 28C2

Place du 8 mai. **GPS**: n44,65060 e0,08363.

5 free 🚰 🔌 Ch WC free. **Surface**: asphalted. ⬛ 01/01-31/12
Distance: ⊗nearby.
Remarks: Max. 48h. No access via La Bastide.

Mont-de-Marsan 28B3

Aire du Camping-Cars du Marsan, 541 avenue de Villeneuve.
GPS: n43,88992 w0,47559.⬆️
45 €5, 01/05-30/09 € 7 🚰€1/5minutes 🔌Ch 🔌€0,50/60minutes.
Location: Rural. **Surface**: asphalted/grassy.
Distance: 🚶2,3km 🛒500m.

Montalivet-les-Bains 20B6

Avenue de l'Europe. **GPS**: n45,37051 w1,14462.⬆️

30 €4-8 🚰 🔌Ch 🔌 included. 🏖️ **Location**: Quiet. **Surface**: forest soil.
⬛ 01/05-30/09
Distance: 🚶800m ⊗nearby 🛒nearby.
Remarks: Max. 48h.

Montalivet-les-Bains 20B6

Boulevard de Lattre de Tassigny, Montalivet-sud. **GPS**: n45,37611 w1,15667.⬆️

30 €5 🚰€1 🔌Ch. **Surface**: grassy/metalled. ⬛ 01/05-30/09
Distance: 🚶on the spot 🏖️on the spot ⊗on the spot 🛒on the spot.
Remarks: At sea, max. 48h, service at Aldi 1km.

Tourist information Montalivet-les-Bains:
🏖️ ⬛ Fri.

Montcaret 28C1

Le Chalet du Gourmet, D936. **GPS**: n44,85349 e0,03964.⬆️

16 €6,50 🚰 🔌Ch 🔌 WC €2 🔌€3.
Surface: grassy.
⬛ 01/01-31/12
Distance: 🚶1,2km ⊗Resto Rapid.
Remarks: Bread-service, fruit-vegetables-wine-regional products for sale.

Monteton 28C2

D423. **GPS**: n44,62226 e0,25635.⬆️

25 �"free 🚰⌐Chfree. **Surface:** grassy. ☐ 01/01-31/12
Distance: ⊗on the spot.
Remarks: Beautiful view.

| 🅢 | Montignac | 28D1 |

P Vieux Quartiers, Rue des Sagnes. **GPS:** n45,06800 e1,16547.➡️

20 ⌐free ⌐€3 🅟 **Location:** Simple, central. **Surface:** gravel.
☐ 01/01-31/12
Distance: ⏁200m ⊗200m ⌐200m.

| 🅢 | Montignac | 28D1 |

Ferme du Bois Bareirou, Les Baraques, Montignac-Lascaux.
GPS: n45,09053 e1,11143.⬆️➡️

20 ⌐free ⌐€3 ⌐Ch ⌐€3. **Surface:** grassy. ☐ 01/01-31/12
Distance: ⏁5km.
Remarks: Max. 3 days.

| 🅢 | Montignac | 28D1 |

Avenue Aristide Briand, D65. **GPS:** n45,06083 e1,15888.⬆️

🚰⌐Chfree. **Location:** Simple. ☐ 01/01-31/12
Distance: ⌐on the spot ⊗300m ⌐500m.

| 🅢 | Montpon-Ménestérol | 28C1 |

Chez Lou Cantou, 46 rue Gustave Eiffel, D730. **GPS:** n45,02101 e0,15997.
4 ⌐€ 10/24h ⌐€3/100liter ⌐Ch ⌐€3.
☐ 01/04-31/10 ◉ frost

| 🅢 | Morcenx | 28A3 |

Chemin des Abattoirs. **GPS:** n44,03811 w0,90914.⬆️

⌐free 🚰⌐Chfree. **Location:** Simple.
Distance: ⏁500m ⌐8,8km.
Remarks: Along railwayline.

| 🅢 | Mugron | 28B4 |

Avenue des Martyrs de la Résistance, D32e. **GPS:** n43,74846 w0,75063.⬆️

4 ⌐free 🚰⌐Ch ⌐(4x)free.
Location: Rural, simple. **Surface:** gravel.
Distance: ⏁300m ⌐on the spot.
Remarks: Max. 24h.

| 🅢 | Nailhac | 28D1 |

D62E3. **GPS:** n45,23276 e1,14214.⬆️
6 ⌐free 🚰⌐Chfree. **Location:** Rural. **Surface:** metalled.

| 🅢 | Naujan-et-Postiac | 28C2 |

Lafuge. **GPS:** n44,78715 w0,17928.⬆️➡️
⌐free. **Location:** Simple. **Surface:** grassy/gravel.

| 🅢 | Nérac | 28C3 |

Place du Foirail. **GPS:** n44,13435 e0,33655.⬆️

2 ⌐free 🚰⌐Ch WC. **Location:** Simple. **Surface:** asphalted.
☐ 01/01-31/12
Distance: ⏁50m ⊗on the spot ⌐on the spot.

| 🅢 | Nontron | 21A6 |

Super U, 26, Avenue Jules Ferry. **GPS:** n45,53670 e0,66660.

3 ⌐free ⌐€2 ⌐Ch ⌐€2. **Location:** Noisy. **Surface:** asphalted.
☐ 01/03-31/10
Distance: ⏁1km ⊗1km ⌐on the spot.

Remarks: Parking supermarket, max. 24h.

♿ S Oloron-Sainte-Marie 28B5

Parking Trivoli, Rue Adour Oloron. **GPS:** n43,18399 w0,60854.⬆➡

7 ☕free ⚡€4/55minutes 🔌 Ch⊞€4/55minutes. **Surface:** asphalted. 🅿 01/01-31/12
Distance: 🚶100m 🅿on the spot 🍴on the spot 🛒400m 🚌400m.
Remarks: Max. 48h, coins at tourist info.

♿ S Ondres 28A4

P3, Avenue de la Plage, Ondres-Plage. **GPS:** n43,57611 w1,48611.⬆

41 ☕€ 7, 01/07-31/08 € 9 ⚡🔌 Ch 🧹 WC free. 🛏 ♻ **Surface:** asphalted. 🅿 15/04-01/11
Distance: 🚶3km 🏊on the spot 🍴on the spot ⊗on the spot 🛒on the spot 🚲on the spot.
Remarks: Max. 48h.

♿ S Parentis-en-Born 🌳 28A2

Site du Lac, Route des Campings. **GPS:** n44,34432 w1,09879.⬆

25 ☕€ 7 ⚡🔌 Ch 🧹(4x)included. **Location:** Comfortable. **Surface:** gravel. 🅿 01/01-31/12 💧 service in winter
Distance: 🚶3km 🏊50m ⊗50m.

♿ S Pau 28B4

Place de Verdun, Rue Ambroise Bordelongue. **GPS:** n43,29848 w0,37811.⬆.

20 ☕free. **Location:** Urban. **Surface:** asphalted. 🅿 01/01-31/12
Distance: 🚶on the spot ⊗on the spot 🛒200m.
Remarks: Max. 48h, free shuttle.

♿ S Payzac 28D1

Le Bourg. **GPS:** n45,40008 e1,21950.
☕free ⚡🔌 Chfree. **Surface:** asphalted. 🅿 01/01-31/12
Distance: 🚶on the spot ⊗on the spot 🛒on the spot 🥾on the spot.

♿ S Pellegrue 28C2

Le Touran, Rue du Lavoir. **GPS:** n44,74514 e0,07416.⬆.

4 ☕free ⚡🔌 Ch 🧹free. **Surface:** metalled. 🅿 01/01-31/12
Distance: 🚶100m ⊗200m 🛒700m.

♿ S Périgueux 28D1

Espace des Prés, Rue des Prés. **GPS:** n45,18770 e0,73081.⬆➡

40 ☕€ 5 ⚡🔌 Ch 🧹included. 🛁 **Location:** Comfortable, central. **Surface:** asphalted. 🅿 01/01-31/12 💧 water disconnected in winter
Distance: 🚶800m 🛒on the spot.
Remarks: Max. 48h.

♿ S Peyrehorade 28A4

Des Gaves, Route de la Pêcherie. **GPS:** n43,54300 w1,1071. ⬆ .
16 ☕€ 8 ⚡🔌 Ch 🧹€2,50 WC 🚰. **Surface:** grassy. 🅿 01/06-30/09
Distance: 🚶150m 🏊on the spot 🍴on the spot ⊗150m 🛒150m 🚌200m.

♿ S Peyrehorade 28A4

Place Jean Bridart, Rue du Sablot, D817. **GPS:** n43,54300 w1,09994.⬆.

10 ☕free ⚡🔌 Chfree. **Surface:** metalled. 🅿 01/01-31/12
Distance: 🚶50m 🏊on the spot 🍴on the spot ⊗100m 🛒on the spot.
Remarks: In front of supermarket Carrefour.

♿ S Port-Sainte-Foy-et-Ponchapt 28C2

Rue Jacques Jasmin. **GPS:** n44,84244 e0,20915.⬆.
4 ☕free ⚡🔌 Chfree. **Surface:** asphalted. 🅿 01/01-31/12
Distance: 🍴on the spot ⊗600m 🛒600m.
Remarks: Along the Dordogne river, service 200m.

🏕 Prats-de-Carlux 29A2

Les Oies du Périgord Noir, D47B. **GPS:** n44,89936 e1,31503.⬆.
3 ☕free. **Location:** Rural.
Remarks: Max. 24h.

© S Ribérac 28C1

Camping de la Dronne, 91 Rue des Etats Unis. **GPS:** n45,25704 e0,34255.⬆.

FR

10 ⛽free, 01/06-15/09 € 5,60 🚰💨 Ch free. 🛶 **Location:** Urban, simple.
Surface: metalled. ⬛ 01/01-31/12 ⬜ Water when frosty
Distance: 🏊1,3km ⊗50m 🛒Leclerc 900m.

🏕️🅂 **Roquefort** 28B3
Allée de Nauton. **GPS:** n44,04754 w0,32255.⬆️
6 ⛽free 🚰💨 Ch. **Surface:** grassy/gravel. ⬛ 01/01-31/12
Distance: 🏊1,7km 🚣5km.
Remarks: Next to camping municipal.

🏕️🅂 **Saint Estèphe** 21A6
Etang de Saint Estèphe. **GPS:** n45,59008 e0,67396.⬆️

10 ⛽€ 5 🚰💨 Ch free. **Location:** Comfortable. **Surface:** gravel.
⬛ 01/01-31/12
Distance: 🏊700m 🏊lake ▶️on the spot ⊗on the spot
🛒3km, bakery 800m.
Remarks: Max. 48h, summer: beach, bar, restaurant.

🏕️🅂 **Saint-Estèphe** 28B1
Rue des Pêcheurs. **GPS:** n45,26544 w0,7582.⬆️

5 ⛽free 🚰💨 Ch➕Service€5. **Surface:** metalled.
Distance: 🚣on the spot ▶️on the spot ⊗on the spot.
Remarks: Free, coins available at restaurant.

🏕️🅂 **Saint-Hilaire-de-Lusignan** 28C3
D813. **GPS:** n44,22491 e0,51364.⬆️
3 ⛽free 🚰€3 💨 Ch. **Surface:** gravel. ⬛ 01/01-31/12

🏕️🅂 **Saint-Pey-d'Armens** 28C1
Château Gerbaud, Gerbaud. **GPS:** n44,85310 w0,10699.⬆️

50 ⛽€ 5 🚰💨 Ch 💨 (8x)€3. **Surface:** grassy. ⬛ 01/01-31/12
Distance: ⊗200m 🛒bakery 200m, supermarket 2km.
Remarks: Max. 48h.

🏕️🅂 **Saint-Romain-la-Virvée** 28B1
Rue des Milonis. **GPS:** n44,96388 w0,4019.⬆️
5 ⛽free 🚰💨 Ch. **Surface:** asphalted. ⬛ 01/01-31/12
Distance: ⊗250m.
Remarks: Next to sports fields.

🏕️🅂 **Sainte-Colombe-en-Bruilhois** 28C3
Lieu-dit Bécade. **GPS:** n44,17889 e0,51692.⬆️

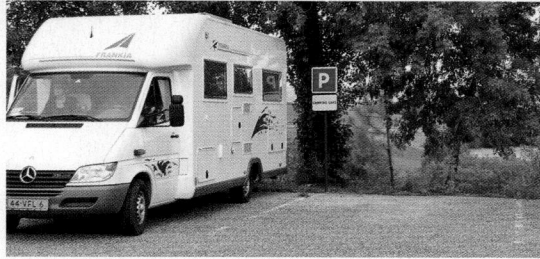

4 ⛽free 🚰💨 Ch WC free. **Surface:** gravel. ⬛ 01/01-31/12
Distance: 🏊on the spot ⊗200m 🛒200m.

🏕️🅂 **Sainte-Nathalène** 28D1
Les Ch'tis, Le Bourg, D47. **GPS:** n44,90409 e1,28765.⬆️

6 ⛽€ 10 🚰💨 Ch 💨 included. **Surface:** gravel. ⬛ 01/01-31/12
Distance: 🏊Sarlat 7km 🛒50m 🛒bread service 50m.
Remarks: Market Wednesday (July-August).

🏕️🅂 **Salies-de-Béarn** ♨️ 28A4
Aire Campincar du Herre, Quartiér du Herre. **GPS:** n43,47270 w0,9339.⬆️➡️

24 ⛽€ 6,50 🚰💨 Ch 💨 included. ⬛🛒 **Surface:** metalled.
⬛ 01/01-31/12
Distance: 🏊300m 🚣on the spot ▶️on the spot ⊗300m 🛒300m 🅿️300m.

🏕️🅂 **Salignac-Eyvigues** 29A1
Rue des Ecoles. **GPS:** n44,97257 e1,32061.⬆️

10 ⛽free 🚰💨 Ch free. **Location:** Comfortable, quiet. **Surface:** grassy.

FR

◻ 01/01-31/12
Distance: 🚰300m ⊗300m 🛒250m.

| 🅿️ | Salignac-Eyvigues | 29A1 |

Les Jardins du Manoir d'Eyrignac. GPS: n44,93875 e1,31609.
🚰free. **Surface:** grassy/gravel.
Distance: 🚰Sarlat 13km ⊗on the spot.

| 🅿️ S | Sanguinet 🚻 🏖️ | 28A2 |

Aire du camping-car Les Bardets, 1131, Avenue de Losa.
GPS: n44,48408 w1,09153.⬆️.

15 🚰free, € 8 (01/05-18/09) 🚰 🛢️ Chfree. **Location:** Simple, quiet.
Surface: metalled. ◻ 01/01-31/12
Distance: 🚰800m ⊘on the spot ➡️on the spot ⊗50m 🛒on the spot.
Remarks: At lake, max. 48h.

| 🅿️ S | Sanguinet 🚻 🏖️ | 28A2 |

Parking du Pavillon, 459, Avenue de Losa. **GPS:** n44,48579 w1,08479.⬆️.

30 🚰free, € 8 (15/6-15/9) 🚰 WC. **Location:** Simple, quiet. **Surface:** forest soil.
◻ 01/01-31/12
Distance: ⊘on the spot ⊗Le Pavillon.
Remarks: Max. 48h.

| 🅿️ S | Sare | 37D4 |

Place de Campingcars de Sare. GPS: n43,31307 w1,57679.⬆️.

15 🚰€6 🚰 🛢️ Chincluded. **Location:** Quiet. **Surface:** metalled.
◻ 01/01-31/12
Distance: 🚰300m ⊗300m 🛒300m 🚲on the spot 🚶on the spot.
Remarks: Max. 48h.

Tourist information Sare:
ℹ️ Office de Tourisme, Bourg, www.sare.fr. Typical Basque village in Labourd-region.
👁 Le petit train de la Rhune, Col de Saint Ignace. The little train runs through the mountains in the Basque Country on the Franco-Spanish border. ◻ 15/03-15/11 from 9h.

| 🅿️ S | Sarlat-la-Canéda 🌿 🍽️ 🛒 | 28D2 |

Place Flandres Dunkerque. **GPS:** n44,89530 e1,21266.⬆️➡️.

50 🚰€ 7/24h, € 15/48h 🚰€2 🛢️ Ch🔌€2 .🛒 **Location:** Simple, noisy. **Surface:** asphalted. ◻ 01/01-31/12
Distance: 🚰300m ⊗100m 🛒bakery 50m.

Tourist information Sarlat-la-Canéda:
🏠 Centre ville. Centre of the French trade in foie grass. ◻ Sa-morning.

| 🅿️ S | Sauvagnon | 28B4 |

Champ de Foire, Rue du Béarn. **GPS:** n43,40361 w0,38635.⬆️.

6 🚰free 🚰 🛢️ Ch WC free. **Surface:** asphalted. ◻ 01/01-31/12
Distance: 🚰on the spot ⊗on the spot 🛒on the spot ➡️on the spot.

| 🅿️ | Sauvagnon | 28B4 |

Rue du Béarn. **GPS:** n43,40310 w0,3876.⬆️.
6 🚰free. **Surface:** grasstiles. ◻ 01/01-31/12
Distance: 🚰on the spot.

| 🅿️ | Sauveterre de Guyenne | 28C2 |

Boulevard de 11 Novembre. **GPS:** n44,69022 w0,08624.⬆️.

4 🚰free 🚰€0,50 🛢️ Ch🔌€1,50/90minutes. **Surface:** metalled.
◻ 01/01-31/12
Distance: 🚰350m.
Remarks: Coins at tourist info, supermarket.

| 🅿️ S | Savignac-Lédrier | 28D1 |

Route de Juillac. **GPS:** n45,36401 e1,22066.
🚰free 🚰 🛢️ Ch 🔧 free. **Surface:** gravel. ◻ 01/01-31/12
Distance: 🚰on the spot ⊗100m.
Remarks: Coins at restaurant des Forges.

| 🅿️ S | Seignosse | 28A4 |

Aire camping-cars, D79. **GPS:** n43,69089 w1,42539.⬆️➡️.

FR

110 🛏€12 ⛽ Ch ✦ WC 📶included 🗑. **Surface:** grassy/gravel.
⬛ 01/01-31/12
Distance: 🚶500m 🏊500m 🛒500m ✖500m ⛽500m.
Remarks: Next to campsite municipal Hourn-Nao, video surveillance.

Sévignacq Méracq 28B5
Aire du gave d'Ossau, Quartier Raguette. **GPS:** n43,10712 w0,419. ⬆➡.

20 🛏€10 ⛽€3 Ch ✦€2 WC ▣. **Surface:** grassy/gravel.
⬛ 01/02-30/11
Distance: 🚶1km 🏊on the spot 🛒on the spot ✖1km ⛽1km.

Soorts-Hossegor 28A4
Route des Lacs. **GPS:** n43,67279 w1,42087. ⬆.
85 🛏€6/24h ⛽€2 Ch WC.🗑 🛒 **Location:** Rural, quiet. **Surface:** gravel.
⬛ 01/01-31/12
Distance: 🏊550m.
Remarks: Max. 5 days.

Sorges 28D1
Aire de repos Grangearias, Le Bourg, N21. **GPS:** n45,30570 e0,87238. ⬆.

4 🛏free ⛽ Ch. **Surface:** metalled. ⬛ 01/01-31/12
Distance: 🚶100m ✖200m ⛽250m.
Remarks: Service 100m.

Soulac-sur-Mer 20B6
Boulevard de L'Amélie. **GPS:** n45,49938 w1,1373. ⬆.

50 🛏€8 ⛽€3,50 Ch 🗑.🗑 🛒 ⬛ 01/01-31/12
Distance: 🏊50m ✖2,5km ⛽2,5km 🎣on the spot 🎿on the spot.

Sourzac 28C1
D6089. **GPS:** n45,05147 e0,39518. ⬆.

8 🛏free ⛽€2/100liter Ch WC. **Location:** Rural, central.
Surface: gravel/metalled. ⬛ 01/01-31/12 ⬤ water disconnected in winter
Distance: 🚶600m ✖100m.
Remarks: Coins at petrol station.

Soustons 28A3
Parking du Lac Marin, Avenue de la Pêtre, Soustons Plage.
GPS: n43,77560 w1,41167. ⬆.

80 🛏01/10-31/04 €6,50, 01/05-30/09 €12,50 ⛽ Ch ✦ WC included.🗑
🗑 **Location:** Simple. **Surface:** gravel/metalled. ⬛ 01/01-31/12
Distance: 🚶city centre 3km 🏊lake 50m, ocean 300m ✖50m ⛽50m
🎣on the spot.
Remarks: Max. 72h.

St.Antoine-Cumond 28C1
Le Bourg, D43. **GPS:** n45,25553 e0,19963. ⬆.

10 🛏free ⛽ Ch WC free. **Location:** Rural, simple.
Surface: asphalted/gravel. ⬛ 01/01-31/12
Distance: 🚶on the spot.

St.Caprais de Blaye 28B1
Route de Saintes, RN137, Ferchaud. **GPS:** n45,29120 w0,5692. ⬆.

8 🛏free ⛽service €2 Ch WC free, cold shower. **Surface:** asphalted.
⬛ 01/01-31/12
Distance: 🚲6,4km ✖on the spot ⛽on the spot.
Remarks: Tourist information and picnic tables available.

St.Cyprien (Dordogne) 28D2
Place Mackenheim, Rue du Priolat. **GPS:** n44,86828 e1,04435.

8 ⌂free ⛽€3/100liter Ch (8x)€3/12h.
Location: Simple. **Surface:** asphalted.
◻ 01/01-31/12
Distance: 50m bakery 50m, supermarket 100m.
Remarks: Max. 24h, coins at tourist info and restaurant La Sivade.

Tourist information St.Cyprien (Dordogne):
⊗ Marché repas gourmand. ◻ summer Thu-evening.

St.Front-la-Rivière 21A6
Chez Boutau, D83. **GPS:** n45,46573 e0,72586.

10 ⌂free Ch (2x)WCfree. **Location:** Rural, isolated, quiet.
Surface: gravel. ◻ 01/01-31/12
Remarks: Max. 72h, picnic area.

St.Jean-de-Côle 21A6
Le Bourg. **GPS:** n45,41984 e0,84048.

6 ⌂free ⛽€2 Ch. **Location:** Comfortable, quiet. **Surface:** gravel.
◻ 01/01-31/12
Distance: on the spot ⊗200m 300m 200m.
Remarks: At tennis-court, coins at tourist info.

St.Jean-de-Luz 37D4
Avenue Pierre Larramendy, D810. **GPS:** n43,38527 w1,6629.

18 ⌂free ⛽ Ch free. **Surface:** asphalted.
Distance: 200m 2,2km 300m 300m ⊗100m 100m.
Remarks: Max. 48h.

Tourist information St.Jean-de-Luz:
ℹ Office de Tourisme, Place du Maréchal Foch, www.saint-jean-de-luz.com. Tourist town with beautiful shops. The local speciality is chipirones, octopus cooked in its own ink.
Halles, Bd Victor Hugo. ◻ morning.

St.Jean-Pied-de-Port 28A5
Parking du Lai Alai. **GPS:** n43,16519 w1,23208.

50 ⌂€ 5,50/24h ⛽ Chfree.
Surface: metalled. ◻ 01/01-31/12
Distance: 350m 350m 350m ⊗350m 350m on the spot.
Remarks: Nearby stadium, max. 48h.

Tourist information St.Jean-Pied-de-Port:
ℹ Office de Tourisme, 14, Place Charles de Gaulle, www.pyrenees-basques.com. Fortified city on the foot of the Roncesvallespass on the road to Santiago de Compostela.
Forêt d'Iraty. Nature reserve, hiking trails available at OT.

St.Laurent Médoc 28B1
Place du 8 mai 1945. **GPS:** n45,14903 w0,8215.
6 ⌂free ⛽ Ch. **Location:** Simple. **Surface:** metalled.
Distance: on the spot ⊗300m 300m.

St.Leon-sur-l'Isle 28C1
Skate Park Bord de l'Isle, D41E2. **GPS:** n45,12002 e0,49628.

6 ⌂free ⛽ Chfree. **Location:** Rural, simple. **Surface:** metalled/sand.
◻ 01/01-31/12
Distance: 2km 5,3km on the spot ⊗2km 2km.
Remarks: Service in village 750m, n45.11515 o0.5003400.

St.Léon-sur-Vézère 28D1
Le Bourg, C201. **GPS:** n45,01230 e1,08978.

⌂free ⛽€2 WC.
Location: Simple, quiet. **Surface:** grassy/gravel. ◻ 01/01-31/12
Distance: 100m 200m 150m.
Remarks: Coins at tourist info, sanitary building 100m, shower € 0,50.

St.Palais 28A4
Parking Place Ste. Elisabeth, Rue Gaztelu Zena. **GPS:** n43,32944 w1,0325.

10 free Ch WC free. **Surface:** asphalted. 01/01-31/12
Distance: 200m 250m 250m.

S St.Paul-les-Dax 28A3

Allée Salvador Allende. **GPS**: n43,73460 w1,07865.

8 free Ch free. **Location:** Simple. **Surface:** gravel/sand.
01/01-31/12
Distance: 500m 500m.
Remarks: Max. 72h, shady.

S St.Pée-de-Nivelle 28A4

Flot bleu park St. Pée sur Nivelle, Promenade du Parlement de Navarre.
GPS: n43,34945 w1,5215.

50 € 9,50/24h €2,50/120liter Ch €2,50/4h.
Surface: asphalted. 01/01-31/12
Distance: 3km on the spot 500m Restaurant Aintzira Le Lac.
Remarks: Parking at lake, max. 48h, bread-service.

St.Saud-Lacoussière 21A6

Étang de la Gourgousse. **GPS**: n45,55957 e0,82366.
free. **Location:** Isolated, quiet. **Surface:** unpaved.
Distance: Sandy beach on the spot on the spot.
Remarks: Max. 72h.

S St.Saud-Lacoussière 21A6

Domaine Sous Chardonnièras, 4, Impasse Sous Chardonnièras.
GPS: n45,54053 e0,81909.

4 € 12,50 WC included. **Surface:** unpaved. 01/01-31/12
Distance: 500m 2km 2km 500m 500m.

S St.Sauveur 28D2

Le Bourg, D21. **GPS**: n44,86850 e0,58834.

3 free Ch WC free. **Location:** Simple. **Surface:** asphalted.
01/01-31/12
Distance: 100m 100m 100m.

S St.Savin 28B1

Aire de Civrac-de-Blaye, Parc de la Mairie, D36, Civrac-de-Blaye.
GPS: n45,11222 w0,44444.

1 free WC free. **Surface:** grassy. 01/01-31/12
Distance: 50m 100m.

S St.Savin 28B1

Aire de St.Girons d'Aiguevives, St.Girons d'Aiguevives. **GPS**: n45,13972 w0,5425.

2 free . **Surface:** grassy/gravel. 01/01-31/12
Distance: on the spot 4km 10km.
Remarks: Parking in front of church.

S St.Savin 28B1

Aire des Lacs du Moulin Blanc, St.Christoly-de-Blaye. **GPS**: n45,15167 w0,47583.

2 free WC free. **Surface:** gravel. 01/01-31/12
Distance: 800m 50m on the spot on the spot 3km.
Remarks: Parking at lake.

S St.Savin 28B1

Aire des Lagunes, St.Mariens. **GPS**: n45,11790 w0,40243.

FR

2 🛏free 🚰 WC free. **Surface:** asphalted. 🔲 01/01-31/12
Distance: 🛒on the spot 🏊6km 🚲6km 🍴2km 🍺3km.

| 🛁S | St.Savin | 28B1 |

Parking Centre Culturel. GPS: n45,13800 w0,4465.

2 🛏free WC. **Surface:** gravel. 🔲 01/01-31/12
Distance: 🛒on the spot 🏊3km 🚲3km ⊗150m 🍺800m, bakery 50m.
Remarks: Max. 48h.

| 🛁 | St.Savin | 28B1 |

Aire de l'Église, Générac. **GPS:** n45,18000 w0,54.
2 🛏free. 🔲 01/01-31/12
Distance: 🛒on the spot ⊗6km 🍺10km.

| 🛁 | St.Savin | 28B1 |

Aire de Marcenais, Marcenais. **GPS:** n45,05808 w0,33889.

2 🛏free. 🔲 01/01-31/12
Distance: 🛒on the spot ⊗6km 🍺6km.
Remarks: Next to community centre.

| 🛁 | St.Savin | 28B1 |

Aire de Saugon, Saugon. **GPS:** n45,17795 w0,50243.
2 🛏free. 🔲 01/01-31/12
Distance: 🛒on the spot 🏊6km 🚲6km ⊗3km 🍺6km.
Remarks: Behind town hall.

| 🛁 | St.Savin | 28B1 |

Aire de St. Vivien, RN137, St.Vivien-de-Blay. **GPS:** n45,09917 w0,51666.

2 🛏free. 🔲 01/01-31/12
Distance: 🛒on the spot 🏊3km 🚲3km ⊗3km 🍺3km.

Remarks: Parking at church.

| 🛁 | St.Savin | 28B1 |

Aire du Dojo, Cézac. **GPS:** n45,09000 w0,41.

1 🛏free. 🔲 01/01-31/12
Distance: 🛒on the spot 🏊6km 🚲6km ⊗3km 🍺3km.
Remarks: Nearby town hall.

| 🛁 | St.Savin | 28B1 |

Aire du Lac des Vergnes, Laruscade. **GPS:** n45,10000 w0,34.
2 🛏free. 🔲 01/01-31/12
Distance: 🏊200m 🛒on the spot ⊗500m 🍺2km.
Remarks: Parking at lake.

| 🛁 | St.Savin | 28B1 |

Aire Maison de la Forêt, Donnezac. **GPS:** n45,24000 w0,44.

2 🛏free. 🔲 01/01-31/12
Distance: 🛒on the spot ⊗6km 🍺6km.
Remarks: Next to community centre.

| 🛁 | St.Savin | 28B1 |

Parking communal Aire de Cavignac, Rue de Paix, Cavignac.
GPS: n45,10019 w0,39192. ⬆.

2 🛏free. 🔲 01/01-31/12
Distance: 🛒on the spot 🚲8km ⊗50m 🍺300m.

| 🛁 | St.Savin | 28B1 |

Parking communal Aire de Saint Yzan, Parking de la Gare, St.Yzan-de-Soudiac.
GPS: n45,14006 w0,40996.
2 🛏free. 🔲 01/01-31/12
Distance: 🛒on the spot 🏊12km 🚲800m ⊗3km 🍺3km 🚿on the spot.

| 🛁 | St.Savin | 28B1 |

Parking de Marsas, Rue Chaignaud, Marsas. **GPS:** n45,06770 w0,3849.
2 🛏free. 🔲 01/01-31/12
Distance: 🛒on the spot ⊗4km 🍺4km.

| 🛁 | St.Savin | 28B1 |

Parking Maison des Jeunes, Cubnezais. **GPS:** n45,07500 w0,40861. ⬆➡.

FR

≋free. **Surface:** asphalted. ◻ 01/01-31/12
Distance: 50m ⊗3km 3km.

| ⌂S | St.Sylvestre-sur-Lot | 28D2 |

Place du Lot, Avenue Jean Moulin. **GPS:** n44,39621 e0,80499. ⬆.

12 ≋free ⚒ Chfree. **Surface:** asphalted. ◻ 01/01-31/12
Distance: 150m, Penne d'Agenais centre 1,8km ⊗100m 50m.
Remarks: Service 100m.

| ⌂⌂S | St.Vincent-de-Cosse | 28D2 |

Ferme d'Enveaux. GPS: n44,82669 e1,09822. ⬆➡.

50 ≋guests free ⚒ Chfree.
Surface: unpaved.
◻ 01/01-31/12
Distance: pebbled beach 50m on the spot ⊗on the spot.
Remarks: Along the Dordogne river, max. 48h, key service at canoe rental.

| ⌂S | St.Vincent-Jalmoutiers | 28C1 |

Le Bourg. **GPS:** n45,20055 e0,19091. ⬆➡.

25 ≋free ⚒ Ch WC free. **Location:** Rural, simple. **Surface:** grassy/sand.
◻ 01/01-31/12
Distance: 350m ⊗350m.

| ⌂S | Ste.Alvére | 28D1 |

Rue de la Fontaine Saint Jean. **GPS:** n44,94500 e0,80499. ⬆.

10 ≋free ⚒€2,50/100liter Ch ⊞€2,50/1h. **Location:** Simple, isolated.
Surface: gravel. ◻ 01/01-31/12
Distance: 500m ⊗500m 500m.
Remarks: At sports centre, coins at town hall.

| ⌂S | Ste.Eulalie-en-Born | 28A2 |

Route du Port, D652. **GPS:** n44,30634 w1,18206. ⬆.

40 ≋€ 7, 01/04-31/10 € 4,50 ⚒ Ch WC included €3.
Location: Comfortable, quiet. **Surface:** grassy.
◻ 01/04-31/10 service 01/11-01/03
Distance: 50m ⊗50m on the spot on the spot.
Remarks: At marina, to be paid at campsite.

| ⌂S | Ste.Livrade-sur-Lot | 28C2 |

Avenue René Bouchon. **GPS:** n44,39588 e0,59179.

8 ≋free ⚒ Chfree. **Surface:** asphalted. ◻ 01/01-31/12
Distance: 850m.
Remarks: At fire-station.

| ⌂S | Taussat | 28A2 |

Allée Albert Pitres. **GPS:** n44,71719 w1,06986. ⬆.
8 ≋free ⚒free. **Location:** Simple. **Surface:** metalled.
Distance: 50m ⊗300m 300m.

| ⌂S | Tocane-Saint-Apre | 28C1 |

Pré Sec, D103. **GPS:** n45,25712 e0,49471. ⬆➡.

8 ≋free ⚒€2/100liter Ch ⊞€2/1h. **Location:** Rural, simple.
Surface: metalled. ◻ 01/01-31/12
Distance: 300m 100m ⊗300m 300m.

FR

Remarks: Coins at the shops in the village.

♿⛽ **Tournon-d'Agenais** 28D2

Base de Loisirs Camp Beau, Pont Roumio, Route de Libos, D102.
GPS: n44,40444 e0,99833.

15 🅿free ⚡🚰 Ch free. **Surface:** metalled. 🅿 01/01-31/12

⛽ **Valeyrac** 20B6

Port de Goulée, Route Castillonaise. **GPS:** n45,40500 w0,91028.

🅿free. **Surface:** asphalted/grassy.
Distance: 🏖50m 🛒on the spot ⊗20m.
Remarks: At harbour.

♿⛽ **Vanxains** 28C1

Le Petit Verteillac, D708. **GPS:** n45,21204 e0,28399. ⬆➡

2 🅿free ⚡🚰 Ch 🔌 WC free. **Location:** Rural, simple. **Surface:** asphalted.
🅿 01/01-3112
Distance: 🏖400m 🛒700m.

♿⛽ **Varaignes** 21A6

Place du Château. **GPS:** n45,59804 e0,53154. ⬆

4 🅿free ⚡🚰 Ch WC free. **Location:** Simple, central. **Surface:** gravel.
🅿 01/01-31/12
Distance: 🏖on the spot ⊗100m 🛒bakery 50m.

♿⛽ **Vertheuil** 28B1

Château Ferré, 3 rue des Aubépines. **GPS:** n45,26225 w0,82798. ⬆

5 🅿free ⚡🚰 Ch WC. **Surface:** gravel. 🅿 01/01-31/12

♿⛽ **Veyrines-de-Domme** 28D2

Boutique des Bois d'Envaux, Route des Milandes, 6-102 Le Falgueyrat.
GPS: n44,82090 e1,10394. ⬆

30 🅿free. **Location:** Simple, isolated. **Surface:** grassy.
Distance: ⊗on the spot.
Remarks: Sale of foie gras and wine, monday evening marché gourmand.

♿⛽ **Vielle St.Girons** 🌳 28A3

Lac de Léon, plage de Vielle. **GPS:** n43,90279 w1,30944. ⬆

30 🅿 € 9-12 + € 0,61/ppp tourist tax, dog € 4,70 ⚡🚰 Ch 🔌 (30x)€4,50/
night WC 🚽. **Location:** Simple. **Surface:** gravel/metalled.
🅿 01/04-30/09
Distance: 🏖100m ⊗300m 🍴50m 🛒100m.
Remarks: Max. 48h.

⛽ **Vielle St.Girons** 🌳 28A3

Les Tourterelles, Saint Girons-Plage. **GPS:** n43,95278 w1,35778. ⬆

40 🅿 € 9, 01/07-31/08 € 15,50 ⚡🚰 €2,70/10liter 🚰 Ch 🔌 55minutes WC 🚽.
Location: Comfortable. **Surface:** gravel/metalled.
🅿 01/01-31/12 ⚙ Service 01/10-26/04
Distance: 🏊300m 🍴500m 🛒500m.

♿⛽ **Vieux-Boucau-les-Bains** 28A3

Aire camping-cars Village, Avenue des Pêcheurs. **GPS:** n43,77971 w1,40041. ⬆

FR

150 🏕€ 6, 01/05-30/09 € 12 🚐🔌Ch 🛠 included. ⬛🚐 ♨ **Location:** Comfortable. **Surface:** gravel/sand. ⬛ 01/01-31/12
Distance: 🚶500m 🏖200m ⊗500m 🛒500m 🚲on the spot.
Remarks: >3,5t not allowed.

🚐S	Vieux-Boucau-les-Bains	28A3

Aire du Marensin Plage, Boulevard du Marensin. **GPS:** n43,79485 w1,4051.⬆️.

35 🏕€ 12 🚐🔌Ch 🛠 . ⬛🚐 **Location:** Simple, quiet. **Surface:** gravel.
⬛ 05/01-30/09
Distance: 🚶1,5km 🏖Ocean 500m ⊗1,5km 🛒1,5km 🚲on the spot.
Remarks: >3,5t not allowed, max. 48h.

🚐S	Villeneuve-de-Marsan	28B3

Avenue du Stade 40. **GPS:** n43,88737 w0,30595.⬆️➡️.

7 🏕free 🚐🔌Ch 🛠 (2x)free,16Amp. **Location:** Rural. **Surface:** asphalted.
⬛ 01/01-31/12
Distance: 🚶400m ⊗500m 🛒400m.
Remarks: Max. 48h.

🚐S	Villeréal	28D2

Aire de Jeux, Boulevard Alphonse de Poitiers, D104. **GPS:** n44,63798 e0,74065.
⬆️.
🏕free 🚐🔌Ch . **Surface:** asphalted. ⬛ 01/01-31/12
Distance: 🚶300m ⊗300m 🛒300m.

🚐S	Villeton	28C2

D120. **GPS:** n44,36386 e0,27279.

4 🏕free 🚐€2/15minutes 🔌Ch 🚐€2/4h. **Surface:** gravel. ⬛ 01/01-31/12
Distance: 🚲10,5km 🏖on the spot 🛒on the spot ⊗on the spot.

🚐S	Vitrac	28D2

Montfort, D703. **GPS:** n44,83558 e1,24852.⬆️➡️.

10 🏕free 🚐€3/100liter 🔌Ch 🚐€3/1h WC . **Location:** Rural, simple.
Surface: grassy/gravel. ⬛ 01/01-31/12
Distance: 🚶50m 🏖2km beach at Dordogne river ⊗200m.
Remarks: Coins available at restaurant Le Point Vue (200m).

Midi Pyrénées

🚐S	Agos-Vidalos	28B5

Le Pibeste, Avenue du Lavedan. **GPS:** n43,03552 w0,07069.⬆️.
30 🏕€ 12 🚐🔌Ch 🛠 📶included. **Location:** Comfortable. **Surface:** grassy.
⬛ 01/01-31/12
Distance: 🚶on the spot.

🚐S	Albi	29B3

Base de Loisirs Pratgraussals. **GPS:** n43,92951 e2,13480.⬆️.
20 🏕free 🚐🔌Chfree. **Surface:** asphalted. ⬛ 01/01-31/12
Distance: 🚶1km.

🚐S	Albi	29B3

Les portes d'Albi. **GPS:** n43,91846 e2,10968.⬆️.
🏕free 🚐🔌Ch . **Surface:** asphalted. ⬛ 01/01-31/12
Distance: ⊗on the spot 🛒on the spot 🚐on the spot.
Remarks: Parking supermarket.

🚐	Albi	29B3

Parking Cathédrale. **GPS:** n43,92750 e2,14111.⬆️➡️.

9 🏕free. **Surface:** asphalted.
Distance: 🚶50m ⊗50m 🛒100m.
Remarks: Parking nearby cathedral Sainte Cécile, max. 48h.

🚐S	Albi	29B3

Rue Michelet. **GPS:** n43,94583 e2,15111.⬆️➡️.
🚐🔌Ch🚐free. ⬛ 01/01-31/12

🚐S	Alblas	28D2

Pech del Gal. **GPS:** n44,47480 e1,23275.⬆️➡️.

10 🏕free 🚐🔌Chfree. **Location:** Simple, isolated, noisy. **Surface:** gravel.
Remarks: At weir.

Alvignac 29A2

Parc du Samayou, Route de Padirac. **GPS:** n44,82504 e1,69711.

10 free Ch WC. **Surface:** asphalted.
Distance: 100m 200m 200m.

Anglès 29B4

Route de Saint-Pons. **GPS:** n43,56553 e2,56544.
4 free Ch. **Surface:** metalled.
Distance: 500m.

Aragnouet 28C5

P5, Piau Engaly. **GPS:** n42,78599 e0,15800.
100 free, Winter € 15 Ch (100x) WC. **Surface:** asphalted.
01/12-31/08
Distance: 300m 300m 300m.
Remarks: Service only during winter period.

Arfons 29B4

Pierron-Les Escudiés. **GPS:** n43,43972 e2,19472.

4 € 5. **Surface:** grassy. 01/01-31/12
Distance: 4km 1km 4km 4km.

Arreau 28C5

Chemin de Fregel, Avenue de la gare. **GPS:** n42,90708 e0,35912.

27 € 2 Ch free. **Surface:** metalled. 01/01-31/12
Distance: 100m 100m 300m 300m 200m.

Arrens-Marsous 28B5

D918. **GPS:** n42,95806 w0,20722.

10 free € 2 Ch € 2. **Location:** Rural, isolated, quiet.

Surface: asphalted. 01/01-31/12
Distance: 1,5km 1,5km 1,5km.

Arvieu 29B3

GPS: n44,19246 e2,65916.

11 € 2 €2/80liter Ch WC. **Surface:** gravel. 01/04-31/10
Distance: 100m on the spot on the spot on the spot.
Remarks: Coins at the shops and town hall.

Aubrac 29C2

D533. **GPS:** n44,62026 e2,98705.
10 free Ch WC free. **Location:** Simple, quiet. **Surface:** gravel.
01/01-31/12
Distance: 50m on the spot on the spot on the spot on the spot.

Auch 28C4

Camping municipal, Rue des Cormorans. **GPS:** n43,63654 e0,58854.

3 € 4 Ch free € 1,50. **Surface:** asphalted. 01/01-31/12
Distance: 15min 15min 15min.

Auterive 29A4

Grande Allée du Ramier. **GPS:** n43,35025 e1,47730.

6 free Ch free. **Surface:** asphalted. 01/01-31/12
Remarks: At fire-station.

Auterive 29A4

Rue des Docteurs Basset. **GPS:** n43,35182 e1,47641.
10 free. **Surface:** asphalted.
Distance: 200m 200m.
Remarks: Along river.

Auzas 28D5

La Grangère. **GPS:** n43,17016 e0,88690.

10 ⌧ € 4 ⛽ 🔧 Ch ✏ (4x)included. **Surface:** asphalted.
Distance: ⚓on the spot.
Remarks: At lake.

🚿S ⛲ Ax-les-Thermes 🎿❄🎣 29A6
A Bonascre, Rue des Chalets. **GPS:** n42,70340 e1,81657.⬆.
40 ⌧free ⛽€2/100liter 🔧Ch ✏€6/24h ✏. **Location:** Isolated, quiet.
Surface: gravel. 🅾 01/01-31/12

🚿S ⛲ Ax-les-Thermes 🎿❄🎣 29A6
N20. **GPS:** n42,72565 e1,83154.⬆.
25 ⌧€6 ⛽€100/liter ⬛ included1h. 🚌 ✏ **Location:** Simple, noisy.
Surface: asphalted.
Distance: 🚶1km.

🚿S ⛲ Ax-les-Thermes 🎿❄🎣 29A6
Parc d'Espagne. **GPS:** n42,71504 e1,84142.⬆.

35 ⌧€5. **Surface:** asphalted. 🅾 01/01-31/12
Distance: 🚶500m ✖500m ⚓500m.

🚿S ⛲ Bagnères-de-Bigorre 🎣 28C5
Rue René Cassin. **GPS:** n43,07319 e0,15256.⬆➡.

10 ⌧free ⛽🔧 Ch WC free. **Surface:** gravel. 🅾 01/01-31/12
Distance: 🚶500m ✖1km ⚓1km.

🚿 Bagnères-de-Bigorre 🎣 28C5
Avenue de Belgique. **GPS:** n43,06917 e0,14889.

10 ⌧free. **Location:** Urban, simple, central. **Surface:** asphalted.
Distance: 🚶200m ✖200m ⚓200m.
Remarks: At station.

🚿S Bagnères-de-Luchon 28C5
Rue Jean Mermoz. **GPS:** n42,79540 e0,59875.⬆.

30 ⌧€4/24h ⛽Service€4 🔧Ch ⬛. **Surface:** asphalted.
🅾 01/01-31/12 ⚫ service: 01/12-01/04
Distance: 🚶1km ✖1km ⚓500m.
Remarks: Coins at tourist info.

🚿S Baraqueville 29B3
Rue du Val de l'Enne. **GPS:** n44,27850 e2,43407.⬆.

10 ⌧free ⛽€3 🔧Ch WC. **Surface:** asphalted.
🅾 01/01-31/12 ⚫ service 01/11-31/03
Distance: 🚶on the spot ⚓50m 🐟 on the spot 🚶 on the spot.
Remarks: Coins at the shops in the village, inclining pitches.

🚿S Barbotan-les-Thermes 28C3
Avenue des Thermes. **GPS:** n43,94884 w0,04344.⬆➡.

6 ⌧free, night € 4,50. **Surface:** asphalted. 🅾 01/01-31/12
Distance: 🚶500m ✖50m ⚓500m.

🚿S Bardigues 🌾🎣 28D3
GPS: n44,03869 e0,89271.⬆➡.

4 ⌧free ⛽€2/100liter 🔧Ch. **Surface:** gravel. 🅾 01/01-31/12
Distance: 🚶150m ✏8,6km ✖150m ⚓150m.

🚿S Bellas 29C3
D995. **GPS:** n44,31256 e3,12689.
10 ⌧€5 ⛽🔧free ✏€3. **Location:** Rural, quiet. **Surface:** grassy/metalled.
🅾 01/01-31/12 🐕 on the spot 🚶 on the spot.

FR

Belmont sur Rance 29B4
Parking de la Mairie, Route de Lacaune. **GPS:** n43,81630 e2,75269.⬆.

3 ⬛free ⬛ Chfree. **Surface:** asphalted. ⬛ 01/01-31/12
Distance: on the spot.

Boisse Penchot 29B2
Rue du Chateau Bas. **GPS:** n44,59201 e2,20567.⬆.

8 ⬛free €3/100liter Ch €3/1h.
Surface: asphalted.
⬛ 01/01-31/12
Distance: 100m on the spot on the spot on the spot on the spot.

Bonac Irazein 28D5
Lac Bonac. GPS: n42,87541 e0,97565.⬆.

10 ⬛€6 ⬛ Ch included. **Surface:** grassy/gravel.
⬛ 01/03-30/11
Distance: on the spot.
Remarks: At artificial lake of Bonac.

Bouillac 29B2
Aire de Bouillac, D840. **GPS:** n44,57333 e2,15750.⬆.

6 ⬛free €3 Ch. **Surface:** metalled. ⬛ 01/03-30/11
Distance: on the spot on the spot on the spot 600m.
Remarks: Max. 24h, coins at the shops.

Branne 28C2
Route de Cabara. **GPS:** n44,83191 w0,18448.
⬛free €2/100liter Ch €2/1h.
Distance: on the spot.

Broquies 29B3
Route de Mazies. **GPS:** n44,00498 e2,69371.⬆.

30 ⬛free ⬛ Ch WC. **Surface:** gravel. ⬛ 01/04-30/11
Distance: 50m on the spot on the spot.
Remarks: Coins at supermarket.

Cadours 28D4
Rue Malakoff. **GPS:** n43,72320 e1,04861.⬆➡.

5 ⬛free ⬛ Chfree. **Location:** Rural. **Surface:** grassy.
⬛ 01/01-31/12 ⬛ tue-evening, wed-morning
Distance: 1km 1km.
Remarks: At football ground.

Cahors 29A2
Parking Chartreux, Rue de la Chartreuse. **GPS:** n44,44062 e1,44170.⬆➡.

3 ⬛free ⬛ Chfree. **Surface:** gravel. ⬛ 01/01-31/12
Distance: 500m on the spot 250m 50m on the spot.
Remarks: Along river.

Cahors 29A2
Parking Saint George, Rue Saint George. **GPS:** n44,43875 e1,44111.⬆➡.
20 ⬛free. **Surface:** asphalted. ⬛ 01/01-31/12
Distance: 1,2km 15km 100m on the spot.
Remarks: Shuttle bus to city centre.
Tourist information Cahors:
⬛ Wed, Sa.

Cahuzac-sur-Vère 29A3
Place du Mercadial. **GPS:** n43,98194 e1,91111.⬆➡.

5 free ⬛🔲 Ch WC. **Surface:** gravel.
Distance: 🔲200m ⊗200m 🔲200m.

Cajarc 29A2
Place de la Gare. **GPS:** n44,48458 e1,84573. ⬆➡.

8 free ⬛€1 🔲 Ch. **Surface:** grassy. ⬛ 01/01-31/12
Distance: 🔲100m ⊗200m 🔲200m.

Camares 29C4
Base de loisirs des Zizines. **GPS:** n43,81654 e2,87988. ⬆.

10 free ⬛🔲 Ch WC free. **Surface:** gravel. ⬛ 01/04-31/10
Distance: 🔲100m ⊿on the spot ⬅on the spot.

Campagnac 29C2
La Sagne. **GPS:** n44,41885 e3,08875. ⬆.

5 free, 13/06-13/09 € 3 ⬛🔲 Ch. **Surface:** metalled. ⬛ 01/01-31/12
Distance: 🔲400m ⊗400m 🔲400m.
Remarks: Coins at campsite and town hall.

Campuac 29B2
GPS: n44,57027 e2,59162. ⬆.
10 free ⬛🔲 Ch WC free. **Surface:** gravel. ⬛ 01/01-31/12
Distance: 🔲100m 🔲on the spot.

Cardaillac 29A2
Le Pré del Prie. **GPS:** n44,67868 e1,99805. ⬆.

12 free ⬛€2/100liter 🔲 Ch ⬛€2/h. **Location:** Isolated, quiet.
Surface: gravel. ⬛ 01/01-31/12
Distance: 🔲100m ⊗on the spot 🔲100m.
Remarks: Behind church.

Castanet 29B3
GPS: n44,27889 e2,28944. ⬆➡.

4 €5 ⬛🔲 Ch ✂included. **Surface:** gravel. ⬛ 01/01-31/12
Distance: 🔲on the spot ⊗on the spot.

Castelnau-de-Montmiral 29A3
Domaine Les Miquels. **GPS:** n43,96667 e1,80278. ⬆➡.

6 € 10,50, 2 pers.incl ⬛🔲 Ch ✂included.
Location: Rural, comfortable, isolated, quiet. **Surface:** grassy. ⬛ 01/01-31/12
Distance: 🔲2,5km ⊗on the spot 🔲2,5km.

Castelnau-Durban 28D5
D117. **GPS:** n42,99994 e1,33976. ⬆.

10 free ⬛€2 🔲Ch⬛€2 WC. **Surface:** metalled.
Remarks: Parking in front of church, max. 48h.

Castelsarrasin 28D3
Allée de la Source. **GPS:** n44,03861 e1,10221. ⬆➡.

40 €3/24h ⬛€2,50/100liter 🔲Ch ✂€2,50/24h. 🔲 **Surface:** gravel.
⬛ 01/01-31/12
Distance: 🔲500m ⊗500m 🔲500m.

Castelsarrasin 28D3
Rue Louis Braille. **GPS:** n44,03833 e1,11473. ⬆.

15 ⌁free ⌁ Ch ⌁free. **Surface:** asphalted. ⬛ 01/01-31/12
Distance: 🚶200m 🚲3km ⊗250m.
Remarks: Along Canal des 2 Mers.

| Castres | 29B4 |

Parc de Gourjade, Avenue de Roquecourbe, D89. **GPS:** n43,62049 e2,25357.⬆.

5 ⌁free. **Surface:** metalled.
Distance: 🚶2km.
Remarks: Max. 24h.

| Castres | 29B4 |

Place Gerard Philipe, Chemin des Porches. **GPS:** n43,60168 e2,24939.

⌁free. **Location:** Urban. **Surface:** asphalted. ⬛ 01/01-31/12
Distance: 🚶2km ⊗2km 🚌2km.
Remarks: Max 3,5t, free bus to centre.

| S | Castres | 29B4 |

Route de l'Industrie Z.I. de Melou. **GPS:** n43,59069 e2,20648.⬆➡.
⌁ Ch free. ⬛ 01/01-31/12

Tourist information Castres:
Palais Episcopal. Episcopal palace.
Tue, Thu-Su.

| Cauterets ⌁⌁❄⌁⌁ | 28B5 |

Avenue Charles Thierry. **GPS:** n42,88628 w0,11522.⬆.
25 ⌁€ 10 ⌁ Ch ⌁ included. **Surface:** asphalted.
Distance: 🚶500m ⊗500m.

| Cauterets ⌁⌁❄⌁⌁ | 28B5 |

Place de la Patinoire, D920. **GPS:** n42,89361 w0,11256.⬆➡.

50 ⌁€ 10/24h ⌁ Ch ⌁ included. **Surface:** asphalted.
⬛ 01/01-31/12
Distance: 🚶300m ⊗300m 🚌300m.
Remarks: Max. 21 nights.

| Caylus | 29A3 |

Base de loisirs Labarthe, D19. **GPS:** n44,23363 e1,77225.⬆.

6 ⌁free ⌁ Ch free. **Surface:** grassy/gravel. ⬛ 01/01-31/12
Distance: 🚶200m ⊗200m 🚌200m.

Tourist information Caylus:
St.Antonin. Small town with the oldest town hall of France.

| Condom | 28C3 |

Avenue des Mousquetaires. **GPS:** n43,94788 e0,36422.⬆.
12 ⌁free ⌁ Ch. **Location:** Comfortable, isolated, quiet.
Surface: metalled.
Distance: 🚶500m.
Remarks: Max. 5 days.

| S | Condom | 28C3 |

Ferme de Parette, Route de Nérac, RN930. **GPS:** n43,98802 e0,35046.⬆➡.

8 ⌁€ 8, 2 pers.incl ⌁ Ch ⌁ included ⬛€4. **Location:** Comfortable,
isolated, quiet. **Surface:** grassy. ⬛ 01/01-31/12
Distance: 🚶2km ⊗2km 🚌2km.

Tourist information Condom:
Musée de l'Armagnac. All about Armagnac.

| S | Cordes-sur-Ciel | 29A3 |

Parking les Tuileries. GPS: n44,06453 e1,95802.⬆➡.

40 🛒 € 5 🚰 €3/100liter 🔌 Ch 🚽 €3/3h. 🚿 **Location:** Isolated, quiet.
Surface: grassy/gravel. ⬛ 01/01-31/12
Distance: 🚶250m.

Coupiac 29B3
Route de Martin. **GPS:** n43,95174 e2,58464. ⬆.
10 🛒free 🚰 Chfree. **Surface:** grassy. ⬛ 01/01-31/12
Distance: 🚶500m 🛒450m.
Remarks: Max. 72h.

Cransac 29B2
Aire de Camping-car Cransac, Route de la Gare. **GPS:** n44,52278 e2,27444.

6 🛒 € 6,80, 2 pers.incl 🚰 🔌 Chincluded. **Surface:** gravel. ⬛ 12/03-25/11
Distance: 🚶500m ⊗500m 🛒500m.
Remarks: Max. 48h.

Donzac 28D3
Lac de Sources, D30. **GPS:** n44,11308 e0,82044. ⬆.

10 🛒free 🚰 🔌 Chfree. **Location:** Rural. **Surface:** gravel.
⬛ 01/01-31/12
Distance: 🚶on the spot.
Remarks: Max. 48h.

Douelle 29A2
Domaine Marcilhac, D8. **GPS:** n44,47927 e1,34947. ⬆➡.

10 🛒free 🚰 €2 🔌 Ch. **Location:** Rural. **Surface:** gravel.
⬛ 01/01-31/12
Distance: 🚶1km ⊗1km 🛒1km 🚌1km.

Entraygues-sur-Truyère 29B2
Route de Villecomtal, D904. **GPS:** n44,64020 e2,56925. ⬆.

🛒free. **Surface:** grassy. ⬛ 01/04-31/12
Distance: 🚶50m ⊿on the spot 🚣on the spot ⊗50m 🛒50m.

Entraygues-sur-Truyère 29B2
Rue de la Grave. **GPS:** n44,64417 e2,56278.

5 🛒free. **Surface:** gravel. ⬛ 01/01-31/12
Distance: 🚶50m ⊗150m 🛒150m.

Entraygues-sur-Truyère 29B2
Rue du 16 Août 1944. **GPS:** n44,64269 e2,56577.

🚰€3 🔌Ch🚿.
Remarks: Coins at tourist info.

Figeac 29A2
Parking le Foiral, Boulevard Colonel Teulié. **GPS:** n44,61089 e2,03674. ⬆.

5 🛒free 🚰€2 🔌 Ch 🚽€2. **Location:** Central, noisy. **Surface:** asphalted.
⬛ 01/01-31/12
Distance: 🚶100m ⊗400m 🛒100m 🚌100m.
Tourist information Figeac:
🎪 Marché régional. Regional market. ⬛ Sa-morning.

Fleurance 28D3
Boulevard de Metz. **GPS:** n43,85164 e0,66184. ⬆➡.

FR

20 🍴free 🚰€2 📶 Ch 🚽€2. **Surface:** gravel.
Distance: 🚶200m 🛒on the spot 🛒on the spot.

| 🏕S | Frejairolles | 29B4 |

Le Grand Chêne, D81. **GPS:** n43,86043 e2,24799. ⬆️
5 🍴€5, free for clients 🚰📶 Ch 🔌 included.

| 🏕S | Gaillac | 29A3 |

Parking des Rives Thomas, Rue Claude Nougaro. **GPS:** n43,89951 e1,89494. ⬆️
➡️

🍴free 🚰📶 Ch free. **Surface:** asphalted. 🔲 01/01-31/12
Distance: 🚶200m ⊗200m 🛒200m.

| 🏕S | Gavarnie 🎿⛰❄ | 28B5 |

Parking Holle, Route de la station des Espécières, D923.
GPS: n42,73857 w0,01959.

20 🍴free, July-Aug €7 🚰📶 Ch included. **Location:** Simple, isolated, quiet.
Surface: metalled. 🔲 01/01-31/12
Distance: 🚶800m ⊘100m 🛒100m ⊗800m 🛒800m 🚌600m 🚠1,5km
⛷1,5km.

| | Gavarnie 🎿⛰❄ | 28B5 |

Parking du Cirque, Chemin du cirque. **GPS:** n42,73694 w0,01278.

20 🍴€5. **Surface:** asphalted. 🔲 01/01-31/12
Distance: 🚶200m ⊘200m ⊗200m 🛒200m.

Tourist information Gavarnie:
👁 Cirque de Gavarnie. Can be reached with a donkey, a horse or by foot. A giant waterfalll, snow pillars and mountain slopes.

| 🏕 | Gèdre | 28C5 |

Aire de stationnement de Héas, D922. **GPS:** n42,74916 e0,08935.
🍴free. **Location:** Rural, simple, isolated, quiet. **Surface:** grassy. 🔲 winter
Distance: 🚶9km ⊗600m.
Remarks: At Chapelle de Héas.

| 🏕 | Gèdre | 28C5 |

Place de la Bergère, Gèdre Débat. **GPS:** n42,78860 e0,01967.
12 🍴free. **Surface:** asphalted.
Distance: 🚶on the spot.

| 🍴 | Gèdre | 28C5 |

Auberge de la Munia, Héas, D922. **GPS:** n42,73643 e0,08631.
5 🍴€6.
Distance: ⊗on the spot.

| 🏕S | Gignac | 29A1 |

Le Moulin, Place des Troubadours. **GPS:** n45,00624 e1,45687. ⬆️

10 🍴free 🚰📶 Ch. **Surface:** metalled. 🔲 01/01-31/12
Distance: 🚶50m ⊗150m 🛒150m.

| 🏕S | Gimont 🌿🍴♨🏛 | 28D4 |

Avenue de Cahuzac, RN124. **GPS:** n43,62987 e0,87009. ⬆️

12 🍴free 🚰📶 Ch 🔌 free.
Location: Simple, noisy. **Surface:** gravel.
🔲 01/01-31/12
Distance: 🚶100m ⊘on the spot 🛒on the spot ⊗300m 🛒300m 🚌300m.
Remarks: At lake, max. 48h, market Wednesday and Sunday.

| 🏕S | Gourdon 🌿🍴♨🏛 | 29A2 |

Esplanade du foirail. **GPS:** n44,73423 e1,38523. ⬆️➡️

8 🍴€1/6h 🚰📶 Ch 🔌 (8x)included. **Location:** Comfortable, quiet.
Surface: gravel. 🔲 01/01-31/12
Distance: 🚶200m ⊗100m 🛒200m 🚌on the spot.

| 🏕S | Gramat | 29A2 |

La Garenne, Avenue Paul Mezet. **GPS:** n44,77966 e1,72904. ⬆️➡️

10 free Ch. **Surface:** gravel. 01/01-31/12
Distance: 400m 400m 400m.
Remarks: Max. 48h.

S Grenade-sur-Garonne 28D4

Quai de Garonne. **GPS**: n43,77201 e1,29673.

4 free Ch. **Surface:** gravel.
Distance: 100m 100m 100m 100m.
Remarks: Service: Allées Alsace Lorraine (100m).

S La Bastide-de-Sérou 29A5

Bargnac, D15. **GPS**: n43,00194 e1,44556.

15 € 14,60, Jul/Aug € 18,60 Ch WC included.
Location: Rural, isolated, quiet. **Surface:** asphalted/gravel. 11/04-03/11

La Couvertoirade 29C3

GPS: n43,91171 e3,31478.

10 € 3 €3/100liter WC. **Location:** Rural, isolated, quiet. **Surface:** gravel.
01/01-31/12
Distance: 50m 50m.
Remarks: Large parking on edge from village.

Tourist information La Couvertoirade:

Citadelle de l'Ordre de Tempeliers. Fortified city in original state. Now many old craft industries are exercised. There is a toll-house at the entrance of the village, entrance fee is charged.

S Labastide-Murat 29A2

Route de Gramat. **GPS**: n44,64944 e1,57061.
free Ch. **Location:** Rural, simple. **Surface:** asphalted.
Distance: 300m on the spot.
Remarks: At supermarket Carrefour.

S Labruguiere 29B4

Domaine d'en Laure, Avenue Arthur Batut. **GPS**: n43,53139 e2,25528.

10 free €2/10minutes Ch €2/minutes.
Location: Rural, simple, isolated, quiet. **Surface:** grassy. 01/01-31/12
Distance: 2km on the spot on the spot 1,3km 1,3km.

S Lacapelle Marival 29A2

Place de Larroque. **GPS**: n44,72806 e1,92944.

50 free €2/100liter Ch €2/h. **Surface:** asphalted.
service 15/05-30/09
Distance: on the spot 100m 50m.

Lacaune 29B4

Rue de la Balme. **GPS**: n43,70795 e2,69010.

20 free. **Surface:** gravel. 01/01-31/12
Distance: on the spot on the spot.

S Lacroix-Barrez 29B2

Le Ventoux. **GPS**: n44,77793 e2,63086.
10 € 2,50 + € 0,30 tourist tax Chfree. **Surface:** grassy.
01/01-31/12 service: 01/11-17/04
Distance: 400m.

S Laguepie 29A3

Quai de l'Aveyron. **GPS**: n44,14485 e1,97226.

6 free Chfree. **Surface:** asphalted. 01/01-31/12
Distance: 200m 200m on the spot.

FR

⛟🅂 **Laquiole** 29C2

Du Bouyssou, La Serre. **GPS**: n44,67199 e2,92451.
🛗€ 8 🚿€3. **Surface**: asphalted.
Distance: 🚶7km 🎣on the spot.

⛟🅂 **Laquiole** 29C2

Rue de Lavernhe. **GPS**: n44,68408 e2,85048. ⬆️➡️.

10 🛗free 🔌🗑️Chfree. **Surface**: gravel.
◼ 01/01-31/12, service: 17/04-15/10
Distance: 🚶on the spot.

🏕️🅂 **Laquiole** 29C2

La Montagnettte, Les Clauzades. **GPS**: n44,70457 e2,84037.
5 🛗free 🚿€2. **Location**: Simple, isolated, quiet. **Surface**: gravel.
Distance: 🚶4km.

⛟🅂 **Laissac** 29B3

Place du Foirail des Ovins, RN88. **GPS**: n44,38590 e2,82160. ⬆️.

6 🛗free 🔌🗑️Chfree. **Surface**: asphalted. ◼ 01/03-30/11
Distance: 🚶500m ⊗500m 🛒500m.
Remarks: Max. 24h.

⛟🅂 **Lanuéjouls** 29B2

Aire Campingcar Lanuéjouls, Avenue du Rouergue, D1.
GPS: n44,42528 e2,16139. ⬆️➡️.

14 🛗€5 🔌🗑️Ch 🚿 WC 🗑️included. **Surface**: gravel. ◼ 01/01-31/12
Distance: 🚶100m ⊗100m 🛒100m.

⛟🅂 **Latronquière** 29A2

Place du Foirail. **GPS**: n44,79917 e2,07917. ⬆️.

4 🛗free 🔌🗑️Ch 🚿 WCfree. **Surface**: asphalted. ◼ 01/01-31/12
Distance: 🚶300m ⛱3km 🚵3km ⊗300m 🛒300m.

⛟🅂 **Lauzerte** 28D3

1, Place du Foirail. **GPS**: n44,25432 e1,13666. ⬆️.

10 🛗free 🔌🗑️Ch WCfree. **Surface**: asphalted.
◼ 01/01-31/12 🅿️ tue-evening, wed-morning
Distance: 🚶500m ⊗on the spot 🛒on the spot.

⛟🅂 **Lauzerte** 28D3

D2, Vignals. **GPS**: n44,26750 e1,14083. ⬆️.

20 🛗free 🔌🗑️Ch WCfree. **Surface**: grassy/gravel. ◼ 01/01-31/12
Distance: 🚶Lauzerte 2km ⊗on the spot 🛒2km.
Tourist information Lauzerte:
⛺ ◻ Wed-morning.

🅲🅂 **Le Fossat** 28D5

Aire des Lallières, Place de la Mairie. **GPS**: n43,17201 e1,41170. ⬆️➡️.

21 🛗€12 🔌🗑️Ch 🚿 WC 🗑️📶included. **Location**: Luxurious.
Surface: gravel. ◼ 01/03-30/11

⛟🅂 **Le Garric** 29B3

Cap Découverte. **GPS**: n44,01361 e2,13778. ⬆️.

18 🛗€8 🔌🗑️Ch 🚿 included. **Surface**: asphalted. ◼ 01/01-31/12
Distance: ⊗300m.

🏕️🅂 **Le Houga** 28C4

Ferme aux Cerfs, Route de Mont de Marsan, D6. **GPS**: n43,78430 e0,20997.

FR

15 🛏 € 3 🚰 🔌 Ch free. **Surface:** grassy. ⬜ 01/01-31/12
Distance: 🚶2,5km ⊗on the spot.
♿ S | **Le Ségur** | 29A3
Place de Marie. **GPS:** n44,10889 e2,05861. ⬆➡.

3 🛏 free 🚰 🔌 Ch WC free. **Surface:** metalled. ⬜ 01/01-31/12
Distance: 🚶50m ⊗100m 🚰100m.
♿ S | **Les Cabannes** | 29A6
Quartier la Bexane. **GPS:** n42,78493 e1,68301. ⬆➡.

30 🛏 € 4/24h 🚰€2/100liter 🔌 Ch WC. **Surface:** asphalted.
Distance: 🚶300m ⊗300m.
♿ S | **Lisle sur Tarn** 🏴 | 29A3
Aire de Bellevue, Rue des Aulnes. **GPS:** n43,86167 e1,81833. ⬆➡.

12 🛏 free 🚰 🔌 Ch. **Location:** Comfortable, isolated, quiet. **Surface:** sand.
⬜ 01/01-31/12
Distance: 🚶1,5km 🏊on the spot 🛒on the spot ⊗1,5km 🚰1,5km.
♿ S | **Lombez** 👥 | 28D4
Route de Toulouse, D632. **GPS:** n43,47417 e0,91592. ⬆➡.

20 🛏 free 🚰 🔌 WC free. **Surface:** gravel.
Distance: 🚶200m ⊗150m 🚰200m.
♿ S | **Loudenvielle** 🏔 | 28C5
GPS: n42,79633 e0,40743.

50 🛏 free, € 3/ski season + Jul/Aug 🚰€2 🔌 Ch 🔌€2.
Surface: asphalted/grassy.
♿ S | **Loudenvielle** 🏔 | 28C5
Chemin du Hourgade. **GPS:** n42,80163 e0,41088. ⬆.
🛏 free, € 3/ski season + Jul/Aug 🚰€2/100liter 🔌 Ch 🔌€2/h.
Surface: gravel.
Distance: 🚶700m ⊗700m 🚰800m.
Remarks: At lake, coins at Tourist Info and Maison de la Presse.
♿ S | **Lourdes** | 28B5
Le Vieux Berger, Route de Julos. **GPS:** n43,10444 w0,03311. ⬆.

27 🛏 € 13 🚰 🔌 Ch 🧹 WC 📶 included. 🏠 **Location:** Rural.
Surface: grassy/gravel. ⬜ 01/01-31/12
Remarks: Next to campsite.
♿ S | **Lourdes** | 28B5
Parking Arrouza, Esplanade du Paradis. **GPS:** n43,08831 w0,05273. ⬆.

🛏 € 10 🚰€5 🔌 Ch. **Surface:** asphalted.
Distance: 🚶city centre 1km.
Tourist information Lourdes:
ℹ Office de Tourisme, Place Peyramale, www.lourdes-infotourisme.com. Lively
place of pilgrimage.
⛪ Basilique St.Pius X. Underground basilica, of the largest sanctuaries in the

FR

world, there is place for 25,000 people.

Luzech 28D2

Les Berges de Caïx, D9. **GPS:** n44,49068 e1,29506. ⬆.

15 🛏 € 8,50 + € 0,22/pp tourist tax ⬅ 🗨 Ch ✎ WC included ⬜ €2.
Surface: gravel. ◻ 01/01-31/12
Distance: 2km.
Remarks: Along Lot river.

L'Hospitalet-près-l'Andorre 29A6

N22. **GPS:** n42,58823 e1,79833.

5 🛏 free ⬅ €2 🗨 Ch ✎ €6. **Surface:** asphalted.
Distance: ⊗100m.

Marbre 28C5

Lac de Payolle, D918, Campan > Col de Aspin. **GPS:** n42,93528 e0,29222.

🛏 free. **Location:** Rural, simple, isolated. **Surface:** grassy/gravel.
Distance: 40m 40m.

Martel 29A1

La Fontanelle, Avenue de Nassogne. **GPS:** n44,93505 e1,60656. ⬆➡.

12 🛏 free ⬅ 🗨 Ch. **Surface:** gravel. ◻ 01/01-31/12
Distance: 250m ⊗250m 🛒250m.

Martel 29A1

Parking Monti. GPS: n44,93957 e1,60827. ⬆.
12 🛏 free. **Surface:** asphalted. ◻ 01/01-31/12
Distance: 400m ⊗400m 🛒400m.

Mazamet 29B4

D118. **GPS:** n43,46278 e2,34609. ⬆➡.

🛏 free ⬅ 🗨 Ch free. **Location:** Rural, isolated, quiet. **Surface:** grassy/gravel.
◻ 01/01-31/12
Distance: 8km on the spot on the spot ⊗on the spot.

Mazamet 29B4

Rue Galibert-Ferret, Champ de la Ville. **GPS:** n43,49089 e2,37918. ⬆.

10 🛏 free ⬅ 🗨 Ch free. **Location:** Urban. **Surface:** asphalted.
◻ 01/01-31/12 ◉ Fri-Sa market
Distance: on the spot ⊗on the spot.
Remarks: At townhall, max. 24h.

Mazères-sur-Salat 28D5

Rue de Vieux Ruisseau. **GPS:** n43,13457 e0,97633. ⬆.

15 🛏 free ⬅ 🗨 Ch ⬛ free. **Surface:** metalled. ◻ 01/01-31/12
Distance: 4,5km river.

Miélan 28C4

Chemin du Cubet. **GPS:** n43,43319 e0,30900. ➡.
6 🛏 free ⬅ 🗨 Ch free. ◻ 01/01-31/12

Millau 29C3

Rue de la Saunerie 19. **GPS:** n44,09610 e3,08577. ⬆➡.

44 🛏 € 9,60, 01/07-31/08 € 12 ⬅ 🗨 Ch 📶 included. 🚰 ✐
Location: Comfortable. **Surface:** gravel.
◻ 01/01-31/12
Distance: 500m.
Remarks: Motorhomes <7.5m, entrance code night: parknight, video surveillance.
Tourist information Millau:
ℹ Office de Tourisme, 1, Place du Beffroi, www.ot-millau.fr. City tourist in the Valley of the Tarn and the Dourbie. Important for the leather trade.
✎ Vieux Millau. Historical hiking route, info at Office de Tourisme.

Mirandol-Bourgnounce 29B3

Place de Foirail. GPS: n44,14167 e2,16667. ⬆.

8 ⌇free ⌇⌇ Ch WC free. **Surface:** asphalted. ☐ 01/01-31/12
Distance: on the spot ⊗on the spot ⌇50m.

| 🖼️S | Mirepoix | 29A5 |

Parking des Capitouls, Alée des Soupirs. **GPS:** n43,08491 e1,87399.⬆️.

20 ⌇free ⌇⌇ChWC free. ☐ 01/01-31/12
Remarks: Next to community centre.

Tourist information Mirepoix:
🎪 Cattle market. ☐ winter 2nd, 4th Mo of the month.
🎪 ☐ Thu, Sa.

| 🖼️S | Moissac | 28D3 |

Promenade Sancert. GPS: n44,10011 e1,08540.

4 ⌇free ⌇ €2/4h. **Location:** Urban, simple. **Surface:** metalled.
☐ 01/01-31/12
Distance: ⊗100m ⌇100m.
Remarks: Coins at tourist info.

| 🖼️S | Mont Roc | 29B4 |

Salle de Fêtes. GPS: n43,80330 e2,37192.⬆️.

8 ⌇free ⌇€2 ⌇Ch ⌇€2 WC. **Surface:** metalled. ☐ 01/01-31/12
Distance: 50m ⊗on the spot ⌇on the spot.

| 🖼️S | Montauban | 28D3 |

Mr. Lacaze, aire camping-car, 225, route de Corbarieu, D21.
GPS: n43,99188 e1,35196.⬆️.

15 ⌇€6 ⌇€1 ⌇Ch ⌇€2 WC ⌇€1. **Surface:** gravel. ☐ 01/01-31/12
Distance: Montauban 3km ⌇1km.
Remarks: Max 3,5t.

| 🖼️S | Montauban | 28D3 |

Port Canal, Rue des Oules. **GPS:** n44,00744 e1,34105.⬆️.
10 ⌇€6 ⌇Ch ⌇. **Location:** Comfortable, quiet. **Surface:** grassy/gravel.
☐ 01/01-31/12
Distance: 2,5km.
Remarks: At the canal.

| 🖼️S | Montauban | 28D3 |

La Ferme des Pibouls, Route de Saint-Antonin. **GPS:** n44,03658 e1,40499.⬆️.
12 ⌇free ⌇Ch.
Surface: grassy.
Distance: 5km.

Tourist information Montauban:
ℹ️ Office de Tourisme, 2, rue du Collège, officetourisme.montauban.com. City
of roses.
🎪 ☐ Sa.

| 🖼️S | Montcuq | 28D3 |

Route de Cahors, D653. GPS: n44,34082 e1,20242.

15 ⌇free ⌇€2 ⌇Ch ⌇€2. **Surface:** gravel.
☐ 01/01-31/12
Distance: 250m ⊗250m ⌇250m.
Remarks: Coins at Tourist Info and petrol station.

| 🖼️S | Monteils | 29A3 |

D47. GPS: n44,26694 e1,99667.⬆️.

4 ⌇free ⌇Ch free. **Surface:** grassy/gravel. ☐ 01/01-31/12
Distance: 100m ⊗100m ⌇50m.

| 🖼️S | Montézic | 29B2 |

Les Prades Sud. GPS: n44,71054 e2,64413.⬆️.

FR

4 🛏️free 🚰🗑️Ch. **Surface:** asphalted. 🅿️ 01/03-31/10
Distance: 🛒500m ⊗on the spot 🍴on the spot.
♨️S | **Montréal (Gers)** | 28C3
Stade André Daubin, D29. **GPS:** n43,95375 e0,19730.⬆️.

🛏️free 🚰🗑️Chfree. **Surface:** gravel. 🅿️ 01/01-31/12
Distance: 🛒200m ⊗500m 🍴500m.
Remarks: Parking at rugby ground.

Tourist information Montréal (Gers):
ℹ️ Office de Tourisme, place de l'Hôtel de Ville, www.montrealdugers.com/.
Fortified city with ramparts, square with arcades and picturesque alleys.

♨️S | **Mur de Barrez** 🌿🏕️ | 29B2
Parc de la Corette, Place du Foirail. **GPS:** n44,84842 e2,65980.⬆️.

6 🛏️free 🚰🗑️Ch. **Surface:** asphalted. 🅿️ 01/04-15/11
Distance: 🛒100m ⊗on the spot 🍴50m.
Remarks: Max. 72h.

♨️S | **Nages** | 29B4
Aire de camping car du Lac, Lac du Laouzas, D162. **GPS:** n43,64694 e2,78194.⬆️.

22 🛏️€7 🚰🗑️Ch🔲included. **Location:** Isolated, quiet.
Surface: grassy/gravel. 🅿️ 31/03-01/11
Distance: 🏊on the spot.
Remarks: Nearby base nautique.

♨️S | **Najac** 🌿🏕️ | 29A3
GPS: n44,22167 e1,96778.⬆️➡️.

10 🛏️free 🚰€2🗑️Ch🔲. **Surface:** asphalted. 🅿️ 01/01-31/12
Distance: 🛒1,8km ⊗on the spot 🍖on the spot 🍴1,8km 🚲on the spot
🚶on the spot.
♨️S | **Naucelle** 🍴 | 29B3
Place du Ségala. GPS: n44,19723 e2,34175.⬆️.

4 🛏️free 🚰🗑️Chfree. **Surface:** asphalted. 🅿️ 01/01-31/12
Distance: 🍴on the spot 🏊500m 🍖500m.
♨️S | **Naussac** | 29A2
Aire de Loisirs de Peyrelevade. **GPS:** n44,52167 e2,07944.⬆️➡️.

10 🛏️€4 🚰🗑️Ch🚿WCincluded. **Surface:** gravel. 🅿️ 01/01-31/12
Remarks: Recreation area.
♨️S | **Oust** | 28D5
Aire camping-car, Foute d'Aulus les Bains. **GPS:** n42,87167 e1,21833.➡️.

10 🛏️€ 14,50, 2 pers.incl. 🚰🗑️Ch🚿WC🔲.
Surface: gravel.
🅿️ 01/01-31/12
Remarks: Next to campsite Les 4 Saisons, arrival >14h departure <12h.
♨️S | **Peyrusse le Roc** | 29B2
D87. **GPS:** n44,49500 e2,13972.⬆️➡️.

8 ⬛free 🚰 ⬛Ch free. **Surface:** sand. ⬛ 01/01-31/12
Distance: 🚶500m ⊗500m 🛒500m.

15 ⬛free 🚰 ⬛Ch WC. **Surface:** grassy/gravel. ⬛ 01/01-31/12

⬛⬛S **Pierrefitte-Nestalas** 28B5

⬛⬛S **Preignan** 28C4

Chemin de la Portere. **GPS:** n42,96037 w0,07743. ⬆.

Rue Emile Zola. **GPS:** n43,71243 e0,63378. ➡.

10 ⬛free 🚰€1 ⬛Ch. **Location:** Isolated, quiet. **Surface:** asphalted.
⬛ 01/01-31/12
Distance: 🚶200m ⊗200m 🛒200m.
Remarks: Max. 1 night.

20 ⬛free 🚰 ⬛Ch free. **Surface:** gravel.
Distance: 🚶1km.
Remarks: At sports park.

⬛⬛S **Pinsac** 29A2

⬛⬛S **Puy l'Eveque** 28D2

Parking Salle des Fêtes, D43. **GPS:** n44,85500 e1,51222.

Place de la Gendarmerie. **GPS:** n44,50699 e1,13560. ⬆.

5 ⬛free 🚰€2 ⬛Ch. **Surface:** gravel. ⬛ 01/01-31/12
Distance: 🚶on the spot 🚲9,5km 🛒700m.

4 ⬛free 🚰 ⬛Ch WC free. **Surface:** gravel.
⬛ 01/01-31/12 ⬛ 05/08-14/08
Distance: 🚶250m ⊗300m 🛒300m.
Remarks: In front of town hall, max. 24h, upper city.

⬛⬛S **Pont-de-Salars** 29B3

⬛⬛S **Puylaurens** 29A4

Place de la Rivière. **GPS:** n44,27822 e2,72853. ⬆.

Rue Albert Thorel. **GPS:** n43,56861 e2,01194. ⬆➡.

5 ⬛free 🚰€3 ⬛Ch WC. **Surface:** asphalted. ⬛ 16/04-15/11
Distance: 🚶100m 🚲1km 🚲1km ⊗on the spot 🛒100m.
Remarks: Along river, max. 3 days.

17 ⬛free 🚰 ⬛Ch free 📶. **Surface:** gravel. ⬛ 01/01-31/12
Distance: 🚶700m ⊗700m 🛒400m.
Remarks: Max. 48h, wifi at supermarket.

⬛⬛S **Prayssac** 👥 28D2

⬛⬛S **Requista** 🏰 29B3

Avenue Maréchal Bessières. **GPS:** n44,50352 e1,19197. ⬆.

Place François Fablé. **GPS:** n44,03465 e2,53599. ⬆.

FR

6 ⬚free ⛽🔧free. **Surface:** gravel. 🅾 01/01-31/12
Distance: 200m.

⬛🅂 **Revel** 29A4

Roy des Eaux, Chemin de la Pergue. **GPS:** n43,45286 e2,01233. ⬆➡.
28 ⬚€ 7, 01/06-31/08 € 9, tourist tax excl ⛽🔧Ch🔧 included. 🔋🚐
Surface: gravel. 🅾 01/01-31/12
Distance: 1km ⊗1km 🚰1km.
Remarks: Max. 7 nights.

⬛🅂 **Rignac** 29B2

Hameau du Lac, La Peyrade. **GPS:** n44,40456 e2,28958. ⬆➡.

12 ⬚free, June-Aug € 5 ⛽🔧Ch. **Surface:** grassy. 🅾 01/01-31/12
Distance: 600m ⊗600m 🚰600m.

⬛🅂 **Rivières** 29A3

Aire de Salta, La Courtade Haute. **GPS:** n43,91072 e1,98889. ⬆.
6 ⬚€ 9,50, € 15 service incl ⛽🔧Ch🔧📶. **Location:** Rural, luxurious.
Surface: grassy/gravel. 🅾 01/06-30/09
Distance: 200m.
Remarks: Along the Tarn river.

⬛ **Rocamadour** 29A2

Le Château, D673. **GPS:** n44,80000 e1,61528. ⬆.

30 ⬚free. **Surface:** gravel. ◉ 15/06-15/09
Distance: ⊗100m.

⬛🅂 **Rodez** 29B3

Route du Gué de Salelles. **GPS:** n44,35731 e2,59374. ⬆.

6 ⬚free ⛽🔧Ch free. **Surface:** asphalted. 🅾 01/01-31/12

Distance: 1km.
Remarks: Max. 72h.

⬛🅂 **Roquecor** 👫 28D3

Place du Foirail. **GPS:** n44,32346 e0,94496. ⬆.

6 ⬚free ⛽🔧Ch free. **Surface:** asphalted. 🅾 01/01-31/12
Distance: 250m ⊗300m 🚰250m.
Remarks: Max. 48h.

⬛🅂 **Roquefort-sur-Soulzon** 29C3

D23. **GPS:** n43,98120 e2,98163. ⬆.

⬚free ⛽🔧Ch WC free. **Surface:** asphalted. 🅾 01/01-31/12
Distance: 100m.
Remarks: Parking behind tourist info, water closed during wintertime.

⬛🅂 **Saint-Antoine** 28D3

GPS: n44,03587 e0,84209. ⬆➡.

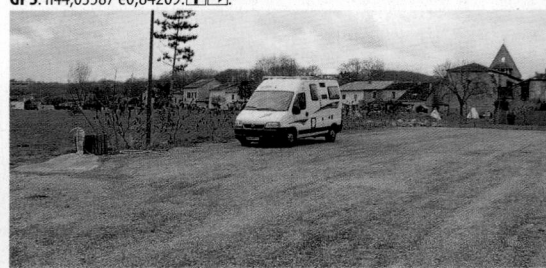

10 ⬚free ⛽🔧Ch free.
Location: Rural, simple, quiet. **Surface:** asphalted.
Distance: 200m ⚓4,3km 🚰200m.

⬛🅂 **Saint-Cirq-Lapopie** 🏖🏛🏘🌳 29A2

Porte Roques, D662. **GPS:** n44,47055 e1,68050. ⬆.

40 ⬚€ 7,50 ⛽€2/100liter 🔧Ch🔌€2 WC🔧€2. ♿ **Location:** Isolated,
quiet. **Surface:** grassy/gravel. 🅾 01/01-31/12
Distance: 1,5km ⊘on the spot ⊗50m.
Remarks: Along Lot river, near campsite, max. 48h.

Tourist information Saint-Cirq-Lapopie:
ℹ Village, entirely under preservation order, has been built on a rock above the

river Lot.

⌂ Grotte de Pech-Merle, Cabrerets. Temple cave, monument from the Paleolithicum with images of mammoth, horses and bizons.

Samatan 28D4

Les Rivages "Vacanciel" Base de Loisirs, Avenue de Lombez, D39. **GPS:** n43,48791 e0,92616. ➡

10 ⓢ€ 3 + € 0,20/pp tourist tax 🚰⚡Ch 🔌 WC included.
Surface: asphalted.
◻ 01/01-31/12
Distance: 🏊500m ⌖ on the spot 🛒on the spot ⊗250m 🗑250m 🚰250m.

Sarrant 28D4

Route de Solomiac. **GPS:** n43,77532 e0,92822. ➡

100 ⓢfree 🚰⚡Chfree. **Surface:** grassy/gravel. ◻ 01/01-31/12
Distance: 🏊150m 🚰150m.
Remarks: In front of football stadium.

Sauveterre-de-Rouergue 29B3

Le Sardou, D997. **GPS:** n44,21613 e2,31700. ⬆
11 ⓢfree 🚰⚡Ch 🔌€2 WC ⚡€1,50. **Surface:** grassy. ◻ 01/05-31/10
Distance: 🏊500m ⊗500m 🚰500m.
Remarks: Coins at tourist info.

Ségur 29B3

GPS: n44,29087 e2,83503. ⬆
5 ⓢfree 🚰⚡Ch 🔌 WC ⚡€2. **Surface:** asphalted. ◻ 01/01-31/12
Distance: 🏊500m 🚰on the spot.
Remarks: Covered picnic area with electricity.

Senergues 29B2

La Ferme des Autruches, La Besse. **GPS:** n44,58861 e2,48361. ⬆
5 ⓢfree, voluntary contribution 🚰⚡Chfree. **Surface:** grassy/gravel.
◻ 01/03-30/11
Distance: 🏊2km.

Serres-sur-Arget 29A5

GPS: n42,96990 e1,51972.

ⓢ€5 🚰⚡Ch 🔌included. **Location:** Isolated, quiet. **Surface:** metalled.
◻ 01/01-31/12
Remarks: Next to community centre.

Souillac 29A2

Parking de Baillot, Chemin de Baillot. **GPS:** n44,89139 e1,47667. ⬆➡

20 ⓢfree 🚰€3 ⚡Ch ⊞€3 🔌. **Surface:** asphalted. ◻ 01/01-31/12
Distance: 🏊400m 🚲4,5km ⊗400m 🚰500m.
Tourist information Souillac:
ℹ Bd Louis-Jean Malvy. Monastery-city, 12th century, between the regions Périgord and Quercy.

Soulom 28B5

Place des Fêtes, D921. **GPS:** n42,95611 w0,0725.

10 ⓢfree 🚰⚡free. **Surface:** asphalted. ◻ 01/01-31/12
Distance: 🏊200m ⌖500m ⊗200m 🚰200m.

Sousceyrac 29A2 ❄

Place des Condamines. **GPS:** n44,87255 e2,03649. ⬆

10 ⓢfree 🚰⚡Ch 🔌 WCfree. **Location:** Simple, central, noisy.
Surface: asphalted. ◻ 01/01-31/12
Distance: 🏊on the spot 🛒on the spot ⊗on the spot 🚰100m.
Remarks: In front of town hall, max. 1 night.

St.Antonin Noble Val 29A3

Chemin de Roumégous. **GPS:** n44,15222 e1,75139. ⬆➡

15 ⓢfree 🚰⚡Chfree. **Surface:** asphalted. ◻ 01/01-31/12
Distance: 🏊200m ⊗300m 🚰100m.

St.Céré 29A2

Rue du Stade. **GPS:** n44,86139 e1,88583. ⬆

FR

FR

3 ⌇free ⊞ & Ch free. **Location:** Simple, central. **Surface:** asphalted. ⊙ 01/01-31/12
Distance: ⚓200m ⊗200m ☕150m.
Remarks: Behind stadium, nearby cemetery.

St.Clar 28D3
Aire de repos, Avenue de la Garlepe. **GPS:** n43,89111 e0,77250. ⬆.

10 ⌇free ⊞ & Ch WC ⌇free. **Location:** Comfortable, isolated, quiet.
Surface: grassy/gravel. ⊙ 01/01-31/12
Distance: ⚓500m ⊗250m.

St.Felix-Lauragais 29A4
Lac de Lenclas, D622. **GPS:** n43,42667 e1,89806.

10 ⌇free ⊞ & Ch WC . **Location:** Simple, isolated, quiet. **Surface:** gravel.
⊙ 01/01-31/12
Distance: ⚓100m ⊗100m.
Remarks: Max. 24h.

St.Geniez-d'Olt 29C2
Avenue de la gare. **GPS:** n44,46305 e2,97563. ⬆.

10 ⌇free ⊞ WC free. **Surface:** gravel. ⊙ 01/01-31/12
Distance: ⚓on the spot ⊿on the spot ⚓on the spot ⊗on the spot
☕on the spot.
Remarks: Max. 24h.

St.Girons 28D5
Rue Aristide Berges. **GPS:** n42,98865 e1,13852. ⬆.

7 ⌇free ⊞€2/150liter ⌇Ch ⊞€2/15minutes. **Surface:** asphalted.
Distance: ⚓100m.
Remarks: Max. 48h.

St.Jean et St.Paul 29C3
Saint Jean d'Alcas. **GPS:** n43,92646 e3,00887. ⬆ →.
10 ⌇free ⊞ & Ch WC free. **Surface:** gravel. ⊙ 01/01-31/12
Distance: ⚓on the spot.

St.Just-sur-Viaur 29B3
Parking La Fabrie, D532. **GPS:** n44,12402 e2,37588. ⬆.
5 ⌇free ⊞ & Ch WC free. **Location:** Isolated, quiet. **Surface:** gravel.
⊙ 01/04-30/11
Distance: ⚓10km ⊿on the spot ⚓on the spot

St.Lary Soulan ⚓ 🏠❄ 28C5
Route de Vieille Aure. **GPS:** n42,82248 e0,32329. ⬆.

60 ⌇€6/night ⊞€2 ⌇Ch ⊞€2. **Surface:** asphalted. ⊙ 01/01-31/12
Distance: ⚓300m ☕300m.
Remarks: Parking behind stadium.

St.Martory 28D5
Place Nationale, D52E, D117. **GPS:** n43,14141 e0,93033.

7 ⌇free ⊞ & Ch WC free. **Surface:** asphalted. ⦿ Thu (market)
Distance: ⚓3km.
Remarks: Along river, max. 1 night.

St.Maurice-en-Quercy 29A2
Place de l'église. **GPS:** n44,74306 e1,94722.

10 ⌇free. **Location:** Simple, quiet. **Surface:** gravel. ⊙ 01/01-31/12

St.Nicolas-de-la-Grave 28D3
Rue de la Calle. **GPS:** n44,06379 e1,02471.➡️.

🛏free 🚰🪑Chfree. **Surface:** asphalted/gravel. ⬜ 01/01-31/12
Distance: 🚰100m ⚓50m ⊗100m.

St.Puy 28C3
Grande Rue, D654. **GPS:** n43,87611 e0,46250.⬆️.

3 🛏free 🚰🪑Ch WC free. **Surface:** gravel. ⬜ 01/01-31/12
Distance: 🚰20m ⚓50m 🪣20m.

St.Thomas 28D4
Ferme Le Gros, D58. **GPS:** n43,50190 e1,07451.⬆️➡️.
10 🛏€3 🚰🪑Ch🔑included.
Location: Rural. **Surface:** grassy/gravel.
Distance: 🚰2km.

Ste.Croix-Volvestre 28D5
Lenclos. **GPS:** n43,12673 e1,17094.⬆️➡️.

🛏free 🚰🪑Chfree. **Location:** Simple, isolated, quiet.
Surface: grassy/gravel. ⬜ 01/01-31/12
Remarks: At football ground.

Ste.Geneviève-sur-Argence 29B2
Rue de l'Argence. **GPS:** n44,80194 e2,76222.⬆️.

30 🛏free 🚰€2 🪑Ch🔑. **Surface:** gravel. ⬜ 01/01-31/12
Distance: 🚰300m ⚓500m ⊗300m 🪣300m.

Tarbes 28C5
Avenue de la Libération. **GPS:** n43,24316 e0,06785.⬆️➡️.

38 🛏€10 🚰€2🪑Ch🔑included. **Surface:** asphalted.
⬜ 01/01-31/12
Distance: 🚰500m ⊗500m 🪣500m.
Remarks: Service only: water €2, water + electricity €5, video surveillance.

Thémines 29A2
Place de L'église. **GPS:** n44,74083 e1,82972.

3 🛏🚰🪑Ch🔑free. **Surface:** asphalted. ⬜ 01/01-31/12
Distance: 🚰on the spot ⊗100m 🪣100m.
Remarks: Near church.

Therondels 29B2
La Cazournie. **GPS:** n44,89833 e2,75937.⬆️.
10 🛏free 🚰🪑Chfree. **Surface:** grassy. ⬜ 01/04-15/11
Distance: 🚰on the spot ⊗100m 🔲100m.

Vabres-l'Abbaye 29B3
Le Coustel, Rue de la Vigne. **GPS:** n43,94575 e2,83957.⬆️.
15 🛏free 🚰🪑Chfree. **Surface:** gravel. ⬜ 01/04-30/10
Distance: 🚰50m ⚓on the spot 🪣on the spot.

Valcabrère 28C5
Parc de la Basilique Saint Just. **GPS:** n43,02812 e0,58370.
🛏free. **Surface:** asphalted. ⬜ 01/01-31/12
Remarks: Nearby Saint Bertrand de Comminges.

Valderiés 29B3
Place de Mairie, D91. **GPS:** n44,01167 e2,23333.⬆️.

5 🛏free 🚰🪑Ch WC free. **Surface:** asphalted. ⬜ 01/01-31/12
Distance: 🚰on the spot ⊗on the spot 🪣on the spot.
Remarks: Weighbridge.

Valence (Tarn-et-Garonne) 28D3
Aire de camping-car à Valence d'Agen, D953EC. **GPS:** n44,10547 e0,88608.⬆️.
🛏€4 🚰🪑Ch➕. **Surface:** asphalted.
Distance: 🚰600m.

Valence (Tarn-et-Garonne) 28D3
M. Cadot, aire privée, 341, Route des Charretiers, Valence-sud.
GPS: n44,09803 e0,89043.⬆️.
8 🛏€8 🚰🪑Ch🔑included. **Location:** Rural, comfortable, isolated, quiet.
Surface: gravel. ⬜ 01/01-31/12
Distance: 🚰1,2km ⊗1,2km 🪣1,2km.

FR

Valence-sur-Baïse · 28C3
Route d'Auch, D930. **GPS**: n43,87272 e0,38787.⬆️

7 🛏free 🚰🔌 Ch WC free. **Location**: Simple, noisy. **Surface**: gravel.
⬛ 01/01-31/12
Distance: 🚶500m ⊗500m 🛒500m 🚌on the spot.

Vénerque · 29A4
Allée du Duc de Ventadour. **GPS**: n43,43356 e1,44021.⬆️

10 🛏free 🚰🔌 Ch 📦free. **Surface**: gravel/metalled.
Distance: 🚶on the spot.

Vers · 29A2
Halte Nautique. **GPS**: n44,48551 e1,55503.⬆️➡️

20 🛏€5 🚰🔌 Ch WC 🗑free. **Surface**: grassy. ⬛ 01/05-30/09
Distance: 🚶100m ⛰100m ⊗200m 🛒100m 🚵on the spot 🚶on the spot.

Vic-en-Bigorre · 28C4
Rue du Stade, Avenue de Pau D6. **GPS**: n43,38472 e0,04917.⬆️➡️

4 🛏free 🚰🔌 Ch free. **Surface**: grassy. ⬛ 01/01-31/12
Distance: 🚶500m ⊗1km 🛒1km.

Vicdessos · 29A6
GPS: n42,76891 e1,50257.⬆️➡️

20 🛏€6 🚰🔌 Ch 🧴included. **Surface**: metalled. ⬛ 01/01-31/12
Distance: 🚶on the spot.

Villefranche-de-Rouergue · 29A3
Parking des Ruelles, Traverse des Ruelles. **GPS**: n44,35111 e2,03333.⬆️

3 🛏free. **Location**: Urban. **Surface**: asphalted. ⬛ 01/01-31/12
Distance: 🚶100m 🛒100m 🍴100m.

Villefranche-de-Rouergue · 29A3
Quai du Temple. **GPS**: n44,34937 e2,03917.⬆️

2 🛏free. **Location**: Urban. **Surface**: asphalted. ⬛ 01/01-31/12
Distance: 🚶300m ⊗200m 🛒300m.
Remarks: At quay in front of the old bridge.
Tourist information Villefranche-de-Rouergue:
🏠 place Notre Dame. ⬛ Thu.

Villeneuve (Aveyron) · 29A2
Place du sol de la Dime. **GPS**: n44,43855 e2,03269.⬆️

13 🛏€5 🚰🔌 Ch WC free. **Surface**: asphalted. ⬛ 12/04-01/11
Distance: 🚶100m ⊗100m 🍴100m.

Andorra

Pas de la Casa · 29A6
Avinguda del Consell General. **GPS**: n42,54468 e1,73525.
🛏20-8h € 2,10 🚰🔌. **Surface**: metalled.

Sant-Julia-de-Lòria · 29A6
Carretera de la Rabassa. **GPS**: n42,46573 e1,49462.⬆️➡️

4 🅿 € 0,50/h, 20.00-08.00 free ⛽🅆 Ch ⚡ (4x)included. 🏠 **Surface:** asphalted. ⭕ 01/01-31/12 **Distance:** 🚶1km.

Languedoc Roussillon

| 🅿S | Agde 〰⚓🍽 | 29C5 |

Les Peupliers. GPS: n43,29846 e3,45194.⬆➡.

30 🅿 € 8, Jul/Aug € 10 ⛽🅆 Ch ⚡ (30x)€2 🍴 📶. **Surface:** gravel/metalled. ⭕ 03/04-14/11 **Distance:** 🚶2km 🏊1,7km 🛒on the spot.

Tourist information Agde:
✝ Cathédrale Ste Étienne. Romanesque fortified cathedral, 12th century.

| 🅿S | Aigues-Mortes 〰⚓🍽 | 29D4 |

Les Poissons d'Argent - Aigues Mortes

contact@lespoissonsdargent.com - www.lespoissonsdargent.com

Excellent location for city visit
Restaurant with regional specialties
Bread-service

Les Poissons d'Argent, CD62. **GPS:** n43,56476 e4,16289.⬆. 120 🅿 € 10 ⛽🅆 Ch included ⚡ (32x)€3/24h,5Amp 📶. **Location:** Simple. **Surface:** gravel. ⭕ 01/03-31/10 **Distance:** 🚶3km 🏊3km 🛒on the spot ✗on the spot 💧1,5km Lidl 🚌500m 🚶500m. **Remarks:** At fish lake, fishing permit incl, bread-service.

| 🅿S | Aigues-Mortes 〰⚓🍽 | 29D4 |

Rue du Port. GPS: n43,56631 e4,18575.⬆.

50 🅿 € 16 ⛽🅆 Ch free. 🏠 **Location:** Simple. **Surface:** metalled. ⭕ 01/01-31/12 **Distance:** 🚶600m. **Remarks:** Max. 24h.

Tourist information Aigues-Mortes:
ℹ Office de Tourisme, Place Saint Louis, www.ot-aiguesmortes.fr. Medieval fortress, 13th century, in the swamp of the Camargue, tourist attraction. 🚮 free. 👁 La Tour Carbonnière, Place Saint Louis. Tower, guard-post for the defence of the city.

| 🅿 | Aiguèze 〰 | 30A3 |

GPS: n44,30530 e4,55250.⬆.

+20 🅿 free. **Location:** Rural. **Surface:** grassy. ⭕ 01/01-31/12 **Distance:** 🚶300m ✗300m.

| 🅿S | Alès 〰⚓🍽🏕 | 29D3 |

Place du camping-car, Avenue Jules Guesde. **GPS:** n44,12013 e4,08207.⬆➡.

6 🅿 free ⛽🅆 Ch free. **Location:** Urban, comfortable, central, noisy. **Surface:** asphalted. ⭕ 01/01-31/12 **Distance:** 🚶on the spot 🏊on the spot 🛒on the spot ✗400m 💧600m 🚌on the spot ✈routes available at tourist office.

| 🅿S | Amélie-les-Bains-Palalda ⛲ | 29B6 |

Carrer de l'Oreneta. GPS: n42,48063 e2,67951. 40 🅿 € 7 ⛽🅆 Ch. 🧺 **Surface:** gravel. ⭕ 01/01-31/12 **Remarks:** Behind hotel du Lion D'Or.

| 🅿S | Amélie-les-Bains-Palalda ⛲ | 29B6 |

Camping Amélie, Avenue Beau Soleil, D115. **GPS:** n42,47894 e2,67414.⬆➡.

Remarks: Max. 48h, Pont du Diable 600m, St.Guilhem-le-Désert 4km, free shuttlebus Mai-Sept: weekend (11-19h), July-Aug daily (10-23h).

⬛S **Aniane** 🌿 **29C4**

Lotissement du Camp de Sauve. **GPS:** n43,68652 e3,58254. ⬆️➡️.

8 📷€6 🔌€3 🚰 Ch. **Surface:** grassy/gravel. ⬛ 01/01-31/12
Distance: 🏊on the spot.
Remarks: Max. 48h, coins at campsite.

⬛S **Anduze** 🌿🏛🏔 **29D3**

Place de la Gare. **GPS:** n44,05000 e3,98444.

20 📷free 🚰 Ch. **Location:** Urban, simple, central, quiet. **Surface:** asphalted.
⬛ 01/01-31/12
Distance: 🏊on the spot ⊗300m 🚰400m 🚲on the spot 🚶on the spot.
Remarks: Max. 48h.

©S **Anduze** 🌿🏛🏔 **29D3**

Camping l'Arche. **GPS:** n44,06889 e3,97282. ⬆️➡️.

5 📷€12/night 🔌🚰Ch🚽WC⬛included,sanitary at campsite.
Location: Rural, simple, isolated, quiet. **Surface:** asphalted.
⬛ 01/04-30/09
Distance: 🏊3km ⊿on the spot ⊗on the spot 🚐100m 🚲on the spot
🚶on the spot.

Tourist information Anduze:
👁 Bambousserie de Prafrance. Bamboo garden laid out in 1835, with a large variety of bamboo species. ⬛ 01/03-15/11.
👁 Train Touristique. Tourist train from Anduze to St. Jean-du-Gard. ⊤ €6,50.

⬛S **Aniane** 🌿 **29C4**

Le Pont du Diable. **GPS:** n43,70270 e3,55988. ⬆️.

📷€4/day, €14/24h 🔌€3 🚰Ch 🧺.📠 **Location:** Rural, isolated.
Surface: gravel. ⬛ 01/01-31/12
Distance: 🚤9km.

15 📷free. **Surface:** gravel. ⬛ 01/01-31/12
Distance: 🏊300m 🚲nearby ⊗300m 🚰300m.

⬛S **Arre** 🏔👫 **29C3**

D999. **GPS:** n43,96771 e3,52139. ⬆️➡️.

6 📷free 🔌€2/100liter 🚰Ch🚽€2/1h WC.
Location: Rural, simple, central, quiet. **Surface:** metalled. ⬛ 01/01-31/12
Distance: 🏊on the spot ⊿on the spot 🚲on the spot ⊗on the spot
🚰bakery 200m 🚶on the spot.

⬛S **Avèze** 🏔 **29C3**

Aire du pont vieux, D999. **GPS:** n43,97517 e3,59899. ⬆️➡️.

4 📷free 🔌stay 🚰Ch free 🚽€2/1h. **Surface:** metalled.
⬛ 01/01-31/12
Distance: 🏊500m ⊿500m 🚲500m ⊗500m 🚰500m 🚶on the spot.
Remarks: Next to campsite municipal.

⬛S **Bagnols-sur-Cèze** **30A3**

Av. de l Europe, D8086. **GPS:** n44,16820 e4,61958. ⬆️.

20 📷free 🔌🚰Chagainst payment. **Surface:** gravel.
Distance: 🏊200m ⊗200m 🚰200m.
Remarks: Max. 24h.

⬛S **Balaruc-les-Bains** 🏛⚓🏛 **29D4**

Avenue des Hespérides 335. **GPS:** n43,44499 e3,67564. ⬆️.

FR

12 ⌷ € 8,50 ⊐ Ch. 🚿 **Location:** Rural, quiet. **Surface:** unpaved.
◻ 01/01-31/12
Distance: 🚶on the spot.

Thermes Hespérides, Avenue des Hespérides. **GPS:** n43,44574 e3,67770. ⬆️➡️

6 ⌷ € 7 ⊐ Ch 🔌 55minutes WC included 📶. 🚿 **Location:** Simple, quiet.
Surface: asphalted. ◻ 01/01-31/12
Distance: 🚶1km.
Remarks: Free bus to centre.

Les Marguilliers, Chemin des Marguilliers. **GPS:** n43,81667 e4,64107. ⬆️

9 ⌷ € 12/24h ⊐ Ch 🔌 included. **Surface:** gravel. ◻ 01/01-31/12
Distance: 🚶500m 🏊500m ⊗500m 🛒500m.

Quai de la Paix. GPS: n43,80615 e4,63739. ⬆️

10 ⌷ free ⊐ € 2/100liter Ch 🔌 € 2/1h. **Location:** Urban, simple.
Surface: asphalted. ◻ 01/01-31/12 ◉ water disconnected in winter
Distance: 🚶300m ⊗300m 🛒bakery 300m.
Remarks: Coins at tourist info.

Avenue Jean Moulin. GPS: n43,61071 e3,15329. ⬆️➡️

10 ⌷ free ⊐ Ch free. **Location:** Urban, simple, central, quiet.
Surface: grassy. ◻ 01/01-31/12
Distance: 🚶on the spot 🏊on the spot 🛒on the spot ⊗800m.
Remarks: Along the Orb river.

Rue des Loisirs. GPS: n42,71560 e2,60786. ⬆️

10 ⌷ € 5 ⊐ € 2 Ch 🔌 € 2. **Surface:** grassy/gravel. ◻ 01/04-31/10
Distance: 🚶100m.

Port de plaisance, Las Courrejos Est. **GPS:** n43,74422 e4,51890. ⬆️

⌷ free ⊐ € 2 Ch 🔌 € 2/1h. **Location:** Rural, simple. **Surface:** gravel/sand.
◻ 01/01-31/12
Distance: 🚶city centre 1,5km.
Remarks: Near marina, max. 48h, coins at harbourmaster.

Stade municipal, Rue du Stade. **GPS:** n43,19864 e1,74472.

15 ⌷ free ⊐ Ch 🔌 free WC. **Surface:** grassy. ◻ 01/01-31/12
Distance: 🚶1km ⊗1km 🛒1km.
Remarks: At football ground.

Parking Cité, P2, Chemin de Montlegun. **GPS:** n43,20534 e2,37189.

⌁€ 5/6h, overnight stay free 🚐 🗑free. **Surface:** gravel.
Distance: 🚶1km 🏖5km.
Remarks: Free shuttle to centre.

Carcassonne 🌿⛲☕ 29B5

Place Gaston-Jourdanne. **GPS:** n43,21000 e2,36028.

20 ⌁free. **Surface:** asphalted/metalled.
◉ 15/06-15/09
Distance: 🚶900m.

Tourist information Carcassonne:
ℹ️ Office de Tourisme, 15, Boulevard Camille Pelletan, www.carcassonne-tourisme.com. Medieval fortified city, museum city with many curiosities.
🛍️ The new city has a modern shopping centre.

FR

Carnon 29D4

Avenue Grassion Cibrand, Carnon-plage. **GPS:** n43,55097 e3,99417.⬆️

15 ⌁€ 11,50, 01/07-31/08 € 13 🚐 🗑Ch 🚿 WC 🗑included, on camp site
◉€5. 📶 ✏️ **Location:** Rural. **Surface:** asphalted. ◻ 01/04-15/10
Distance: 🚶1km 🏊80m 🚉50m.
Remarks: Next to campsite Les Saladelles.

Casteil 29B6

D116. **GPS:** n42,53324 e2,39230.⬆️

5 ⌁free. **Location:** Rural, simple, isolated, quiet. **Surface:** forest soil.
◻ 01/04-31/10
Distance: 🚶1km.

Castelnaudary 29A5

Camping-Car Park Castelnaudary, Passage des Lavandières.
GPS: n43,31427 e1,94899.⬆️
14 ⌁€ 12 🚐🗑Ch 🚿 (5x). 📶 ✏️ **Surface:** grassy/gravel.
◻ 01/01-31/12
Distance: 🚶on the spot ⊗on the spot 🚉on the spot.
Remarks: At Canal du Midi.

Chusclan 30A3

Cave Chusclan, Route d'Orsan, D138. **GPS:** n44,14552 e4,67762.⬆️

6 ⌁free 🚐🗑Chfree. **Surface:** gravel. ◻ 01/01-31/12
Distance: ⊗500m 🚉500m.
Remarks: Max. 48h.

Clermont-l'Hérault 🌿☕🏞️ 29C4

Aire de stationnement camping-car, Lac du Salagou.
GPS: n43,64677 e3,38915.⬆️➡️

8 ⌁€ 5-7 🚐€2/100liter 🗑Ch 🚿 (6x). **Location:** Rural, simple, isolated,
quiet. **Surface:** gravel. ◻ 01/01-31/12
Distance: 🚶7km 🏊on the spot 🛥️on the spot ⊗on the spot 🚉7km
🚲 on the spot 🎣on the spot.
Remarks: Coins at campsite.

Collioure 🌿⛲🏞️ 29C6

Route de Madeloc. **GPS:** n42,52566 e3,06861.⬆️

12 + 80 ⌁€ 15/24h 🚐🗑Ch 🚿 (12x) WC included. 📶
Location: Comfortable, quiet. **Surface:** asphalted. ◻ 01/05-31/10
Distance: 🚶2km 🏊2,3km ⊗2km 🚉2km.
Remarks: Monitored parking, may-Sep free shuttle to Collioure.

Comps 30A4

Place des Arènes. **GPS:** n43,85402 e4,60724.⬆️

50 🏕€5 🚰€2/110liter 🔌 Ch 🚿€2/50minutes WC 🧹 ♨️
Location: Rural. **Surface:** grassy/gravel. 🅾️ 01/01-31/12
Distance: 🚲50m 🏊on the spot 🛒on the spot 🚌50m 🛍on the spot
🚶on the spot.

	Comps	30A4

GPS: n43,85390 e4,60912.

30 🏕€5. 🛍 **Location:** Rural. **Surface:** unpaved. 🅾️ 01/01-31/12
Remarks: Along river.

	Cuxac-Cabardès	29B4

La Cabasse. **GPS:** n43,36126 e2,30185. ⬆️➡️.
8 🏕€5 🚰€2 🔌 Ch 🚿€3.
Location: Isolated, quiet. **Surface:** metalled.

	Duilhac-sous-Peyrepertuse	29B5

Route du château. **GPS:** n42,86160 e2,56527. ⬆️.

25 🏕free 🚰€2 🔌 Ch 🚿€2 WC. **Surface:** asphalted. 🅾️ 01/04-31/10
Distance: 🚲200m ✖️200m.

	Espéraza	29B5

Promenade François Mitterand. **GPS:** n42,93370 e2,21589. ⬆️.
20 🏕free 🚰 🔌 Ch. **Surface:** grassy.
Distance: 🚲500m ✖️500m.

	Fanjeaux	29A5

Chemin des Fontanelles. **GPS:** n43,18611 e2,03222. ⬆️➡️.

15 🏕free 🚰 🔌 Ch 🚿free. **Surface:** grassy/gravel. 🅾️ 01/01-31/12
Distance: 🚲100m.
Remarks: Next to maison de retraite (home for the elderly), max. 48h.

	Félines-Termenès	29B5

Av. de Termenes, dir Mouthoumet. **GPS:** n42,98691 e2,61285.

3 🏕free 🚰 🔌 Ch 🚿free. **Surface:** gravel. 🅾️ 01/01-31/12
Distance: 🚲50m.
Remarks: Closed when frosty.

Tourist information Félines-Termenès:
👁 Cité Médiéval, Villerouge Termenes. Medieval village and castle from 12-14th century. 🅾️ 01/07-30/09.

	Fitou	29C5

Aragon, Route Nationale 9, Les Cabanes de Fitou. **GPS:** n42,89275 e2,99672. ⬆️.

15 🏕€5/12h, €7/24h 🚰 🔌 Ch 🚿 🛒€2,50 📶 included. **Location:** Rural.
Surface: gravel. 🅾️ 01/01-31/12
Distance: 🛣A9 6,5km 🛒on the spot 🚂500m.
Remarks: Video surveillance.

	Fleury-d'Aude	29C5

Base de Loisirs Étang de Pissevache, Saint-Pierre-la-Mer.
GPS: n43,18972 e3,19694. ⬆️.

100 🏕€6,50 🚰€2 🔌 Ch 🚿€2/4h 🧹 🏪 🧽 **Surface:** unpaved.
🅾️ 01/01-31/12
Distance: 🏊sandy beach 300m.
Remarks: Parking directly behind the beach, next to tennis park and small surf lake, follow Base de Loisirs.

	Fleury-d'Aude	29C5

Les-Cabanes-de-Fleury. **GPS:** n43,21529 e3,23315. ⬆️.

100 🏕€6,50 🚰€2 🔌 Ch. 🛍 **Surface:** metalled/sand.

FR

◻ 01/01-31/12
Distance: 🚿on the spot ⚓on the spot ⊗200m.
Remarks: Next to campsite municipal Rive d'Aude, coins at capitainerie (1km).

| 📷S | Florac 🌿⚓🏔 | 29C3 |

D16. **GPS:** n44,32582 e3,59032.⬆➡.

23 🚐free ⛽€2/100liter 🔋Ch🔌€2/1h WCfree. **Location:** Rural, comfortable, central, quiet. **Surface:** asphalted. ◻ 01/01-31/12
Distance: 🚿150m ⚓300m 🚲300m ⊗150m 🛒150m
🚵mountainbike trail 🥾on the spot.
Remarks: Nearby cemetery.

| 📷S | Fraïsse-sur-Agout 🏔👫 | 29B4 |

Allée des Tilleuls. **GPS:** n43,60583 e2,79778.⬆➡.

15 🚐€7 ⛽🔋Ch🔌 (1x)included. **Surface:** asphalted/grassy.
◻ 01/01-31/12
Distance: 🚿400m ⚓20m 🚲20m ⊗400m.
Remarks: At the edge of village, on the Agout river.

| 📷S | Génolhac 🏔🌳 | 29D3 |

Les Taillades, Place du 19 Mars 1962, D906. **GPS:** n44,35388 e3,94844.⬆➡.

10 🚐free ⛽🔋Chfree. **Location:** Rural, simple, isolated, quiet.
Surface: metalled. ◻ 01/01-31/12
Distance: 🚿200m ⊗800m 🥾on the spot.

| 📷S | Gruissan ⚓ | 29C5 |

Aire des 4 Vents, Avenue des quatre vents. **GPS:** n43,10444 e3,09944.⬆➡.

80 🚐free, 01/03-30/11 € 8,50 ⛽🔋Ch🔌 WC 🗑included. 🚻
Surface: gravel. ◻ 01/01-31/12

Distance: 🚿on the spot ⚓on the spot 🚲on the spot ⊗on the spot 🛒on the spot.

| 📷S | Gruissan ⚓ | 29C5 |

Aire des Châlets, Avenue de la Jetée, Gruissan-plage. **GPS:** n43,09583 e3,11111.⬆➡.

80 🚐free, 01/03-30/11 € 8,50 ⛽🔋Ch🔌included. **Surface:** gravel.
◻ 01/03-30/11
Distance: 🚿2km ⚓on the spot 🚲on the spot ⊗2km 🛒2km.

| 📷S | Gruissan ⚓ | 29C5 |

Étang de Mateille, Gruissan dir Narbonne-Plage, base de voile, D332.
GPS: n43,12083 e3,11417.⬆.

150 🚐€ 8,50-10 ⛽🔋Ch🔌 (24x)€1 WC🗑.
Surface: grassy/metalled.
◻ 01/07-31/08
Distance: 🚿4km ⚓on the spot 🚲on the spot ⊗800m 🛒Lidl 2km.

Tourist information Gruissan:
👁 L'Hospitalet. Probably the largest wine-cellar of the world.
👁 Vieux Port. Old fishing-port.

| 📷S | Ispagnac 🌿🏔 | 29C3 |

Le Pavillon, D907. **GPS:** n44,37077 e3,53687.⬆➡.

6 🚐free ⛽🔋Ch🔌€2 WCfree. **Location:** Rural, simple, central, quiet.
Surface: asphalted/gravel. ◻ 01/04-31/10
Distance: 🚿100m ⚓river 200m 🚲100m 🥾on the spot.

| 📷S | La Canourgue 🌿🏔 | 29C2 |

Avenue du Lot, D998. **GPS:** n44,43325 e3,20775.⬆.

10 ⌇free ⟿⊟Chfree. **Location:** Rural, simple, isolated, quiet.
Surface: metalled. ◻ 01/01-31/12 ◉ Jul/Aug: tue
Distance: ⟿500m ⟋1,3km ⊗600m ⚓600m ⚘600m.
Remarks: Max. 24h.

🛁S	La Grande Motte ⚐	29D4

Aire camping-car Les Cigales, Avenue de la Petite Motte.
GPS: n43,56789 e4,07404.⬆⬆.

50 ⌇€ 11, May-Sep € 16 ⟿⊟Ch WC ⌷.⊞⌸ **Location:** Rural.
Surface: gravel. ◻ 01/01-31/12
Distance: ⟿2km ⚓1,2km ⊗2km ⚘2km.

🛁S	La Palme	29C5

Les Salins de La Palme, Route de Port la Nouvelle. **GPS:** n42,98033 e3,01858.⬆.
49 ⌇€ 12 ⟿⊟Ch ⚓(49x) ⌇.⊞ **Location:** Rural, comfortable, isolated,
quiet. **Surface:** grassy. ◻ 01/01-31/12
Distance: ⟿2,5km ⚓2km ⚘on the spot.

🛁S	Lagrasse ❀⚐🏛	29B5

Parking de la Promenade, P2, Les Condamines. **GPS:** n43,09273 e2,62004.

40 ⌇€ 3, 01/06-30/09 € 5 ⟿⊟Ch. **Surface:** grassy/gravel. ◻ 01/01-31/12
◉ Market day
Distance: ⟿on the spot ⚓on the spot ⟿on the spot ⊗on the spot
⚘on the spot.

🛁S	Langogne ⚐	29D2

Base Nautique l'Espace Bleu. GPS: n44,73598 e3,83489.⬆➡.

50 ⌇€ 12 ⟿⊟Ch ⚓(1x) ⌇included. ⊞⌸ **Location:** Rural, simple,
quiet. **Surface:** unpaved. ◻ 01/01-31/12
Distance: ⟿2km ⚓beach 1km ⟿on the spot ⊗2km ⚘2km.
Remarks: At lake Naussac, max. 48h.

🛁S	Langogne ⚐	29D2

Centre Polyvalente. GPS: n44,72281 e3,85419.⬆.

10 ⌇free ⟿€2/100liter ⊟Ch. **Location:** Central, quiet. **Surface:** asphalted.
◻ 01/01-31/12
Distance: ⟿on the spot ⊗300m ⚘300m ⚓on the spot.
Remarks: Coins at tourist info.

🛁S	Lapradelle Puilaurens	29B6

D117. **GPS:** n42,81003 e2,30854.⬆.

6 ⌇free ⟿⊟Chfree. **Surface:** gravel.
Distance: ⟿on the spot ⊗on the spot ⚘on the spot.
Remarks: At fire-station.

📷S	Latour-Bas-Elne	29C6

Aire de Latour Bas Elne, Route de la Mer. **GPS:** n42,60017 e3,00667.⬆➡.

40 ⌇€ 10, € 14 Jun-Aug, trailer € 4 ⟿⊟Ch ⚓included ⌇€3/2day.⛽
Location: Comfortable. **Surface:** grassy. ◻ 01/01-31/12
Distance: ⚓3km.
Remarks: Baker at 9am, monitored parking.

🛁S	Latour-de-Carol 🏛⚐	29A6

Village Club Yravals, 2 Rue de Saneja. **GPS:** n42,45829 e1,89460.⬆.

5 ⌇€ 10, 2 pers.incl, extra pers € 1 ⟿⊟Ch ⚓WC included ⌇€2/day.
Surface: grassy. ◻ 01/04-31/10
Distance: ⟿2km.

🛁S	Laudun-l'Ardoise	30A3

Place des Arènes. GPS: n44,10791 e4,65556.⬆.

FR

3 🅢free ⛽€4 Ch📷. **Surface:** asphalted. 📅 01/01-31/12
Distance: 🚰300m ⊗300m 🍽300m.

Laudun-l'Ardoise 30A3
Route d'Avignon, N580. **GPS:** n44,09527 e4,70164.⬆️
🅢free ⛽🍽Chfree. **Surface:** asphalted. 📅 01/01-31/12
Distance: 🚰5,5km.

Laudun-l'Ardoise 30A3
Vignerons de Laudun, Avenue du Général de Gaulle. **GPS:** n44,10388 e4,66362.⬆️
10 🅢free ⛽🍽Ch. **Surface:** grassy/gravel.
Distance: 🚰750m⊗300m 🍽750m.
Remarks: Max. 3 days.

Le Bosc 29C4
Parc Activités Méridienne. **GPS:** n43,68932 e3,35328.⬆️➡️

10 🅢free ⛽€2/100liter 🍽Ch📷€2/1h. **Location:** Highway, simple, isolated.
Surface: asphalted. 📅 01/01-31/12
Distance: ⚓400m⊗on the spot 🍽Intermarché 50m.

Le Boulou 29B6
Chemin du Moulin Nou. **GPS:** n42,52719 e2,83704.⬆️➡️

21 🅢free ⛽€2 🍽Ch WC. **Surface:** asphalted. 📅 01/01-31/12
Distance: 🍽300m.
Remarks: In front of cemetery, max. 24h.

Le Cap d'Agde 29C5
Rue du Gouverneur. **GPS:** n43,28600 e3,51739.⬆️➡️

30 🅢€5 02/11-26/03, € 10 27/03-02/11 ⛽€2/25 🍽Ch✂included.

Location: Rural, comfortable, central. **Surface:** asphalted/metalled.
📅 01/01-31/12
Distance: 🚰on the spot ⚓500m ⊗500m 🍽500m.
Remarks: Nearby Camping La Clape, video surveillance.

Le Caylar 29C4
Domaine des Templiers, Route de la Couvertoirade, D609.
GPS: n43,86944 e3,31466.

30 🅢€3 ⛽€2,10/100liter 🍽Ch📷€2,10/15minutes ✂(9x)€2,10/4h.
Location: Comfortable, isolated, quiet. **Surface:** gravel. 📅 01/04-31/10
Distance: 🚰600m ⚓500m ⊗on the spot.

Le Grau du Roi 29D4
Parking de la plage, Rue du Commandant Marceau. **GPS:** n43,54061 e4,13349.⬆️

40 🅢€ 8,80, June-Aug € 12,50 ⛽€2/100liter 🍽Ch📷€2/55minutes.
Surface: asphalted.
📅 01/01-31/12
Distance: 🚰centre 550m ⚓sandy beach 20m ⊗on the spot 🍽on the spot.
Remarks: Beach parking, video surveillance.

Le Malzieu-Ville 29C2
Place Foirail. **GPS:** n44,85506 e3,33385.⬆️➡️

6 🅢free ⛽🍽Ch WCfree 📶. **Location:** Rural, simple, comfortable, central,
quiet. **Surface:** asphalted. 📅 01/01-31/12
Distance: 🚰on the spot ⚓10km ⚓on the spot ⊗200m 🍽200m
🚶on the spot.

Le Monastir 29C2
Place de la Gare. **GPS:** n44,50896 e3,25162.⬆️➡️

4 ⌇free ⊐⚫Ch WC free. **Location:** Rural, simple, isolated, quiet.
Surface: asphalted. ⬛ 01/01-31/12
Distance: 1km ⬅1,5km 1km.
Remarks: 2013: during inspection service out of order, coins at petrol station (200m), picnic area.

| ⌇S | Le Ségala | 29A4 |

Esplanade du Canal. **GPS:** n43,34089 e1,83544.

10 ⌇free ⊐€1 ⚫Ch ⊞€2 WC. **Surface:** gravel. ⬛ 01/01-31/12
Distance: on the spot ⌇on the spot on the spot ⊗on the spot.

| ⌇S | Les Anges | 29A6 |

Pla del Mir. **GPS:** n42,56365 e2,06599.⬆.

100 ⌇free ⊐€3,50 ⚫Ch WC. **Surface:** asphalted. ⬛ 01/01-31/12
⬤ winter08-18h
Distance: 2,6km ⌇on the spot.

| ⌇S | Les Mages | 29D3 |

Serre Marine, D904, St. Ambroix/Alès. **GPS:** n44,23442 e4,16967.⬆➡.

7 ⌇free ⊐⚫Ch free. **Location:** Rural, simple, isolated, noisy.
Surface: metalled. ⬛ 01/01-31/12
Distance: 700m ⊗700m 800m.
Remarks: Picnic area.

| ⌇S | Leucate | 29C5 |

Aire camping-car, Chemin du Mouret, Leucate Plage. **GPS:** n42,90022 e3,05272.
⬆.

100 ⌇€ 7,20/24h ⊐€2 ⚫Ch ⬚.⬛ ⌇ **Location:** Rural, simple.
Surface: asphalted/gravel. ⬛ 01/01-31/12
Distance: 300m ⌇on the spot on the spot.
Remarks: Beach parking, baker on site (20/03-31/10).

| ⌇S | Leucate | 29C5 |

Chemin des Coussoules, La Franqui. **GPS:** n42,94329 e3,02917.⬆.

70 ⌇€ 6 ⊐⚫Ch on camp site €5. **Surface:** unpaved. ⬛ 01/02-30/11
Distance: 2km ⌇on the spot on the spot ⊗2km 2km.
Remarks: Next to campsite Coussoules, check in at reception campsite.

| ⌇S | Leucate | 29C5 |

Le Goulet, D627. **GPS:** n42,91145 e3,01946.⬆.

150 ⌇free, 15/02-15/11 € 7,20/24h ⊐€2 ⚫Ch ⊞€2.⬛ ⌇
Location: Rural, simple. **Surface:** unpaved.
⬛ 01/01-31/12
Distance: centre Leucate 850m ⌇on the spot on the spot.
Remarks: Terraces, at lake of Leucate, baker on site (20/03-31/10).

| ⌇S | Limoux | 29B5 |

Parking, Rue Louis Braille. **GPS:** n43,05741 e2,21490.➡.
10 ⌇free ⊐⚫Ch free. **Surface:** metalled. ⬛ 01/01-31/12

| ⌇S | Lunas | 29C4 |

Base de Loisirs Prade, D35. **GPS:** n43,70555 e3,18555.⬆➡.

75 ⌇free ⚫Ch free. **Location:** Urban, simple, isolated, quiet. **Surface:** grassy.
⬛ 01/01-31/12
Distance: 900m ⌇on the spot on the spot ⊗200m 700m 200m.

FR

FR

Marseillan-Plage ⬆️ 29C5
Rue des Goélands. **GPS:** n43,31902 e3,54864. ⬆️➡️.

122 🗑️ € 4-6-10/24h ⚡ €2/10minutes 🔌 Ch 🧹.🛒 ♻️
Location: Comfortable, quiet. **Surface:** gravel. 🅾️ 01/01-31/12
Distance: 🛒on the spot 🏖️sandy beach 600m ⊗on the spot 🍺on the spot.

Marvéjols 🌲🏖️ 29C2
Boulevard Aurelle de Paladines, Le Pré de Suzon. **GPS:** n44,55406 e3,28753. ⬆️.

10 🗑️free ⚡ 🔌 Ch WC free.
Location: Central. **Surface:** asphalted.
Distance: 🛒on the spot 🚲7,5km ⊗on the spot 🍺on the spot.
Tourist information Marvéjols:
ℹ️ Maison de Tourisme, Porte du Soubeyran, www.ville-marvejols.fr.
Old fortress city, gates with battlements and towers.

Matemale 🏔️🏖️❄️ 29A6
GPS: n42,57964 e2,10227. ⬆️.
🗑️free ⚡€2 🔌 Ch. **Location:** Rural, isolated, quiet. **Surface:** grassy.
🅾️ 01/01-31/12
Distance: 🛒1,8km.
Remarks: Parking at lake.

Matemale 🏔️🏖️❄️ 29A6
Rue de la Truite. **GPS:** n42,57106 e2,10984. ⬆️.

10 🗑️free. **Location:** Rural, isolated, quiet. **Surface:** gravel.
🅾️ 01/01-31/12
Distance: 🛒500m 🚲20m 🏖️20m ⊗500m 🍺500m.
Remarks: Parking at lake.

Mende 🏞️🏔️ 29C2
Rue du Faubourg Montbel. **GPS:** n44,52063 e3,49660. ⬆️.

23 🗑️free ⚡€2/10minutes 🔌 Ch free 🛒€2/55minutes.
Location: Urban, comfortable, central, quiet. **Surface:** asphalted.
🅾️ 01/01-31/12
Distance: 🏊on the spot 🚲on the spot ⊗200m 🍺400m 🚌on the spot 🚶on the spot.
Remarks: Along Lot river, max. 4 days.

Mèze 29C4
Complexe sportif des Sesquiers, Route de Villeveyrac.
GPS: n43,44135 e3,59436. ⬆️.

6 🗑️free ⚡ 🔌 Ch free. **Location:** Noisy. **Surface:** gravel.
Distance: 🛒2,5km 🚲10km.

Mont-Louis 🏔️🏖️ 29A6
Parking des Remparts. GPS: n42,50765 e2,12273.

20 🗑️€5 ⚡ 🔧 included. **Surface:** asphalted.
Distance: 🛒200m ⊗200m 🍺200m.
Remarks: Parking at city wall.

Montagnac 29C4
D613. **GPS:** n43,47520 e3,49129. ⬆️➡️.

3 🗑️free ⚡ 🔌 Ch free. **Surface:** gravel.
Distance: 🛒1km ⊗1km 🍺1km.

Montcalm 29D4
Le Caveau du Chêne, Route d'Aigues Mortes, D58. **GPS:** n43,57322 e4,30505. ⬆️.

40 ⛺free for clients. **Location:** Rural, isolated, quiet. **Surface:** grassy.
◻ 01/01-31/12

◫S **Montferrand** 29A4
Col de Naurouze, Route du Ségala, N113> D218. **GPS:** n43,35238 e1,82390.⬆.

20 ⛺free ⛽. **Surface:** gravel. ◻ 01/01-31/12
Distance: 🚲2km ⊗on the spot 🛒2km.

P **Montpellier** 🌿⚓🍴 29D4
Parking Joffre, Rue D'Argencour. **GPS:** n43,61316 e3,88608.
⛺€ 1/1h. **Surface:** asphalted. ◻ 01/01-31/12
Distance: ✈4km.
Remarks: Overnight stay possible. Via avenue Jean Mermoz.

Tourist information Montpellier:
👁 Corum. Opera-complex.
👁 Place de la Comédie. Square with many cafés.

◫S **Mourèze** 🌿⚓🚶🍴 29C4
D8. **GPS:** n43,61728 e3,36111.⬆.

6 ⛺€ 6 ⛽ Ch WC included. 🚿 **Location:** Simple, isolated, quiet.
Surface: gravel. ◻ 01/01-31/12
Distance: 🚲on the spot ⊗300m 🚶 on the spot.

◫S **Murviel-lès-Béziers** 🚶🍴 29C4
Route de Réals, D36. **GPS:** n43,43953 e3,13420.⬆.

12 ⛺€ 3 ⛽🥤Ch 🔑 (6x) WCincluded. **Location:** Rural, comfortable,
isolated, quiet. **Surface:** unpaved. ◻ 15/04-15/10
Distance: 🚲700m ✈10km ⊗700m 🚶 on the spot.
Remarks: Max. 7 nights.

◫S **Narbonne** 29C5
Parking du Parc des Sports, Avenue de la Mer. **GPS:** n43,18017 e3,02294.⬆.

36 ⛺€ 9/day ⛽€2 🥤Ch 🔑€2 🚿.🛒 🗑
Surface: asphalted.
◻ 01/01-31/12
Distance: 🚲on the spot ✈2,3km 🛒Carrefour.
Remarks: Free bus to centre every 30 minutes.

Tourist information Narbonne:
👁 Autorail Touristique du Minervois. Train tourist from Narbonne to Bize.
◻ 01/07-17/09.
🏛 Palais des Archevêques. Palace, 11th century, with cathedral.
⛱ ◻ Thu, Su.

◫S **Nîmes** 🌿⚓🍴 29D4
Domaine de Fontbespierre, 3359, route d'Anduze. **GPS:** n43,87142 e4,27746.
⬆.

50 ⛺€ 12 ⛽€2 🥤Ch 🔑€2/day WC. **Surface:** grassy/gravel.
◻ 01/01-31/12
Distance: 🚲6km ⊗6km 🛒6km.
Remarks: Terrain with video surveillance.

◫ **Octon** 🚶 29C4
Avenue de la Molière. **GPS:** n43,65390 e3,30378.

⛺free. **Surface:** gravel.
Distance: 🚲50m ⊗50m 🛒50m 🏊Lac du Salagou 🚶Lac du Salagou.
Remarks: Parking behind 'Clamery', Lac du Salagou.

◫S **Ouveillan** 29C5
Place Cave Coopératieve. **GPS:** n43,29204 e2,97080.⬆.

FR

7 ⌂free ⚡🔌 Chfree. **Surface:** gravel/metalled. ☐ 01/01-31/12
Distance: 🚶2km ⊗2km ⛲2km.

♨S | **Palavas-les-Flots** | 29D4
D62E2. **GPS:** n43,53281 e3,92654. ⬆.

23 ⌂€11-19 ⚡🔌 Ch 🔧 included. **Surface:** asphalted. ☐ 01/01-31/12
Distance: 🚶centre 600m ⛱sandy beach 800m.

♨S | **Palavas-les-Flots** | 29D4
Port Fluvial, Base Paul Riquet, Avenue de Lattre Tassigny.
GPS: n43,53091 e3,92316. ⬆.

200 ⌂€11, Jul-Aug €19 + €0,22/pp tourist tax, extra charge >8m and trailer ⚡€3 🔌 Ch 🔧€2 WC ⚡included 📶.
Surface: asphalted. ☐ 01/01-31/12
Distance: 🚶1km ⊗1km ⛲1km.

♨S | **Peyriac-de-Mer** | 29C5
Rue des Étangs. **GPS:** n43,09372 e2,96205. ⬆.

20 ⌂€5 ⚡🔌 Ch WC ⚡. 🚿 **Location:** Rural, simple, simple.
Surface: grassy/metalled. ☐ 01/01-31/12
Distance: 🚶1km ⛱on the spot ⊗1km ⛲1km 🚲on the spot 🏕on the spot.
Remarks: Next to rugby ground.

♨ | **Pézenas** | 29C4
Promenade du Pré St.Jean, Avenue du Maréchal Leclerc.
GPS: n43,46054 e3,42622.

⌂free. **Surface:** metalled. ☐ 01/01-31/12
Distance: 🚶on the spot 🚲1km.
Remarks: Parking centre.

Tourist information Pézenas:
✈ ☐ Sa.

♨S | **Pezens** | 29B5
Place de la Liberté, D6113. **GPS:** n43,25528 e2,26361.

5 ⌂free ⚡🔧 free. **Surface:** gravel. ☐ 01/01-31/12
Distance: 🚶50m ⊗50m ⛲50m.

♨S | **Port Vendres** | 29C6
Plage des Tamarins, Route de la Jetée. **GPS:** n42,51778 e3,11375. ⬆.

30 ⌂€5,50, Jul/Aug €9 ⚡€2/100liter 🔌Chincluded WC. 🚿
Location: Rural, simple. **Surface:** gravel. ☐ 01/01-31/12
Distance: 🚶1,3km ⛱100m ⊗on the spot.

♨S | **Port-la-Nouvelle** | 29C5
Chemin des Vignes. **GPS:** n43,01366 e3,04077. ⬆➡.

30 ⌂free, May-Jun, Sep €4, Jul/Aug €7 ⚡€2/15minutes 🔌
Ch 🔋€2/15minutes ⚡included, on camp site 🚿. 🚿
Location: Rural, simple. **Surface:** grassy/gravel.
Distance: 🚶2km 🚲8,6km ⛱2km ⊗2km ⛲1km Huit-à-huit, Passage de l'Abbé Gavanon.

♨S | **Port-la-Nouvelle** | 29C5
Parking Super U, Avenue du Général de Gaulle. **GPS:** n43,01609 e3,04933.
⌂free ⚡€2/10minutes 🔌 Chfree 🔧€2/55minutes ☐against payment.
Surface: asphalted. ☐ 01/01-31/12, 19.30-08.30h

Distance: 🛒1km ⚓1km ⊗1km 🚿on the spot.

| | Portiragnes | 29C5 |

Avenue de la Grande Maïre. **GPS**: n43,27558 e3,35156.⬆️.

± 15 🗑free. **Location**: Rural, simple, quiet. **Surface**: unpaved.
🅿 01/01-31/12
Distance: ⚓sandy beach 200m.
Remarks: Max. 2 days.

| | Quillan | 29B5 |

Parking Joseph Courjétaire, D117. **GPS**: n42,87366 e2,18266.⬆️.

10 🗑free 🚰€3,10 🚽Ch WC. **Surface**: asphalted. 🅿 01/01-31/12
Distance: 🛒on the spot ⚓on the spot ↪on the spot ⊗on the spot
🚿on the spot.
Remarks: Nearby railwayline, coins available at Office du Tourisme and bar.

| | Remoulins | 30A3 |

N86. **GPS**: n43,93789 e4,55851.

10 🗑free 🚰€5/20minutes 🚽Ch. **Location**: Urban. **Surface**: asphalted.
Distance: 🛒100m ⊗100m 🚿100m.
Remarks: Parking nearby river, service on the other side of the bridge: Route du Pont du Gare.

Tourist information Remoulins:
⌒ Pont du Gard. Roman aqueduct.

| | Rennes-les-Bains | 29B5 |

Plateau Sport Nature, Route des Corbières. **GPS**: n42,91479 e2,31814.
7 🗑€ 5/24h.
Distance: 🛒500m.

| | Rieutort-de-Randon | 29C2 |

Lac de Charpal. **GPS**: n44,62491 e3,56046.⬆️.

10 🗑free. **Location**: Rural, isolated, quiet. **Surface**: unpaved.
🅿 01/01-31/12
Distance: 🛒8km 🏊18km ⚓on the spot ↪on the spot ⊗on the spot
🏃on the spot.
Remarks: At lake Charpal.

| | Rigarda | 29B6 |

Aire 66, Route de Finestret. **GPS**: n42,62585 e2,52898.⬆️.

30 🗑€ 10 🚰🚽Ch 🔌included. 🐕 **Location**: Rural, simple, isolated, quiet.
Surface: grassy/gravel. 🅿 01/01-31/12
Distance: 🛒Vinça 2,7km ⊗2,7km 🚿2,7km.

| | Routier | 29A5 |

Sous la Serre. **GPS**: n43,10813 e2,12362.⬆️➡️.

± 7 🗑free 🚰free. **Surface**: gravel/metalled. 🅿 01/01-31/12
Distance: 🛒on the spot.

Tourist information Routier:
ℹ️ Corbières. Region is known for its wines and the Cathar citadels, the castle of Queribus in Cucugan is one of the last bastions of the Cathars.

| | Saillagousse | 29A6 |

Rue des Sports. **GPS**: n42,45764 e2,03766.⬆️.

7 🗑free 🚰€4 🚽Ch 🚽WC. **Surface**: asphalted. 🅿 01/01-31/12
Distance: 🛒on the spot ⊗on the spot 🚿on the spot.
Remarks: Coins at tourist info and town hall.

| | Saint-André | 29C6 |

Parking de Taxo. **GPS**: n42,55248 e2,97303.⬆️➡️.

6 ⌇€ 2,30 ⌇€2 ⌇Ch ⌇€2. **Surface:** asphalted. ⬚ 01/01-31/12
Distance: ⌇on the spot.
Remarks: Max. 3 nights, coins at tourist info.

5 ⌇free ⌇⌇Ch free. **Location:** Urban, simple, central, noisy.
Surface: metalled. ⬚ 01/01-31/12
Distance: ⌇50m ⌇50m ⌇on the spot.

	Saint-Cyprien	29C6

Aire du Théâtre de la Mer, Quai Arthur Rimbaud. **GPS:** n42,61776 e3,03512.⬆.

	Sérignan-Plage	29C5

Parking Mini-Golf, Avenue de la Plage. **GPS:** n43,26892 e3,33629.⬆.

49 ⌇€ 12,50/24h15/10-31/03 € 10,15/24h ⌇⌇Ch ⌇included. ⌇⌇
Location: Comfortable. **Surface:** asphalted.
⬚ 01/01-31/12 ⬚ service 15/10-31/03
Distance: ⌇450m marina ⌇300m.

20 ⌇€ 13, Jul/Aug € 17 ⌇⌇Ch ⌇WC ⌇included ⬚€4. **Location:** Rural,
comfortable, quiet. **Surface:** unpaved. ⬚ 01/01-31/12
Distance: ⌇150m ⌇on the spot ⌇150m.
Remarks: Behind restaurant, bread-service, swimming pool.

	Saint-Marsal	29B6

GPS: n42,53755 e2,62242.⬆.
25 ⌇€ 3 ⌇⌇Ch WC free. **Surface:** asphalted. ⬚ 01/01-31/12
Distance: ⌇on the spot ⌇nearby ⌇nearby.

	Servian	29C4

Servian Camping-cars, Zone d'Activité de la Baume, D18E5.
GPS: n43,38994 e3,31368.⬆.
⌇€ 8 ⌇€2 ⌇⌇Ch ⌇€2. **Surface:** asphalted. ⬚ 01/01-31/12
Distance: ⌇2km.
Remarks: Motorhome dealer, on industrial area.

	Saint-Thibéry	29C4

Domaine de la Vière, Chemin de la Vière. **GPS:** n43,38301 e3,40137.⬆.
⌇€ 10 ⌇⌇Ch ⌇WC ⌇included. ⌇ **Surface:** unpaved.
⬚ 01/01-31/12
Distance: ⌇2km ⌇A9 3km ⌇14km.
Remarks: During the weekend possible inconvenience of motocross.

	Sète	29C5

Parking Les 3 Digues. GPS: n43,36663 e3,61523.⬆.

	Salles-sur-l'Hers	29A5

Allée des Platanes. **GPS:** n43,29194 e1,78844.⬆➡.

30 ⌇free ⌇€2/10 ⌇Ch ⌇. **Location:** Rural, simple. **Surface:** gravel.
⬚ 01/01-31/12
Distance: ⌇50m ⌇on the spot ⌇on the spot.
Remarks: Beach parking, 01/06-30/09 no dogs allowed on the beach.

	Sommières	29D4

Chemin de la Princesse. **GPS:** n43,78701 e4,08717.⬆.

10 ⌇free ⌇⌇Ch ⌇free. **Location:** Simple, isolated, quiet. **Surface:** gravel.
⬚ 01/01-31/12
Distance: ⌇on the spot ⌇100m ⌇100m.

	Sauve	29D3

D999. **GPS:** n43,94017 e3,95218.⬆➡.

25 ⌇free ⌇€3 ⌇Ch. **Surface:** gravel.
Distance: ⌇500m.

FR

Remarks: In front of campsite municipal.

St.Chély-d'Apcher 29C2

Parking du Péchaud, Boulevard G. d'Apcher, N9. **GPS:** n44,80084 e3,27296.

2 free €2/100liter Ch €2/10minutes. **Location:** Simple, central, quiet. **Surface:** asphalted. 01/01-31/12
Distance: 200m 2,5km 200m 200m on the spot.
Remarks: Coins at tourist info.

St.Gilles 30A4

Quai du Canal. **GPS:** n43,67154 e4,43281.

free. **Location:** Rural. **Surface:** asphalted. 01/01-31/12
Distance: 500m 200m 500m.

Tourist information St.Gilles:
Abbay St.Gilles. Abbey with underground church.

St.Jean-du-Gard 29D3

Av. de la Resistance. **GPS:** n44,10210 e3,88347.

20 free Ch WC free. **Location:** Urban, simple. **Surface:** metalled. 01/01-31/12
Distance: on the spot 100m 100m 50m 300m on the spot.
Remarks: 2013: during inspection service out of order, tourist train.

St.Mamert-du-Gard 29D4

Rue des Fraisses. **GPS:** n43,88965 e4,19039.
6 free. **Location:** Simple. **Surface:** asphalted. 01/01-31/12
Distance: 400m.

St.Mamert-du-Gard 29D4

Route du Stade. **GPS:** n43,88491 e4,19054.

Ch free. 01/01-31/12

St.Mathieu-de-Tréviers 29D4

D17. **GPS:** n43,76206 e3,86016.

8 € 5 Ch included. **Surface:** gravel. 01/01-31/12
Distance: 1km.
Remarks: Check in at gymnasium.

Thues-entre-Valls 29B6

Gorges de la Carança. **GPS:** n42,52346 e2,22517.

25 € 8 Ch included. **Surface:** grassy/gravel.
01/01-31/12 frost
Distance: 2km.

Tournissan 29B5

M. Bailly, Clot Nelty, Route de Saint Laurent B452, Lieu-dit la Paulette.
GPS: n43,08068 e2,67280.

3 free Ch free. **Location:** Isolated, quiet. **Surface:** gravel.
01/04-31/10
Distance: 500m.

Vailhan 29C4

Parking de l'Eglise. **GPS:** n43,55527 e3,29882.

FR

6 🅿️ €5 🔌 Ch included. **Surface:** gravel. ⬛ 01/01-31/12
Distance: 1km 200m 50m.

🅿️S **Vallabrègues** 30A4
Route d'Aramon, D183A. **GPS:** n43,85763 e4,62639.⬆️

5 🅿️free 🔌€2 🔌 Ch €2. **Location:** Rural. **Surface:** gravel.
⬛ 01/01-31/12 🔆 high water
Distance: 500m.
Remarks: At lake and along the Rhone river.

🅿️S **Valras-Plage** 29C5
Avenue du Casino. **GPS:** n43,28162 e3,24230.⬆️

30 🅿️free 🔌€2 Ch. **Surface:** asphalted/metalled.
⬛ 01/10-30/06 🔆 summer
Distance: on the spot 200m on the spot on the spot on the spot.
Remarks: Behind casino/disco, service: Boulevard Pierre Giraud 200m, no camping activities.

🅿️S **Villasavary** 29A5
Camping-Car Park des Collines, Zone du Pradel. **GPS:** n43,21881 e2,03242.⬆️
11 🅿️€12 🔌 Ch. **Location:** Rural, comfortable, isolated, quiet.
Surface: asphalted. ⬛ 01/01-31/12
Distance: 650m 10km on the spot.
Remarks: Video surveillance.

🅿️S **Villeneuve-lès-Maguelone** 29D4
Avenue René Poitevin. **GPS:** n43,52980 e3,86584.⬆️➡️

26 🅿️€9, 26/04-30/09 €14/24h 🔌 Ch included. 🔌

Location: Rural. **Surface:** asphalted.
⬛ 01/01-31/12
Distance: 500m 8km 2,5km 500m 250m 50m on the spot.
Remarks: 26/04-30/09: also cash payment at office de tourisme (200m).

🅿️S **Villeneuve-Minervois** 29B5
Avenue du Jeu de Mail. **GPS:** n43,31516 e2,46432.⬆️

20 🅿️free 🔌 Ch WC. **Surface:** asphalted/metalled. ⬛ 01/01-31/12
Distance: on the spot on the spot on the spot.
Remarks: In front of town hall, max. 48h.

Provence-Alpes-Côte d'Azur

🅿️S **Allos** 30D3
Les Prés. **GPS:** n44,24289 e6,62220.⬆️

30 🅿️€6 🔌 Ch (9x)included WC. **Surface:** asphalted.
⬛ 01/01-31/12
Distance: 500m 200m 500m 500m 200m 200m.
Remarks: Max. 72h.

🅿️ **Allos** 30D3
Parking de la Cluite. **GPS:** n44,24677 e6,66918.⬆️

6 🅿️free. **Location:** Isolated, quiet. **Surface:** gravel.
Distance: Allos 6,5km.
Remarks: Isolated parking, jul/Aug shuttle bus to Lac d'Allos.

🅿️ **Allos** 30D3
La Foux d'Allos. **GPS:** n44,29583 e6,56944.⬆️➡️

5 ⌇free ⎓ ⊠ Ch WC free. **Surface:** asphalted.
Distance: ⟿1km ⊗100m ▯100m ⇥Skibus 50m ⚡50m.

| ⌖ S | Annot | 30D3 |

Chemin de la Colle Basse. **GPS:** n43,96351 e6,66386. ⬆➡.

20 ⌇free ⎓ ⊠ Ch free. **Surface:** grassy/gravel. ◻ 01/01-31/12
Distance: ⟿400m ⊗400m ▯400m.

| ⌖ S | Arles ⚘⚓⛴ | 30A4 |

Place Lamartine. **GPS:** n43,68151 e4,63046. ⬆.

6 ⌇free ⎓ ⊠ Ch free. **Location:** Urban. **Surface:** asphalted.
◉ Wed 5-15h, market
Distance: ⟿50m ⛱on the spot ⇤on the spot ⊗50m ▯100m.

Tourist information Arles:
ℹ Office de Tourisme, Boulevard des Lices, www.tourisme.ville-arles.fr. City
on the border of the nature reserve Camargue with Roman ruin. The painter Van
Gogh lived in Arles, 1888-89.
✝ Église St.Trophine. Romanesque and Gothic construction.
⌒ Palais Constantin.

| ⌖ | Avignon ⚘⚓⛴ | 30A3 |

Chemin de l'Ile Piot. **GPS:** n43,95167 e4,79361. ⬆.

20 ⌇free. **Surface:** asphalted. ◻ 01/01-31/12
Distance: ⟿800m ⊗800m ▯800m ⇤on the spot.
Remarks: Max. 24h, free bus to centre every ten minutes.

Tourist information Avignon:
ℹ Office de Tourisme, 41, cours Jean Jaurès, www.ot-avignon.fr. Roman city
dominated by the Palais du Papes. ◻ 01/04-31/08, 01/10-31/12 9-17h, 01/09-
30/09 9-20h, 01/11-31/03 9-12.45h, 14-18h.
◉ Place d'Horloge. Cosy square in the old centre of the city.
◉ Pont Saint Bénézet. Known as the Pont d'Avignon.
⚔ Petit Palais. Former residence of the archbishop.

| ⌖ S | Bagnols-en-Fôret | 30D4 |

Parc de Notre-Dame Les Merles, 1 chemin des Meules, D47.
GPS: n43,53590 e6,68893.

⌇€ 5 ⛽ €4. ☕ **Location:** Rural. **Surface:** grassy. ◻ 01/01-31/12
Distance: ⟿1km ⊗1km ▯1km.

| ⌖ S | Banon ⋔ | 30B3 |

Espace de la Grand Fontaine, Rue de la Grande Fontaine.
GPS: n44,03982 e5,63006. ⬆.

± 15 ⌇€ 3/24h ⎓ ⊠ Ch free WC. ☕ **Location:** Rural, simple.
Surface: gravel/metalled.
Distance: ⟿250m ⊗250m ▯100m ⚲on the spot ⚶on the spot.
Remarks: Max. 7 days, tuesday morning market.

| ⌖ S | Barcelonnette ⛰ | 30D3 |

Parking du Bouguet, Chemin des Alpages. **GPS:** n44,38222 e6,65778. ⬆➡.

15 ⌇€ 6 ⎓€2/100liter ⊠ Ch ⊞€2/1h ⊿. **Location:** Isolated, quiet.
Surface: grassy. ◻ 01/01-31/12
Distance: ⟿500m ⊗200m ⊗500m ▯500m.

| ⌖ | Barcelonnette ⛰ | 30D3 |

GPS: n44,38717 e6,64626. ⬆.
3 ⌇free. **Location:** Simple. **Surface:** asphalted. ◻ 01/01-31/12
Distance: ⟿500m ⊗500m ▯600m.
Remarks: Max. 48h.

| ⌖ S | Bédoin ⋔ | 30B3 |

Chemin des Sablières. **GPS:** n44,12472 e5,17167. ⬆➡.

⌇€ 3 ⎓€2/10minutes,only 2-euro coins ⊠ Ch free ⛽ €2/55minutes,only
2-euro coins. ☕ **Location:** Rural, simple, quiet. **Surface:** grassy/metalled.
◻ 01/01-31/12
Distance: ⟿600m ⊗600m ▯600m ⚶Mont-Ventoux ⚲on the spot.

FR

Remarks: Next to campsite La Pinède, max. 3 nights.

⛰️ S **Bollène** 30A3

Centre Leclerc, Route de Saint Paul Trois Châteaux, D26.
GPS: n44,32222 e4,74306.⬆️.

🚿free 🚰🔌Ch free. ⬛ 01/01-31/12
Distance: 🛒4,3km.
Remarks: Service only during opening hours shop.

Tourist information Bollène:
👁️ Village Troglodyte. Cave dwelling village. ⬛ 01/04-31/10 9.30-19h, 01/11-31/03 Sa-Su, holidays 14-18h ⬛ 01/12-31/01.

🚐 S **Briançon** 〰️🏕️⛰️🌊 30C2

Parc des Sports, Rue Jean Moulin. **GPS:** n44,89028 e6,62883.⬆️.
4 🚿free 🚰€2/100liter 🔌Ch 🚽€2. **Surface:** asphalted.
Distance: 🚉1km.
Remarks: At sports park, max. 24h.

Tourist information Briançon:
ℹ️ Office de Tourisme, 1, place du Temple, www.ot-briancon.fr. Highest city of Europe, fortress is now a tourist centre, in winter as winter sports resort and in summer parapente, rafting and biking.
🌿 Parc des Écrins. Nature reserve.

🚐 S **Caille** ⛰️ 30D4

Aire de Caille, Chemin de la Plaine. **GPS:** n43,77893 e6,73331.⬆️➡️.

3 🚿free 🚰€2/15minutes 🔌Ch 🚽€2/15minutes. ⬛ 01/01-31/12
Distance: 🚉50m ⊗50m 🍴100m 🚲on the spot.

©️ S **Carpentras** 🏛️ 30A3

Parking de Coubertin, Avenue de Coubertin. **GPS:** n44,04398 e5,05372.⬆️.

8 🚿free 🚰🔌Ch free.
Location: Urban, simple. **Surface:** asphalted.
Distance: 🚉1,5km.
Remarks: At sports centre P.de Coubertin, max. 24h.

Tourist information Carpentras:
👁️ Hôtel Dieu. Former hospital, 18th century.
🌳 Centre-ville. ⬛ Fri-morning.

🚐 S **Carro** 30A5

Quai Jean Verandy. **GPS:** n43,32931 e5,04076.

70 🚿€ 6, 01/04-30/06 € 8, 01/07-31/08 € 10 🚰🔌Ch 🌿included. 🚐♻️
Surface: metalled. ⬛ 01/01-31/12
Distance: 🏖️on the spot 🚤on the spot ⊗200m 🍴200m.
Remarks: Max. 72h, fish sales from 08h.

🚐 **Carry-le-Rouet** 30B5

Avenue Pierre Sémard. **GPS:** n43,33829 e5,15921.
5 🚿free. **Location:** Simple.
Remarks: Max. 48h.

🚐 S **Castellane** ⛱️⛰️🌊 30C4

Ancienne Route de Grasse. **GPS:** n43,84630 e6,51484.⬆️.

28 🚿€ 6 🚰🔌Ch 🌿included. **Surface:** asphalted.
Distance: 🚣100m 🌊on the spot.
Remarks: Directly at the river, near Pont du Roc.

Tourist information Castellane:
🌳 ⬛ Sa-morning.

🚐 S **Cavalière** 30C5

Avenue du Cap Nègre, D559. **GPS:** n43,15228 e6,43078.⬆️.

50 🚿€ 16-18 🚰🔌Ch 🌿🚿📶included. **Surface:** sand.
Distance: 🚉50m 🏖️50m ⊗50m 🍴200m.

🚐 S **Château-Arnoux-Saint-Auban** 30C3

Avenue Gén. de Gaulle, N85. **GPS:** n44,09543 e6,01022.⬆️➡️.

+10 🚿free 🚰🔌Ch free. **Location:** Urban, central, noisy. **Surface:** asphalted.
Distance: 🚉on the spot 🍴2,3km.
Remarks: Max. 48h, service 50m.

FR

Chorges 30C2

Place du champ de foire. **GPS**: n44,54600 e6,28008.

10 free free. **Surface**: gravel. 01/01-31/12
Distance: 400m 400m 1km.
Remarks: Max. 12h.

Tourist information Chorges:

Lac de Serre Ponçon, Serre Ponçon. Clear blue artificial lake, many water sports.

Colmars-les-Alpes 30D3

GPS: n44,17943 e6,62695.

10 free €2 Ch . **Surface**: asphalted. 01/01-31/12
Distance: 300m 50m 50m 300m 300m.
Remarks: Tuesday market.

Comps-sur-Artuby 30C4

D955. **GPS**: n43,70652 e6,50678.

8 free €3 Ch WC. **Location**: Rural, isolated, quiet. **Surface**: gravel.
01/01-31/12
Distance: 350m pizzeria/crêperie.

Cuges-les-Pins 30B5

Le Jardin de la Ville. **GPS**: n43,28150 e5,70558.

10 € 3/12-12h Ch included. **Location**: Rural, isolated, quiet.
Surface: grassy/gravel. 01/01-31/12
Distance: 500m 500m 500m.
Remarks: Monitored parking.

Tourist information Cuges-les-Pins:

Musée Légion Etrangères, Aubagne. Museum about the French Foreign Legion.

Dauphin 30B4

Route de la Rencontre. **GPS**: n43,90028 e5,78417. .

4 free. **Location**: Rural, simple, quiet. **Surface**: metalled.
Distance: 300m 300m on the spot on the spot.
Remarks: Near Salle des Fêtes.

Digne-les-Bains 30C3

Le Vallon des Sources, Avenue des Thermes. **GPS**: n44,07998 e6,26091.

25 free €2 Ch. 01/01-31/12
Distance: 2,5km 750m 2km 100m.
Remarks: Coins available at pay-desk of theTherme.

Esparron de Verdon 30C4

D82. **GPS**: n43,74233 e5,97366.

7 free . **Location**: Rural, simple.
Distance: 500m 500m 500m 500m on the spot.

Fayence 30D4

Allée des Jardins. **GPS**: n43,62308 e6,68982.
5 free €4 Ch.
Distance: 750m 750m 300m.
Remarks: At tennis-court and swimming pool, max. 48h.

Fontaine-de-Vaucluse 30B3

Camping-Car Park, Route de Cavaillon. **GPS**: n43,92024 e5,12452.

€ 12 Ch (2x) included. **Location**: Rural, comfortable,

FR

quiet. **Surface:** gravel/metalled. ☐ 01/01-31/12
Distance: 🚶500m ⊗500m 🚲on the spot ⚓on the spot.

🛇S 🚐 Fontvieille 30A4

Parking du Moulin de Daudet, Allée des Pins. **GPS:** n43,72000 e4,71200.⬆

🚐€5 ⛽€2 🍽Ch.🅿🧺 **Location:** Rural, comfortable, quiet.
Surface: gravel.
Distance: 🚶800m ⊗800m.

🛇S 🚐 Gap 30C2

Parking Dumont, Avenue Commandant Dumont, N85. **GPS:** n44,56544 e6,08447.
⬆➡

3 🚐free ⛽€3 🍽Ch 🔌€3 🧺. **Surface:** asphalted.
Distance: 🚶500m ⊗on the spot ⚡on the spot.
Remarks: Stay overnight allowed at other pitches.

🛇S 🚐 Gémenos 30B5

Cours Sudre. **GPS:** n43,29772 e5,62953.⬆

3 🚐free ⛽🍽Ch 🔧 free. **Surface:** metalled.
Distance: 🚶100m ⊗100m ⚡100m.
Remarks: Max. 24h.

🛇S 🚐 Gigondas 🍴 30A3

Domaine des Florets, Route des Dentelles, D80. **GPS:** n44,16220 e5,01725.⬆

3 🚐free ⛽free. **Location:** Rural, simple, quiet. **Surface:** gravel.
☐ 01/01-31/12
Distance: 🚶1,7km ⊗500m 🚲on the spot ⚓Des Dentelles.
Remarks: Check in at tasting room.

🛇 Gordes 🌿🏖 30B4

D2. **GPS:** n43,90056 e5,19306.⬆

20 🚐free. **Location:** Rural, simple. **Surface:** gravel.
☐ 01/01-31/12
Distance: 🚶2km ⊗2km 🗑2km.

🛇S 🚐 Greasque 30B4

Musée de la Mine, Route de Puits Hely d'Oissel. **GPS:** n43,43281 e5,53439.⬆

15 🚐free ⛽🍽Chfree. **Surface:** gravel. ☐ 16/01-20/12
Distance: 🚶600m.

🛇S 🚐 Gréoux-les-Bains 🏖🏛 30C4

Aire Camping-car, Chemin de la Barque. **GPS:** n43,75562 e5,88862.⬆➡

80 🚐€9/24h ⛽🍽Ch 🔧 WC included. 🅿🧺 **Location:** Urban, simple,
noisy. **Surface:** gravel. ☐ 01/01-31/12
Distance: 🚶150m ⊗150m ⚡150m ⚓on the spot.
Remarks: Max 3,5t, max. 30 days.

🛇S 🚐 Grimaud 🏖 30C5

Saint Pons Les Mûres, D98. **GPS:** n43,28000 e6,57806.⬆

12 🚐€13 ⛽€2,50 🍽Ch 🔌€2,50 🧺. 🅿 **Location:** Simple.
Surface: asphalted. ☐ 01/01-31/12
Distance: 🚶800m 🏊800m 200m ⚡500m.
Remarks: Max. 72h.

🛇S 🚐 Guillaumes 30D3

D2202. **GPS:** n44,08861 e6,85285.⬆➡

FR

10 ⌷free ⌁€2/100liter ⌷Ch⌷€2/1h. ◻ 01/01-31/12
Distance: 50m on the spot on the spot ⊗50m 🛒50m.
Remarks: Coins at Bar-Tabac, tourist info, town hall.

Le Mérou, D42, L'Ayguade. **GPS:** n43,10897 e6,18117. ⬆.

6 ⌷free ⌁€3/15minutes ⌷Ch ⌷.
Distance: on the spot ⊗on the spot.

Les Etangs de Sauvebonne, 566 Route de Pierrefeu. **GPS:** n43,16120 e6,12133.
⬆.

20 ⌷€ 10 ⌷Ch included 💧€3/day. **Location:** Rural, quiet.
Surface: grassy. ◻ 01/01-31/12
Distance: on the spot on the spot.

Route de Jausiers-Barcelonette, D900. **GPS:** n44,41266 e6,72936. ⬆➡.

3 ⌷free ⌁€3 ⌷Ch⌷. **Surface:** metalled. ◻ 01/01-31/12
Distance: 600m 🛒50m ⊗100m 🛒400m.

Pont de Barnuquel, Lotissement des Neiges. **GPS:** n44,41278 e6,72472.

20 ⌷free. **Surface:** unpaved. ◻ 01/01-31/12
Distance: 600m on the spot ⊗100m 🛒400m.
Remarks: Service 200m.

Rue des Bailes. **GPS:** n43,73806 e6,62583.

4 ⌷free ⌁⌷Ch. **Location:** Noisy. **Surface:** asphalted.
◻ 01/01-31/12
Distance: 200m ⊗100m 🛒100m.

Bourg La Bréole. **GPS:** n44,45777 e6,29194. ➡.

6 ⌷free ⌁⌷Ch WC free. **Location:** Simple, quiet. **Surface:** asphalted.
◻ 01/01-31/12
Distance: on the spot 2km 2km Lac de Serre Ponçon ⊗100m
🛒100m.

Espace Lavage Auto Grand Bleu, La Moutonne. **GPS:** n43,12417 e6,07444.

3 ⌷€ 4 ⌁⌷Ch 💧WC included. **Surface:** concrete. ◻ 01/01-31/12
Remarks: Free after washing the motor home (€ 10).

Rond-point Ducourneau, chemin du Pansard. **GPS:** n43,13185 e6,23053. ⬆.

FR

4 ⬛free ⚡€3 🔧Ch 🔲.
Distance: 🚶800m.
Remarks: Max. 24h.

| 📷S | La Motte | 30C4 |

Chemin des Correns. **GPS:** n43,48860 e6,54212. ⬆️➡️
12 ⬛free ⚡€2 🔧Ch.
Location: Rural, simple, quiet. **Surface:** gravel.
Distance: 🚶800m ✖️300m.
Remarks: At tennis-courts, max. 24h, coins at the shops.

| 📷S | La Roche-des-Arnauds | 30C2 |

D994, Chemin des Digues. **GPS:** n44,56134 e5,95637. ⬆️

5 ⬛free. **Surface:** asphalted. 🔲 01/01-31/12
Distance: 🚶100m 🛒on the spot 🚰on the spot 💧100m.
Remarks: Max. 24h.

| 📷S | La Salle-les-Alpes 🏔️❄️ | 30C2 |

Aire camping car Pontillas, Hameau de Bez. **GPS:** n44,94805 e6,55564. ⬆️
20 ⬛€8 ⚡🔧Ch 🔌 included. **Surface:** metalled.
Distance: 🚶400m ✖️400m 💧400m 🎿20m.
Remarks: Pay at tourist office.

| 📷S | La Salle-les-Alpes 🏔️❄️ | 30C2 |

Chemin de l'Oratoire, Villeneuve. **GPS:** n44,94417 e6,55583.

15 ⬛€8, winter €18 ⚡🔧Ch 🔌 included. **Surface:** gravel.
🔲 01/01-31/12
Distance: 🚶200m ✖️50m.
Remarks: Parking at skipistes.

| 📷S | Laragne-Montéglin | 30B3 |

Avenue de Provence, D1075. **GPS:** n44,31212 e5,82543. ⬆️

15 ⬛free ⚡🔧Ch 🔲free. **Surface:** asphalted. 🔲 01/01-31/12
Distance: 🚶300m ✖️300m 💧300m.

| 🏕️S | Laragne-Montéglin | 30B3 |

Intermarché, D1075. **GPS:** n44,30300 e5,83700. ⬆️

30 ⬛free ⚡€2 🔧Ch. 🔲 01/01-31/12
Distance: 🚶2km.

| 📷S | Le Lauzet-Ubay 🏔️🚤❄️ | 30C2 |

D900. **GPS:** n44,42833 e6,43389. ⬆️

10 ⬛free. **Location:** Isolated, quiet. **Surface:** gravel. 🔲 01/01-31/12
Distance: 🚶50m 🛒50m ✖️50m 💧100m.
Remarks: At small lake.

| 📷S | Le Monêtier-les-Bains ❄️ | 30C1 |

Aire camping car les Charmettes, Route des Bains. **GPS:** n44,97602 e6,50933.
⬆️
40 ⬛€4,80/day + tourist tax ⚡🔧Chfree. **Surface:** metalled.
🔲 01/01-31/12
Distance: 🎿on the spot.
Remarks: Parking at skipistes.

| 📷S | Le Thoronet | 30C4 |

D17, boulevard du 17 aout 1944. **GPS:** n43,45097 e6,30411. ⬆️

3 ⬛free ⚡€3 🔧Ch. **Location:** Rural. **Surface:** asphalted.
🔲 01/01-31/12
Distance: 🚶on the spot 💧50m.
Remarks: Coins at tourist info.

Les Arcs-sur-Argens — 30C4

Cellier des Archers, Avenue des Laurons. **GPS:** n43,45509 e6,47750.

10 free ⚡ Ch free. **Surface:** gravel/sand. 01/01-31/12
Distance: 1km 8km 100m Super U 1km 1km 200m.

Tourist information Les Arcs-sur-Argens:
Thu morning.

Les Issambres — 30D4

Chez Marcel, Plage La Gaillarde, N98. **GPS:** n43,36559 e6,71202.

50 € 12, peak season € 16 ⚡ Ch included €3/day €0,50 €5.
Location: Simple, comfortable. **Surface:** gravel/sand.
01/01-31/12
Distance: 50m 200m 200m.

Les Salles-sur-Verdon — 30C4

L'Ermitage, D957. **GPS:** n43,77434 e6,21773.

5 € 6, Jul/Aug € 8 ⚡ Ch €5 included. **Location:** Rural, simple.
Surface: gravel/sand.
Distance: 700m Lac de Ste Croix 1km on the spot on the spot
on the spot.
Remarks: Service passerby € 5, swimming pool incl.

Malaucène — 30B3

Avenue Charles de Gaulle. **GPS:** n44,17792 e5,12970.

€ 3 ⚡ Ch free. **Location:** Rural, simple, noisy.
Surface: asphalted/metalled. 01/01-31/12
Distance: 150m 150m 150m Mont-Ventoux on the spot.
Remarks: Between sports fields and gendarmerie.

Tourist information Malaucène:
Marché Provencal. Wed-morning.

Malemort-du-Comtat — 30B3

Avenue Docteur Tondut, D5. **GPS:** n44,02175 e5,15714.

free ⚡ Ch free. **Location:** Rural, simple. **Surface:** gravel.
Distance: 200m on the spot.
Remarks: Near Salle des Fêtes.

Marseille — 30B5

Marlyparc, Chemin de Morgiou 120. **GPS:** n43,24085 e5,40693.
12 € 12 ⚡ Ch included. **Location:** Urban, simple.
Surface: metalled. 01/01-31/12
Distance: on the spot 1km on the spot.

Ménerbes — 30B4

Parking Longue Durée. **GPS:** n43,83193 e5,20828.

free. **Location:** Rural, simple. **Surface:** gravel.
Distance: 250m 100m on the spot.

Montgenèvre — 30D2

Aire des Marmottes. **GPS:** n44,93417 e6,73317.

250 € 10 ⚡ Ch (80x) included. **Location:** Comfortable, isolated,
quiet. **Surface:** metalled. 01/01-31/12
Distance: 500m 500m on the spot.

Moustiers Ste.Marie — 30C4

P5, D952. **GPS:** n43,84361 e6,21874.

€ 8,50/night ⚡ €2/10minutes Ch €2/10minutes.
Location: Rural, simple. **Surface:** gravel.

FR

Distance: 10 min walking on the spot on the spot.
Remarks: Max. 2 nights.

Névache 30C1

D994G. **GPS:** n45,01666 e6,64261.

free, 01/07-31/08 € 5 free. **Location:** Isolated. **Surface:** grassy. 01/01-31/12

Oppède-le-Vieux 30B4

Parking Oppéde-le-Vieux. GPS: n43,83094 e5,15897.

2 € 5/day free WC.
Location: Rural, simple. **Surface:** gravel.
Distance: 500m 500m.

Tourist information Oppède-le-Vieux:
Hiking route through medieval top-hill village.

Orcières-Merlette 30C2

Camping-car Casse Blanche, Pra Palier, P2. **GPS:** n44,69517 e6,32567.
24 € 10/24h Ch included. **Surface:** asphalted.
01/01-31/12
Distance: on the spot on the spot.
Remarks: Summer pay at tourist office.

Pélissanne 30B4

Prouvenque, Chemin de la Prouvenque. **GPS:** n43,62805 e5,15307.

6 free Ch free.
Location: Urban, simple, quiet. **Surface:** asphalted.
Distance: 500m 8km.
Remarks: Parking stadium.

Plan-de-la-Tour 30C5

Parking Boulodrôme, D74. **GPS:** n43,33827 e6,54902.

free. **Surface:** asphalted. 01/01-31/12 Thu
Distance: 100m 100m 100m.
Remarks: At tennis-courts.

Tourist information Plan-de-la-Tour:
Thu morning 6-12h.

Port Saint-Louis-du-Rhône 30A4

Av. de la 1 Dfl. **GPS:** n43,38424 e4,81909.

50 € 6,50 Ch included. **Location:** Simple, isolated, quiet.
Surface: asphalted/gravel. 01/01-31/12
Distance: 2km 50m 2km 2km.
Remarks: Baker every morning.

Pra-Loup 30C3

Parking des Choupettes. GPS: n44,36806 e6,60611.

50 free €3 Ch €3 WC. **Surface:** asphalted. 01/01-31/12
Distance: 400m 400m 400m 50m.
Remarks: Parking at skipistes.

Puget Theniers 30D3

Aire de la Condamine, Route des Grandes Alpes. **GPS:** n43,95306 e6,89944.

10 € 3,50 Ch included. **Surface:** asphalted. 01/01-31/12
Distance: 300m 20m 300m 300m.

Puy-Saint-Vincent 30C2

Clôt de Saint-Romain, D4. **GPS:** n44,83245 e6,48331.
20 € 6 Ch included. 18/12-25/04
Remarks: Altitude 1600m, max. 15 days, information at cableway.

Puyvert · 30B4

Super U, D118. **GPS**: n43,74763 e5,33727.

5 free (2x)free €4/time.
Location: Rural. **Surface:** asphalted. 01/01-31/12
Distance: 1,5km on the spot.
Remarks: Parking near Super-U.

Quinson · 30C4

Les Prés du Verdon, Allée des Prés du Verdon. **GPS**: n43,69801 e6,03911.

5 free Ch free. **Location:** Rural, simple, quiet. **Surface:** gravel/sand.
01/01-31/12
Distance: 100m 100m 300m 500m on the spot.
Remarks: Near the prehistoric museum of the gorges du Verdon.

Ramatuelle · 30D5

Parking de Tamaris, Plage de Pamplonne, Route des Tamaris.
GPS: n43,23893 e6,66149.

60 € 5/day, € 5/night, 1/7-31/8 € 9day, € 9/night, dog € 1 Ch
(20x)€7/day. **Location:** Rural. **Surface:** gravel.
Distance: on the spot on the spot on the spot.
Remarks: Beach parking.

Ramatuelle · 30D5

Parking Municipal, Plage de Pamplonne, Route de Bonne-Terrasse.
GPS: n43,21126 e6,66217.

90 € 8 Ch WC. **Location:** Rural. **Surface:** gravel.
01/04-31/10
Distance: 200m 200m 2km.

Remarks: Beach parking, bread-service.
Tourist information Ramatuelle:
La place de l'Ormeau. Provencal Market. Thu, Su.

Riez · 30C4

P de l'Auvestre, Chemin du Relais. **GPS**: n43,82180 e6,09197.

30 € 5/24h Ch free.
Location: Rural, comfortable, quiet. **Surface:** gravel.
Distance: 500m 500m 100m on the spot on the spot.

Roussillon · 30B4

Parking Saint Joseph, D149. **GPS**: n43,89660 e5,29593.

20 € 2/day, € 7/night.
Location: Rural, comfortable. **Surface:** gravel.
Distance: 800m 800m on the spot on the spot.
Remarks: Max. 48h, no camping activities.

Tourist information Roussillon:
Sentier des Ocres. Hiking trail, 45 min.

Sablet · 30A3

Domaine du Parandou, D977. **GPS**: n44,19325 e4,99522.

5 € 2 Ch (2x)€3 WC included. **Location:** Rural, simple.
Surface: gravel. 01/01-31/12
Distance: 2km.

Saint-Crépin · 30C2

D138. **GPS**: n44,70562 e6,60196.

€ 6 + € 0,40/pp tourist tax Ch WC included. **Location:** Quiet.

Surface: grassy. 🔲 01/01-31/12
Distance: 🚶500m ⌁on the spot.
Remarks: Service on the other side of the bridge.

Salin-de-Giraud 30A4
Rue de la Bouvine. **GPS:** n43,41222 e4,73056. ⬆️

20 🅿free ⚡€2 Ch €0,80. **Surface:** gravel. 🔲 01/04-31/10
Distance: 🚶1km 🛒1km.
Remarks: At fire-station.

Sarrians 30A3
Avenue de la Camargue. **GPS:** n44,07943 e4,97788. ⬆️

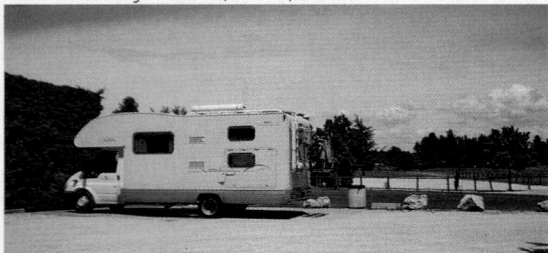

10 🅿€3/day ⚡Chfree 📦. **Location:** Rural, simple.
Surface: gravel. 🔲 01/01-31/12
Distance: 🚶800m 🛒500m.

Sault 30B3
P3, Route de Saint-Trinit. **GPS:** n44,09434 e5,41308. ⬆️

15 🅿free ⚡€2/10minutes Ch stay. **Location:** Rural, simple.
Surface: gravel. 🔲 01/01-31/12
Distance: 🚶500m 500m on the spot 🥾4km chemin des Lavandes.

Sausset-les-Pins 30A5
Avenue Pierre Matraja. **GPS:** n43,33890 e5,10916. ⬆️

15 🅿free ⚡€2/100liter Ch €2/1h. **Surface:** asphalted.
🔲 01/01-31/12
Distance: 🚶1,2km 1,2km 🛒1,2km 5m.
Remarks: At stadium, max. 72h.

Savines-le-Lac 30C2
Parking du Barnafret, Av. du Faubourg, D954. **GPS:** n44,52495 e6,40090. ⬆️

17 🅿€8 ⚡€2/120liter Ch (20x). 🏠 **Location:** Comfortable, central.
Surface: asphalted.
Distance: 🚶300m 500m 100m.

Selonnet 30C3
Quartier de Boulangère. **GPS:** n44,36862 e6,31525. ⬆️➡️

7 🅿free ⚡€2/10minutes Ch €2/55minutes. **Location:** Rural.
Surface: gravel. 🔲 01/01-31/12
Distance: 🚶300m 300m 🛒300m.
Remarks: Coins at town hall, supermarket, bakery and Tabac, free wifi at town hall.

Sénas 30A4
Avenue des Jardins. **GPS:** n43,74403 e5,08020. ➡️

6 🅿free ⚡€3/10minutes Ch. **Location:** Urban, simple.
Surface: asphalted. 🔲 01/01-31/12
Distance: 🚶200m 1,5km 200m 🛒200m.
Remarks: Coins at tourist info and maison de presse.

Sillans-la-Cascade 30C4
Route de Salernes. **GPS:** n43,56692 e6,18277. ⬆️➡️
🅿free, July-Aug €2 ⚡€3 Ch. 🔲 01/01-31/12
Distance: 🚶500m 500m.
Remarks: Free entrance swimming pool.

Sisteron 30C3
Aire camping-cars, Avenue de la Libération. **GPS:** n44,19105 e5,94542. ⬆️
12 🅿€2/12h ⚡€2/20minutes Ch €2/4h. **Surface:** asphalted.
🔲 01/01-31/12
Distance: 🚶800m.
Remarks: Along railwayline.

Sisteron 30C3
Parking Melchior Donnet, D4085. **GPS:** n44,20028 e5,94389. ⬆️

10 free €2 Ch €2/12h. **Surface:** asphalted. 01/01-31/12
Distance: 4,5km.

S Six-Fours-les-Plages 30B5
Promenade Gén. Charles de Gaulle. **GPS:** n43,11252 e5,81172.
€3 Ch. 01/01-31/12
Remarks: Behind tourist info, 8-12, 14-19h.

S Six-Fours-les-Plages 30B5
Port de la Coudoulière. **GPS:** n43,09750 e5,81194.

5 € 10 WC included. **Surface:** asphalted. 01/10-30/04
Distance: 100m 100m 100m.

S Sospel 31A3
Stade E. Donato, D2566. **GPS:** n43,87876 e7,44213.

4 free Ch free. **Surface:** asphalted. 01/01-31/12
Distance: 300m 300m 300m.

S St.André-les-Alpes 30C3
Grand Rue. **GPS:** n43,96525 e6,50735.

30 free €3/10minutes Ch . **Location:** Comfortable, quiet.
Surface: asphalted. 01/01-31/12
Distance: 250m 100m 250m.

S St.Etienne-de-Tinée 30D3
Camping du Plan d'Eau, Boulevard de la Digue. **GPS:** n44,25847 e6,92307.
6 € 10 €3 Ch . **Location:** Comfortable, quiet. **Surface:** gravel.
01/06-30/09
Remarks: At lake, in the village.

S St.Laurent-du-Var 30D4
Route des Pugets. **GPS:** n43,68584 e7,18459.

7 free Ch free. **Surface:** asphalted.
Distance: 1,2km 4,5km 1,2km 1,2km.
Remarks: Max. 7 days.

S St.Laurent-du-Var 30D4
Avenue Francis Teisseire. **GPS:** n43,66628 e7,19595.
5 free. **Location:** Central, noisy. **Surface:** asphalted.
01/01-31/12
Distance: city centre 2km 200m 500m.
Remarks: Max. 8M.

S St.Mandrier 30C5
Pin Roland, Impasse de la Mer. **GPS:** n43,07771 e5,90444.

6 free Ch free. **Surface:** asphalted. 01/01-31/12
Distance: 500m 500m.
Remarks: Max. 48h.

S St.Martin-de-Crau 30A4
Place François Miterrand. **GPS:** n43,63859 e4,81454.
3 free Ch WC free. **Location:** Urban. **Surface:** metalled.
01/01-31/12
Distance: 400m 400m 1,5km.
Remarks: In front of town hall, max. 48h.

St.Michel-l'Observatoire 30B3
GPS: n43,90908 e5,71750.

10 free . **Location:** Simple. **Surface:** gravel. 01/03-15/11
Distance: 200m 200m on the spot.
Remarks: Beautiful panorama.

S St.Paul-lez-Durance 30B4
Rue du Camping le Retour. **GPS:** n43,68700 e5,70588.

FR

6 🛏free 🚰🚻 Chfree. **Location:** Rural, simple, quiet. **Surface:** gravel.
🅿 01/01-31/12
Distance: 🚶500m 🚲4km ⊗500m 🛒700m.
Remarks: Max. 48h.

| 🛏🅂 | St.Tropez | 30D5 |

Aire camping-car, Chemin Fontaine du pin, Chemin de la Moutte.
GPS: n43,26468 e6,67227.⬆️

15 🛏€ 13 🚰€2 🚻 Ch 🚿€2,50 WC€1. **Location:** Comfortable, isolated,
quiet. **Surface:** grassy/sand. 🅿 01/01-31/12
Distance: 🚶3km 🏖800m.

Tourist information St.Tropez:
🏰 La Citadelle, musée de la Marine. Navy museum.
🛒 Place des Lices. Week market. 🅿 Wed + Sa morning.

| 🛏🅂 | St.Véran ❄🏔❄ | 30D2 |

D5. **GPS:** n44,70447 e6,86091.
20 🛏€ 2/day, € 5/night 🚰🚻 Ch WC free. **Location:** Isolated, quiet.
Surface: metalled. 🅿 01/01-31/12
Distance: 🚶100m ⊗100m 🛒200m 🎿on the spot ⛷200m.

| 🛏🅂 | Ste.Croix-de-Verdon | 30C4 |

Route du Lac. **GPS:** n43,76077 e6,15102.⬆️

50 🛏€ 10/24h 🚰🚻 Chfree. 🅿 **Surface:** metalled. 🅿 01/01-31/12
Distance: 🚶city centre 1km 🏖1,2km ⊗McDonalds 50m 🛒Lidl 200m.
Remarks: Max. 48h.

Tourist information Ste.Maxime:
🏰 🅿 Thu-morning.
🏰 Les Greniers du Golfe, Aire des Magnoti. Bric-a-brac. 🅿 Wed 08-18h.

| 🛏🅂 | Stes.Maries-de-la-Mer 🏖 | 30A4 |

Avenue d'Arles, D570. **GPS:** n43,45535 e4,42750.⬆️➡️

60 🛏€ 10, > 7,5m € 20 🚰🚻 Ch WC included. 🚿 **Surface:** asphalted.
🅿 01/01-31/12
Distance: 🚶200m 🏖beach 400m ⊗100m 🛒50m ▣100m.
Remarks: Max. 48h, service: 8.30-11.30h, 16-19.30h.

| 🛏🅂 | Stes.Maries-de-la-Mer 🏖 | 30A4 |

Plage Ouest, Route d'Aigues-Mortes, D38. **GPS:** n43,44991 e4,40407.⬆️
50 🛏€ 10, >7.50m € 20 🚰🚻 Chincluded. **Surface:** asphalted/gravel.
🅿 01/01-31/12
Distance: 🚶1,5km 🏖50m.

| 🛏🅂 | Stes.Maries-de-la-Mer 🏖 | 30A4 |

Valée des Lys, Parking Plage Est, Avenue Cousteau. **GPS:** n43,45364 e4,43695.
⬆️➡️

150 🛏€ 10 🚰🚻 Chfree WC. **Surface:** metalled. 🅿 01/01-31/12
Distance: 🚶250m 🏖beach 50m ⊗100m 🛒250m.

| 🔺🅂 | Stes.Maries-de-la-Mer 🏖 | 30A4 |

Camping de la Brise. GPS: n43,45572 e4,43620.⬆️
50 🛏€ 16 + tourist tax 🚰🚻 Ch 🚿 WC ▣📶. 🅿 16/12-11/11
Distance: 🚶850m 🏖direct access to sandy beach 🏊on the spot
🎣on the spot.

| 🛏🅂 | Thorenc | 30D4 |

Lac de Thorenc, D2. **GPS:** n43,79665 e6,80819.⬆️

| 🛏🅂 | Ste.Maxime | 30D5 |

D25, le Muy dir Ste.Maxime. **GPS:** n43,31730 e6,62999.⬆️

20 🛏€ 6,50/24h 🚰€2/10minutes 🚻 Ch WC included. 🚿 **Location:** Rural,
simple. **Surface:** asphalted.
Distance: 🚶100m ⊗100m 🏊on the spot 🎣on the spot.
Remarks: Max. 3 nights, water closed during wintertime.

FR

10 ⎵free ⚡⚍ Ch free. **Location:** Rural, simple, isolated, quiet.
Surface: metalled. ⊡ 01/01-31/12
Distance: ⎯750m ⚓on the spot ⊗on the spot ⚑épicerie 750m.
Remarks: Along Lake Thorenc.

⚹S	Trigance	30C4

Quartier Saint Roch. **GPS:** n43,76060 e6,44255.⬆.

10 ⎵€5 ⚡⚍Ch☐free. **Location:** Isolated, quiet.
Surface: asphalted/gravel. ⊡ 01/01-31/12
Remarks: Max. 2 days.

⚹S	Uvernet-Fours 🏔🌲❄	30D3

Losissement Le Bachelard, D902. **GPS:** n44,36816 e6,62783.⬆.

6 ⎵free ⚡€2 ⚍Ch☐€2. **Location:** Isolated, quiet. **Surface:** gravel/sand.
⊡ 01/01-31/12
Distance: ⎯900m.

⚹S	Vaison-la-Romaine 🌾⛰	30A3

Aire camping-car, Avenue André Coudray. **GPS:** n44,24650 e5,07392.⬆➡.

25 ⎵€7,50/24h ⚡⚍Ch free.🚲 **Location:** Urban, comfortable.
Surface: gravel. ⊡ 01/01-31/12 ⊙ Tue-morning
Distance: ⎯800m.

Tourist information Vaison-la-Romaine:
👁 Le Pont Romain. Bridge from the Roman Empire.
⌂ Le Château. Ruins of the castle of the Counts of Toulouse.
🎪 ⊡ Tue.

⚹S	Valberg ⛲🏔❄	30D3

Le Lagopède, Route de Rouya. **GPS:** n44,09615 e6,93675.⬆➡.

21 ⎵€ 10 + € 0,20/pp tourist tax ⚡⚍Ch 🔧(21x) WC included.
Location: Comfortable, isolated, quiet. **Surface:** asphalted. ⊡ 01/01-31/12
Distance: ⎯500m ⚓on the spot ⊗500m ⚑500m ⚒600m.

⚹	Valréas	30A3

Aire camping-car. GPS: n44,38713 e4,99245.⬆➡.

5 ⎵free. **Location:** Simple. **Surface:** asphalted. ⊡ 01/01-31/12
Distance: ⎯400m ⊗250m.
Remarks: Behind tourist info, max 3,5t.

⚹S	Valréas	30A3

Domaine du Lumian, Route de Montélimar, D941. **GPS:** n44,39384 e4,96325.
⬆➡.

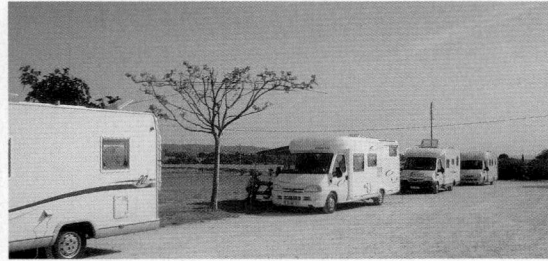

6 ⎵free ⚡⚍Ch 🔧free. **Surface:** gravel. ⊡ 01/01-31/12
Distance: ⎯2,5km.

⚹S	Veynes	30B2

Base de Loisirs Les Iscles, Les Graviers, D994. **GPS:** n44,51830 e5,79860.⬆.
⎵€5,50 📶. **Location:** Rural, simple, quiet. **Surface:** gravel.
Distance: ⚓on the spot ⊗on the spot.
Remarks: Wifi at restaurant.

⚹S	Villeneuve	30B4

GPS: n43,89611 e5,86167.⬆➡.

12 ⎵free ⚡⚍Ch free. **Location:** Rural, simple, quiet. **Surface:** gravel.
⊡ 01/01-31/12 ⊙ service: 30/11-01/03
Distance: ⎯200m 🚲5,5km 🛁on the spot 🚶on the spot.
Remarks: Max. 48h.

FR

S **Vinon sur Verdon** 30B4

Chemin du Plan. **GPS:** n43,72952 e5,80141. ⬆.

20 free €2/20minutes Ch included. **Location:** Rural, simple.
Surface: asphalted.
Distance: 3km ⊗on the spot on the spot.
Remarks: Parking Carrefour Market, coins at petrol station.

S **Visan** 30A3

Domaine de Lucena, 1600 chemin du Rastelet. **GPS:** n44,31576 e4,98406. ⬆.
5 Ch . **Location:** Isolated, quiet. **Surface:** gravel.
☐ 01/01-31/12
Distance: 4km.

S **Visan** 30A3

Domaine des Lauribert, D976. **GPS:** n44,34833 e4,97276. ⬆.

20 free Ch (8x)€2 WC. **Surface:** unpaved. ☐ 01/01-31/12
Remarks: At wine-grower, max. 72h.

FR

SPAIN

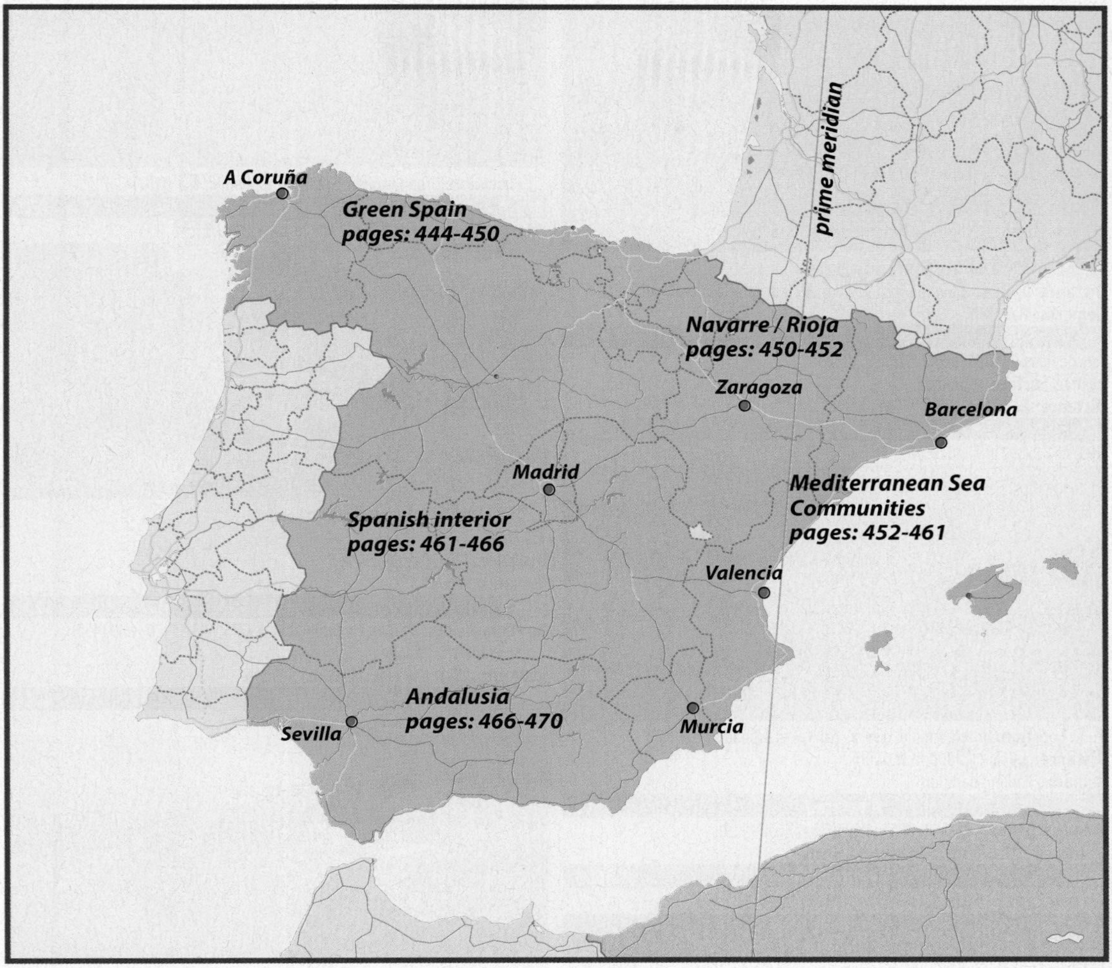

A Coruña

Green Spain
pages: 444-450

prime meridian

Navarre / Rioja
pages: 450-452

Zaragoza

Barcelona

Madrid

**Mediterranean Sea
Communities**
pages: 452-461

Spanish interior
pages: 461-466

Valencia

Andalusia
pages: 466-470

Sevilla

Murcia

Capital: Madrid
Government: Constitutional monarchy
Official Language: Spanish
Population: 47,265,000 (2013)
Area: 505,782 km²

General information
Dialling code: 0034
General emergency: 112
Currency: Euro

Regulations for overnight stays
Wild camping is allowed having gained permission from the municipality, olice or property owner. Along the Mediterranean coast wild camping is almost always forbidden. Parking places (P) mentioned here can be considered as tolerated places to stay overnight.

Additional public holidays 2015
January 6 Epiphany
April 3 Good Friday
May 1 Labor Day
June 4 Corpus Christi
August 15 Assumption of the Virgin Mary
October 22 National Holiday
November 1 All Saints' Day
December 6 Constitution Day
December 8 Immaculate Conception

Green Spain

⬛S A Coruña 〰🏖🍦🐚 36C3
Puerto de San Pedro de Visma, Zona de O Portiño. **GPS**: n43,37167 w8,44472.⬆️

12 🏕free 🚰🗑Ch free. **Surface**: metalled.
Distance: 🚶3km 🏊on the spot ⊗50m 🛒1km Carrefour 🚌1km.
Remarks: Max. 48h.

⬛ A Coruña 〰🏖🍦🐚 36C3
Tore de Hercules. **GPS**: n43,38378 w8,40228.
🏕free. **Surface**: asphalted.
Distance: 🚶on the spot ⊗50m 🛒50m.

⬛ A Guarda 🐚 36B5
GPS: n41,89892 w8,87825.⬆️.

5 🏕. **Location**: Urban, simple, central. **Surface**: asphalted.
Distance: 🚶1km ⊗300m 🛒500m.
Remarks: Parking harbour.

⬛S A Laracha 36C3
Area de O Regado, AC-552. **GPS**: n43,24972 w8,61694.⬆️.
3 🏕free 🚰🗑Ch free. **Surface**: asphalted.

⬛S A Pontenova 36D3
Rua de la Estación. **GPS**: n43,34739 w7,19171.⬆️➡️.

8 🏕free 🚰🗑Ch free. **Surface**: asphalted.
Distance: ⊗200m 🛒100m.
Remarks: Max. 48h.

⬛S A Rúa 36D4
Área Recreativa O Aguillón. **GPS**: n42,38800 w7,11459.⬆️.
10 🏕free 🚰🗑Ch free. **Surface**: asphalted/grassy. 🗓01/01-31/12
Distance: 🚶500m 🏊on the spot ⊗500m 🛒500m.
Remarks: Next to football ground.

⬛S Arcade 🐚 36B4
Rúa do Peirao. **GPS**: n42,33946 w8,61329.
5 🏕free 🚰🗑Ch free. **Surface**: metalled. 🗓01/01-31/12
Distance: ⊗nearby 🛒nearby.

⬛ Arrigorriaga 37C4
Carretera Buia Etorbidea. **GPS**: n43,23772 w2,91938.⬆️.

🏕. **Location**: Urban, simple. **Surface**: asphalted. 🗓01/01-31/12

⬛S As Neves 36C5
Camino del Emenjeric. **GPS**: n42,08726 w8,41374.⬆️➡️.

1 🏕free 🚰🗑Ch free. **Location**: Rural.
🗓 01/01-31/12
Distance: ⊗200m 🛒200m.
Remarks: Max. 48h.

🍴⬛S Avilés 37A3
Restaurante Rias Baixas, Camino Heros, 3. **GPS**: n43,55120 w5,93451.
7 🏕€ 8/24h 🚰🗑Ch.
Distance: ⊗on the spot 🛒500m.

⬛S Bakio 🏔 37C4
Parking, BI 3101. **GPS**: n43,42783 w2,80442.⬆️.

20 🏕free 🚰WC free. **Location**: Urban, simple. **Surface**: grasstiles.
🗓 01/01-31/12
Distance: 🚶100m 🏊200m ⊗100m 🚌on the spot.
Remarks: Behind tourist info.

⬛S Bárzana 🏔 37A4
Area de Bárzana-Quirós, El Felguere. **GPS**: n43,15611 w5,97306.
15 🏕free 🚰🗑Ch free. **Location**: Simple. **Surface**: asphalted.
🗓 01/01-31/12

⬛ Behobia 🛡 37D4
N10, Calle de Aria Juncal. **GPS**: n43,34310 w1,7598.⬆️.

6 🏕€ 3/2h < 19.30, overnight stay free. **Location**: Urban, simple, noisy.
Surface: asphalted. 🗓 01/01-31/12

ES

Distance: 🚰on the spot 🚿500m ⊗200m 🗑500m on the spot.

📷 S | **Bermeo** 🌿 | 37D4

Área de la Pérgola, Itsasoan Galdurakoen Lamera. **GPS**: n43,42306 w2,72556.
⬆➡

10 📷free 🚰🗑 Ch free. **Location**: Urban, simple. **Surface**: asphalted.
◻ 01/01-31/12
Distance: 🚰500m ⊗500m 🗑500m 🚌300m.
Remarks: Nearby football ground, max. 48h.

📷 S | **Bertamirans** ⌚ | 36C4

Paseo Fluvial. **GPS**: n42,86009 w8,64838. ⬆

15 📷free 🚰🗑 Ch free. **Surface**: asphalted. ◻ 01/01-31/12
Distance: 🚰100m 🗑50m Carrefour 🚌dir. Santiago every 30 min.
Remarks: Max. 48h.

📷 S | **Bilbao** 🌿 | 37C4

Kobetamendi, Monte Kobeta, 31. **GPS**: n43,25961 w2,96355. ⬆➡

72 📷€ 15/day 🚰🗑 Ch 🔧included.
Location: Urban, comfortable, quiet.
Surface: grasstiles.
◻ 15/06 - 15/10
Distance: 🚰centre 4,5km ⊗2,8km 🚌Bilbao-bus 58.
Remarks: 16/10-14/05 free parking, asphalt, max. 72h, service passerby € 6.
Tourist information Bilbao:
ℹ Bilbao. Capital of the Basque Country and previously centre of the iron industry.
⛪ Basilica de Begoña, Virgen de Begoña, 38, Bilbao-Vizcaya. Basilica.

📷 S | **Boiro** 🍴 | 36B4

Playa Jardín de Barraña. **GPS**: n42,64183 w8,89481. ⬆➡

10 📷€ 3-6 🚰🗑 Ch free. **Surface**: asphalted. ◻ 01/01-31/12
Distance: 🚰500m 🚿20m ⊗200m Bistro Prima 🗑400m.
Remarks: Max. 48h.

📷 S | **Boiro** 🍴 | 36B4

Playa Mañons, S/n 15930 Chancelas–Abanqueiro. **GPS**: n42,63138 w8,85311.
⬆➡
8 📷free 🚰🗑 Ch free.
Distance: 🚿on the spot.

📷 | **Bueu** | 36B4

P0315 dir Cabo Udra. **GPS**: n42,33460 w8,8248.
📷free. **Surface**: sand.
Remarks: Max. 48h.

📷 | **Bueu** | 36B4

Puerto, Avda. de Montero Rios. **GPS**: n42,32732 w8,7838.
📷.

📷 S | **Burela** | 36D3

Area de Burela, Parque de O Campón, parking Hospital de Burela.
GPS: n43,65216 w7,35891. ⬆

5 📷free 🚰🗑 Ch free. **Surface**: asphalted.
Distance: 🚰200m ⊗300m 🗑200m.
Remarks: Max. 48h.

📷 S | **Cabárceno** | 37C4

Área Lago del Acebo, N634> dir Parque de la naturaleze de Cabárceno.
GPS: n43,35802 w3,81959. ⬆

30 📷free 🚰🗑 Ch free. **Surface**: asphalted.
Distance: 🚰100m 🗑50m 🗑50m ⊗on the spot.
Remarks: Max. 48h.

📷 | **Camariñas** | 36B3

Puerto Club Nautico, Rúa Castelo. **GPS**: n43,12694 w9,18333.
5 📷free. **Surface**: asphalted.

📷 S | **Cangas de Onís** | 37B4

Parking Lanzadera Picos de Europa, Calle del Llreau.
GPS: n43,35211 w5,12536. ⬆

ES

4 🛏free 🚰🗑 Chfree. **Surface:** asphalted.
Distance: ⊗100m.
Remarks: Max. 48h.

🛏S Carnota 🏖 36B4
Area de Mar de Lira, Calle Miñarzo s/n. **GPS:** n42,80306 w9,12944.

4 🛏free 🚰🗑 Chfree. **Surface:** sand.
Distance: 🚶Carnota 5km ⚓10m ⊗on the spot.
Remarks: Parking next to hatchery.

🛏S Cartelle 36C5
Camperpark O Mundil, Antigua Carretera OU-659. **GPS:** n42,21444 w8,03306.

24 🛏€10 🚰🗑 Ch 🔌 WC ▯▫ 📶free. **Surface:** gravel.
🔲 01/01-31/12
Distance: ⚓1km zona fluvial Río Arnoia ⊗10m.

🛏 Castro Urdiales 37C4
Parking Parco Cotolino. **GPS:** n43,37364 w3,20899.
🛏€2/3h (10.00-20.00). **Surface:** asphalted.

🛏S Chantada 36C4
Champ de Sangoñedo, Ctra. De Barrela o Seixo. **GPS:** n42,60598 w7,77989.⬆
5 🛏free 🚰🗑 Chfree.
Distance: 🚶500m.
Remarks: At footballstadium.

🛏S Coaña 36D3
Area de Ortiguera, Barrio Nueva Rasa. **GPS:** n43,56082 w6,73352.⬆
2 🛏free 🚰🗑 Chfree.
Location: Rural, simple. **Surface:** asphalted.
Distance: ⊗on the spot 🍽on the spot.

🍴S Colombres 37B4
Area de Casa Junco, N-634. **GPS:** n43,38056 w4,55472.
15 🛏free 🚰🗑 Chfree.
Distance: ⊗on the spot.

🛏S Colunga 37A3
Area de Los Llanos, Avda de Asturias N-632. **GPS:** n43,48472 w5,26491.⬆
20 🛏€4 🍴€3 🗑. **Location:** Simple. **Surface:** asphalted.

🛏 Comillas 37B4
Parking, Calle de Manuel Noriega. **GPS:** n43,38821 w4,28319.
🛏free. **Surface:** asphalted. 🔲 01/07-31/08

🛏S Cospeito 36D3
Camino de la Laguna. **GPS:** n43,23984 w7,55579.
5 🛏free 🚰🗑 Ch 🔌 free. **Surface:** asphalted. 🔲 01/01-31/12
Distance: ⊗300m.

🛏 Cudillero 37A3
Puerto. **GPS:** n43,56568 w6,1517.
5 🛏.
Remarks: Parking in harbour.

🍴S Cudillero 37A3
Hotel Rest. Casa Fernando II, N-632. **GPS:** n43,56028 w6,17722.⬆
5 🛏free 🚰🗑 Ch€3. **Location:** Simple. **Surface:** asphalted.
Distance: ⊗on the spot.

🛏S Ferrol 36C3
Ctra. de la Malata. **GPS:** n43,49333 w8,23972.⬆

15 🛏free 🚰🗑 Chfree. **Surface:** asphalted.
Distance: 🚶700m ⊗300m.

🛏S Finisterre ⛵🏖 36B4
Praia de Langosteira. **GPS:** n42,92320 w9,26149.

5 🛏free 🚰.
Distance: ⚓on the spot ⊗1km 🛒1km.
Remarks: Beach parking, max. 48h.

🛏 Fuente Dé 37B4
Picos de Europa, C621. **GPS:** n43,14433 w4,81274.
🛏free. **Surface:** sand.
Remarks: Parking funicular railway.

🛏S Gijón 37A3
Polígono Puerto Musel. **GPS:** n43,54467 w5,69562.⬆

15 🛏free 🚰🗑 free. **Surface:** asphalted. 🔲 01/01-31/12
Distance: 🚶3km ⚓on the spot 🚌on the spot.
Remarks: Max. 48h.

🛏 Gijón 37A3
Camino de las Mimosas, El Rinconín. **GPS:** n43,54708 w5,63648.
20 🛏free. **Surface:** asphalted.
Distance: ⚓300m.

🛏 Gorliz 🏖🏖 37C4
Paseo de Astondo. **GPS:** n43,41220 w2,94194.⬆

🛏free. **Location:** Urban, simple. **Surface:** asphalted. ▢ 01/01-31/12
Distance: 🚶500m 🏖50m 🚌on the spot.
Remarks: Parking beach.

| 🛏S **Gozon** | 37A3 |

El Molino, Ctr. Luanco-Cabo Peñas. **GPS:** n43,62541 w5,81125. ⬆➡.
25 🛏€ 10 ⛽ 🗑 Ch ⚡ included. **Location:** Rural, comfortable.
Surface: grassy. ▢ 01/01-31/12
Distance: 🏖500m ⊗on the spot 🚰on the spot.

| 🛏S **Guitiriz** | 36C3 |

Rua do Voluntariado. **GPS:** n43,17727 w7,88062. ⬆.
5 🛏free ⛽ 🗑 Ch ⚡ free. **Surface:** gravel. ▢ 01/01-31/12
Distance: 🚶800m 🚰100m.

| 🛏S **Hermandad De Campoo De Suso** | 37B4 |

Estación Invernal Alto Campoo, C 628 Reinosa - Espinilla, dir: Alto Campoo.
GPS: n43,03839 w4,37036.
20 🛏 ⛽ Ch.
Distance: 🚴on the spot.

| 🛏S **Hondaribbia** 🌿🪂 | 37D4 |

Ramón Iribarren Pasalekua. **GPS:** n43,37929 w1,79768. ➡⬆.

20 🛏€12/day ⛽ 🗑 Ch included. 🐕 **Location:** Urban, simple, quiet.
Surface: asphalted. ▢ 01/04-31/09
Distance: 🚶2km 🚲8km ⊗on the spot 🚌on the spot.
Remarks: Beautiful view.

| 🛏S **Illano** | 36D3 |

Area de Folgueirou, Area recreativa de Folgueirou. **GPS:** n43,34333 w6,85116.
30 🛏free ⛽ 🗑 Ch included. **Location:** Rural, simple. **Surface:** grassy/gravel.
▢ 01/01-31/12
Distance: ⊗on the spot.

| 🛏S **Legazpi** | 37D4 |

Parque Mirandaola de Legazpi, Carretera Legazpia, GI 2630.
GPS: n43,03678 w2,33758. ⬆➡.

5 🛏free ⛽ 🗑 Ch free. **Location:** Urban, simple, noisy. **Surface:** asphalted.
▢ 01/01-31/12
Distance: 🚶1,5km ⊗on the spot 🏕on the spot.
Remarks: Max. 48h.

| 🛏S **Lekeitio** 🌿🪂 | 37D4 |

Iñigo Artieta Etorbidea. **GPS:** n43,35849 w2,50743. ⬆➡.

14 🛏free ⛽€1/100liter 🗑 Ch. **Location:** Urban, comfortable, quiet.
Surface: asphalted. ▢ 01/01-31/12
Distance: 🚶500m 🚲500m ⊗500m 🚰300m.
Remarks: Coins at tourist info.

| 🛏S **Liérganes** | 37C4 |

Calle de Puente Romano. **GPS:** n43,34479 w3,74183.
10 🛏free ⛽ 🗑 Ch free. **Location:** Urban. **Surface:** asphalted.
Distance: 🚰100m.
Remarks: Parking nearby train station, max. 48h.

| 🛏S **Lugo** 🍲 | 36C4 |

Pabellón Municipal de Deportes, Avda. de Santiago. **GPS:** n43,00452 w7,56144.
⬆.

10 🛏free ⛽ 🗑 Ch free. **Surface:** asphalted.
Distance: 🚶10min 🚲5,2km 🚰10min.
Remarks: Parking gymnasium, max. 48h.

| P S **Lugo** ⬭ | 36C4 |

Plaza de Asturias, Rúa Ánxel Fole. **GPS:** n43,00972 w7,55805.
15 🛏€ 12/24h ⛽ 🗑 free. **Surface:** asphalted.

| 🛏S **Lugones** | 37A3 |

Area de Lugones, Calle Conde de Santa Bárbara. **GPS:** n43,40694 w5,81139. ⬆.
4 🛏free ⛽ 🗑 Ch included. **Location:** Urban, simple.
Surface: asphalted/metalled.
Distance: 🚶9 km Oviedo ⊗on the spot 🚰on the spot 🚌200m.

| 🛏S **Mieres** | 37A4 |

Area de Mieres, Calle Asturias. **GPS:** n43,25194 w5,78083. ⬆.
5 🛏free ⛽ 🗑 Ch free. **Location:** Simple. **Surface:** asphalted.
Distance: 🚶100m 🚲500m ⊗on the spot 🚰on the spot.

| 🛏S **Milladoiro** | 36C4 |

Traversia do Porto. **GPS:** n42,84512 w8,58079. ⬆.

20 🛏free ⛽ 🗑 Ch free. **Surface:** asphalted.
Distance: ⊗200m 🚰200m 🚌dir. Santiago every 15 min.
Remarks: At swimming pool, max. 48h.

| 🛏S **Miño** | 36C3 |

AP-9 Coruña-Ferrol ><, km 15,5. **GPS:** n43,37404 w8,18736. ⬆.

ES

12 free Ch WC free. **Surface:** asphalted.
Distance: on the spot on the spot.
Remarks: Parking nearby motorway.

Miranda de Ebro 37C5
Calle de Burgos. **GPS:** n42,68880 w2,95403.

7 free Ch free. **Location:** Urban, simple, noisy. **Surface:** metalled.
01/01-31/12
Distance: 1km 3km river.

Tourist information Miranda de Ebro:
Medieval annual fair. around May 1.
Week market. Sa.

Mondoñedo 36D3
Calle de Vicedo. **GPS:** n43,42778 w7,37028.
10 free Ch free. **Surface:** metalled.

Monforte de Lemos 36C4
Auditorio Multiusos de Monforte, Calle de la Circunvalación / Calle de Santa Clara.
GPS: n42,52750 w7,5119.

20 free Ch free. **Surface:** asphalted.
Distance: 500m 550m 300m.
Remarks: Max. 48h.

Nava 37A4
Area de Nava, Avda. de la Constitución. **GPS:** n43,35722 w5,49917.
6 free Ch free. **Surface:** asphalted/metalled.
Distance: 900m.

Navelgas 36D3
Area de Navelgas, Recinto Ferial. **GPS:** n43,40402 w6,54167.
15 free Ch free. **Location:** Urban. **Surface:** asphalted/metalled.
Distance: 100m.

Navia 36D3
Area de la Granja, C/ Travesía de la Granja. **GPS:** n43,54528 w6,72028.
10 free Ch free.
Location: Urban. **Surface:** gravel/metalled.
Distance: on the spot on the spot.

Noia 36B4
Rúa de Pedra Marques. **GPS:** n42,78783 w8,8906.

free. **Surface:** asphalted.

Distance: on the spot 50m 50m Bus 20m.
Tourist information Noia:
El Pendo, 5km S. Santander. Cave with petroglyphs.

O Barco 36D4
Malecón Campiño. **GPS:** n42,41063 w6,97493.

12 free Ch free. **Surface:** unpaved. 01/01-31/12
Distance: 400m 250m 250m.

Pajares 37A4
Valgrande-Pajares, Brañillín. **GPS:** n42,97889 w5,77194.
15 free Ch free. **Location:** Rural. **Surface:** asphalted.

Parada do Sil 36C4
Rural Pepe, Campo da Feira 17. **GPS:** n42,38287 w7,57106.
4 guests free Ch €2. 01/01-31/12
Distance: on the spot on the spot.

Pobra do Brollòn 36D4
Campo Municipal de Fut. **GPS:** n42,56944 w7,39417.
8 free Ch free. **Surface:** metalled.

Pola de Laviana 37A4
Area de Pola de Laviana, Av. Real Titánico. s/n.. **GPS:** n43,25478 w5,56836.
8 free Ch free. **Surface:** metalled.
Distance: 1500m 1500m 1500m.

Potes 37B4
Santo Toribio de Liébana, CA885. **GPS:** n43,15028 w4,65389.

free free.
Location: Isolated, quiet. **Surface:** asphalted.
Distance: Potes 3km on the spot.
Remarks: Parking monastery.

Tourist information Potes:
Local products. Mo.
Historical cattle market, since 1379. 01/08-15/08.

Redondela 36B4
Avda. de Mendiño. **GPS:** n42,28972 w8,61055.
15 free Ch.
Distance: 600m 500m 600m 600m.

Rentería 37D4
Área Rural de Listorreta-Barrengoloia. **GPS:** n43,26800 w1,90135.

2 🛏free ⌐🔌 Ch free. **Location:** Rural, simple, isolated, quiet.
Surface: asphalted. ◼ 01/01-31/12
Distance: 🚉Renteria 7km 🚶on the spot.
Remarks: Parking nature reserve.

| 🛏S | **Ribadeo** | 36D3 |

Eroski, Camino de Vilar. **GPS:** n43,54000 w7,06055.
10 🛏free ⌐🔌 Ch free. **Surface:** asphalted. ◼ 01/01-31/12
Distance: 🚉500m 🚲1km ⚓on the spot.
Remarks: At supermarket.

| 🛏S | **Ribamontán al Monte** | 37C4 |

A8 Bilbao > Santander. **GPS:** n43,40282 w3,62877.
10 🛏free ⌐🔌 Ch free.

| 🛏S | **Ribamontán al Monte** | 37C4 |

A8 Santander > Bilbao. **GPS:** n43,40446 w3,62476.
10 🛏free ⌐🔌 Ch free. **Location:** Highway. **Surface:** asphalted.

| 🛏S | **Riosa** 🏔 | 37A4 |

Area de El Angliru, Viapará s/n. **GPS:** n43,24806 w5,90667.⬆.
15 🛏€ 5 ⌐🔌 Ch included 🔊. **Location:** Rural, simple.
Surface: asphalted/metalled.
Distance: ⊗on the spot.

| 🛏S | **San Clodio** | 36D4 |

Parque de Pena da Mula, Calle del Troque. **GPS:** n42,46750 w7,28583.⬆.

3 🛏free ⌐🔌 Ch free. **Surface:** asphalted. ◼ 01/01-31/12
Distance: 🚉200m 🏊Playa Fluvial 25m ⊗cafetaria.

| 🛏S | **San Martín del Rey Aurelio** | 37A4 |

Área del Pozo Entrego, Avda. de la Vega, AS17. **GPS:** n43,28639 w5,63889.⬆.
3 🛏free ⌐🔌 Ch free. **Location:** Urban. **Surface:** asphalted.
Distance: ⊗on the spot ⚓Alcampo 1km.
Remarks: Max. 48h.

| 🛏S | **San Sebastian** 🌊🏖 | 37D4 |

Paseo de Berio nº 2. **GPS:** n43,30797 w2,01426.⬆.

44 🛏€ 6,45, 01/10-31/05 € 3,20 ⌐🔌 Ch included. 🏠🧹
Location: Urban, simple, noisy. **Surface:** grasstiles.
◼ 01/01-31/12
Distance: 🚲2km ⊗50m 🚌100m.
Remarks: Max. 48h, marked pitches, registration with licence plate number.

Tourist information San Sebastian:
ℹ Centro de Atracción y Turismo (CAT), Reina Regente, www.donostia.org. Old city with, Parte Vieja, historical city centre with numerous cafés, restaurants and tapa bars.
Ⓜ Palacio del Mar. Museum for oceanografics. ◼ 10-19h, Sa-Su 10-21h, 15/06-15/09 10-21h.
🎋 ◼ Su-morning.

| 🛏 | **San Vicente de la Barquera** 🌊🏖 | 37B4 |

Barrio Rupuente, C6316. **GPS:** n43,39372 w4,36166.

🛏free.
Remarks: Not suitable for big motorhomes.

| P S | **Santiago de Compostela** 🌊🏖 | 36C4 |

Rúa Manuel María. **GPS:** n42,89560 w8,5317.
100 🛏8-20h € 3 ⌐🔌€3🔌 Ch.
Surface: asphalted.
◼ 01/01-31/12
Distance: 🚉centre 2,5km 🚲3km ⊗50m 🚌line 1 > centre.
Remarks: Ticket for overnight stay € 12.

Tourist information Santiago de Compostela:
ℹ Oficina de Turismo, Rúa del Villar, 43, www.santiagoturismo.com. City known for the termination of the pilgrime route.
👁 Plaza de la Quintana. Impressive square.
🎆 Fiesta del Apóstol Santiago. Most important festival of Galicia. ◼ 15/07-31/07.

| | **Santillana del Mar** 🌊🍃 | 37B4 |

Ctra. C6316. **GPS:** n43,38845 w4,10803.

🛏€ 2/24h. **Surface:** asphalted.

| 🛏S | **Sanxenxo** 🍃 | 36B4 |

Área de Cachadelos, PO-308. **GPS:** n42,41652 w8,86833.⬆➡.
65 🛏€ 10 ⌐🔌 Ch 🔧 included 🔘. **Surface:** grassy.
Distance: 🏊200m 🚲2km ⚓on the spot.

| 🛏S | **Sarria** | 36D4 |

Calle de Castelo. **GPS:** n42,77194 w7,41028.⬆.

12 🛏free ⌐🔌 Ch free. **Surface:** asphalted.
Distance: 🚉800m ⊗on the spot 🚉800m.

| 🛏S | **Saturrarán** 🍃 | 37D4 |

GPS: n43,31968 w2,41165.⬆.

5 ⓢfree WC. **Location:** Rural, simple. **Surface:** grasstiles.
◖ 01/01-31/12
Distance: 500m ≃on the spot ⛲700m.
Remarks: Parking beach.

⌇S | **Tapia** ◖ | **36D3**
Area de Playa Grande, Av. de la Playa. **GPS:** n43,56667 w6,94639.⬆
15 ⓢfree ⌁⌇Chfree. **Location:** Rural. **Surface:** grasstiles.
Distance: 500m ⛲500m ⛲500m.

⌇S | **Teverga** | **37A4**
Parking Senda del Oso, Entrago. **GPS:** n43,17178 w6,09562.
20 ⓢfree ⌁⌇Chfree. **Surface:** asphalted.
Distance: ⊗on the spot.
Remarks: Max. 48h.

⌇S | **Tui** | **36B5**
Puente Tripes, Avenida de Portual. **GPS:** n42,04333 w8,64656.⬆

3 ⓢfree. **Location:** Urban, simple. **Surface:** asphalted.
◖ 01/01-31/12
Distance: 1,3km ⊗500m ⛲Lidl 1,5km.
Remarks: Max. 48h.

S | **Vegadeo** | **36D3**
Area de Vegadeo, Calle Emilio Cotarelo, s/n. **GPS:** n43,46667 w7,05167.⬆
8 ⓢfree ⌁⌇Chfree. **Location:** Urban. **Surface:** asphalted/metalled.
Distance: ⊗on the spot ⛲on the spot.
Remarks: Max. 72h.

⌇S | **Vilalba** | **36C3**
Rua da Feira. **GPS:** n43,29556 w7,67694.⬆
15 ⓢfree ⌁⌇Chfree. **Surface:** asphalted.
Distance: ⊗300m ⛲300m.

⌇S | **Villanueva de Oscos** | **36D3**
Area de Villanueva, Lugar de Villanueva. **GPS:** n43,31056 w6,98583.⬆
2 ⓢfree ⌁⌇Chfree. **Surface:** gravel.
Remarks: Max. 48h.

⌇S | **Vitoria Gasteiz** 🏵⌁⊜ | **37D4**
Área de Lakua, Portal de Foronde. **GPS:** n42,86684 w2,68539.⬆➡

10 ⓢfree ⌁⌇Ch free. **Location:** Urban, comfortable, central, quiet.
Surface: asphalted. ◖ 01/01-31/12

Distance: 2km ⌁5km ⊗100m ⛲bakery 50m ⌁50m.
Remarks: Max. 72h, market Wednesday.

⌇S | **Zumaia** ◖ | **37D4**
Calle de la Estación. **GPS:** n43,29279 w2,24684.⬆➡

25 ⓢfree ⌁⌇Chfree. **Location:** Simple, noisy. **Surface:** asphalted.
◖ 01/01-31/12
Distance: 2km ⌁4,4km 🚲on the spot 🚶on the spot.

Navarre and Rioja

⌇ | **Aínsa** 🏵 | **28C6**
Plaza del Castillo. **GPS:** n42,41916 e0,13515.
ⓢfree.
Surface: sand.
Tourist information Aínsa:
ℹ The capital of a medieval kingdom by surrounded fortress walls.
⌇ ◖ Tue.

⌇ | **Albarracín** 🏵 | **39D1**
Quesería Sierra de Albarracín, Pol. Los Rubiales, 1. **GPS:** n40,43286 w1,4405.

6 ⓢfree. ◖ 01/01-31/12
Distance: 1km ⌁200m ⊗1km ⛲1km.

⌂ | **Alquézar** 🏵 | **40B1**
Alquézar, Ctra.Barbastro,. **GPS:** n42,17097 e0,02382.
ⓢ€ 21-25. ◖ 01/01-31/12
Tourist information Alquézar:
ℹ Historical city.

⌇S | **Ansó** | **28A5**
Ctra. de Ansó a Fago. **GPS:** n42,75648 w0,83102.
2 ⓢ⌁.

⌇⌇S | **Aoiz** | **28A5**
Hotel Ekai. **GPS:** n42,77624 w1,38536.⬆

10 ⓢfree ⌁⌇⌇free. **Location:** Rural, simple. **Surface:** gravel/metalled.
◖ 01/01-31/12
Distance: 3km ⊗on the spot.

🅂 Arguedas 37D5
Aparcamiento Municipal de Autocaravanas de Arguedas, Calle Bordón.
GPS: n42,17270 w1,5913. ⬆➡.

9 ⬛free ⚡€2/100liter ⬛Ch. **Location:** Rural, simple, quiet. **Surface:** gravel.
⬛ 01/01-31/12
Distance: 🚶800m ⊗800m 🛒800m.
Remarks: At Parque de Bardenas Reales, max. 48h.

🅂 Ariza 37D6
Area de Servicios La Cadiera, A2 Madrid > Zaragoza. **GPS:** n41,31210 w2,00329.
5 ⚡.

🅂 Arnedillo 37D5
Calle Miguel del Pozo. **GPS:** n42,21361 w2,23972. ⬆➡.

40 ⬛€ 10 ⚡⬛Ch ✎ (40x)€1/4h WC ⬛,cold shower 🚿included. ⬛
Location: Rural, comfortable. **Surface:** asphalted. ⬛ 01/01-31/12
Distance: 🚶200m ⊗200m 🛒200m 🏊on the spot.
Remarks: Follow the signs in the village.

🅂 Berriozar 37D5
Av. Berriozar. **GPS:** n42,84043 w1,66557. ⬆➡.

20 ⬛free ⚡€2/100liter ⬛Ch. **Location:** Urban, simple. **Surface:** concrete.
⬛ 01/01-31/12
Distance: 🚶4km Pamplona 🚌500m.
Remarks: Max. 72h, coins at sports centre (9-21h).

🄱 Bielsa 28C6
Calle Mayor. **GPS:** n42,63437 e0,21893.
3 ⬛.

🄱 Botaya 28B6
Parking Monasterio de San Juan la Peña. **GPS:** n42,50699 w0,66414.

3 ⬛free.

🅂 Cascante 40C1
Av. Fuentes Dutor Parking Termolúdico. **GPS:** n41,99361 e1,00000. ⬆.
40 ⬛free ⚡⬛free. **Location:** Urban, simple. **Surface:** asphalted.
⬛ 01/01-31/12
Distance: 🚶750m ⊗800m.

🅂 Estelle 37D5
Calle St. Barbara Calea. **GPS:** n42,67306 w2,03972.

3 ⬛free. **Surface:** asphalted. ⬛ 01/01-31/12

Tourist information Estelle:
🏛 Puebte la Reine. ⬛ Sa.

🅂 Falces 28D6
Calle la Mota. **GPS:** n42,39258 e1,00000. ⬆.
6 ⬛free ⚡⬛Chfree. **Location:** Simple. **Surface:** metalled.
⬛ 01/01-31/12
Distance: 🚶700m 🛒300m.

🅂 Haro 37C5
LR111. **GPS:** n42,57253 w2,86739. ⬆.

10 ⬛free ⚡free. **Location:** Rural, simple, quiet. **Surface:** gravel.
⬛ 01/01-31/12
Distance: 🚶1,5km ⊗1,3km 🛒1,5.

🅂 Haro 37C5
Parking centro deportivo, Av de los Ingenieros del Ministerio Obras Públicas,
LR-111. **GPS:** n42,57677 w2,85222. ⬆.

4 🛏free 🚰free.
Location: Urban, simple.
Surface: asphalted.
◻ 01/01-31/12
Distance: 🚂500m 🚗14km ⊗on the spot.
Remarks: At sports park, Haro, Rioja Wine Capital, wine museum, wine cellars.
Tourist information Haro:
ℹ Capital of Rioja wine.

🛏S	Irura	37D4

Área del Frontón, Calle Zilar. **GPS:** n43,16778 w2,0652.⬆➡

4 🛏free 🚰🔧Chfree. **Location:** Urban, simple, noisy. **Surface:** asphalted.
◻ 01/01-31/12
Distance: 🚗100m.

🛏S	Logroño	37D5

Avenue de la Sonsierra, LR132. **GPS:** n42,47916 w2,4571.⬆

3 🛏free 🚰🔧Chfree. **Location:** Urban, simple, noisy. **Surface:** metalled.
◻ 01/01-31/12
Distance: 🚂700m 🏊100m ⊗400m 🛒300m 🚌20m.
Remarks: Max. 48h.

🛏S	Logroño	37D5

Emblase de la Grajera, Pontano de la Grajera. **GPS:** n42,44909 w2,50189.⬆ .

15 🛏free. **Location:** Rural, simple. **Surface:** concrete.
◻ 01/01-31/12
Distance: 🚂7km 🚗1km 🏊on the spot.
Remarks: Parking at lake, golf court and park La Grajera.

🛏	Navarrete 🌿	37D5

Calle de la Carretera. **GPS:** n42,42458 w2,55584.⬆ .

🛏free. **Location:** Urban, simple. **Surface:** asphalted. ◻ 01/01-31/12
Distance: 🚂1km 🚗3km ⊗600m 🛒800m.
Remarks: Parking at sports park.

🛏	Roncesvalles 🏔	28A5

Paseo Ibaneta. **GPS:** n43,02018 w1,32401.⬆ .

5 🛏. **Location:** Rural, simple. **Surface:** asphalted. ◻ 01/01-31/12
Distance: 🚂1,5km.
Remarks: Beautiful view.

	Zaragoza	40A1

Parque de Atracciones de Zaragoza. **GPS:** n41,61994 w0,90122.
10 🛏.
Distance: 🚗4,5km.

Mediterranean Sea Communities

🛏S	Alqueria de la Comtessa	40A4

Camperpark Km zero, Metge Panella nº 1. **GPS:** n38,93878 w0,15276.➡.

35 🛏€ 8-12 🚰🔧Ch📦 🔧(35x),6Amp WC 🚿€3/3 📶included.
Surface: asphalted. ◻ 01/01-31/12
Distance: 🚂100m 🚗1,5km 🏊4km ⊗200m 🛒200m 🚌150m 🚲300m 🚶500m.

🛏	Altafulla	40C2

Área de Servicio Mèdol, AP-7 km 237, Barcelona > Taragona.
GPS: n41,14157 e1,34590.
10 🛏free 🚰🔧Chfree. **Surface:** asphalted. ◻ 01/01-31/12
Distance: ⊗on the spot 🛒on the spot.

🛏	Altafulla	40C2

Área de Servicio Mèdol, AP-7 km 237, Taragona > Barcelona.
GPS: n41,14054 e1,34746.
10 🛏free 🚰🔧Chfree. **Surface:** asphalted. ◻ 01/01-31/12
Distance: ⊗on the spot 🛒on the spot.

🛏S	Altea 🏖	40A5

San Antonio Camperpark, Ctra. del Albir 5/6, CV7651.
GPS: n38,58544 w0,05989.⬆.

50 🛏€ 15, 2 pers.incl 🚰 🔌 Ch 🔌 €0,45/kWh WC 🚻 ◉ €3 ✳included.
Location: Comfortable. ⬛ 15/09-30/04
Distance: 🚶Altea > 1km < Albir ⛱100m ⊗500m ⏚500m 🚌200m, tram 1km.
Remarks: Bread-service, discount longer stays.

| ♿ S | Amposta | 40B2 |

Masia Vora Riu, Calle Zamora, 8. **GPS:** n40,75006 e0,56069.
5 🛏€ 10 🚰 Ch 🔌 included. **Surface:** sand. ⬛ 01/01-31/12

| 🚻 S | Amposta | 40B2 |

Casa de Fusta, Partida L'Encanyissada. **GPS:** n40,65851 e0,67475.⬆

15 🛏free 🚰 €3 🔌 Ch.
Location: Rural, comfortable. **Surface:** unpaved.
Distance: ⊗on the spot 🚶on the spot.

| 🅿 S | Ascó | 40B2 |

C/ Alcalde Tomas Biarnes Radua. **GPS:** n41,18673 e0,56802.⬆

25 🛏free 🚰 🔌 Ch free. **Surface:** asphalted.

| 🅿 S | Avinyo | 40C1 |

Area Municipal de Avinyó, Calle Industria. **GPS:** n41,86556 e1,97472.⬆
10 🛏free 🚰€1/50liter 🔌 Ch free. **Surface:** gravel/sand.
Distance: 🚶300m ⊗300m ⏚300m.

| 🅿 S | Avinyonet del Penedès | 40C2 |

Area Cellar Can Batlle - Artcava, Masia Can Batlle s/n, BV2411.
GPS: n41,36790 e1,77306.⬆

🛏free 🚰 🔌 Ch free. **Location:** Rural, isolated, quiet. **Surface:** grassy/gravel.
⬛ 01/01-31/12

Distance: 🚶1km 🚤6km.
Remarks: Wine tasting.

| 🅿 S | Ayora | 40A4 |

El Nogal, Romeral 5. **GPS:** n39,05870 w1,0324.
20 🛏€ 10 🚰 🔌 Ch included 🔌 free. **Location:** Rural, comfortable.
Surface: grassy.

| 🅿 S | Ayora | 40A4 |

Ayora, N330. **GPS:** n39,04382 w1,04126.

5 🛏€ 10 🚰€1 🔌 Ch 🔌€2 WC 🚻included ◉€5 🚿. **Surface:** gravel.
⬛ 01/01-31/12
Distance: 🚶2,5km.

| 🅿 S | Barcelona | 40D2 |

CityStop, Rambla Guipúzcoa. **GPS:** n41,42433 e2,20748.⬆
80 🛏€ 30 🚰 🔌 Ch 🔌€4 WC 🚻 🚿. **Location:** Urban, comfortable.
Surface: asphalted.
Distance: 🚶on the spot.

| 🅿 S | Barcelona | 40D2 |

Park & Ride del Besòs, Carrer del Taulat, B10 > salida 24 / 25, Sant Adrià del Besos. **GPS:** n41,41333 e2,22222.⬆

20 🛏€ 30/24h, € 3/h 🚰 🔌 Ch 🔌 WC 🚻included 🧹. **Location:** Urban.
Surface: metalled. ⬛ 01/01-31/12
Distance: 🚶1km ⊗300m ⏚300m 🚋Tram 100m, metro 500m.
Remarks: Max. 72h, monitored parking.

| 🅿 S | Benicasim 🌿 | 40B3 |

Calle de Ausias March. **GPS:** n40,05527 e0,05916.⬆
🚰 Ch free.

| 🅿 S | Bicorp | 40A4 |

Area de Bicorp, Junto al Polideportivo. **GPS:** n39,13278 w0,79056.⬆
20 🛏€ 5 🚰 Ch included. **Location:** Rural. **Surface:** gravel.
Distance: 🚶200m.

| 🅿 S | Cadaqués | 40D1 |

Parking, Riera de Sant Vicenç. **GPS:** n42,28964 e3,27260.

🛏€ 20,20/24h WC 🚻 🚐 🔌 **Surface:** asphalted.
Distance: 🚶100m ⛱1km ⏚1,5km ⊗100m ⏚100m.
Tourist information Cadaqués:
⛪ La Riera. Week market. ⬛ Mo 8-14h.

ES

Calaf 40C1
Calle de Leida-Girona. **GPS:** n41,73306 e1,52667. ⬆.

5 ⛺free ⛽ 🍽Chfree. **Location:** Comfortable. **Surface:** asphalted.
Remarks: At petrol station.

Calaf 40C1
Carrer Berlin. **GPS:** n41,73500 e1,51389. ⬆.

4 ⛺free ⛽ 🍽Chfree. **Surface:** gravel/metalled.
Remarks: Max. 24h, market Saturday.

Calnegre 39D5
Camperpark Taray, RM-D21, Puntas Calnegre. **GPS:** n37,51515 w1,39845. ⬆.

50 ⛺€ 6 ⛽€1/100liter 🍽 Ch 🔲€4. **Surface:** sand. ◼ winter
Distance: 🏖100m ⊗500m 🛒500m.

Calnegre 39D5
Puntas Calnegre, Ctra. Puntas de Calnegre, nº 42. **GPS:** n37,51179 w1,41198. ⬆.

17 ⛺€ 10,50 ⛽ 🍽 Ch 🚿 included. **Surface:** metalled. ◼ 15/09-01/04
Distance: 🏖600m.

Calpe 40A5
Odissea Camper Area Calpe, Avda. Bulgaria. **GPS:** n38,64893 e0,06665. ⬆.

58 ⛺€ 12 (discount longer stay) , 01/07-31/08 € 15 ⛽ 🍽
Ch 🚿 WC ⬜included 📶€2/day. 🎯 **Location:** Comfortable, central.
Surface: gravel. ◼ 01/01-31/12
Distance: 🚶on the spot 🏖1km 🛒100m.

Calpe 40A5
Euro Nautica, Ctra. N233. **GPS:** n38,65578 e0,03660.
10 ⛺€ 10 ⛽ 🍽 Ch. **Surface:** metalled. ◼ 01/01-31/12 🔲 Sa-Su
Remarks: Motorhome dealer, arrival during opening hours.

Cañada de Callego 39D5
Loma de St.Antonio, Camino de Perchèles. **GPS:** n37,53542 w1,37226.

⛺free. **Surface:** sand.
Remarks: Parking at sea.

Carcaixent 40A4
Hort de Soriano. **GPS:** n39,07045 w0,40918. ⬆.

15 ⛺€ 15 ⛽ 🍽 Chfree.
Surface: sand.
Distance: 🚶7km 🏊on the spot.
Remarks: Max. 48h, picnic and barbecue place. At recreation area, first drive into
Carrer Julián Ribera (39°7'19"N 00°27'04"W) ± 5km, than follow Hort de Soriano.

Cartagena 39D5
Area Autocaravanas Cartagena. **GPS:** n37,65373 w1,00345. ⬆.

30 ⛺€ 7, € 10 service incl ⛽ 🍽 Ch 🚿 WC ⬜€2 🔲€4 📶. **Surface:** gravel.
◼ 01/01-31/12
Distance: 🚶centre 5km, port 8km ⊗400m 🛒400m 🚌400m 🏊on the spot
🏊on the spot.

Remarks: Bread-service, sunday market Bohio 500m, Thursday market Dolores 1km.

| 🏕️S | **Cartagena** 🌿🛒🗑️🥾 | 39D5 |

Área Belmonte Plus, Ctra. de Tentegorra, 1. **GPS:** n37,61500 w1,00555. ⬆️.
7 🏕️ € 10 🚰🗑️Ch 🥾 included. **Surface:** asphalted.
Distance: 🚶500m 🚌on the spot.

| 🏕️S | **Dénia** 🌿🛒🥾 | 40A4 |

Los Llanos, Partida Deveses 32. **GPS:** n38,86811 w0,016.
10 🏕️ € 10-25 🚰🗑️Ch 🥾 WC ⬜included.

Tourist information Dénia:
🏛️ Torrecremada Esplanade. ⏰ Mo 8.30-14h.

| 🏕️S | **El Campello** 🌿🥾 | 40A5 |

Camper Park Alicante, Carrer Llauradors. **GPS:** n38,42599 w0,40914. ⬆️.
35 🏕️ € 9 🚰🗑️Ch 🥾 📶included.
Location: Comfortable. **Surface:** gravel.
Distance: 🚶500m 🚌1km.

| 🏕️S | **El Campello** 🌿🥾 | 40A5 |

Bar-Restaurant, N332 km124. **GPS:** n38,45746 w0,36129. ⬆️.

2-3 🏕️free 🚰🥾 WC ⬜📶included. **Surface:** sand.
Distance: ⊗on the spot.
Remarks: 3 days free.

| 🍴S | **El Pinós** | 39D4 |

Bonnie's Bar. GPS: n38,40917 w1,08639.

5 🏕️ € 10-12 🚰🗑️Ch 🥾 WC ⬜included. **Surface:** metalled.
⏰ 01/01-31/12

| 🏕️S | **Elche** | 40A5 |

MH VICKY, Partida de Pusol 153, Deramador. **GPS:** n38,19711 w0,7314. ⬆️➡️.

9 🏕️ € 9,50 🚰🗑️Ch 🥾€0,25/kWh WC ⬜€1 🔌€3 📶€2/day.
Surface: gravel. ⏰ 01/01-31/12
Distance: 🚶Elche 6km ⊗2km 🚌4km 🏖️1,5km.
Remarks: Bread-service, 2 bicylcles available, jacuzzi € 1.

| 🏕️S | **Els Muntells** | 40B2 |

Carrer Major. **GPS:** n40,66869 e0,75929. ⬆️.

10 🏕️ € 6 🚰🗑️Ch 🥾 WC included. **Location:** Rural, isolated.
Surface: asphalted/gravel.
Distance: 🏖️1,2km.

| 🏕️S | **Figueres** | 40D1 |

Parking Supermercado Esclat, Avda. de los Paisos Catalans, N260.
GPS: n42,26042 e2,95096.

5 🏕️free. **Surface:** asphalted.
Distance: 🚶on the spot ⊗500m 🚌on the spot 🚌50m.
Remarks: Max. 48h.

Tourist information Figueres:
🏛️ Rambla. Antiques market. ⏰ 3rd Sa of the month.
🏛️ Plaza Catalunya en Plaza del Gra. ⏰ Tue-Thu-Sa 9-14h.

| 🏕️S | **Gandia** | 40A4 |

Area Camper Dunes, Carrer Garbi 2a, Daimús. **GPS:** n38,96981 w0,14509. ⬆️.

50 🏕️ € 9 🚰🗑️Ch 🥾€3 ⬜included 📶€1/3h. **Location:** Comfortable.
Surface: gravel.
Distance: 🏖️350m 🚌50m 🚌100m ⬜on the spot.

| 🏕️S | **Garrigàs** | 40D1 |

Área del Empordà Norte, A7 km-35. **GPS:** n42,17333 e2,93194. ⬆️.
10 🏕️free 🚰 WC free. **Surface:** metalled. ⏰ 01/01-31/12

| 🏕️S | **Garrigàs** | 40D1 |

Área del Empordà Sur, A7 km-35. **GPS:** n42,17456 e2,93074. ⬆️.

10 🏕️free 🚰🗑️ WC free. **Surface:** metalled. ⏰ 01/01-31/12

ES

🛁S **Ibi** 40A5
Área Chambit, Calle Pedro Valdivia. **GPS:** n38,62222 w0,56694. ⬆.
25 🅿free ⟶ 🚰Chfree. **Surface:** sand. ⬜ 01/01-31/12
Distance: 🏖 2,3km.

🛁S **Jalance** 40A4
N330. **GPS:** n39,18740 w1,0761. ⬆.

10 🅿free ⟶ 🚰Chfree. **Surface:** asphalted.
Distance: 🚶300m.
Remarks: Parking next to swimming pool, max. 48h.

🅿 **Jávea** 40B5
Avda. de Tamarits. **GPS:** n38,76982 e0,19097.
5 🅿. **Surface:** unpaved.

🅿 **Jérica** 40A3
Carre del Rio. **GPS:** n39,91116 w0,57385.

5 🅿. ⬜ 01/01-31/12
Distance: 🏖 2,2km 🅿on the spot.
Remarks: Along river, max. 7m.

🅿 **La Azohia** 🌊 39D5
Carretera a La Azohía. **GPS:** n37,56332 w1,17393.

🅿free. **Surface:** unpaved.
Distance: 🌊50m ⊗100m 🚶100m.

🛁S **La Marina** 40A5
Finca La Escuera, Escuera 300. **GPS:** n38,14360 w0,66939.

6 🅿€10 ⟶ 🚰Ch 🔌€0,20/kWh WC 🚿 ⬛. **Surface:** sand. ⬜ 01/01-31/12
Distance: 🚶300m 🏊3km ⊗300m 🛒300m 🚌300m 🧍on the spot.

🛁S **La Marina** 40A5
La Marina Elche, Cami del Molar o Pinet. **GPS:** n38,15628 w0,63791.

20 🅿€8 ⟶ 🚰Chincluded 🔌€0,50/kWh,16Amp. ⬜ winter

🅿 **La Marina** 40A5
Camino del Pinet, La Marina nord. **GPS:** n38,15087 w0,63276.

40 🅿free. **Surface:** asphalted.

🛁S **La Romana** 40A5
Camperpark EuroPeCa, Cuevas de San Anton 2. **GPS:** n38,35662 w0,90378.

7 🅿€9,00 ⟶ 🚰Ch 🔌€0,30/kWh WC 🚿€1 ⬛€4 📶included. 🛁
Location: Rural, comfortable. **Surface:** gravel. ⬜ 01/01-31/12
Distance: 🚶1,5km ⊗1,5km 🛒1,5km 🧍on the spot.
Remarks: Possibility for reservation: 0034638278693.

🅿 **La Salzadella** 40B3
Av. Tomas Molins. **GPS:** n40,41611 e0,17305. ⬆➡.

5 🅿free ⟶ 🚰Chfree. **Surface:** asphalted.
Distance: 🚶250m.
Remarks: Village of cherries: cherry soap, cherry jam.

🅿 **La Seu dÚrgell** 28D6
Portal de cerdanya. **GPS:** n42,35888 e1,46447.
8 🅿.

🛁S **Lleida** 40B1
AP-2 Zaragoze > Barcelona km 143. **GPS:** n41,54111 e0,63917.
10 🅿 ⟶ 🚰Ch.
Distance: 🏖 on the spot.

ES

📷S **L'Alfàs del Pi** **40A5**
Camper Park Costa Blanca, Cami des Alguers, 79. **GPS**: n38,58389 w0,08139.
⬆️➡️.

42 🛏€ 12, 01/05-30/09 € 10 🚰🔌Ch 🚿 (42x)€2 WC 🚽€0,50 🔌€4/4
📶included. **Location:** Rural, comfortable, quiet. **Surface:** metalled.
🔲 01/01-31/12
Distance: 🏪L'Alfas del Pi 1km, Playa Albir 1km 🏄5km 🏊sandy beach 2km
🚶2km 🛒500m 🚉1km 🚋Tram 600m.

📷S **L'Alfàs del Pi** **40A5**
Camper Park Orange Grove, Cami d'Alguers 65. **GPS**: n38,58526 w0,08405.⬆️
30 🛏€ 12 🚰🔌Ch 🚿€3 WC 🚽🔲 01/01-31/12

📷S **L'Arboç** **40C2**
Área del Penedés Norte, AP7 dir Barcelona. **GPS**: n41,28794 e1,59117.
10 🛏🚰🔌Chfree. **Surface:** metalled. 🔲 01/01-31/12
Distance: ⊗on the spot 🚉on the spot.

📷S **L'Arboç** **40C2**
Área del Penedés Sur, AP7 dir Taragona. **GPS**: n41,29029 e1,59235.

10 🛏🚰🔌Chfree. **Surface:** asphalted. 🔲 01/01-31/12
Distance: ⊗on the spot 🚉on the spot.

📷S **Mataro** **40D1**
Autocaravanas del Sol, Calle de Torrent de Madá, El Cros.
GPS: n41,53564 e2,41790.⬆️

4 🛏€ 10 🚰🔌Ch 🚿 WC 📶included. 🔲 01/01-31/12
Distance: 🚉300m 🚌> Barcelona 100m.
Remarks: At motorhome dealer, max. 7 nights.

📷S **Montseny** **40D1**
Área de Montseny, AP7-Nord km-117 > Francia. **GPS**: n41,64700 e2,42586.⬆️

20 🛏free 🚰🔌free. **Surface:** metalled. 🔲 01/01-31/12
Distance: ⊗on the spot 🚉on the spot.

📷S **Montseny** **40D1**
Área de Montseny, AP7-Sur>Barcelona. **GPS**: n41,65000 e2,44222.⬆️

20 🛏free 🚰🔌free. **Surface:** metalled. 🔲 01/01-31/12
Distance: ⊗on the spot 🚉on the spot.

📷S **Morella** **40A2**
N232. **GPS**: n40,62398 w0,09141.⬆️

30 🛏free 🚰🔌Chfree. **Surface:** metalled. 🔲 01/01-31/12
Distance: 🏪2km ⊗2km.
Remarks: Max. 72h.

📷S **Mula** **39D4**
Camino de las Curtis. **GPS**: n38,03972 w1,48139.⬆️
5 🛏free 🚰🔌Ch free. **Surface:** asphalted. 🔲 01/01-31/12
Distance: 🏪500m 🚉500m.

📷S **Murcia** **39D4**
Camperpark Huerta de Murcia, Carril los Cánovas, Rincón de Almodóvar, Los
Ramos. **GPS**: n38,00722 w1,04361.

32 🛏€ 12 🚰🔌Ch 🚿 WC 🚽included 🔌€3 📶free. **Surface:** gravel.
🔲 01/01-31/12
Distance: 🏪Alquerías 1,7km ⊗500m 🚉500m 🚌on the spot.
Remarks: Bread-service.

📷S **Navarcles** **40C1**
Calle de la Font de la Cura. **GPS**: n41,75661 e1,90833.⬆️

ES

5 🛏 free 🚰🗑️ Ch 🔧 free. **Location:** Isolated, quiet.
Surface: gravel.
Distance: 🚴500m 🚶on the spot.

🍴 S — Navata — 40D1
Restaurante Can Janot, Ctra. de Olot nº 2. **GPS:** n42,22600 e2,86325. ⬆️

20 🛏 € 4 🚰 €2 🗑️ 📶. **Location:** Quiet. **Surface:** grassy.
Distance: ❌on the spot 🛒100m.
Remarks: Guests free.

🛏 S — Olimar — 40A4
Area de Ocio Nostrum Caravaning. GPS: n39,47051 w0,64056. ⬆️
100 🛏 € 15 🚰🗑️ Ch 🔧included. **Surface:** metalled/sand.
Distance: 🏖️300m.
Remarks: 100m from camper/caravan Ocio Nostrum.

S — Oliva — 40A4
Area Camper Kikopark, C/ Assagador de Carro. **GPS:** n38,93282 w0,09742. ⬆️
15 🛏 € 18-26,50 🚰🗑️ Ch 🔧 WC included. ⬛ 01/01-31/12
Distance: 🏖️on the spot ❌on the spot.
Remarks: Stop & Go arrival >15h, departure <15h.

🛏 S — Palamós — 40D1

EmpordArea - Palamós

empordarea@empordarea.com - www.empordarea.com

Point of interest
Reservations possible
Bicycle rent

EmpordArea, C/ Pui Gorgoll s/n - C/ Pla del Llop s/n. **GPS:** n41,85740 e3,11467.
45 🛏 € 7, 18/06-13/09 € 11 🚰🗑️ Ch 🔧 €3/24h,8Amp WC 🗑️€2 ⬛€4
📶included. **Surface:** grassy/gravel. ⬛ 01/01-31/12
Distance: 🚴1km 🏖️1,3km 🏊1km 🚶1km ❌450m 🛒300m 🚌500m
🚲1,2km 🚶1,2km.

🛏 S — Peñíscola — 40B3
Area camper Vizmar, Camí de la Volta. **GPS:** n40,39357 e0,40778. ⬆️
25 🛏 € 6 🚰🗑️ Ch 🔧 WC 📶. **Surface:** grassy. ⬛ 01/01-31/12
Distance: 🏖️500m.

🛏 S — Peñíscola — 40B3
Stop&Go La Volta, Camino de la Volta. **GPS:** n40,39793 e0,40316. ⬆️
70 🛏 € 7, 01/07-31/08 € 13, 2 pers incl., 1 pers + € 1-2 🚰🗑️ Ch 🔧 €3,6Amp
WC 🗑️⬛€4/4 📶free. **Location:** Rural. **Surface:** grassy/gravel.
⬛ 01/01-31/12

S — Peñíscola — 40B3
Camper Park Los Pinos, C/ Abellers, 2. **GPS:** n40,37912 e0,38827. ⬆️
30 🛏 15/09-15/06 € 10 🚰 Ch 🔧 WC included ⬛ 📶.
Surface: gravel/metalled. ⬛ 01/01-31/12
Distance: 🏖️2km.

🛏 S — Platja d'Aro — 40D1
Calle Roma. GPS: n41,81028 e3,05767. ⬆️

30 🛏 € 8 🚰🗑️ Ch included. **Location:** Comfortable, quiet.
Surface: asphalted.
Distance: 🏖️750m.
Remarks: Max. 2 days.

🛏 S — Quart — 40D1
Avinguda de la Bòbila. GPS: n41,93944 e2,83917. ⬆️

4 🛏 free 🚰🗑️ Ch free. **Surface:** metalled. ⬛ 01/01-31/12
Distance: 🚴on the spot 🏖️6,5km ❌on the spot 🛒on the spot.
Remarks: Max. 48h, max. 8M.

🛏 S — Ramonete — 39D5
Wo-Mo Puerto Villa Brisa, Los Curas, D21, Puntas de Calnegre.
GPS: n37,52589 w1,4336. ⬆️➡️

50 🛏 € 6 🚰 €0,10/10liter 🗑️ Ch 🔧 €0,50 🗑️€2 ⬛€4/4 📶. **Surface:** gravel.
⬛ 19/09-30/05
Distance: 🚴5km 🏖️5km ❌5km 🛒5km.
Remarks: Bread-service.

🛏 — Ripoll — 40D1
Raval de Barcelona. GPS: n42,20008 e2,18695. ⬆️ .

5 🚐free. **Surface:** asphalted.
Distance: 🚶300m ⊗500m 🛒500m.
Remarks: Max. 24h, no camping activities.
Tourist information Ripoll:
⌂ Centrum. Week market. 🅿 Sa-morning.

San Feliu de Guixols 🏖 40D1
Parking Narcis Massanas, Ronda Narcis Massanas. **GPS:** n41,78020 e3,02303. ⬆.

15 🚐free 🚰 🔌Chfree. **Location:** Simple, quiet.
Surface: unpaved.

San Fulgencio 40A5
Camper Park San Fulgencio, Mar Cartabrico 7, Centro Comercial las Dunas.
GPS: n38,12080 w0,66005. ⬆.

38 🚐first day € 14, then € 12 🚰 🔌 Ch 🛠 WC 🗑⊡€3 📶included.
Location: Comfortable. **Surface:** gravel. 🅿 01/01-31/12
Distance: 🏊1,5km ⊗200m 🛒150m 🚌150m.

San Fulgencio 40A5
Oasis, Caminal del Convenio. **GPS:** n38,11972 w0,66194. ⬆.

14 🚐€ 14, from 15th night € 12 🚰 🔌 Ch 🛠 WC 🗑⊡€3/2 📶included.
Surface: gravel.
🅿 01/09-30/04
Distance: 🚶San Fulgencio 7km 🏖beach 1,5km ⊗200m 🛒200m 🚌300m.

San Raphael del Río 40B2
Restaurante Spätzle-Fritz, Planes del Reine, San Jorge, CV-11.
GPS: n40,57507 e0,39333. ⬆.

50 🚐€ 8, guests free 🚰🔌Ch🛠€4 WC🗑 📶. **Location:** Quiet.
Surface: gravel. 🅿 01/01-31/12
Distance: 🚶3,5km 🏊9km ⊗on the spot.

Sant Hilari Sacalm 🏞 40D1
Carretera de la Font Picant. **GPS:** n41,88417 e2,50778. ⬆.

10 🚐free 🚰🔌Chfree 🔌. **Location:** Rural. **Surface:** gravel/sand.
🅿 01/01-31/12
Distance: 🚶200m ⊗200m 🛒200m.
Remarks: Max. 48h.

Santa Cristina d'Aro 40D1
Costa Brava Park, Carretera Platje d'Aro. **GPS:** n41,81306 e3,01119. ⬆.

46 🚐€ 15 🚰€3 🔌Ch 🛠 included 📶€6. **Surface:** metalled/sand.
Distance: 🏊6km ⊗100m.

Segorbe 40A3
Area de Segorbe, Escalera de la Estación. **GPS:** n39,84805 w0,48166. ⬆.
12 🚐free 🚰🔌Chfree. **Surface:** asphalted/metalled.
Remarks: Max. 48h.

Sitges 🏖 40C2
Avda. del Cami Pla. **GPS:** n41,25083 e1,81838. ⬆.

10 🚐€ 5 1/11-31/3, € 8 1/4-31/10 🚰🔌Ch 🧹. **Location:** Simple.
Surface: asphalted. 🅿 01/01-31/12
Distance: 🚶Boulevard/beach Sitges 2,5km 🛒50m.
Remarks: Industrial area, max. 7 days, Barcelona 40km.

Sta.Pola 40A5
Europa-Area, Carrer dels Electricistas. **GPS:** n38,20805 w0,57416. ⬆➡.

ES

33 🛏️8 ⚡ Ch ✋€3 🍽️◻️🛜. **Surface:** gravel/metalled.
◻️ 01/01-31/12
Distance: 🚶1,7km ⛱️1,8km ⊗1,7km.

Tortosa 40B2

Área de Tortosa, Camí de la Toïa. **GPS:** n40,80277 e0,51388.⬆️➡️.

30 🛏️€5/24h ⚡€1 Ch. **Surface:** asphalted. ◻️ 01/01-31/12
Distance: 🚶1,1km ✈️10km ⊗900m 🚉1km.

Tremp 40B1

Passeig de Conca de Tremp. GPS: n42,16312 e0,89043.⬆️.

10 🛏️free ⚡free ✋€1/2h. **Surface:** asphalted.
Remarks: Max. 48h.

Turis 40A4

Carretera de Silla Tunis. **GPS:** n39,38944 w0,69777.⬆️.
10 🛏️free ⚡ Ch free. **Surface:** unpaved. ◻️ 01/01-31/12
Distance: 🚶500m.

Valencia 🐚🍽️ 40A4

Valencia Camper Park - Valencia

valcampark@gmail.com - http://www.valenciacamperpark.com

Excellent location for city visit
Free wifi access
Baker every morning

Valencia Camper Park, Calle Universo, Bétera. **GPS:** n39,56126 w0,43213.⬆️.
80 🛏️€12 ⚡€0,50/40liter Ch ✋(50x)€3/24h,6Amp WC 🍽️◻️€3

🛜included. **Location:** Luxurious. **Surface:** gravel. ◻️ 01/01-31/12
Distance: 🚶Valencia 12km 🚉1,5km 🚂train 300m.

Valencia 🐚🍽️ 40A4

Area Camping-car La Marina, Carrer del Rio 556B, El Saler.
GPS: n39,38727 w0,33213.⬆️.
70 🛏️€11 ⚡ Ch WC. **Surface:** gravel.
Distance: 🚶Valencia 10km ⛱️beach 150m ⊗600m 🚂on the spot.
Remarks: Discount longer stays.

Valencia 🐚🍽️ 40A4

Parking Valencia, Avda. Peris y Valero, 27. **GPS:** n39,45627 w0,37806.⬆️.

8-10 🛏️€25 ⚡ Ch ✋WC included. **Location:** Urban, central, noisy.
Surface: asphalted/gravel.
Distance: 🚶city centre 1,7km ✈️2,5km 🚂200m.
Remarks: Monitored parking.

Vic 40D1

Carrer de la Fura. **GPS:** n41,93444 e2,24000.⬆️➡️.

10 🛏️€5 ⚡€2/100liter Ch ✋€6/3h. **Surface:** grassy.
Distance: 🚶1,8km 🚂400m.
Remarks: Max. 48h.

Viladrau 🏔️ 40D1

Carrer Montseny s/n. **GPS:** n41,84544 e2,38732.⬆️.

16 🛏️free ⚡ Ch 🛜free. **Location:** Rural. **Surface:** gravel/sand.
◻️ 01/01-31/12
Distance: 🚶500m ⊗500m 🚂500m.
Remarks: Max. 48h, nature reserve.

Yelca 39D4

Finca Caravana, Paraje Fuente del Pinar A-14. **GPS:** n38,71443 w1,11948.
10 🛏️€8 ⚡ Ch included. **Surface:** gravel/sand. ◻️ 05/06-30/06

Yelca 39D4

Portichuelo, Paraje el Portichuelo. **GPS:** n38,52833 w1,03944.⬆️➡️.

3 ⬛€ 10 🔌🚰 Ch 🔧 included 📶. **Surface:** grassy. ⬛ 01/01-31/12
Distance: 🚉 Yelca 10km ⊗on the spot.
Remarks: Check in at B&B <22h.

Spanish interior

🔲S **Aguilar de Campoo** 37B4
N611, Ctra Palencia-Aguillar de Campoo. **GPS:** n42,78631 w4,25757. ⬆️➡️

10 ⬛free 🚰🔌 Chfree. **Location:** Urban, simple. **Surface:** asphalted.
⬛ 01/01-31/12
Distance: 🚉1km 🏊3,1km ⊗1km ⛽1km.
Remarks: Max. 48h.

🔲S **Aldeadávila de la Ribera** 36D6
GPS: n41,22028 w6,61333. ⬆️

5 ⬛free 🚰🔌 Chfree. **Surface:** asphalted. ⬛ 01/01-31/12
Distance: ⊗on the spot ⛽200m.
Remarks: Max. 48h.

🔲 **Almazán** 37C6
Camino Viejo del Cubo de la Solana. **GPS:** n41,49259 w2,53385.
⬛.
Remarks: Parking at swimming pool.

🔲S **Ampudia** 37B5
Area de San Martín, Glorieta. S. Martín. **GPS:** n41,91130 w4,78082. ⬆️➡️

6 ⬛free 🚰🔌 Chfree. **Location:** Rural, simple. **Surface:** gravel/metalled.
⬛ 01/01-31/12
Distance: 🚉400m.

Remarks: No camping activities.

🔲S **Aranda de Duero** 37B6
Dª Ruperta Baraya/Manzane M1. **GPS:** n41,66833 w3,69583. ⬆️

10 ⬛free 🚰🔌 Chfree. **Surface:** asphalted. ⬛ 01/01-31/12
Distance: ⊗150m ⛽on the spot.
Remarks: Max. 48h.

🔲S **Astorga** 🌼 37A5
Parking plaza de Toros. **GPS:** n42,45138 w6,06593. ⬆️➡️

15 ⬛free 🚰🔌 Chfree. **Surface:** metalled.
Distance: 🚉500m 🏊1,4km ⊗500m ⛽500m.
Remarks: Max. 48h.

🔲S **Astudillo** 37B5
Area de la Joya, Urbanizacion de don Bosco. **GPS:** n42,18944 w4,3. ⬆️

10 ⬛free 🚰🔌 Chfree.
Location: Rural, simple. **Surface:** gravel.
Distance: 🚉1km ⛽300m.
Remarks: No camping activities.

🔲 **Avila** 🌼 🏔️ 39A1
Parking del Palacio de Congresos, Calle Molino dell Carril.
GPS: n40,66111 w4,70472.

10 ⬛free. **Surface:** asphalted.
Distance: 🏊2,2km.

Tourist information Avila:
ℹ️ Small medieval town surround by ramparts.
✝ The San Vicenta basilica is a Roman building.

⌖S Baltanàs 🍴   37B5
Area de la Ermita de Revilla, Plaza Arrañales de Revilla.
GPS: n41,93472 w4,2475. ⬆➡.

5 ⌖free 🚰⌗Chfree. **Location:** Rural, simple. **Surface:** concrete.
◻ 01/01-31/12
Remarks: No camping activities.

⌖S Bretocino   37A5
Area para Autocaravanes, Cuesta de los Nogales. **GPS**: n41,88654 w5,75517. ⬆.

5 ⌖€7 🚰⌗Ch 🔌includedtime WC 🔧 Location: Rural, comfortable,
quiet. **Surface:** concrete. ◻ 01/01-31/12
Distance: 🚶300m 🏪300m.
Remarks: Service passerby € 3, swimming pool.

⌖S Burgo de Osma   37C6
Calle de Santos Iruela. **GPS**: n41,58662 w3,07338. ⬆.

10 ⌖free 🚰. **Location:** Rural, simple. **Surface:** metalled.
◻ 01/01-31/12
Distance: 🚶500m ⊗200m 🏪500m.

⌖ Burgos   37C5
N120, Calle de Cartuja de Miraflores. **GPS**: n42,34037 w3,69361.

5 ⌖€ 0,60/h, max. € 2,60, 20-10h free. **Surface:** asphalted.
Distance: 🚣2,6km.
Remarks: Parking beside river.

Tourist information Burgos:
ℹ City, 8th century, with a lot of curiosities such as the cathedral, the castle and
Monasterio de las Huelgas.

△S Cabrerizos   37A6
Don Quijote, Ctra. Aldealengua km 4. **GPS**: n40,97500 w5,60306.
⌖€ 22 🚰Ch. ◻ 01/03-31/10
Remarks: Formula Camper.

⌖ Cáceres 🐚   38D2
Avda. Lope de Vega. **GPS**: n39,48041 w6,36649. ⬆➡.

15 ⌖free 🚰⌗Ch 🚻free. **Surface:** asphalted.
Distance: 🚶600m 🚣6,7km.
Remarks: Monitored parking.

Tourist information Cáceres:
ℹ Oficina de Turismo, Plaza Mayor, nº 3, www.inedito.com/caceres/. City with
historical centre.
🎭 PeroPalo. Traditional celebration. ◻ 21/02-24/02.

⌖S Carrión de los Condes 🐚   37B5
C/ Las Huertas. **GPS**: n42,33875 w4,60808. ⬆➡.

10 ⌖free 🚰⌗Chfree.
Location: Rural, simple. **Surface:** metalled.
Distance: 🚶200m ⊗200m 🏪200m.
Remarks: Max. 48h.

⌖S Cervera de Pisuerga   37B4
C/ El Maderao. **GPS**: n42,87139 w4,49972. ⬆.

10 ⌖free 🚰⌗Chfree.
Location: Rural, simple, isolated. **Surface:** sand.
Distance: 🚶500m ⊗500m 🏪500m.
Remarks: Along river, max. 48h.

⌖ Coca ⛲   37B6
GPS: n41,21348 w4,52733. ⬆.

5 ⊒free. **Location:** Urban, simple. **Surface:** metalled.
🅿 01/01-31/12
Remarks: Parking castle.

| | **Consuegra** | 39B2 |

GPS: n39,45339 w3,6106.
⊒free. **Surface:** sand.
Remarks: Isolated parking at foot of hill with windmills.

| S | **Cuellar** | 37B6 |

Área El Castillo, Calle del Alamillo, 40. **GPS:** n41,40083 w4,32028. ⬆️.

6 ⊒free ⛽🚿free. **Location:** Rural, simple. **Surface:** metalled.
Distance: 🚲 2km.
Remarks: At castle.

| S | **Don Benito** | 38D3 |

Avda. de los Deportes. **GPS:** n38,96250 w5,86305. ⬆️➡️.
3 ⊒free ⛽Chfree. **Surface:** metalled. 🅿 01/01-31/12
Distance: ⊗on the spot 🛒on the spot 🚌on the spot.

| S | **Espinosa de los Monteros** | 37C4 |

Parking Las Cocinas, BU-570 > Bárcenas. **GPS:** n43,08556 w3,5575. ⬆️.
10 ⊒free ⛽Chfree. **Surface:** asphalted.
Remarks: Max. 48h.

| S | **Foncastín** | 37A6 |

Estación de Servicios La Loba, A6, salida 175. **GPS:** n41,44131 w4,97957. ⬆️.

5 ⊒free ⛽🚿Chfree. **Location:** Rural, simple. **Surface:** asphalted.
🅿 01/01-31/12
Distance: 🚲 250m ⊗on the spot.

| S | **Frómista** 🐚 | 37B5 |

Paseo de Julio Senador, P-980. **GPS:** n42,26494 w4,41198. ⬆️➡️.

6 ⊒free ⛽🚿Chfree. **Location:** Urban, simple. **Surface:** metalled.
🅿 01/01-31/12
Distance: 🚏600m 🚲 200m ⊗500m 🛒500m.
Remarks: At sports park, max. 48h, weigh bridge nearby € 0,50.

| S | **La Alberca** | 38D1 |

Casa del Parque. GPS: n40,48833 w6,11583. ⬆️.
10 ⊒free ⛽🚿Chfree. **Surface:** metalled.
Distance: 🚏300m.
Remarks: Max. 48h.

| S | **La Joyosa** | 40A1 |

Área de Marlofa, Calle Sobradiel. **GPS:** n41,73744 w1,06664. ⬆️➡️.
21 ⊒free ⛽🚿Ch 🔌€3 WC 🚽. **Surface:** asphalted/grassy.
Distance: 🚲 9km.

| S | **Lagartera** | 39A2 |

Camino de la Estacion. **GPS:** n39,91151 w5,19978. ⬆️.

3 ⊒free ⛽🚿free. **Surface:** asphalted. 🅿 01/01-31/12
Distance: 🚏on the spot 🚲 1,4km 🛒100m.
Remarks: Max. 48h.

| S | **León** | 37A4 |

Avda. De los Peregrinos, 5. **GPS:** n42,60471 w5,58525. ⬆️.

10 ⊒free ⛽🚿Chfree. **Surface:** metalled.
Distance: ⊗300m.
Remarks: Max. 48h.

| S | **Logrosán** | 39A2 |

El Palomar, Calle Palomar. **GPS:** n39,33188 w5,48044. ⬆️➡️.
10 ⊒free ⛽🚿free. 🅿 01/01-31/12
Remarks: Max. 48h.

| | **Mérida** 🐚 | 38D3 |

P Hernan Cortez, Calle Cabo Verde. **GPS:** n38,91861 w6,33611. ⬆️.
20 ⊒€ 18/24h. **Surface:** metalled. 🅿 01/01-31/12
Distance: 🚏250m 🚲 4km ⊗250m 🚌500m.

Tourist information Mérida:
ℹ️ Oficina de Turismo, Calle Santa Eulalia, 64. Also called Spanish Rome. Former stopover on the old silver trail.

ES

�️Ⓢ **Olmedo** 37B6
Parque del Mudejar, N601, km 148,1. **GPS**: n41,29167 w4,68194.⬆️.

9 🅂free ⛽🚰Chfree. **Location:** Rural, simple. **Surface:** metalled.
🅿 01/01-31/12
Distance: ⊗100m.🚰200m.

⚧Ⓢ **Osorno** 37B5
Los Chopos, N611 Osorno > Herrera de Pisuerga. **GPS**: n42,41694 w4,35111.⬆️.

30 🅂free ⛽🚰Chfree. **Surface:** asphalted.
Distance: 🚶700m 🚲2,2km ⊗on the spot.
Remarks: Max. 48h, monitored parking.

Ⓢ **Palazuelos de Eresma** 39B1
Calle Cordel. **GPS**: n40,92848 w4,05529.⬆️➡️.

⛽€1 🚰Chfree. 🅿 01/01-31/12
Distance: 🚲4km.

⚧Ⓢ **Palencia** 37B5
Parque Isla Dos Aguas, Avda. Ponce de León, 12. **GPS**: n42,00389 w4,53333.⬆️
➡️

23 🅂free ⛽🚰Chfree. **Surface:** asphalted.
Distance: 🚶on the spot 🚲4km ⊗on the spot 🚰El Arbol 50m 🚌100m.
Remarks: Max. 48h.

🈂 **Peñafiel** 37B6
Calle de Los Destiladeros. **GPS**: n41,59440 w4,11582.⬆️.

5 🅂free. **Location:** Rural, simple. **Surface:** asphalted.
🅿 01/01-31/12
Distance: ⊗150m.
Remarks: Parking castle.

⚧Ⓢ **Peñaflor** 40A1
Parking Surrecreo, Urbanizacion Los Rosales Peñaflor. **GPS**: n41,72777 w0,79194.
⬆️➡️.
150 🅂€ 15 ⛽🚰Ch 🔌 WCincluded.
Distance: 🚶8 km.

⚧Ⓢ **Pollos** 37A6
Estación de Servicios La Loba 2000, A62, salida 169. **GPS**: n41,41004 w5,13396.
⬆️.

10 🅂free ⛽🚰Chfree. **Location:** Highway, simple. **Surface:** metalled.
🅿 01/01-31/12
Distance: 🚲200m ⊗on the spot 🚰on the spot.
Remarks: At petrol station.

⚧ **Salamanca** 🌿🍜 37A6
Parking Turismus, Avenida del Padre Ignacio Ellacuria. **GPS**: n40,95758 w5,67646.
⬆️.

15 🅂free. **Location:** Urban. **Surface:** asphalted.
Distance: 🚶city centre 1,5km 🚰50m Lidl/Mercadona 🚌on the spot.

⚧Ⓢ **Saldaña** 37B5
Calle de los Sauces. **GPS**: n42,51882 w4,74125.⬆️.

6 🅂free ⛽🚰Ch. **Location:** Rural, simple. **Surface:** concrete.
🅿 01/01-31/12

Distance: 🚶1 km ⊗1 km.
Remarks: Next to sports fields, max. 48h.

🍴 S | **Sancti-Spiritus** | 36D6

Hostal-Restaurante La Ponderosa, Carretera nacional 620 km303.
GPS: n40,73481 w6,36093.

🥤customers free 🚰🗑.
Distance: 🚲3km.
Remarks: Daily menu € 8.

🅿 | **Sepúlveda** 🌿 | 37B6

Calle de el Postiguillo. **GPS:** n41,29897 w3,74479.

10 🥤free. **Surface:** asphalted.
Distance: 🚶300m 🚲12km ⊗100m.

🅿 | **Soria** | 37D6

Monte de las Animas. **GPS:** n41,76769 w2,45391.

🥤free. **Surface:** gravel.

🅿 S | **Terradillos** | 37A6

Area del Encinar, Paseo de Poniente. **GPS:** n40,88000 w5,58194. ⬆.
10 🥤free 🚰🗑Chfree. **Location:** Simple. **Surface:** asphalted.
Distance: ⊗200m.

🅿 | **Toledo** 🌿 | 39B2

Parking de la Estación, Avda. de Castilla la Mancha. **GPS:** n39,86472 w4,01944.
50 🥤free.
Surface: asphalted.
Distance: 🚲1,3km.

Tourist information Toledo:
✝ Catedral. Cathedral known for its richness.
⌂ El Alcázar. Roman castle ruins, 16th century.

🅿 S | **Turégano** | 37B6

CL603. **GPS:** n41,15241 w4,00749. ⬆.

10 🥤free 🚰🗑Chfree. **Location:** Rural, simple. **Surface:** asphalted.
📅 01/01-31/12
Distance: ⊗200m.
Remarks: Behind former grain factory, max. 48h.

🅿 S | **Valencia de Don Juan** | 37A5

Area de Coyanza, Calle Tres de Abril. **GPS:** n42,28750 w5,51333. ⬆➡.

7 🥤free 🚰🗑Chfree. **Location:** Urban, simple. **Surface:** concrete.
📅 01/01-31/12
Distance: 🚶500m ⊗300m.
Remarks: Max. 48h.

🅿 S | **Valladolid** 🌿🍽 | 37B6

San Lorenzo, Avda. Ramon Pradera, 6. **GPS:** n41,65583 w4,73722. ⬆.

10 🥤€ 2,50/24h 🚰🗑🧹 included.
Location: Urban. **Surface:** asphalted.
Distance: 🚶city centre 1km 🚲3,2km ⊗400m.
Remarks: Max. 48h.

🅿 S | **Villada** | 37B5

C/ San Fructuoso, Calle del Ferial Nuevo 10. **GPS:** n42,25533 w4,9649. ⬆➡.

5 🥤free 🚰🗑Chfree. **Location:** Rural, simple, quiet. **Surface:** gravel.
📅 01/01-31/12
Distance: 🚶200m ⊗200m 🏊200m.
Remarks: Max. 48h, no camping activities.

🅿 S | **Villalpando** | 37A5

Area de Servicios Villalpando, A6, salida 236. **GPS:** n41,85906 w5,41993. ⬆.
5 🥤free. **Location:** Highway, simple, isolated, noisy. **Surface:** asphalted.

ES

⬜ 01/01-31/12
Distance: 🛣200m ⊗on the spot 🚻on the spot.
Remarks: At petrol station.

| 🚰S | **Zafra** | 38D3 |

Ctra. de los Santos de Maimona, Ex101. **GPS:** n38,42527 w6,41083. ⬆.

30 🛏free 🔧 🔌Ch free. **Surface:** asphalted. ⬜ 01/01-31/12

| 🚰S | **Zafra** | 38D3 |

Ferial Zafra, Ctra. Badajoz-Granada. **GPS:** n38,42558 w6,4116. ⬆→.
30 🛏free 🔧 🔌Ch free. **Location:** Urban. **Surface:** asphalted.

| 🅿 | **Zamora** 🪣 | 37A6 |

Estadio Barrio 3 Arboles, Calle de los Pisones. **GPS:** n41,50337 w5,75585.

18 🛏free. **Location:** Urban, simple, central. **Surface:** asphalted.
Distance: 🚰1km ⊗1km.
Remarks: Playground.

Andalusia

| 🅿 | **Agua Amarga** | 39D5 |

GPS: n36,93883 w1,93657.

20 🛏free. **Surface:** gravel/sand. ⬜ 01/01-31/12
Distance: 🚰on the spot ⛱100m ⊗50m 🚻500m 🛒2km.
Remarks: Riverbed.

| 🚐S | **Alcalá de Guadaíra** | 38D5 |

Autocaravanas Hidalgo, A92 Sevilla>‹Malaga km 7. **GPS:** n37,32856 w5,8056.

18 🛏€ 10 🔧€0,50 🔌Ch 🧹 included 🚿.

Distance: 🛣170m exit 15.
Remarks: Motorhome dealer, max. 2 nights.

| 🚐S | **Alhaurín del la Torr** | 39A5 |

Área de Autocaravanas Sol, Camino de las Curtis. **GPS:** n36,68083 w4,53611. ⬆.
150 🛏€ 10 🔧 🔌Ch 🧹included.
Distance: 🚰9 km 🚌100m.
Remarks: Monitored parking.

| 🅿 | **Alicún de las Torres** | 39B5 |

GR6104. **GPS:** n37,50836 w3,10802.

3 🛏free. **Surface:** metalled. ⬜ 01/01-31/12
Distance: 🚰100m ⊗100m.
Remarks: Next to the spa resort.

| 🚐S | **Almayate** 🌊 | 39A5 |

Area AMB, Carretera Nacional 340, km 266,5. **GPS:** n36,72372 w4,13999. ⬆.
🛏€ 6 🔧 🔌Ch included 🧹€3. **Surface:** metalled.
Distance: ⛱100m ⊗100m 🚻4km.
Remarks: At motorhome dealer.

| 🍴S | **Almensilla** | 38D5 |

San Diego, A-8054. **GPS:** n37,31361 w6,09333.
15 🛏free 🔧 🔌Ch free.
Remarks: At petrol station BP and restaurant, restaurant visit appreciated.

| 🅿 | **Almería** | 39C6 |

Area Autocaravanas Playa de Almería, Av. Cabo de Gata 280.
GPS: n36,81602 w2,43228. ⬆.
40 🛏€ 10 🔧 🔌Ch included 🧹€2 WC €1 🚿€1. **Surface:** asphalted.
Distance: ⛱200m ⊗on the spot.
Remarks: Behind petrol station, max. 72h.

| ⚓S | **Almerimar** | 39C6 |

Area del Puerto Deportivo Almerimar, Torre del puerto.
GPS: n36,69612 w2,79425. ⬆.

20 🛏€ 7,95 🔧 🔌Ch 🔌€3,50 WC included 🚿€3,50. **Surface:** asphalted.
⬜ 01/01-31/12
Distance: ⛱on the spot ⊗150m 🚻100m 🛒100m.
Remarks: Check in at harbourmaster 9-14h, 16-21h.

| 🚐S | **Archidona** 🌿 | 39A5 |

A7200. **GPS:** n37,09097 w4,38879. ⬆.

ES

12 🗆free 🍴 Ch free. **Surface:** concrete. 🅾 01/01-31/12
Distance: 🚶250m ⊗1km 🚰500m 🗑1km.

| 🅢 | **Cabra** | 39A5 |

Auditorio Municipal Alcalde Juan Muños, Juanita la Larga.
GPS: n37,46608 w4,42361.⬆.

10 🗆free 🚰 🍴 Ch free. **Surface:** asphalted. 🅾 01/01-31/12
Distance: 🚶300m ⊗300m 🗑300m.
Remarks: Max. 48h.

| 🖼 | **Chipiona** | 38C5 |

Carretera de la Playa. **GPS:** n36,70442 w6,42915.

8 🗆free. **Surface:** asphalted. 🅾 01/01-31/12
Distance: 🚶4km 🛁on the spot ⊗on the spot 🗑1,5km.

| 🖼 | **Conil de la Frontera** | 38D6 |

Avda. del Rio. **GPS:** n36,27282 w6,08994.

20 🗆free. **Surface:** asphalted. 🅾 01/01-31/12
Distance: 🛁on the spot ⊗500m 🗑500m.
Remarks: Parking along coast road.

| 🖼 | **Córdoba** | 39A4 |

Avda. de los Custodios. **GPS:** n37,87528 w4,78778.
30 🗆 € 11. **Surface:** asphalted/gravel. 🅾 01/01-31/12
Distance: 🚶historical centre 300m 🚤2,3km.
Remarks: In front of police station.

| 🅿 | **Córdoba** | 39A4 |

Avda. del Campo de la Verdad/Calle del Compositor Rafael Castro.
GPS: n37,87515 w4,76626.

🗆free.
Surface: asphalted.
🅾 01/01-31/12
Distance: 🚶1km.

Tourist information Córdoba:
Ⓜ Museo Municipal Taurino, Plaza de las Bulas. Museum about bull-fighting.
🅾 Tue-Sa 8.30-15h, Su 8.30-14.30h ⊙ Mo. 🅣 € 4.
Ⓜ Torre de la Calahorra. Urban museum.
🅾 10-14, 16.30-20.30. 🅣 € 4,50.
❌ Oficina de Turismo, Torrijos, 10 (Palacio de Congresos), www.ayuncordoba.es.
Historical and culturally rich city, city of the flamenco and bull-fighting.
❌ Palacio del Marqués de Viana. Palace with collections of leather, silverware,
porcelain etc. 🅾 Mo-Sa 10-19h, Su 10-15h. 🅣 € 8.
✝ Mezquita. World-famous Moorish mosque. 🅾 10-19h.

| 🅢 | **Cuevas de San Marcos** 🌿🏔🎭 | 39A5 |

GPS: n37,26059 w4,40237.⬆.

15 🗆free 🚰 🍴 Ch free. **Surface:** asphalted.
Distance: 🚶1km ⊗500m 🗑1km.
Remarks: Parking at swimming pool.

| 🅢 | **Cullar** | 39C5 |

Venta de Peral2, A-92. **GPS:** n37,55336 w2,6144.

20 🗆free 🚰 WC 🍴free. **Surface:** asphalted. 🅾 01/01-31/12
Distance: 🚶3km ⊗10m 🗑10m.

| 🅢 | **El Bosque** | 38D5 |

Calle de Juan Ramón Jiménez. **GPS:** n36,75670 w5,51056.

5 🗆free 🚰 🍴 Ch free. **Surface:** metalled. 🅾 01/01-31/12
Distance: 🚶on the spot ⊗100m 🗑300m.

| 🅢 | **Gelves** | 38D4 |

Puerto Gelves, Calle de Puerto Gelves. **GPS:** n37,33934 w6,02405.

ES

20 🛏 € 12 ⟜🔧 Ch 🚰 €2,80 WC 🗑️ 📶 🧺. **Surface:** asphalted.
🅾️ 01/01-31/12
Distance: 🚶on the spot 🏊4,3km ⊗on the spot 🍽️on the spot
🚌on the spot.
Remarks: Sevilla 10km, good bus connection.

| 🅿️S | **Granada** 🌿 | 39B5 |

Área de Geysepark-Cármenes, Torre de Comares. **GPS:** n37,15136 w3,59533. ⬆️

30 🛏 € 16/day ⟜🔧 Ch 🚰 included. **Surface:** asphalted. 🅾️ 01/01-31/12
Distance: 🚶200m 🏊2km ⊗200m 🍽️200m 🚌200m.
Remarks: Covered parking, entrance motorhomes 2nd ramp.

| 🅿️ | **Granada** 🌿 | 39B5 |

Alhambra, P5. **GPS:** n37,17168 w3,57974. ⬆️

50 🛏 € 46,65/24h, 01/10-31/05 € 26,60/24h.
Surface: gravel.
🅾️ 01/01-31/12
Distance: 🚶1,5km ⊗200m 🍽️200m 🚌100m.

Tourist information Granada:
👁 Alhambra. Most important curiosity of the city, the best kept Arab palace.
🅾️ 9-20h, winter, Sa 20-22h, Su 9-18h, summer Tue,Thu, Sa 22-24h.
👁 Cuevas del Sacromonte. Caves in Sacromonte mountain, gypsies previously lived here. Now important tourist attraction and stage of flamenco shows.
👁 El Albaicín. Moorish district facing the Alhambra.

| 🅿️ | **Grazalema** | 38D5 |

Calle Juan de la Rosa. **GPS:** n36,75807 w5,36365.

4 🛏 free. **Surface:** asphalted. 🅾️ 01/01-31/12
Distance: 🚶300m ⊗200m 🍽️500m.

| 🅿️ | **Huelva** ⚓ | 38C4 |

Monumento a Colón, Avenida Francesco Montenegro. **GPS:** n37,21333 w6,93972.

15 🛏 free. **Surface:** asphalted. 🅾️ 01/01-31/12
Distance: 🚶6km 🏊50m ⊗on the spot 🍽️6km 🚌500m.

| 🅿️ | **La Isleta** | 39C6 |

Playa del Pénom blanca, Carreta Noria. **GPS:** n36,81670 w2,05146.

15 🛏 free. **Surface:** gravel.
Distance: 🚶100m ⛱sandy beach 20m ⊗150m 🍽️300m.
Remarks: Parking at sea.

| 🅿️ | **La Línea de Concepción** | 38D6 |

Av. Principe de Asturias. **GPS:** n36,15583 w5,34553.

50 🛏 € 1/h, € 15/24h. **Surface:** metalled. 🅾️ 01/01-31/12
Distance: 🚶500m ⛱1km ⊗200m 🍽️1km.
Remarks: Market Wednesday.

| 🅿️S | **La Línea de Concepción** | 38D6 |

Area de Alcaidesa Marina, Av. Principe de Asturias. **GPS:** n36,15528 w5,35389.
60 🛏 € 12 ⟜🔧 Ch included. **Surface:** metalled.
Distance: ⊗on the spot 🍽️on the spot.

| 🅿️ | **Marchena** | 38D5 |

Calle Sevilla s/n. **GPS:** n37,33083 w5,42416. ⬆️
20 🛏 free ⟜🔧 Ch free. **Surface:** metalled.
Distance: 🚶1km.

ES

🆓S **Olvera** 38D5

Vía Verde de la Sierra. **GPS**: n36,94138 w5,25305.⬆️.
48 🛏️€ 5 🚰🔧 Ch 💧 included. 🔌 01/01-31/12
Distance: 🚶1km.

🆓S **Peñarroya-Pueblonuevo** 39A3

El Pantano. **GPS**: n38,27694 w5,27722.⬆️.

20 🛏️€ 5-7 🚰🔧 ChService€1,50 💧€2 📶included. **Location:** Comfortable, isolated, quiet. 🔌 01/01-31/12
Distance: 🚶4km ⛱️lake 🛒on the spot 🚿on the spot 🎣on the spot.
Remarks: Direct access to the lake, motorhome washing place € 1, swimming pool.

🆓S **Priego de Córdoba** 39A5

Calle del Carrusel s/n. **GPS**: n37,44361 w4,21186.⬆️.

10 🛏️free 🚰🔧 Ch WC free. **Surface:** concrete. 🔌 01/01-31/12
Distance: 🚶500m ⊗500m 🛒500m.

Tourist information Priego de Córdoba:
⛪ Iglesia de la Aurora.

🆓S **Rute** 39A5

Calle de Jésus Obrero. **GPS**: n37,33113 w4,37323.⬆️➡️.

6 🛏️free 🚰🔧 Chfree. **Surface:** asphalted.
Distance: 🚶500m ⊗500m 🛒300m.
Remarks: Parking next to police station, max. 48h.

🆓S **San Juan de los Terreros** 39D5

Playa de Entrevista, A332. **GPS**: n37,35083 w1,67972.

>20 🛏️free 🚰. **Surface:** gravel/sand. 🔌 01/01-31/12
Distance: 🚶500m ⛱️100m ⊗2km 🛒2,5km.

Remarks: Parking beach.

🆓S **Sancti Petri La Barrosa** 38C6

Carretera de la Barossa. **GPS**: n36,38612 w6,2053.

20 🛏️free. **Surface:** metalled. 🔌 01/01-31/12
Distance: 🚶2km ⛱️200m ⊗1km 🛒5km.
Remarks: Parking beach.

🆓S **Sanlúcar de Barrameda** 38C5

Sanlúcar AC Parking - Sanlúcar de Barrameda

info@protecor.es - facebook Sanlœcar AC Parking

Located directely on the beach
Open all year
Walking and bicycle area

Sanlúcar AC Parking, Camino de la Reyerta, s/n. **GPS**: n36,76195 w6,39617.⬆️.
58 🛏️01/07-30/09 € 12, 01/04-30/06 € 10, 01/10-31/03 € 8 🚰🔧 Ch 💧
(30x)€3/day,5Amp WC 🚿€3/3 📶included. 🔌 01/01-31/12
Distance: 🚶4km ⛱️100m 🛒100m ⊗300m 🛒350m 🚌400m 🚲500m.

🆓S **Sevilla** 38D4

Area Sevilla Centro - Sevilla

areasevilla@gmail.com - http://areasevilla.blogspot.com

Historical center
Free wifi access
Located directly at the river

Area Ac Sevilla Centro, Carretera de la Esclusa, Seville (Sevilla)
GPS: n37,36239 w5,99452. 100 🛏️€ 12 🚰🔧 Ch 💧 (40x)€3
WC 📶included. **Surface:** asphalted. 🔌 01/01-31/12 **Distance:** 🚶200m
⊗200m 🛒300m 🍽️on the spot 🚌200m 🚲200m.

🅿️ **Sevilla** 38D4

Parking Kansas City, Avda. de Kansas City, Seville (Sevilla).
GPS: n37,39194 w5,97333.
🛏️€ 18/24h. **Surface:** asphalted.

Tourist information Seville (Sevilla):
♜ Alcazar, Plaza del Triumfo.

ES

⋂ Italica. Roman ruins, 9 km at north of Sevilla on N630.
⚘ Almeda de Hercules. ▢ Su-morning.
☺ Parque de los Descubrimientos. Theme park science, in pavilion of Expo 1992.
▢ Fri-Su, summer Tue-Thu from 18h ◉ 10/01-28/02.

▨ S | **Sierra Nevada** ⛰ ❄ | **39B5**

Los Peñones de San Francisco. GPS: n37,09995 w3,3947. ⬆ ➡

60 ☕ € 10/day ⛽ ≋ Ch included. **Surface:** asphalted.
Distance: 🚶3km ①1km ♒300m.
Remarks: Shuttle bus to village.

Tourist information Sierra Nevada:
🌿🏔☃ Parc Natural de Sierra Nevada. Large nature park with Europe's most southern ski resort.

▨ S | **Taberno** | **39C5**

Área El Rancho, Los Llanos (La Carrasquilla), Santopetar.
GPS: n37,46028 w2,03833. ⬆
8 ☕€ 8 ⛽ ≋ Ch ⚡ (4x)included. **Surface:** gravel.
Distance: 🚶600m ✈ A7 13km.
Remarks: Swimming pool.

▨ S | **Tarifa** ✿ | **38D6**

GPS: n36,06804 w5,6856.

20 ☕free. **Surface:** sand. ▢ 01/01-31/12
Distance: 🚶10km ⚓on the spot ⊗50m ♒100m.
Remarks: Parking beach.

Tourist information Tarifa:
ℹ Tourist Office, Duke of Kent House, Cathedral Square, Gibraltar, www.gibraltar.gi. British colony at the northwest end of the Rock of Gibraltar.
👁 Siege Tunnels, Gibraltar. Labyrinth of tunnels, ingenious defence system.

▨ S | **Valverde del Camino** | **38C4**

Ctra. de Zalamea. **GPS:** n37,58111 w6,75138. ⬆

10 ☕free ⛽ ≋ Ch free. **Surface:** asphalted/sand. ▢ 01/01-31/12
Distance: 🚶500m.

▨ S | **Vélez-Rubio** | **39C5**

Área Puerta Oriental de Andalucía, Calle Granada. **GPS:** n37,65194 w2,07555.
⬆➡

10 ☕free ⛽ ≋ Ch free. **Surface:** metalled.
▢ 01/01-31/12 ◉ 1st week Aug
Distance: 🚶500m ✈2,2km ⊗500m ♒500m.

▨ S | **Vera** | **39D5**

Acvera Motorhome Park & Aire. GPS: n37,26030 w1,85347. ⬆
150 ☕€ 7-9 ⛽ ≋ Ch ⚡ included. **Location:** Rural, comfortable.
Surface: metalled.
Distance: 🚶Vera 2km ✈4,7km ⚓beach 7km ⊗on the spot.
Remarks: Tennis & padel lessons, 11 tennis courts.

▨ S | **Vera** | **39D5**

Oasis al Mar, Av del Salar. **GPS:** n37,22731 w1,82819. ⬆
50 ☕€ 7-9, trailer € 1 ⛽ ≋ Ch ⚡ €3/day ◉€3 ⚡included.
Location: Rural, comfortable. **Surface:** gravel. ▢ 01/10-01/05
Distance: 🚶centre Vera 4,4km ⚓2km.
Remarks: Motorhome washing place € 4.

▨ S | **Villanueva de Algaidas** | **39A5**

Calle de la Archidona, A-7201. **GPS:** n37,17824 w4,44858. ⬆

20 ☕free ⛽ ≋ Ch free. **Surface:** asphalted.
Remarks: Max. 48h.

PORTUGAL

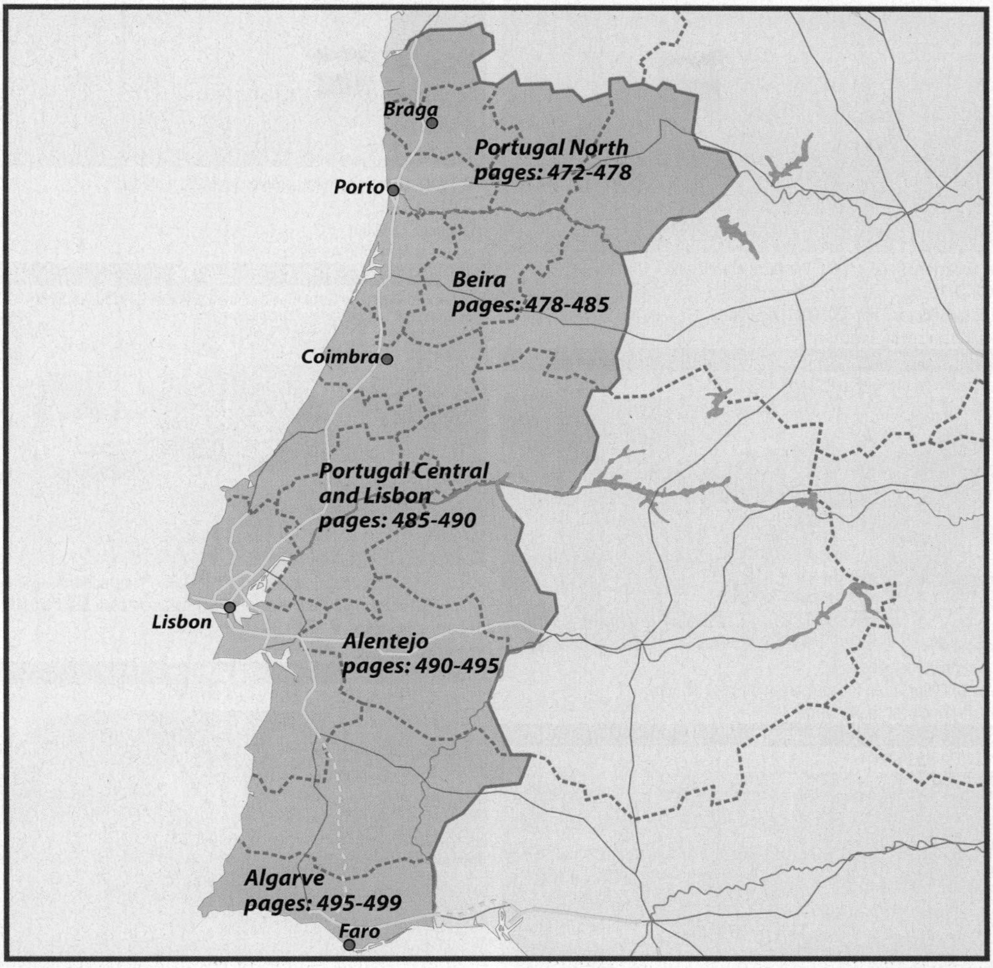

Braga

Porto

Portugal North
pages: 472-478

Beira
pages: 478-485

Coimbra

Portugal Central
and Lisbon
pages: 485-490

Lisbon

Alentejo
pages: 490-495

Algarve
pages: 495-499

Faro

Capital: Lisbon
Government: Parliamentary democracy
Official Language: Portuguese
Population: 10,800,000 (2013)
Area: 91,642 km²

General information
Dialling code: 00351
General emergency: 112
Currency: Euro
Payments by credit card are accepted almost
everywhere.

Regulations for overnight stays
Wild camping is not officially allowed. Overnight
parking places mentioned here are not official
motorhome stopovers but tolerated areas. You will
not find an official motorhome sign.

Additional public holidays 2015
January 6 Epiphany
April 3 Good Friday
April 25 Liberationday
May 1 Labor Day
June 4 Corpus Christi
June 10 National Holiday
August 15 Assumption of the Virgin Mary
October 5 Republic day
November 1 All Saints' Day
December 8 Immaculate Conception

Portugal North

Aguçadoura — 36B5

Aguaçadoura Futebol Clube. **GPS**: n41,44389 w8,77722. 🔼 .

5 free. **Location:** Rural, simple. **Surface:** gravel/sand.
◻ 01/01-31/12
Distance: 500m 50m 500m 500m.
Remarks: Parking at the beach.

Amarante — 36C6

Av. Alexandre Herculano. **GPS**: n41,27286 w8,07178.

. **Surface:** metalled.
Distance: 800m on the spot on the spot 50m.
Remarks: Parking near sports centre.

Amarante — 36C6

GPS: n41,27020 w8,07708.

. **Surface:** metalled. 🔘 Wed
Distance: ⊗on the spot on the spot.
Remarks: Market square along the river.

Amarante — 36C6

Penedo da Rainha, São Gonçalo. **GPS**: n41,28031 w8,06925.
Ch . ◻ 01/02-30/11
Distance: 1km ⊗on the spot on the spot 1km.

Tourist information Amarante:
Ⓜ✝ Museu Municipal Amadeu de Souza Cardoso, Alameda Teixeira Pascoaes.
Modern art.

Arcos de Valdevez — 36C5

N202. **GPS**: n41,84749 w8,41524. 🔼 .

10 free. **Location:** Rural, simple. **Surface:** metalled.
◻ 01/01-31/12
Distance: 300m.
Remarks: Along the Vez river.

Avintes — 36B6

Parque Biológico de Gaia, Rue da Cunha. **GPS**: n41,09730 w8,55414. 🔼➡️.

9 €4 + €4 /pp, entrance park incl Ch included WC free,at
reception. **Location:** Luxurious, quiet. **Surface:** grasstiles. ◻ 01/01-31/12
Distance: 10km 800m 100m.
Remarks: Check in at reception.

Barcelos — 36B5

R.Rosa Ramalho. **GPS**: n41,52829 w8,61547. 🔼 .

12 free. **Location:** Rural, simple. **Surface:** metalled.
◻ 01/01-31/12
Distance: centre 800m 3,5km on the spot.
Remarks: Parking swimming pool.

Tourist information Barcelos:
Ⓜ Museu de Olaria de Barcelos, R. Cónego Joaquim Gaiolas. Ceramics and
archeology. ◻ Tue-Su 10-12.30h, 14-18h, Thu 10-18h.

Bico — 36B6

R. Vasco da Gama. **GPS**: n40,73016 w8,64747. 🔼 .

30 free free. **Location:** Rural, simple, isolated, quiet. **Surface:** metalled.
◻ 01/01-31/12
Distance: 300m on the spot on the spot ⊗on the spot.
Remarks: In fishing port.

Braga — 36C5

Bom Jesus do Monte. **GPS:** n41,55278 w8,38137. ⊕ .

25 ⛺ free ⟊ Ch WC free. **Location:** Urban, simple. **Surface:** concrete. ☐ 01/01-31/12
Distance: 🚉6km ⊗20m 🚌100m.
Remarks: Parking at funicular railway.

Braga — 36C5

Sameiro. **GPS:** n41,53928 w8,36743.

10 ⛺ free.
Location: Simple.
Surface: gravel/sand.
Remarks: Parking at place of pilgrimage.

Tourist information Braga:
🎆 Semana Santa. Procession. ☐ week before Easter.
🌿 Parque Nacional da Peneda-Gerês. Hiking routes.

Bragança 🐚 — 36D5

Parque de Merendas, Rue Miguel Torga. **GPS:** n41,80417 w6,74611. ⊕ .

30 ⛺ free ⟊ 🔧 Ch free.
Location: Rural, comfortable, quiet. **Surface:** metalled.
☐ 01/01-31/12
Distance: 🚉200m ⊗200m 🚌200m.
Remarks: P below the castle, 01/07-15/09, max. 24h, beautiful view.

Tourist information Bragança:
ℹ️ Medival upper city and castle.
Ⓜ Museu Militar. ☐ 9-11.45h, 14-18.15h.
🌿 Parque Natural de Montesinho. Nature reserve.

Cabedelo — 38B1

R.do Cabedelo. **GPS:** n40,14403 w8,86395.

10 ⛺. **Location:** Simple. **Surface:** sand. ☐ 01/01-31/12
Distance: 🏊on the spot ⊗on the spot.
Remarks: Beach parking.

Caminha — 36B5

Largo da Feira. **GPS:** n41,87490 w8,84113. ⊕ .

10 ⛺ free. **Location:** Urban, simple. **Surface:** metalled.
☐ 01/01-31/12
Distance: 🚉500m 🚌100m.

Carrazeda de Ansiães — 36C6

Rua Engenheiro Camilo de Mendonça. **GPS:** n41,24498 w7,30386.
⛺ ⟊ 🔧 Ch. ☐ 01/01-31/12
Remarks: Parking swimming pool.

Carregal do Sal — 38C1

Quinta de Cabriz. **GPS:** n40,42465 w8,01856.
⛺ free. **Surface:** unpaved.
Distance: ⊗on the spot.
Remarks: Portugal Tradicional, max. 24h.

Carregal do Sal — 38C1

Luzio, Arruamento Urbano a Sul da Vila. **GPS:** n40,43116 w7,99471. ⊕ .

3 ⛺ free ⟊ 🔧 Ch free. **Location:** Simple. **Surface:** grassy.
☐ 01/01-31/12
Distance: 🚉1km.
Remarks: Behind petrol station.

Castelo do Neiva — 36B5

Av, de Santoinho. **GPS:** n41,67501 w8,78243.
⛺.

Chaves 🐚 — 36C5

Alameda do Trajano. **GPS:** n41,73694 w7,46917. ⊕ .

6 ⛺free. **Location:** Urban, simple. **Surface:** metalled.
🅿 01/01-31/12
Distance: 🏛historical centre 300m 🏖8,6km ⊗100m 🚰100m.
Remarks: Along the Tâmega river.

| △ S | Chaves 🌿 | 36C5 |

Quinta do Rebentão, Vila Nova de Veiga. **GPS:** n41,70127 w7,50013.
⛺🚿Ch🔧. 🅿 01/01-30/11
Distance: 🏊4km ⊗400m 🚰1km 🚌800m.

Tourist information Chaves:
🏛 Torre de Mengem. Military museum.

| △ S | Covas | 36B5 |

Parque Campismo de Covas, Lugar de Pereiras. **GPS:** n41,88758 w8,69497.
⛺🚰Ch🔧. 🅿 01/01-31/12

| △ S | Covas | 36B5 |

Camping Quinta do Retiro *** - Covas (TBU)

quintadoretiro@gmail.com - http://www.quintadoretiro.com

Beautiful view
Sanitary facilities
Swimming pool

Quinta do Retiro, Lugar Quinta do Retiro s/n. **GPS:** n40,35230 w7,91583.
5 ⛺01/09-30/06 € 17,50, 01/07-31/08 € 22 🚰🚿Ch🔧 (5x),10Amp
WC🅿⊡€1/1 🛜included. **Surface:** grassy. 🅿 01/01-31/12
Distance: 🏛800m 🏊3km ⊗3km 🚰3km 🚌8km 🎣on the spot.

| 🅿 S | Entre-os-Rios | 36B6 |

GPS: n41,08357 w8,29322. 🔼.

4 ⛺ WC 🛜Lunchroom & co. **Location:** Simple, central, noisy.
🅿 01/01-31/12
Distance: 🏛100m 🏊on the spot 🛒on the spot ⊗100m 🚰100m.
Remarks: Parking along the Douro river.

| 🅿 S | Espinho 🏖 | 36B6 |

GPS: n40,98889 w8,64306. 🔼.

40 ⛺free 🚰free,beach. **Location:** Rural, simple, isolated, quiet.
Surface: gravel/sand. 🅿 01/01-31/12
Distance: 🏛1km 🏊25m ⊗1km 🚰1km.
Remarks: Beach parking.

| △ | Espinho 🏖 | 36B6 |

Municipal de Espinho, Zona da Ribeira dos Mochos. **GPS:** n41,01402 w8,63743.
⛺. 🅿 01/01-31/12

| 🅿 S | Esposende 🏖 | 36B5 |

Forte de S.João Baptiste, Rue do Farol. **GPS:** n41,54222 w8,79111.

5 ⛺free 🚰🛜 🛜free.
Location: Urban, simple. **Surface:** asphalted.
🅿 01/01-31/12
Distance: 🏛1,5km 🏊on the spot ⊗on the spot 🚰1,5km.
Remarks: Parking at lighthouse, free wifi for clients restaurant.

| △ S | Esposende 🏖 | 36B5 |

Parque de Campismo de Fão, Lírios - Fão. **GPS:** n41,50778 w8,77833.
⛺🚰🛜Ch🔧. 🅿 01/01-31/12
Distance: 🏊500m ⊗500m 🚰on the spot 🚌500m.

| 🅿 S | Freixo de Espada a Cinta | 36D6 |

Espaço Multiusos, R. do Samiteiro de Cima. **GPS:** n41,08826 w6,81751.🔼.
12 ⛺free 🚰🛜Ch🔧 (12x)free. **Surface:** metalled. 🅿 01/01-31/12
Distance: ⊗900m 🚰900m.
Remarks: Arrival <18h.

| 🅿 S | Freixo de Numão | 36C6 |

Area de autocaravanas Jean Pierre Rossi, Sebarigos.
GPS: n41,06000 w7,22111.🔼.

30 ⛺€ 5/night 🚰🛜Ch🔧 WC included. 🚿 **Surface:** metalled.
Distance: 🏛900m ⊗500m 🚰500m.

| 🅿 S | Gerês 🏔 | 36C5 |

Vila do Gerês. GPS: n41,73538 w8,15969. 🔼.

4 🚐 🚰 free. **Location:** Rural, simple. **Surface:** asphalted.
📅 01/01-31/12
Distance: 🏘 1km 🍴 on the spot.

[△] [S] Gondomar 36B6

Medas, Gavinho - Medas. **GPS**: n41,03917 w8,42694.
🚐 🚰 🕳 Ch. 📅 01/01-31/12

🍇 Gosende 36C6

Cooperativa Capuchinhas CRL, Campo Benfeito. **GPS**: n40,99799 w7,9269.
🚐 free. **Surface:** unpaved.
📅 01/01-31/12
Distance: ⛽ 5,1km.
Remarks: Portugal Tradicional.

🚐 [S] Guilhufe 36B6

EM594. **GPS**: n41,19541 w8,31605. [↑][→].

8 🚐 free 🚰 🕳 Ch free. **Location:** Simple, noisy. **Surface:** metalled.
📅 01/01-31/12
Distance: 🏘 1km ⛽ 1,6km 🍴 1km 🛒 1km.

🚐 [S] Izeda 36D5

Largo do Toural. **GPS**: n41,56750 w6,72333. [↑][→].

30 🚐 free 🚰 🕳 Ch free. **Location:** Rural, simple, central, quiet.
Surface: metalled. 📅 01/01-31/12
Distance: 🏘 centre 🍴 200m 🛒 200m.

🚐 [S] Lamego 36C6

Parque Lamego, N2, Lugar da Raposeira. **GPS**: n41,09016 w7,82214. [↑][→].

40 🚐 € 5 + € 3/pp 🚰 🕳 Ch 🔌 €4/day WC 🚿 📶. **Location:** Luxurious, isolated, quiet. **Surface:** unpaved. 📅 01/01-31/12
Distance: 🏘 1,2km ⛽ 4,5km 🍴 500m 🛒 2km 🚌 on the spot.
Remarks: Baker every morning, beautiful view, near Caves da Raposeira, sale of wines.

🚐 [S] Lamego 36C6

GPS: n41,09501 w7,80372.

🚐 🚰 free. **Surface:** metalled. 📅 01/01-31/12
Distance: 🏘 on the spot 🍴 on the spot 🛒 on the spot.
Remarks: At the foot of monumental stairs of the Santuari.

Tourist information Lamego:

👁 Bodega Raposeira. [T] free.
✳ Nossa Senhora dos Remédios. Pilgrimage in Portugal, most important festivity of the country. 📅 end Aug-beginning Sep.

🚐 [S] Macedo de Cavaleiros 36D5

Rua das Piscinas. **GPS**: n41,53756 w6,95715. [↑][→].

8 🚐 free 🚰 €2/100liter 🕳 Ch 🔌 €2/1h. **Location:** Urban, simple, central, quiet. **Surface:** asphalted. 📅 01/01-31/12
Distance: 🏘 200m 🍴 200m 🛒 300m 🚌 on the spot.

🚐 Macedo de Cavaleiros 36D5

Barragem do Azibo, Frada da Pegada. **GPS**: n41,58333 w6,89944. [⇡] .

10 🚐 free. **Location:** Rural, simple, quiet. **Surface:** metalled.
📅 01/01-31/12
Distance: 🏘 2km ⛱ Sandy beach 🍴 on the spot (peak season).
Remarks: At barrage, guarded during summer period.

🚐 Matosinhos 36B6

Av. de Praia. **GPS**: n41,26044 w8,72434. [⇡] .

PT

10 🛏free. **Location:** Simple, noisy. **Surface:** metalled.
⬤ 01/01-13/12
Distance: 🚶200m ⊗200m 🛒600m 🚌on the spot.
Remarks: Beach parking.

| △S | Matosinhos | 36B6 |

Municipal de Angeiras. GPS: n41,26722 w8,71972.
🛏🚰⚡Ch. ⬤ 01/01-31/12
Remarks: Service only € 3,15-5,40.

| 🅿 | Melgaço | 36C5 |

Porta de Lamas de Mouro, Lamas de Mouro. **GPS:** n42,05202 w8,19413.
🛏free. **Surface:** metalled.

| 🏛 | Melgaço | 36C5 |

Rua do Mercado. **GPS:** n42,11549 w8,26095. 🔼 .

6 🛏free. **Location:** Rural, simple. ⬤ 01/01-31/12
Distance: ⊗on the spot.

| 🅿 | Miranda do Douro 🌿🚶🎭 | 36D6 |

Av. Eduardo Quero. **GPS:** n41,49167 w6,27333.

🛏free. **Surface:** metalled.
Distance: 🚶25m ⊗200m.
Remarks: Near city wall.

| 🅿 | Miranda do Douro 🌿🚶🎭 | 36D6 |

Largo do Cestelo. **GPS:** n41,49611 w6,275.

🛏free. **Surface:** metalled.
Distance: 🚶on the spot ⊗50m 🛒50m.
Remarks: Parking near ruins of castle.

| 🅿S | Mirandela 🌿 | 36D5 |

Largo Cardal. **GPS:** n41,48685 w7,18391. 🔼 .

15 🛏free 📶Fon. **Location:** Rural, simple, central, noisy.
Surface: metalled.
Distance: 🚶centre ⊗on the spot 🛒on the spot 🚌on the spot.
Remarks: Large parking along the river.

| △S | Mirandela 🌿 | 36D5 |

Três Rios-Maravilha. GPS: n41,50683 w7,19716.
🛏🚰⚡Ch.
⬤ 15/05-31/09

Tourist information Mirandela:
🅼 Museu municipal. Modern Portuguese painting art. ⊤ free.
🅼 Villa Flôr. Village museum. ⊤ free.

| △S | Mogadouro | 36D6 |

Mogadouro, Complexo Desportivo Municipal. **GPS:** n41,33528 w6,71861.
🛏🚰⚡Ch.⚡ ⬤ 01/04-30/09
Distance: ⊗500m 🛒on the spot 🚌500m.

| 🅿S | Mondim de Basto | 36C5 |

Area Mondim de Basto. GPS: n41,41199 w7,95137. 🔼

30 🛏free 🚰🛢Chfree. **Location:** Urban, simple, central. **Surface:** metalled.
⬤ 01/01-31/12
Distance: 🚶300m ⊗300m 🛒300m.
Remarks: Friday market.

| 🅿S | Montalegre | 36C5 |

Rua João Rodrigues Cabrilho. **GPS:** n41,82280 w7,78684. 🔼
🛏free 🚰🛢Chfree. **Surface:** metalled. ⬤ 01/01-31/12
Distance: 🚶500m.

| 🅿 | Murça | 36C6 |

Murça-Estádio, Variante à N15. **GPS:** n41,40421 w7,44994. 🔼 .

🛏free. **Surface:** asphalted. ⬤ 01/01-31/12
Distance: 🚶500m ⊗300m.
Remarks: At footballstadium.

| 🏚 | Nelas | 36C6 |

Paço dos Cunhas de Santar, Largo do Paço, Santar. **GPS:** n40,57229 w7,89154.
🛏free.
Remarks: Portugal Tradicional, max. 24h, vineyard/restaurant, awning and

generator prohibited.

🛏️	**Parada**	36C5

Santuàrio. **GPS:** n41,68806 w8,20167.

🛏️ S	**Peso da Régua** ⬆️ 🔌	36C6

Parque Ovar, Av. de Ovar. **GPS:** n41,16278 w7,79222.⬆️.

4 🏕️free ⚡(4x)WCfree,150m. **Location:** Urban, simple, central, noisy.
Surface: asphalted. ⬛ 01/01-31/12
Distance: 🚰on the spot 🛒4km 🅿️on the spot ⊗on the spot 🍴on the spot.

🛏️	**Ponte de Lima** 🌿 ⬆️	36B5

Alameda de São João. **GPS:** n41,77052 w8,5847.⬆️.

15 🏕️. **Location:** Urban, simple. **Surface:** metalled. ⬛ 01/01-31/12
Distance: 🚰300m 🅿️on the spot.
Remarks: Along river.

⚠️ S	**Póvoa de Varzim**	36B5

Rio Alto, Estela. **GPS:** n41,46277 w8,77369.
🏕️🔌⬛Ch. ⬛ 01/01-31/12
Remarks: Service passerby € 3,50-6.

⚠️ S	**Queimadela**	36C5

Parque de Campismo do Baragem. **GPS:** n41,50379 w8,16216.
🏕️€5 🔌⬛Ch ⚡🍴. **Surface:** grassy/metalled. ⬛ 01/01-31/12
Distance: 🏊100m 🚰100m 🍴on the spot.

🛏️	**Santa Maria da Feira** 🌿	36B6

GPS: n40,91972 w8,54306.⬆️.

5 🏕️free. **Location:** Rural, simple, quiet. **Surface:** gravel/sand.
⬛ 01/01-13/12
Distance: 🚰600m ⊗600m.
Remarks: Parking at castle.

🛏️ S	**São Romão do Corgo**	36C5

Quinta de Bourça, Lugar de Vila Nova. **GPS:** n41,44348 w7,9932.
🏕️free 🔌€2,50 ⚡€2,50. **Location:** Rural.
Distance: 🛒11km.
Remarks: Portugal Tradicional.

🛏️ S	**São Salvador de Lordelo**	36B6

R. da Igreja. **GPS:** n41,23472 w8,41139.⬆️➡️.

20 🏕️free 🔌⬛Chfree. **Location:** Simple, quiet. **Surface:** gravel/sand.
⬛ 01/01-31/12
Distance: 🚰400m ⊗400m 🍴400m.

🛏️	**Soajo** ⛰️	36C5

M530. **GPS:** n41,87197 w8,2633.⬆️.

5 🏕️free. **Location:** Rural, simple. **Surface:** metalled.
⬛ 01/01-31/12
Distance: 🚰100m ⊗100m.
Remarks: Parking near school.

🛏️ S	**Torre de Moncorvo**	36D6

GPS: n41,18083 w7,04167.⬆️.
9 🏕️free 🔌⬛Chfree 🍴. **Surface:** metalled. ⬛ 01/01-31/12
Distance: 🚰1,5KM.
Remarks: At sports park.

🛏️	**Valadares-SP do Sul** ⛰️	36B6

Cooperativa Mimos, Largo do Cruzeiro 1. **GPS:** n40,75704 w8,19997.⬆️.

3 🏕️free. **Location:** Simple. **Surface:** grassy.
⬛ 01/01-31/12
Distance: 🚰on the spot.
Remarks: Portugal Tradicional.

⚠️ S	**Valpaços**	36C5

Do Rabaçal, Rua Gago Coutinho. **GPS:** n41,63222 w7,24778.
🏕️🔌⬛Ch. ⬛ 01/01-31/12

🛏️	**Viana do Castelo** 🐚	36B5

Rua de Lima. **GPS:** n41,69534 w8,81875.⬆️.

PT

15 🛌free. **Location:** Urban, simple. **Surface:** metalled/sand.
Distance: 🚶centre 700m.
Remarks: Large parking along the Limia river.

△S **Viana do Castelo** 36B5
Cabedelo/Orbitur, Cabedelo - Darque. **GPS:** n41,67862 w8,82611.
🛌 ⛽€5,40 🍴Ch. ⬛ 16/01-15/11

Tourist information Viana do Castelo:
⛺ Campo do Costelo. Market. ⬛ Fri.
☀ Romaria da Nossa Senhora da Agonia. Procession with Gigantes (giants).
⬛ 3rd week Aug.

△S **Vila Chã** 36B5
Sol de Vila Chã, Rua do Sol, Facho. **GPS:** n41,29825 w8,73263.
🛌 ⛽🍴Ch🧹. ⬛ 01/01-31/12
Distance: 〰300m ⊗10m 🚰on the spot 🚗100m.

▢ **Vila do Conde** 36B5
Av. Júlio Graça. **GPS:** n41,34476 w8,74541. ⬆.

20 🛌free. **Location:** Urban, simple, central, noisy. **Surface:** metalled.
⬛ 01/01-31/12
Distance: 🚶400m 〰150m 🚐150m ⊗200m 🚰400m.
Remarks: Along the Este river.

▢ **Vila do Conde** 36B5
Av. Marques de Sa Bandiera. **GPS:** n41,34270 w8,74587. ⬆.

20 🛌free. **Location:** Urban, simple, central. **Surface:** gravel/sand.
⬛ 01/01-31/12
Distance: 🚶500m 🚐on the spot ⊗200m 🚰400m.
Remarks: Parking at sea.

🛌S **Vila Nova de Cerveira** 36B5
Av. dos Pescadores. **GPS:** n41,93823 w8,74685. ⬆.

4 🛌free ⛽🍴Ch🏊free. **Location:** Rural, simple. **Surface:** asphalted.
⬛ 01/01-31/12
Distance: 🚶historical center 150m 🏖river-beach.
Remarks: Near Minho river and public pool park.

🛌S **Vila Nova de Foz Côa** 36C6
Autocross, N102. **GPS:** n41,06727 w7,15496. ⬆➡.
🛌free ⛽🍴Ch🔑 free. **Location:** Isolated, quiet.
Distance: 🚶2km.

🛌 **Vila Nova de Foz Côa** 36C6
Rua Engenheiro Eugénio Nobre. **GPS:** n41,08028 w7,14806. ⬆➡.
+50 🛌free. **Location:** Rural. ⬛ 01/01-31/12
Distance: 🚶500m ⊗500m.

△S **Vila Nova de Gaia** 36B6
Madalena, Rua de Cerro, Praia de Madalena. **GPS:** n41,10750 w8,65556.
🛌 ⛽🍴Ch. ⬛ 01/01-31/12
Remarks: Service only € 3,15-5,40.

Tourist information Vila Nova de Gaia:
ℹ City of the port wine, at the left bank of the river Douro, Port houses can be visited daily.

△S **Vila Real** 🍃 36C6
Municipal de Vila Real, Rua Dr. Manuel Cardona, Quinta da Carreira.
GPS: n41,30333 w7,73667.
🛌 ⛽🍴Ch.
⬛ 01/01-31/12

Tourist information Vila Real:
👁 Solar de Mateus. Baroque country house, 18th century, known from label of the Matheus wine.

🛌S **Vinhais** 36D5
GPS: n41,83381 w7,00271. ⬆.

6 🛌free ⛽🍴Chfree. **Location:** Urban, simple. **Surface:** gravel.
⬛ 01/01-31/12
Distance: 🚶200m ⊗100m.
Remarks: Nearby swimming pool.

Beira

🛌S **Aldeia da Ponte** 38D1
Caminho do Freguil. **GPS:** n40,41092 w6,87159. ⬆.

4 🛌free ⛽🍴Chfree. **Location:** Rural, simple. **Surface:** metalled.
⬛ 01/01-31/12
Distance: 🚶300m.
Remarks: Near old Roman bridge.

🛌 **Almeida** 🍃 36D6
Rua da Guerreira. **GPS:** n40,72295 w6,90489.

🛌free. **Surface:** metalled. ⬛ 01/01-31/12

Remarks: At fort-castle.

Anadia 38B1

Rua Seabras de Castro. **GPS:** n40,44056 w8,4375. 🔼 .

🛏free. **Surface:** asphalted.
Distance: ⊗100m 🚰100m.
Remarks: At restaurants.

Aveiro 36B6

Parcue de S João, Canal São Roque. **GPS:** n40,64328 w8,65859.

10 🛏free 🚰free. **Surface:** grasstiles. ⬛ 01/01-31/12
Distance: 🚶200m 🏊25m ⊗200m 🚰200m.
Remarks: Parking at the Canal and A25.

Tourist information Aveiro:
Ⓜ Ecomuseu da Troncalhada, Canal das Pirâmides. Salt-making. ⬛ summer.
Ⓜ Museu de Aveiro, Av. Sta. Joana Princesa. Collection baroque art. ⬛ Tue-Su 10-17.30h.

Barril de Alva 38C1

EM517-1. **GPS:** n40,28611 w7,96167.🔼 .

50 🛏free 🚰🚽Ch WC free. **Location:** Rural, simple, quiet. **Surface:** unpaved.
⬛ 01/01-31/12
Distance: 🚶500m 🏊river-beach ⊗on the spot.

Barriosa 38C1

Poço da Broca. **GPS:** n40,29366 w7,75376.

🛏free. **Location:** Rural.
Distance: 🏊on the spot ⊗on the spot.
Remarks: Portugal Tradicional, restaurant and regional products for sale.

Belmonte 38C1

Parque de Santiago, N345. **GPS:** n40,27512 w7,35856.🔼.

4 🛏free 🚰 Ch WC 🛏free. **Surface:** metalled. ⬛ 01/01-31/12
Distance: 🚶500m ⊗on the spot 🚰150m 🚌on the spot.

Castelo Bom 38D1

Avenida Santa Maria, N16. **GPS:** n40,61261 w6,83398. 🔼 .

3 🛏free. **Location:** Rural, simple. **Surface:** metalled.
⬛ 01/01-31/12
Distance: 🚶on the spot.
Remarks: Less suitable for motorhomes >6,5m, typical village nearby spanish border.

Castelo Branco 38C1

Municipal de Castel Branco, N18. **GPS:** n39,85815 w7,49351.
🛏🚰🚽Ch free. ⬛ 02/01-15/11

Tourist information Castelo Branco:
⌒ Castelo. Ruins of castle of the Templars.
🌳 Alameda da Liberdade. ⬛ Mo.

Castelo de Paiva 36B6

R. Emidio Navarro. **GPS:** n41,03955 w8,27406. 🔼 .

50 🛏free 🚰🚽Ch WC free. **Location:** Simple, central, quiet.
Surface: metalled. ⬛ 01/01-31/12
Distance: 🚶on the spot ⊗on the spot 🚰on the spot.
Remarks: Market square.

Castelo Mendo 38D1

P5, N16. **GPS:** n40,59444 w6,94833. 🔼 .

PT

3 🛏️free ⚡free. **Location:** Rural, simple. **Surface:** grassy/sand.
⬛ 01/01-31/12
Distance: ⬇️on the spot ⚡6,8km.

Castelo Rodrigo 🌿 36D6
GPS: n40,87778 w6,96611.

🛏️free. **Surface:** sand.
Remarks: At the entrance of fort.

Celorico da Beira 36C6
GPS: n40,63389 w7,40472.

10 🛏️. **Location:** Isolated. **Surface:** metalled.
Distance: ⬇️2km.
Remarks: Parking sports park.

Cinfães 36C6
GPS: n41,07167 w8,08719.

🛏️. **Surface:** metalled. ⬛ 01/01-31/12
Distance: ⬇️100m ✕100m ⚡100m.

Coimbra 🌿 38B1
Parque do Choupalinho, Av. Inês de Castro. **GPS:** n40,19970 w8,42905. ⬆️

20 🛏️free ⚡🔌Ch🚿free. **Surface:** metalled.
⬛ 01/01-31/12
Remarks: Max. 24h.

Tourist information Coimbra:
👁️ Portugal dos Pequeninos. Miniature Portugal. ⬛ 9-19h.

Coimbrão 38B1
Praia do Pedrógão. GPS: n39,91500 w8,95.
🛏️ ⚡€2,15 🔌Ch🚿. ⬛ 16/02-15/12
Distance: ⬇️50m ✕on the spot ⚡on the spot 🚌10m.

Condeixa 38B1
Av. Bombeiros Voluntarios de Condeixa. **GPS:** n40,11291 w8,49336. ⬆️➡️

6 🛏️free ⚡🔌Chfree. **Surface:** asphalted. ⬛ 01/01-31/12
Distance: ⬇️500m ✕on the spot ⚡300m.
Remarks: Max. 48h, market Friday-morning.

Condeixa 38B1
Conímbriga, Praça da Republiça Condeixa. **GPS:** n40,09895 w8,4894. 🎪.

5 🛏️free. **Location:** Simple. **Surface:** grassy/metalled. ⬛ 01/01-31/12
Remarks: Parking next to archaeological site.

Covas do Monte-SP do Sul 36C6
Covas do Monte.
GPS: n40,88873 w8,09823.
🛏️free ⚡free.
Distance: ⬇️250m.
Remarks: Portugal Tradicional.

Escalos de Baixo 38C1
Hanmar, Estrada National 352. **GPS:** n39,89917 w7,40028. ⬆️

20 🛏️€ 8, May-Aug € 10 ⚡🔌Ch ✂️WC 🔲included. **Surface:** grassy.
⬛ 01/01-31/12
Distance: ✕1km ⚡1km.

Estarreja 36B6
R. Dr.Antonio Madureira. **GPS:** n40,75417 w8,56611. ⬆️➡️

6 ₹ € 2/24h ⌐ ⏚ Ch 🖊 included. **Location:** Urban, simple, central.
Surface: metalled. ◘ 01/01-31/12
Distance: ⬇on the spot ⊗on the spot ⬇on the spot.
Remarks: Max. 48h, check in Cafe Piscina, Ag. Seguros Rebelo, tuesday market 100m.

10 ₹free ⌐ ⏚ Chfree. **Surface:** grassy. ◘ 01/01-31/12
Distance: ⬇200m 🚲1km ⊗300m ⬇300m.

⚠S	Estarreja	36B6
Ribeira do Maurão. **GPS:** n40,81328 w8,61588. ⬆➡.

⚠S	Fundão	38C1
Quinta do Convento. **GPS:** n40,13276 w7,51205.
₹ ⌐ ⏚Ch 🖊 WC ⏚ ⌐. ◘ 01/01-31/12

6 ₹free ⌐ ⏚ Chfree. **Location:** Rural, simple, isolated, quiet.
Surface: metalled. ◘ 01/01-31/12
Distance: ⬇on the spot 🚶on the spot.
Remarks: Nature reserve.

⚠S	Furadouro	36B6
Praia do Furadouro. **GPS:** n40,87645 w8,67381. ⬆.

30 ₹free WC 50m. **Location:** Rural, simple, quiet. **Surface:** asphalted.
◘ 01/01-31/12
Distance: ⬇on the spot ⊗300m ⬇300m.
Remarks: Beach parking.

⚠S	Figueira da Foz ⛱	38B1
Av. de Espanha. **GPS:** n40,14856 w8,86791. ⬆.

⚠S	Guarda 🍦	38C1
Parque Pólis, Rua da Direcção Geral de Viação. **GPS:** n40,54894 w7,24083. ⬆➡.

30 ₹ WC. **Surface:** asphalted. ◘ 01/01-31/12
Distance: ⬇on the spot ⬇on the spot ⊗100m.

20 ₹free ⌐ ⏚ Chfree. **Location:** Simple. **Surface:** metalled.
◘ 01/01-31/12
Distance: ⬇historical centre 4km 🚲2,4km ⬇700m.
Remarks: Recreation park.

⚠S	Figueira da Foz ⛱	38B1
Gala/Orbitur, Matas Nacias, Gala. **GPS:** n40,11861 w8,85639.
₹ ⌐ ⏚Ch. ◘ 16/01-15/11
Remarks: Service only € 3,15-5,40.

⚠S	Guarda 🍦	38C1
Rossio de Valhelhas. **GPS:** n40,40333 w7,40528.
₹ ⌐ ⏚Ch. ◘ 01/05-30/09
Distance: ⬇50m ⊗300m ⬇150m ⬇100m.

⚠S	Figueira da Foz ⛱	38B1
Praia de Quiaios. **GPS:** n40,22083 w8,885.
₹ ⌐ ⏚Ch 🖊. ◘ 01/07-30/09
Distance: ⬇500m ⊗on the spot ⬇on the spot ⬇500m.
Remarks: Service only € 2,60-4,40.

Tourist information Guarda:
🏛 Medieval city.

⚠S	Idanha-a-Nova	38C1
Municipal de Idanha-a-Nova, Albufeira da Barragem Marechel Carmona.
GPS: n39,95056 w7,18722.
₹ ⌐ ⏚Ch 🖊. ◘ 01/01-31/12
Distance: ⬇50m ⊗on the spot ⬇on the spot ⬇8km.
Remarks: Service only € 2,60-4,40.

⚠S	Fratel	38C2
Vila Velha de Ródão. **GPS:** n39,63250 w7,74694. ⬆➡.

	Idanha-a-Velha	38C1
N332. **GPS:** n39,99830 w7,1445.
₹.

Tourist information Idanha-a-Velha:
⌒ Archeological tour.

⚠S	Ilhavo	36B6
Av Ns.da Saude. **GPS:** n40,61417 w8,75222. ⬆.

7 ⬚free ⌐ Ch WC. **Surface:** metalled. 🅾 01/01-31/12
Distance: ⌐on the spot ⌐on the spot.
Remarks: Beach parking.

| 🅰🅂 | Ilhavo ◁ | 36B6 |

Av. Infante Dom Henrique, Praia da Barra. **GPS:** n40,64375 w8,74456.⬆

30 ⬚free. **Surface:** metalled. 🅾 01/01-31/12
Distance: ⌐300m. ⌐300m.

| 🅂 | Ilhavo ◁ | 36B6 |

Costa Nova do Prado. **GPS:** n40,61222 w8,74917.⬆

7 ⬚free. **Surface:** metalled. 🅾 01/01-31/12
Distance: ⌐on the spot ⌐on the spot ⊗on the spot ⌐on the spot.
Remarks: Beach parking.

Tourist information Ilhavo:
Ⓜ Museu Histórico da Vista Alegre, Fábrica de Porcelanas da Vista Alegre.
Collection of porcelain. 🅾 Tue-Fri 9-18h, Sa-Su 9-12.30h, 14-17h.
Ⓜ Museu Marítimo de Ílhavo, Av. Dr. Rocha Madahil. Shipping museum.
🅾 Tue-Fri 10-12.30h, 14.30-18h, Sa-Su 14.30-17.30h.

| 🅂🅂 | Lorvão | 38B1 |

Rua do Malhao. **GPS:** n40,25896 w8,31468.

10 ⬚free ⌐ Ch free. **Surface:** metalled.
Distance: ⌐on the spot.

| 🅂 | Luso | 38B1 |

GPS: n40,38639 w8,38139.

10 ⬚free. **Surface:** metalled. 🅾 01/01-31/12
Remarks: Parking next to Hotel de Terme.

Tourist information Luso:
🌿 Mata Nacional do Buçaco. Nature reserve.

| 🅰🅂 | Melo-Gouveia | 38C1 |

Quinta das Cegonhas, Nabainhos. **GPS:** n40,52057 w7,54169.
50 ⬚€ 14,50-18 ⌐ Ch ⌐ WC ⌐ ⌐.

| 🅰🅂 | Mira ⌐ | 36B6 |

Praia de Mira. GPS: n40,44472 w8,79806.
⬚⌐Ch. 🅾 16/01-15/11
Remarks: Service only € 3,15-5,40.

| 🅂🅂 | Miranda do Corvo ⌐ | 38B1 |

Rua Porto Mourisco. **GPS:** n40,08803 w8,33232.⬆➡

8 ⬚free ⌐ Ch free. **Location:** Rural. **Surface:** asphalted.
🅾 01/01-31/12
Distance: ⌐700m.

| 🅂🅂 | Oleiros | 38C1 |

R. Dr. Barata Relvas. **GPS:** n39,92056 w7,91389.⬆
⬚free ⌐ Ch free. **Surface:** metalled. 🅾 01/01-31/12

| 🅂🅂 | Pardilhó ⌐ | 36B6 |

Parque de Merendas, R. Joaquim Maria Resende. **GPS:** n40,80111 w8,63472.
⬆➡

15 ⬚€ 2/48h ⌐ Ch ⌐ included. **Location:** Rural, comfortable, isolated,
quiet. **Surface:** metalled. 🅾 01/01-31/12
Distance: ⌐600m ⌐on the spot ⌐on the spot.
Remarks: Max. 48h, check in at bar (service).

| 🅂🅂 | Penacova | 38B1 |

Bairro de Carrazedos. **GPS:** n40,26722 w8,28306.➡

PT

10 🛏free ⛽🚿 Ch WC free. **Surface:** metalled. 🅿 01/01-31/12
Distance: 🛒400m 🏊3km ⛰800m ⊗400m.

20 🛏free. **Surface:** sand.
Distance: 🛒500m.
Remarks: Beach parking.

🏧S	Penamacor ⛰	38C1

Benquerença. **GPS:** n40,22938 w7,22136. ⬆.

🏧S	Praia de Quiaos	38B1

Praia de Quiaos. **GPS:** n40,22034 w8,89116.

10 🛏free ⛽ 🚿 Ch free. **Location:** Rural, simple, quiet. **Surface:** gravel/sand.
🅿 01/01-31/12
Distance: 🛒2km ⛰on the spot.

15 🛏 ⛽free. **Location:** Simple. **Surface:** metalled. 🅿 01/01-31/12
Remarks: Beach parking.

🏧	Pinhel	36C6

GPS: n40,77389 w7,06194.

🏧S	Sabugal	38C1

Rua do Cemitério. **GPS:** n40,34843 w7,08653. ⬆➡.

🛏.
Distance: ⊗on the spot 🍴on the spot.
Remarks: At townhall.

6 🛏free ⛽ 🚿 Ch free. **Surface:** metalled. 🅿 01/01-31/12
Distance: 🛒500m ⊗400m.

🏧S	Praia de Mira 🏖	36B6

Praia da Mira. **GPS:** n40,45800 w8,8025.

🏧S	Sangalhos	36B6

R. do Mercado. **GPS:** n40,48639 w8,47528. ⬆➡.

6 🛏 ⛽free. **Location:** Simple. **Surface:** metalled. 🅿 01/01-31/12
Distance: 🛒on the spot.
Remarks: Beach parking.

20 🛏free ⛽🚿Ch free. **Location:** Simple. **Surface:** metalled.
🅿 01/01-31/12
Remarks: At sports centre.

🏧	Praia de Mira 🏖	36B6

GPS: n40,44620 w8,80447.

⚠S	Santa Ovaia	38C1

Ponte das Três Entradas, Avô. **GPS:** n40,30667 w7,87139.
🛏⛽🚿🏧. **Surface:** grassy. 🅿 01/01-31/12
Distance: ⛰10m 🛒on the spot ⊗on the spot 🍴on the spot 🚌10m.

🏧S	São João da Pesqueira	36C6

Rua General Ramalho Eanes. **GPS:** n41,14682 w7,40187.
10 🛏€ 10 ⛽🚿 Ch 🚿 WC 🛏.
Distance: 🛒400m.
Remarks: At fire-station.

PT

🍴 S | **São João da Pesqueira** | 36C6
Restaurant Carocha, N222. **GPS:** n41,15120 w7,42378.
50 ⚡free 🚰🔌 Ch free. ⊡ 01/01-31/12
Distance: 🚶1km ⊗on the spot.
Remarks: Next to restaurant and Port wine cellar Cave Cadão.

🅿 S | **Sao Joao de Areias** | 38C1
Terra de Iguanas, Estrada principal 76, Vila Dianteira. **GPS:** n40,39045 w8,08574.
4 ⚡€ 7,50, 01/06,50-31/08 € 10 🚰🔌Ch 🔑included. ⊡ 01/01-31/12
Remarks: Max. 3 nights, swimming pool incl., vegetables and fruit from the garden.

🅿 | **São Lourenço do Bairro** | 38B1
Quinta do Encontro, N334. **GPS:** n40,44136 w8,49014.
⚡free. ⊡ 01/01-31/12
Remarks: Portugal Tradicional, max. 24h, vineyard/shop/restaurant, awning and generator prohibited.

🅿 | **São Pedro do Sul** ♨ | 36C6
Termas São Pedro do Sul, N46. **GPS:** n40,74056 w8,08639. ⬆➡.

6 ⚡free 🚰🔌 Ch free. **Location:** Simple. **Surface:** asphalted.
⊡ 01/01-31/12
Distance: 🚶1km.
Remarks: Max. 48h.

🅿 S | **Sertã** ♨ | 38B1
R. Amaro Vicente Martins. **GPS:** n39,79729 w8,09588. ⬆.

4 ⚡free 🚰🔌 Ch 🔑free. **Location:** Simple. **Surface:** asphalted.
⊡ 01/01-31/12
Distance: 🚶500m 🚲3km 🛒50m.
Remarks: At sports park.

🅿 | **Sertã** ♨ | 38B1
Palácio da Justiça, R. Baden Powell. **GPS:** n39,80028 w8,09944. ⬆.

⚡free. **Location:** Simple. **Surface:** gravel/sand.
Distance: 🚶100m 🚲3km ⊗50m 🛒100m.

🅿 S | **Sertã** ♨ | 38B1
Albergue do Bonjardim, Nesperal, Sertã. **GPS:** n39,81306 w8,16278.

2 ⚡€ 6 🚰🔌 🔑€4 WC ▯. **Location:** Luxurious, isolated.
Surface: unpaved.
⊡ 01/04-31/10
Distance: 🚶200m ⊗2,5km 🛒1km 🚂50m.
Remarks: Sauna, steam bath and covered pool € 7,50, breakfast € 7,50.

🅿 | **Tabua** | 38C1
Piscina. GPS: n40,36306 w8,03.

3 ⚡free. **Surface:** metalled.

🅿 | **Tabua** | 38C1
Rua Aurora Jesus Goncalves. **GPS:** n40,36306 w8,02278.

10 ⚡free. **Surface:** metalled.

🅿 | **Trancoso** | 36C6
Parque Sportivo. GPS: n40,77160 w7,35621.

3 ⚡free. **Surface:** metalled.

🅿 | **Trancoso** | 36C6
Av. Heróis de São Marcos. **GPS:** n40,77583 w7,35056.

10 ⛺. **Surface:** metalled.
Distance: ⊗50m.
Remarks: Note: Friday market day.

📷S **Vagos** 36B6
Praia da Vagueira. GPS: n40,54944 w8,77056.⬆.
20 ⛺€7,50, 01/10-31/05 €5 ⚡🍴Ch⚙€2 ⬚€0,50. **Surface:** sand.
🅾 01/01-31/12
Remarks: Service passerby € 2,50.

⚠S **Vagos** 36B6
Vagueira, Gafanha da Boa Hora. **GPS:** n40,55806 w8,74528.
⛺🍴Ch 🅾 01/01-31/12
Distance: 🚲1km ⊗on the spot 🍽1km 🚌500m.
Remarks: Service only € 2,60-4,40.

📷 **Vagueira** 36B6
Rua Arménio, Praia da Vagueira. **GPS:** n40,56506 w8,76697.⬆➡.

20 ⛺free. **Surface:** metalled.
Distance: 🚲200m 🏖sandy beach 50m.
Remarks: Beach parking.

📷S **Vila Nova de Oliveirinha** 38C1

Quinta do Tapadinho - Vila Nova de Oliveirinha

info@campingtapadinho.com - www.campingtapadinho.com
Beautiful view
Convenient for longer stays
Bread-service

Quinta do Tapadinho, Rua dos Brandões. **GPS:** n40,36520 w7,92195.
5 ⛺€13,25 ⚡€2/100liter Ch⚙(5x)€5/24h,10Amp WC⬚€4
📶included. **Surface:** grassy/sand. 🅾 01/01-31/12
Distance: 🚲1km 🚲6km ⊗1km 🍽8km 🚌1km ⚲on the spot.

📷S **Vila Pouca da Beira** 38C1
Despinheiro, Avenida Principal. **GPS:** n40,30159 w7,9257.

4 ⛺€8, 2 pers.incl ⚡WC⬚€1 €4. **Location:** Rural, isolated, quiet.
Surface: grassy. 🅾 01/01-31/12
Distance: 🚲500m 🚲2km 2km ⊗800m on the spot ⚲on the spot.

📷S **Vilar Formoso** 38D1
Zaza, Avenida das Tilia's, N332. **GPS:** n40,61528 w6,83833.⬆.

12 ⛺€5/24h ⚡€2 Chincluded ⚙(12x)€1,50/day. **Location:** Simple.
Surface: asphalted/gravel. 🅾 01/01-31/12
Distance: 🚲500m 🍽baker on site.

📷S **Viseu** 36C6
Av. Europa. **GPS:** n40,66533 w7,91681.⬆.
8 ⛺free ⚡Chfree.
Surface: asphalted.
🅾 01/01-31/12
Distance: 🚲on the spot 🚲6km.

Tourist information Viseu:
ℹ Centre of Vinho do Dão.
Ⓜ Museu municipal, Castro Daire. Etnographical collection.

Portugal Central

📷S **A-dos-Cunhados** 38A2
R. Monsenhor José Fialho. **GPS:** n39,15222 w9,30083.⬆.

⛺free ⚡Chfree. **Surface:** asphalted. 🅾 01/01-31/12
Distance: 🚲100m 🚲6km 🏖beach 7km ⊗200m.

📷S **Abrantes** 38B2
Aquapolis, São Joao. **GPS:** n39,45489 w8,18977.⬆.

PT

⌁free ⊣ ᗕ Ch ⟫free. **Surface:** metalled. ▯ 01/01-31/12
Distance: 📍3km ⚓4,7km ⊗100m 🚰6km.
Remarks: Service 100m.

Abrantes 38B2

Aquapolis, São Joao. **GPS:** n39,45333 w8,19056.⬆.

10 ⌁free ⊣ ᗕ Ch ⟫free. **Surface:** metalled.
Distance: 📍3km ⚓4,8km ⌂Sandy beach.
Remarks: Along the Tagus river.

Abrantes 38B2

Largo do Pralvo. **GPS:** n39,44956 w8,18968.⬆.

10 ⌁free. **Surface:** metalled. ▯ 01/01-31/12
Distance: 📍1km ⚓6,5km ⊗1km 🚰1km.
Remarks: Along the Tagus river.

Abrantes 38B2

Parque Urbano de São Lourenço, São Vincente. **GPS:** n39,47530 w8,21541.⬆.

10 ⌁free. **Surface:** grassy/gravel. ▯ 01/01-31/12
Distance: 📍centre 2,4km ⚓4,4km ⊗50m 🚰3,5km.
Remarks: Max. 48h.

Tourist information Abrantes:
⌂ Posto de Turismo, Esplanada 1º de Maio, www.cm-abrantes.pt. City with historical centre.

Alenquer 38A2

Alenquer camping, Casal das Pedras. **GPS:** n39,05917 w9,02833.
4 ⌁€ 15,50 ⊣€2,50 ᗕ Ch. ▯ 01/01-31/12
Distance: 🚰on the spot 🚰on the spot.

Almourol 38B2

Castelo de Almourol, Praia do Ribatejo. **GPS:** n39,46295 w8,38297.

10 ⌁free. **Location:** Simple. **Surface:** metalled.
Distance: 📍2km ⚓4km ⊗on the spot 🚰2km.
Remarks: On the banks of the Tejo river, parking castle.

Arruda dos Vinhos 38A2

Casal da Pevide. **GPS:** n38,99861 w9,08417.⬆.

3 ⌁free ⊣ ᗕ Ch free. **Surface:** asphalted. ▯ 01/01-31/12
Distance: 📍2km ⊗on the spot 🚰on the spot.
Remarks: Parking Intermarché.

Baleal 38A2

Estrada do Baleal. **GPS:** n39,37240 w9,33702.

⌁free. **Surface:** asphalted. ▯ 01/01-31/12
Distance: 📍2km ⌂sandy beach 50m ⊗on the spot 🚰2km.
Remarks: Parking next to bar restaurant in village square, not recommended at the weekend.

Batalha 38B1

Parque Cónego M. Simões Inácio, Rua Cerca Conventual.
GPS: n39,66134 w8,82516.⬆.

15 ⌁free ⊣ ᗕ Ch 📧 ⟫free. **Surface:** asphalted.
▯ 01/01-31/12 ◉ Mo
Distance: 📍100m ⊗250m 🚰on the spot.
Remarks: At football ground/tennis, max. 48h.

Cabo Espichel 38A3

P Cabo Espichel. **GPS:** n38,42031 w9,21353.

♨free. **Location:** Isolated. **Surface:** unpaved. ▢ 01/01-31/12
Distance: ⌂Sesimbra 13km ⚓At the sea.
Remarks: Beautiful view.

Cascais 🏖 — 38A2
Cap Raso. GPS: n38,71134 w9,48498.

♨free. **Location:** Isolated. **Surface:** sand. ▢ 01/01-31/12
Distance: ⌂6km ⊗on the spot ⚓6km.
Remarks: Parking near the cliffs Also possibility for overnight stay at restaurant Maremonte.

Cascais 🏖 — 38A2
Guincho, Areia, Guincho. **GPS:** n38,72167 w9,46639.
♨ ⛽🍽Ch. ▢ 01/01-31/12
Remarks: Service only € 3,15-5,40.

Cerradas — 38A2
Estrada Á-dos-Serrados. **GPS:** n38,91798 w9,38292.
20 ♨free ⛽Chfree.
Distance: ⌂on the spot ⚓5km.

Constância — 38B2
Estrada National. **GPS:** n39,47670 w8,34365.⬆

20 ♨free ⛽🍽Chfree. **Location:** Comfortable. **Surface:** metalled.
▢ 01/01-31/12
Distance: ⌂500m ◢2,3km ⚓on the spot ⊗500m ⚓300m.
Remarks: Along the Zêzere river.

Coruche — 38B2
Area autocaravana, Rua 5 de Outubro. **GPS:** n38,96139 w8,51944.

100 ♨free ⛽🍽Chfree. **Surface:** metalled. ▢ 01/01-31/12 ◉ last Sa of the month
Distance: ⚓on the spot ⚓on the spot.

Costa da Caparica 🏖 — 38A2
Caravanismo da Costa da Caparica, Santo António da Caparica.
GPS: n38,65389 w9,23833.
♨⛽🍽Ch ◢ ▢ 01/01-31/12
Distance: ⚓500m ⚓on the spot ⚓on the spot ⚓100m.
Remarks: Service only € 3,15-5,40.

Dois Portos — 38A2
GPS: n39,03689 w9,18098.

♨⛽free. **Surface:** metalled. ▢ 01/01-31/12

Ericeira 🏖 — 38A2
Municipal de Mil Regos, N247, Casal do Moinho Velho.
GPS: n38,97778 w9,41861.
♨⛽🍽Chfree.
▢ 01/01-31/12
Remarks: Service in front of campsite.

Tourist information Ericeira:
👁 Aldeia Museu de José Franco, Sobreiro. Miniature village. ▢ 9-19h. 🇹 free.

Fátima — 38B1
Rua de Sao Vicente de Paulo. **GPS:** n39,63389 w8,67111.⬆

10 ♨free ⛽WCfree. **Surface:** asphalted. ▢ 01/01-31/12
Distance: ⌂1km ◢3,2km ⊗100m ⚓1km.
Remarks: May 12-13 festivities.

Foz do Arelho — 38A2
Av. do Mar. **GPS:** n39,42888 w9,22201. ⬆.

10 ♨free WC. **Surface:** metalled. ▢ 01/01-31/12
Distance: ⌂1km ⚓50m ⊗on the spot ⚓1,5km.
Remarks: Beach parking.

Lisbon — 38A2
Av. de Brasilia. **GPS:** n38,69463 w9,19966.

50 ♨free. **Surface:** asphalted.
Distance: ⌂city centre 6km ⊗300m ⚓500m ⚓400m bus-tram.

PT

△S **Lisbon** 🍳🎣🍲🥗 **38A2**
Municipal de Lisboa-Monsanto, Monsanto, Estrada da Circunvalação.
GPS: n38,72472 w9,20805.
🅱️ 🔌 Ch 🔧 WC 🚰🔲 📹.
🅾️ 01/01-31/12
Distance: 🚶3km ⊗on the spot 🚆on the spot 🚌50m.
Tourist information Lisbon:
ℹ️ Lisboa Card. Card gives entrance to museums, public transport, available at: Rua Jardim do Regedor 50 (10-18), Mosteiros do Jeronimos, Museu dos Coches.
📞 € 18,50/24h, € 31,50/48h, € 39/72h.
⚘ Market. 🅾️ Tue, Sa.
⚘ 32 Covered markets, most important market: Av. 24 de Julho. 🅾️ 6-14h
💿 Su.
⚘ Campo de Sta Clara. Flea market.
⚘ Rua de São Bento. Antiques market.
😊 Arena near metro Campo Pequeno. 🅾️ 01/05-30/09 Thu.
😊 Feira Popular. Fairground, opposite the Entrecampos metro. 🅾️ 01/05-30/09.
😊 Oceanário, Parque das Nações. Aquarium. 🅾️ 10-19h.
🥗 Chiado. Elegant shopping district. 🅾️ elevator 7-24h.

🅱️S **Mação** **38B2**
Campo de Feiras, Av. Vicente Mirrado. **GPS:** n39,55723 w7,99303.⬆️

10 🅱️free 🔌 💬 Ch 🔧 WC free. **Location:** Simple. **Surface:** metalled.
🅾️ 01/01-31/12
Distance: 🚶500m 🚲6km ⊗500m 🚆500m.
Remarks: Max. 48h.

🅱️S **Mafra** **38A2**
Palacio Nacional. GPS: n38,93758 w9,33548.
🅱️ 🔌free. 🅾️ 01/01-31/12
Tourist information Mafra:
✖️ Posto do turismo, Palácio Nacional de Mafra - Torreão Sul, Terreiro D. João V, www.cm-mafra.pt/turismo.
😊 Parque Tapada Nacional, Portão do Codeçal. Safaripark. 🅾️ 10-19h.

🅱️ **Marinha Grande** **38B1**
São Pedro de Moel. **GPS:** n39,76974 w9,02752.

🅱️free. **Location:** Simple. **Surface:** metalled. 🅾️ 01/01-31/12
Distance: 🚶10km 🚲100m ⊗50m.
Remarks: Beach parking.

△S **Marinha Grande** **38B1**
Parque de Campismo Orbitur, São Pedro de Moel. **GPS:** n39,75806 w9,02583.
🅱️ 🔌💬Ch. 🅾️ 01/01-31/12
Remarks: Service only € 3,15-5,40.

🅱️ **Montijo** **38A2**
GPS: n38,70286 w8,97665.

50 🅱️free. **Surface:** metalled.
Distance: 🚶800m 🚲200m ⊗100m 🚆200m 🅿️2km.
Remarks: Parking at ferry-boat to Lisbon.

🅱️S **Nazaré** ⚓🍲 **38B1**
Rua Nossa Senhora da Vitória. **GPS:** n39,64696 w9,06936.
20 🅱️free 🔌💬Chfree 📶. **Location:** Rural, isolated, quiet.
Surface: metalled.
Distance: 🚶on the spot ⊗on the spot.

🅱️ **Nazaré** ⚓🍲 **38B1**
Avenue do Municipio. **GPS:** n39,59741 w9,0696.

7 🅱️free. **Surface:** asphalted. 🅾️ 01/01-31/12
Distance: 🚶200m 🚲250m ⊗250m 🚆750m.

🅱️S **Obidos** 🍳 **38A2**
Rue do Ginasio. **GPS:** n39,35628 w9,15672.⬆️

20 🅱️€ 6/24h 🔌 💬Ch 🔧 WC included. **Location:** Simple.
Surface: gravel/sand. 🅾️ 01/01-31/12
Distance: 🚶500m 🚲1km ⊗500m 🚆500m.

🅱️S **Odivelas** **38A2**
Rolarlivre, Rua Alm. Gago Coutinho, Póvoa de Santo Adrião.
GPS: n38,79605 w9,16384.⬆️
3 🅱️€5 🔌💬Ch 🔧included. **Surface:** metalled. 🅾️ 01/01-31/12
Distance: 🚲700m ⊗100m.
Remarks: Motorhome dealer, service passerby € 2,50, video surveillance.

🅱️S **Outeiro da Cabeça** **38A2**
Rua do Pavilhão Gimnodesportivo. **GPS:** n39,19306 w9,1825.⬆️

⅀free 🚰🔌Chfree. **Surface:** gravel. ⏺ 01/01-31/12
Distance: 🚶300m 🚲2,5km ⊗300m 🛒300m.

| 📷 | **Palmela** | 38A3 |

GPS: n38,56664 w8,90032.
⅀.
Remarks: Parking at castle.

| 📷 | **Peniche** | 38A2 |

Av. Porto De Pesca. **GPS:** n39,35852 w9,37752. 🔼.

⅀free. **Location:** Simple, central. **Surface:** metalled.
⏺ 01/01-31/12
Distance: 🚶500m 🚲900m ⚓1km ⊗500m 🛒500m.
Remarks: At fire-station and marina.

| 📷 | **Peniche** | 38A2 |

Farol do Cabo Cavoeiro, Caminho do Farol. **GPS:** n39,35989 w9,4082. 🔼.

⅀. **Location:** Simple, isolated. **Surface:** metalled. ⏺ 01/01-31/12
Distance: 🚲5km ⚓300m ⊗1,5km 🛒3km.
Remarks: At lighthouse.

| 📷 | **Peniche** | 38A2 |

Praia de Consolação, Avenida do Mar, Consolação. **GPS:** n39,32567 w9,35713.
🔼.

⅀free. **Surface:** asphalted.
Distance: 🚶on the spot ⚓Sandy beach.
Remarks: Beach parking.

| 📷 | **Peniche** | 38A2 |

R. de Liberdade. **GPS:** n39,36577 w9,37417. 🔼.

⅀. **Location:** Simple. **Surface:** sand. ⏺ 01/01-31/12
Distance: 🚶1,7km ⚓50m ⊗200m 🛒200m.
Remarks: Nearby Intermarché.

| 📷S | **Peniche** | 38A2 |

Peniche Praia, Estrada Marginal Norte. **GPS:** n39,36959 w9,392. 🔼.

23 ⅀€ 15,20, 2 pers.incl 🚰🔌Ch ⚡ WC included 📷 📶. **Surface:** grassy.
⏺ 01/01-31/12
Distance: ⚓At the sea ⊗on the spot 🛒1,5km 🚌1,5km.
Tourist information Peniche:
ℹ️❌ Fortaleza de Peniche. Bathing resort.
ℹ️❌ Posto de Turismo, Rua Alexandre Herculano, www.cm-peniche.pt. Bathing resort.

| 📷S | **Praia de Santa Cruz** | 38A2 |

GPS: n39,14418 w9,37482.
⅀free 🚰WC free. **Location:** Simple. **Surface:** asphalted.
⏺ 01/01-31/12
Distance: 🚶300m ⚓20m ⊗on the spot 🛒300m.
Remarks: Parking at the beach or near the cliffs.

| 📷 | **Praia de Santa Cruz** | 38A2 |

GPS: n39,13640 w9,38006.
⅀free. **Surface:** metalled.
Distance: 🚶on the spot ⚓50m ⊗on the spot 🛒on the spot.
Remarks: Beach parking.

| 📷 | **Ribamar** | 38A2 |

R. do Cacho Longo, São Lourenço. **GPS:** n39,01120 w9,42078.
⅀free. **Location:** Simple, isolated. **Surface:** asphalted.
⏺ 01/01-31/12
Distance: ⚓Sandy beach ⊗on the spot 🛒6km.

| 📷 | **São Martinho do Porto** | 38A1 |

Av. Marigal. **GPS:** n39,50176 w9,14132. 🔼.

⅀free. **Surface:** metalled. ⏺ 01/01-31/12
Distance: 🚶1,4km 🚲5,5km ⚓sandy beach 50m ⊗850m.

| 📷S | **Sintra** | 38A2 |

Avenida Conde Sucena, São Pedro de Penaferrim. **GPS:** n38,78883 w9,37473. 🔼.
⅀€5 🚰🔌Chincluded. **Surface:** asphalted.
Distance: 🚶2km.
Remarks: At footballstadium.

| 📷S | **Tomar** | 38B1 |

Av. Gen. Bernardo Faria. **GPS:** n39,59972 w8,41306.

PT

free WC. **Location:** Simple. **Surface:** gravel/sand.
🗓 01/01-31/12
Distance: 🚆200m ⊗200m 🛒300m.
Remarks: Nearby railway station.

Tourist information Tomar:
Ⓜ Sinagoga de Tomar, Museu Luso-Hebraico, Rua Dr. Joaquim Jacinto, 75.
Synagogue and Jewish Portuguese history. Ⓣ free.
✝ Convento de Cristo. Fortified monastery.
Festa dos Tabuleiros. 🗓 Whitsuntide.
Barragem de Castelo de Bode. Artificial lake, 15km east of the city.

△S Torres Vedras 38A2
Municipal da Praia de Santa Cruz. GPS: n39,13444 w9,37472.
🚰 Ch against payment. 🗓 01/01-31/12

△S Turcifal 38A2
Largo Brigadeiro França Borges. **GPS:** n39,04288 w9,26581.⬆
free 🚰 Ch free. **Location:** Central. **Surface:** metalled.
Distance: 🚆on the spot.

△S Vermoil 38B1
R. Vale de Fojo, Pombal. **GPS:** n39,85080 w8,66125.⬆

5 free 🚰 Ch free. **Surface:** gravel/sand. 🗓 01/01-31/12
Distance: 🚆200m ⊗300m 🛒300m.
Remarks: At cemetery.

Alentejo

△S Alcácer do Sal 38B3
Barragem Pego do Altar, Alcácer do Sal > N253 > Montemoro o Novo > N380.
GPS: n38,42055 w8,39384.

15 free 🚰 Ch WC free. **Location:** Rural. **Surface:** sand.
🗓 01/01-31/12
Distance: 🚆Alcácer do Sal 13km on the spot ⊗100m.

△S Alcácer do Sal 38B3
Rua do Cabo da Vila. **GPS:** n38,36903 w8,50276.
free.
🗓 01/01-31/12
Distance: 🚆Old city 600m 🚲5,6km ⊗400m.
Remarks: Near arena.

ℹ Little town on the Rio Sado.

△S Almograve 38A4
Avenida da Praia. **GPS:** n37,65303 w8,80059. 🅿.

30 free 🚰 free. **Location:** Simple. **Surface:** grasstiles.
🗓 01/01-31/12
Distance: on the spot.

△S Alvito 38B3
Rua de Tapadinha. **GPS:** n38,25917 w7,99222.
free.
Remarks: At swimming pool.

△S Avis 38B2
Municipal Albufeira do Maranhão, Barragam Albufeira do Maranhão.
GPS: n39,05682 w7,91145.
🚰 Ch.
Distance: on the spot.
Remarks: Service only € 1,90.

△S Campo Maior 38C2
Barragem do Caia. **GPS:** n39,00308 w7,14219.

.

△S Castelo de Vide 38C2
Estr. de São Vincente. **GPS:** n39,41028 w7,44917.

Remarks: At stadium.

△S Castelo de Vide 38C2
Rua Luís de Camões. **GPS:** n39,41583 w7,45778.⬆

free.
Remarks: Near city wall.
Tourist information Castelo de Vide:
ℹ www.cm-castelo-vide.pt. Historical centre with medieval citadel.

△S Cavaleiro 38A4
Cabo Sardano. **GPS:** n37,59810 w8,80608. 🅿.

PT

30 🛏️free. **Location:** Simple. **Surface:** sand. ◯ 01/01-31/12
Distance: ⚓on the spot.
Remarks: At lighthouse.

🅢 Comporta 38A3
GPS: n38,38308 w8,78712.

🛏️⚓free. **Surface:** sand. ◯ 01/01-31/12
Distance: 🚰250m ⚡1km ⊗300m 🚻500m.
Remarks: Near church.

Comporta 38A3
GPS: n38,37849 w8,78544.
🛏️. **Surface:** sand. ◯ 01/01-31/12

Elvas 🌀 38C3
Intermarché, Rue Paco Bandera. **GPS:** n38,87458 w7,18429.⬆️.

15 🛏️free ⛽🔋Chfree. **Surface:** asphalted. ◯ 01/01-31/12
Distance: 🚰historical centre 1,7km 🚻on the spot.
Remarks: At petrol station and supermarket, max. 48h.

Elvas 🌀 38C3
GPS: n38,87766 w7,17763.

🛏️. **Surface:** metalled.
Remarks: Parking at aqueduct.
Tourist information Elvas:
ℹ️ Fortified city.

🅢 Estremoz 38C3
Rossio Marquês de Pombal. **GPS:** n38,84252 w7,5858.

10 🛏️ 📶. **Surface:** metalled.
Distance: 🚰on the spot ⊗50m 🚻50m.
Tourist information Estremoz:
⛺ Market. ◯ Sa.

Evora 🌀 38B3
GPS: n38,57529 w7,90519.

🛏️free. **Surface:** gravel/metalled. ◯ 01/01-31/12
Remarks: Parking university, illuminated.

Evora 🌀 38B3
Ave Túlio Espanca, N114. **GPS:** n38,56655 w7,91541.

🛏️free. **Surface:** gravel/metalled. ◯ 01/01-31/12
Distance: 🚰500m ⊗800m 🚻600m ⊡1km.

Evora 🌀 38B3
Lago da Porta de Avis. **GPS:** n38,57672 w7,91096.

🛏️free. **Surface:** gravel/metalled.
◯ 01/01-31/12
Remarks: Parking at aqueduct.
Tourist information Evora:
ℹ️ Posto de Turismo, Praça do Geraldo, www.cm-evora.pt. City with historical centre.

PT

✝ Igreja de S. Francisco, Capela dos Ossos. Chapel of the bones.
🚻 8-18h 📷 12-14h.
🎍 🚻 Tue.

PT

📲 S **Ferreira do Alentejo** 38B3
GPS: n38,05675 w8,11955.

🅿️free 🚰. **Surface:** asphalted.
Distance: 🚰500m ⊗100m 🛒1km 🗒1,5km.
Remarks: Parking sports park.

📲 S **Grândola** 38B3
Parque de Grândola. **GPS:** n38,18525 w8,564. ⬆️➡️.

7 🅿️free 🚰 🚽 Ch. **Location:** Simple. **Surface:** asphalted.
🚻 01/01-31/12
Distance: 🚰1km ⚓7,4km ⊗600m 🛒500m 🚌1,4km.
Remarks: At sports grounds.

📲 S **Lousal** 38B3
Rua 25 Abril. **GPS:** n38,03591 w8,42908. ⬆️➡️.

6 🅿️free 🚰 🚽 Chfree. **Surface:** gravel. 🚻 01/01-31/12
Distance: ⚓15km ⊗250m 🛒400m bakery 🎍on the spot.
Remarks: At the site of the old mines of Lousal.

📲 S **Luz** 38C3
R. de Mourão. **GPS:** n38,34278 w7,37389. ⬆️➡️.

🅿️free 🚰 🚽 Chfree. **Surface:** metalled.

📲 S **Marvão** 🌿 38C2
N359-6. **GPS:** n39,39556 w7,37667. ⬆️.

12 🅿️free 🚰 🚽 Chincluded WCfree.
Location: Simple. **Surface:** metalled.
Distance: 🚰on the spot ⊗500m.

📲 **Melides** 38A3
Praia de Melides. **GPS:** n38,12897 w8,79262.

🅿️. **Surface:** metalled. 🚻 01/01-31/12
Distance: 🚰Melides 6,2km ⛱Sandy beach ⊗on the spot.

📲 **Mértola** 38B4
N122/IC27. **GPS:** n37,64250 w7,65833.

🅿️.
Distance: ⊗200m 🛒200m.

📲 **Mértola** 38B4
Rua dos Bombeiros Voluntários. **GPS:** n37,64114 w7,66326.
10 🅿️free. **Surface:** gravel/sand.
Remarks: At fire-station.

📲 **Mértola** 38B4
Rua Doutor Afonso Costa.
GPS: n37,64103 w7,6574.
🅿️.
Remarks: Along river.

Tourist information Mértola:
✝ Convento São Francisco.
Former convent, exposition room and atelier.
🚻 10-17h.

📲 S **Messejana** 38B4
GPS: n37,83167 w8,24694. ⬆️.

50 🏕 € 7 🚰 🕾 Ch. **Location:** Rural. ⏹ 01/01-31/12
Distance: 🚶on the spot 🏖 10km.

| 📷 S | Mina de São Domingos 🌿 | 38C4 |

Rua Catarina Eufémia. **GPS:** n37,67052 w7,50194.
🏕 free 🚰 € 2 🕾 Ch.

| 📷 S | Mina de São Domingos 🌿 | 38C4 |

Praia Fluvial, R265. **GPS:** n37,67228 w7,50418.⬆.

20 🏕 free. **Location:** Simple. **Surface:** metalled/sand.
Distance: 🚶750m. 🏊50m.
Remarks: At recreation area, marked pitches.

| 📷 | Monsaraz 🌿 | 38C3 |

GPS: n38,44250 w7,38003.⬆.

±15 🏕 free. **Location:** Quiet. **Surface:** metalled. ⏹ 01/01-31/12
Distance: 🚶100m ⊗100m.
Remarks: Near city wall, beautiful view.

| S | Monsaraz 🌿 | 38C3 |

Rue da Fonte. **GPS:** n38,45317 w7,38117.

🚰€3,50 🕾Ch.
⏹ Mo-Fr 8-21h, Sa-Su 8-12h
Remarks: Call for the key.
Tourist information Monsaraz:
ℹ️ www.monsaraz.com.pt/. Small medieval town.

| ⚠S | Montargil | 38B2 |

Ponte de Sôr. **GPS:** n39,09972 w8,145.
🚰🚐🕾Ch. ⏹ 01/01-31/12
Remarks: Service only € 3-5.

| 📷 S | Montemor-o-Novo | 38B3 |

A6-IP7. **GPS:** n38,61791 w8,08014.
🏕free 🚐free. **Location:** Highway. **Surface:** gravel/sand.
Remarks: Note: toll ticket is valid for 12 hours!.

| 📷 | Odeceixe | 38A4 |

GPS: n37,43750 w8,79833. ⬆.

30 🏕free. **Location:** Simple. **Surface:** sand. ⏹ 01/01-31/12
Distance: 🚶6km 🏊on the spot.
Remarks: Beach parking.

| 📷 | Odemira | 38A4 |

GPS: n37,59839 w8,64615.

🏕free. **Surface:** asphalted. ⏹ 01/01-31/12
Remarks: Along river.

| 📷 S | Pedrogão do Alentejo 🌿🏖🍴 | 38B3 |

Alqueva Camping-Car Park, Estrada nacional 258, Km38,5.
GPS: n38,11705 w7,63571.⬆.

25 🏕first night € 7,50, € 6 each additional night 🚰🕾Ch.🏌 **Location:**
Rural. **Surface:** gravel. ⏹ 01/01-31/12
Distance: 🚶1km 🏊1km 🚣1km ⊗1km 🍴on the spot 🎣on the spot
🎿on the spot.

| 📷 S | Ponte de Sôr | 38B2 |

Avenida da Liberdade. **GPS:** n39,24996 w8,00824.
🏕free. **Surface:** asphalted. ⏹ 01/01-31/12
Distance: ⊗100m 🍴100m.

| 📷 S | Porto Covo | 38A3 |

Rua Francisco Albino. **GPS:** n37,85225 w8,78874.⬆➡.
30 🏕free 🚰🕾Chfree. **Surface:** metalled. ⏹ 01/01-31/12
Distance: 🚶centre 250m 🏊750m.

| 📷 | Porto Covo 🍴 | 38A3 |

Forte do Pessegueiro, Praia da Ilha. **GPS:** n37,49389 w8,47268.

PT

10 ⌇. **Location:** Simple. **Surface:** sand. ☐ 01/01-31/12
Distance: 4km on the spot.
Remarks: Parking at castle.

⌇free. **Location:** Isolated. **Surface:** metalled/sand.
Distance: on the spot.
Remarks: Follow 'Pousada/Zona recreitiva balnear'.

Porto Covo	38A3

Praia Grande, Rua do Mar. **GPS:** n37,85054 w8,79299.

S	Santiago do Cacém	38A2

Rua das Nogueiras. **GPS:** n38,80437 w9,22871.

15 ⌇. **Location:** Simple. **Surface:** gravel.
Distance: 1km 100m 100m 1km.
Remarks: Beach parking.

7 ⌇free Ch free. **Surface:** grasstiles.
Distance: 600m 100m 600m.
Remarks: At swimming pool.

Reguengos de Monsaraz	38C3

N255. **GPS:** n38,43077 w7,53315.

S	Santo André	38A3

Praia de Santo André, Lagoa de Santo Andre. **GPS:** n38,10067 w8,78943.

⌇free. **Surface:** asphalted.
Remarks: Parking at swimming pool.

S	Reguengos de Monsaraz	38C3

Campo 25 de Abril. **GPS:** n38,42150 w7,53534.

15 ⌇. **Location:** Simple. **Surface:** sand.
Distance: 5km on the spot on the spot bakery 1km.
Remarks: Beach parking.

S	Santo André	38A3

Lagoa de Santa André. **GPS:** n38,10972 w8,78722.
Ch . ☐ 01/01-23/12
Distance: 1km 500m on the spot 500m.
Remarks: Service passerby € 2,50.

S	Santo António das Areias	38C2

Camping Asseiceira, Asseiceira. **GPS:** n39,41012 w7,34062.
10 ⌇ € 15-20 Ch WC . **Surface:** grassy. ☐ 01/01-11/11

São Martinho das Amoreiras	38B4

N503. **GPS:** n37,56250 w8,34139.

€3,50 Ch.
Remarks: Next to fire-station.

Santa Clara-e-Velha	38B4

Barragem de Santa Clara. **GPS:** n37,51303 w8,44024.

⌇free. **Surface:** metalled.
Remarks: At barrage.

⊠S **Terrugem** **38C3**
Largo Joaquim Codero Vinaigre. **GPS**: n38,84556 w7,34861. 🔼🏕 .

10 🚐 free 🚰🚱 Ch free.
Location: Rural, simple, quiet. **Surface:** asphalted.
Distance: ⊗300m.

⊠S **Vendas Novas** **38B3**
GPS: n38,67795 w8,45609.
🚐🚰 free. ⏰ 01/01-31/12

⊠S **Vila Viçosa** **38C3**
Avenida do Alandroal. **GPS**: n38,76988 w7,4154.🔼
🚐€5 🚰€2🚱 Ch. **Location:** Simple, quiet. **Surface:** asphalted.
Distance: 🚶1km ⊗1km.
Remarks: At fire-station, monitored parking.

⊠ **Vila Viçosa** **38C3**
Largo Gago Coutinho. **GPS**: n38,77661 w7,42034.

10 🚐 free. **Surface:** sand.
Distance: 🚶250m ⊗25m 🛒100m.

Algarve

⊠S **Albufeira** 🏕🏖 **38B4**
Parque da Galé, Rua do Barranco Vale Rabelho. **GPS**: n37,09347 w8,31125.

28 🚐€6,50 🚰🚱 Ch 🚿 (28x) 📶 included. **Location:** Comfortable.
Surface: unpaved. ⏰ 01/01-31/12
Distance: 🚶600m 🏖1,8km ⊗200m 🛒500m.

⊠S **Albufeira** 🏖 **38B4**
Parque da Palmeira, Rua da Palmeira. **GPS**: n37,09829 w8,24339.🔼

90 🚐€8 🚰🚱 Ch 🚿 WC 🚽⊙€4,50 📶included. **Location:** Urban.
Surface: gravel. ⏰ 01/01-31/12
Distance: 🚶Old city 1,7km 🏖7km 🏊1,5km 🛒800m Lidl 🚌bus terminal 300m.

Tourist information Albufeira:
🔵 Posto de Turismo, R. 5 de Outubro,, www.cm-albufeira.pt. ⏰ 10-20h.
😊 ZooMarine, N125. Attractions park, dolphinarium, aquarium. ⏰ 10-20h.

⊠S **Alcoutim** **38C4**
Estrada da Pousada da Juventude. **GPS**: n37,47500 w7,47472.🔼
🚐free 🚰🚱 Ch free. **Surface:** sand.
⏰ 01/01-31/12
Distance: ⊗200m.
Remarks: Next to 'Centro de Saude'.

Tourist information Alcoutim:
ℹ️ Fortified city. ⏰ 9-17.30h.

⊠S **Aljezur** 🌙🏔 **38A4**
Largo do Mercado. **GPS**: n37,31611 w8,80278.🔼 .

10 🚐free WC free. **Location:** Simple. **Surface:** metalled.
⏰ 01/01-31/12
Distance: ⊗200m 🛒500m.

⊠ **Altura** 🏖 **38B4**
Rua de Alagoa. **GPS**: n37,17138 w7,49952.

+10 🚐free. **Surface:** sand.
Distance: 🚶100m 🏖on the spot ⊗100m.
Remarks: Beach parking.

⊠S **Alvor** 🏖 **38A4**
Zona para autocaravanas, Praia de Alvor. **GPS**: n37,12482 w8,59506.🔼

PT

150 ⌖€4 ⟶🔲Ch ⚐included. **Location:** Central. **Surface:** sand.
🔲 01/01-31/12
Distance: ⚓centre 400m ⚓100m ⚓on the spot.

🔲S | **Ameixial** | 38B4
Estacionamento de Autocaravannas. GPS: n37,36539 w7,97165.⬆️
10 ⌖free ⟶🔲Chfree. **Location:** Rural, isolated, quiet. **Surface:** unpaved.
🔲 01/01-31/12

🔲 | **Cabo de São Vicente** 🌾🏖 | 38A4
N268. **GPS:** n37,02361 w8,995.

8 ⌖free. **Surface:** metalled. 🔲 01/01-31/12
Distance: ⚓Sagres 6km.
Remarks: Parking at lighthouse.

🔲S | **Caldas de Monchique** 🏔 | 38A4
Parque Rural Autocaravanas Vale da Carrasqueira, Barracão 190.
GPS: n37,27667 w8,54333.⬆️

14 ⌖€ 12,50/24h ⟶🔲Ch ⚐WC 🔲included 🔲📶. **Location:** Rural,
comfortable. **Surface:** gravel. 🚶on the spot.

🔲 | **Carrapateira** 🏖 | 38A4
Praia de Amado. GPS: n37,19623 w8,90156.⬆️.

30 ⌖free. **Location:** Simple. **Surface:** gravel.
Distance: ⚓Carrapateira 2km ⊗100m 🚶on the spot.
Remarks: Beach parking.

🔲 | **Carrapateira** 🏖 | 38A4
Praia de Bordeira. GPS: n37,19735 w8,90726.⬆️.

10 ⌖free. **Location:** Simple. **Surface:** metalled.
Distance: ⚓Carrapateira 2,5km.
Remarks: Parking near the cliffs.

🔲S | **Carvoeiro** | 38B4
Casa Long Yin, Sitio nas Travessadas. **GPS:** n37,11547 w8,47011.

5 ⌖€ 10 ⟶🔲Ch ⚐WC 🔲🔲€2,50 📶included.
Surface: grassy.
🔲 01/01-31/12
Distance: ⚓1,5km ⚓1,5km ⊗300m ⚌600m 🏊on the spot 🚶on the spot.
Remarks: Swimming pool incl.

🔲 | **Carvoeiro** | 38B4
Estr. do Farol. **GPS:** n37,08774 w8,44285.

8 ⌖. **Location:** Isolated. **Surface:** sand.
Distance: ⊗500m 🚶on the spot.
Remarks: Parking at lighthouse.

🔲 | **Carvoeiro** | 38B4
Praia Marinha. GPS: n37,09026 w8,41254.

⌖free. **Location:** Isolated. **Surface:** unpaved. 🔲 04/01-31/12
Distance: ⚓4km ⚓on the spot.
Remarks: Beach parking, beautiful view.

🔲S | **Castro Marim** 🌾 | 38B4
Av. Dr. José Afonso Gomes. **GPS:** n37,21984 w7,44434.⬆️.

PT

± 20 �📷 free 🚰€2 🗑 Ch. **Surface:** gravel.
🅾 01/01-31/12 🅾 2rd Sa of the month
Distance: ⛟1,3km ⊗50m.
Remarks: Coins at the shops in the village.

Faro 🌊🍽☕ 38B5
Parking Largo de São Francisco. **GPS:** n37,01132 w7,93184.⬆️.

±6 ⏲free. **Surface:** metalled. 🅾 14-08h

Lagos 🌊⛲🚤 38A4
Area de servico, Junto ao Estadio Municipal de Lagos. **GPS:** n37,11563 w8,678.
⬆️➡️.

20 ⏲€3, from 4th night € 2,50 🚰€2/100 🗑 Ch WC free 📶 against payment.
Surface: gravel.
🅾 01/01-31/12
Distance: city centre 2km ⛟7,3km ⛴2,3km ⊗McDonalds 450m.
Remarks: Check in and pay at reception stadio, market 1st Saturday each month.

Tourist information Lagos:
Ⓜ Museu Municipal, Rua General Alberto da Silveira. Regional museum.
🅾 9.30-12.30h, 14-17h 🅾 holiday.

Manta Rota 🏖 38B4
Praia de Manta Rota, Quinta Manta Rota 15. **GPS:** n37,16513 w7,52096.

80 ⏲€4 🚰🗑 Ch 🔧3h,€2/day 📶included. 🛵 **Surface:** metalled.
Distance: on the spot ⛟6,5km ⛴100m ⊗100m 🚢500m.

Moncarapacho 38B5
Far West Style Camp. **GPS:** n37,08344 w7,76608. ⬆️➡️.
40 ⏲€7 🚰🗑 Ch 🔧 WC 📶included. 🛵 **Location:** Rural, comfortable.

Surface: gravel/sand. 🅾 01/01-31/12
Distance: on the spot ⛴3km.

Moncarapacho 38B5
Caravanas Algarve. **GPS:** n37,09502 w7,77427.

20 ⏲€ 11 🚰🗑 Ch 🔧. **Surface:** gravel. 🅾 01/01-31/12
Distance: 1km ⛱beach 6km ⊗1km.

Odeleite 38B4
Almada D´Ouro Club-Algarve, M1063, Alcarias-Odeleite.
GPS: n37,33187 w7,46865.⬆️.

10 + 20 ⏲€ 4,50 🚰€2,50 🗑 Ch 🔧€2,50 🅾€5 📶included. 🛵
Location: Isolated, quiet. **Surface:** gravel. 🅾 01/01-31/12
Distance: Odeleite 2,3km 🚶on the spot.
Remarks: At hunting club, discount longer stays.

Paderne 38B4
Motorhome Friends. GPS: n37,15643 w8,20972.⬆️.

16 ⏲€ 4,50 🚰🗑 Ch 🔧(9x)€3 WC 🅾€5 📶included. **Location:** Rural.
Surface: gravel. 🅾 01/01-31/12
Distance: 1km ⛴10km 🚶on the spot.
Remarks: Bicycle rental € 5, car rental € 15.

Paderne 38B4
Cm 1177 920N. **GPS:** n37,16801 w8,20897.

12 ⏲free 🚰🗑 Ch free. **Surface:** metalled. 🅾 01/01-31/12
Distance: 1km ⊗1km.

Pereiro 38B4
Parque de merendas do Pereiro, Pereiro. **GPS:** n37,44695 w7,5924.⬆️.

PT

16 🛏free 🚰🗑Chfree. **Surface:** unpaved. ⬛ 01/01-31/12

🛏S **Portimão** 🏖⚓ **38A4**

Praia da Rocha, Avenida Rio Arade,. **GPS:** n37,11898 w8,53037.⬆.

200 🛏€ 2,50 🚰€2/100liter 🗑 Ch 🔌free.🚿 **Surface:** metalled/sand.
Distance: 🏖on the spot ⚓100m ⊗on the spot 🛒200m 🚌on the spot.

🛏 **Portimão** 🏖⚓ **38A4**

Rue Três Castelos. **GPS:** n37,11969 w8,54723.

25 🛏free. **Surface:** asphalted.
Distance: 🏖Praia da Rocha 700m ⚓sandy beach 250m 🛒1km.

🛏S **Quarteira** 🌿 **38B4**

Estrada Fonte Santa, M527-2. **GPS:** n37,07322 w8,07716.⬆➡.

100 🛏€ 2/24h 🚰€2 🗑 Ch 🔌€2.🚿
Surface: gravel.
⬛ 01/01-31/12
Distance: 🏖2km 🚴6,8km ⚓sandy beach 2,5km ⊗50m 🛒150m Lidl
🚌on the spot.
Remarks: Tue 17h-Wed 17h adjacent parking because of Gypsy Market.

🛏S **Sagres** 🏖⚓ **38A4**

Fortaleze de Sagres. **GPS:** n37,00523 w8,94545.⬆ .

50 🛏free WC. **Surface:** asphalted. ⬛ 01/01-31/12
Distance: 🏖500m.
Remarks: At fort-castle.

🛏 **Sagres** 🏖⚓ **38A4**

Rua Mareta. **GPS:** n37,00968 w8,93687.⬆ .

10 🛏free. **Location:** Simple. **Surface:** gravel/sand.
⬛ 01/01-31/12
Distance: 🏖400m ⚓on the spot.
Remarks: Parking behind tourist info, service at the left-hand dir harbor.

🛏 **Salema** 🏖⚓ **38A4**

Praia Boca do Rio. **GPS:** n37,06563 w8,82434.⬆ .

20 🛏free. **Location:** Simple. **Surface:** sand. ⬛ 01/01-31/12
Distance: 🏖2,2km ⚓50m.
Remarks: Forbidden during Summer period.

🛏S **São Bartolomeu de Messines** **38B4**

Camperstop Messines. **GPS:** n37,27979 w8,24133.⬆➡.

40 🛏€ 6, Jul/Aug € 10 🚰🗑 Ch WC 🔌⬛€4/4 🔌included. **Location:** Rural,
isolated, quiet. **Surface:** gravel. ⬛ 01/11-01/08
Distance: 🏖6,5km 🚴6,4km ⊗1,2km.

🛏S **São Bartolomeu de Messines** **38B4**

Rua António Aleixo. **GPS:** n37,25514 w8,2847.⬆.

4 🛏free 🚰🗑Chfree. **Location:** Rural. **Surface:** gravel.
⬛ 01/01-31/12
Distance: 🏖centre 150m 🚴2,7km.
Remarks: Monday regional market.

🛏S **Silves** 🏖⚓ **38B4**

Algarve Motorhome Park Silves, N124. **GPS:** n37,18722 w8,45158.⬆.

50 🚐€ 8 🚰 ⛆ Ch ⚡ 📶included. ☐ 01/01-31/12
Distance: 🏙1km ⊗800m.

🚐 S Silves ⛱ ≋ 38B4
Club Autocaravana, N124. **GPS**: n37,21834 w8,36924.⬆➡.

15 🚐€ 5 🚰 ⛆ Ch ⚡ WC 🚿 ▣ 📶included. **Location:** Rural, comfortable.
Surface: gravel/metalled. ☐ 01/01-31/12
Distance: 🏙9km 🚌100m.

🅿 Silves ⛱ ≋ 38B4
Barregem do Arade, N124-3. **GPS**: n37,23960 w8,37699.

10 🚐free. **Location:** Isolated. **Surface:** sand.
Distance: 🏙Silves 10km.

Tourist information Silves:
Ⓜ Museu Municipal de Arqueologia. Archeological findings.
♜ Castello. ☐ 9-18h.
✵ Festival da cerveja. Beer festival. ☐ July.

🚐 S Tavira 38B4
Parque de Autocaravanes. **GPS**: n37,13637 w7,64013.⬆.

20 🚐€ 9,90 🚰 ⛆ Ch ⚡ WC 🚿 ▣€2 📶included. 🐕
Surface: grassy/gravel. ☐ 15/09-15/06 ◙ summer
Distance: 🏙1km.
Remarks: Swimming pool.

Tourist information Tavira:
♜ Castello. ☐ Mo-Fri 8-17.30h.

🅿 Vila do Bispo 38A4
Praia da Barriga, N1265. **GPS**: n37,09970 w8,94445.

🚐free. **Surface:** asphalted.
Distance: 🏙Vila do Bispo 3,8km ⛱on the spot.
Remarks: Beach parking.

🅿 Vila do Bispo 38A4
Praia de Ingrina-Zavial. **GPS**: n37,04667 w8,88057.⛰.

4 🚐free. **Location:** Simple. **Surface:** gravel/sand. ☐ 01/01-31/12
Distance: 🏙Vila do Bispo 6,7km ⛱100m ⊗200m 🚶on the spot.
Remarks: Beach parking.

△ S Vila do Bispo 38A4
Sagres, Cerro da Moita. **GPS**: n37,02278 w8,94583.
🚐 🚰 ⛆ Ch 🪙. ☐ 01/01-31/12
Distance: ⛱2km ⊗on the spot 🛒on the spot 🚌500m.

🚐 S Vila Real de Santo António ≋ 38C4
Avenida de República. **GPS**: n37,19955 w7,4153.⬆.

70 🚐€ 4,50 🚰 ⛆ Ch ⚡€2,50 📶included. **Surface:** metalled/sand.
Distance: 🏙500m ⊗on the spot.

PT

DENMARK

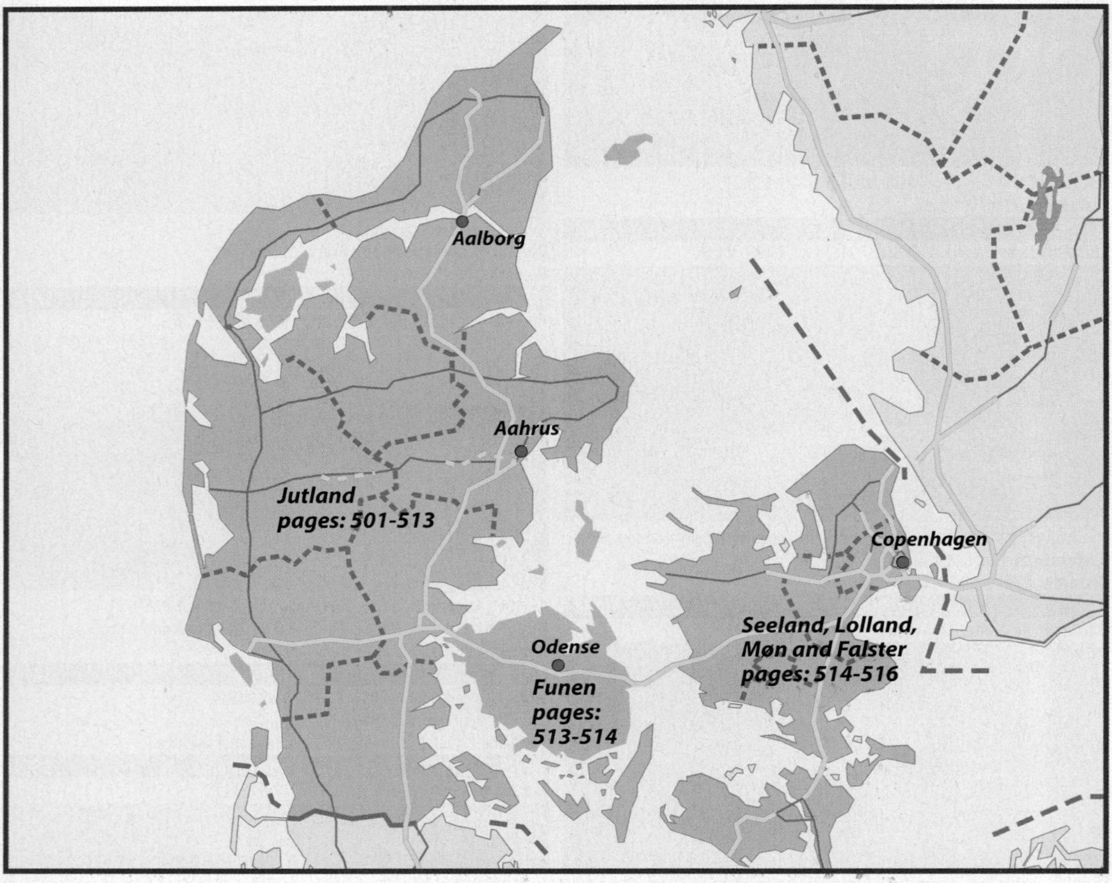

Aalborg

Aahrus

Jutland
pages: 501-513

Copenhagen

Seeland, Lolland,
Møn and Falster
pages: 514-516

Odense

Funen
pages:
513-514

Capital: Copenhagen
Government: Constitutional monarchy
Official Language: Danish
Population: 5,605,000 (2013)
Area: 44,000m²

General information
Dialling code: 0045
General emergency: 112
Currency: Danish Krone (DKK), 1 DKK= 100 øre,
DKK 1 = € 0,13, € 1 = DKK 7,44,
DKK1 = £ 0,11, £ 1 = DKK 9,45 (October 2014)
Payments by credit card are accepted at almost every
shop and restaurant.

Regulations for overnight stays/campsites
Overnight parking is allowed: for 1 night, if there is
no local prohibition, but no "camping" activities are
allowed.

Camping Key Europe is obligatory when using Danish
campsites: the card can be purchased at any campsite
for DKK 110 (± € 14,30/ £11,64), valid for one year.

Additional public holidays 2015
May 1 Great Prayer Day
June 5 Danisch Constitution Day
June 23 Sankt Hans Eve

Denmark

Jutland

| 🏕 | Aabybro | 2B3 |

Birthe&Leif Brinkmann, Kanalvej 164. **GPS**: n57,11947 e9,73156. ⬆.

3 🛏DKK 50. 🏕 **Location:** Simple, isolated. **Surface:** grassy.
⬛ 01/01-31/12
Distance: 🚶5km.

| 🏕 S | Aalbæk 🚤 | 2B2 |

Aalbæk Havn, Sdr. Havnevej 65. **GPS**: n57,59306 e10,42686. ⬆.

6 🛏DKK 170 ⛽ 💧 (6x) WC ⬚included. 🏕 **Location:** Simple, quiet.
Surface: gravel.
⬛ 01/01-31/12
Distance: 🚶800m ⛵on the spot 🚆on the spot ⊗800m 🍽800m 🚌250m.
Remarks: Pay at harbourmaster.

| 🏕 | Aalbæk 🚤 | 2B2 |

Galleri & Selskabslokal Gyllegaard, Hirtshalsvej 48. **GPS**: n57,60619 e10,41757.
⬆➡.

5 🛏DKK 100. 🏕 **Location:** Simple, isolated, quiet. **Surface:** grassy.
⬛ 01/01-31/12
Distance: 🚶4km ⛵1km ⊗4km 🍽4km.

| 🏕 S | Aarhus | 2B5 |

Aarhus centrum parkerinsplads, Kalkværksvej 2. **GPS**: n56,14815 e10,21015.
⬆➡.

6 🛏free 🚰free. **Location:** Urban, simple, central. **Surface:** asphalted.
⬛ 01/01-31/12

Distance: 🚶500m ⊗on the spot 🍽on the spot.
Remarks: Behind petrol station, max. 24h.

| 🏕 S | Aarhus | 2B5 |

Aarhus Nord, Randersvej 400. **GPS**: n56,22672 e10,16335.
🛏DKK 100 ⛽Ch💧against payment. ⬛ 01/01-31/12
Remarks: Quick-Stop: >20h - <10h.

| 🏕 S | Aarhus | 2B5 |

Marselisborg Havn, Marselisborg Havnevej 54. **GPS**: n56,13927 e10,21916.
🛏⛽🚰Ch💧WC⬚ 📶against payment. 🏪🚮
Distance: 🚶on the spot ⊗on the spot.

| 🏕 S | Åbenrå 🌿🍴🍽🚤 | 2B6 |

Camperstop Aabenraa, Sønderskovvej 104. **GPS**: n55,02513 e9,41471. ⬆.

34 🛏€ 14 ⛽DKK 20/120liter 🚰Ch💧DKK 4,50/kWh WC⬚DKK 10/5minutes.
Surface: grassy/gravel. ⬛ 01/01-31/12
Distance: 🚶2km 🚲8km 🏊400m.
Remarks: Chip-card available at campsite.

| 🏕 S | Åbenrå 🌿🍴🍽🚤 | 2B6 |

Lystbådehavn, Kystvej 55. **GPS**: n55,03434 e9,42352. ➡.

48 🛏€ 17 ⛽🚰Ch💧WCincluded ⬚📶against payment. 📶free. 🏪🚮
🔧. **Location:** Comfortable. **Surface:** gravel. ⬛ 01/04-31/10
Distance: 🚶1km 🏊on the spot 🚆on the spot ⊗on the spot 🍽50m
🚌200m 🚲on the spot 🚶on the spot.
Remarks: Harbour Åbenrå.

| 🏕 S | Augustenborg 🍽🚤 | 2B6 |

Augustenborg Slot, Palævej. **GPS**: n54,94694 e9,85389.

70 🛏DKK 100 ⛽🚰Ch💧WC⬚. 🏕 **Location:** Rural, comfortable.
Surface: grassy. ⬛ 01/01-31/12
Distance: 🚶1,5km 🚆on the spot 🚲on the spot.

| 🏕 S | Augustenborg 🍽🚤 | 2B6 |

Yachthavn, Langdel 6. **GPS**: n54,94074 e9,86942. ⬆.

DK

19 ⌒DKK 130 🚰🔌Ch 🔧 DKK 25 WC 🚽. 🚿 **Location:** Luxurious, central.
Surface: gravel. 🔌 01/04-15/10
Distance: 🚶1km 🚃1km 🚌 on the spot.

🚩S	**Bindslev**	

Tannisbugt Hallen, Stadion allé 7. **GPS:** n57,54559 o10,19943
20 ⌒€ 10 🚰🔌Ch WC. **Location:** Urban. **Surface:** metalled. 🔌 15/07-07/08

🚩S	**Bredebro**	2A6

Claus Cornelsen, Galgemark 9. **GPS:** n55,04853 e8,83270. 🔼.

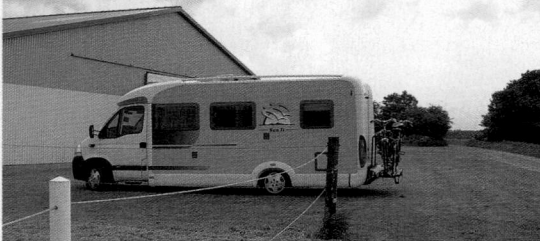

50 ⌒free 🚰🔌Ch 🔧 against payment 🚽. **Location:** Rural, simple, quiet.
Surface: gravel. 🔌 01/01-31/12
Distance: 🚶1km.

🚩S	**Brovst**	2B3

Vilsbæk Rideskole ved Brovst, Kanalvej 34. **GPS:** n57,11895 e9,53640. 🔼.

10 ⌒DKK 60 🚰🔌Ch 🔧 WC included. 🚿 **Location:** Rural, simple, isolated,
quiet. **Surface:** grassy. 🔌 01/01-31/12
Distance: 🚶2km.

🚩S	**Brønderslev**	2B3

Serritslev Fiskepark, Agårdsvej 35. **GPS:** n57,29750 e9,99597. 🔼.

20 ⌒DKK 50 🚰free WC. 🚿 **Location:** Rural, simple, isolated, quiet.
Surface: grassy. 🔌 01/01-31/12
Distance: 🚃 on the spot.

🔺S	**Bylderup-Bov**	2B6

Kristianshåb Autocamper Park, Kristianshåbvej 5. **GPS:** n54,96189 e9,06950.
➡️.

50 ⌒DKK 100 incl. 2 pers 🚰🔌Ch 🔧 DKK 4/24h WC 🚽🔲. 🚿🎣
Location: Rural, comfortable, isolated. **Surface:** grassy.
🔌 01/01-31/12
Distance: 🚶6km 🚲1km ⊗5km.

🚩S	**Bylderup-Bov**	2B6

Boskov, Kvænholtvej 15. **GPS:** n54,94488 e9,06078. 🔼.

10 ⌒DKK 60 🚰🔌Ch 🔧 included. 🚿 **Location:** Rural, simple, isolated.
Surface: grassy/gravel.
Distance: 🚃200m.

🚩S	**Bylderup-Bov**	2B6

B&B Bredevad, Bredevadvej 5. **GPS:** n54,96885 e9,12138. 🔼.

2 ⌒€ 13, 2 pers.incl 🚰🔌Ch 🔧 WC 📶included. 🚿
Location: Rural.
Distance: 🚃4km.

Tourist information Bylderup-Bov:
🏰 Schackenborg Slot, Schackenborg 2, Tønder. Visit the castle garden.

🚩S	**Bælum**	2B4

Bakgaarden, Hælskovvej 2. **GPS:** n56,83815 e10,12007. 🔼.

4 ⌒DKK 50 🚰🔌Ch 🔧 included. 🚿 **Surface:** grassy. 🔌 01/01-31/12
Distance: 🚶1km 🚃1km.

🚩S	**Bønnerup** 🚢	2C4

Bønnerup Lystbådehavn, Vestre Mole 2, Glesborg. **GPS:** n56,53139 e10,71139.
🔼.

DK

20 ⌂ DKK 150 ⊶ Ch ⚓ (12x)included WC ⬚ ▣ 🔊 against payment. 🚻
Location: Rural, comfortable, quiet. **Surface:** gravel. ⬛ 01/01-31/12
Distance: 🚶500m ⚓on the spot ⊷on the spot ⊗250m 🛒400m.
Remarks: Parking at marina.

⚓S	Børkop	2B5

Brejning Lystbådehavn, Brejning Strand. **GPS:** n55,67431 e9,68920. ⬆️ .

12 ⌂ € 16 ⊶ ⚓ (12x) WC ⬚ included 🔊 . ▣ 📇 ⊘ **Location:** Rural, simple,
isolated, quiet. **Surface:** gravel/metalled. ⬛ 01/01-31/12
Distance: 🚶Børkop 5km ⚓4,1km ⚓10m ⊗10m.
Remarks: Restaurant only in summer.

⚓	Ebeltoft	2C5

Skøvgarde, Havmøllevej 5. **GPS:** n56,24475 e10,77902. ⬆️➡️ .

2 ⌂DKK 50. 🚻 **Location:** Rural, simple, isolated, quiet. **Surface:** grassy.
⬛ 01/01-31/12 🕺on the spot.
Remarks: Pay at Havmøllevej 5 or 20.

ⓔS	Ebeltoft	2C5

Dråby Strand, Dråby Strandvej 13. **GPS:** n56,22172 e10,73778.
⌂DKK 150 ⊶ ⚓ Ch ⚓against payment. ⬛ 04/04-14/09
Remarks: Quick-Stop: >20h - <10h.

⚓S	Egå	2B5

Egå Marina, Egå Havvej 35. **GPS:** n56,21069 e10,28819. ⬆️ .

7 ⌂ € 19 ⊶ ⚓ Ch ⚓ (7x) WC ⬚ included ▣ 🔊 . ▣ 📇 ⊘ **Location:** Urban,
comfortable. **Surface:** asphalted.
⬛ 01/01-31/12
Distance: 🚶2km ⚓400m ⊷on the spot ⊗on the spot 🛒600m 🚌600m.

Remarks: Tallycard: service, electricity, sanitary building, caution DKK 50.

⚓S	Ejerslev ⛵	2A4

Ejerslev Havn, Utkærvej 5. **GPS:** n56,91855 e8,92096. ⬆️➡️ .

10 ⌂DKK 110 ⊶ ⚓ Ch ⚓ (10x) WC ⬚included ▣ . 🚻 **Location:** Rural,
isolated, quiet. **Surface:** gravel. ⬛ 01/01-31/12
Distance: 🚶4km ⚓on the spot 🛒4km 🚲on the spot 🕺on the spot.
Remarks: Bread-service, last 2km gravel road, borrow cycles for free.

⚓S	Engesvan	2B5

Pårup Autocamperplads, Silkeborgvej 8. **GPS:** n56,13694 e9,35028. ⬆️ .
4 ⌂DKK 50 ⊶ ⚓ Ch ⚓ included. 🚻 **Location:** Urban, simple, central.
Surface: gravel. ⬛ 01/04-01/11
Distance: 🚶on the spot.

⚓	Erslev	2A4

Inger-Marie og Knud Erik Nielsen, Bindeleddet 4. **GPS:** n56,83881 e8,68060.
⬆️ .

4 ⌂DKK 40 ⚓ . 🚻 **Location:** Rural, simple, isolated, quiet. **Surface:** gravel.
⬛ 01/01-31/12
Distance: 🚶1km.

⌂S	Esbjerg	2A6

Nebelso, Vestervadsvej 17 Vester Nebel. **GPS:** n55,55000 e8,54361. ⬆️➡️ .

25 ⌂DKK 50 ⊶ DKK 10 ⚓ DKK 25. 🚻 **Location:** Rural, simple, isolated, quiet.
Surface: grassy/gravel.
⬛ 01/04-01/11
Distance: 🚶15km ⊷on the spot.
Remarks: Fishpond, fishing license DKK90 www.nebelsoe.dk.

⚓S	Fanø	2A6

Fanø Fiskesø, Storetoft 30. **GPS:** n55,43401 e8,39294.
4 ⌂ € 14 ⊶ ⚓ Ch ⚓ WC 🔊against payment. **Surface:** gravel.
Distance: ⊷on the spot.
Remarks: At fish pond.

⚓	Fjerritslev	2B3

Erna K Nielsen, Holmsøvej 31, Haverslev. **GPS:** n57,04102 e9,39252. ⬆️ .

6 🛏 DKK 50 ⚡ 💧 included. 🚐 **Location:** Rural, simple, quiet. **Surface:** grassy. 🔲 01/01-31/12
Distance: 🏊 Limfjord 1,7km.

20 🛏 DKK 150 ⚡ 🔌 Ch 💧 (10x) WC 🚿 🔊 included. 🚐 **Location:** Urban, comfortable, central, quiet. **Surface:** grassy/gravel. 🔲 01/01-31/12
Distance: 🏪 800m 🏊 on the spot 🛒 on the spot 🚻 on the spot 🚂 700m.
Remarks: Pay at harbourmaster.

Fjerritslev 2B3
Niels Balle, Hedegardsvey 19. **GPS:** n57,12505 e9,33422. ⬆️.

🔲🇸 **Gistrup** 2B4
Kirsten og Karl Age, Gunderupvej 164. **GPS:** n56,93476 e9,95844. ⬆️.

4 🛏 DKK 70 💧 (1x)included. 🚐 **Location:** Rural, simple, isolated. **Surface:** grassy. 🔲 01/01-31/12
Distance: 🏪 7km 🏊 4km.

4 🛏 DKK 100 ⚡ 💧 included. 🚐 **Location:** Rural, simple, isolated.
Surface: gravel.

🔲🇸 **Flauenskjold** 2B3
Markedsplad, Agertoften 4. **GPS:** n57,24854 e10,28477. ⬆️➡️.

🔲🇸 **Glejbjerg** 2A6
Betina & Klaus Jørgensen, Gammelgårdsvej 3. **GPS:** n55,55052 e8,78705.
4 🛏 free ⚡ 🔌 Ch free 💧 against payment WC 🚿. **Location:** Comfortable.
Surface: grassy/gravel. 🔲 01/01-31/12

🔲🇸 **Grenaa** 2C4
Fornæs Skibsophug, Folshøjvej. **GPS:** n56,41879 e10,91709.
10 🛏 free. **Surface:** grassy. 🔲 01/01-31/12

Tourist information Grenaa:
⚫ Kattegat Centret. The underwater world and shark centre. 🔲 10-16/17h
🔲 13/12-26/12.

🔲🇸 **Haderslev** 🌿 2B6
Fam. Nowak, Felstrupvej 37. **GPS:** n55,25488 e9,52556. ⬆️.

10 🛏 DKK 50 ⚡ 🔌 💧 DKK 25 WC included. 🚐 **Location:** Rural, simple, quiet.
Surface: grassy. 🔲 01/01-31/12
Distance: 🚲 5km.
Remarks: Money in envelope in mail box, festival and market place.

🔲🇸 **Fredericia** 🌿⚓🌊 2B6
Lystbådehavnen, Strandvejen 115/Sanddalbakke. **GPS:** n55,55246 e9,72805.
✈️.

2 🛏 free ⚡ Service DKK 30 💧 🔊. **Location:** Rural. **Surface:** gravel.
🔲 01/01-31/12
Distance: 🏪 3km 🏊 100m 🛒 on the spot.

⚓🇸 **Haderslev** 🌿 2B6
Haderslev Sejl Club, Sydhavnsvej 1F. **GPS:** n55,24806 e9,50028. ⬆️.
6 🛏 € 15 ⚡ 🔌 Ch WC 🚿 🔊 included. **Surface:** gravel.
Distance: 🚻 on the spot.

Tourist information Haderslev:
👁 Sillerup Mølle, Sillerup Møllevej 33. Mill, bake bread yourself. 🔲 15/06-15/09 Tue 10h.
🚲 Wachman's Tour. Excursion with the night watch in the old part of the city.
🔲 01/07-31/08 Thu 21h.

8 🛏 € 11 ⚡ 🔌 Ch 💧 (8x) WC 🚿 🔊 included. 🖨 🌊 🔧.
Location: Rural, simple, quiet. **Surface:** metalled.
🔲 01/01-31/12
Distance: 🏪 1km 🏊 on the spot 🛒 on the spot 🚻 on the spot 🚂 1km
🚌 200m.
Remarks: Tallycard: service, electricity, sanitary building, caution DKK 50.

🔲🇸 **Frederikshavn** 🌊 2B3
Frederikshavn Marina, Søsportsvej 8. **GPS:** n57,42375 e10,52709. ✈️.

🔲🇸 **Hadsund** 🌊 2B4
Hvirvelkærgård, Kystvejen 202, Als. **GPS:** n56,76414 e10,28565. ⬆️.

10 ⑤DKK 90 ☕ ✍DKK30 WC ⬚included. 🚐 **Location:** Rural, simple, quiet. **Surface:** grassy. ⬛ 01/01-31/12
Distance: 🚶1km ⊗1km.

Hadsund Havn, Skovvej 67. **GPS:** n56,70988 e10,10428. ⬆ .

10 ⑤DKK 130 ☕ ✍ WC ⬚included. 🚐 **Location:** Rural, comfortable, quiet. **Surface:** grassy. ⬛ 01/01-31/12
Distance: 🚶2km ⊗2km 🛒2km.

Ingrid og Kristen Gade, Hobrovej 62. **GPS:** n56,70773 e10,07975. ⬆ .

4 ⑤DKK 100 ☕ ✍(2x) WC ⬚included. 🚐 **Location:** Rural, simple. **Surface:** grassy. ⬛ 01/01-31/12

THy Minicamping (Rær Autocamperplads), Kærbakken 2.
GPS: n57,08945 e8,67104. ⬆➡ .

20 ⑤DKK 100 ☕ ⬚Ch ✍ WC ⬚included. 🚐 **Location:** Rural, comfortable. **Surface:** grassy. ⬛ 01/01-31/12
Distance: 🚶Hanstholm 4km ⛰5km.

Hanstholm, Hamborgvej 95. **GPS:** n57,10909 e8,66724.
⑤DKK 165 ☕ ⬚Ch ✍against payment. ⬛ 01/03-30/09
Remarks: Quick-Stop: >20h - <10h.

Tourist information Hanstholm:
👁 Frøstrup mini-village, Søndergade 36, Frøstrup. Miniature village. ⬛ 01/05-15/10 Wed-Thu 10-13h, 01/07-31/08 daily 13-16h.

Udbyhøj Havn, Havnevej 62 Udbyhøj. **GPS:** n56,61111 e10,30583. ⬆ .

10 ⑤DKK 150 ☕ ⬚Ch included. ✍against payment WC ⬚ 📶 . 🚐 ✎
Location: Rural, comfortable. **Surface:** asphalted. ⬛ 01/01-31/12
Distance: ⏚on the spot 🚶on the spot 🛒500m.

Randers Fjord, Midtvasen 21. **GPS:** n56,60997 e10,29334.
2 ⑤DKK 130 ☕ ⬚Ch ✍against payment. ⬛ 01/04-15/09
Remarks: Quick-Stop: >20h - <10h.

Rethe og Hans Jørn Mogensen, Klattrupgade 36, Klattrup.
GPS: n56,66397 e10,21208. ⬆ .

4 ⑤DKK 50 ☕ ⬚Ch ✍included. 🚐 **Location:** Rural, simple, quiet. **Surface:** grassy/gravel. ⬛ 01/01-31/12
Distance: 🚶2km 🛒2km.

Banegårdspladse, Banegårdspladsen 1. **GPS:** n57,59119 e9,96308. ⬆➡ .

30 ⑤free. **Location:** Simple, central. **Surface:** metalled.
⬛ 01/01-31/12
Distance: 🚶600m 🚲 4,8km ⊗600m 🛒on the spot.
Remarks: At station and ferry terminal.

Willemoesvej. **GPS:** n57,59097 e9,98601.

40 ⑤free. **Location:** Simple, quiet. **Surface:** unpaved.
⬛ 01/01-31/12

DK

Distance: 🏖1km ⛵Sandy beach ⊗1km.
Remarks: Parking ferry to Norway.
Tourist information Hirtshals:
Ⓜ Nordsømuseet, Willemoesvej 2. Oceanarium, large aquarium.
⭕ 11/01-01/12 10-17.

| ⓈⓈ | Hjallerup | 2B3 |

Peter Bastholm Galleri Retro, Alborgvej 715. **GPS:** n57,17919 e10,15856. ⬆ .

5 ⅏DKK 100 ⚡🔧. 🛁 **Location:** Rural, isolated, quiet. **Surface:** gravel.
⭕ 01/01-31/12
Distance: 🎣fish pond.

| ⓈⓈ | Hjørring | 2B3 |

Somo-Art, Tverstedvej 41, Uggerby. **GPS:** n57,57523 e10,12868. ⬆.
6 ⅏€ 16 🔌🍴 Ch included ⚡ free. **Location:** Rural, quiet. **Surface:** grassy.
⭕ 01/04-20/10
Distance: 🏖3km ⊗3km 🛒3km.

| ⓈⓈ | Hjørring | 2B3 |

Thomas Lindrup, Tverstedvej 31. **GPS:** n57,57256 e10,12775. ⬆➡.

6 ⅏DKK 120 🔌🍴 Ch ⚡(6x) WC ⌐included. 🛁 **Location:** Rural,
comfortable, isolated, quiet. **Surface:** grassy. ⭕ 01/01-31/12

| ©Ⓢ | Hobro | 2B4 |

Hobro Camping Gattenborg, Skivevej 35. **GPS:** n56,64015 e9,78265.
3 ⅏DKK 160 🔌🍴Ch⚡against payment. ⭕ 01/04-02/10
Remarks: Quick-Stop: >20h - <10h.

| ⓈⓈ | Holsted | 2A6 |

Holsted Golfbanen, Bergardsvej 4, Vejen-Esberg. **GPS:** n55,52353 e8,93228.

15 ⅏€ 10 🔌⚡ WC . **Surface:** gravel. ⭕ 01/04-30/10
Distance: 🏖1km.

| ⓈⓈ | Horsens 🚤 | 2B5 |

Lystbådehavn, Jens Hjernøes Vej 32. **GPS:** n55,85764 e9,87417. ⬆➡.

5 ⅏DKK 150 🔌🍴Ch⚡ WC ⌐included 📷.📶.🔌🔧 🗑
Location: Rural, comfortable, quiet. **Surface:** gravel.
⭕ 01/01-31/12
Distance: 🏖3km ⛵on the spot 🔌on the spot ⊗on the spot.
Remarks: Harbour Horsen, special motorhome parking, tallycard: service,
electricity, sanitary building, caution DKK 50.
Tourist information Horsens:
👁 Dolmen "Jættestuen", åbjerg Skov. Dolmen. ⭕ 01/01-31/12.

| ⓈⓈ | Hoven | 2A5 |

Kvindehojskole, Bredgade 10, Tarm. **GPS:** n55,85065 e8,75938. ⬆.

6 ⅏free WC free. **Location:** Urban, simple. **Surface:** gravel.
⭕ 01/01-31/12
Distance: 🏖on the spot.
Remarks: Parking and stay overnight possible at several places; Brugsen 2/3
campers; sport hall.

| ⓈⓈ | Hurup 🌿🚤 | 2A4 |

Nordisk Folkecenter, Kammersgaardsvej 16. **GPS:** n56,69358 e8,41306. ⬆ .

8 ⅏DKK 60 ⚡ WC included. 🛁 **Location:** Rural, simple, isolated, quiet.
Surface: gravel. ⭕ 01/01-31/12
Distance: 🔌on the spot 🛒4km.
Remarks: Check in at reception, access energy-park incl.

| ⅏ | Hvide Sande 🚤🗑 | 2A5 |

Autocamper Fabriksvej 31, Fabriksvej 31. **GPS:** n56,00245 e8,11979. ⬆.
45 ⅏€ 12,50. 🔌 🗑 **Location:** Rural, simple. **Surface:** gravel/sand.
⭕ 01/01-31/12
Distance: 🏖800m ⛵500m 🛒500m.

| ⅏ | Hvide Sande 🚤🗑 | 2A5 |

Autocamper Fabriksvej 42. **GPS:** n56,00475 e8,11754. ⬆.
20 ⅏€ 12,50. 🔌 🗑 **Location:** Rural, simple.
Surface: gravel/sand.
Distance: 🏖200m ⛵on the spot 🛒200m.

| ⅏ | Hvide Sande 🚤🗑 | 2A5 |

Autocamper P, Tungevej 6. **GPS:** n55,99722 e8,12222. ⬆.

40 ⌇DKK 75. 🖃 ⬛ **Location:** Rural, simple, quiet.
Surface: gravel/metalled.
🔲 01/01-31/12
Distance: 🚰200m ⚓on the spot ⊗200m 🏊300m 🚶on the spot.
Remarks: Beach parking, service Hvide Sande Camping, 1km, DKK 37,50.

©S	Hvide Sande 🏖🚤	2A5

Bjerregaard, Sdr. Klitvej 185. **GPS:** n55,90620 e8,16565.
⌇DKK 120 ⛽🔌Ch 🚿against payment. 🔲 15/04-01/10
Remarks: Quick-Stop: >20h - <10h.

©S	Hvide Sande 🏖🚤	2A5

Hvide Sande (Beltana), Karen Brands Vej 70. **GPS:** n55,98689 e8,13478.
⌇DKK 110 ⛽🔌Ch 🚿against payment. 🔲 03/04-26/10
Remarks: Quick-Stop: >20h - <10h.

P S	Højslev	2B4

Virksund Lystbådehavn, Sandkrogen 10. **GPS:** n56,61014 e9,29139.
12 ⌇€ 16 ⛽🚿WC🔌📶included. **Surface:** gravel.
Distance: ⚓on the spot.

S	Ikast	2B5

Jens Jørgen Billlo, Bangsvej 50, Tulstrup. **GPS:** n56,15480 e9,16197.⬆ .

5 ⌇free ⛽🔌Ch 🚿against payment. **Location:** Rural, simple, isolated, quiet. **Surface:** grassy.
Distance: 🚰1,5km 🚤4km.

S	Juelsminde 🚤	2B5

Havn & Marina, Havnegade 15. **GPS:** n55,71457 e10,01509.⬆ .

12 ⌇€ 20 ⛽🔌Ch 🚿(12x) WC🔌📶included. 🖃 ⬛
Location: Rural, comfortable, central, quiet.
Surface: gravel.
🔲 01/05-30/09
Distance: 🚰200m ⚓on the spot 🛒on the spot ⊗on the spot 🚤200m.
Remarks: Tallycard: service, electricity, sanitary building, caution DKK 50.

S	Karup	2B4

2B Pack, Ulvedalsvej 43. **GPS:** n56,31528 e9,27361.⬆ .
4 ⌇€ 14 ⛽🔌Ch 🚿. 🔲 23/03-29/10

⚓S	Kolding 🍴🚤	2B6

Kolding Marina, Skamlingvejen 5. **GPS:** n55,48746 e9,50051.⬆ .

15 ⌇€ 15 ⛽🔌Ch 🚿WC🔌📶against payment. 🖃 ⬛ **Location:**
Rural, comfortable, quiet. **Surface:** grassy/gravel. 🔲 01/05-01/10
Distance: 🚰2,6km ⚓on the spot ⊗on the spot.
Remarks: Near marina, tallycard: service, electricity, sanitary building, caution DKK 50.

S	Kvissel	2B3

Bondegård Hansen, Mejlingvej 65. **GPS:** n57,46753 e10,39556.⬆ .

10 ⌇DKK 75 ⛽🔌Ch 🚿WC included 🔌DKK 10. **Location:** Rural, comfortable, quiet. **Surface:** grassy. 🔲 01/01-31/12
Distance: 🚰1km 🚤5km.

S	Lemvig 🚤	2A4

Fjaltring Strand Høfte, Kjeldjergvej (Fjaltring). **GPS:** n56,47596 e8,12477.⬆ .

10 ⌇free ⛽🚿WC free 🔌. **Location:** Rural, simple, isolated, quiet.
Surface: metalled.
Distance: 🚰1km ⚓on the spot 🚤1km.
Remarks: Beach parking.

S	Lemvig 🚤	2A4

Lemvig Havn, Toldbodgade. **GPS:** n56,55395 e8,30956.
10 ⌇free. **Surface:** gravel. 🔲 01/01-31/12
Distance: ⊗250m 🚤250m.
Remarks: Max. 12h.

Tourist information Lemvig:
👁 Bovbjerg Fyr, Fyrvej 27. Lighthouse.

S	Løgstør 🏖🍴🚤	2B3

Løgstør Golfklub, Viborgvej 13, Ravnstrup. **GPS:** n56,94689 e9,25390.⬆ .

DK

10 ℥DKK 110 ✏ (4x)included. 🚿 **Location:** Simple, isolated, quiet. **Surface:** gravel.
Distance: 🚶2km ⊗2km 🚲2km.

Ⓒ Ⓢ **Løgstør** 🚣🏠 | 2B3
Løgstør Lysbadehavn, Kanalvejen 19. **GPS:** n56,96728 e9,24528. ⬆➡

12 ℥DKK 110 🚰🍺✏ (12x) WC 🚽📺📶 included. 🚿🧺 **Location:** Comfortable, central. **Surface:** grassy/metalled. ⬛ 01/01-31/12
Distance: 🚶200m ⚓on the spot ⊗on the spot 🚲200m.

🍴 **Løgstør** 🚣🏠 | 2B3
Café Bondestuen, Over Aggersund 49. **GPS:** n57,00835 e9,28776. ⬆.

6 ℥free. **Location:** Rural, simple. **Surface:** gravel.
⬛ 01/01-31/12

Ⓒ Ⓢ **Løkken** 🚣🏠 | 2B3
Hugo Ottesen, Kettrupvej 80. **GPS:** n57,31135 e9,67861. ⬆.

5 ℥DKK 100 🚰✏ 🚿 **Location:** Rural, simple, isolated. **Surface:** grassy.
⬛ 01/01-31/12

Ⓒ **Løkken** 🚣🏠 | 2B3
Galleri Munkens Klit, Munkensvej 11. **GPS:** n57,33871 e9,70522. ⬆➡

10 ℥DKK 100 🚰✏ DKK 5 WC 📶 included. 🚿 **Location:** Rural, comfortable, isolated, quiet. **Surface:** grassy. ⬛ 01/01-31/12
Distance: 🚶3km.

Ⓒ Ⓢ **Løkken** 🚣🏠 | 2B3
Gl.Klitgaard, Lyngbyvej 331. **GPS:** n57,41784 e9,76017.
℥DKK 140 🚰🍺Ch ✏against payment. ⬛ 15/04-23/10
Remarks: Quick-Stop: >20h - <10h.

Ⓒ Ⓢ **Løkken** 🏠 | 2B3
Grønhøj Strand, Kettrupvej 125. **GPS:** n57,32127 e9,67293.
℥DKK 100 🚰🍺Ch ✏against payment. ⬛ 15/04-18/09
Remarks: Quick-Stop: >20h - <10h.

Ⓒ Ⓢ **Løkken** 🚣🏠 | 2B3
Løkken Strand, Furreby Kirkevej 97. **GPS:** n57,38533 e9,72571.
℥DKK 100 🚰🍺Ch ✏against payment. ⬛ 05/05-04/09
Remarks: Quick-Stop: >20h - <10h.

Ⓒ Ⓢ **Løkken** 🚣🏠 | 2B3
Rolighed, Grønhoj Strandvej 35. **GPS:** n57,32143 e9,67818.
℥DKK 75 🚰🍺Ch ✏against payment.
⬛ 04/04-18/10
Remarks: Quick-Stop: >20h - <10h.

Tourist information Løkken:
Ⓜ Vendsyssel historiske museum "Jens Thomsens Gård", Strandfogedgården i Rubjerg, Langelinie 2. Cultural past of the coast area. Hiking-trails. ⬛ 16/06-15/09 Mo, Wed-Fri, Su 11-17h. Ⓣ free.
☺ Familiy Farm Fun Park, Lyngbyvej 86, Vittrup. Animal park. ⬛ 01/05-30/09.

Ⓢ **Mariager** | 2B4
Kongsdl Bådelaug, Kongsdal Havn 8. **GPS:** n56,68383 e10,07023. ⬆.

24 ℥DKK 120 🚰🍺Ch ✏ (24x) WC 🚽DKK 5/3minutes 📺📶 included.
🚾🚿 **Location:** Rural, comfortable, isolated, quiet. **Surface:** gravel.
⬛ 01/01-31/12
Distance: 🚶7km ⚓on the spot ⊸on the spot.

Ⓒ Ⓢ **Mariager** | 2B4
Mariager, Ny Havnevej 5A. **GPS:** n56,65399 e9,97640.
2 ℥DKK 100 🚰🍺Ch ✏against payment. ⬛ 08/04-25/09
Remarks: Quick-Stop: >20h - <10h.

Ⓢ **Nordborg** | 2B6
Kvickly, Gartnervænget. **GPS:** n55,05611 e9,74150. ➡
10 ℥free. **Surface:** asphalted. ⬛ 01/01-31/12
Remarks: At supermarket.

Ⓢ **Nordborg** | 2B6
Lone & Henning Carlsson, Kådnervej 7. **GPS:** n55,03194 e9,73111. ⬆.

5 ℥DKK 100 🚰 WC 📶. 🚿 **Location:** Rural, comfortable, quiet.
Surface: gravel. ⬛ 01/01-31/12
Distance: 🚶5km.
Remarks: Narrow entrance.

Ⓢ Ⓢ **Nykøbing Mors** 🛒 | 2A4
Morsø Sejlklub & Marin, Jernbanevej 3A. **GPS:** n56,79282 e8,86370. ⬆➡

18 🗓€ 16 🔧🍳Ch 💦WC 🗐🖵 📶included. 🖐🚗 🧽
Location: Comfortable, quiet. **Surface:** gravel.
🅾 01/01-31/12
Distance: 👟150m 🛶on the spot 🚤on the spot ⊗on the spot 🔌200m.
Remarks: Tallycard: service, electricity, sanitary building, caution DKK 25.

| 🛐S | Nykøbing Mors 🚽🥢 | 2A4 |

Ejerslev Havn, Utkærvej 5, Ejerslev. **GPS:** n56,91868 e8,92093.
🗓€ 11 Ch 💦€4 🗐🖵. 🅾 01/01-31/12

| 🛐S | Nørager | 2B4 |

Stellplads E45 Autocamper, Fyrkildevej 39, Ladelund. **GPS:** n56,77505 e9,70986.
⬆️.

15 🗓DKK 75 🔧included 💦. 🖐 **Location:** Rural, simple, isolated, quiet.
Surface: grassy. 🅾 01/01-31/12
Distance: ✒E45 5km.

| 🛐S | Odder | 2B5 |

Jørgen Petersen, Aarhusvej 354. **GPS:** n56,01650 e10,18157.⬆️➡️.

3 🗓DKK 75 🔧🍳Ch 💦WC 🗐included. 🖐 **Location:** Rural, luxurious,
isolated, quiet. **Surface:** grassy/gravel. 🅾 01/01-31/12
Distance: 👟5km.

| ©S | Odder | 2B5 |

Odder strand Camping, Toldvejen 50. **GPS:** n55,93891 e10,25054.
🗓DKK 150 🔧🍳Ch 💦againstpayment. 🅾 01/04-21/09
Remarks: Quick-Stop: >20h - <10h.

| 🛐S | Randers 🥢 | 2B4 |

Mellerup Bådelaug, Amtsvejen 153 Mellerup. **GPS:** n56,52431 e10,22213.⬆️.

3 🗓DKK 100 🔧💦WC 📶included. 🖐 **Location:** Rural, simple, quiet.
Surface: gravel. 🅾 01/01-31/12
Distance: 👟Mellerup 1,2km 🛶on the spot 🚤on the spot.
Remarks: Pay at harbourmaster.

| 🛐 | Randers 🥢 | 2B4 |

Randers havn, Toldbodgade 14. **GPS:** n56,46229 e10,05122.⬆️.

10 🗓free. **Location:** Urban, simple. **Surface:** gravel.
🅾 01/01-31/12
Distance: 👟500m ⊗on the spot.
Remarks: Max. 24h.

| 🛐S | Ribe 🌊🏖🚽🥢 | 2A6 |

Fabelbo, Hølleskovvej 48. **GPS:** n55,24076 e8,86077.
🗓free 🔧free. **Location:** Isolated, quiet. **Surface:** grassy.
🅾 01/01-31/12

| 🛐S | Ribe 🌊🏖🚽🥢 | 2A6 |

Stampemøllevej. **GPS:** n55,32480 e8,75740.⬆️.

25 🗓free 🔧🍳WC free. **Location:** Urban, simple. **Surface:** asphalted.
🅾 01/01-31/12
Distance: 👟500m ⊗100m 🔌400m.
Remarks: Parking south of centre, max. 48h.

| 🛐S | Ribe 🌊🏖🚽🥢 | 2A6 |

Storkesøen, Haulundvej 164. **GPS:** n55,31703 e8,76022.⬆️➡️.

24 🗓DKK 140 🔧🍳Ch 💦included. **Location:** Rural, comfortable, quiet.
Surface: grassy. 🅾 01/01-31/12
Distance: 👟1km 🚤on the spot.
Remarks: At fish pond.

| 🛐S | Ribe 🌊🏖🚽🥢 | 2A6 |

Maglegaard, Toftlundvej 6. **GPS:** n55,31067 e8,79151.

3 ⌛DKK 100 🚰 ✎ DKK 20. 🚐
Location: Rural, simple, quiet.
Surface: grassy.
Distance: 🚶3km.

Tourist information Ribe:
👁 Vadehavscentret, Okholmvej 5. Wadden Sea centre.
🅾 10-16/17h. 🅾 01/12-31/01.
Ⓜ Museet Ribes Vikinger, Odins Plads. Viking period in Denmark. 🅾 daily 10-16h, summer 10-18h 🅾 01/11-31/03 Mo.
Ⓜ Ribe Vikingecenter. Open air museum. 🅾 01/05-30/06, 01/09-15/10 Mo-Fri 10-15.30h, 01/07-31/08 daily 11-17h.
⊗ Weis Stue, Torvet 2. Oldest inn of Denmark with traditional Danish kitchen.

🏕S	Ringkøbing ⛱	2A5

Annemette & Svend Erik Jensen, Birkmosevej 6. **GPS:** n56,08806 e8,26722. ➡
15 ⌛free 🚰 🍽 Ch against payment. **Location:** Simple. **Surface:** grassy.
🅾 01/01-31/12
Distance: ⚓500m ⊗500m 🛒200m.

🏕S	Ringkøbing ⛱	2A5

Lystbadenhavn, Fiskerstraede 60. **GPS:** n56,08611 e8,24056. ⬆

10 ⌛€14 🚰 🍽 Ch ✎ (6x)DKK 2,30/kWh WC included ⊐DKK 10/3minutes.
🚾 ♨ **Location:** Urban, comfortable, quiet. **Surface:** gravel.
🅾 01/01-31/12
Distance: 🚶on the spot ⚓on the spot ⛵on the spot ⊗500m 🛒500m.
Remarks: Parking at pier.

🏕	Ringkøbing ⛱	2A5

Autocamperplads, Vesterled 11. **GPS:** n56,09338 e8,23740. ⬆

20 ⌛DKK 70. 🚾 **Location:** Urban, simple. **Surface:** gravel.
🅾 01/01-31/12
Distance: 🚶700m ⚓400m ⛵400m ⊗700m 🛒700m.
Remarks: Pay with Danish coins.

©S	Ringkøbing ⛱	2A5

Søndervig, Solvej 2. **GPS:** n56,11186 e8,11760.
⌛DKK 115 🚰 🍽 Ch ✎ against payment. 🅾 04/04-25/10
Remarks: Quick-Stop: >20h - <10h.

Tourist information Ringkøbing:

---

❽ Fishing and Family Park West, Hovervej 56. Recreation park with swimming pool. 🅾 10h-sunset.

⚓S	Roslev	2A4

Sallingsund Sejlklub, Færgevej 7. **GPS:** n56,76333 e8,86667.
⌛€16 🚰 🍽 Ch ✎ WC ⊐ 📶 included. 🚐
Distance: ⊗on the spot 🛒on the spot.

⚓S	Roslev	2A4

Sundsøre Lystbådehavn, Sundsørevej. **GPS:** n56,70991 e9,17324.
⌛€16 🚰 ✎ WC ⊐ included. **Location:** Isolated, quiet.
Surface: grassy/gravel. 🅾 01/01-31/12
Distance: ⚓on the spot ⊗on the spot.
Remarks: At marina and ferry-boat.

🏕S	Rødding	2B6

Inga & Ejnar Gejl, Skodborgskovvej 25, Skodborgskov. **GPS:** n55,40056 e9,15722.
4 ⌛🚰 ✎ against payment WC free. **Location:** Rural, simple.
Surface: grassy. 🅾 01/01-31/12
Distance: 🚶5km.

🚐S	Rødding	2B6

Brændekilde, Haderslevvej 59. **GPS:** n55,35750 e9,18833. ⬆

10 ⌛free 🚰 DKK 25 Ch ✎ DKK 25 WC. **Location:** Rural, simple, noisy.
Surface: metalled. 🅾 01/01-31/12
Distance: 🚶1km.
Remarks: Max. 1 week.

🚐S	Rødding	2B6

FB Camping Service, Industriparken 13. **GPS:** n55,42556 e9,16083.
15 ⌛free 🚰 DKK 10 Ch free ✎ DKK 40. **Location:** Urban, simple.
Surface: gravel. 🅾 01/01-31/12

🚐S	Rødekro	2B6

Rødekro Fiskepark, østermarkvej 3-7. **GPS:** n55,08806 e9,30889. ➡

50 ⌛DKK 100 🚰 🍽 Ch ✎ DKK 2/kWh WC ⊐DKK 5 ⊐DKK 25. 🚐
Location: Rural, simple, quiet. **Surface:** grassy. 🅾 01/01-31/12
Distance: 🚶2km ⚓on the spot ⛵on the spot 🛒on the spot 🚌100m.
Remarks: At fish lake.

🚐S	Silkeborg ⛱ 🍽	2B5

Anne & Gert Lassen, Ellinglund, Ellingvej 16, Funder Kirkeby.
GPS: n56,16556 e9,40917.
⌛€14 🍽 Ch ✎ WC ⊐ 📶. **Location:** Rural, comfortable.
Surface: grassy. 🅾 01/01-31/12
Distance: 🚶2km.

🚐S	Silkeborg ⛱ 🍽	2B5

Jørgen Engebjerg, Lemmingvej 12. **GPS:** n56,22124 e9,53991.
3 ⌛€10 🚰 ✎ included. **Location:** Rural. **Surface:** grassy. 🅾 01/01-31/12
Distance: 🚶5km.

Tourist information Silkeborg:
👁 AQUA, Vejlsøvej 55. Aquarium. 🅾 01/09-31/05 Mo-Fri 10-16h, Sa-Su 10-17h, 01/06-31/08 10-18h.

ⓒⓈ Sindal 2B3
Sindal, Hjørringvej 125. **GPS**: n57,46849 e10,17945.
3 🅿DKK 120 🚰🔧Ch against payment 🔧DKK 25. 🔲 01/04-20/09
Remarks: Quick-Stop: >20h - <10h.

🅿 Skagen 2C2
P-plads på Grenen i Skagen, Akandevej. **GPS**: n57,73895 e10,63283. ⬆.

20 🅿DKK 150. 🛁 ♨ **Location:** Rural, simple, isolated. **Surface:** asphalted.
🔲 01/01-31/12
Distance: 🚶2km ⊗100m 🚲3km.

ⓒⓈ Skals 2B4
Ulbjerg, Skråhedevej 6. **GPS**: n56,64495 e9,33915.
🅿€ 10,50 🚰🔧Ch 🔧against payment. 🔲 01/01-31/12
Remarks: Quick-Stop: >20h - <10h.

🅿Ⓢ Skjern 2A5
Stauning Havn, Strandvejen, Stauning. **GPS**: n55,95488 e8,37352. ⬆.
6, <10m 🅿€ 14 🚰Ch WC 🛁included. **Surface:** metalled. 🔲 01/01-31/12
Distance: 🚶Skjern 8km ⊗on the spot.

ⓒⓈ Skærbæk 2A6
Skærbæk, Ullerupvej 76. **GPS**: n55,16584 e8,77909.
🅿DKK 100 🚰🔧Ch 🔧against payment. 🔲 01/01-31/12
Remarks: Quick-Stop: >20h - <10h.

🖐 Snedsted 2A4
Kaj Foget, Skyumvey 105. **GPS**: n56,84380 e8,59720. ⬆➡.

6 🅿DKK 50. 🛁 **Location:** Rural, simple, isolated, quiet. **Surface:** grassy.
🔲 01/01-31/12

🅿Ⓢ Spøttrup 2A4
Gyldendal hav, Vester Hærup Strandvej 34. **GPS**: n56,58107 e8,71066. ⬆.

6 🅿DKK 110 🚰🔧(6x) WC 🔲. 🛁 **Location:** Rural, simple, quiet.
Surface: metalled. 🔲 01/01-31/12
Distance: 🏊on the spot 🚶on the spot 🚲1km.
Remarks: Pay at harbourmaster.

ⓒⓈ Stouby 2B5
Løgballe Autocamperplads, Løgballevej 12. **GPS**: n55,70765 e9,84359. ⬆➡.

7 🅿DKK 75 🚰DKK 15 🔧Ch 🔧(7x)DKK 30 WC. 🛁 **Location:** Rural, simple,
isolated, quiet. **Surface:** gravel. 🔲 01/04-01/10

🅿Ⓢ Strandby 2B3
Strandby havn, Søndre Havnevej 27. **GPS**: n57,49249 e10,50245. ⬆.

6 🅿DKK 120 🚰🔧 WC included. 🛁 **Location:** Urban, simple.
Surface: metalled. 🔲 01/01-31/12
Distance: 🚶on the spot 🏊on the spot 🚶on the spot ⊗on the spot
🚲on the spot.
Remarks: Pay at harbourmaster.

🚻Ⓢ Struer 2A4
Holstebro-Struer Lystbådehavn, Fjordvejen. **GPS**: n56,49380 e8,59068. ⬆➡.

15 🅿€ 16 🚰🔧Ch 🔧(4x) WC 🛁 📶included. 🛁 **Location:** Rural, simple,
quiet. **Surface:** gravel/sand. 🔲 01/01-31/12
Distance: 🏊Sandy beach 🚶on the spot ⊗on the spot.

4 🅿€ 16 🚰🔧 WC 🛁Access sanitary building DKK 20 🔲 📶included. 🏪 ♨
Location: Urban, comfortable, quiet. **Surface:** gravel. 🔲 winter
Distance: 🚶100m 🚲100m.
Remarks: Tallycard: service, electricity, sanitary building, caution DKK 50.
Tourist information Struer:
👁 Gimsinghoved, Gimsinghoved 1. Former large Danish farm.

🅿Ⓢ Storvorde 2B3
Egense Lystbådehavan, Kystvej 1. **GPS**: n56,98270 e10,30451. ⬆.

DK

⚙S **Sæby** 2B3
Top Plads hos Ase en Helmer, Understedvej 65, Understed.
GPS: n57,37249 e10,46447.⬆

20 🚐DKK 100 🚰📶Ch 🔌 WC ⬜🔲. 🚿 **Location:** Rural, comfortable,
isolated, quiet. **Surface:** grassy. ⬛ 01/01-31/12

⚙ **Sæby** 2B3
Lene en Knut Holdensgård, Holdenggårdvej 16, Sønder.
GPS: n57,21616 e10,45253.⬆

3 🚐DKK 50 🚰 🔌. 🚿 **Location:** Rural, simple, isolated, quiet.
Surface: grassy. ⬛ 01/01-31/12

⚙ **Sæby** 2B3
Sæby Havn, Havnen 20. **GPS:** n57,33218 e10,53373.⬆➡

20 🚐DKK 150 🚰 🔌 (20x)included. 🚿 **Location:** Urban, simple, central.
Surface: asphalted. ⬛ 01/01-31/12
Distance: 🏙100m ⊗100m 🛒100m.

⚙S **Sæby** 2B3
Danbjerg, Hjørringvej 160. **GPS:** n57,32544 e10,36967.⬆➡

6 🚐DKK 50 🔌. **Location:** Rural, simple, isolated, quiet.
Surface: grassy/gravel. ⬛ 01/01-31/12
Distance: 🏙1km 🛒1km.

⚙ **Tarm** 2A5
Par3Golf, Grimlundvej. **GPS:** n55,83819 e8,71321.
🚐free. **Location:** Isolated, quiet. ⬛ 01/01-31/12
Distance: 🏙Tarm 19km.

⚙S **Tårs (Hjørring)** 2B3
Vendelbo Vans Autocampere, Damhusvej 23. **GPS:** n57,38972 e10,11500.⬆

8 🚐DKK 50 🚰📶Ch 🔌 (8x) WC ⬜included. 🚿 🧺 **Location:** Urban,
comfortable, central, quiet. **Surface:** grassy/gravel. ⬛ 01/01-31/12
Distance: 🏙100m ⛰500m 🛍500m ⊗300m 🛒300m 🚌200m.
Remarks: At motorhome dealer, max. 48h, sanitary 9-17h.

⚙ **Thorsager** 2C4
Dagli Brugsen, Thorsgade 26. **GPS:** n56,34305 e10,46286.⬆

4 🚐free. **Location:** Urban, simple. **Surface:** gravel/metalled.
⬛ 01/01-31/12
Distance: 🏙on the spot 🛒on the spot.
Remarks: Behind supermarket Brugsen.

⚙S **Thyholm** 🚤 2A4
Jegindø Havn, Havnegade. **GPS:** n56,65219 e8,63575.
🚐€ 15 🚰 WC ⬜🔲📶included. **Surface:** gravel. ⬛ 01/01-31/12
Remarks: At harbour.

⚙S **Tinglev** 2B6
Uge Green 2. **GPS:** n54,97365 e9,34601.

6 🚐€ 10 🚰📶Ch 🔌 (6x)DKK 27,10Amp WC ⬜DKK 10 📶included.
Location: Rural. **Surface:** grassy. ⬛ 01/01-31/12
Distance: 🚲2km ⛰on the spot 🛍on the spot ⊗800m 🛒on the spot
🚲on the spot 🏊on the spot.

⚙S **Toftlund** 2B6
Dahl, Lebækvej 2. **GPS:** n55,17839 e9,07768.
5 🚐DKK 35 🚰📶Ch 🔌 included.

⚙S **Ulfborg** ⚡🎣👥 2A5
Rejkjær, Ringkobingvej 24. **GPS:** n56,23319 e8,30966.
🚐DKK 100 🚰📶Ch 🔌against payment. ⬛ 03/04-18/10
Remarks: Quick-Stop: >20h - <10h.

⚙S **Ulfborg** ⚡🎣👥 2A5
Tvind Skolecenter, Skorkærvej 8. **GPS:** n56,25636 e8,28110.⬆

DK

15 ⌇free. **Location:** Rural, simple, isolated.
◘ 01/01-31/12
Distance: 8km 8km 8km.

| | | | Vandel | 2B5 |
Dagli' Brugsen, Hans Thomsens Vej. **GPS:** n55,71285 e9,21800.
⌇free. **Surface:** asphalted. ◘ 01/01-31/12
Remarks: At petrol station and supermarket, Legoland 6km.

| | | | Vandel | 2B5 |
Rastplads, Billundvej. **GPS:** n55,70687 e9,26709.
⌇free ⌇ WC free. **Surface:** forest soil. ◘ 01/01-31/12
Distance: on the spot 4km.
Remarks: Parking in the forest with place for campfire, Legoland 10km.

| | | | Vejers Strand | 2A6 |
Stjerne, Vejers Havvej 7. **GPS:** n55,61915 e8,14090.
⌇DKK 115 ⌇ Ch against payment. ◘ 01/01-31/12
Remarks: Quick-Stop: >20h - <10h.

| | | | Vejers Strand | 2A6 |
Vejers Familicamping, Vejers Havvej 15. **GPS:** n55,61950 e8,13594.
⌇DKK 115 ⌇ Ch against payment.
◘ 01/04-18/09
Remarks: Quick-Stop: >20h - <10h.

Tourist information Vejers Strand:
Tirpitz. German bunker.

| | | | Vesløs | 2A3 |
Vejlernes Grill & Kiosk, Aalborgvej 219B. **GPS:** n57,02518 e9,01585.

⌇free. **Surface:** gravel. ◘ 01/01-31/12

| | | | Vesløs | 2A3 |
Amtoft Havn, Gårdbækvej 12. **GPS:** n57,00647 e8,94068.

10 ⌇€ 14 ⌇ Ch (10x) WC included ⌇free. **Location:** Rural, comfortable, quiet. **Surface:** grassy. ◘ 01/01-31/12
Distance: on the spot on the spot on the spot on the spot.

| | | | Vinderup | 2A4 |
Handbjerg Marina, Strandvejen. **GPS:** n56,47568 e8,71337.
5 ⌇€ 10.
◘ 01/01-31/12
Distance: on the spot.

Tourist information Vinderup:
Hjerl Hedes Frilandsmuseum, Hjerl Hedevej 14. Open air museum. ◘ 01/04-31/10 10-17h.
Stubber Kloster, Stubbergård sø. Ruins of former Benedictine monastery. ◘ 01/01-31/12. free.

| | | | Voerså | 2B3 |
Parking Havn, Havstokken 11. **GPS:** n57,20389 e10,49389.

20 ⌇DKK 120 ⌇ Ch (20x) WC included. **Location:** Rural, comfortable, isolated. **Surface:** gravel. ◘ 01/04-31/10
Distance: 3km on the spot on the spot 3km 3km.
Remarks: Money in envelope in mail box.

Funen

| | | | Aarup | 2B6 |
Annemette & Lars Mogensen, Frøbjerg Vænge 31. **GPS:** n55,34907 e10,08323.
3 ⌇free free. **Surface:** gravel. ◘ 01/01-31/12

| | | | Assens | 2B6 |
Britta Bang, Lilletoftevej 7, Lilletofte Gamtofte. **GPS:** n55,28165 e9,98850.
3 € 13,50 ⌇ Ch included WC. **Location:** Rural.
Surface: metalled.
Distance: 7,5km 7km 7km.

Tourist information Assens:
Vestfyns Hjemstavnsgård, Klaregade 23.,Gummerup, Glamsbjerg. Open air museum. ◘ 01/04-31/10 10-16h Mo.

| | | | Bagenkop | 5B1 |
Koldkrigsmuseum Langelandsfor, Vognsbjergvej 4A.
GPS: n54,75306 e10,71583.
⌇DKK 95. **Surface:** metalled. ◘ 01/04-31/10
Remarks: Check in at museum.

| | | | Bogense | 2B6 |
Autocamper - Bogense, Vestre Havnevej 29-31. **GPS:** n55,56806 e10,07833.
5 € 14 ⌇ included. **Surface:** gravel. ◘ 01/01-31/12
Distance: 300m on the spot.

| | | | Faaborg | 2B6 |
Faaborg Havn, Kanalvej 19. **GPS:** n55,09658 e10,23429.
6 ⌇DKK 120 ⌇ DKK 5 Ch DKK 3/kWh WC. **Surface:** asphalted.
◘ 01/01-31/12
Distance: 200m on the spot on the spot on the spot 500m 200m.
Remarks: Check in at harbourmaster.

| | | | Ferritslev | 2C6 |
Jørgen Christensen, Rolfvej 45. **GPS:** n55,32111 e10,56806.
47 ⌇free. **Location:** Urban, simple. **Surface:** metalled.
◘ 01/01-31/12

| | | | Gram | 2A6 |
Anholm Fiskesø, Folevej 11. **GPS:** n55,30564 e8,99888.

15 ⌇€ 6,75 ⌇ Ch included. **Location:** Rural, simple, isolated, quiet. ◘ 01/04-01/11

DK

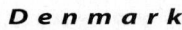

Distance: 🚶5km 🚐on the spot ⊗1km 💧5km.
Remarks: At fish pond.

🚾S | Gram | 2A6
Annemettes, Ribelandevej 18. **GPS:** n55,28647 e9,00098. ⬆ .

3 🍴€ 14 ⛽🔌Ch 🧹. 🚾 **Location:** Rural, simple, isolated, quiet.
Surface: grassy/gravel.

🚾S | Middelfart | 2B6
Lystbådehavn, østre Hougvej 112. **GPS:** n55,49250 e9,73028. ⬆.

12 🍴€ 17 ⛽🔌Ch 🧹 (12x) WC ⬜🔊included. 📷 🚾**Location:** Rural,
luxurious, isolated, quiet. **Surface:** asphalted/metalled. ⬛ 01/01-31/12
Distance: 🚶2km ⛴on the spot 🚐on the spot ⊗on the spot 💧on the spot.
Remarks: Harbour Middelfahrt, tallycard: service, electricity, sanitary building,
caution DKK 50.

🚾S | Nyborg | 2C6
GPS: n55,29734 e10,83963.

🍴free ⛽🔌Chfree. **Surface:** metalled.

🚾S | Nyborg | 2C6
Sulkendrup Vandmølle, Sulkendrupvej 1, Sulkendrup.
GPS: n55,29384 e10,71334.
3 🍴€ 10 ⛽DKK 25 🔌Ch 🧹 against payment WC ⬜DKK 10/time.
Location: Rural, comfortable. **Surface:** grassy. ⬛ 01/01-31/12
Distance: 🚶5km.
Tourist information Nyborg:
🏰 Nyborg Fæstning, Slotsgade 1. Fortress.
🏰 Nyborg Slot / Danehofslottet, Slotsgade 34. Castle, end 12th century.
⬛ 01/04-31/10 10-15/17h.

📷 | Odense | 2C6
Tarup Campingcenter, Agerhatten 31. **GPS:** n55,36110 e10,46722.
20 🍴free. **Surface:** grassy.
Distance: 🚶6km ✈2km.

🚾S | Stenstrup | 2C6
Tronbjerggård Strandhave, Højbjergvej 13. **GPS:** n55,12944 e10,58306.
3 🍴against payment ⛽🔌🧹 WC .

🚾S | Svendborg | 2C6
Mogens Nielsen, Tordensgårdevej 3. **GPS:** n55,08750 e10,55389.
10 🍴 ⛽🧹 WC ⬜included. **Location:** Rural, comfortable.

Surface: grassy/metalled. ⬛ 01/01-31/12
Distance: 🚶5km ⛴5km ⊗on the spot.

S | Svendborg 🏰🏛 | 2C6
Idrætshallen, Ryttervej 70. **GPS:** n55,05668 e10,57613.
⛽🔌Ch.

Tourist information Svendborg:
🏛🏰 Egeskov Slot, Kværndrup. Citadel with park and 6 museums. ⬛ 01/05-
31/10 10-17/20h.
🏰 Valdemars Slot, Slotsalléen 100, Troense, Tåsinge. Castle on the island Tåsinge,
fully furnished. ⬛ 01/05-31/10 10-17h ⬛ May, Sep, Oct: Mo.

🚾S | Varde | 2A6
Fritidscenter, Lerpøtvej 55. **GPS:** n55,63294 e8,47447.
20 🍴against payment ⛽🔌🧹against payment. **Surface:** grassy.
⬛ 01/05-31/10
Remarks: At sports centre.

🚾S | Varde | 2A6
Jensen, Ringkøbingvej 143. **GPS:** n55,65762 e8,48942. ⬆.

4 🍴DKK 75 ⛽🔌🧹 WC . 🚾 **Location:** Rural, comfortable, isolated, quiet.
Surface: grassy/metalled.
Distance: 🚶5km.

🚾S | Varde | 2A6
Joan & Preben Christensen, Ringkøbingvej 259, Hindsig.
GPS: n55,72077 e8,49345. ⬆ .

5 🍴DKK 50 ⛽🔌Ch. 🚾 **Location:** Rural, comfortable, quiet.
Surface: grassy. ⬛ 01/01-31/12
Distance: 🚶12km 💧3km.

Seeland, Møn, Lolland and Falster

🍴S | Bogø By | 2D6
Café-Restaurant Stalden, Hougårdsbanke 5. **GPS:** n54,93000 e12,02806.
4 🍴free for clients ⛽🔌Ch 🧹 WC ⬜🔊against payment.
Location: Rural. **Surface:** grassy. ⬛ 01/01-31/12
Distance: 🚶1km ⊗on the spot.

🚾S | Copenhagen 〰🏰🏛🍰 | 2D5
Copenhagen City Camp, Fisketorvet, Kalvebod Pladsvej.
GPS: n55,65889 e12,55778.

50 DKK 35, DKK 75/pp Ch DKK35. 01/06-31/08
Distance: within walking distance on the spot on the spot.
Remarks: Next to harbour and new shopping center Fisketorv.

Copenhagen 2D5
Svanemøllehavnen, Strandvænget 45. **GPS:** n55,71583 e12,58556.
10 € 17 WC included against payment.
Surface: metalled.
15/05-01/10
Distance: 5km.

Tourist information Copenhagen:
Copenhagen Card. Card gives free entrance to public transport, 60 museums and attractions. Available at Tourist Offices, hotels, camp-sites.
Dyrehavsbakken, Dyrehavevej 62, Klampenborg (ten n. van Kopenhagen). Popular amusement park, oldest park of Denmark, with among other things 100 attractions and 35 restaurants. free.
Tivoli, Vesterbrogade 3. Large amusement park in the centre of the city with among other things 32 restaurants, 26 attractions, shows, concerts etc.
11-21/1h.

Dannemare 5C1
Hummingen, Pumpehusvej 1. **GPS:** n54,71317 e11,24606.
DKK 140 Ch against payment. 04/04-17/10
Remarks: Quick-Stop: >20h - <10h.

Farum 2D5
Hovedgade 32. **GPS:** n55,81222 e12,36917.
3 free. **Location:** Urban, simple. **Surface:** metalled.
01/01-31/12

Farum 2D5
Stavnsholt Renseanlæg. **GPS:** n55,81278 e12,40556.
Ch free. Mo-Thu 7-15.30h, Fr 7-11.30h

Farø 2D6
Farø, Grøsundvej. **GPS:** n54,94876 e11,98696.
20 free Ch WC free. **Location:** Noisy. **Surface:** asphalted.

Frederikssund 2D5
Marbæk Lystbådehavn, Strandlystvej 26 D. **GPS:** n55,82778 e12,06389.
4 € 17 Ch WC included against payment. **Location:** Comfortable. **Surface:** gravel. 01/01-31/12

Gedser 5D1
Gedser Lystbådehavn, Vestre Strand 3. **GPS:** n54,58194 e11,92361.
5 € 16 included. **Surface:** gravel. 01/01-31/12
Distance: 200m.

Gørlev 2C6
Reersø Havn, Strandvejen 101, Reersø. **GPS:** n55,51750 e11,11833.
5 against payment included WC against payment. 01/11-01/04

Hundested 2D5
Hundested Havn, Havnegade 8. **GPS:** n55,96557 e11,84845.
5 € 16 Ch WC against payment.
Location: Comfortable. **Surface:** metalled. 01/01-31/12
Distance: 500m on the spot on the spot on the spot 200m 200m.

Hundested 2D5
Lynæs Havn, Lynæs Havnevej 15 B, Lynæs. **GPS:** n55,94167 e11,86667.
10 € 16 Ch WC against payment. **Surface:** metalled.
01/01-31/12

Hørve 2C5
Teglværksgårdens, Teglværksvej 9A. **GPS:** n55,75794 e11,36568.
DKK 110 Ch against payment. 01/01-31/12
Remarks: Quick-Stop: >20h - <10h.

Kalvehave 2D6
Lystbådehavn, Kalvehave Havnevej 26. **GPS:** n54,99584 e12,16641.
2 against payment against payment. **Surface:** grassy/gravel.

Karrebæksminde 2D6
Naestved Sjelklub, Ved Broen 29. **GPS:** n55,17706 e11,65018.
6 € 18 Ch WC against payment included.
Distance: on the spot on the spot.

Kirke Hyllinge 2D5
Gershøj Havn, Gershøj Havnevej 5, Gershøj. **GPS:** n55,71667 e11,98000.
10 € 8 Ch against payment WC included. **Location:** Simple.
Surface: gravel. 01/01-31/12
Distance: 5km.

Korsør 2C6
Pit-Stop Storebælt, Storebæltsvej 85. **GPS:** n55,34833 e11,11556.
40 € 10. **Location:** Simple. 01/01-31/12
Distance: 500m,.

Korsør 2C6
Lystbådehavn, Sylowsvej 10. **GPS:** n55,32664 e11,13190.

€ 17 included WC against payment. **Surface:** gravel.
01/01-31/12

Tourist information Korsør:
The Great Belt Bridge and Nature Centre, Storebæltsvej 88. Exhibition about the construction of the bridge over the Grote Belt. 01/03-31/12 10-17/19h.
Korsør Fæstning, Korsør Coastal Battery, The Fortress, Søbatteriet 7. Fortress.
01/04-30/11 Tue-Su 11-16h.

Lynge 2D5
Irene & Aage Andersen, Stengårdsvej 12. **GPS:** n55,81972 e12,27376.
3 free. **Location:** Simple. 01/01-31/12

Maribo 5C1
Skelstrupgåren Bed and Breakfast, Skelstupvej 3. **GPS:** n54,78774 e11,52095.
5 DKK 50 against payment. **Surface:** grassy.
Distance: 2,2km 4km.

Munke Bjergby 2D6
Dojringevej 40a. **GPS:** n55,49637 e11,55065.

10 free DKK 10,07 DKK 10,07 DKK 29,83. **Surface:** grassy.
01/01-31/12
Distance: 5km on the spot on the spot.
Remarks: Max. 48h.

Nykøbing 2D5
Lystbådehavn, Snekkevej 9. **GPS:** n55,91610 e11,67287.
10 DKK 110 Ch WC included against payment.
Surface: metalled.
Distance: on the spot.

Nykøbing F. 5D1
Falster City Camping, østre Allé 112. **GPS:** n54,76243 e11,89479.
DKK 120 Ch against payment. 01/04-01/12
Remarks: Quick-Stop: >20h - <10h.

DK

⚓️ S | **Nykøbing F.** | 5D1

Toreby Sejlklub, Dæmningen 2, Sundby Lolland. **GPS**: n54,76051 e11,86041.
5 ⌁€14 ⌁ ⚡ WC ⌁included. **Surface**: gravel.
Distance: ⊗on the spot ⚑on the spot ⚘on the spot.

⚓️ S | **Præstø** | 2D6

Præstø Havn, Fjordstien 1. **GPS**: n55,12444 e12,04333.⬆️.
5 ⌁€16 ⌁ ⚡ ⌁ ⚐included. ⊞ ⚘ **Surface**: asphalted.
Distance: ⊗on the spot.

⚒️ S | **Ringsted** | 2D6

Mogens Madsen, Vibevej 34. **GPS**: n55,44222 e11,80667.
3 ⌁free ⚡ against payment. **Surface**: metalled. ☐ 01/01-31/12
Distance: ⫽4 km ⚑800m.

🅖 | **Rødvig** | 2D6

Rødvig Camping, Højstrupvej 2 A. **GPS**: n55,24346 e12,34999.
⌁DKK 100. ☐ 01/04-28/09
Remarks: Quick-Stop: >20h - <10h.

⚓️ S | **Rødvig** | 2D6

Rødvig Fiskerihavn, Fiskerihavnen 8. **GPS**: n55,25417 e12,37500.
4 ⌁€16 ⌁ ⚐ Ch ⚡ WC ⌁⊡included. ⊞ ⚘ **Surface**: metalled.
☐ 01/01-31/12
Distance: ⊗on the spot.
Remarks: Check in at harbourmaster.

⚓️ S | **Sakskøbing** | 5C1

Sakskøbing Lystbådehavn, Maltrup Vænge 38. **GPS**: n54,81078 e11,61957.
5 ⌁€14 ⌁ ⚡ WC ⌁against payment ⚐included.
Distance: ⊗500m.

⚓️ S | **Sjællands Odde** | 2C5

Sjællands Odde Havn, Østre Havnevej 42. **GPS**: n55,97139 e11,36956.
2 ⌁€16 ⌁ ⚡ included WC against payment. **Surface**: gravel.
☐ 01/01-31/12

⚓️ S | **Skælskør** | 2C6

Skælskør Havn, Havnevej 20. **GPS**: n55,25223 e11,28992.
15 ⌁€14 ⌁ ⚐ Ch ⚡ WC included ⌁⊡ ⚐against payment.
Surface: metalled. ☐ 01/01-31/12
Distance: ⊗on the spot.

🏨 S | **Taastrup** | 2D5

Park Hotel, Brorsonsvej 3. **GPS**: n55,65389 e12,30000.⬆️.
10 ⌁DKK 125 ⚡ DKK 25 WC ⌁. **Surface**: metalled. ☐ 01/01-31/12
Distance: ⚞300m ⫽1,5km ⊗on the spot ⚑300m.
Remarks: Breakfast buffet DKK 75.

⚓️ S | **Tårs (Harpelunde)** | 2C6

Fiskeri & lystbådehavn, Tårsvej 15, Harpelunde. **GPS**: n54,87811 e11,02381.
2 ⌁€17 ⌁ ⚡ WC ⌁included. ☐ 01/01-31/12
Remarks: Harbour Tårs.

⌁ | **Værløse** | 2D5

Furesø Museer, Skovgårds alle 37. **GPS**: n55,78528 e12,37722.
4 ⌁free. **Location**: Urban, simple. **Surface**: metalled.
☐ 01/01-31/12
Distance: ⊗250m ⚑250m.

🏨 S | **Værløse** | 2D5

Bryggeri Skovlyst, Skovlystvej 2. **GPS**: n55,76317 e12,38365.
3 ⌁free ⌁ WC . **Location**: Simple. **Surface**: gravel. ☐ 01/01-31/12
Distance: ⚞5km ⊗on the spot ⚘on the spot ⚘on the spot.

DK

GERMANY

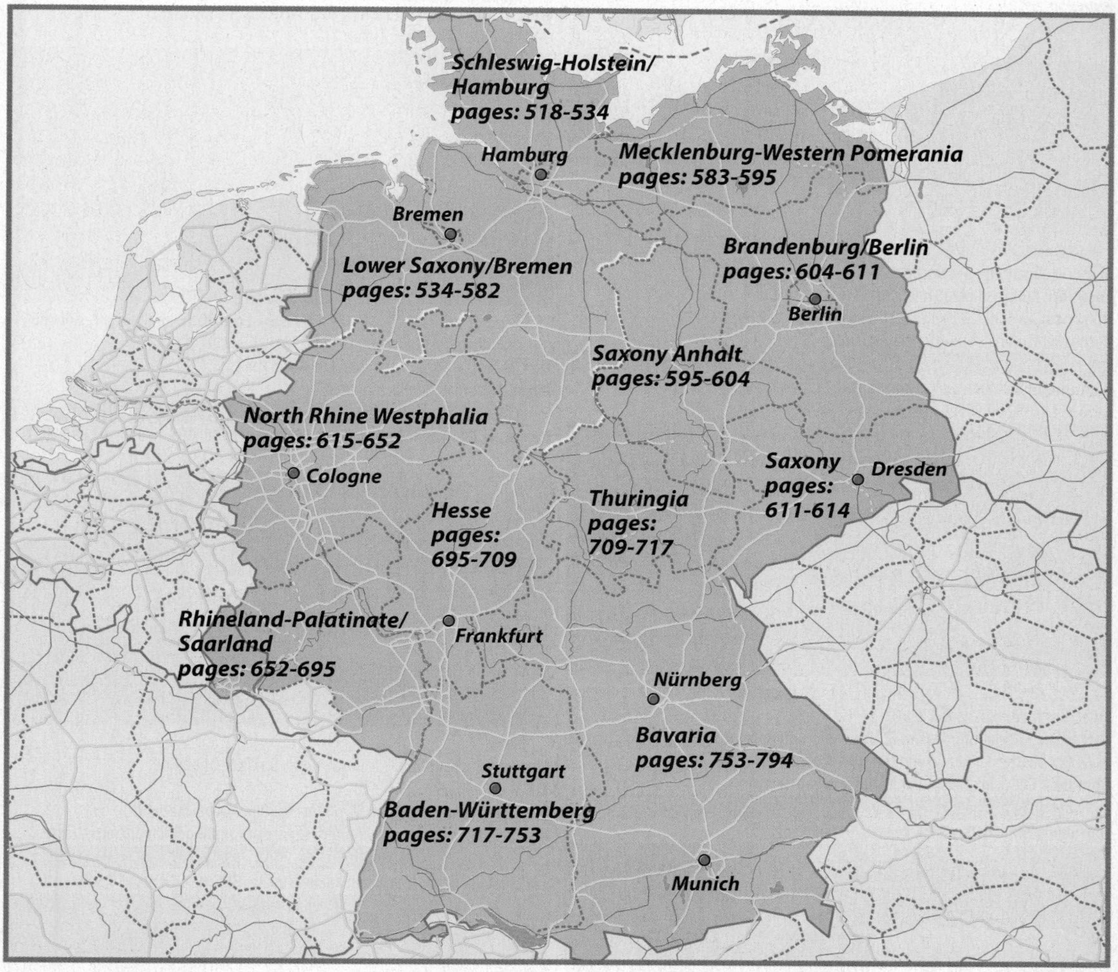

Schleswig-Holstein/ Hamburg
pages: 518-534

Hamburg

Mecklenburg-Western Pomerania
pages: 583-595

Bremen

Lower Saxony/Bremen
pages: 534-582

Brandenburg/Berlin
pages: 604-611

Berlin

Saxony Anhalt
pages: 595-604

North Rhine Westphalia
pages: 615-652

Cologne

Saxony
pages:
611-614

Dresden

Hesse
pages:
695-709

Thuringia
pages:
709-717

Rhineland-Palatinate/ Saarland
pages: 652-695

Frankfurt

Nürnberg

Bavaria
pages: 753-794

Stuttgart

Baden-Württemberg
pages: 717-753

Munich

DE

Capital: Berlin
Government: Federal republic
Official Language: Germany
Population: 82,000,000 (2013)
Area: 356,970 km²

General information
Dialling code: 0049
General emergency: 112
Currency: Euro

Regulations for overnight stays
Overnight stays on the public highway are allowed,
if there is no local prohibition, but no "camping"
activities are allowed.

Additional public holidays 2015
January 6 Epiphany
April 3 Good Friday
April 6 Eastermonday
May 1 Labor Day
May 25 White Monday
June 4 Corpus Christi
August 15 Assumption of the Virgin Mary
October 3 Day of German Unity
November 1 All Saints' Day

Schleswig-Holstein

DE

🌊S Albersdorf 4D2

Freizeitbad Albersdorf, Weg zur Badeanstalt 18. **GPS:** n54,15350 e9,28055.

6 🕙 € 15 swimming pool incl 🚰🔌Ch 🔌(6x)included.
Location: Rural, isolated, quiet. **Surface:** grassy. 🔲 01/05-31/08
Distance: 🚂1km ⊗100m 🛒300m on the spot 🏊on the spot.
Remarks: Parking at swimming pool, max. 3 days.

🌊S Altenhof 5A2

Wohnmobilpark Ostsee 'Grüner Jäger', Grünen Jäger.
GPS: n54,44392 e9,90526. ⬆➡.

80 🕙 € 8 🚰🔌Ch 🔌€3/24h WC 🔌€1 🧹. **Location:** Rural, simple, isolated, quiet. **Surface:** grassy. 🔲 01/01-31/12
Distance: 🚂Eckernförde 6km 🏊2km ⊗on the spot 🛒6km
🚌200m busstop -> Kiel 🚲on the spot 🏊on the spot.
Remarks: Check in at restaurant Grüner, bread-service.

🌊S Aukrug 5A3

Zum Sportplatz 1. **GPS:** n54,07441 e9,79160. ⬆➡.

8 🕙 € 8 🚰Ch 🔌included. **Location:** Rural. **Surface:** grassy/metalled.
🔲 01/01-31/12
Distance: 🚂1km ⊗800m 🛒1km 🚲on the spot 🏊on the spot.
Remarks: Max. 3 days, check in and key service at pay-desk of swimming pool.

🌊S Aventoft 4C1

Bauernhof Clausen, Gotteskoogstrasse 5. **GPS:** n54,88250 e8,80722. ⬆➡.

5 🕙 € 6 🚰🔌€2 WC 🔌€2. 🛒 **Location:** Rural, simple, isolated, quiet.

Surface: grassy. 🔲 01/01-31/12
Distance: 🚂5km 🛒5km.
Remarks: <3000kg.

🌊S Aventoft 4C1

Wohnmobilstellplatz Zu den Fuchswiesen, Revtoftweg 1.
GPS: n54,87661 e8,84562. ⬆.

15 🕙 € 5, dog € 1 🚰Ch 🔌€1,50. 🛒 **Location:** Rural, simple, isolated, quiet. **Surface:** asphalted/grassy. 🔲 01/01-31/12
Distance: 🚂3km ⊗3km 🛒3km 🚲on the spot.
Remarks: Bread-service.

🌊S Bad Bramstedt 👥 5A3

Parkplatz P7, Am Bahnhof, König Christian Strasse. **GPS:** n53,92167 e9,88967. ⬆➡.

5 🕙 free.
Location: Urban, simple, central, noisy. **Surface:** metalled.
🔲 01/01-31/12
Distance: 🚂centre 500m ⊗500m 🛒500m 🚌on the spot.
Remarks: At station, max. 1 night, service at camping Roland, Kielerstrasse.

🌊S Bad Malente 5B2

Parkplatz Krützen, Sebastian Kneipp strasse. **GPS:** n54,17198 e10,54919. ⬆.

8 🕙 € 2/pp 🚰€1 🔌€1 Ch. 🚻 **Location:** Rural, simple. **Surface:** metalled.
🔲 01/01-31/12
Distance: 🚂on the spot ⊗500m 🛒1km.

🌊S Bad Oldesloe 🪣 5B3

Wohnmobilplatz Exer, Am Bürgerpark. **GPS:** n53,81101 e10,36915. ⬆➡.

8 🛏free 🚰€1/10minutes 🔌Ch 🚿(8x)€2/10h WC 🚻.
Location: Urban, simple, quiet. **Surface:** metalled. 📅 01/01-31/12
Distance: 🚶on the spot 🚲3km ⊗on the spot 🚉400m.

Bad Segeberg 5B3
Kalkbergblick, Kastanienweg 1b. **GPS:** n53,93872 e10,31423.⬆➡.

25 🛏€8 🚰🔌Chincluded 🚿(15x)€3/night,6 Amp.
Location: Rural, comfortable, quiet. **Surface:** gravel. 📅 01/01-31/12
Distance: 🚶500m 🚲A7 3km 🛒600m Segerberger See 🛒600m ⊗500m 🚉500m 🛒on the spot 🛒on the spot.
Remarks: Jun/Aug Karl May Spiele, open air theater.

Barmstedt 5A3
Am Rantzauer See, Seestrasse 12. **GPS:** n53,78640 e9,76420.⬆.

5 🛏€5 🚰🔌Ch 🚿WC 🚻included. **Surface:** metalled. 📅 01/01-31/12
Distance: 🚶on the spot ⊗on the spot 🚉500m.

Behrensdorf 5B2
Campingpark Waldesruh, Neuland. **GPS:** n54,35754 e10,60216.⬆.

18 🛏€ 10-12 2 pers.incl, dog € 1,50 🚰🔌Ch 🚿€1/24h WC 🚻.
Location: Rural, comfortable. **Surface:** grassy. 📅 01/04-31/10
Distance: 🚶2km 🛒on the spot 🛒on the spot ⊗on the spot 🚉on the spot.

Bistensee 5A2
Ferienplatz bei Matz, Mühlenweg 1. **GPS:** n54,39538 e9,71386.⬆.

5 🛏€3 + € 3/pp 🚰🚿included WC 🚻. **Location:** Rural, simple, isolated, quiet. **Surface:** grassy. 📅 01/01-31/12
Distance: 🚶500m 🛒600m Bistensee 🛒on the spot ⊗2km 🚉1km 🛒on the spot 🛒on the spot.

Blekendorf 5B2
Am Sehlendorfer Strand, Strandstrasse 24. **GPS:** n54,30571 e10,69358.⬆.

40 🛏€ 15,50 🚰€1 🔌Ch 🚿included WC 🚻. **Location:** Rural, comfortable. **Surface:** grassy. 📅 01/01-31/12
Distance: 🚶1km 🛒on the spot 🛒on the spot ⊗on the spot 🚉5km.

Bordesholm 5A2
Festplatz, Kielerstrasse. **GPS:** n54,18389 e10,02667.

6 🛏free. **Location:** Rural, simple, quiet. **Surface:** grassy/sand.
📅 01/01-31/12
Distance: 🚶1,5km 🚲4km.
Remarks: Max. 18h, service at petrol station.

Bordesholm 5A2
Shell tankstelle, Bahnofstrasse 78. **GPS:** n54,17343 e10,03497.
🚰🔌Ch 🚿. 📅 01/01-31/12

Bosau 5B3
Dat Gröne Huus, Stadtbeker Strasse 97. **GPS:** n54,09198 e10,42886.⬆.

3 🛏€ 5, guests free 🚿€3 🚉.
Location: Rural, simple, quiet. **Surface:** gravel.
📅 01/04-30/11
Distance: 🚶100m 🛒Großer Plöner See 🛒on the spot ⊗on the spot 🚉1km.
Remarks: Bread-service.

Bösdorf 5B2
Wohnmobilcamp Augustfelde, Vierer See, Augustfelde.
GPS: n54,12898 e10,45506.⬆➡.

16 🛏€ 11,50-13,50 🚰🔌Ch 🚿(16x) WC included 🚻€0,75.

Surface: grassy. ☐ 01/04-25/10
Distance: ⚓on the spot ⚓on the spot ⊗on the spot ⚓on the spot.

Campingpark Gut Ruhleben, Missionsweg 2, Ruhleben.
GPS: n54,14308 e10,45021.

10 ⌁ € 10,50-13,50 ⛽🔌Ch 🔫〰included. 🛁 **Location:** Rural, simple.
Surface: grassy/gravel. ☐ 01/04-30/09
Remarks: Max. 3 nights.

Süderstraße. **GPS:** n54,61307 e8,97082. ↑→.

5 ⌁free. **Location:** Rural. **Surface:** asphalted. ☐ 01/01-31/12
Distance: ⚓900m ⚓Aldi 650m.
Remarks: Nearby swimming pool.

Camping Am Mussinder Fährhaus, Mussinder Fahrstrasse 33.
GPS: n54,52500 e9,71583. 🗙.

20 ⌁ € 12 ⛽🔌Ch 🔫WC⚓. **Surface:** grassy. ☐ 01/04-31/10

Ferienhof Lassen, Grossbrodersbyer weg 5. **GPS:** n54,53829 e9,71443. 🗙.

3 ⌁ € 10 ⛽🔌Ch 🔫included. **Location:** Rural, simple, quiet.
Surface: grassy.
Distance: ⚓500m ⊗2km ⚓500m.

Parkplatz, Dorfstrasse. **GPS:** n53,86417 e9,31667. ↑.

30 ⌁free ⛽€1/5minutes 🔌€1 Ch 🔫 (30x)€0,50/kWh WC⚓€0,50.
Location: Rural, comfortable. **Surface:** metalled. ☐ 01/01-31/12
Distance: ⚓800m ⚓400m ⊗on the spot ⚓500m 🚲on the spot
🏊on the spot.

An der Braake, Am Freizeitbad. **GPS:** n53,89832 e9,13138. ↑.

12 ⌁free ⛽€1 🔌Ch. **Location:** Rural, comfortable, central, quiet.
Surface: grassy/metalled. ☐ 01/01-31/12
Distance: ⚓500m ⊗500m ⚓500m 🚲on the spot.

Hermann-Ehlers-Platz, Agnes Miegel Strasse. **GPS:** n54,31583 e9,69306. ↑→.

10 ⌁free. **Location:** Simple, central. **Surface:** metalled.
☐ 01/01-31/12
Distance: ⚓on the spot ⊗1km ⚓1,5km.
Remarks: Max. 1 night.

Wohnmobilstellplatz Nordsee, Dr. Martin Bahr Strasse.
GPS: n54,12889 e8,86889. ↑→.

100 ⌁ 1/11-28/2 € 10, 1/3-31/10 € 13 ⛽€0,50/50liter 🔌
Ch 🔫WC⚓〰€0,50/day. 🏠 **Location:** Rural, comfortable, isolated, quiet.
Surface: grassy. ☐ 01/01-31/12
Distance: ⚓1km ⚓500m ⊗300m.

Deichmuseum P2, Westereck 2. **GPS:** n54,14210 e8,84212. ↑.

50 ⌁free. **Location:** Simple, isolated, quiet.
Distance: 500m. 500m.
🆂 **Dagebüll** 4C1
Am Nordseedeich, Am Badedeich 15. **GPS:** n54,72666 e8,69527.⬆.

10 ⌁€6 €2. **Location:** Rural. **Surface:** grassy.
01/01-31/12
Distance: 5km 100m 100m on the spot bakery 300m.
🆂 **Damp** 5A1
Wohnmobilpark Damp, Parkstrasse 2. **GPS:** n54,57750 e10,01667.⬆➡.

70 ⌁€12 €1/100liter Ch (60x)€0,60/kWh WC €1/3minutes
Location: Rural, comfortable, quiet. **Surface:** grassy/gravel.
01/01-31/12
Distance: on the spot on the spot on the spot 150m.
🆂 **Drelsdorf** 4D1
Drelsdörper Krog, Dorfstrasse 23. **GPS:** n54,60555 e9,03555.⬆.

15 ⌁€5, guests free €2 WC. **Location:** Simple, central, noisy.
Surface: grassy. 01/01-31/12
Distance: 200m 2km.
Remarks: Along through road.
🆂 **Eckernförde** 5A2
Parkplatz P1, Grüner Weg, B76. **GPS:** n54,46549 e9,83574.⬆➡.

46 ⌁€1,60/h 10-20h, overnight stay free €0,50/120liter €0,50 Ch€0,50
€0,50/kWh. **Location:** Urban, simple, central. **Surface:** metalled.
01/01-31/12
Distance: 200m 250m 300m 300m 200m on the spot
on the spot.
Remarks: Along busy through road, parking nearby centre and beach.
🆂 **Elmshorn** 5A3
Stellplatz Elmshorn, Nordufer. **GPS:** n53,75157 e9,65268.⬆.

6 ⌁free €1/80liter Ch WC. **Location:** Urban, simple, central, quiet.
Surface: metalled. 01/01-31/12
Distance: 800m on the spot on the spot.
⌁ **Eutin** 5B2
Elisabethstrasse. **GPS:** n54,13507 e10,60935.⬆.

5+3 ⌁free. **Location:** Urban. **Surface:** metalled. 01/01-31/12
Distance: on the spot.
Remarks: Parking at station.
Eutin 5B2
Schloss-Parkplatz P11, Schlossstraße. **GPS:** n54,13828 e10,61990.⬆.
5 ⌁free. **Surface:** metalled. 01/01-31/12
Distance: Großer Eutiner See.
🆂 **Fehmarn** 5C2
Wohnmobilpark Wulfener Hals, Wulfener-Hals-Weg 16, Wulfen.
GPS: n54,40687 e11,17489.⬆.

100 ⌁from € 11,80-27,40 Ch €2,10 WC €0,90
Location: Rural, luxurious. **Surface:** grassy. 01/01-31/12

DE

Distance: ⌐on the spot.

⚄S | **Fehmarn** | 5C2
Hintz-Heizungsbau, Landkirchenerweg 1b, Burg. **GPS:** n54,44228 e11,18967.⬆

16 ⚄€ 10 ⌐€1 ⍾Ch ✦ (16x)€5. **Location:** Simple, quiet.
Surface: metalled. ◻ 01/01-31/12
Distance: ⌐on the spot.

⚄ | **Fehmarn** | 5C2
Parkplatz Ost, Osterstrasse, Burg. **GPS:** n54,43754 e11,19990.⬆

30 ⚄€ 8 (21-8h). ⌂ **Location:** Urban, simple. **Surface:** metalled.
◻ 01/01-31/12
Distance: ⌐100m.

©S | **Fehmarn** | 5C2
Camping Strukkamphuk, Strukkamp. **GPS:** n54,41239 e11,10223.⬆

21 ⚄€ 14,50-31 ⌐ ⍾Ch ✦ WC ⌐included. 🛁 **Location:** Rural.
Surface: grassy. ◻ 01/01-31/12
Distance: ⊗10m.

⚓ | **Fehmarn** | 5C2
Kommunal- und Yachthafen Burgstaaken, Burgstaaken/am Binnensee,
Burgstaaken. **GPS:** n54,42028 e11,19224.⬆

15 ⚄€ 10 21-08h. ⌂ **Location:** Rural, simple. **Surface:** metalled.
◻ 01/01-31/12
Distance: ⊗100m. ⚑100m.

⚄ | **Flensburg** 🌿⚓🍽🏄 | 4D1
Am Industriehafen, dir Flensburg Mürwick. **GPS:** n54,80444 e9,44388.⬆

20 ⚄free.
Location: Urban, simple, isolated, quiet. **Surface:** gravel.
Distance: ⌐1,5km ⌐on the spot ⌐on the spot.

⚄S | **Fockbek** | 5A2
Am Freibad, Grosse Rheie 17. **GPS:** n54,30190 e9,60331.⬆

3 ⚄free ⌐ ⍾Ch WC ⌐. **Location:** Rural, quiet. **Surface:** grassy/sand.
◻ 01/01-31/12
Distance: ⌐800m ⊗800m ⚑800m 🚴on the spot 🏃on the spot.
Remarks: Parking swimming pool, max. 24h.

⚄ | **Friedrichskoog** | 4D3
P2, Nordseestrasse. **GPS:** n54,03272 e8,84833.⬆➡

30 ⚄€ 2, overnight stay free. **Location:** Rural, comfortable, isolated, quiet.
Surface: asphalted/grassy. ◻ 01/03-31/10
Distance: ⌐1km ⌐550m ⊗800m.
Remarks: Bread-service.

⚄S | **Gelting** ⚓🏄 | 5A1
Hafen Wackerballig, Strandweg, Wackerballig. **GPS:** n54,75564 e9,87842.⬆

18 ⚄€ 8 ⌐€0,50/40liter ⍾Ch ✦€1,50/day WC ⌐€0,50. 🛁
Location: Rural, simple. **Surface:** grassy/gravel. ◻ 01/04-31/10
Distance: ⌐1,5km ⊗on the spot ⚑2km.
Remarks: Key sanitary building/waste dump at harbour master, caution € 20.

⚄ | **Glückstadt** | 4D3
Park & Ride platz, Bahnhofstrasse. **GPS:** n53,78776 e9,43145.

DE

10 ⬛free. **Location:** Urban, simple. **Surface:** asphalted.
🔵 01/01-31/12
Distance: 🚶900m 🚊200m 🚲on the spot 🚶on the spot.
🔷 | **Glückstadt** | 4D3
Am Außenhafen, Am Hafen. **GPS:** n53,78560 e9,41088.⬆️➡️.

16 ⬛€ 5. 🔌 **Location:** Rural, comfortable. **Surface:** metalled.
🔵 01/01-31/12 💧 high water
Distance: 🚶1km 🏊on the spot 🎣on the spot ⊗on the spot 🚲on the spot
🚶on the spot.
Remarks: Along the river Elbe.
🔷S | **Grödersby** | 5A1
WSG Arin/Grödersby, Friedenshöher Straße 21. **GPS:** n54,63444 e9,92944.⬆️.

15 ⬛€ 15 🔌🔵Ch 🔌 WC 🚽€3/2 🚿included. 🔌 **Location:** Rural,
simple, quiet. **Surface:** gravel/metalled. 🔵 01/05-30/09
Distance: 🚶200m 🏊on the spot 🎣on the spot ⊗200m 🚿on the spot.
🔷S | **Grömitz** | 5C2
Wohnmobilstellplatz am Lensterstrand, Blankwasserweg.
GPS: n54,15650 e10,99134.⬆️.

60 ⬛winter € 6, summer € 12 🔌€0,50 🔵Ch 🔌 (20x)€1/kWh.🔵
Location: Rural, comfortable. **Surface:** metalled. 🔵 01/01-31/12
Distance: 🏊200m 🔌on the spot ⊗200m.
🐑 | **Großenaspe** | 5A3
Wildpark Eekholt, Eekhol 1. **GPS:** n53,94819 e10,02916.

10 ⬛free. **Location:** Rural, simple, isolated, quiet. **Surface:** grassy/sand.
🔵 01/01-31/12
Distance: 🚶4km Grossenaspe ⊗Kiek ut Stuben 🚌> Wildpark.
🔷S | **Großenbrode** | 5C2
Wassersportzentrum, Am Kai 29. **GPS:** n54,35583 e11,07798.⬆️➡️.

50 ⬛€ 8-10 🔌€0,50/100liter 🔵Ch 🔌€1/kWh WC 🚽€0,50 🚿.🔌
Location: Rural. **Surface:** grassy/metalled. 🔵 01/01-31/12
Distance: 🏊300m 🔌on the spot 🚿2km.
🔷S | **Großenbrode** | 5C2
Wohnmobilhafen Reise, Südstrand 1. **GPS:** n54,36170 e11,08567.⬆️➡️.

36 ⬛€ 10-14 🔌🔵Ch 🔌 WC 🚽€0,50 🚿. **Location:** Rural, comfortable.
Surface: gravel. 🔵 01/01-31/12
Distance: ⊗on the spot 🚿500m 🚌on the spot.
🔷S | **Großsolt** | 4D1
Stellplatz Mühlenbrück, Flensburger strasse, Mühlenbrück.
GPS: n54,70853 e9,52243.⬆️.

50 ⬛winter free, summer € 7,50 🔌 WC.🔵 **Location:** Rural. **Surface:** grassy.
🔵 01/01-31/12 💧 water disconnected in winter
Distance: 🏊on the spot 🎣on the spot.
🔷S | **Grömitz** | 5C2
Wohnmobilstellplatz, Gildestraße 14. **GPS:** n54,14490 e10,95262.⬆️➡️.

DE

50 🛏 € 10 🚰 🔌 Ch 🚿 (13x) €2/day WC 🚽 €0,50. 🛒
Location: Rural, comfortable, quiet. **Surface:** gravel. ⬛ 01/03--01/10
Distance: 🚉 200m.

6 🛏 € 10 🚰 🔌 Ch 🚿 (6x) WC 🚽. 🛒 **Location:** Rural, comfortable, isolated, quiet. **Surface:** grassy. ⬛ 01/01-31/12
Distance: 🚲 2km.

| 🏕 S | **Hamburg** 🌴⚓🧁🚤 | 5A4 |

Wohnmobilhafen Hamburg, Grüner Deich 8, Hammerbrook.
GPS: n53,54303 e10,02814. ⬆️➡️

| 🏕 S | **Harrislee** | 4D1 |

Skandic Camping, Am Oxer 17a. **GPS:** n54,79800 e9,36960. 🏕️ .

60 🛏 € 19 🚰 🔌 Ch 🚿 WC 🚽. 🛒 **Location:** Urban, simple, central, noisy.
Surface: gravel. ⬛ 01/01-31/12
Distance: 🚲 4km 🚌 200m.

5 🛏 € 5 🚰 🔌 Ch 🚿 included WC €1. 🛒 **Location:** Urban, simple, isolated.
Surface: metalled. ⬛ 01/01-31/12
Distance: 🚲 6km.
Remarks: Motorhome dealer, accessory shop.

| 🏕 S | **Hamburg** 🌴⚓🧁🚤 | 5A4 |

Wohnmobilplatz Hamburg Süd, Finkenrieker Hauptdeich 5.
GPS: n53,47440 e10,00134. ⬆️➡️

| C S | **Hasselberg** | 5A1 |

Camping Oehe-Draecht, Drecht. **GPS:** n54,71590 e9,99030. ⬆️➡️

80 🛏 € 12 🚰 €1 🔌 €1 Ch €1 🚿 (10x) €1/2kWh WC 🚽 €1 📶. 🚐
Location: Urban, simple, noisy. **Surface:** metalled. ⬛ 01/01-31/12
Distance: 🚲 14km 🏊 100m 🚌 100m 🚶 5 min.

10 🛏 €11 🚰 🔌 Ch 🚿 €3 WC 🚽 included. **Location:** Rural, simple, quiet.
Surface: grassy. ⬛ 01/04-30/09
Distance: 🚲 3km 🏊 on the spot ⊗ on the spot.

| 🏕 | **Hamburg** 🌴⚓🧁🚤 | 5A4 |

Am Strand Pauli, St. Pauli Hafenstraße. **GPS:** n53,54598 e9,96099.
20 🛏 € 8,50, weekend € 13.
Surface: asphalted.
⬛ 01/01-31/12
Distance: 🚲 Hamburg Altstadt 2,4km 🏊 on the spot ⊗many restaurant 100m 🚌 600m.

| 🏕 S | **Heide** | 4D2 |

Wohnmobilplatz Heide, Langvogt-Johannsen-strasse. **GPS:** n54,20181 e9,11319.
⬆️ .

Tourist information Hamburg:

ℹ️ Hamburg-card. Card offers free entrance to public transport and museums, discounts on boat trips, zoo etc. Available at Tourist Information. 🎫 € 9,50/1 day, € 22,90/3 days, 1 adult + max. 3 children.
👁 Sankt Pauli. City district with well-known Reeperbahn.
🎪 Flohschanze, Rinderschlachthalle St Pauli. Antiques and flea market. ⬛ Sa 8-16h.
😀 Tierpark Hagenbeck, Stellingen. Zoo.
🏛 Antikpassage, Klosterwall 9-21. Arcade with 39 antique stores. ⬛ Tue-Fri 12-18h, Sa 10-16h.

16 🛏 € 5/€ 7 🚰 €1/100liter 🔌 €1 Ch 🚿 €1/2kWh.
Surface: grasstiles/metalled. ⬛ 01/01-31/12
Distance: 🚲 800m 🏊 5,5km ⊗100m 🚉 300m.

| 🏕 S | **Heiligenhafen** ⚓🚤 | 5C2 |

Parkplatz Steinwarder, B207 Abfahrt Heiligenhafen. **GPS:** n54,37896 e10,97875.
⬆️➡️

| 🏕 S | **Hanerau-Hademarschen** | 4D3 |

Ferienhof Sievers, Wilhelmsburg. **GPS:** n54,12360 e9,38627. ⬆️

90 🚐 € 7,50, peak season € 12/24h 🚰 €0,50 ♨ Ch 💧 (42x)€2 WC 🚿. 🚐
Surface: asphalted. ⚡ 01/01-31/12
Distance: 🚶400m 🏖on the spot 🎣on the spot.
Remarks: Direct access to the beach.

Reisemobilstellplatz Binnensee, Eichholzweg. **GPS:** n54,37721 e10,95548. 🔼

20 🚐 € 7,50-10 💧 (21x)€2. 🚐 **Location:** Urban. **Surface:** metalled.
⚡ 01/01-31/12
Distance: 🚶1km 🏖on the spot.
Remarks: Max. 24h.

Campingpark Ostseestrand, Strandstraße. **GPS:** n54,38588 e10,49152. 🔼➡️.

25 🚐 € 15 🚰 ♨ Ch 💧 WC 🚿included 📷. **Location:** Rural, luxurious.
Surface: grassy. ⚡ 01/04-15/10
Distance: 🚶1km 🏖beach 150m 🎣150m ⊗on the spot 🚿on the spot.

Wohnmobilplatz Radeland, Strandstraße 18. **GPS:** n54,38278 e10,49295. 🔼
➡️.

20 🚐 € 5 🚰 ♨ Ch 💧 €0,60/kWh WC 🚿 €3/day. **Location:** Rural.
Surface: grassy/sand. ⚡ 01/04-30/09
Distance: 🏖300m.

Parkplatz Alt-Hohwacht, Strandstrasse. **GPS:** n54,31902 e10,67529. 🔼➡️.

20 🚐 € 10 🚰 €1/80liter ♨ €1 Ch 💧 (20x)€1/kWh. 🚐
Location: Urban. **Surface:** metalled. ⚡ 01/01-31/12
Distance: 🏖on the spot 🎣on the spot.

Loof's Wohnmobilhafen, Dockoogstrasse 7. **GPS:** n54,47451 e9,04249.

30 🚐 € 12 🚰 €1 ♨ €2 Ch €2 💧 (30x)€3 WC 🚿€0,50. 🚿
Location: Rural, simple, central, quiet. **Surface:** gravel. ⚡ 01/01-31/12
Distance: 🚶200m 🏖200m 🎣200m ⊗200m 🍽200m 🚴on the spot
🚶‍on the spot.

Wohnmobilplatz Am Dockkoog, Dockoogstrasse 17. **GPS:** n54,47888 e9,01138.
🔼.

40 🚐 € 12 2 pers.incl, dog € 1 🚰 ♨ Ch WC 🚿included 🚿€1. 🚿
Location: Rural, simple, quiet. **Surface:** grassy. ⚡ Easter-31/10
Distance: 🚶500m 🏖200m 🎣200m 🍽on the spot 🚴on the spot
🚶‍on the spot.
Remarks: Max. 3 nights.

Malzmüllerwiesen, Schuhmacherallee. **GPS:** n53,91970 e9,51815. 🔼➡️.

5 🚐 free 🚰 €1/100liter ♨ €1 Ch €1.
Location: Rural, simple, central, quiet. **Surface:** metalled/sand.
⚡ 01/01-31/12 📷 during event
Distance: 🚶600m 🏖20m 🎣on the spot 🚶‍on the spot.

Wohnmobilhafen Jagel, Bundesstrasse 13. **GPS:** n54,45388 e9,53416. 🔼.

DE

31 ⛺ € 10 🚰 Ch ☕ day WC 🚿. **Location:** Rural, comfortable, quiet.
Surface: grassy. 🅾 01/01-31/12
Distance: 🚶250m 🚢 4,5km.

🅾🆂 Kaltenkirchen ♨ 5A3
Reisemobilstellplatz Holstentherme, Norderstrasse 8.
GPS: n53,84056 e9,94650. ⬆➡

20 ⛺ free 🚰 €1/80liter 🔌€1 Ch€1 🚿. **Location:** Quiet.
Surface: grassy/gravel. 🅾 01/01-31/12
Distance: 🚶1,5km 🚴1km 🛒on the spot 🎣1,5km 🚌on the spot.
Remarks: Coins available at pay-desk of theTherme.

🅾🆂 Kappeln ⛵ 5A1
Aral-Tankstelle, Eckernförder Strasse 9/B. **GPS:** n54,65688 e9,94480.

10 ⛺ free 🚰 Ch ☕ €5/day. **Location:** Urban, simple. **Surface:** metalled.
🅾 01/01-31/12
Distance: 🚶300m 🚴2km 🛒on the spot.
Remarks: Caution key electricity € 25.

⚓🆂 Kappeln ⛵ 5A1
Anker Yachting, Am Hafen. **GPS:** n54,66715 e9,93718. ⬆
20 ⛺ € 10-14 🚰 Ch ☕ €0,50/kWh 🔌1. 🅾 01/01-31/12
Distance: 🚶1km 🛒1km 🎣1km.
Remarks: Near marina.

🅾🆂 Kellinghusen ⛲ 5A3
Am Freibad, Jacob-Fleischer-Strasse 6. **GPS:** n53,94715 e9,71035. ⬆➡

10 ⛺ free 🚰 €0,50/100liter 🔌€0,50 Ch ☕ (4x)€1/h WC 🚿use sanitary
facilities at swimming pool. **Location:** Rural, quiet. **Surface:** gravel.

🅾 01/01-31/12
Distance: 🚶centre 500m 🛒500m 🎣500m.
Remarks: Check in at swimming pool.

🅾🆂 Kiel 🌊🐚 5A2
Wohnmobilstellplatz Kiel, Förde und Kanalblick, Mecklenburgstrasse 58.
Kiel-Wik. **GPS:** n54,36362 e10,14705. ⬆➡

30 ⛺ € 11-13 🚰 Ch ☕ (33x)€3,50/24h WC 🔌€1/5minutes 🚿€3/1.
Location: Urban, simple, central, noisy. **Surface:** metalled.
🅾 01/01-31/12
Distance: 🚶6,5km 🛒Imbiss on the spot 🎣1,5km 🚲on the spot
🚶on the spot.
Remarks: Check in and pay at reception, bread-service.

⚓🆂 Kiel 🌊🚢 5A2
Olympiahafen Schilksee, Soling 26. **GPS:** n54,43033 e10,16634. ⬆

20 ⛺ € 10 🚰 €0,50/3minutes 🔌€1 Ch ☕ WC 🚿. **Surface:** metalled.
🅾 01/01-31/12 ☀ last 2 weeks of Jun
Distance: 🚶13km 🏊400m 🏖400m.
Remarks: Check in and coins service at harbourmaster.

Tourist information Kiel:
Ⓜ Schleswig-Holsteinisches Freilichtmuseum, Molfsee. Open air museum.
🅾 01/04-31/10 daily 9-18h, 01/11-31/03 Su 11-16h.
🎫 € 4,50, family card € 11.

🏕 Krempe 5A3
Am Schul- und Sportzentrum, Am Freibad. **GPS:** n53,83356 e9,49447. ⬆

3 ⛺ free. **Location:** Rural, simple, quiet. **Surface:** gravel.
🅾 01/01-31/12
Distance: 🚶200m.

🍴 Kremperheide 5A3
Heidekrug, Dorfstraße. **GPS:** n53,88006 e9,47967.
4 ⛺ € 5, guests free. 🅾 01/01-31/12
Distance: 🛒on the spot.
Remarks: In front of restaurant.

🍴🆂 Kropp 5A2
Hotel Wikingerhof, Tetenhusener Chaussee 1. **GPS:** n54,40638 e9,51055. ⬆

8 ⌇ € 5, guests free ☕ WC 🚿. **Location:** Urban, simple, quiet. **Surface:** metalled. ◻ 01/01-31/12 **Distance:** 🚶300m ⊗on the spot 🚂300m.

| 🍴S | Kropp | 5A2 |

Restaurant Rosengarten, Rheiderweg 7. **GPS:** n54,41388 e9,50138.⬆

4 ⌇ € 5, € 10 swimming pool incl ⛽🔌Ch ☕ WC ◻included.🚽

Location: Rural, comfortable, isolated, quiet. **Surface:** grassy. ◻ 01/01-31/12

Distance: 🚶1km ⛱on the spot.

| ⌂S | Langballig 🐟 | 5A1 |

Campingplatz Langballigau, Strandweg 3, Langballigau. **GPS:** n54,82234 e9,65969.

5 ⌇ € 5 WC. **Location:** Urban, simple, quiet. **Surface:** metalled. ◻ 01/01-31/12

Distance: 🚶200m ⊗on the spot 🚂200m.

| 🚐S | Kropp | 5A2 |

Garage Audi-VW Thomsen, Werkstrasse 2. **GPS:** n54,41361 e9,52833.

50 ⌇ € 10, dog € 1 ⛽🔌Ch ☕ €2,50/night WC included ◻€1/time.🚽

Location: Rural, simple. **Surface:** grassy/gravel. ◻ 01/01-31/12

Distance: ⛱100m ⊗on the spot.

| 🚐S | Langwedel 🎡 | 5A2 |

Caravanpark am Brahmsee, Mühlenstraße 30a. **GPS:** n54,21462 e9,91943.⬆ ➡.

5 ⌇ € 5 ⛽🔌Ch ☕. **Location:** Urban, simple, noisy. **Surface:** metalled. ◻ 01/01-31/12

Distance: 🚶300m ⊗300m 🚂300m.

| 🚐S | Laboe | 5B2 |

Ostseebad Laboe Ehrenmal, Steinerweg/Prof. Munzerring. **GPS:** n54,41029 e10,23289.⬆

20 ⌇ € 10 ⛽€1/80liter ☕Ch ☕ €2,50/24h,6 Amp WC ◻sanitary at campsite.

Location: Rural, comfortable, quiet. **Surface:** grassy/gravel. ◻ 01/01-31/12

Distance: 🚶600m 🛣A7 3 km ⛱Brahmsee 500m 🚏500m 🚂7km. **Remarks:** Check in at reception campsite, bread-service.

| ⛵S | Lauenburg/Elbe 🎡⚓ | 5B4 |

Marina Lauenburg/Yachthafen, Hafenstrasse 14. **GPS:** n53,37156 e10,56527.⬆

18 ⌇ € 12 ⛽€1/5minutes ☕€1 Ch. 🏠 **Location:** Urban, simple. **Surface:** metalled. ◻ 01/01-31/12

Distance: 🚶1km ⛱400m 🚏400m ⊗on the spot 🚂1km.

| 🚐S | Ladelund | 4D1 |

Am Naturbad, Stato. **GPS:** n54,84919 e9,03629.⬆

10 ⌇ € 7 ⛽€1/100liter ☕ (8x)€1/kWh WC €0,50 ◻€1 ⊗€4/4.

Location: Rural, comfortable. **Surface:** metalled. ◻ 01/01-31/12

Distance: 🚶10 min walking ⊗on the spot 🚂10 min walking.

🏕S   Lensahn   5C2
Reisemobilplatz Lensahn, Dr. Julius-Stinde strasse. **GPS**: n54,21446 e10,87745. ⬆➡.

15 🛢€ 8 🚰€1/80liter 🗑Ch 🚿 (4x)€2. 🚽 **Location:** Rural, simple. **Surface:** grasstiles. ⬛ 01/01-31/12 **Distance:** 🚶1,5km ⚓on the spot ⊗200m 🚊2,5km.

🏕S   Lübeck 🌿🚤⛵   5B3
Wohnmobil Treff Lübeck, An der Hülshorst 11. **GPS**: n53,89510 e10,71088. ⬆.

40 🛢€ 9/day 🚰🗑Ch 🚿 WC €1/5minutes 📶€1,50. 🚽 **Location:** Urban, luxurious, quiet. **Surface:** gravel. ⬛ 02/01-31/10 **Distance:** 🚶4,5km ⚓5km ⊗on the spot 🚌50m.

S   Lübeck 🌿🚤⛵   5B3
Wohnmobilstellplatz Lübeck Marienbrücke P4, Lastadie. **GPS**: n53,87147 e10,67904. ⬆➡.

16 🛢free, 18-10h. **Location:** Urban, simple. **Surface:** asphalted. ⬛ 01/01-31/12 **Distance:** 🚶500m ⚓2km ⚓on the spot 🚌on the spot.

Tourist information Lübeck:
Ⓜ Museum Holstentor, Holstentorplatz. Historical museum. ⬛ 10-16/17h. Ⓣ € 4 (incl. 3 children).
Ⓜ Niederegger Einkaufserlebnis, Café und Marzipan-Museum, Breite strasse 89. Marzipan, Lübecker speciality, museum, café and shop.

🏕S   Maasholm 🌿🚤⛵   5A1
Stellplatz am Yachthafen, Uleweg 31. **GPS**: n54,68334 e9,99436. ⬆.

80 🛢€ 10 🚰🗑Ch 🚿€2/day WC €0,50 ⊗€2 📶. 🚽 **Location:** Rural, comfortable, quiet. **Surface:** grassy/gravel. ⬛ 01/01-31/12 **Distance:** 🚶100m ⚓5km ⚓on the spot 🚌on the spot ⊗100m. **Remarks:** Parking marina.

🏕S   Meldorf   4D3
Reisemobil-Stellplatz am Deich, Deichstraße 2. **GPS**: n54,09409 e8,95070. ⬆.

80 🛢€ 7, only overnight stay € 3,50 🚰🗑Ch 🚿 (18x)€3 WC €2. 🚽 **Location:** Rural, comfortable, isolated, quiet. **Surface:** grassy/metalled. ⬛ Easter-31/10 **Distance:** 🚶7km ⚓on the spot ⊗Imbiss 10-18 uur 🚲on the spot 🚶on the spot.

🏛   Molfsee 🌿   5A2
Freilichtmuseum/Restaurant Drathenhof, Hamburger Landstrasse 99. **GPS**: n54,27411 e10,07571. ⬆.

20 🛢free, use of a meal desired WC at restaurant. **Location:** Central. **Surface:** gravel. ⬛ 01/01-31/12 **Distance:** 🚶on the spot ⊗on the spot 🚌on the spot 🚲on the spot 🚶on the spot. **Remarks:** At open air museum.

🏕S   Mölln   5B4
Alt Möllner strasse. **GPS**: n53,62564 e10,68314. ⬆.

20 🛢€ 7/24h 🚿 (20x)included. 🔌 **Location:** Rural. **Surface:** gravel. ⬛ 01/01-31/12 **Distance:** 🚶1km ⊗250m 🚊300m. **Remarks:** Service: Vorkamp 19, GPS n53,62024, o10,67701.

🏕S   Neumünster 🏛   5A3
Bad am Stadtwald, Hansaring 177. **GPS**: n54,08078 e9,96064. ⬆➡.

22 🛏 € 10 🚰 €0,50/100liter 🔌€0,50 Ch ✈ (22x)€0,50/kWh WC 🗑€0,50
📶. **Location:** Rural, comfortable, central, quiet. **Surface:** grassy/gravel.
📷 01/01-31/12
Distance: 🚶2km ✈ A7 1 km ⊗on the spot 🛒300m 🚌on the spot.
Remarks: Check in at swimming pool.

🅂 **Neustadt in Holstein** 5C2
Wohnmobilstellplatz Ostsee, Auf der Pelzer Wiese 45, Pelzerhaken.
GPS: n54,08889 e10,87250.⬆➡.

90 🛏 € 12 + tourist tax (summer) 🚰€1 🔌€1 Ch ✈ (90x)€1/2kWh
WC 🗑€2. 🎥 **Location:** Rural, luxurious, noisy. **Surface:** grassy.
📷 01/01-31/12
Distance: 🚶900m 🏖150m ⊗900m 🛒400m 🚌on the spot.

🅂 **Neustadt in Holstein** 5C2
P5, Am Binnenwasser. **GPS:** n54,11096 e10,81496.⬆➡.

10 🛏 Mo-Fr € 5/24h, Sa-Su free ✈ (2x)€0,50/kWh. 🏧 **Location:** Urban,
simple. **Surface:** metalled. 📷 01/01-31/12
Distance: 🚶on the spot.

🅂 **Niebüll** 4C1
Parkplatz, Lornsenstrasse 19. **GPS:** n54,78901 e8,82546.⬆.

25 🛏 € 5 🚰€1 🔌€1 Ch ✈ (12x)€1. **Location:** Urban, simple, central, quiet.
Surface: grassy. 📷 01/01-31/12
Distance: 🚶on the spot ⊗200m.
Remarks: Parking swimming pool, max. 24h.

🅂 **Nordstrand** 4D2
Wohnmobilplatz Margarethenruh, Süderhafen 8. **GPS:** n54,46944 e8,91000.
⬆.

21 🛏 € 14,80-17,50, 2 pers.incl. 🚰 🔌 Ch ✈ €2,60 WC 🗑€3 📶. 🚿
Location: Rural, comfortable, central, quiet. **Surface:** gravel.
📷 01/01-31/12
Distance: 🚶3km 🏖300m 🛒150m 🚌3km.

🅂 **Nordstrand** 4D2
Womoland, Norderquerweg 2. **GPS:** n54,51736 e8,93012.

38 🛏 € 7 + € 3,50/pp 🚰 🔌 Ch ✈ €2,50 WC 🗑. **Surface:** grassy/gravel.
📷 01/01-31/12

🅂 **Nordstrand** 4D2
Landgasthof Pohnshallig, Pohnshalligkoogstrasse 17. **GPS:** n54,49772 e8,92906.
⬆.

4 🛏 € 5, guests free 🚰€2,50. 🚿 **Location:** Rural, simple. **Surface:** metalled.
📷 01/07-31/10 ◉ Thu
Distance: 🚶3km ⊗on the spot 🛒3km.
Remarks: Along through road.
Tourist information Nordstrand:
ℹ Former Wadden island.

🅲🅂 **Norgaardholz** 5A1
Campingplatz Nordstern, Nordstern 1. **GPS:** n54,78528 e9,79889.⬆.

10 🛏 € 6, dog € 1 🚰 🔌 Ch ✈ €2/day WC 🗑use sanitary €4/night 🗑free. 🚿
Location: Rural, simple, quiet. **Surface:** gravel/metalled. 📷 01/01-31/12
Distance: 🏊on the spot ⊗on the spot.

DE

⚙S Ockholm 4C1

Wohnmobilstellplätze Altes Pastorat Ockholm, Baderstrasse 5/6. **GPS:** n54,66517 e8,82940.⬆.

5 ⬛€8 ⬛ ⬛ Ch ⬛(5x)€1,60 WC ⬛ ⬛€5/5. ⬛ **Location:** Rural, simple, isolated, quiet. **Surface:** grassy. ◻ 01/01-31/12
Remarks: Along through road, bread-service.

⚙S Oeversee ♥ 4D1

Kranzbinderei Schnell, Frörupsand 2. **GPS:** n54,69134 e9,43602.⬆.

9 ⬛€6 ⬛ ⬛ Ch ⬛€1/night ⬛free. ⬛ **Location:** Rural, simple, quiet. **Surface:** grassy. ◻ 01/01-31/12
Distance: ⊗500m.

⚙S Osterhever 4C2

Stellplatz Norderheverkoog, Norderheverkoogstraße 12, Norderheverkoog. **GPS:** n54,39656 e8,76163.⬆.

10 ⬛€6 ⬛ ⬛€1 Ch ⬛(10x)€3 WC ⬛€1. ⬛
Location: Rural. **Surface:** grassy. ◻ 01/04-31/10
Distance: ⬛1km ⬛2km ⬛1km ⬛on the spot ⬛on the spot.
Remarks: Bread-service.

⬛S Pahlen 4D2

Fischerstrasse 17. **GPS:** n54,27101 e9,30015.⬆➡.

12 ⬛€6 + €1/pp ⬛ ⬛(12x) WC ⬛included. ⬛
Location: Rural, comfortable, quiet. **Surface:** grassy. ◻ 01/01-31/12
Distance: ⬛200m ⬛50m ⬛50m ⊗200m ⬛200m.

⬛S Plön ⚓⬛ 5B2

Wohnmobilhafen Plön, Ascheberger straße 76. **GPS:** n54,14709 e10,39841.⬆ ➡.

14 ⬛€15 ⬛ ⬛Ch ⬛ WC ⬛ ⬛included. **Location:** Comfortable, noisy.
Surface: grassy/gravel. ◻ 01/04-15/12
Distance: ⬛1,5km ⊗on the spot.

⬛S Plön ⚓⬛ 5B2

Womo-Stop Kleinen Plöner See, Hamburgerstrasse/Aschenberg strasse, B430. **GPS:** n54,15278 e10,40417.⬆➡.

16 ⬛€5 ⬛€0,50 ⬛€0,50 Ch. ⬛ **Location:** Simple. **Surface:** metalled.
◻ 01/01-31/12
Distance: ⬛on the spot.
Remarks: In front of passage to beach, max. 24h.

⬛S Pommerby ⬛ 5A1

Campingplatz Seehof, Gammeldam 5. **GPS:** n54,76495 e9,96782.⬆.

5 ⬛€ 3,75 + € 4,50/pp, child € 2, dog € 2 ⬛ ⬛Ch ⬛€2/day WC ⬛€0,50/5 ⬛€2,50/time. ⬛ **Location:** Rural, simple, quiet. **Surface:** grassy/gravel.
◻ 01/04-31/10
Distance: ⬛on the spot ⬛on the spot.

⬛S Preetz ♥⬛ 5B2

Wohnmobilpark Kirchsee, Kahlbrook 25a. **GPS:** n54,22811 e10,28616.⬆➡.

10 ⬛€ 5, 01/04-30/10 € 15 ⬛ ⬛ ⬛included WC ⬛ ⬛. ⬛ **Surface:** gravel.
◻ 01/01-31/12 ⬛ service 01/11-31/03
Distance: ⬛10min ⬛on the spot ⊗on the spot.
Remarks: Bread-service, canoe and bicycle rental.

🅢 Puttgarden   5C1
Wohnmobilplatz Johannisberg, Johannisbergstrasse.
GPS: n54,50208 e11,18000. ⬆️➡️

50 🛏 € 6 + € 4/pp, dog € 2 ⚡€2,50 💧 Ch ⚡€2,50 WC 🚰 🔷 💧
Location: Rural, simple, quiet. **Surface:** grassy/metalled. 🅾 01/01-31/12
Distance: 🚶2,5km 🏖800m 🛥800m ⊗on the spot.
Remarks: In nature reserve Am Grüner Brink, bread-service.

🅢 Puttgarden   5C1
Bade- und Surfstrand Grüner Brink, Krögenweg. **GPS:** n54,51174 e11,18285.
30 🛏 € 8 ⚡€2,50 💧 Ch. **Surface:** gravel. 🅾 01/01-31/12
Distance: 🏖on the spot.

🅢 Quickborn bei Burg   4D3
Am Helmschen-Bach, Hauptstraße 2. **GPS:** n54,01165 e9,21648. ⬆️➡️

6 🛏 € 5 🛢 💧 **Location:** Rural, comfortable, quiet. **Surface:** grassy.
🅾 01/04-30/09
Distance: 🚶300m ⊗on the spot.

🅢 Ratzeburg   5B3
Hallenbad Aqua Siwa, Fischerstrasse 43. **GPS:** n53,69567 e10,77598. ⬆️➡️

12 🛏 € 7 ⚡€1/80liter 💧 Ch ⚡€0,50/kWh. 🏠 **Location:** Urban, simple,
central, noisy. **Surface:** gravel. 🅾 01/01-31/12
Distance: 🚶500m 🏖on the spot 🛥on the spot ⊗on the spot.

🅢 Reinfeld   5B3
Am Herrenteich, Klosterstraße. **GPS:** n53,83024 e10,48362. ⬆️

5 🛏 free ⚡€0,50/70liter ⚡€0,50 Ch ⚡€0,50/kWh.
Location: Urban, simple, quiet. **Surface:** metalled. 🅾 01/01-31/12

Distance: 🚶500m.

🅢 Rendsburg 🍰 🎔 🚲   5A2
Wohnmobil-Hafen Eiderblick, An der Untereider 9. **GPS:** n54,30406 e9,65610.
⬆️➡️

45 🛏 € 13 ⚡€1/75liter 💧 Ch ⚡(45x)€0,50/kWh WC 🚰€0,50/7minutes
🚿against payment 🧺 🏠 **Location:** Urban, luxurious, central, quiet.
Surface: gravel. 🅾 01/01-31/12
Distance: 🚶800m ⊗on the spot 🚆800m 🚌on the spot 🚲on the spot
🚶on the spot.
Remarks: Bread-service, internetcafé.
Tourist information Rendsburg:
- 👁 Eiserne Lady. Train-bridge North Sea-Baltic Canal, 42m high.
- 🚶 Blue Line. City walk 3 km.
- 🚶 Hausbrauerei Niewarker, Paradeplatz. Guided tour and tastery.

🅢 Reußenköge 🏖 🚲   4D1
Amsinck Haus, Sönke Nissenkoog 36a. **GPS:** n54,61666 e8,87027. ⬆️➡️

9 🛏 € 7 🛢 💧 🚿(6x)€2/day WC 🚰 🔷 €3. 💧 **Location:** Rural, comfortable,
isolated, quiet. **Surface:** asphalted. 🅾 01/01-31/12

🅢 Schacht-Audorf 🌿 🎔   5A2
WohnmobilPark Schacht-Audorf, K76. **GPS:** n54,30611 e9,71250. ⬆️

38 🛏 € 10 ⚡€0,50/100liter 💧 Ch ⚡(33x)€0,60/kWh WC€0,50/time 🚰€1/
time. 🏠 **Location:** Rural, comfortable. **Surface:** gravel.
🅾 01/01-31/12
Distance: 🚶700m 🛣A7 2km ⊗800m 🚆800m 🚌on the spot.
Remarks: Max. 3 nights.

🅢 Scharbeutz   5B3
Reisemobilplatz Hamburger Ring, Hamburgerring/Trelleborg Strasse.
GPS: n54,03028 e10,75222. ⬆️

DE

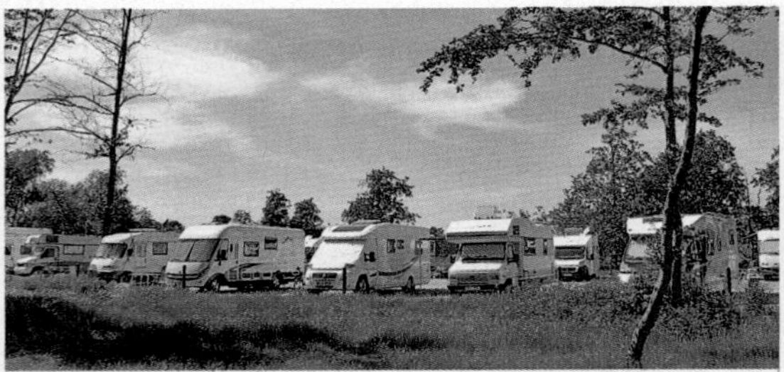

70 🚐€ 10/24h, 01/04-31/10 beach tax € 3,50 🚰€1/100liter 🚽 Ch 🔌 (2x)€1. 🚌 **Location:** Rural. **Surface:** sand. 📅 01/01-31/12
Distance: 🏙300m ⛱300m, dog friendly beach 1km 🍴400m.

[S] Schashagen ⛱ 5C2

Wohnmobilpark Ostseeblick, Biesdorf. **GPS**: n54,11934 e10,92108.[↑→].

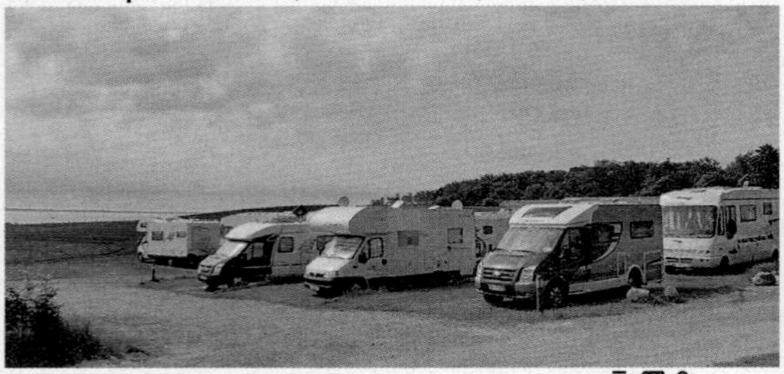

30 🚐01/04-30/09 € 14,50-16,50, 2 pers.incl., dog € 2,50-3,50 🚰 🚽 Ch 🔌 €0,50/kWh WC 🚿. 🐕 **Location:** Rural, comfortable, quiet.
Surface: grasstiles. 📅 01/01-31/12 ◼ Service facilities
Distance: ⛱300m.
Remarks: € 7 if campsite is closed.

[S] Schleswig 🐚⛱🚤 5A2

Am Stadthafen, Am Hafen 5. **GPS**: n54,51167 e9,56917.[↑].

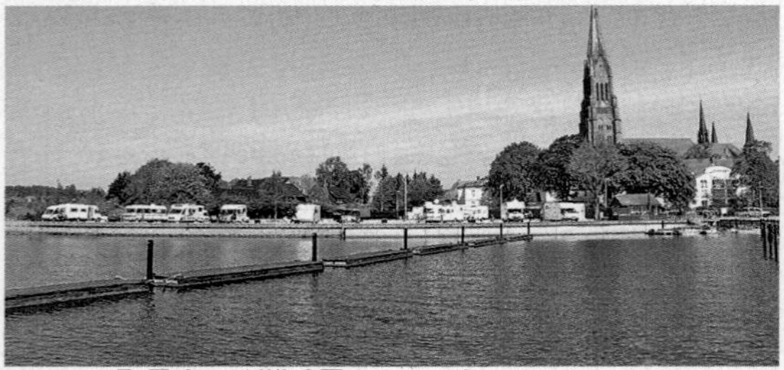

45 🚐€ 14 🚰 🚽 Ch 🔌 WC 🚿 🧺€2,50/time 📶included. 🐕
Location: Urban, comfortable, central.
Surface: gravel/metalled.
📅 01/01-31/12
Distance: 🏙150m 🛣5km ⛱on the spot 🎣on the spot 🍴50m 🛒300m 🧺nearby 🚌50m.
Remarks: Max. 48h, check in at harbourmaster.

Tourist information Schleswig:

ℹ Tourist Information Schleswig, Plessenstrasse 7. Historical city, founded by the Vikings, Haithabu.

[M]🏰 Schloß Gottorf. Regional museum, archeological museum and museum for art and culture.

[M] Museum am Danewerk, Ochsenweg 5, Dannewerk. Fortifications, 650-1200. 📅 winter 10-16h, 01/04-31/10 Tue-Fri 9-17h, Sa-Su 10-18h.

[M] Wikinger Museum Haithabu, Haddeby-Busdorf. All about the life of the Vikings. 📅 01/04-31/10 9-17h, 01/11-31/03 Tue-Su 10-16h.

[S] Schönberg/Ostsee 5B2

Brasilien, Seesternweg. **GPS**: n54,42408 e10,39116.[↑→].

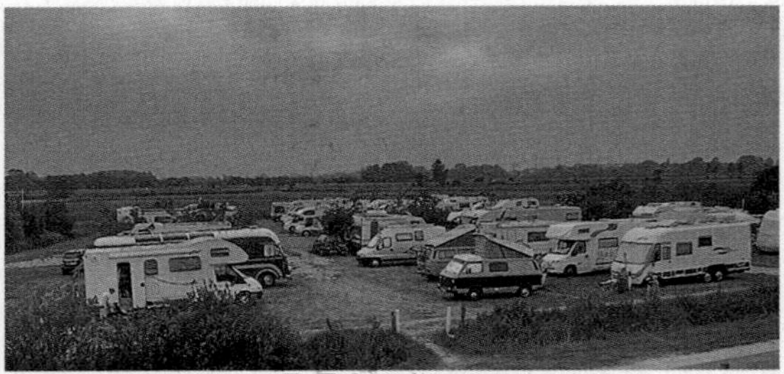

40 🚐€ 9, 15/05-15/09 € 11 🚰 🚽 Ch 🔌 included. 🐕
Location: Rural, simple. **Surface:** grassy. 📅 01/01-31/12
Distance: ⛱200m 🎣200m.

[S] Schönberg/Ostsee 5B2

Stellplatz Mittelstrand, Mittelstrand. **GPS**: n54,42233 e10,39573.[↑→].

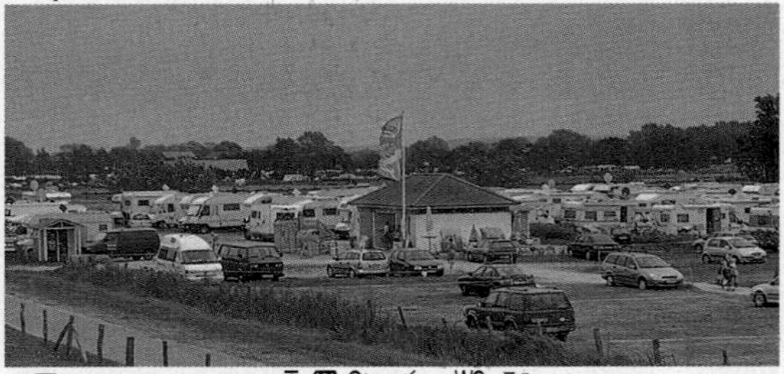

50 🚐€ 9, 15/05-15/09 € 11 🚰 🚽 Ch 🔌 €2 WC. 🐕
Location: Rural. **Surface:** grassy. 📅 01/01-31/12
Distance: ⛱200m 🎣200m 🍴on the spot.
Remarks: Bread-service in summer period.

Seestermühe 5A4

Achtern Diek. **GPS**: n53,70333 e9,56232.[↑].
4 🚐free. **Surface:** metalled. 📅 01/01-31/12
Distance: 🍴200m.

[S] Sehestedt 🐚🎈🚤 5A2

Wohnmobilstellplatz Sehestedt, Fährstrasse 1. **GPS**: n54,36466 e9,81973.[↑→].

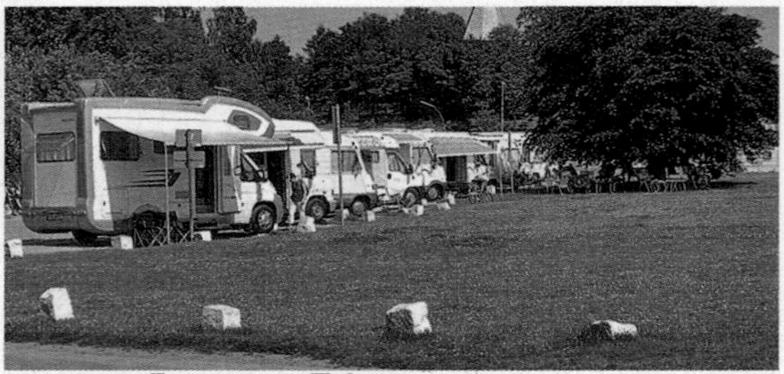

13 🚐€ 7/24h 🚰€0,50/80liter 🚽 Ch. 🚌
Surface: gravel. 📅 01/01-31/12
Distance: 🏙750m 🛣A7 13km 🍴on the spot 🛒200m.
Remarks: Directly at North Sea-Baltic canal.

[S] Sierksdorf 5B3

Wohnmobilstellplatz Hof Sierksdorf, Altonaer Straße.
GPS: n54,06013 e10,75737.[↑].
15 🚐€ 11 🚰€1 🚽€1 Ch 🔌 €0,50/kWh WC 🚿 🧺. **Surface:** gravel.
📅 01/04-15/10
Distance: ⛱beach 100m.

[S] Simonsberg 4D2

Nordsee Camping Zum Seehund, Lundenbergweg 4. **GPS**: n54,45515 e8,96958.[↑→].

DE

30 ⌀ € 15 ⚡ 🚰 Ch 🔌 WC ⬜included 🔲€5. ♨ **Location:** Rural, comfortable, isolated, quiet. **Surface:** gravel. ⬜ Easter-31/10
Distance: 🚲2km 🏊500m 🛒on the spot 🍴on the spot.
Remarks: Use steam bath, sauna, fitness-studio incl.

Sörup 5A1
Südensee, Seeblick. **GPS:** n54,71216 e9,66611. ⬆➡.

5 ⌀ € 4 ⚡ 🚰 Ch 🔌€2/night WC. ♨ **Location:** Rural, simple, quiet.
Surface: grassy. ⬜ 01/01-31/12
Distance: 🏊on the spot 🛒on the spot ⊗kiosk.
Remarks: Parking at small lake.

St.Peter Ording 🛁🍴 4C2
Reisemobilhafen St.Peter-Ording, Am Ketelskoog. **GPS:** n54,30881 e8,63522. ⬆➡.

70 ⌀ € 12 ⚡€1/50liter 🚰 Ch 🔌 (70x)€0,60/kWh WC€0,20 ⬜€1 📶€1. 🚽
Location: Rural, comfortable. **Surface:** gravel. ⬜ 01/01-31/12
Distance: 🚲300m 🏊1km ⊗300m 🛒300m.
Remarks: Market Wednesday.

Tourist information St.Peter Ording:
😊 Westküstenpark, Wohldweg 6. Animal park. ⬜ summer 9.30-19h, winter 10.30h-sunset.

Süderlügum 4D1
Wohnmobilplatz Mehrzweckhalle, Jahnstrasse. **GPS:** n54,87472 e8,90306. ⬆.

5 ⌀free. **Location:** Rural, central, quiet. **Surface:** metalled. ⬜ 01/01-31/12
Distance: 🚲500m 🛒300m.

Timmendorfer Strand 5B3
Am Vogelpark, P4, Bäderrandstraße, B76. **GPS:** n53,99136 e10,81439. ⬆➡.

50 ⌀ € 7,50 + tourist tax ⚡€0,50/120liter 🚰 Ch 🔌. ⬜🚽
Location: Rural. **Surface:** grassy/sand. ⬜ 01/01-31/12
Distance: ⊗180m.
Remarks: Max. 1 night.

Tönning 4D2
Wohnmobilplatz Eiderblick - Kapitänshaus, Am Strandweg. **GPS:** n54,30920 e8,93684. ⬆.

33+15 ⌀ € 11 2p incl., excl. tourist tax ⚡€1/100liter 🚰 Ch 🔌€0,50/kWh ⬜included 🔲€3,50/3. ♨ **Location:** Rural, luxurious, isolated, quiet.
Surface: grassy. ⬜ 01/01-31/12
Distance: 🚲500m 🏊on the spot 🛒on the spot 🍴on the spot.
Remarks: Along the Eider river.

Travemünde 🛁🍴 5C3
Wohnmobilparkplatz Kowitzberg, Kowitzberg. **GPS:** n53,97598 e10,87830. ⬆➡.

49 ⌀15/5-14/9 € 10, 15/9-14/5 € 6 ⚡€1/100liter 🚰 Ch 🔌 (48x)€1/5kWh.
Location: Urban. **Surface:** grassy. ⬜ 01/01-31/12
Distance: 🚲2,5km 🏊800m 🛒800m ⊗300m 🛒250m 🚌50m.

Travemünde 🛁🍴 5C3
Parkplatz am Fischerreihafen, Auf dem Baggersand 15. **GPS:** n53,95556 e10,86139. ⬆.

120 ⌀ € 12-14 ⚡€1/50liter 🚰 Ch 🔌 (5x)€3/kWh WC ⬜€2. ♨
Location: Urban, simple. **Surface:** gravel. ⬜ 01/01-31/12

DE

Distance: 🏊beach 1,8km ⚓max. 250m 🚌express bus Altstadt Lubeck.
Remarks: Parking fishing port, no camping activities.

| ⚓ | **Uetersen** | 5A4 |

Am Stichhafen, Ziegelei. **GPS:** n53,67977 e9,66861.⬆.
4 🚐free. **Surface:** metalled. 🅾 01/01-31/12
Distance: 400m 🚲7,4km ⊗300m.

| 🚐S | **Wedel** | 5A4 |

Am Freibad. **GPS:** n53,57860 e9,69520.⬆.

20 🚐€6 🔌€1/10minutes 💧 Ch 🚿 (14x)€1/8h WC 🚽. 🚽
Location: Rural, simple, quiet. **Surface:** grassy/metalled.
🅾 01/01-31/12 🅾 during event
Distance: 800m.
Remarks: Max. 3 days.

| ⒸS | **Westerholz** | 5A1 |

Campingplatz Fördeblick, Kummle 1. **GPS:** n54,81998 e9,66686.⬆.
45 🚐€7 🔌€1 💧 Ch 🚿€2,50/night WC 🚽. 🚽
Location: Rural, simple, quiet. **Surface:** grassy. 🅾 01/04-15/10
Distance: 🏊150m.
Remarks: At Flensborg Fjord, max. 24h.

| 🚐S | **Wilster** | 4D3 |

Colosseumplatz, Etatsrätin-doos-strasse 14-17. **GPS:** n53,92419 e9,37449.⬆➡.

15 🚐free 🔌 💧 Ch 🚿€0,50. **Location:** Urban, simple, central, quiet.
Surface: grassy/gravel. 🅾 01/01-31/12 🅾 fair
Distance: 200m ⚓100m ⊗on the spot.

| 🚐S | **Wischhafen** | 4D3 |

Hafenstrasse 6. **GPS:** n53,77278 e9,32278.⬆➡.

15 🚐€3 🚿 (6x)€1/kWh. 🚽 **Location:** Rural, simple. **Surface:** grassy/gravel.
🅾 01/01-31/12
Distance: ⊗500m ⚓1km.

| 🚐S | **Wischhafen** | 4D3 |

Ziegelstraße, Gewerbegebiet Wischhafen. **GPS:** n53,76417 e9,32111.⬆➡.

8 🚐€3 🔌 💧Chfree. 🚽 **Location:** Rural, simple. **Surface:** gravel.
🅾 01/01-31/12
Distance: 1km ⚓200m.

| 🚐 | **Wischhafen** | 4D3 |

Süder-Elbe, Glückstädter Straße. **GPS:** n53,78678 e9,34017.⬆➡.

15 🚐€3. 🚽 **Location:** Rural, simple, isolated. **Surface:** sand.
🅾 01/01-31/12
Distance: 3km ⊗150m.
Remarks: Parking at ferry-boat.

| 🚐 | **Wischhafen** | 4D3 |

Unterm Deich 7. **GPS:** n53,77528 e9,32111.⬆➡.

6 🚐€3. 🚽 **Location:** Rural, simple. **Surface:** grassy.
🅾 01/01-31/12
Distance: 300m ⊗on the spot ⚓1km.

Lower Saxony/Bremen

| 🚐 | **Adendorf** | 5B5 |

Freizeitzentrum, Scharnebecker Weg. **GPS:** n53,28925 e10,45398.🏊.

10 🚐free 🚿 (4x)€0,50/kWh.
Location: Rural, simple, noisy.
🅾 01/01-31/12
Distance: 500m.
Remarks: Parking sports centre, max. 3 days, swimming pool and sauna on site.

| 🍴🍽S | **Aerzen** | 9D2 |

Restaurant Waldquelle, Waldquelle 1. **GPS:** n52,05952 e9,26146.⬆➡.

DE

4 🛏 € 4,50 🚿 (1x)€1,50/day. **Location:** Rural, isolated. **Surface:** gravel.
⬛ 01/01-31/12 ⬤ Tue
Distance: 🚶2km 🛒1km 🚌500m on the spot.
Remarks: Check in at hotel.

20 🛏 € 10 + € 2/pp tourist tax 🚰€0,50/40liter 🔲 Ch 🔌€0,50/kWh.
Location: Rural, quiet. **Surface:** metalled. ⬛ 01/01-31/12
Distance: 🚶1,5km ⊗on the spot 🛒on the spot 🚌on the spot.
Remarks: Pay at pay-desk of theTherme.

🏕S	Ahlerstedt	5A4

Ahlerstedt Ottendorf, Rickstücken 2. **GPS:** n53,38908 e9,41017. ⬆➡

🏕S	Amelinghausen 🌿🏕👫🏖	5B5

Lopausee, Auf der Kalten Hude. **GPS:** n53,13324 e10,23441. ⬆➡

25 🛏 € 8 🚰 🔲 Ch 🔌 included. 🚿 **Location:** Rural, simple.
Surface: metalled. ⬛ 01/01-31/12
Distance: 🚶3km 🛒3km.

🏕	Alfeld/Leine	10A2

Bornstrasse. GPS: n51,98586 e9,82769. ⬆

50 🛏 € 5, 1/9-1/7 € 3,50 🚰 🔲 Ch included. **Location:** Simple, isolated, quiet.
Surface: gravel/sand. ⬛ 01/01-31/12
Distance: 🚶1km 🏊100m 🚤100m ⊗1km 🛒1km 🚴on the spot
🧍on the spot.
Remarks: Ticket available at petrol stations, kiosk Lopausee, pay-desk Waldbad
and tourist office.

🏕S	Amelinghausen 🌿🏕👫🏖	5B5

Waldbad, Zum Lopautal. **GPS:** n53,12402 e10,23018. ⬆

4 🛏 free. **Location:** Simple. **Surface:** metalled. ⬛ 01/01-31/12
Distance: 🚶on the spot ⊗80m 🛒200m.
Remarks: Parking in city centre behind the evangelical church.

🏕S	Altenau 🌿👫🏖❄🐏	10B2

Alter Bahnhof Altenau, Rothenbergerstrasse 52. **GPS:** n51,79879 e10,43320.
⬆➡

40 🛏 € 8 🚰 🔲 Ch 🔌 included. 🚿 **Location:** Comfortable.
⬛ 01/01-31/12
Distance: 🚶1km 🏊500m ⊗1km 🛒1km 🚴on the spot 🧍on the spot.
Remarks: Bread-service, incl. access swimming pool.

🏕	Amelinghausen 🌿🏕👫🏖	5B5

Kronsbergheide, Hochseilgarten. **GPS:** n53,13500 e10,23389. ⬆➡

20 🛏 € 13, tourist tax incl 🚰€1/50liter 🔲€1 Ch 🔌(10x)€2,50/day WC.
Location: Quiet. **Surface:** gravel. ⬛ 01/01-31/12
Distance: 🚶1km ⊗2km 🛒1km 🚴on the spot 🧍on the spot 🚵2km
🐟on the spot.

🏕S	Altenau 🌿👫🏖❄🐏	10B2

Kristall-Saunatherme Heißer Brocken, Karl-Reinecke-Weg 35.
GPS: n51,79836 e10,44408. ⬆

10 🛏 € 5, 1/9-1/7 € 3,50. **Location:** Rural, simple, isolated, quiet.
⬛ 01/01-31/12
Distance: 🚶1km 🏊500m 🚤on the spot ⊗1km 🛒1km 🚴on the spot
🧍on the spot.
Remarks: Ticket available at petrol stations, kiosk Lopausee, pay-desk Waldbad

DE

and tourist office.

Amelinghausen 🌿⛺👥🌾 5B5

Schwindbeckerheide, Steinbeckerstrasse, Soderstorf. **GPS**: n53,12247 e10,09934. ⬆.

15 ⌇€ 5. **Location**: Rural, simple, isolated. **Surface**: metalled/sand.
🅿 01/01-31/12
Distance: 🚲6km 🐴on the spot 🚶on the spot.
Remarks: Ticket available at petrol stations, kiosk Lopausee, pay-desk Waldbad and tourist office.

🍴S Amelinghausen 🌿⛺👥🌾 5B5

Gasthaus Eichenkrug, Unter den Eichen 10, Dehnsen.
GPS: n53,12804 e10,16817.

4 ⌇€ 5 🚰 🔌 included. 🛒🔌 **Location**: Simple, isolated. **Surface**: metalled.
🅿 01/01-31/12
Distance: 🚲4km 🛒on the spot 🍽4km 🐴on the spot 🚶on the spot.
Remarks: Max. 3 nights.

🍴S Amelinghausen 🌿⛺👥🌾 5B5

Gasthaus Schenck, Lüneburgerstrasse 48. **GPS**: n53,12568 e10,21426. ⬆.

15 ⌇€ 5 🚰 🔌 WCincluded. 🛒🔌 **Location**: Simple, central.
Surface: metalled.
Distance: 🚲on the spot 🛒on the spot 🍽on the spot 🐴on the spot 🚶on the spot.

Tourist information Amelinghausen:
👁 Oldendorfer Totenstatt. Hunnebed cineraria from the ice-age. 🅿 guided tour 01/05-30/09.
Ⓜ Jachtmuseum Wulff, Hässelmühler WegOerrel. 🅿 Wed-Sa 14-18h, Su 11-17h.

🌿S Ankum 9B1

Ferienhof Buse-Glass, Tütingen 5. **GPS**: n52,51431 e7,86842. ⬆.

5 ⌇€ 14 🚰 🔌 WCincluded 📷. **Location**: Quiet. **Surface**: grassy.
🅿 01/01-31/12
Distance: 🚲2,5km 🛒500m 🍽2,5km.

Apen 4B5

Am Freibad, Hauptstraße, Hengstforde. **GPS**: n53,21795 e7,78706. ⬆.

10 ⌇free. **Location**: Rural, simple. **Surface**: metalled.
🅿 01/05-15/09
Distance: 🚴5,8km 🛒50 m.
Remarks: Along railwayline, swimming pool Hengstforde.

Apen 4B5

Viehmarktplatz, Hauptstraße. **GPS**: n53,21820 e7,80221.

10 ⌇free. **Location**: Simple. **Surface**: metalled. 🅿 01/01-31/12
Distance: 🚲100m 🚴5km.

🍴S Artlenburg 🌊 5B4

Am Sportboothafen, Am Deich 9. **GPS**: n53,37680 e10,48550.

40 ⌇€ 10 🚰 🍴Ch 🔌 WC 🚻. **Location**: Comfortable, quiet.
Surface: grassy.
🅿 15/04-15/10
Distance: 🚲500m 🏊on the spot 🚣on the spot 🛒500m 🍽500m 🚍500m.
Remarks: Along the river Elbe.

🌿S Aurich 4B4

Familienbad De Baalje, Tannenbergstraße. **GPS**: n53,46540 e7,47568. ⬆.
20 ⌇€ 9 🚰€1/100liter 🍴Ch 🔌(24x)€1/kWh 🚻€1. **Surface**: metalled.
🅿 01/01-31/12
Distance: 🚲500m 🛒100m.

DE

Remarks: Check in and pay at pay desk swimming pool.

Aurich 4B4

An den Kiesgruben, Tannenhausen. **GPS:** n53,52173 e7,47834.

free. **Surface:** unpaved.
Distance: 10m on the spot.
Remarks: At the lake of Tannenhausen.

Aurich 4B4

Landgasthof Alte Post, Essenerstrasse. **GPS:** n53,54573 e7,60736.

6 €6, guests €3 €1 Ch WC. **Surface:** metalled.
01/01-31/12
Distance: on the spot.
Remarks: Caution key electricity € 10.

Bad Bentheim 9A1

Am Mühlenberg, Mühlenberg. **GPS:** n52,29360 e7,10095.

30 € 10, 2 pers.incl Ch included €1. **Location:** Rural, simple, quiet. **Surface:** gravel/sand. 01/01-31/12
Distance: 1km on the spot 1km 600m.

Bad Essen 9C1

Wohnmobilstellplatz Falkenburg, Falkenburg 3. **GPS:** n52,32352 e8,36384.

50 €7 €1/100liter Ch €2/4kWh WC €0,50. **Location:** Rural, comfortable, quiet. **Surface:** grassy/metalled. 01/03-30/10
Distance: 1,2km 900m 300m.
Remarks: At the Mittelland canal, near marina.

Bad Gandersheim 10B2

Wohnmobil-Stellplatz Rio Gande, An der Wiek. **GPS:** n51,87191 e10,01881.

24 € 8/24h, tourist tax incl €1/100liter Ch (14x)€0,50/kWh.
Location: Rural, simple. **Surface:** gravel. 01/01-31/12
Distance: 400m 100m on the spot on the spot.
Remarks: Max. 3 nights, bread-service only in summer.

Bad Lauterberg 10B3

Erlebnisbad Vitamar, Mast Tal 1. **GPS:** n51,63358 e10,48661.

10 €7 €1/80liter Ch €0,50/kWh WC. **Location:** Rural.
Surface: metalled. 01/01-31/12
Distance: 200m 50m on the spot on the spot.

Bad Bentheim 9A1

Am Schloßpark, Funkenstiege. **GPS:** n52,30328 e7,15448.

5 free €1 €1 Ch €1. **Location:** Simple, quiet. **Surface:** metalled.
01/01-31/12
Distance: 1,5km 30km 1,5km on the spot.

Bad Lauterberg 10B3

Wiesenbeker Teich, Wiesenbek 75. **GPS:** n51,61719 e10,49074.

30 €7 €1/80liter Ch €0,50/kWh WC. **Surface:** metalled.
01/01-31/12
Distance: 200m 100m.

Bad Bevensen 5B5

Reisemobilplatz, Am Waagekai. **GPS:** n53,07417 e10,60139.

DE

4 ⅃ €13 ⟿ ⍰ Ch ⚭ included.
Location: Isolated, quiet. **Surface:** gravel.
☐ 01/01-31/12
Distance: ⚲2km ✈30km ⚲on the spot ⚲on the spot ⚲on the spot ⚲2km ⚲2 km ⚲on the spot.
Remarks: Check in and pay at reception campsite, max. 1 night.

🏳	Bad Münder	10A1

Rhomelbad, Lindenallee. **GPS:** n52,19305 e9,47111.⬆.

5 ⅃free. **Location:** Simple. **Surface:** metalled. ☐ 01/01-31/12
Distance: ⚲400m ⚲on the spot ⚲400m ⚲200m.

🏳 S	Bad Nenndorf	10A1

Wohnmobilstellplatz am Schulzentrum, Bahnhofstrasse 77.
GPS: n52,34294 e9,37666.⬆.

15 ⅃free ⟿€2/45liter ⍰Ch ⚭(8x)€1/6h WC⍰. **Location:** Simple.
Surface: gravel/metalled. ☐ 01/01-31/12
Distance: ⚲700m ✈3,4km ⚲on the spot ⚲on the spot ⚲on the spot.

🏳 S	Bad Pyrmont 🛁🍴♨	9D2

Reisemobilhafen in den Emmerauen, Hauptmann Boelke-Weg.
GPS: n51,98092 e9,25108.⬆➡.
65 ⅃€9 + €2,30-3,20/pp tourist tax ⟿€0,10/10liter ⍰Ch ⚭(44x)€0,60/
kWh WC⍰free.🚌
Location: Urban, central. **Surface:** grassy/gravel.
☐ 01/01-31/12
Distance: ⚲historical centre 400m ⚲200m ⚲400m ⚲100m.
Remarks: Bread-service, free swimming < 9AM, e-bike rental, free shuttle to spa resort.

Tourist information Bad Pyrmont:
ℹ Bad Pyrmont Tourismus GmbH, Europa-Platz 1, www.badpyrmont.de. Health resort.

🏳 S	Bad Sachsa 🌿🛁🍴❄♨	10C3

Wohnmobilplatz auf dem Schützenplatz, Im Osteral.
GPS: n51,60470 e10,54949.⬆.

72 ⅃€7 ⟿€0,50 ⍰€0,50 ⚭(10x)€0,50/kWh WC. 🚌 **Location:** Rural, simple, quiet. **Surface:** gravel. ☐ 01/01-31/12
Distance: ⚲on the spot ⚲500m ⚲800m ⚲500m.
Remarks: Service 200m, discount on access terme.

🏳	Bad Sachsa 🌿🛁🍴❄♨	10C3

Harzer Schnitzelhaus & Waffelbäckerei, Schützenstrasse 13.
GPS: n51,59778 e10,55056.⬆.

2 ⅃guests free. **Location:** Rural, simple, central. **Surface:** asphalted.
☐ 01/01-31/12
Distance: ⚲on the spot ⚲on the spot ⚲100m.
Remarks: Max. 2 days.

🏳 S	Bad Salzdetfurth ♨	10B2

Am Solebad, Solebadstraße, Detfurth. **GPS:** n52,07193 e10,01859.⬆➡.

10 ⅃free ⟿€1/50liter ⍰Ch ⚭€1/6h. **Location:** Rural, simple.
Surface: asphalted. ☐ 01/01-31/12
Distance: ⚲2km ⚲Bistro 50m ⚲100m ⚲on the spot ⚲on the spot.
Remarks: Market Friday-morning.

♨ S	Bad Zwischenahn	4B5

Wohnmobilstellplatz Am Badepark, Am Badepark. **GPS:** n53,18722 e8,00021.
⬆➡.

35 ⅃€8,50 ⟿€0,50/70liter ⍰Ch ⚭(35x)€1/2kWh WC⍰€3,(spa resort).
🚌 **Location:** Urban, simple. **Surface:** metalled. ☐ 01/01-31/12
Distance: ⚲on the spot ✈6,8km ⚲on the spot ⚲on the spot ⚲100m ⚲500m ⚲on the spot.

[S] Balge 4D6
Blenhorster Bauernhof, Klünderberg 1. **GPS**: n52,71361 e9,13011. ⬆.

20 ⌁€ 5 ⚷ 🔌 included. **Surface**: grassy. ◻ 01/01-31/12
Distance: ⊗on the spot.

[⚓] Balje 4D3
Naturkundemuseum Niederelbe, Neuenhof, Neuhaus.
GPS: n53,81958 e9,03867. ⬆.

6 ⌁free. **Location**: Rural, simple, isolated.
◻ 01/01-31/12
Distance: ⚓4km ⚲on the spot ⊗4km ⚑4km.

[S] Barßel 🚣 4B5
Am Bootshafen, Deichstrasse. **GPS**: n53,16754 e7,73441. ⬆➡.

14 + 20 ⌁€ 6 ⚷ 🔥Ch 🔌 (34x)€2/24h WC included ▣€1. 🚿
Location: Urban, simple. **Surface**: grasstiles. ◻ 01/01-31/12
Distance: ⚓500m ⚲on the spot ⊗on the spot ⚑500m.

[S] Barsinghausen 🌼 10A1
Wohnmobilstellplatz am Besucherbergwerk Klosterstollen, Conrad-
Bühreweg. **GPS**: n52,29858 e9,46943. ⬆➡.

5 ⌁€ 6,50 ⚷ 🔌 (5x)included. 🚿 **Location**: Rural, simple. **Surface**: gravel.
◻ 01/01-31/12
Distance: ⚓300m ⊗nearby ⚑300m.
Remarks: Max. 3 days, visit coalmine possible.

[S] Berge 4B6
Stift Börstel, Börstel 5. **GPS**: n52,64957 e7,69438.
2 ⌁€ 5, in envelope in mail box ⚷ 🔌on demand. **Surface**: metalled.

◻ 01/01-31/12
Remarks: Near abbey, max. 2 nights.

Berge 4B6
Dorfteich Berge, Schienenweg 19. **GPS**: n52,62011 e7,75099.
2 ⌁free. ◻ 01/01-31/12

[S] Bergen 5A6
Ziegeleiweg. **GPS**: n52,81273 e9,96457. ⬆.

6 ⌁€ 3,50 ⚷€1 🔥Ch 🔌. **Surface**: gravel.
◻ 01/01-31/12
Distance: ⚓nearby ⊗on the spot.
Remarks: Caution key € 20 at town hall.

Tourist information Bergen:
◉ Wildpark Lüneburger Heide, Nindorf. Game preserve. ◻ 01/03-31/10
8-19h, 01/11-28/02 9-16.30h.

[S] Berne 🚣 4C5
Fähranleger Motzen, Motzener Strasse. **GPS**: n53,17972 e8,55778. ⬆.

4 ⌁free ⚷€1/60liter 🔥Ch 🔌 (4x)€1/6h. **Location**: Urban, simple, isolated,
noisy. **Surface**: gravel/sand. ◻ 01/01-31/12
Distance: ⚓3,5km ⚲on the spot ⊗1km ⚑100m 🚲100m.
Remarks: Parking at ferry-boat at river Weser.

[⚓] Bevern 10A2
Schwimm- und Freizeitzentrum, Jahnstrasse. **GPS**: n51,85750 e9,50805. ➡.

5 ⌁free. **Location**: Rural, simple. **Surface**: asphalted.
◻ 01/01-31/12
Distance: ⚓1,2km ⚑500m 🚲500m.

[S] Bienenbüttel 🚣 5B5
Wohnmobilstellplatz Ilmenauwiese, Niendorfer strasse, K42.
GPS: n53,14514 e10,49051. ⬆.

DE

12 ⚏ € 6 🚰 €1/8minutes ⚡ Ch ⚓ (12x)€1/8h WC 🗑 €1. ♨
Location: Rural, comfortable, quiet. **Surface:** metalled. 🅿 01/01-31/12
Distance: 🛒500m 🍴on the spot ⊗on the spot ⚕500m ⚌500m
🚶special sculpture route.

5 ⚏free. **Location:** Simple, central. **Surface:** metalled.
🅿 01/01-31/12
Distance: 🛒on the spot ⚲1km ⊗100m ⚕100m 🚲on the spot
🚶on the spot.

| | Bippen � 👪 | 9B1 |

Dorfteich, Hauptstrasse. **GPS:** n52,58209 e7,73887.
2 ⚏free. 🅿 01/01-31/12

| | Bispingen 🚤 | 5A5 |

Reiter- und Ferienhof Cohrs, Volkwardingen 1, Moorweg.
GPS: n53,13409 e10,00047.

| | Bippen 🚤 👪 | 9B1 |

Ferienhof Neyenhuis, Hallweg. **GPS:** n52,59360 e7,73005. ➡

20 ⚏ € 10 🚰 ⚓ WC 🗑 €2. ♨ **Location:** Rural, simple, quiet. **Surface:** grassy.
🅿 01/01-31/12
Distance: 🛒1km.

10 ⚏ € 14 🚰 ⚡ Ch ⚓ included WC 🗑 €3. ♨
Location: Comfortable, isolated, quiet. **Surface:** grassy. 🅿 01/01-31/12
Distance: 🛒3km ⚲5,5km ⊗500m ⚕5km 🚲on the spot.
Remarks: Bread-service.

| | Bippen 🚤 👪 | 9B1 |

Gasthof Mol, Einigkeitsstraße 20, Lonnerbecke. **GPS:** n52,54337 e7,67118.
10 ⚏free ⚓ Service €7/day.
Distance: ⊗on the spot.

| | Bissendorf | 9C1 |

Reisemobil-Center Veregge & Welz, Gewerbepark 14, A30 Abfahrt Bissendorf.
GPS: n52,24026 e8,13977. ⬆

| | Bippen 🚤 👪 | 9B1 |

Hotel-Restaurant-Café Sülte Mühle, Ölmühle 1, Lonnerbecke.
GPS: n52,54972 e7,69594.
2 ⚏free ⚓ €2.

| | Bispingen 🚤 | 5A5 |

Parkplatz Oberhaverbeck, Oberhaverbeck. **GPS:** n53,14281 e9,91998.

Sie die *HEIDEPFLEGE*! Danke!

100 ⚏ € 3/day, € 6/night 🚰 €1/10minutes ⚡ Ch ⚓ (8x)€1/10h. 🚐
Location: Rural, simple, isolated. **Surface:** grassy/gravel.
🅿 01/01-31/12 ⚏ Service: winter
Distance: ⊗on the spot 🚲on the spot 🚶on the spot.
Remarks: In nature reserve the the Lüneburg Heide (heath).

5 ⚏free 🚰 €1/5minutes ⚡ Ch ⚓ (4x)€1/6h. **Location:** Urban, simple, quiet.
Surface: metalled. 🅿 01/01-31/12
Distance: 🛒1km ⚲650m ⊗800m ⚕800m.

| | Bispingen 🚤 | 5A5 |

Parking Rathaus, Borsteler Straße 4-6. **GPS:** n53,08499 e9,99789.

| | Bleckede 👪 | 5C5 |

Campingpark Elbtalaue, Am Waldbad 23. **GPS:** n53,25948 e10,80526. ⬆ ➡

15 ⚏ € 14, 2 pers incl 🚰 €1 ⚡ Ch ⚓ €3,50/night,or €0,50/0,8kWh
WC 🗑 included ⚡ €3,50/3 💧 €4/day, € 9/3 days. **Location:** Rural, luxurious,
isolated, quiet. **Surface:** grassy. 🅿 01/01-31/12
Distance: 🛒2km 🍴300m ⊗800m ⚕6km ⚌50m.

| | Blomberg | 4B4 |

Dorfplatz Blomberg, Hauptstrasse. **GPS:** n53,57718 e7,55815. ⬆ ➡

20 🛏free ⛽€1 🚰Ch€1 🔌€0,50/kWh WC. **Surface:** grassy/metalled. 🅿 01/01-31/12
Distance: 🏪on the spot ⊗200m 🚉200m 🚌50m.

🍽 | Bockenem | 10B2
Am Freibad, In den Reesen. **GPS:** n52,00787 e10,13610.⬆.

5 🛏free. **Location:** Rural, simple, quiet. **Surface:** gravel.
🅿 01/01-31/12
Distance: 🏪800m ⊗200m 🚉300m.

🍽 S | Bockenem | 10B2
Hotel Sauer am Aral Autohof, Allensteiner strasse 7. **GPS:** n52,00224 e10,13379.⬆.

20 🛏guests free ⛽€1,50 🚰Ch 🔌(8x)€2,50 WC 🗑€1,50. **Location:** Rural, simple. **Surface:** metalled. 🅿 01/01-31/12
Distance: 🏪300m ⊗on the spot 🚉500m.

🍽 S | Bockhorn | 4B5
Reisemobilplatz Germer, Am Geeschendamm 1. **GPS:** n53,38575 e8,00857.⬆.

5 🛏free. **Location:** Rural. **Surface:** metalled. 🅿 01/01-31/12
Distance: 🚶on the spot.
Remarks: Parking swimming pool, max. 1 day.

🍽 S | Bockhorn | 4B5
Gaststätte Altdeutsche Diele, Landesstrasse 11, Steinhausen.
GPS: n53,41539 e8,03622.⬆.

3 🛏free 🔌(3x)against payment. **Location:** Simple. **Surface:** metalled.
🅿 01/01-31/12

🍽 | Bockhorn | 4B5
Gaststätte Zum Sandkrug, Sandkrugsweg 21,Grabstede.
GPS: n53,35893 e8,00186.⬆.

4 🛏free. **Location:** Rural, simple, quiet. **Surface:** grassy.
🅿 01/01-31/12
Distance: ⊗on the spot.

🍽 S | Bodenwerder | 10A2
Wohnmobilstellplatz Bodenwerder, Am Mühlentor. **GPS:** n51,98037 e9,51795.
⬆➡.

30 🛏€6 ⛽€1,50 🚰Ch 🔌(30x)€1,50/24h WC 🗑€2. 🚿 **Location:**
Comfortable. 🅿 01/01-31/12

🍽 | Bockhorn | 4B5
Erlebnisbad, Urwaldstrasse 35a. **GPS:** n53,39876 e7,99410.⬆.

25 🛏€6 + €1/pp tourist tax ⛽€2/10minutes 🚰Ch 🔌€2,50/day
WC 🗑€1,50. 🚿 **Location:** Urban, simple. **Surface:** grassy.
🅿 01/01-31/12
Distance: 🏪200m 🏊Weser 200m ⊗200m 🚉500m 🚌200m.
Remarks: Check in and pay at pay desk swimming pool.

🍽 | Bohmte | 9C1
Golfclub Arenshorst, Arenshorster Kirchweg 2. **GPS:** n52,35651 e8,28450.➡.

DE

3 🛏guests free. **Location:** Rural, simple. **Surface:** grassy/metalled.
🅾 01/01-31/12
Distance: ⚓3km ⊗on the spot ⛽3km.

| 🍴S | Bohmte | 9C1 |

Landgasthaus Gieseke-Asshorn, Bremer strasse 55. **GPS:** n52,36674 e8,31261.

4 🛏guests free 🚰 ♨ free. **Location:** Urban, quiet. **Surface:** metalled.
🅾 01/01-31/12
Distance: ⚓on the spot ⊗on the spot ⛽200m.

| 🏕S | Bohmte | 9C1 |

VARIOmobil Fahrzeugbau GmbH, Bremer strasse. **GPS:** n52,38623 e8,30761. ➡

2 🛏free 🚰 ♨ Ch free. **Location:** Rural, quiet. **Surface:** metalled.
🅾 01/01-31/12
Distance: ⚓500m ⊗1km ⛽1km.
Remarks: Service only during opening hours.

| 🔵 | Bomlitz | 5A6 |

Am Weltvogelpark, Am Vogelpark. **GPS:** n52,88425 e9,59720.⬆

50 🛏free. **Location:** Rural, simple, central. **Surface:** grassy.
🅾 01/01-31/12
Distance: ⚓2,5km ⊗on the spot ⛽2,5km.
Remarks: Max. 1 night.

| 🏕S | Brake 〰🏖🍦 | 4C5 |

City-Parkplatz, Breite Strasse. **GPS:** n53,32534 e8,47982.⬆➡

2 🛏free. **Location:** Urban, simple, central, noisy. **Surface:** metalled.
🅾 01/01-31/12
Distance: ⚓on the spot ⊗on the spot ⛽200m 🚌200m 🚶on the spot.

| ⚓S | Brake 〰🏖🍦 | 4C5 |

Am Binnenhafen, Hafenstrasse. **GPS:** n53,32802 e8,48296.⬆

4 🛏free 🚰€1/10minutes 🗑 Ch ♨(4x)€0,50/6h.
Location: Urban, simple, central, noisy. **Surface:** grasstiles.
🅾 01/01-31/12
Distance: ⚓on the spot ⚡1km ⊗100m ⛽200m 🚌200m 🚶on the spot.

| 🏕S | Bramsche | 9C1 |

Wohnmobilstellplatz Waldwinkel, Zum Dreschhaus 4.
GPS: n52,39591 e8,10244.⬆➡

60 🛏€6 🚰€1,50/70liter 🗑 Ch ♨(80x)€2 WC 🚿€1.
Location: Rural, comfortable, quiet. **Surface:** grassy. 🅾 01/01-31/12
Distance: ⚓3,5km ⊗100m ⛽3,5km 🚶on the spot 🏃on the spot.
Remarks: Next to campsite Waldwinkel.

| 🏕 | Bramsche | 9C1 |

Hasebad, Malgartener strasse 49. **GPS:** n52,41493 e7,99423.⬆

10 🛏free. **Location:** Urban, simple, quiet. **Surface:** metalled.
🅾 01/01-31/12
Distance: ⚓500m.

| 🏕S | Bramsche | 9C1 |

Reisemobile Lewandowsky, Am Kanal 1b. **GPS:** n52,38524 e7,92958.⬆➡

2 🛏free 🚰 🗑 Ch free 🔌 €2/day. **Location:** Rural, simple. **Surface:** gravel.
📅 01/01-31/12
Distance: 🛒1km ⊗1km 🍴1km.
Remarks: Also repairs possible, service during opening hours, walking and bicycle area.

| 🚐S | Braunlage ⛺ ❄ | 10C2 |

Schützenplatz, Schützenstrasse 21. **GPS:** n51,71658 e10,60847. ⬆

85 🛏€ 9,50 + € 2,20/pp tourist tax 🚰 🗑 Ch 🔌 €0,50/kWh WC included 🗑€1
💧€3. 🚿 **Location:** Rural, luxurious, quiet. **Surface:** gravel.
📅 01/01-31/12
Distance: 🛒400m ⊗Café Restaurant Hubertushöhe 🚲 on the spot
🏃 on the spot 🐕 on the spot.

| 🚐S | Braunschweig | 10B1 |

Theodor-Heuss-Straße. **GPS:** n52,24964 e10,51835. ⬆ ➡

16 🛏free 🚰 €1/10minutes 🗑 Ch 🔌 (16x)€1/8h.
Location: Urban, simple, noisy. **Surface:** asphalted. 📅 01/01-31/12
Distance: 🛒2km ⊗400m 🍴200m 🚋on the spot.
Remarks: Max. 2 nights.

| 🚐S | Bremen 🌿🏕🍴🗑 | 4D5 |

Wohnmobil Oase Bremen, Schoster born, via Emil von Behringstrasse.
GPS: n53,06778 e8,86333. ⬆

8 🛏€ 15 + tourist tax € 1/pp 🚰 €2/time 🗑 Ch 🔌 WC included 🗑€1,50,use
luxurious bathroom €5, sauna €5 🗑€6/time 🚿 🚲 **Location:** Urban,
comfortable, central. **Surface:** gravel. 📅 01/01-31/12
Distance: 🛒4km ⊗on the spot 🍴50m 🚋Tram 🚲 on the spot.

Remarks: Motorhome < 7m.

| 🚐S | Bremen 🌿🏕🍴🗑 | 4D5 |

Am Kuhhirten, Kurhirtenweg. **GPS:** n53,06500 e8,81871. ⬆ ➡

70 🛏€ 13 🚰 €1/100liter 🗑 Ch 🔌 (70x)€0,50/kWh WC €1/24h 🗑€1.
Location: Urban, comfortable, central. **Surface:** gravel.
📅 01/01-31/12
Distance: 🛒Old city centre 1,3km 🏊500m ⊗on the spot 🍴800m
🚋Tram 700m 🚲 on the spot.

| 🚐S | Bremen 🌿🏕🍴🗑 | 4D5 |

Bremer Schweiz, Im Pohl, Lesum. **GPS:** n53,16765 e8,69560. ⬆ ➡

7 🛏€ 5/24h 🚰 €1/10minutes 🗑 Ch 🔌 (8x)€1/8h. 🚗
Location: Urban, comfortable, quiet. **Surface:** gravel. 📅 01/01-31/12
Distance: 🛒on the spot 🚲2,4km ⊗on the spot 🍴300m 🚋on the spot
🚲on the spot.

| 🚐S | Bremen 🌿🏕🍴🗑 | 4D5 |

Maritime Meile, Schulkenstrasse. **GPS:** n53,17298 e8,60906. ⬆ ➡

5 🛏€ 5 + tourist tax 🚰 €1/80liter 🗑 Ch 🔌 (4x)€1/8h. 🚿
Location: Urban, comfortable, central, quiet. **Surface:** asphalted.
📅 01/01-31/12
Distance: 🛒Bremen 20km ⊗100m 🍴200m 🚲 on the spot.

| 🚐S | Bremen 🌿🏕🍴🗑 | 4D5 |

Camping Stadtwaldsee, Hochschulring 1. **GPS:** n53,11381 e8,84389. ⬆

20 🛏€ 12-15 🚰 €1/80liter 🗑 Ch 🔌 (20x)€1/5h WC included. 🚿
Location: Rural, luxurious. **Surface:** grasstiles.
📅 01/01-31/12

DE

Distance: 5,5km ⬦ 3km ⚓ on the spot ⬅ on the spot ⊗ on the spot 🚗 100m ⛟ on the spot.

Tourist information Bremen:

ℹ Tourist Information, Obernstrasse en Hauptbahnhof, www.bremen-tourism. de. Hanseatic city and second harbour of Germany.

👁 Böttcherstrasse. Pedestrian passage.

☗ Weserpromenade Schlachte. Antiques and flea market. ⬛ Sa 8-14h.

🏕 S **Bremerhaven** 🌊 ⛱ 🍺 ⛵ 4C4

Reisemobil-Parkplatz Doppelschleuse, An der Neuen Schleuse. **GPS:** n53,53230 e8,57607. ⬆➡.

63 🍴 € 10 ⛽ €1/100liter 🔋 Ch ⚡ (40x)€0,50/kWh WC €0,50/time €0,50/time. 🅿 **Location:** Urban, comfortable, luxurious, central, quiet. **Surface:** asphalted. ⬛ 01/01-31/12

Distance: 1km ⬦ 8km ⚓1km ⊗1,5km ⬛1,2km ⛟ on the spot.

Remarks: Bread-service.

🏕 S **Bremerhaven** 🌊 ⛱ 🍺 ⛵ 4C4

Reisemobil-Parkplatz Fischereihafen, Hoebelstrasse, Fischereihafen 1. **GPS:** n53,52634 e8,57610. ⬆➡.

47 🍴 € 10, tourist tax incl ⛽ €1/100liter 🔋 Ch ⚡ (36x)€0,50/kWh WC included. 🅿 **Location:** Urban, luxurious, central, quiet. **Surface:** asphalted/metalled. ⬛ 01/01-31/12

Distance: 4km ⚓ on the spot ⬅ on the spot ⊗500m ⬛500m 🚗200m ⛟200m.

Remarks: At harbour, caution key sanitary € 5.

🏕 S **Bremervörde** ⛵ 4D4

Wohnmobilstation - Bremervörde

touristik@bremervoerde.de - www.bremervoerde.de

Located directly at lake
Ideal base for walking and cycling
Bread-service

Wohnmobilstation Bremervörde, Kiebitzweg 1. **GPS:** n53,49453 e9,15576. ⬆➡.

---

40 🍴 € 9,50, 01/11-28/02 € 6,50 ⛽ 🔋 Ch ⚡ (21x)€3/day,10Amp WC included €1. 💈 ⚡ **Location:** Rural, comfortable, quiet.

Surface: metalled. ⬛ 01/01-31/12

Distance: 1,5km ⚓100m ⬅100m ⊗300m ⬛1km 🚗1,5km ⛟ on the spot ☗ on the spot.

🏕 S **Brietlingen** ⛵ ⚓ 5B4

Reihersee, Grosse strabe. **GPS:** n53,34344 e10,45844. ⬆.

50 🍴 € 8. **Location:** Rural, simple, isolated. **Surface:** grassy. ⬛ 01/03-31/10

Distance: ⊗ on the spot.

🍴 **Brietlingen** ⛵ ⚓ 5B4

Hotel Franck, Bundesstrasse 31b. **GPS:** n53,32951 e10,44491. ☗.

5 🍴 free ⚡ (1x)€2/night.

Location: Rural, simple, quiet.

Distance: on the spot ⊗ on the spot ⬛500m.

🏕 S **Bruchhausen-Vilsen** 4D6

Reisemobilstellplatz Bruchhausen-Vilsen, Bollenstrasse. **GPS:** n52,82671 e8,99536. ⬆➡.

20 🍴 € 6 ⛽ €1/100liter 🔋 Ch ⚡ (6x)included WC.

Surface: gravel. ⬛ 01/01-31/12

Distance: 200m ⚓ on the spot ⊗200m ⬛200m.

🏕 S **Buchholz/Nordheide** ⛱ 🍺 ⛵ 5A5

Buchholz/Nordheide, Weg zum Badeteich 20. **GPS:** n53,28202 e9,87495. ⬆.

12 🍴 € 12-15 ⛽ €1/100liter 🔋 Ch ⚡ (6x)€2 WC included 🗑. 💈 ⚡

Location: Rural, comfortable. **Surface:** metalled/sand. ⬛ 01/01-31/12

DE

Distance: 200m on the spot on the spot 200m.

S | **Bückeburg** | 9D1

Am Schloss, Georgstrasse/Liebesallee. **GPS:** n52,25777 e9,04583.

20 €5 €1 Ch (24x)€1/12h . **Location:** Urban, quiet.
Surface: gravel/metalled. 01/01-31/12
Distance: 500m 500m 500m 200m on the spot.

S | **Bückeburg** | 9D1

Neumarktplatz, Unterwallweg 5c. **GPS:** n52,26326 e9,05040.

15 free €1/80liter Ch (6x)€0,50/kWh.
Location: Urban, simple. **Surface:** gravel. 01/01-31/12
Distance: 250m 250m 250m.

| **Büddenstedt** | 10C1

Am Sportplatz. GPS: n52,17567 e11,01843.

3 free. **Location:** Rural, simple, quiet. **Surface:** asphalted.
01/01-31/12
Distance: 1km on the spot 2km.
Remarks: Parking swimming pool.

| **Büddenstedt** | 10C1

Parking K22, Barneberger Straße, Offleben. **GPS:** n52,13738 e11,04409.

2 free. **Location:** Rural, simple. **Surface:** asphalted.
01/01-31/12
Distance: 500m 500m 500m.

S | **Bühren** | 10A3

Alter Festplatz, Im Teich. **GPS:** n51,48378 e9,67451.

20 €2 €2. **Location:** Rural, isolated. **Surface:** grassy.
01/01-31/12
Distance: 700m 5km on the spot on the spot.

S | **Bunde** | 4A5

Am Friedhofsweg. GPS: n53,18500 e7,26639.

10 €3 €1 €1 Ch €1/10h.
Surface: grasstiles. 01/01-31/12
Distance: 100m 2,3km 350m 200m.
Remarks: At townhall, max. 3 days.

S | **Bunde** | 4A5

Freizeitgelände, Denkmalstrasse 11, Ditzumerverlaat. **GPS:** n53,26028 e7,26861.

10 €3/24h €0,50 Ch (8x)€1/8h. **Surface:** metalled.
01/01-31/12 during event
Distance: 250m on the spot on the spot 350m 250m.
Remarks: Max. 3 days.

| **Bunde** | 4A5

Möhlenlandbad, Kellingwold 25. **GPS:** n53,18683 e7,27418.
10 €3. **Surface:** metalled. 01/01-31/12
Distance: 500m.

S | **Butjadingen** | 4C4

Henken's Stellplatz, Am Hafen 6, Fedderwardersiel. **GPS:** n53,59581 e8,35669.

80 €5 + €1,10-2,20/pp tourist tax €0,01/1liter Ch €1/24h
(48x)€2,50/day. **Location:** Rural, comfortable, central, quiet.

DE

Surface: grassy. ◘ 01/01-31/12
Distance: ⛟500m ⚓on the spot ⊷on the spot ⊗on the spot ⚏on the spot ⛟500m ♨on the spot ⚘on the spot.
Remarks: Bread-service.

©S **Butjadingen** ☀⚓⚘ 4C4
Knaus Campingpark Burhave, Strand Allee, Burhave. **GPS:** n53,58306 e8,37000. ⬆➡.

50 ⛺€ 9,80 + € 2,20/pp tourist tax ⛽€2,20 ⚑Ch ⚡€0,70/kWh WC ⬧€3,30. **Surface:** grassy. ◘ 15/04-15/10
Distance: ⛟1km ⚓on the spot ⊷200m ⚏1km.

⛺S **Butjadingen** ☀⚓⚘ 4C4
Hof Iggewarden, Iggewarden 1. **GPS:** n53,58622 e8,32653. ⬆➡.

20 ⛺€ 8 ⛽€1/100liter ⚑Ch ⚡(2x)€2/day WC. ♨ **Location:** Rural, comfortable, isolated, quiet. **Surface:** gravel. ◘ 01/01-31/12
Distance: ⛟2km ⚓2km ⊗on the spot ⚏on the spot ⊷300m ♨on the spot ⚘on the spot.

⚓S **Butjadingen** ☀⚓⚘ 4C4
Jachthaven Fedderwardersiel. **GPS:** n53,59518 e8,35700. ⬆.

30 ⛺€ 10 excl. tourist tax ⛽Ch €1,50/time ⚡(20x)€2,50/day WC ⬧4minutes ⬡€6/time. ♨ **Location:** Rural, comfortable, isolated, quiet.
Surface: grassy. ◘ 01/01-31/12
Distance: ⛟800m ⚓on the spot ⊷on the spot ⊗800m ⚏800m ⊷on the spot ♨on the spot ⚘on the spot.

⛺S **Buxtehude** ☀⬡⚘ 5A4
Pfingstmarktplatz, Cuxhavenerstrasse, Neukloster, B73.
GPS: n53,47974 e9,63528. ⬆.

40 ⛺free ⛽€0,50/90liter ⚑Ch ⬧€2. **Location:** Rural, simple.
Surface: asphalted. ◘ 01/01-31/12 ⬡ week before/after Whitsuntide
Distance: ⛟3km ⊗Imbiss ⚏bakery 200m.
Remarks: Key shower at Imbiss.

⛺S **Buxtehude** ☀⬡⚘ 5A4
Schützenplatz, Genslerweg. **GPS:** n53,47139 e9,69528. ⬆➡.

30 ⛺free ⛽€1/90liter ⚑Ch ⚡(36x)€1/kWh. **Location:** Urban, central.
Surface: gravel. ◘ 01/01-31/12
Distance: ⛟nearby Old city centre ⊗50m ⚏bakery 50m.
Tourist information Buxtehude:
👁 Das Fleth. Old inland-port.

⛺S **Cadenberge** 4D3
Reisemobilvermietung Hennig, Alter Postweg 1. **GPS:** n53,76686 e9,05681. ⬆.

4 ⛺€ 5 ⛽€0,50/100liter ⚡€1,50/24h. ♨ **Location:** Rural, simple.
Surface: grassy. ◘ 01/01-31/12
Distance: ⛟on the spot ⊗on the spot ⚏50m.

⛺S **Celle** 5B6
Schützenplatz, Hafenstraße. **GPS:** n52,62794 e10,07348. ⬆.

35 ⛺free ⛽€1 ⚑Ch WC. **Surface:** grassy/metalled. ◘ 01/01-31/12
Distance: ⛟150m ⊗100m.

⛺S **Celle** 5B6
Langensalzaplatz. **GPS:** n52,61842 e10,08052. ➡.

DE

3 🛏free. **Surface:** metalled. 🅿 01/01-31/12
Distance: 🚶on the spot.

| 🏕 | Clausthal-Zellerfeld 🎿 🎎 | 10B2 |

Busbahnhof, Bahnhofstraß2 5. **GPS:** n51,81360 e10,33602.⬆.

4 🛏tourist tax € 1,50. **Location:** Rural, simple. **Surface:** metalled.
🅿 01/01-31/12
Distance: 🚶on the spot 🛒200m 🚉600m 🚌on the spot 🚲on the spot
🚶on the spot.

| 🏕 S | Clenze 🎎 | 5C5 |

Regenbogen-Hof, Mützen. **GPS:** n52,94079 e10,93899.⬆➡.

5 🛏€ 5/pp 🚰 🗑 Ch 🚿 WC �included. **Location:** Rural, simple, isolated,
quiet. **Surface:** grassy. 🅿 01/01-31/12
Distance: 🚶3km 🛒on the spot 🚉3km 🚌on the spot.
Remarks: Arrival <22h.

| 🏕 S | Cloppenburg | 4C6 |

Am Stadtpark, Hagenweg. **GPS:** n52,84649 e8,04687.⬆.

3 🛏free 🚰€0,50/80liter 🗑 Ch. **Location:** Urban, simple. **Surface:** metalled.
🅿 01/01-31/12
Distance: 🚶100m 🚲2km.
Remarks: Max. 3 days.

| 🏕 | Cloppenburg | 4C6 |

Museumsdorf Cloppenburg, Bether Straße. **GPS:** n52,85197 e8,05335.⬆.

20 🛏free. **Location:** Rural, simple. **Surface:** metalled.
🅿 01/01-31/12
Distance: 🚶900m 🚲1km.
Remarks: Parking in front of museum village, max. 24h.

| 🏕 S | Coppenbrügge 🎎 | 10A2 |

Parkplatz am Frei- und Hallenbad, Felsenkellerweg. **GPS:** n52,11613 e9,53676.
⬆➡.

12 🛏€ 3,50 🚰€2,50 🗑 Ch 🚿 (12x)€1. **Location:** Rural, simple.
Surface: grassy/gravel. 🅿 01/01-31/12
Distance: 🚶1,5km 🛒500m 🚉500m 🚲on the spot 🚶on the spot.
Remarks: Check in at campsite.

| 🏕 S | Cuxhaven ⚓ | 4C3 |

Duhner Allee, Duhnen. **GPS:** n53,88284 e8,64814.⬆.

60 🛏€ 10, 1/9-1/7 € 6 🚰🗑Ch 🚿€2/day WC€0,50 �€1. 🚗
Location: Simple. **Surface:** asphalted. 🅿 01/01-31/12
Remarks: Beach parking, in front of campsite am Bäderring.

| 🏕 S | Cuxhaven ⚓ | 4C3 |

Elbe-Ferry, Am Fährhafen. **GPS:** n53,87508 e8,70315.⬆➡.

100 🛏€ 10-13, tourist tax incl 🚰🗑Ch. 🚗
Location: Urban, simple. **Surface:** asphalted. 🅿 01/01-31/12
Distance: 🚶1km 🚉500m.
Remarks: Bread-service.

| 🏕 S | Cuxhaven ⚓ | 4C3 |

Privatparkplatz Kugelbake Halle, Nordfeldstraße. **GPS:** n53,89033 e8,67703.
⬆.

80 🏕 € 8 🚰 🗑 Ch WC . 🚐 **Location:** Urban, simple. **Surface:** metalled.
📅 01/01-31/12
Distance: 🏊 200m ⊗ 100m.

⚓S **Cuxhaven** 4C3
Campingplatz Finck, Am Sahlenburger Strand 25. **GPS:** n53,86039 e8,59167.
⬆️➡️

12 🏕 € 15,00 🚰 🗑 Ch 🔌 (12x) WC . 🚿 **Location:** Comfortable.
📅 01/01-31/12
Distance: 🏊 3km ⊗ on the spot ⊗ on the spot 🛒 on camp site 🚍 100m.

🏕S **Damme** 9C1
Am Flugplatz 8. **GPS:** n52,49055 e8,17925. ⬆️➡️

25 🏕 € 5 🚰 €0,50/80liter 🗑 Ch 🔌 (12x)€0,50/kWh WC 🧻€1.
Location: Luxurious. **Surface:** grassy/gravel. 📅 01/01-31/12
Distance: ⊗ on the spot.
Remarks: Parking airport Damme.

🏕 **Damme** 9C1
Parkplatz Altes Amtsgericht, Große Straße. **GPS:** n52,52381 e8,19486. ⬆️
5 🏕 free. **Surface:** metalled. 📅 01/01-31/12
Distance: 🏊 300m.

♨S **Damme** 9C1
Olgahafen, Dümmerstrasse, Dümmerlohausen. **GPS:** n52,52917 e8,31098. ⬆️

12 🏕 free 🚰 €1 🗑 Ch 🔌€1. **Location:** Rural, simple, quiet. **Surface:** gravel.
📅 01/01-31/12
Distance: 🏊 100m 🚶 100m ⊗ on the spot 🛒 bakery.
Remarks: At lake Dümmer, max. 3 days.

♿S **Dassel** 10A2
Am Badesee in der Ortschaft, Lauenberg. **GPS:** n51,75750 e9,76389. ⬆️➡️

8 🏕 free, 01/05-01/10 € 5 🚰 €1/80liter 🗑 Ch 🔌 €1/8h
🧻included,01/05-30/09. 🚿 **Location:** Rural, isolated, quiet.
Surface: asphalted. 📅 01/01-31/12
Distance: 🚲8,5km 🏊 on the spot ⊗300m 🛒300m 🚍300m 🏍 on the spot
🚶 on the spot.

♿S **Dassel** 10A2
Am Sollingbad, An der Badeanstalt. **GPS:** n51,80722 e9,68917. ⬆️➡️

5 🏕 free. **Location:** Rural, isolated. 📅 01/01-31/12
Distance: 🏊 Old city centre 500m 🛒1km 🏍 on the spot 🚶 on the spot.

🏕S **Delmenhorst** 4C5
Reisemobilhafen Delmenhorst, An den Graften. **GPS:** n53,04722 e8,62278.
⬆️➡️

8 🏕 free 🚰 🗑 Ch free 🔌 €1/kWh.
Location: Urban, simple, central, quiet. **Surface:** gravel/sand.
📅 01/01-31/12 🔘 during event
Distance: 🏊 on the spot 🚴 2,8km ⊗ on the spot 🛒200m.
Remarks: Max. 7 days.

🏕S **Detern** 4B5
Reisemobilhafen Detern, Alte Heerstrasse 6, Stickhausen.
GPS: n53,21560 e7,64743. ⬆️➡️

40 🏕 € 5 🚰 €1/100liter 🗑 Ch 🔌 (44x)€2/24h WC 🧻€1 🚿 €0,50. 🚿
Location: Urban, luxurious. **Surface:** asphalted/gravel. 📅 01/01-31/12
Distance: 🏊 on the spot 🚤 6km 🏊 on the spot 🚶 on the spot ⊗ on the spot

🏍 on the spot 🚶 on the spot.
Remarks: Behind tourist info, bread-service.

🚲S Diepenau 9D1
Am Bahnhof. **GPS:** n52,42470 e8,74106. ⬆.

6 🚐free ⌐€1 🍳Ch ⚡€1/8h. **Surface:** metalled. ⬛ 01/01-31/12
Distance: 🏊500m ⊗500m 🛒500m.

🚲S Diepholz 4C6
Parkplatz Am Heldenhain, Am Heldenhaim (B69). **GPS:** n52,61250 e8,37056. ⬆➡.

12 🚐free ⌐€1 🍳Ch ⚡(12x)€0,50/kWh. **Location:** Urban.
Surface: grassy. ⬛ 01/01-31/12
Distance: 🏊500m ⊗500m 🛒500m.

🚲S Ditzum 4A5
Nah und Gut Blank, Pogumer Straße. **GPS:** n53,31489 e7,27619. ⬆.

14 🚐€7/24h ⌐€1/100liter 🍳Ch ⚡(10x)€1/kWh. **Surface:** metalled.
⬛ 01/01-31/12
Distance: 🏊100m ⊗300m 🚆300m ⊗100m 🛒on the spot.

🚲S Ditzum 4A5
Reisemobilstellplatz Ditzum, Am Deich. **GPS:** n53,31555 e7,28666. ⬆.

45 🚐€7 ⌐€1/100liter 🍳Ch ⚡(45x)€1/2kWh. **Surface:** metalled.
⬛ 01/01-31/12
Distance: 🏊100m ⛱100m 🚆100m ⊗100m 🛒300m.
Remarks: Bread-service, waste dump €1, shower €1.

🚲S Dornum 4B4
Wohnmobilplatz, Schöpfwerkstraße, Dornumersiel. **GPS:** n53,67272 e7,48092. ⬆.

30 🚐€9, Nordsee-ServiceCard incl ⚡€1/8h. **Surface:** metalled.
⬛ 01/01-31/12
Distance: 🏊500m ⊗100m 🛒100m.

🚲S Dornum 4B4
Wohnmobilplatz, Schützenplatz. **GPS:** n53,64850 e7,42365. ⬆ ⬆.

30 🚐€9, Nordsee-ServiceCard incl ⌐€1/65liter 🍳Ch ⚡€1/8h.
Surface: grassy. ⬛ 01/01-31/12
Distance: 🏊on the spot ⊗300m 🛒50m.
Remarks: Max. 1 night.

ⒸS Dornum 4B4
Am Nordseestrand, Hafenstraße 7. **GPS:** n53,68063 e7,48294. ⬆.
13 🚐€17 Nordsee-ServiceCard incl ⌐🍳Ch ⚡included. ⬛ 01/04-30/09
Distance: 🏊on the spot ⊗300m 🛒500m.
Remarks: Bread-service.

🚲S Dörpen 🍽 4A6
Festplatz, Veeneweg. **GPS:** n52,97115 e7,33425. ⬆➡.

10 🚐free. **Location:** Simple. **Surface:** grassy/metalled.
⬛ 01/01-31/12 ◉ 1st week in June: fair
Distance: 🏊500m ⊗on the spot 🛒500m 🚶on the spot.

🚲S Dorum 4C4
Wohnmobilhafen Am Deich, Am Neuen Deich 2a. **GPS:** n53,73838 e8,51966. ⬆➡.

24 🚐€12,50 + €1,50/pp tourist tax ⌐🍳Ch ⚡included WC 🗑€1 🔌 ♻
Location: Simple. **Surface:** metalled. ⬛ 01/01-31/12
Distance: 🏊on the spot 🚆on the spot ⊗on the spot.
Remarks: Check in at Deichhotel.

🚲S Dörverden 🌿⛺🍽 4D6
In der Worth. **GPS:** n52,84529 e9,22568. ⬆➡.

5 🛢free 🚰€1/80liter ⚡(5x)€1/8h.
Location: Urban, simple, quiet. **Surface:** gravel.
⊙ 01/01-31/12
Distance: 🚰200m ⊗200m 🛒200m 🚌Bremen/Hanover 🚲100m 🚶1km.
Remarks: Behind town hall, max. 3 nights.

| 🚻 | Dörverden 🌿🍽️🎡 | 4D6 |

Wolfcenter, Kasernenstraße, Barme. **GPS:** n52,82635 e9,21417.
10 🛢free. **Location:** Simple. **Surface:** concrete. ⊙ 01/01-31/12
Distance: 🚰Dörverden 3km ⊗on the spot 🛒Aldi 3km.
Remarks: Parking wolf park.

| 🅿️S | Drage/Elbe 🌊 | 5B4 |

Reisemobilplatz Stover Strand, Stover Strand 10. **GPS:** n53,42467 e10,29213.
⬆️.

100 🛢€ 12 🚰€1/80liter 🔌Ch ⚡(100x)€0,50/kWh WC 🚾€0,50/4minutes
🚿€4/4 💧€2/h. **Location:** Comfortable. **Surface:** grassy.
⊙ 01/01-31/12
Distance: 🏊on the spot 🍽️on the spot ⊗on the spot 🛒on the spot 🚌500m
🚲on the spot 🚶on the spot.
Remarks: Next to campsite.

| 🅿️S | Drochtersen ⛱️ | 4D4 |

Krautsand, Deichverteitigungsweg. **GPS:** n53,75167 e9,39028. ⬆️➡️.

12 🛢€ 10 ⚡(12x)included. 📶 **Location:** Rural, simple. **Surface:** metalled.
⊙ 01/01-31/12
Distance: 🏊Elbestrand 🛒300m.

| 🅿️ | Drochtersen ⛱️ | 4D4 |

Hallenbad Drochtersen, Am Sportplatz. **GPS:** n53,70548 e9,38215. ⬆️.

6 🛢free. **Location:** Simple. **Surface:** metalled. ⊙ 01/01-31/12
Distance: 🚰1km 🛒1km.
Remarks: Parking at swimming pool.

| ⚓ | Drochtersen ⛱️ | 4D4 |

Am Alten Hafen, Asseler Sand. **GPS:** n53,69418 e9,43928. ⬆️.

6 🛢free. **Location:** Rural, simple. **Surface:** gravel.
⊙ 01/01-31/12
Distance: ⊗500m 🛒1km.

| 🅿️S | Duderstadt 🌿⛱️ | 10B3 |

P&R Parkplatz, Adenauerring. **GPS:** n51,51043 e10,27278. ⬆️➡️.

50 🛢free 🚰€1/120liter 🔌€1/time Ch€1/time ⚡(4x)€0,50/kWh.
Location: Rural, quiet. **Surface:** gravel. ⊙ 01/01-31/12
Distance: 🚰800m 🚲17km ⊗800m 🛒200m 🚌100m.

| 🅿️ | Duderstadt 🌿⛱️ | 10B3 |

Eichsfeldhalle, August Werner Allee. **GPS:** n51,50662 e10,25890. ⬆️.

5 🛢free.
Location: Rural, simple. **Surface:** gravel.
⊙ 01/01-31/12
Distance: 🚰900m 🚲17km ⊗900m 🛒900m 🚌700m.
Remarks: Max. 1 night.
Tourist information Duderstadt:
ℹ️ Gästeinformation der Stadt Duderstadt, Marktstrasse 66, www.duderstadt.
de. Old part of town with half-timbered houses.

| 🅿️S | Edewecht | 4B5 |

Rathhausstrasse. **GPS:** n53,12834 e7,98201. ⬆️.

DE

20 🚐free ⚡€1/80liter 🗑Ch ♨ (8x)€1/6h. **Location:** Urban, simple.
Surface: grasstiles. 🅾 01/01-31/12
Distance: 🚰on the spot ⊗400m 🛒Aldi 50m.

🛟S **Egestorf** 5A5
Naturerlebnisbad Acquadies, Ahornweg 5. **GPS:** n53,19796 e10,05455. ⬆➡

40 🚐€7 ⚡€1 🗑Ch ♨ (30x)€2/10h WC 🚽 🚿 **Location:** Simple, quiet.
Surface: gravel/metalled. 🅾 01/01-31/12
Distance: 🚰1km 🏊2,2km 🛒on the spot ⊗700m 🛒1km.
Remarks: At swimming pool.

🛟S **Eggermühlen** 9B1
Reiterhotel Vox, OT Bockraden 1. **GPS:** n52,57278 e7,79553. ⬆➡

8 🚐€ 25, clients € 7,50 ⚡€1 🗑Ch ♨ WC 🚽included.
Location: Rural. **Surface:** grassy. 🅾 01/01-31/12
Distance: 🚰3km 🛒3km.

🚐 **Eggestedt** 4C5
Eggestedt, Betonstrasse/Habichthorsterweg. **GPS:** n53,22819 e8,63902. ⬆➡

8 🚐free. **Location:** Simple, isolated, noisy. **Surface:** metalled/sand.
🅾 01/01-31/12
Distance: 🚰4km 🏊400m.

🚐S **Einbeck** 🌿♨🛒 10A2
Am Schwimmbad, Ochsenhofweg. **GPS:** n51,82433 e9,86464. ⬆➡

30 🚐free ⚡€1/60liter 🗑€1 Ch ♨ (18x)€0,50/kWh. **Location:** Simple.
Surface: gravel. 🅾 01/01-31/12
Distance: 🚰800m ⊗500m 🛒500m 🚴on the spot 🚶on the spot.
Remarks: Parking at swimming pool.

Tourist information Einbeck:
🏛 Alte Marktplatz. 🅾 Wed + Sa morning.

⚓S **Elsfleth** 🌿♨🛒 4C5
Im Hafen, An der Kaje. **GPS:** n53,23771 e8,46545. ⬆➡

20 🚐€ 8/24h ⚡€1/80liter 🗑Ch ♨ (16x)€2/8h WC 🚽€2/time. 🚐
🚿**Location:** Urban, comfortable, central, noisy. **Surface:** concrete.
🅾 01/01-31/12
Distance: 🚰150m 🏊900m 🚃on the spot ⊗100m 🛒500m 🚆on the spot
🚴on the spot.

⚓S **Emden** 4A5
Alter Binnenhafen, Am Eisenbahndock. **GPS:** n53,36306 e7,20778. ⬆

45 🚐€ 8 ⚡€0,50/100liter 🗑€0,50 Ch ♨ (36x)€0,50/kWh WC€0,50 🚽€1
🚿€3. **Surface:** metalled. 🅾 01/01-31/12
Distance: 🚰500m ⊗500m 🛒500m.
Remarks: Pay at harbourmaster.

🚐 **Emden** 4A5
Wohnmobilstellplatz Knock, Jannes Ohling Strasse. **GPS:** n53,35559 e7,00367.
⬆.

25 🚐€ 4,50. **Surface:** metalled. 🅾 01/01-31/12
Distance: 🚰13km 🏖500m ⊗on the spot 🛒13km.
Remarks: Beautiful view.

⚓ **Emden** 4A5
Außenhafen Emden, An der Nesserlanderschleuse. **GPS:** n53,34571 e7,19132.
⬆.
10 🛏 € 5. **Surface:** asphalted. 🄾 01/01-31/12
Distance: 🚶3,5km ⛵on the spot. 🚂on the spot.

⚓ **Emden** 4A5
Nordkai, Zum Nordkai 6. **GPS:** n53,35037 e7,21712.⬆.
9 🛏 € 8. **Surface:** metalled. 🄾 01/01-31/12
Distance: 🚶centre 2,5km ⊗Hafenbistro 🚂on the spot.

🍴S **Emsbüren** 9A1
Landgasthof Elberger Schlipse, Elbergen 1, Elbergen.
GPS: n52,46825 e7,30103.

40 🛏 € 3 🚰🍽 Ch 🔌 (15x)€2,50/24h WC 🚽. ♨ **Location:** Rural, quiet.
Surface: grassy. 🄾 01/01-31/12
Distance: 🚶2km ⛵100m 🚂2km 🚲on the spot. 🧍on the spot.

📷S **Eschershausen** 🌿 10A2
Reisemobil-Stellplatz am Angerplatz, Angerweg. **GPS:** n51,92965 e9,62806.
⬆➡.

10 🛏free 🚰€1/100liter 🍽€1 Ch 🔌€0,50/kWh. **Surface:** metalled.
🄾 01/01-31/12
Distance: 🚶1km.

📷S **Esens** 4B4
Wohnmobil-Stellplatz Esens, Schützenplatz. **GPS:** n53,63921 e7,61077.⬆.

20 🛏 € 2 + € 2,80/pp tourist tax 🚰🍽 Ch 🔌 included. ♨ **Surface:** grassy.
🄾 01/01-31/12
Distance: 🚶500m ⊗50m 🚂200m.
Remarks: Max. 2 nights.

🍴S **Essel** 5A6
Hotel Heide-Kröpke, Esseler Damm 1. **GPS:** n52,73240 e9,69419.⬆.

5 🛏free 🚰🔌 📶. **Surface:** grassy. 🄾 01/01-31/12
Distance: ⊗on the spot 🚂9km.
Remarks: Use of a meal desired, bird reserve Ostenholzer-Moor.

📷S **Esterwegen** ⛵ 4B6
Am Erikasee. GPS: n52,99366 e7,66768.⬆.

6 🛏free 🚰€1/100liter 🍽 Ch 🔌 (6x)€1/2kWh WC 🚽.
Location: Rural, simple, isolated. **Surface:** gravel/metalled. 🄾 01/01-31/12
Distance: 🚶2km ⛵100m ⊗Imbiss 80m.
Remarks: Walking and bicycle area.

📷 **Eystrup** 4D6
Bahnhofstrasse 21. **GPS:** n52,78004 e9,21840.⬆➡.

5 🛏free. **Surface:** grassy. 🄾 01/01-31/12
Distance: 🚂100m.
Remarks: Max. 5 days.

📷S **Faßberg** 5B6
Am Schützenplatz, Moorweg. **GPS:** n52,90518 e10,16991.⬆.

50 🛏 € 2 🚰€1 🍽 Ch WC. **Surface:** grassy. 🄾 01/01-31/12
Distance: 🚂700m.

📷S **Faßberg** 5B6
Parkplatz Heidesee, Unterlüßerstraße, L280, Müden. **GPS:** n52,87889 e10,12472.
⬆.

20 🗓️€ 2 ⎌€1 ᄅCh ⚡€1. **Surface:** grassy.
🅿️ 01/01-31/12 ⏹️ end Sep

🚐 **Faßberg** 5B6

Parkplatz am Wildpark, Willinghäuser Kirchweg, Müden.
GPS: n52,87222 e10,10861.⬆️.

20 🗓️€ 2. **Surface:** grassy. 🅿️ 01/01-31/12
Distance: 🚶1km ⊗1km.

🚐S **Freiburg/Elbe** 4D3

Am Bassin. **GPS:** n53,82285 e9,29305.⬆️➡️.

50 🗓️€ 8 ⎌ ᄅCh ⚡ WCincluded 🗑️€1. 🚿 **Location:** Rural, simple.
Surface: metalled. 🅿️ 01/01-31/12
Distance: 🚶200m ⛽50m ⊗300m 💧400m.
Remarks: Find more possibilities on the city plan.

🚐S **Friedeburg** 4B4

Schützenplatz. GPS: n53,45488 e7,83349.⬆️.

20 🗓️free ⎌ ᄅChfree ⚡ (6x)€1/1. **Location:** Rural, simple.
Surface: grassy. 🅿️ 01/01-31/12
Distance: 🏊15/05-15/09 💧400m.
Remarks: Max. 3 days.

🚐 **Fürstenau** 9B1

Schlossinsel Fürstenau, Schlossplatz 1. **GPS:** n52,51638 e7,67333.⬆️.

2 🗓️free ⎌€3 ᄅCh ⚡€2/day. **Location:** Quiet. **Surface:** metalled.
🅿️ 01/01-31/12
Distance: 🚶100m ⊗100m 💧100m 🚲on the spot 🚶on the spot.
Remarks: Next to castle.

🚐S **Gartow** 5D5

Imbiss am See, Springstraße 88. **GPS:** n53,02944 e11,44944.⬆️.

20 🗓️€ 5 WC. **Surface:** gravel/metalled. 🅿️ 01/04-30/10
Distance: 🚶1km ⚓on the spot ⛵on the spot ⊗on the spot.
Remarks: Imbiss 11-21h.

🚐 **Geeste** 9A1

Am Speicherbecken, Biener Straße. **GPS:** n52,59407 e7,27417.⬆️.

50 🗓️free. **Location:** Quiet. **Surface:** metalled. 🅿️ 01/01-31/12
Distance: 🚶2km ⊗100m.
Remarks: Max. 1 night.

🚐 **Geeste** 9A1

P Biotop/Ausblick, Osterbrocker Strasse. **GPS:** n52,59840 e7,29279.⬆️.

4 🗓️free. **Surface:** metalled. 🅿️ 01/01-31/12
Distance: 🚶1,5km ⊗1,5km 🚲on the spot 🚶on the spot.
Remarks: Max. 1 night, hiking area.

🚐S **Gehrden** 10A1

An den Sporthallen, Lange Feldstraße 12. **GPS:** n52,31197 e9,60971.⬆️.

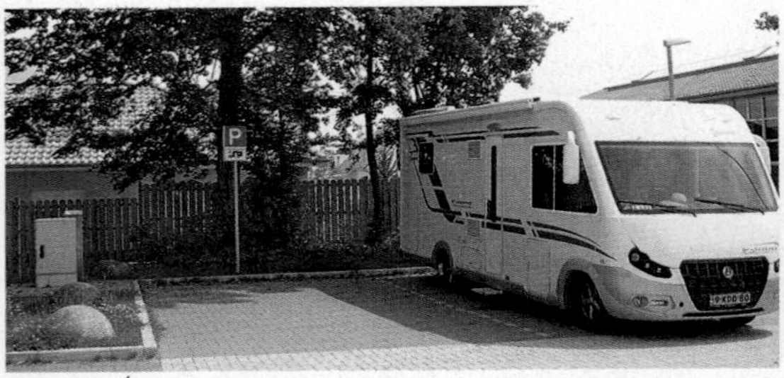

2 🚐 free ⚡ (2x)€0,50/kWh. **Location:** Simple. **Surface:** metalled.
[■] 01/01-31/12
Distance: 🏙 centre 700m 🍴 200m.

[🏭] [S] Gifhorn 10B1
Fischer Camping + Gas, Schmiedeweg 4, Wische. **GPS**: n52,50863 e10,48462. [↑].

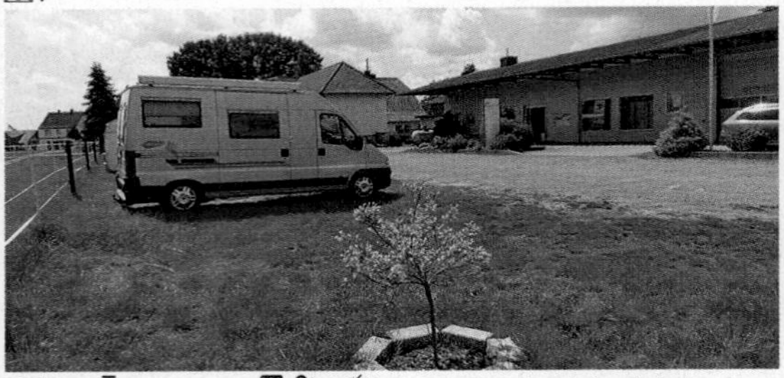

8 🚐 free 🚰 €0,50/50liter 🚽 Ch ⚡ (8x). **Location:** Rural, simple, isolated.
Surface: grassy. [■] 01/01-31/12
Distance: 🏙 3km 🍴 500m 🛒 3km.
Remarks: Accessory shop.

[🚐] [S] Gnarrenburg 4D4
Parkplatz Brillit, Alte Strasse, Brillit. **GPS**: n53,41390 e9,00007. [↑][→].

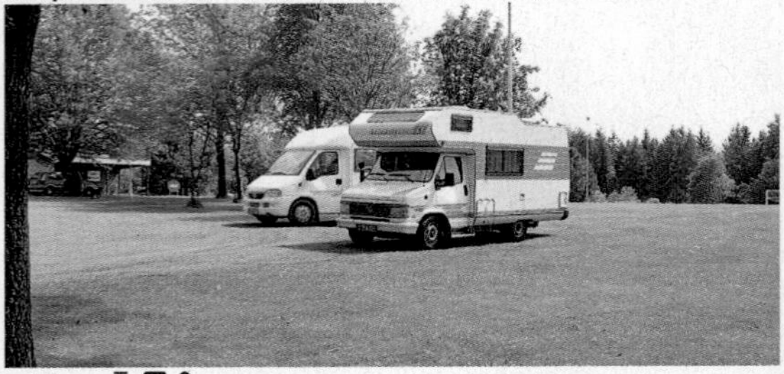

15 🚐 free 🚰 🚽 Ch free. **Location:** Rural, simple. **Surface:** gravel.
[■] 01/01-31/12
Distance: 🏙 1km 🍴 3km 🛒 1km.
Remarks: At community centre.

[🚐] [S] Gnarrenburg 4D4
Schulzentrum, Brilliterweg. **GPS**: n53,39000 e9,00028. [↑][→].

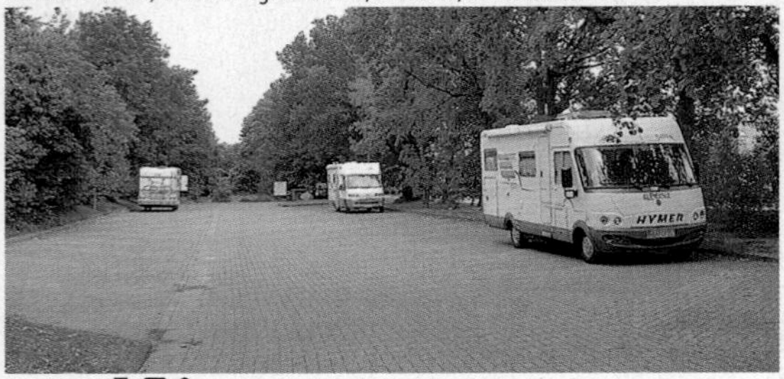

15 🚐 free 🚰 🚽 Ch free. **Surface:** metalled. [■] 01/01-31/12
Distance: 🍴 1km 🛒 500m.
Remarks: Sports centre.

[⚓] [S] Gorleben 5C5
Am Sportboothafen, Ringstraße. **GPS**: n53,04972 e11,35111. [↑].

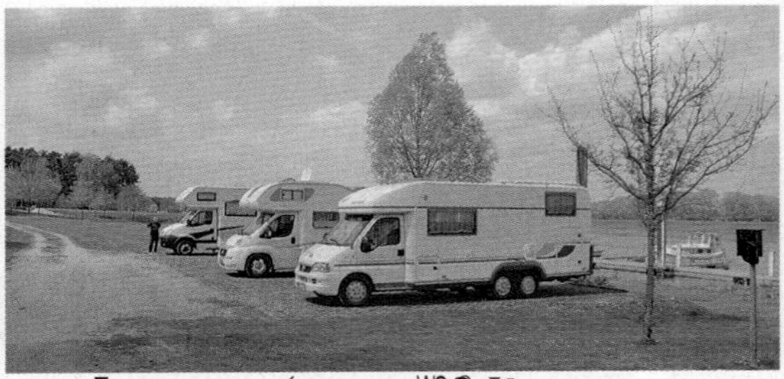

5 🚐 € 5 🚰 €1/10minutes ⚡ (4x)€1/10h WC 🚿. 🧺
Location: Rural, comfortable, quiet. **Surface:** grasstiles. [■] 01/01-31/12
Distance: 🏊 on the spot 🎣 on the spot 🍴 500m.
Remarks: Bakery 500m.

[🚐] [S] Göttingen 10B3
Reisemobilhafen Eiswiese, Windausweg 6. **GPS**: n51,52320 e9,92965. [↑][→].

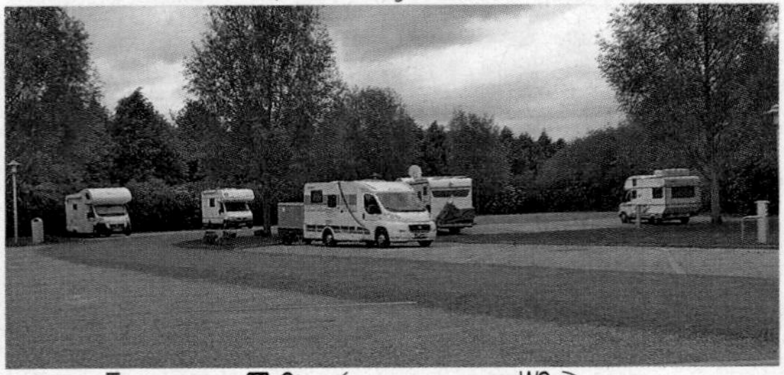

28 🚐 € 9 🚰 €1/100liter 🚽 Ch ⚡ (24x)€0,50/kWh WC 📶 €1/15h.
Location: Comfortable. **Surface:** gravel. [■] 01/01-31/12
Distance: 🏙 500m ⛽ 5,2km 🏊 100m 🎣 20-400m 🍴 100m 🛒 500m 🚌 100m.
Remarks: Max. 3 nights.

[🚐] [S] Grasberg 4D5
P&R, Wörpedorfer Straße. **GPS**: n53,18411 e8,98433. [↑].

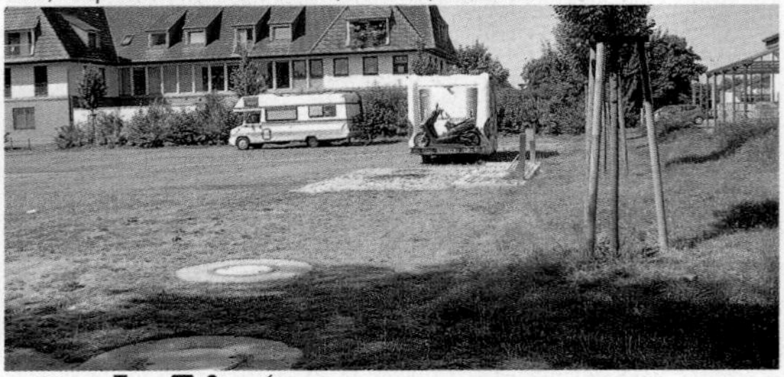

10 🚐 free 🚰 €1 🚽 Ch ⚡ (8x)€1/6h. **Location:** Simple. **Surface:** gravel.
[■] 01/01-31/12
Distance: 🏙 on the spot 🍴 on the spot 🛒 on the spot 🚌 > Bremen.

[🚐] [S] Gronau/Leine 10A2
Kuhmasch. **GPS**: n52,08265 e9,77034. [↑][→].

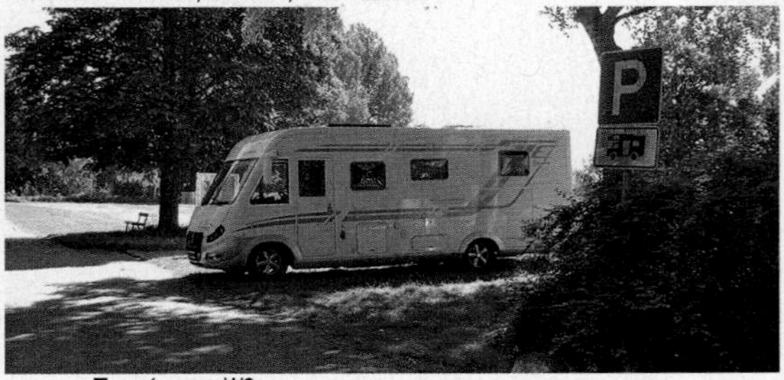

4 🚐 € 5 🚰 ⚡ €1,50 WC included. **Location:** Rural, simple. **Surface:** grassy.
[■] 01/01-31/12
Distance: 🏙 200m 🍴 300m 🛒 300m 🚶 on the spot.
Remarks: Check in at swimming pool, caution key electricity € 10.

[🍴] [S] Großefehn 4B5
Ostfriesen-Bräu Bagband, Voerstad 8, Badband. **GPS**: n53,35034 e7,61060. [↑].

DE

4 🍴€ 5,70, after consumption € 7/pp free ⛽🔲 ♨ 16Amp WC. **Surface:** metalled. 🅾 01/01-31/12
Distance: 🚶10km 🚲4km ⊗on the spot 🛒600m.

🔲 **Großenkneten** 4C6

Dorfplatz, Bahnhofstrasse, Huntlosen. **GPS**: n52,99139 e8,28611.⬆.

6 🍴free. **Location:** Rural, simple. **Surface:** grasstiles.
🅾 01/01-31/12
Distance: 🚶on the spot ⊗50m 🛒1km.

🔲 **Großenkneten** 4C6

Wilhelm-Wellman-Platz, Ahlhorner Strasse. **GPS**: n52,94274 e8,25751.⬆.

15 🍴free. **Location:** Rural, simple. **Surface:** grasstiles.
🅾 01/01-31/12
Distance: 🚶200m ⊗200m 🛒on the spot.

🔲 **Großenwieden** 🚣 9D1

Am Steinbrink. GPS: n52,17191 e9,18982.⬆➡.

5 🍴free. **Location:** Rural. **Surface:** gravel.
Distance: 🚶on the spot ⊗Gasthaus/Biergarten 300m 🚴 Weserradweg
🚶on the spot.

🔲 **Großheide** 4A4

Kirchweg, Berumerfehn. **GPS**: n53,56040 e7,34713.⬆.

6 🍴free. **Surface:** metalled. 🅾 01/01-31/12
Distance: 🚶on the spot ⊗on the spot 🛒2km.
Remarks: Max. 2 nights.

🔲 **Großheide** 4A4

P Freizeitanlage Am Kiessee, Doornkaatsweg. **GPS**: n53,58656 e7,35787.
🍴free.
Distance: 🏊on the spot.

🔲S **Hage** 4A4

Kurzentrum, Wichter Weg, Blandorf-Wichte. **GPS**: n53,60373 e7,31998.⬆.
12 🍴€ 9 ⛽€0,50/80liter ♨Ch ⚡€1/2kWh 📶included. **Surface:** metalled.
🅾 01/01-31/12

🔲S **Hagenburg** 10A1

Grillplatz, Steinhuder-Meer-Straße. **GPS**: n52,43684 e9,32388.⬆.

8 🍴free ⚡(8x)€1/6h. **Location:** Rural, isolated. **Surface:** gravel.
🅾 01/01-31/12
Distance: 🚶500m 🏊Lake Steinhude 1,1km 🛒200m.
Remarks: At sports park.

🔲S **Hambergen** ⚓ 4D5

Festplatz, Kirchweg/Am Langenend. **GPS**: n53,31050 e8,82389.⬆➡.

20 🍴€ 3,50 ⛽♨Ch⚡.
Location: Urban, simple. **Surface:** gravel/sand.
🅾 01/01-31/12
Distance: 🚶on the spot ⊗50m 🛒50m 🚲1km 🚴on the spot 🚶on the spot.
Remarks: Caution key service € 25.

🔲S **Hameln** ⚓ 10A2

Hannes Weserblick, Ruthenstrasse 14. **GPS**: n52,09623 e9,35853.⬆➡.

DE

27 🛏 € 8/24h ⛽€1/100liter 🗑 Ch 💧 (27x)€1/8h. **Location:** Urban, simple. **Surface:** metalled. 📅 01/01-31/12 **Distance:** 🚶1km ⊗600m 🚉600m 🚌800m 🚴Weser-Radweg.

🏕 S **Hankensbüttel** 5B6
Parkplatz Am Boldhamm, Wiesenweg. **GPS:** n52,73111 e10,61417. ⬆➡.

10 🛏 free. **Location:** Simple. **Surface:** gravel. 📅 01/01-31/12 **Distance:** 🚶700m 🚴on the spot. **Remarks:** Along the Werra river.

©S **Hannoversch Münden** 10A3
Grüne Insel Tanzwerder, Tanzwerder 1. **GPS:** n51,41694 e9,64751. ⬆.

20 🛏 € 6 ⛽🗑 Ch included. 🐕 **Location:** Rural. **Surface:** grassy. 📅 01/01-31/12 **Distance:** 🚶900m ⊗1km 🚉1km. **Remarks:** Service: Mo/Fr 6-12h, Sa/Su 8-10h.

Tourist information Hankensbüttel:
☺ Otter-Zentrum. Zoo. 📅 15/03-31/10 9.30-18h, 01/11-14/03 9.30-17h 📅 15/12-15/01.

20 🛏 € 6 + € 1,50/pp 💧€1/80 🗑 Ch 💧 (6x)€0,60/kWh,+ €2 WC 🚿 📶€3/h. **Location:** Simple. **Surface:** grassy. 📅 01/01-31/12 **Distance:** 🚶100m ⊗150m 🚉150m 🚴on the spot 🚶‍♂️on the spot. **Remarks:** Max. 3t.

Tourist information Hannoversch Münden:
ℹ️ Touristik Naturpark Münden e.V, Rathaus, www.hann-muenden.net/spontan. Old city centre with 430 half-timbered houses.

🏕 S **Hannoversch Münden** 10A3
Am Weserstein, Tanzwerder. **GPS:** n51,42000 e9,64888. ⬆➡.

🏕 S **Hardegsen** 10A3
Wohnmobilhafen Steinbreite, Alte Uslarer Straße 1. **GPS:** n51,65093 e9,82267. ⬆➡.

30 🛏 € 6/24h 💧€1 🗑 Ch 💧 (16x)€1/8h. 🚻 **Location:** Central. **Surface:** metalled. 📅 01/01-31/12 📅 Easter Market, service: 01/11-31/03 **Distance:** 🚶900m ⊗100m 🚴on the spot 🚶‍♂️on the spot. **Remarks:** 01/11/- 31/03 no service.

15 🛏 € 6 ⛽€1/100 🗑 Ch 💧 (16x)€1/8h WC €2/day 🚿€2/day 📶€2,50/day. 🐕 **Location:** Comfortable. **Surface:** grasstiles. 📅 01/01-31/12 **Distance:** 🚶500m 🚉on the spot 🚴on the spot.

🏕 **Hannoversch Münden** 10A3
Am Hochbad, Rattwerder. **GPS:** n51,40595 e9,64643. ⬆.

🏕 S **Haren/Ems** 🚤 ⛪ 4A6
Freizeitzentrum Schloss Danken, Rentmeisterstrasse. **GPS:** n52,79724 e7,20530. ⬆.

15 🛏 free. **Location:** Rural. **Surface:** asphalted. 📅 01/01-31/12 **Distance:** 🚶1,7km 🚴on the spot.

🏕 **Hannoversch Münden** 10A3
Am Werraweg, Werraweg. **GPS:** n51,41701 e9,66176. ➡.

17 🛏 € 10/24h ⛽🗑 Ch 💧 (18x) WC 🚿 €1. **Location:** Rural, simple. **Surface:** grassy/gravel. 📅 21/03-25/10 **Distance:** 🚶1km 🚤2,8km 🚌on the spot ⊗on the spot 🚉on the spot

DE

🐾 on the spot.

Haren/Ems 🚤 🚇 **4A6**

Schleusenstraße. **GPS:** n52,78873 e7,24705.
15 🚐 free. **Surface:** grasstiles. 🅾 01/01-31/12
Distance: 🚶500m ⊗550m.

Harsefeld **5A4**

Klosterpark, Kirchenstrasse. **GPS:** n53,45384 e9,50344. ⬆️➡️.

5 🚐 free. **Location:** Rural, simple. 🅾 01/01-31/12
Distance: 🚶100m ⊗100m 🚰100m 🚮100m 🐾on the spot 🚶on the spot.
Remarks: Parking park of monastery, max. 5 days.

S **Haselünne** **4B6**

Plesseparkplatz, Plessestrasse. **GPS:** n52,67210 e7,48865. ⬆️.

3 🚐 free 🔌€2/10minutes 🚮 Ch WC. **Location:** Urban, simple, noisy.
Surface: metalled. 🅾 01/01-31/12
Distance: 🚶400m ⊗300m 🚰300m.
Remarks: Parking behind town hall.

Haselünne **4B6**

Lingener Strasse. **GPS:** n52,66778 e7,48222. ⬆️.

4 🚐 free. **Location:** Simple, quiet. **Surface:** metalled.
🅾 01/01-31/12
Distance: 🚶400m ⊗400m 🚰400m 🚮100m 🚶on the spot.
Remarks: Parking swimming pool.

🍴 **Haselünne** **4B6**

Restaurant Esders-Ab der Hasebrücke, Lingenerstrasse 1.
GPS: n52,66992 e7,48638.

10 🚐 € 10, guests free. **Location:** Urban. **Surface:** metalled. 🅾 Mo
Distance: 🚶200m ⊗on the spot.

Helmstedt 🌿 🚇 **10C1**

Am Maschweg, Maschweg. **GPS:** n52,23535 e11,01128. ⬆️➡️.

25 🚐 free. **Location:** Rural, simple. **Surface:** metalled.
🅾 01/01-31/12
Distance: 🚶500m 🚲800m ⊗50m 🚰200m 🐾on the spot 🚶on the spot.
Remarks: Other parking in case of festivities.

Helmstedt 🌿 🚇 **10C1**

Brunnentheater, Brunnenweg 6A, Bad Helmstedt. **GPS:** n52,23676 e11,06411.
⬆️➡️.

5 🚐 free. **Location:** Rural, simple, isolated, quiet. **Surface:** asphalted.
🅾 01/01-31/12
Distance: 🚶3km ⊗500m 🚰4km 🐾on the spot 🚶on the spot.

S **Hermannsburg** **5B6**

Parkplatz Waldschwimmbad, Lotharstrasse 66. **GPS:** n52,82718 e10,10807. ⬆️.

6 🚐 free 🔌€1 🚮€1 Ch. **Surface:** metalled. 🅾 01/01-31/12
Distance: 🚶500m.
Remarks: Parking at swimming pool.

S **Hermannsburg** **5B6**

Schützenplatz, Lotharstraße 75. **GPS:** n52,82787 e10,10963. ⬆️.

40 🚐 € 2 🔌 🚮 Ch. **Surface:** grassy. 🅾 01/01-31/12
Distance: 🚶500m ⊗on the spot.
Remarks: Max. 1 night, service at Waldbad (50m).

DE

Hermannsburg 5B6

Grillplatz Bonstorf, Schulstrasse. **GPS:** n52,86492 e10,05134. ⬆.

4 🗓 free. **Surface:** grassy. ⬛ 01/01-31/12
Distance: 🚰 5km.
Remarks: Parking sports park.

Hermannsburg 5B6

Parkplatz am Feuerwehrhaus, Weesenerstrasse, Weesen.
GPS: n52,83645 e10,13692. ⬆.

3 🗓 free. **Surface:** grassy. ⬛ 01/01-31/12
Distance: 🚶 500m.
Remarks: Parking fire-station.

Hermannsburg 5B6

Parkplatz Örtzetal- Halle, Lutterweg. **GPS:** n52,83363 e10,09579. ⬆.

5 🗓 free. **Surface:** metalled. ⬛ 01/01-31/12
Distance: 🚰 100m.

Hermannsburg 5B6

Lutter Hof, Waldstrasse, Lutter. **GPS:** n52,84188 e10,09894. ⬆.

5 🗓 €5 🚰 included. **Surface:** grassy. ⬛ 01/01-31/12

Herzlake 4B6

Hasetal, Im Mersch. **GPS:** n52,68211 e7,60780. ⬆.

30 🗓 free 🚰 Ch WC free. **Surface:** grassy. ⬛ 01/03-30/11
Remarks: Parking sports centre.

Hesel 4B5

Marktplatz, Kirchstrasse. **GPS:** n53,30497 e7,59174. ⬆ ➡.

12 🗓 €4 🚰 €1 Ch 🚿 €1/8h €1,at swimming pool Hesel.
Surface: metalled. ⬛ 01/01-31/12
Distance: 🚶 on the spot 🚰 1km.

Hessisch Oldendorf 9D1

Südwall P1, Weserstraße. **GPS:** n52,16693 e9,25049. ⬆ ➡.

4 🗓 free 🚰 €0,50/5minutes €0,50 Ch €0,50. **Location:** Rural, simple.
Surface: grassy/gravel. ⬛ 01/01-31/12
Distance: 🚶 400m ⊗500m 🚰 500m 🚲 Weserradweg 1km.
Remarks: Max. 5 days.

Hitzacker 5C5

Bleichwiesen, K36, Elbufferstrasse. **GPS:** n53,15074 e11,04941. ⬆.

40 🗓 free 🚰 €1/70liter Ch 🚿(17x)€1/6h WC.
Location: Rural, comfortable. **Surface:** metalled. ⬛ 01/01-31/12
Distance: 🚶 200m ⊗450m.
Remarks: Max. 2 nights.

Hohne 5B6

Am Waldbad, Am Schwimmbad 23. **GPS:** n52,59340 e10,37398. ⬆.

4 ⬛€5 🅿 🔌 Ch 🚿 (4x) WC ⬛ included. **Location:** Rural, comfortable, quiet.
Surface: gravel. 📅 01/01-31/12
Distance: 🚶1km ⊗50m 🚊200m.
Remarks: Max. 7 days, caution key € 50, use sanitary only during opening hours swimming pool.

145 ⬛€ 7,50 🅿€1/100liter 🔌 Ch 🚿€0,60/kWh WC ⬛€0,50 🔲.
Location: Comfortable. **Surface:** grassy. 📅 01/01-31/12
Distance: 🚶550m 🚴100m ⊗100m 🚊100m 🚕200m 🚲 on the spot
🧗 on the spot.
Remarks: Bread-service.

📷🅂	Hohnstorf/Elbe 🚤	5B4

Wohnmobilstellplatz Hohnstorf, Schulstraße 1. **GPS:** n53,36234 e10,56223. ⬆️

🍴🅂	Hornburg 🌿🌳	10C2

Iberg-Gaststätte, Schützenallee 1. **GPS:** n52,03133 e10,59677. ⬆️➡️

8 ⬛€ 8 🅿 🔌 Ch 🚿 (3x)€1/10h. 🚮 **Location:** Comfortable.
Surface: metalled. 📅 01/01-31/12
Distance: 🛒on the spot ⊗500m 🚊500m.
Remarks: Along the river Elbe.

20 ⬛€ 2 🅿 🚿 (6x)€1/night. **Location:** Rural, simple, quiet.
Surface: grassy/metalled. 📅 01/01-31/12
Distance: 🚶600m 🚴5,6km ⊗on the spot 🚊1km 🧗on the spot.

🚐🅂	Holdorf	9C1

Erholungszentrum Heidesee, Zum Heidesee 53. **GPS:** n52,57696 e8,11533. ⬆️
➡️

🚐🅂	Hoya/Weser	4D6

Reisemobilstellplatz Weserblick, Stettiner Straße. **GPS:** n52,80106 e9,13987.
⬆️➡️

60 ⬛€ 4/pp 🅿 🔌 Ch 🚿 €2. **Surface:** grasstiles. 📅 01/03-15/10
Distance: 🚶1,5km 🚴3,4km ⛱Sandy beach ⊗on the spot 🚊1,5km.

10 ⬛voluntary contribution 🅿€1/150liter 🔌 Ch. **Surface:** grassy/gravel.
📅 01/01-31/12
Distance: 🚶500m ⛱100m ⊗500m.

🚐	Hollern ⛵🚤	5A4

Am Deich, Twielenfleth. **GPS:** n53,60417 e9,55917. ⬆️➡️

📷🅂	Hude 🌳🚤	4C5

Wohnmobilstellplatz Hude, Schützenstrasse. **GPS:** n53,10758 e8,45867. ⬆️➡️

15 ⬛€ 5/0-24h. 🚮 **Location:** Rural, simple. **Surface:** metalled.
📅 01/01-31/12
Distance: 🚶200m 🍴Imbiss 300m.
Remarks: Along the river Elbe.

10 ⬛€ 5 🅿€1/time 🔌 Ch 🚿 (12x)€0,50/kWh. 🚮 **Location:** Urban, quiet.
Surface: gravel. 📅 01/01-31/12
Distance: 🚶on the spot ⊗on the spot 🚊400m 🚕on the spot 🚲on the spot
🧗1km.

📷🅂	Holzminden ⛵🚤	10A2

Mobilcamping Holzminden, Stahler Ufer 16. **GPS:** n51,82681 e9,43909. ⬆️➡️

📷🅂	Hüde (49448)	9C1

Freizeitarena Dümmer See, Rohrdommelweg 33. **GPS:** n52,50176 e8,35425. ⬆️

50 ⊠ € 10 ⚏ ⚑ Ch ⚓ €2,50 WC ⚑. **Location:** Rural, quiet. **Surface:** grassy.
◯ 15/04-15/10
Distance: ⚓150m ⊗on the spot.

⌖S | Jade ⚜ ⦅⦆ ⬕ | 4C5
Quittenweg, Süderschweiburg. **GPS:** n53,39139 e8,26639.⬆.

8 ⊠free ⚏€1 ⚑ Ch ⚓ (8x)€1/8h. **Location:** Rural, comfortable, isolated.
Surface: gravel/metalled. ◯ 01/01-31/12
Distance: ⚓800m ⚓500m ⊗1km ⚓800m ⚓ on the spot ⚓ on the spot.

⚑S | Jade ⚜ ⦅⦆ ⬕ | 4C5
Drei Eichen, Kreuzmoorstrasse 28. **GPS:** n53,31531 e8,23084.⬆.

10 ⊠€10 ⚏ ⚑ Ch ⚓ (3x) WC included ⚑against payment. ⚓ **Location:**
Rural, simple, quiet. **Surface:** grassy/gravel. ◯ 01/01-31/12
Distance: ⚓4km.
Remarks: At manege.

⚑S | Jade ⚜ ⦅⦆ ⬕ | 4C5
Schützenhof, Am Schützenplatz, Vareler Strasse. **GPS:** n53,34111 e8,18667.⬆.

10 ⊠guests free ⚏on demand ⚓ (3x)€2/night. ⚓ **Location:** Simple.
Surface: metalled. ◯ 01/01-31/12
Distance: ⚓on the spot ⊗on the spot ⚓on the spot.
Remarks: Parking of Shooting Club.

⌖ | Jade ⚜ ⦅⦆ ⬕ | 4C5
Jaderberg, Tiergartenstrasse 69, Jaderberg. **GPS:** n53,32679 e8,18521.⬆ .

20 ⊠free. **Location:** Simple. **Surface:** gravel. ◯ 01/01-31/12
Distance: ⚓on the spot ⊗on the spot.
Remarks: Parking Jarderpark, zoo and adventure park.

⚑S | Jever ⚜ ⦅⦆ ⬕ | 4B4
Jahnstrasse. **GPS:** n53,57733 e7,89074.⬆➡.

20 ⊠€ 8 ⚏€2 ⚑ Ch ⚓ (20x)€2. **Surface:** metalled. ◯ 01/01-31/12
Distance: ⚓Old city centre 750m ⚓100m.
Remarks: Sports centre, max. 3 days, coins at petrol station Henn.

Tourist information Jever:
Ⓜ⚔ Schloßmuseum. Castle, English gardens and museum. ◯ Tue-Su 10-18h,
01/07-31/08 Mo-Su 10-18h.
Ⓜ Frisiesches Brauhaus. Brewery with museum. Guided tour 2 hours, 2 drinks
included. ◯ Mo-Fri 9.30-16.30h, Sa 9.30-12.30h.

⊠S | Jork ⚓ | 5A4
Festplatz, Schützenhofstrasse/Festplatzweg. **GPS:** n53,53100 e9,68336.⬆➡.

80 ⊠free ⚏€1/100liter ⚑ Ch WC ⚑€0,50. **Location:** Rural, simple.
Surface: metalled. ◯ 01/01-31/12
Distance: ⚓200m ⊗200m ⚓200m.
Remarks: Parking event ground, max. 24h.

⚑ | Jork ⚓ | 5A4
Stellplatz Lühe-Anleger, Fährstraße, Grünendeich. **GPS:** n53,57271 e9,63129.
⬆.
10 ⊠€ 10/24h. **Surface:** gravel. ◯ 01/01-31/12

⚑S | Jork ⚓ | 5A4
Stubbe's Gasthaus, Lühe 46. **GPS:** n53,56861 e9,63333.⬆.

DE

7 🛏 €8 ⚡ €2 📶 🗑. **Location:** Rural, comfortable. **Surface:** grasstiles.
🅿 01/01-31/12
Distance: ⊗on the spot.
Remarks: Bread-service, picnic area Am Gartenteich.

🚻💧S Jork 🚣 5A4
Am Yachthafen, Neuenschleuse. **GPS:** n53,55375 e9,66858. ⬆➡.

18 🛏 free 💧€1/90liter ⚡ Ch ⚡ (18x)€0,50/kWh WC 🚽€2.
Location: Urban, simple. **Surface:** unpaved. 🅿 01/01-31/12
Distance: 🛒Jork 3km ⊗on the spot 🚲 on the spot 🏊 on the spot.
Remarks: Along the river Elbe.

🚻💧S Kirchlinteln 🍺 4D6
Auf dem Kleberhof, Scharnhorster Weg 1. **GPS:** n52,95562 e9,30651.

7 🛏 €10 💧 ⚡ (4x) WC 🚽included 🚿€3. 🛝
Location: Rural, comfortable, quiet. **Surface:** grassy. 🅿 01/01-31/12
Distance: 🛒3,5km 🚲6km ⊗3,5km 🛒3,5km.
Remarks: Bread-service.

🚻💧S Königslutter am Elm 🌿🍺 10C1
P1 Niedernhof, Amtsgarten. **GPS:** n52,25009 e10,81996. ⬆➡.

5 🛏 free 💧€1/5minutes ⚡€1/time Ch€1/time ⚡ (4x)€1/8h.
Location: Urban, comfortable, central, noisy. **Surface:** grasstiles.
🅿 01/01-31/12
Distance: 🛒on the spot ⊗on the spot 🛒on the spot.

🚻💧S Krummendeich 4D3
Stellplatz Krummendeich, Schulweg 107. **GPS:** n53,83145 e9,20231. ⬆➡.

5 🛏 free WC€0,50 🚽€0,50. **Location:** Rural, simple. **Surface:** gravel.

🅿 01/01-31/12
Distance: 🏊100m 🛒300m.

🚻💧S Krummhörn 🌿⛵📷 4A4
Reisemobilhafen Greetsiel, Mühlenstrasse 3, Greetsiel.
GPS: n53,49711 e7,10181. ⬆.

55 🛏 €11 incl. 2 pers., tourist tax incl 💧€2/90liter ⚡ Ch ⚡ (40x)€1/8h. 🚗
Surface: gravel. 🅿 01/01-31/12
Distance: 🛒250m.

🚿 Lamspringe 10B2
Am Bahnhof. GPS: n51,95404 e10,00656. ⬆➡.

3 🛏 free. **Location:** Rural, isolated. **Surface:** gravel.
🅿 01/01-31/12
Distance: 🛒750m ⊗1km 🛒400m 🚌250m 🚲 Radweg zur Kunst
🏊 on the spot.
Remarks: Max. 3 days.

🚻💧S Lauenau 10A1
Brauhaus Felsenkeller, Feggendorfer Straße 10. **GPS:** n52,27914 e9,36906.

10 🛏 free 💧 ⚡ 📶 free. **Location:** Rural, simple. **Surface:** gravel.
🅿 01/01-31/12
Distance: 🛒500m 🚲2,4km 🚌on the spot.
Remarks: Check in at restaurant.

🚻💧S Lauenförde 10A3
Yachthafen Dreiländereck, Würgasser Straße. **GPS:** n51,65045 e9,37983. ⬆➡.

50 🛏 €7 💧🚰 Ch included ⚡ (35x)€2,20/day WC 🚽€0,50 🚿€2,50
📶€4,95. **Location:** Rural, comfortable. **Surface:** gravel. 🅿 01/04-01/11

DE

Distance: 🚲3km ⛵on the spot 🚂3km 🚴on the spot 🚶on the spot.
Remarks: Bread-service.

| 🛁S | Lautenthal 🏔🏕 | 10B2 |

Kaspar Bitter Strasse 7b. **GPS:** n51,87020 e10,28729.⬆️.

25 🛌€4 + € 1/pp tourist tax 🚰€1/60liter 🔲€2/time Ch€2/time 🚿(8x)€1/6h. **Location:** Rural, comfortable, quiet. **Surface:** gravel.
⭕ 01/01-31/12
Distance: 🚲300m ⊗300m 🚂500m 🚏50m.

| 🛁S | Leer | 4B5 |

P9, Grosse Bleiche. **GPS:** n53,22577 e7,44686.⬆️.

6 🛌free 🚰€1/100liter 🔲€1 Ch 🚿(6x)€1/24h WC€0,50 🔲€1.
Location: Urban, simple. **Surface:** metalled. ⭕ 01/01-31/12
Distance: 🚲200m ⊗on the spot 🚂2km.
Remarks: Caution key sanitary € 30, sanitary at offices Bruchbrücke.

| 🛁S | Leer | 4B5 |

Hallen- und Freibad, Burfehnerweg 32. **GPS:** n53,23927 e7,44998.⬆️.

10 🛌free. **Location:** Urban, simple. **Surface:** metalled.
⭕ 01/01-31/12
Distance: 🚲on the spot ⊗on the spot 🚂1km.

| 🍴S | Leer | 4B5 |

Windmühlenhof Eiklenborg, Logabirumer Straße, Logabirum.
GPS: n53,24745 e7,51582.⬆️.
5 🛌€11 🚰🔲Ch🚿WC🔲€2. **Surface:** grassy/metalled. ⭕ 01/01-31/12
Remarks: Near old Dutch windmill.

| 🛁S | Leer | 4B5 |

Am Hafen, Nessestrasse. **GPS:** n53,22527 e7,45472.⬆️➡️.

10 🛌free WC€0,50 🔲€1. **Location:** Urban, simple. **Surface:** asphalted/gravel.
⭕ 01/01-31/12
Distance: 🚲500m ⊗300m 🚂2km.
Remarks: Caution key sanitary € 30, sanitary at offices Bruchbrücke.

| 🛁 | Leese | 9D1 |

Loccumer straße. **GPS:** n52,50272 e9,11733.⬆️.

4 🛌free. **Surface:** metalled. ⭕ 01/01-31/12
Distance: 🚲200m ⊗on the spot 🚂200m.

| 🍴S | Leese | 9D1 |

Rasthaus Leeser Tanger, Bahlweg. **GPS:** n52,49372 e9,12055.⬆️.

8 🛌€ 15, discount for clients 🚰🚿🔲included. **Surface:** metalled.
⭕ 01/01-31/12
Distance: 🚲800m ⊗on the spot.

| 🛁 | Lembruch 🏖🌊 | 9C1 |

Stellplatz Dümmer-See Lembruch, Seestraße. **GPS:** n52,52439 e8,36703.⬆️.

20 🛌free. **Location:** Rural. **Surface:** grassy. ⭕ 01/01-31/12
Distance: ⛵300m ⊗100m.

| ©S | Lembruch 🏖🌊 | 9C1 |

Campingplatz Seeblick, Birkenallee. **GPS:** n52,52583 e8,36056.⬆️.

DE

20 △ € 9 ⟷ ⚑ Ch on camp site. **Location:** Rural. **Surface:** grassy.
◐ 01/01-31/12
Distance: ⤳50m ⊗50m.
Remarks: Max. 1 night.

4 △ free. **Location:** Urban, simple, quiet. **Surface:** grassy.
◐ 01/01-31/12
Distance: ⤳600m ⫞1km ⤳Stoteler See ⊗100m ⟶ on the spot.

	Lemwerder	4C5

⊞S	Loxstedt	4C4

Reisemobilhafen Peter-Baxmann-Platz, Schulstrasse 44.
GPS: n53,15784 e8,61783. ⬆➡.

Am Bootshafen, Fährstrasse. **GPS:** n53,44438 e8,49942. ⬆.

50 △ € 3 ⟷ ⚑ Ch included ⚡ (40x) € 1/8h. ⬚
Location: Urban, comfortable, isolated, quiet. **Surface:** gravel.
Distance: ⤳on the spot ⊗200m ⚐500m ⤳500m ⚵300m.
Remarks: Nearby swimming pool.

5 △ free ⚡ (6x) € 0,50/kWh. **Location:** Rural, simple. **Surface:** gravel/sand.
◐ 01/04-15/10
Distance: ⤳300m ⤳on the spot ⊗on the spot ⚵on the spot.
Remarks: Along the Weser river.

	Lemwerder	4C5

	Lüchow	5C5

Vulkanparkplatz, Uferweg. **GPS:** n53,17000 e8,60028. ⬆➡.

Parkstraße. **GPS:** n52,96983 e11,14594. ⬆.

5 △ free.
Location: Urban, simple, quiet. **Surface:** asphalted/metalled.
◐ 01/01-31/12
Distance: ⤳2km ⤳on the spot ⊗2km ⚐2km ⚌on the spot ⚵on the spot.

2 △ free. **Location:** Urban, simple. **Surface:** asphalted/metalled.
◐ 01/01-31/12
Distance: ⤳900m ⊗900m ⚐1,7km.
Remarks: Max. 3 nights.

⊞S	Lingen/Ems	9A1

⍾⊞S	Lüdersfeld	9D1

Linus Bad, Teichstrasse. **GPS:** n52,51863 e7,30606. ⬆⬆➡.

Heinrichs'Reisemobil Stellplatz, Am Hülsebrink 10+11.
GPS: n52,35972 e9,25512. ⬆.

16 △ free ⟷ € 1 ⚑ Ch ⚡ (16x) € 0,50/kWh. **Location:** Rural. **Surface:** gravel.
◐ 01/01-31/12
Distance: ⤳1km ⚐on the spot ⚵on the spot.
Remarks: Max. 3 days.

30+15 △ € 6 ⟷ ⚑ Ch ⚡ (8x) included. **Location:** Rural, simple.
Surface: gravel. ◐ 01/01-31/12
Distance: ⤳500m ⊗on the spot.
Remarks: Check in at hotel, bread-service.

	Loxstedt	4C4

⊞S	Lüneburg	5B5

Stotel, Alte Schulstraße 75. **GPS:** n53,44067 e8,59356. ➡.

Am Sülzwiesen, Pieperweg. **GPS:** n53,24556 e10,39694. ⬆.

DE

50 ⚏ € 8/24h ⛽€1/10minutes 🛢Ch ⚡(40x)€1/8h,30/09-01/05 €2/8h. 🏠 **Location:** Rural, comfortable, isolated, quiet. **Surface:** metalled.
☐ 01/01-31/12
Distance: 🚶1km ⚓300m.
Remarks: Max. 1 night.

⚏S | Mardorf | 9D1
Wohnmobilstellplatz Steinhuder Meer, Rote-Kreuz-Strasse 16. **GPS:** n52,48704 e9,30065. ⬆️➡️.

60 ⚏ € 6 ⛽€1/100liter 🛢Ch ⚡(60x)€3. **Surface:** grassy.
☐ 01/01-31/12
Distance: 🚶1km 🚣300m ⊗1km.
Remarks: Bread-service.

⚏S | Melle | 9C1
Am Wellenbad 43. **GPS:** n52,20497 e8,32368.⬆️.

10 ⚏free. **Location:** Simple, quiet. **Surface:** metalled.
☐ 01/01-31/12
Distance: 🚶on the spot ⚓1,2km ⊗nearby 🛒300m.
Remarks: Parking swimming pool.

⚏S | Meppen | 4A6
Reisemobilplatz am Hallenbad, An der Bleiche. **GPS:** n52,69107 e7,28399.⬆️.

10 ⚏ € 6 2 pers, swimming pool incl ⛽€2/100liter 🛢Ch ⚡(4x)€1/12h.
Surface: metalled. ☐ 01/01-31/12
Distance: 🚶200m ⊗on the spot 🛒300m.
Remarks: Parking swimming pool, max. 2 nights.
Tourist information Meppen:

⛺ ☐ Tue-Sa morning.

⚏ | Moormerland | 4B5
Am Rathaus, Theodor Heussstrasse 12, Warsingsfehn. **GPS:** n53,31062 e7,48618. ⬆️➡️.

4 ⚏free. **Surface:** metalled. ☐ 01/01-31/12
Distance: 🚶50m ⊗250m 🛒50m 🚌50m.
Remarks: Parking townhall, max. 3 nights.

🍴⚏S | Moormerland | 4B5
Bei Cassi, Deichlandstraße 10, Rorinchem. **GPS:** n53,32010 e7,35473. ⬆️➡️.

15 ⚏ € 5, free with a meal ⛽€1 🛢Ch ⚡2 🍽€1. **Surface:** gravel.
☐ 01/04-31/10 🍽 Restaurant: Mo
Distance: ⊗on the spot.

⚏ | Moringen | 10A3
Domänenhof, Amtsfreiheit. **GPS:** n51,69833 e9,86861. ⬆️➡️.

3 ⚏free. **Location:** Rural, simple. **Surface:** gravel.
☐ 01/01-31/12
Distance: 🚶on the spot ⚓5,5km ⊗300m.
Remarks: At city park.

⚏S | Neuharlingersiel | 4B4
Wohnmobilstellplatz am Ostanleger, Am Hafen Ost. **GPS:** n53,70173 e7,70741. ⬆️.

23 ⚏ € 12 ⛽€1 🛢Ch ⚡included WC. 🏠 **Location:** Rural, comfortable, quiet. **Surface:** metalled. ☐ 01/01-31/12
Distance: 🚶500m 🚣800m 🛒1km.
Remarks: Max. 3 nights.

Neuharlingersiel 🚤🌊 4B4

Neuharlingersiel, Alt Addenhausen 4. **GPS:** n53,69580 e7,69021.⬆️

8 🚐 € 12, tourist tax incl 🚰€1 🔌Ch 🔧included WC on camp site 🚮on camp site.🚿 **Location:** Rural, simple. **Surface:** metalled.
🅿️ 01/01-31/12
Distance: 🚶800m 🏖️sandy beach 1km.
Remarks: Max. 1 night.

Nienburg 4D6

Reisemobilstellplatz Nienburg/Weser, Oyler Straße. **GPS:** n52,64094 e9,20137.⬆️➡️

25 🚐€ 5 🚰€1/120liter 🔌Ch 🔧(12x)€1/8h.
Surface: gravel.
🅿️ 01/01-31/12
Distance: 🚶10 min walking 🏊on the spot 🚲on the spot 🚲300m 🚏500m.
Remarks: Along the river Weser.

Nienburg 4D6

Am Theaterparkplatz, Mühlenstraße. **GPS:** n52,63651 e9,20563.
🚐. **Surface:** metalled. 🅿️ 01/01-31/12
Distance: 🚶on the spot.

Norddeich 🌊🚤🏖️ 4A4

Wohnmobilhafen Norddeich, Itzendorferstrasse. **GPS:** n53,61073 e7,15649.⬆️➡️

44 🚐€ 10/24h, 2 pers. + tourist tax, incl. 50% discount Erlebnisbad Ocean Wave 🚰🔌Ch 🔧(48x)€1/2kWh WC 🚮€1. **Surface:** metalled.
🅿️ 01/01-31/12
Distance: 🚶100m 🏖️100m 🚲100m 🚏500m 🚏100m.

Norddeich 🌊🚤🏖️ 4A4

Womo Park Norddeich, Deichstraße 24. **GPS:** n53,60166 e7,13527.⬆️

44 🚐€ 11, tourist tax excl., dog € 2 🚰€1/100liter 🔌Ch 🔧€1/kWh WC 🚮€1
🔲€3/1,50 💧. **Surface:** gravel. 🅿️ 01/01-31/12
Distance: 🚶2km 🏖️beach 1,5km, beach (dog allowed) 1km 🚲on the spot 🚏500m 🚏100m.
Remarks: Bread-service.

Nordenham 🌿 4C4

Freizeitbad Störtebeker, Atenser Allee. **GPS:** n53,49478 e8,47368.⬆️➡️

15 🚐€ 6 🚰€1/liter 🔌Chfree 🔧(16x)€1/8h 🚲€2,at sauna. 🚌
Location: Urban, comfortable, noisy. **Surface:** grasstiles.
🅿️ 01/01-31/12
Distance: 🚶1km 🚲2km 🚲on the spot 🚏400m 🚏on the spot 🚴on the spot.
Remarks: Max. 3 days, bread-service.

Nordenham 🌿 4C4

Volkers, Deichstrasse 158. **GPS:** n53,54003 e8,50905.⬆️

6 🚐€ 5 🚰€1/100 🔌Ch 🔧(6x)€2/day WC 💧on demand. 🚿
Location: Rural, comfortable, quiet. **Surface:** gravel. 🅿️ 01/01-31/12
Distance: 🚶2km 🏖️100m 🚏500m 🚴on the spot.

Nordholz 4C4

Wuster Strasse 12, Spieka. **GPS:** n53,75772 e8,59409.⬆️

5 🚐free 🚰€1/100liter 🔌€1 Ch 🔧(5x)€1/2kWh. **Location:** Rural, simple.
Surface: metalled.
Distance: 🚶on the spot 🚲100m.

Nordhorn 🔵 9A1

Vechtesee, Heseperweg. **GPS:** n52,43683 e7,08190.⬆️

35 ⏚€5 🚰€1/100liter 🗑Ch. ♨€1/5h. 🛉 **Location:** Rural.
Surface: grassy. ☀ 01/01-31/12
Distance: 🚶400m ⊗300m 🛒300m 🚲on the spot 🧗on the spot.

8 ⏚€5 🚰€1/100liter 🗑Ch. 🛉 **Location:** Urban, simple.
Surface: asphalted. ☀ 01/01-31/12
Distance: 🚶on the spot ⊗300m 🛒300m.

🗺S | Northeim | 10B3
Grosser Freizeitsee, Am Nordhafen. **GPS:** n51,72920 e9,96286.⬆.

🗺S | Osnabrück 🌿⛺🍴 | 9C1
Wohnmobilplatz Netebad, Im Haseesch 6. **GPS:** n52,30470 e8,05413.⬆.

10 ⏚€6 🚰€0,50/50liter 🗑Ch. ♨(8x)€1/kWh. 🛉 **Location:** Rural, simple,
noisy. **Surface:** gravel. ☀ 01/01-31/12
Distance: 🚶on the spot 🚴3km ⊗2km.

5 ⏚€5 🚰€1/100liter 🗑Ch. ♨€1/6h. 🛉 **Location:** Urban, simple, quiet.
Surface: grassy/metalled. ☀ 01/01-31/12
Distance: 🚶on the spot.
Remarks: Max. 48h.

🗺 | Oberndorf/Oste | 4D4
Wohnmobilplatz Bentwisch, Hoffmann-von-Fallersleben-Straße 10.
GPS: n53,75398 e9,15054.⬆➡.

🗺 | Osnabrück 🌿⛺🍴 | 9C1
Natruper Straße / Nobbenburger Straße. **GPS:** n52,28116 e8,03651.
⏚€5. **Surface:** metalled. ☀ 01/01-31/12
Distance: 🚶1,5km.

🗺 | Osten | 4D4
Festhalle, Altendorf 13. **GPS:** n53,69602 e9,18813.⬆➡.

8 ⏚€5 🚰€2/100liter 🗑Ch. ♨(6x)€2/8h WC€0,50 🚿€0,50. 🛁
Location: Rural, comfortable. **Surface:** grassy/gravel. ☀ 01/01-31/12
Distance: 🚶2km 🏊100m 🛒100m 🚲on the spot.

🗺 | Oldenburg 🛶⛺🍴 | 4C5
Am Küstenkanal, Westfalendamm. **GPS:** n53,12927 e8,21465.⬆.

5 ⏚€5 🗑Ch. ♨(2x)included. 🛁 **Location:** Rural, simple.
Surface: metalled. ☀ 01/01-31/12
Distance: 🚶on the spot ⊗on the spot 🛒500m.
Remarks: Pay at Hotel Fährkrug.

🗺S | Osterholz-Scharmbeck | 4D5
August Schlüter Turnhalle, Lange Strasse. **GPS:** n53,22562 e8,79000.⬆➡.

3 ⏚free. **Location:** Rural, simple. **Surface:** gravel.
☀ 01/01-31/12
Distance: 🚶on the spot 🚴1km 🏊on the spot ⊗100m 🛒400m.
Remarks: Alternative: in front of campsite Am Flötenteich, 53,166944 8,235,
2 pitches free.

🗺S | Osnabrück 🌿⛺🍴 | 9C1
Schlosswallhalle, Heinrichstrasse. **GPS:** n52,27074 e8,03953.⬆.

4 ⏚free 🚰€1 🗑. **Location:** Urban, simple, central. **Surface:** metalled.
☀ 01/01-31/12

🗺S | Osterode 🍴 | 10B3
Aloha-Aqualand, Schwimmbadstraße. **GPS:** n51,72263 e10,24998.⬆➡.

DE

7 🛏 € 8-10 ⛽ €1/75liter 💧€1/time Ch ⚡ (7x)€1,50/8h. 🚿
Location: Rural, noisy. **Surface:** metalled. 📅 01/01-31/12
Distance: 🛒1km ⊗200m ⚓500m.
Remarks: Max. 2 nights.

Osterode 10B3
Campingplatz Eulenburg, Scheerenberger Straße 100.
GPS: n51,72766 e10,28347. ⬆️➡️

13 🛏 € 8, 2 pers.incl ⛽ €1/100liter 💧 Ch ⚡ (12x)€1/kWh
WC 🚽€0,70/4minutes 🚿€4/day. **Location:** Rural, comfortable, quiet.
Surface: gravel. 📅 01/01-31/12
Distance: 🛒2km ⊗on the spot ⚓2,5km 🏊on the spot.
Remarks: Bread-service, swimming pool incl.

Ostrhauderfehn 4B5
Reisemobilhafen Ostrhauderfehn, Hauptstrasse 115.
GPS: n53,13872 e7,62318. ⬆️

20 🛏 € 5 ⛽ 💧 Ch ⚡ (12x)€1/2kWh WC 🚽€0,50 ⊡ 🚼
Surface: asphalted.
📅 01/01-31/12 ⊙ during fair in June
Distance: 🛒100m ⊗100m ⚓100m.
Remarks: Caution key € 10, sanitary at bar.

Otterndorf 4D3
Parking Mitte, Jahnstrasse. **GPS:** n53,80861 e8,89444. ⬆️➡️

8 🛏free. **Location:** Rural, simple. **Surface:** metalled. 📅 01/01-31/12
Distance: 🛒on the spot ⊗200m.

Otterndorf 4D3
Seglertreff, Schleuse 5. **GPS:** n53,82250 e8,89472. ⬆️

12 🛏free, 01/04-31/10 € 7,00 ⛽ 💧 Ch ⚡ €2,50/24h WC 🚽 🚼 📹
Location: Rural, comfortable. **Surface:** metalled. 📅 01/01-31/12
Distance: 🛒2km ⚓50m 🔌on the spot ⊗on the spot ⚓2km 🚲on the spot
🏊on the spot.

Ottersberg 4D5
Am Sportzentrum, Fährwisch. **GPS:** n53,10721 e9,13558. ⬆️

8 🛏free ⛽€1 Ch ⚡ €1/8h. **Location:** Simple. **Surface:** gravel/sand.
📅 01/01-31/12
Distance: 🛒500m ⊗200m.

Ovelgönne 4C5
Burgdorf Ovelgönne, Am Sportplatz. **GPS:** n53,34333 e8,42750. ⬆️➡️

5 🛏free ⛽€1/100liter 💧 Ch ⚡ free.
Location: Urban, simple, isolated, quiet. **Surface:** grassy. 📅 01/01-31/12
Distance: 🛒700m ⊗700m ⚓700m 🚲on the spot.

Oyten 4D5
KNAUS Reisemobilpark, Oyter See 1. **GPS:** n53,04645 e9,00396.

20 🛏 € 12-15 ⛽€2,20 💧 Ch ⚡ €0,70/kWh WC 🚽included ⊡ 🚿€1 🚼
📹**Location:** Rural, comfortable. **Surface:** metalled. 📅 01/04-01/11
Distance: 🛒2,5km 🚲3km ⚓Oyter See 150m.
Remarks: Caution key € 5.

Papenburg 4B5
Roten Kreuz, Rathausstraße. **GPS:** n53,07646 e7,39266.
30 🛏free. **Surface:** gravel. 📅 01/01-31/12

DE

Distance: 🚶on the spot ⊗300m.

© S **Papenburg** 4B5

Poggenpoel, Zum Poggenpoel. GPS: n53,06526 e7,42630. ⬆️➡️.

20 ⌇€ 8 🚰€3/100liter 🔌€3 Ch 🚿 (8x)€2/24h WC ⌇€2 ♻️ 🚮

Location: Rural, simple. **Surface:** gravel. 🔲 01/01-31/12

Distance: 🚶3,5km 🏊Badesee.

Remarks: At lake, max. 3 nights.

© S **Polle** 10A2

Weserpromenade, Mühlenweg 2. GPS: n51,89871 e9,40830. ⬆️.

15 ⌇€ 8 + € 1/pp tourist tax, 01/10-31/05 free 🚰 🔌Ch included 🔌.

Location: Rural, simple. **Surface:** grassy. 🔲 01/01-31/12

Distance: 🚶100m 🏊on the spot 🛒on the spot ⊗100m 🍴100m 🚴‍♂️Weser-Radweg.

Remarks: Along the Weser river, check in at campsite.

© S **Rastede** 4C5

Mühlenstraße. GPS: n53,24806 e8,20944. ⬆️.

4 ⌇free. **Location:** Urban, simple. **Surface:** metalled. 🔲 01/01-31/12

Distance: 🚶1km 🚲2,7km ⊗1km 🍴2km.

© S **Rastede** 4C5

Bauernmuseum, Raiffeisenstraße 60. GPS: n53,24627 e8,18579. ⬆️.

5 ⌇€ 5 🚰€1 🚿 (5x)€1/24h. 🚮 **Location:** Rural, simple, quiet. **Surface:** grassy. 🔲 01/01-31/12

Distance: 🚲1km ⊗400m 🍴100m.

🚾 S **Rehburg-Loccum** 9D1

Wohnmobilstellplatz Rehburg, Auf der Bleiche. GPS: n52,47370 e9,23227. ⬆️➡️.

8 ⌇€ 5 🚿€1/12h. **Surface:** gravel. 🔲 01/01-31/12

Distance: 🚶400m.

Tourist information Rehburg-Loccum:

😀 Dinosaurierpark Münchehagen. Attractions park around the dinosaur.

😀 28/02-30/11 10h, summers 9h.

🚾 S **Rhauderfehn** 4B5

Paddel- und Pedalstation, Am Siel 8. GPS: n53,13878 e7,58689. ⬆️➡️.

16 ⌇€ 5 🚰€1/100liter 🔌Ch 🚿 (16x)€1/8h WC ⌇€2. 🚮

Location: Rural, luxurious, quiet. **Surface:** grassy. 🔲 01/01-31/12

Distance: 🚶500m 🏊on the spot 🛒on the spot ⊗50m.

Remarks: Caution key sanitary € 10, canoe and bicycle rental.

🚾 S **Rhede/Ems** 4A5

Emspark, Am Sportplatz 6. GPS: n53,05853 e7,27621. ⬆️.

5 ⌇free. **Location:** Simple. **Surface:** metalled. 🔲 01/01-31/12

Distance: 🚶500m ⊗500m 🍴500m.

Remarks: Parking in front of sports park.

🚾 S **Rinteln** 9D1

Reisemobilplatz am Weseranger, Dankerser strasse. GPS: n52,19226 e9,07842. ⬆️➡️.

40 ⌇free 🚰€2/100liter 🔌€2 Ch€2 🚿 (36x)€0,50/kWh.

Location: Rural, simple. **Surface:** grassy/gravel. 🔲 01/01-31/12

Distance: 🚶600m 🏊on the spot 🛒on the spot ⊗100m 🍴400m 🚌400m

🚴 Weserradweg 🚶 on the spot.
Remarks: Max. 3 days.

🏕 Ⓢ **Rodewald** 5A6

Am Freibad, Im Zentrum. **GPS:** n52,66369 e9,48020. ⬆️

10 🅿free ⚡ (10x)€0,50/kWh. **Surface:** grasstiles. ☐ 01/01-31/12
Distance: 🚉200m 🚍on the spot.

🏕 Ⓢ **Rotenburg (Wümme)** ⛴ 5A5

Am Weichelsee, Bremer Straße. **GPS:** n53,11960 e9,38230. ⬆️➡️

20 🅿€5 ⛽€2 🗑 Ch ⚡ (20x)€2. 🛒 🗑 **Location:** Rural, simple.
Surface: metalled. ☐ 01/01-31/12
Distance: 🚉2km 🏊on the spot ⊗Strandhaus 🚍2km 🚴on the spot.
Remarks: Check in at StrandHouse.

🏕 Ⓢ **Salzgitter** 🌾 10B1

Reisemobilstellplatz am Salzgittersee, Zum Salzgittersee.
GPS: n52,15222 e10,31306. ⬆️➡️

18 🅿free ⛽€2/100liter 🗑 Ch ⚡ (14x)€1/6h. **Location:** Rural, comfortable.
Surface: grassy/metalled. ☐ 01/01-31/12
Distance: 🚉1km 🏊on the spot ⊗500m 🚊1km 🚴on the spot
🚶 on the spot.
Remarks: Max. 4 days, boat rental.

🏕 **Salzgitter** 🌾 10B1

Thermalsolebad, Parkallee 3, Salzgitter-Bad. **GPS:** n52,03724 e10,38351. ⬆️➡️

6 🅿free. **Location:** Rural, simple, quiet. **Surface:** metalled.
☐ 01/01-31/12
Distance: 🚉1,5km ⊗on the spot 🚊1,5km 🚍on the spot 🚴on the spot

🚶 on the spot.
Remarks: Max. 4 days, no camping activities.

🏕 Ⓢ **Salzhausen** 5B5

Am Waldbad, Schwienbrink. **GPS:** n53,22199 e10,17841. ⬆️

6 🅿free ⛽€1/10minutes 🗑Chfree ⚡ (4x)€1/8h. **Location:** Rural, simple.
Surface: gravel. ☐ 01/01-31/12
Distance: 🚉1km 🚊500m.

🏕 Ⓢ **Salzhemmendorf** 🏺 10A2

Ith-Sole-Therme, In der Saale-Aue. **GPS:** n52,07093 e9,58564. ⬆️

20 🅿€7,50 ⛽€0,20/20liter 🗑€1 Ch ⚡ (20x)€1/kWh.
Location: Rural, quiet. **Surface:** grassy/gravel. ☐ 01/01-31/12
Distance: 🚉400m 🚍on the spot.
Remarks: Check in at pay-desk of the Therme.

🏕 **Salzhemmendorf** 🏺 10A2

Rasti-land, Quanthofer strasse 9. **GPS:** n52,09706 e9,66451. ⬆️ .

5 🅿free. **Location:** Isolated. **Surface:** gravel/sand.
Distance: 🚉1km.
Remarks: Bus parking amusement park.

Tourist information Salzhemmendorf:
☺ Rasti-Land, Quanthofer strasse 9. Amusement park. ☐ 01/04-31/10 10-17/18h, Apr, Sep: Mo, Sa, Su.

🏕 **Sande (Nieder-Sachsen)** 4B4

Am Markt. GPS: n53,50251 e8,01113. ⬆️

4 🅿free. **Location:** Urban, simple. **Surface:** metalled. ☐ 01/01-31/12
Distance: 🚉100m ⊗100m 🚊100m.

DE

🛢 **Sande (Nieder-Sachsen)** 4B4
Paddel- und Pedalstation, Altmarienhausen. GPS: n53,51174 e8,01076.⬆.
4 🅿 free. **Surface:** gravel. 🅿 01/01-31/12
Distance: 🚲1km 🏖Sander See 50m.

🛢 **Sande (Nieder-Sachsen)** 4B4
Sander See, Loppelter Weg. GPS: n53,51162 e8,00206.⬆.

4 🅿 free. **Surface:** metalled. 🅿 01/01-31/12
Distance: 🚲2km 🏖on the spot.

🅂 **Sande (Nieder-Sachsen)** 4B4
Freizeitmobile von der Kammer, Huntestraße 1. GPS: n53,49076 e8,02292.
⬆ .

🚰🧺Ch 🔌on demand. 🅿 winter

⚓🅂 **Sandstedt** 〰️⚓ 4C5

Wohnmobilstellplatz Sandstedt - Sandstedt

info@hagen-cux.de · www.hagen-cux.de
Beautiful view
Paved and flat motorhome pitches
Snackbar

Wohnmobilstellplatz Sandstedt, Am Radarturm 5.
GPS: n53,36317 e8,51231.⬆➡.
10 🅿 free 🚰€1/100liter 🧺€1 Ch€1 🔌€1 WC 🚽150m on campsite.
Location: Rural, comfortable, isolated, quiet. **Surface:** grassy/gravel.
🅿 01/04-30/09
Distance: 🚲500m 🚣3km 🏖100m 🛒950m ⊗3km ⚓on the spot
🎣on the spot.

🅂🅂 **Saterland** 👫⚓ 4B5
Reisemobilhafen am Maiglöckchensee, Am Sportplatz, Scharrel.
GPS: n53,07060 e7,70116.⬆➡.

28+7 🅿€4 🚰€1/100liter 🧺€1 Ch€1 🔌(28x)€2/24h WC 🚽€0,50 🔵€2.🛗
Location: Rural, luxurious, quiet. **Surface:** grassy. 🅿 01/01-31/12
Distance: 🚲300m 🏖50m 🛒50m ⊗1km ⚓500m 🚏500m.

⚓🅂 **Saterland** 👫⚓ 4B5
Reisemobilplatz Am Bootshafen, Hauptstrasse 640, Strücklingen.
GPS: n53,12819 e7,66762.⬆.

15 🅿€3 🚰€1/100liter 🧺€1 Ch 🔌€1,50/24h WC€1 🚽€0,50. 🛗 **Location:**
Rural, simple. **Surface:** grassy/gravel. 🅿 01/01-31/12
Distance: 🚲100m 🏖on the spot 🛒on the spot ⊗on the spot 🚏on the spot
🚏100m.

🅂🅂 **Scharnebeck** 〰️⚓ 5B5
Wohnmobilstellplatz Am Schiffshebewerk, Adendorfer Straße 40.
GPS: n53,29196 e10,49320.⬆.

15 🅿€6/24h, park €2 🚰€1/10minutes 🧺Ch 🔌(8x)€1/8h. 🚗🚐
Location: Rural, comfortable, isolated, quiet. **Surface:** metalled.
🅿 01/01-31/12
Distance: 🚲1km ⊗200m 🛒Aldi 400m.
Remarks: Climbing wall 100m, boat lift Scharnebeck.

DE

⎇S Schneverdingen 🌲👥🏊 **5A5**
Wohnmobil-Hafen Lüneburger Heide - Schneverdingen

info@camping-LH.de - www.camping-LH.de
Comfortable motorhome stopover
Located in nature reserve
Restaurant with regional specialties

Wohnmobilhafen Lüneburger Heide, Badeweg 3, Heber.
GPS: n53,07104 e9,86481.⬆.
40 🛏€12 🚰€1/80liter 🚻Ch 💧(40x)included,10Amp WC€2/day
🚽use sanitary €2/pp 📷 📶. 💧 **Location:** Rural, comfortable.
Surface: grassy/metalled. 🅿 01/04-31/10
Distance: 🚶7km ⛵5km 🛒on the spot ⊗on the spot 💧on camp site
🚲on the spot 🅰on the spot.
Remarks: Use sanitary facilities at campsite.

⎇S Schneverdingen 🌲👥🏊 **5A5**
Am Quellenbad, Inseler Straße. **GPS:** n53,13110 e9,77280.⬆➡.

20 🛏free 🚰€2 🚻Ch WC €1. **Location:** Urban, simple. **Surface:** grassy.
🅿 01/01-31/12
Distance: 🚶2km 🛒on the spot 🚲on the spot 🅰on the spot.
Remarks: Use sanitary only during opening hours swimming pool.

⎇ Schneverdingen 🌲👥🏊 **5A5**
Parkplatz Festhalle, Im Osterwald. **GPS:** n53,11893 e9,80681.⬆.

4 🛏free. **Location:** Simple. **Surface:** metalled. 🅿 01/01-31/12
Distance: 🚶2km 💧2km.
Remarks: Entrance via Festhalle.

©S Schneverdingen 🌲👥🏊 **5A5**
Reisemobilhafen Lüneburgerheide, Badeweg 3, Heber.
GPS: n53,07108 e9,86464.⬆.

5 🛏€12 🚰 🚻Ch 💧(5x) WC €2,50. 🚲 🏊 **Location:** Rural, luxurious,
quiet. **Surface:** grasstiles/metalled. 🅿 01/04-31/10
Distance: 🚶5km 💧on camp site.
Remarks: Sanitary at campsite.

⎇S Schneverdingen 🌲👥🏊 **5A5**
Mariechens Hoff, Voßbarg 15, Reinsehlen. **GPS:** n53,17122 e9,83316.⬆➡.

8 🛏€8 🚰 🚻Ch included 💧(8x)€0,40/kWh. 🚲 **Location:** Rural, simple,
isolated, quiet. **Surface:** grassy. 🅿 01/01-31/12
Distance: 🚶7km ⛵15km ⊗3km 💧4 km 🚲on the spot 🅰on the spot.

⎇ Schöppenstedt **10C1**
Elm-Asse-Platz, Schützenplatz am Berge. **GPS:** n52,14756 e10,77737.⬆.

15 🛏free. **Location:** Rural, simple, noisy. **Surface:** asphalted.
🅿 01/01-31/12
Distance: 🚶600m ⊗1km 💧km.
Remarks: Next to sports fields.

Tourist information Schöppenstedt:
ℹ The region of Till Eulenspiegel. Tills-Tauf-Tour: cycle and hiking routes in the
country of Jester Till, start at the Till Eulenspiegel museum. 🅿 Tue-Fri 14-17h,
Sa-Su 11-17h.
Ⓜ Till Eulenspiegelmuseum, Nordstrasse 4a. 🅿 Tue-Fri 14-17h, Sa-Su 11-17h
🅿 Mo.

⎇ Schortens **4B4**
Aqua-toll, Beethovenstrasse. **GPS:** n53,53961 e7,93780.

2 🛏free. **Surface:** metalled. 🅿 01/01-31/12
Distance: 💧200m 🚋25m.

Remarks: Parking swimming pool, max. 6,5m.

Schortens 4B4

Reisemobilstellplatz Fair-Cafe, Birkenstraße. **GPS:** n53,55281 e7,97650.

6 guests free. **Surface:** unpaved. 01/01-31/12
Distance: 3km 100m.

Schulenberg 10B2

Wiesenbergstrasse. **GPS:** n51,83535 e10,43464.

20 € 5 + € 1,50/pp tourist tax €1/80liter Ch (6x)€0,60/kWh WC.
Location: Rural, comfortable, quiet. **Surface:** gravel.
01/01-31/12
Distance: on the spot on the spot 6km on the spot on the spot.
Remarks: Check in at tourist office, view at Okerstausee.

Schüttorf 9A1

Am Kuhmplatz, Graf-Egbert-Straße. **GPS:** n52,32123 e7,22642.

10 free Chfree. **Location:** Rural, simple. **Surface:** gravel.
01/01-31/12
Distance: 2,4km 100m.
Remarks: Parking swimming pool.

Schwanewede 4C5

Am Markt, Am Markt. **GPS:** n53,22412 e8,59644.

3 free. **Location:** Simple, central. **Surface:** metalled.
01/01-31/12
Distance: on the spot on the spot on the spot.

Schwanewede 4C5

Brücke zu Harriersand, Inselstraße. **GPS:** n53,26489 e8,49762.

5 free. **Location:** Rural, simple, isolated. **Surface:** grassy.
01/01-31/12
Distance: 7km.

Schwanewede 4C5

Löhnhorst, Hammersbeckerweg/Am Fosshall. **GPS:** n53,20355 e8,62453.

2 free. **Location:** Rural, simple, isolated, quiet. **Surface:** metalled.
01/01-31/12
Distance: 6km 6km 6km.

Schwanewede 4C5

Wohnmobilstellplatz, Klint, Neuenkirchen. **GPS:** n53,23670 e8,50919.

5 free. **Location:** Rural, simple, quiet. **Surface:** unpaved.
01/01-31/12
Distance: 500m.
Remarks: Dead end street.

Seelze 10A1

Marina Rasche Werft, Werftstraße 10. **GPS:** n52,39560 e9,56435.

13 € 6,50 Chincluded (13x)€3 WC €2 . 01/04-15/10
Distance: 2km 4,5km on the spot.
Remarks: Bread-service.

Selsingen 5A4

Wohnmobilstation, Im Sick. **GPS:** n53,42764 e9,50764.

25 ⏚free 🚰🔌 Ch free. **Location:** Rural, simple, quiet. **Surface:** metalled. ⬛ 01/01-31/12
Distance: 🚶500m 🛒100m.

▨S | **Sittensen** 🌿⚓🍦 | 5A5
Parkplatz, Mühlenstrasse. **GPS:** n53,27652 e9,50750.⬆.

5 ⏚free 🚰🔌 Ch WC free. **Location:** Simple, central. **Surface:** metalled. ⬛ 01/01-31/12
Distance: 🚶centre ⊗200m 🚰on the spot 🚶on the spot.

▨ | **Soltau** 🌿⚓🍦🍷 | 5A5
Soltau Therme, Stubbendorffweg. **GPS:** n52,99301 e9,84443.

10 ⏚free. **Location:** Simple, central, quiet. **Surface:** metalled. ⬛ 01/01-31/12
Distance: 🚶1km ⊗on the spot 🚲on the spot 🚶on the spot.
Remarks: Max. 1 night.

▨ | **Soltau** 🌿⚓🍦🍷 | 5A5
Heidepark. GPS: n53,02166 e9,87370.

100 ⏚€ 5.🚲
Location: Rural, simple, isolated. **Surface:** grasstiles.
⬛ 01/01-31/12
Remarks: Parking amusement park.

Tourist information Soltau:
🅘 Heidepark. Amusement park. ⬛ 01/04-31/10 9-18h, 01/07-15/08 Sa 9-21h.

▨S | **Spieka-Neufeld** | 4C3
Wohnmobilhafen, Deichweg. **GPS:** n53,78899 e8,55060.⬆.

40 ⏚€ 8 🚰€1/100liter 🔌Ch 🔌(18x)€1/2kWh. **Location:** Rural, simple.
Surface: gravel/metalled. ⬛ 01/01-31/12
Distance: 🚶300m 🏊on the spot 🚰on the spot ⊗200m.
Remarks: Bread-service.

▨ | **Springe** | 10A1
Auf dem Burghof. **GPS:** n52,20765 e9,55717.⬆.

5 ⏚free. **Location:** Simple. **Surface:** asphalted. ⬛ 01/01-31/12
Distance: 🚶Old city centre 200m ⊗300m.

▨S | **St.Andreasberg** 🏔❄ | 10B3
Silbererzgrube Samson, Am Samson 4. **GPS:** n51,71398 e10,51625.⬆.

20 ⏚€ 11 🔌(20x)included. 🚲 **Location:** Rural, simple, quiet.
Surface: gravel. ⬛ 01/01-31/12
Distance: 🚶1km ⊗400m 🛒1km 🚶on the spot.
Remarks: At Historical Mine of SIlver Ores.

▨S | **Stade** | 5A4
Wohnmobilstellplatz Am Schiffertor, Schiffertorsstrasse 21.
GPS: n53,60278 e9,46667.⬆➡.

79 ⏚€ 8,50/24h 🚰€1/80liter 🔌Ch 🔌€0,50/kWh.🏚 **Location:** Urban, central. **Surface:** gravel. ⬛ 01/01-31/12
Distance: 🚶500m ⊗700m.

▨S | **Stadland** ⚓🍦 | 4C4
Am Sportplatz, Hauptstrasse, Seefeld. **GPS:** n53,45639 e8,35778.⬆.

DE

5 ⌂free ⛽€1/10minutes ⚡(4x)€1/8h. **Location:** Urban, simple, quiet.
Surface: asphalted. ☐ 01/01-31/12
Distance: 🛒on the spot ⊗on the spot 🍴on the spot 🚆on the spot
🚲on the spot.
Remarks: Next to sports fields.

S Stadland 🏕 �* 🛶 **4C4**
Deichparkplatz, Fährstrasse, Kleinensiel. **GPS:** n53,44250 e8,47833. ⬆.

5 ⌂free ⛽€1/100liter ⚡(4x)€1. **Location:** Rural, simple, isolated, quiet.
Surface: gravel. ☐ 01/01-31/12
Distance: 🛒500m ⚓200m Weserstrand 🚲300m 🚲on the spot.

S Stadland 🏕 �* 🛶 **4C4**
Rathausplatz, Am Markt, Rodenkirchen. **GPS:** n53,39944 e8,45444. ⬆.

10 ⌂free ⛽€1/10minutes 🔌Ch ⚡(4x)€1/8h.
Location: Urban, simple, central, quiet. **Surface:** grasstiles/metalled.
☐ 01/01-31/12 ◉ Thu 5-13h market
Distance: 🛒on the spot ⊗500m 🍴500m 🚆on the spot 🚲on the spot.

S Stadland 🏕 �* 🛶 **4C4**
Birkenweg, Kleinensiel. **GPS:** n53,44194 e8,47444.

0free 🔌Chfree. **Location:** Urban, simple. **Surface:** metalled.
☐ 01/01-31/12
Distance: 🛒on the spot.

S Stadthagen **9D1**
Reisemobilplatz am Tropicana, Jahnstraße 2. **GPS:** n52,32236 e9,18896. ⬆.

15 ⌂free ⛽€1/100liter 🔌Ch ⚡(4x)€1/2kWh WC 🚿 📶 . 🔲🍴
Location: Rural, quiet. **Surface:** gravel. ☐ 01/01-31/12
Distance: 🛒2km ⊗1km 🍴1km 🚲on the spot 🚶on the spot.
Remarks: Max. 3 days, service at Tropicana.

S Stadtoldendorf **10A2**
Mobilcamping unter den Homburg, Linnenkämper Strasse 33.
GPS: n51,87777 e9,63500. ⬆➡.

30 ⌂€5/day ⛽€1 🔌€1 Ch ⚡(25x)€2/day.🐕 **Location:** Simple.
Surface: grassy. ☐ 01/01-31/12
Distance: 🛒1km 🍴1km.
Remarks: Check in at restaurant.

S Steinfeld **9C1**
Zur Schemder Bergmark, Dammer Strasse. **GPS:** n52,58308 e8,21476. ⬆➡.

20 ⌂free ⛽€1/100liter 🔌€0,50 Ch€0,50. **Location:** Rural, quiet.
Surface: metalled. ☐ 01/01-31/12
Distance: 🛒500m 🍴500m.
Remarks: Parking swimming pool.

S Steinhude **10A1**
Wohnmobilstellplatz Steinhude, Am Bruchdamm. **GPS:** n52,44874 e9,35478.
⬆.

180 ⌂€7,50 ⛽ 🔌€1 Ch ⚡(60x)€3/day WC 🍴€1 🔲€2,50/2,50.
Surface: grassy.
☐ 01/01-31/12
Distance: 🛒500m ⚓500m ⊗500m 🍴500m.
Remarks: Max. 3 nights, bread-service.

DE

Tourist information Steinhude:

ℹ️ Marina on lake of the same name.

🏕️ **S** | **Steyerberg** | 4D6

Waldferienpark Steyerberg, Zum Ferienpark 37. **GPS:** n52,57395 e9,01096.⬆️

40 🛏️€5 🚰€1 🅿️Ch ♿€2 WC 🚽€2. **Surface:** metalled.

☀️ 01/01-31/12

Distance: 🚶1km ⊗1km 🛒1km.

🏕️ **S** | **Steyerberg** | 4D6

Wohnmobilstellplatz Steyerberg, Kleine Straße 7. **GPS:** n52,56655 e9,02505.⬆️

4 🛏️free 🚰€1/100liter 🅿️€1 Ch€1 ♿(8x)€1/8h. **Surface:** gravel.

☀️ 01/01-31/12

Distance: 🚶on the spot.

🍴 **S** | **Steyerberg** | 4D6

Gasthaus Zur Eiche, Sarninghausen 2. **GPS:** n52,56944 e8,99444.⬆️

15 🛏️guests free 🚰. **Surface:** grassy. ☀️ 01/01-31/12

🏕️ **S** | **Stolzenau** | 9D1

Reisemobilstellplatz Stolzenau, Weserstrasse. **GPS:** n52,51021 e9,08104.⬆️➡️

33 🛏️€4 🚰€1/60liter 🅿️Ch ♿(24x)€2/12h. **Surface:** grasstiles.

☀️ 01/01-31/12 ⬛ service 01/11-31/03

Distance: 🚶250m ⚓on the spot ⛽on the spot ⊗300m 🛒300m.

Remarks: Along the Weser river.

🏕️ **S** | **Sulingen** | 4D6

Am Stadtsee, Kornstraße. **GPS:** n52,67653 e8,80127.⬆️

10 🛏️free 🚰€1/5minutes 🅿️€1 Ch€1. **Surface:** metalled.

☀️ 01/01-31/12

Distance: 🚶600m ⚓300m.

🏕️ **S** | **Surwold** | 4B5

Erholungsgebiet Surwolds Wald, Waldstrasse. **GPS:** n52,96743 e7,51535.⬆️

20 🛏️€5 🚰€1/100liter 🅿️Ch ♿€2 WC 🚽€0,50. **Surface:** grassy.

☀️ 01/01-31/12

Distance: 🚶800m ⊗250m.

🏕️ **S** | **Surwold** | 4B5

Privatplatz Klapper, Papenburgerstrasse 57. **GPS:** n53,01774 e7,48470.⬆️

10 🛏️€10 🚰🅿️Ch ♿(4x)€1/24h WC 🚽€2. **Location:** Rural, simple.

Surface: grassy. ☀️ 01/01-31/12

Distance: 🚶1km ⚓1,5km ⊗1km 🛒1km.

Remarks: Swimming pool and picnic area available.

🏕️ **S** | **Tarmstedt** | 4D5

Landtechniek Grabau, Bahnhofstraße. **GPS:** n53,22421 e9,08728.⬆️➡️

15 🛏️€6 🚰🅿️Ch ♿included. 🚿 **Location:** Simple. **Surface:** metalled.

☀️ 01/01-31/12

Distance: 🚶on the spot ⊗500m 🛒on the spot.

🏕️ **S** | **Thedinghausen** | 4D6

Reisemobilstellplatz Erbhof, Braunschweiger Straße. **GPS:** n52,96188 e9,03020.⬆️

8 🛏️€5 🚰€1/10minutes 🅿️Ch ♿€1/6h WC. **Surface:** grasstiles.

☀️ 01/01-31/12

Distance: 🚶500m 🚲on the spot 🚶on the spot.

DE

🏕️S **Twist** 4A6
Am Hallenbad. **GPS**: n52,64719 e7,08918.⬆️.

6 🚐free 🚰€1/100liter 🚽Ch ⚡(8x)€1/2kWh. **Surface:** metalled.
⭕ 01/01-31/12
Distance: 🏊on the spot 🏖️on the spot.
Remarks: Barefoot path.

🏕️S **Uchte** 9D1
Balkenkamp. **GPS**: n52,49761 e8,90618.⬆️.

3 🚐free 🚰€1 🚽Ch. **Surface:** metalled. ⭕ 01/01-31/12
Distance: 🏊100m 🏖️500m ⚓100m.

🏕️S **Uelsen** 9A1
Festplatz, Hardinghauserstrasse. **GPS**: n52,49575 e6,88840.⬆️➡️.

10 🚐free 🚰€2 🚽Ch WC. **Surface:** asphalted. ⭕ 01/01-31/12

🛥️S **Uelzen** 5B5
Im Sportboothafen, Riedweg 7. **GPS**: n52,95722 e10,59444.⬆️.

8 🚐€8 + €1/pp 🚰€1/70liter 🚽€1 Ch ⚡(8x)€1/6h WC included
⚡€2,50/2,50. **Location:** Rural, simple, quiet. **Surface:** metalled.
⭕ 01/01-31/12
Distance: 🏖️on the spot 🚶on the spot ⊗on the spot ⚓1,9km
🏃on the spot 🏊on the spot.
Remarks: Max. 3 nights, free bicycles available, playground.

🏕️ **Undeloh** 5A5
Am Naturschutzpark, Wilseder Straße. **GPS**: n53,19253 e9,97709.

30 🚐€3/day, €6/night. 🏠 **Location:** Rural, simple. **Surface:** unpaved.
⭕ 01/01-31/12
Distance: 🏊500m ⊗100m 🏃on the spot.
Remarks: In nature reserve the the Lüneburg Heide (heath).

🏕️S **Uplengen** 4B5
Remelser Paddel- & Pedalstation, Uferstrasse. **GPS**: n53,30123 e7,75151.⬆️.

5 🚐€5 🚰 🚽Ch ⚡(4x)€2. **Surface:** metalled. ⭕ 01/01-31/12
Distance: 🏊500m 🏖️50m ⚓500m.
Remarks: Max. 3 days, canoe and bicycle rental.

🏕️S **Uplengen** 4B5
Schützenplatz, Schützenstraße. **GPS**: n53,30719 e7,74708.⬆️➡️.

10 🚐€5 🚰 🚽Ch ⚡€1/12h. **Surface:** grasstiles. ⭕ 01/01-31/12
🅿️ 10/06-15/06
Distance: 🏊500m.
Remarks: Max. 3 nights.

🏕️S **Uslar** 10A3
Reisemobilpark am Badeland, Zur Schwarzen Erde. **GPS**: n51,66753 e9,62831.
⬆️➡️.

20 🚐€6 + reduction swimming pool 🚰€1/10minutes 🚽Ch ⚡€1/8h
WC€0,50. **Location:** Quiet. **Surface:** grasstiles. ⭕ 01/01-31/12
Distance: 🏊1km ⊗on the spot ⚓500m 🚌on the spot.

🏕️S **Uslar** 10A3
Am Lindenhof, Lindenhof 1. **GPS**: n51,67213 e9,62952.⬆️➡️.

5 🅿free night € 8, € 2 each additional night ⌐🔲Chincluded ⚡€0,40/kWh.
Location: Rural, simple. **Surface:** grassy/gravel. 🔲 01/01-31/12
Distance: 🚶2,5km ⊗2,5km 🚊2,5km ⛽ on the spot.
Tourist information Uslar:
🏕 Market, city centre. 🔲 Fri 9-13h.
🦋 Alaris Schmetterlingspark. Butterfly park in tropical rain forest.
🔲 01/04-31/10 Tue-Su 9.30-17.30h.
🏊 Uslarer Badeland. Swimming pool complex. 🔲 Sa/Su 10-18h, Tue-Fri
10-20h, Mo 10-13h.

🅿S	Vechta	4C6

Am Hallenwellen- und Freibad, Dornbusch. **GPS:** n52,74000 e8,29639.⬆.

10 🅿free. **Location:** Urban, simple. **Surface:** grassy/metalled.
🔲 01/01-31/12
Distance: 🚶1km ⊗1km 🚊1km.
Remarks: Parking swimming pool, max. 3 days, service Bokenerddamm 40.

🅿	Vechta	4C6

Oldenburgerstraße. **GPS:** n52,73245 e8,28833.⬆.

5 🅿free. **Location:** Urban, simple. **Surface:** metalled.
🔲 01/01-31/12
Distance: 🚶on the spot ⊗on the spot 🚊on the spot.

🅿S	Verden 🎏	4D6

Conrad-Wode-Straße. **GPS:** n52,92572 e9,22738.⬆➡.
14 🅿€ 6/24h ⌐€1/90liter 🔲Ch ⚡€1/8h. 🏠
Location: Urban, comfortable, central.
Surface: grassy.
🔲 01/01-31/12 🔲 26/05-05/06
Distance: 🚶350m ⊗300m 🚊300m ⛽300m.
Tourist information Verden:
ⓘ Reiterstadt, horse city of international reputation.
Ⓜ Deutsches Pferdemuseum, Holzmarkt 9 . Horse museum. 🔲 Tue-Su 10-17h.
🏕 Verdener Bauernmarkt. 🔲 Sa 8-13h.

🅿	Vienenburg 🎏	10B2

Schacht I. **GPS:** n51,95705 e10,56772.⬆➡.

4 🅿free. **Location:** Rural, simple, quiet. **Surface:** metalled.
🔲 01/01-31/12
Distance: 🚶700m ⊗700m 🚊600m ⛽on the spot 🚶on the spot.
Remarks: At Vienenburg Lake, max. 24h.

🅿	Visselhövede	5A5

Zu den Visselwiesen, Wüstenhof 1. **GPS:** n52,98530 e9,57772.⬆➡.

8 🅿free. **Location:** Urban, simple. **Surface:** metalled.
🔲 01/01-31/12
Distance: ⊗100m 🚊200m.

🅿S	Walchum 🎏	4A6

Marinapark Emstal, Steinbilder Straße. **GPS:** n52,92680 e7,29624.

10 🅿€ 10 ⌐🔲Ch ⚡(6x) WC 🔲€1,50. **Location:** Rural.
Surface: grassy. 🔲 01/01-31/12
Distance: fishing permit obligatory ⊗300m 🚊on the spot ⛽on the spot
🚶on the spot.

🍴S	Walsrode	5A6

Forellenhof, Hünzingen 3. **GPS:** n52,89855 e9,59122.

10 🅿€ 10 ⌐🔲 ⚡(2x). **Location:** Rural, simple, isolated, quiet.
Surface: grasstiles/grassy.
Distance: 🚶3km ⊗on the spot 🚊3km.
Remarks: Free with a meal.
Tourist information Walsrode:
🐦 Vogelpark Walsrode. Bird park and botanical garden. 🔲 01/03-31/10 8-19h.

🅿S	Wangerland	4B4

An der Ostdüne, Bäderstrasse, Hooksiel. **GPS:** n53,64103 e8,03514.⬆➡.

DE

75 ⌁ € 12 + € 2,90/pp Kurtaxe, dog € 3,10 ⚓ 🔧 Ch 🚿 WC 🗑 📶 included.
Surface: gravel. ⬛ 01/04-30/10
Distance: 🚶1,7km ⚓beach ±250m.

🔥 S		**Wangerland**	4B4

Nordsee-Camping-Schillig, Jadestraße, Schillig. **GPS:** n53,69986 e8,02338. ⬆
➡

80 ⌁ € 12 + € 2,90/pp Kurtaxe, dog € 3,10 ⚓ 🔧 Ch 🚿
(80x) WC 📶 included. **Surface:** grassy. ⬛ 01/04-31/10
Distance: 🚶200m.

⚓ S		**Wangerland**	4B4

Am Yachthafen, Zum Hafen, Horumersiel. **GPS:** n53,68293 e8,02091. ⬆➡

22 ⌁ € 15,80 ⚓ 🔧 Ch 🚿 WC 🗑 included. **Surface:** concrete.
⬛ 01/04-30/10
Distance: 🚶600m ⚓on the spot.

⚓ S		**Wardenburg**	4C5

Keilstrasse, Astrup. **GPS:** n53,04770 e8,21197. ⬆

5 ⌁free 🚿 (3x). **Location:** Urban, simple. **Surface:** gravel.
⬛ 01/01-31/12
Distance: 🚲2,5km.

⌁	**Wardenburg**	4C5

Marktplatz, Huntestraße. **GPS:** n53,06401 e8,19832. ⬆➡

3 ⌁free. **Location:** Urban, simple. **Surface:** metalled.
⬛ 01/01-31/12
Distance: 🚶on the spot 🚲3,6km.

⚓ S		**Weener** ⚓	4B5

Am Alten Hafen, Panneborgstrasse. **GPS:** n53,16953 e7,36167. ⬆

45 ⌁ € 7,50/24h ⚓ €1/100liter 🔧 Ch 🚿 (45x)€2,50/24h WC 🗑 €1. 🚐
Location: Urban, comfortable. **Surface:** asphalted.
⬛ 01/01-31/12 ⭕ during harbor festival 3rd week of June
Distance: 🚶on the spot ⊗on the spot 🏊on the spot.
Remarks: Max. 3 days.

⚓ S		**Weener** ⚓	4B5

Am Yachthafen, Am Marina-Park. **GPS:** n53,16570 e7,36480. ⬆➡
24 ⌁ € 7,50 🚿 €2,50 🗑€2. **Surface:** metalled. ⬛ 01/04-30/09
Distance: 🚶centre 1,2km ⊗50m.

⌁ S	**Werlte**	4B6

Kreutzmanns Mühle, Kirchstraße. **GPS:** n52,85463 e7,68155. ⬆

6 ⌁free ⚓ €1/100liter 🔧 Ch 🚿 (8x)€1/2kWh. **Location:** Urban,
comfortable. **Surface:** metalled. ⬛ 01/01-31/12
Distance: 🚶200m ⊗200m 🏊200m.

⌁ S	**Westergellersen**	5B5

Turniergelände Luhmühlen, Westergellerser Heide. **GPS:** n53,23306 e10,21623.
⬆➡

35 ⌁ € 8 ⚓ €1 🔧 Ch 🚿 (35x)€1/8h WC 🗑. 🐾 **Location:** Rural, comfortable,
isolated, quiet. **Surface:** grassy. ⬛ 01/01-31/12
Distance: 🚶4km ⚓1,5km ⊗4km 🏊4km 🚌2km.

DE

Westerholt 4B4

Am Schul- und Sportzentrum, Ewigsweg. **GPS**: n53,59089 e7,44907.
5 free ⊟ Ch free. **Surface**: metalled. 01/01-31/12
Distance: 500m 600m.

Westerstede 4B5

Albert-Post-Platz, Auf der Lohe. **GPS**: n53,25883 e7,92685.

5 free. **Location**: Urban, simple. **Surface**: metalled.
01/01-31/12
Distance: 100m 2km 250m.

Westerstede 4B5

Badesee Karlshof, Bekassinenweg. **GPS**: n53,18811 e7,86954.

5 free. **Location**: Rural, simple, isolated. **Surface**: gravel.
01/01-31/12
Distance: Badesee.
Remarks: Max. 3 days.

Westerstede 4B5

Wohnmobilhafen Westerstede, Süderstraße 2. **GPS**: n53,24968 e7,93438.

50 €5 ⊟ Ch €2/24h WC €2/pppd use sanitary €2,50.
Location: Urban, comfortable, quiet. **Surface**: grassy/gravel.
01/01-31/12
Distance: 800m 1,4km McDonalds 200m.

Westoverledingen 4B5

Rathausplatz, Bahnhofstrasse 18, Ihrhove. **GPS**: n53,16634 e7,45173.

3 free €1/100liter Ch. **Location**: Urban, simple. **Surface**: grassy.
01/01-31/12 last week Jun

Distance: on the spot 50m.
Remarks: At townhall.

Westoverledingen 4B5

Reisemobilhafen zur Mühle, Mühlenstrasse 214, Steenfelderfehn.
GPS: n53,12944 e7,44051.

30 €5 ⊟ Ch (18x)included. **Location**: Rural, simple.
Surface: grassy/metalled. 01/01-31/12
Distance: on the spot 1km.

Westoverledingen 4B5

Schützenplatz Flachsmeer, Papenburger strasse 74, Flachsmeer.
GPS: n53,12700 e7,46367.

10 €5 ⊟ (10x)included. **Location**: Rural, simple.
Surface: grassy. 01/01-31/12
Distance: on the spot 100m.

Wiefelstede 4C5

Wohnmobilstellplatz am Bernsteinsee, Dorfstrasse 11, Conneforde.
GPS: n53,32657 e8,06362.

25 €6 €0,50 ⊟ €2 Ch (25x)€0,50/kWh WC €0,50 on camp site.
 Location: Rural, comfortable. **Surface**: grassy. 01/01-31/12
Distance: on the spot on the spot.
Remarks: In front of campsite, caution sepkey € 5.

Wiefelstede 4C5

Freibad Wiefelstede, Alter Damm 11. **GPS**: n53,26146 e8,10713.

10 free. **Location**: Rural, simple, quiet. **Surface**: metalled. 01/01-31/12
Distance: 500m on the spot 1,5km.

DE

⚓ S **Wiesmoor** 4B4

Bootshafen Ottermeer, Am Stadion. **GPS**: n53,40951 e7,71841.⬆➡.

14 🛏 € 5,50 🚰 ♨ Ch ⚡ included. **Surface:** grassy/metalled.
📅 01/01-31/12
Distance: 🚶1,5km.
Remarks: Key service at Gaststätte (12-19h).

🏕 S **Wietzendorf** 5A6

Übernachtungsoase Südsee Camp, Südsee camp 1, K41.
GPS: n52,93120 e9,96474.⬆.

40 🛏 € 14 🚰 €1/100liter ♨ ⚡ €0,50/kWh WC 🚽. **Location:** Comfortable.
Surface: metalled.
Distance: 🚶2km ⛰100m 🛒 on the spot.
Remarks: Caution key service € 3.

🏕 S **Wildeshausen** 4C6

Am Krandel, Krandelstrasse. **GPS**: n52,90042 e8,42728.⬆➡.

16 🛏 € 5 🚰 €1/80liter ♨ Ch ⚡ (15x)included. 🐕 **Location:** Rural, simple.
Surface: grassy/metalled. 📅 01/01-31/12
Distance: 🚶500m 🚴4,4km ⛰400m 🛒700m.
Remarks: Parking at swimming pool.

🏕 S **Wilhelmshaven** 〰⛵🌊 4C4

Reisemobilhafen Nautimo - Wilhelmshaven

bernd.lohss@sww-gmbh.de - www.nautimo.de

Paved and flat motorhome pitches
Bread-service
Swimming pool

Wohnmobilhafen Nautimo, Friedenstrasse 99. **GPS**: n53,53546 e8,10104.⬆➡.
26 🛏 € 8 🚰 €1/100liter ♨ Ch ⚡ (26x)€1/6h,10Amp WC included 🚽 €1 🚿€2/h.
Surface: metalled. 📅 01/01-31/12
Distance: 🚶2km 🚴3km 🏊4km 🚤1,5km ⊗on the spot 🚆200m 🚏1,5km 🚌100m 🚲on the spot ♁on the spot.
Remarks: Max. 7 days.

🏕 S **Wilhelmshaven** 4C4

Wohnmobilstellplatz Schleuseninsel, Schleussenstrasse 37.
GPS: n53,51478 e8,15218.⬆.

30 🛏 € 9, trailer € 5 🚰 €0,50/50liter ♨ Ch ⚡ (28x)€3/24h WC 🚽.
Surface: gravel. 📅 01/01-31/12
Distance: ⊗250m 🚌Jadebus.

🏕 S **Wilhelmshaven** 〰⛵🌊 4C4

Am Freibad Nord, Möwenstraße 30. **GPS**: n53,57032 e8,10368.⬆➡.

6 🛏 € 3,50, free with use of swimming pool 🚰 ♨ Ch ⚡ €1/6h WC 🚽.
Surface: gravel. 📅 01/05-31/08
Distance: 🚶1,5km.
Remarks: Use sanitary only during opening hours swimming pool.

🏕 S **Wilhelmshaven** 〰⛵🌊 4C4

Reisemobilstellplatz Wilhelmshaven Südstadt, Banterweg 12.
GPS: n53,51559 e8,09072.⬆.

20 🍴 € 8 🚰 🚾 Ch 💧 (16x)included 📶. **Surface:** gravel. 🅾 01/01-31/12

Wilhelmshaven 〰️⚓〰️ 4C4

Fliegerdeich West, Fliegerdeich. **GPS**: n53,50996 e8,12718.⬆️.

40 🍴 € 0,75/h, € 12/day. 🚐 **Location:** Rural. **Surface:** metalled.
🅾 01/01-31/12
Distance: 🚶2,5km 〰️sea ✖️nearby.
Remarks: No camping activities.

Wilhelmshaven 〰️⚓〰️ 4C4

Wohnmobilstellplatz Jade, Bunsenstraße 10. **GPS**: n53,51110 e8,08153.⬆️.

10 🍴 € 10 🚰 💧 included. **Surface:** asphalted.
🅾 01/01-31/12 🅾 water: 01/11-31/03

Tourist information Wilhelmshaven:
👁 Aquarium Wilhelmshaven, Südstrand. Sea aquarium. 🅾 10-18h.

Winsen/Luhe 5B4

Festplatz Bleiche, Tönnhäuserweg. **GPS**: n53,36452 e10,21228.⬆️.

10 🍴free. **Location:** Simple, central. **Surface:** asphalted.
🅾 01/01-31/12
Distance: 🚶100m ✖️100m. 🚲100m.

Winsen/Luhe 5B4

GreenEagle Golf, Radbrucher Straße 200. **GPS**: n53,32278 e10,22778.
15 🍴free, playing golf obligatory. **Location:** Simple. **Surface:** gravel.
🅾 01/01-31/12
Distance: 🚶6km 🏊2,2km ✖️on the spot.

Winsen/Luhe 5B4

Freizeit Center Albrecht, Porchestrasse 15, Gewerbegebiet Lühdorf.
GPS: n53,33750 e10,21947. ⬆️ .

11 🍴free 🚰€2 🚾 Ch 💧 (11x) WC. **Location:** Rural, simple.
Surface: metalled. 🅾 01/01-31/12
Distance: 🚶4,5km 🚲 on the spot.

Wittingen 〰️〰️ 5B6

Wittinger Sporthafen, Am Sporthafen 1. **GPS**: n52,72706 e10,66187.⬆️➡️.

20 🍴€ 9 + € 0,50 pp 🚰 🚾 Ch 💧 (20x) WC 🚿 included 💡€2,50/2,50.
Location: Rural, comfortable. **Surface:** grassy. 🅾 01/04-01/10
Distance: 🚶4km 🚲on the spot 🎣on the spot ✖️on the spot 🚲4km
〰️200m 🚲 on the spot.
Remarks: Near marina.

Wittmund 4B4

Schützenplatz, Auricherstrasse. **GPS**: n53,55763 e7,69156.⬆️.
30 🍴free. **Surface:** grassy. 🅾 01/01-31/12
Distance: 🚶800m 🍞bakery 200m.

Wittmund 4B4

Hafen Harlesiel, Am Harlesiel. **GPS**: n53,70853 e7,80888.⬆️➡️.

54 🍴€ 10-13 + € 2 Kurtaxe 🚰 🚾 Ch 💧 €3 WC 🚿. **Surface:** metalled.
🅾 15/03-31/10
Distance: 〰️on the spot.
Remarks: Caution key electricity € 10.

Wolfenbüttel 〰️⚓〰️ 10B1

Alte Spinnerei, Am Seeligerpark. **GPS**: n52,16228 e10,52632.
10 🍴free 🚰€1 💧 (3x)€1. **Surface:** metalled. 🅾 01/01-31/12
Distance: 🚶800m ✖️300m.
Remarks: Max. 3 days, quiet at night, crowdy during the day.

Wolfenbüttel 〰️⚓〰️ 10B1

Sporthalleninsel, Vor dem Wehre. **GPS**: n52,16168 e10,52646.⬆️➡️.

DE

2 ⌷ free ⌷ € 1/80liter ⌷ (4x)€ 1/8h. **Location:** Urban, central, noisy.
Surface: metalled. ⬛ 01/01-31/12
Distance: 250m ⊗500m 500m 200m.
Remarks: Along railwayline.

Ⓒ S | **Wolfsburg** 🌿 | **10C1**
Autostadt, Berliner Brücke. **GPS:** n52,43485 e10,79716.⬆️.

9 ⌷ € 3/day, € 10/24h ⌷ included. 🚐**Location:** Urban, noisy.
Surface: asphalted. ⬛ 01/01-31/12
Distance: 2km ⊗on the spot 2km.

Tourist information Wolfsburg:
😊 Autostadt. Of the Volkswagen-concern; with pavilion of several car makes, car tower of 20 floors, test driving. ⬛ 9-20h.

⌷ S | **Zetel** 🏕️ 👤 | **4B4**
Johann Quathamer, Fuhrenkampstrasse 60. **GPS:** n53,40084 e7,91893.⬆️.

15 ⌷ € 7 ⌷ € 1/100liter Ch ⌷ (15x) WC included €0,50. ⌷
Location: Rural, comfortable, quiet. **Surface:** grassy. ⬛ 01/01-31/12
Distance: 4km.

⌷ S | **Zetel** 🏕️ 👤 | **4B4**
Markthamm, Neuenburger Strasse. **GPS:** n53,41706 e7,97000.⬆️.

40 ⌷ free ⌷ Ch free ⌷ (6x)€ 1/kWh. **Location:** Urban, simple, central.
Surface: grasstiles. ⬛ 01/01-31/12
Distance: on the spot ⊗Imbiss.
Remarks: Parking centre, max. 2 days, service Kläranlage open: Mo/Tue 11-23h, Thu/Sa 11-23h, Su 16-23h.

⌷ | **Zetel** 🏕️ 👤 | **4B4**
Driefeler Esch. **GPS:** n53,41835 e7,98445.⬆️.

10 ⌷ free. **Location:** Simple. **Surface:** gravel. ⬛ 01/01-31/12
Remarks: Parking swimming pool, max. 48h.

⌷ | **Zetel** 🏕️ 👤 | **4B4**
Schulmuseum Bohlenbergerfeld, Wehdestrasse. **GPS:** n53,41322 e7,92143.⬆️.

25 ⌷ free. **Location:** Rural, simple, isolated. **Surface:** grassy/gravel.
⬛ 01/01-31/12
Distance: 2,5 km.

⌷ | **Zetel** 🏕️ 👤 | **4B4**
Urwald, Urwaldstrasse, Neuenburg. **GPS:** n53,39293 e7,96547.⬆️.

20 ⌷ free. **Location:** Rural, simple, quiet.
⬛ 01/01-31/12
Remarks: Max. 1 day.

S | **Zetel** 🏕️ 👤 | **4B4**
Kläranlage, Mohrstrasse. **GPS:** n53,42302 e7,97937.
⌷ Ch free. ⬛ 01/01-31/12
Remarks: Mo/Thu 7-16h, Fri 7-13h, Sa/Su 9-9.30h.

⌷ | **Zeven** | **4D5**
Viehmarkt, Meyerstrasse/Godenstedterstrasse. **GPS:** n53,29764 e9,27514.⬆️➡️.

4 ⌷ free. **Location:** Simple. **Surface:** metalled. ⬛ 01/01-31/12
Distance: 500m.

Ⓒ S | **Zorge** 👤 | **10C3**
Campingplatz im Waldwinkel, Kunzental 2. **GPS:** n51,64188 e10,64881.⬆️➡️.

DE

30 🛏 € 9,50, 2 pers.incl 🚰 €0,20/10liter 🔌 Ch 🚿 (15x)€2/day WC 🚽€1/pp.
Location: Rural, simple, quiet. **Surface:** grassy/gravel. ⭕ 01/01-31/12
Distance: 🛒1,5km 🚲on the spot 🏖6km 🚌300m 🚶on the spot
🎿 on the spot. **Remarks:** Max. 2 nights.

Mecklenburg-Western Pomerania

🚲S **Ahlbeck** ⚓ 6C2
Caravanplatz Am Wiesenrand, Gothenweg 5a. **GPS:** n53,94100 e14,17600.⬆️
➡️.

24 🛏 € 10, peak season € 12,50 🚰 🔌 Ch 🚿€2 WC 🚽€1 📶€3/3.
Surface: grassy. ⭕ 01/03-31/10
Distance: 🛒10min 🚲10min 🚾500m 🛒200m.
Remarks: Bread-service.

🚲S **Ahlbeck** ⚓ 6C2
Wohnmobilstellplatz Rauthe, Waldstrasse 7. **GPS:** n53,93660 e14,18660.⬆️➡️.

30 🛏 € 15 🚰 🔌 Ch 🚿 WC 🚽€2 📶€4. **Surface:** grassy. ⭕ 01/01-31/12
Distance: 🛒on the spot 🚲5 min 🚾200m 🛒200m.

🚲S **Ahlbeck** ⚓ 6C2
Parkplatz an der Grenze, Swinemüdestrasse. **GPS:** n53,92380 e14,21280.⬆️.

30 🛏 € 5. **Surface:** metalled. ⭕ 01/01-31/12
Distance: 🛒3km.
Remarks: Max. 24h.

🚲 **Ahrenshoop** ⚐ 6A2
Dorfstraße. **GPS:** n54,39155 e12,43914.

🛏 € 7,50 day/€ 7,50 night. **Surface:** gravel. ⭕ 01/01-31/12
Distance: 🛒2km 🏖beach 50m.

⚓S **Alt Schwerin** 6A4
Insel Camping Werder, Wendorf 8. **GPS:** n53,48696 e12,31833.➡️.

13 🛏 € 9,80 🚰 🔌 Ch 🚿€2 📶€3/3. **Surface:** grassy. ⭕ 01/01-31/12
Distance: 🛒4km 🚲on the spot 🛒on the spot 🛒on the spot.

⚓S **Altwarp** 6D3
Hafen, Seestrasse. **GPS:** n53,73905 e14,27147.⬆️.

40 🛏 € 11 🚰 🔌 Ch 🚿 WC 🚽included 📶. ⭕ 01/01-31/12
Distance: 🛒on the spot 🚲300m 🛒on the spot 🚾300m 🛒400m.

🚲S **Anklam** 6C3
Wasserwanderrastplatz, Demminer strasse. **GPS:** n53,85610 e13,67870.⬆️.

5 🛏 € 9,50, dog € 1 🚰 🔌 Ch 🚿€0,40/kWh WC 🚽€0,50. **Surface:** metalled.
⭕ 01/01-31/12
Distance: 🛒500m 🚲on the spot.

🚲S **Bansin** 6C2
Waldparkplatz Bansin. **GPS:** n53,99800 e14,11260.➡️.

DE

80 ⌘ € 4-5 + € 2,50-3/pp, dog € 1,50 ⌁ ⌁ Ch ⌁ €2,50 WC ⌁€1.
Surface: metalled. ⬤ 01/05-30/09
Distance: ⌁3km ⌁400m ⊗300m ⌁on the spot.

Barth · 6A2
Segelverein, Am Westhafen. **GPS:** n54,37130 e12,72510.

20 ⌘ € 10 ⌁ ⌁ Ch ⌁ €2 WC ⌁€1. **Surface:** grassy. ⬤ 01/05-01/10
Distance: ⌁on the spot ⌁on the spot ⌁on the spot.

Barth · 6A2
Wohnmobilparkplatz Barth, Am Osthafen. **GPS:** n54,36870 e12,77770. ⬆.

10 ⌘ € 7 ⌁ (8x)€0,50/kWh. ⌁ **Surface:** metalled. ⬤ 01/01-31/12
Distance: ⌁300m.

Beckerwitz · 5C3
Ostseecamping Beckerwitzer Strand, Haus 2a. **GPS:** n53,94137 e11,31682. ⬆➡.

12 ⌘ € 6-8 ⌁ ⌁ Ch ⌁ WC ⌁⬤. **Surface:** grassy. ⬤ 01/04-15/10
Distance: ⌁on the spot.

Bergen/Rügen · 6B1

Wohnmobilstellplatz Rügen, Tilzower Weg 32A.
GPS: n54,40757 e13,42949. ⬆➡.
16 ⌘ € 12 ⌁ €1/80liter ⌁ Ch ⌁ (16x)€2/day,25Amp WC included
⌁€2/6minutes ⌁€4/4 ⌁€2. **Surface:** metalled. ⬤ 01/01-31/12
Distance: ⌁1km ⊗400m ⌁500m ⌁100m ⌁on the spot.
Remarks: Bread-service.

Binz · 6B1
Wohnmobil-Oase Rügen, Proraer Chaussee 60. **GPS:** n54,44819 e13,56181. ⬆ ➡.

150 ⌘ € 11, Jul/Aug € 14 ⌁€1 ⌁€1 Ch ⌁ €1/kWh WC €0,50 ⌁€0,50
⬤€4/4. **Location:** Luxurious, isolated, quiet. **Surface:** grassy/gravel.
⬤ 01/04-31/10
Distance: ⌁Binz 5km ⌁1,5km ⌁700m ⌁on the spot.
Remarks: Bread-service.

Binz · 6B1
Parkplatz Zentrum, Proraer Chaussee 5. **GPS:** n54,40278 e13,60194. ⬆ .

60 ⌘ € 14/24h, € 3/2h ⌁€1/50liter ⌁ Ch ⌁ included WC ⌁€1.
Surface: grassy/metalled. ⬤ 01/01-31/12
Distance: ⌁on the spot ⊗50m ⌁on the spot.
Remarks: Next to petrol station.

Boiensdorf · 5D3
Am Strand, Werder. **GPS:** n54,02412 e11,54744. ⬆➡.

⌁€7 🚰 🅗Ch WC€0,30. **Surface:** grassy. ☀ 01/01-31/12
Distance: 🏊on the spot 🛒on the spot ⊗50m.

| 🏖S | Boltenhagen ⛵ | 5C3 |

Krämer's Wohnmobilhafen, Ostsee-allee 58b. **GPS:** n53,98122 e11,21908. ⬆.

45 ⌁€ 10-14, 2 pers.incl 🚰€0,20/20liter 🅗Ch ✂€2,50 WC 🚽€0,50. ☀ 01/01-31/12
Distance: 🏊800m ⛱200m 🛒200m ⊗on the spot 🛒700m 🚌on the spot.
Remarks: Bread-service in summer period.

| 🏖S | Boltenhagen ⛵ | 5C3 |

Wohnmobilpark Boltenhagen, Ostsee-allee 58. **GPS:** n53,98133 e11,21854. ⬆.

50 ⌁€ 9-13 + € 2,10/pp tourist tax 🚰€2 🅗Ch ✂€2,50 WC 🚽€1 ☀ 📶. **Surface:** grassy. ☀ 01/01-31/12
Distance: 🏊700m ⛱200m 🛒200m ⊗on the spot 🛒700m.

| 🏖S | Boltenhagen ⛵ | 5C3 |

Regenbogen Boltenhagen, Ostseeallee 54. **GPS:** n53,98196 e11,21714. ⬆.

20 ⌁€ 20 🚰 ✂ WC 🚽included ☀. **Surface:** grassy/metalled. ☀ 01/01-31/12
Distance: 🏊600m ⛱200m 🛒200m ⊗on the spot 🛒700m 🚌on the spot.
Remarks: Max. 1 night.

| 🏖S | Boltenhagen ⛵ | 5C3 |

Swin Golf Boltenhagen, Ausbau 15, Redewisch. **GPS:** n54,00851 e11,17180. ⬆.

10 ⌁€ 10-13 🚰€2 ✂€2. **Surface:** grassy. ☀ 01/04-31/10
Distance: 🏊on the spot.

| 🍴S | Brenz | 5D4 |

Landhaus Böttcher, Parchimer strasse 11. **GPS:** n53,38688 e11,67103. ⬆.

5 ⌁€ 10, guests free 🚰€1,50 ✂(4x)€2/day WC included.
Location: Rural, simple. **Surface:** grassy/metalled. ☀ 01/01-31/12
Distance: 🏊on the spot 🚲3km ⊗on the spot 🛒5km 🚌200m.

| 🍴S | Broock | 5D4 |

Hotel-Restaurant Am Worns-Berg, Am Worns-Berg 1.
GPS: n53,46734 e12,10698. ⬆.

6 ⌁€ 5, free with a meal 🚰 🅗Ch ✂€2 WC 🚽€1,50. **Surface:** gravel.
☀ 01/01-31/12
Distance: 🏊5km ⛱1,5km 🛒1,5km ⊗on the spot 🛒5km 🚌500m.

| 🍴S | Carpin | 6B4 |

Landgasthof Am Schlesersee, Hauptstrasse 25. **GPS:** n53,35424 e13,24028. ⬆.

10 ⌁€ 5, guests free 🚰 ✂ WC included. **Surface:** metalled.
☀ 01/01-31/12
Distance: 🏊500m ⛱on the spot 🛒on the spot ⊗on the spot 🛒4km.

| ⚓ | Dabitz ⛵ | 6A2 |

Hafen Dabitz, Boddenstraße. **GPS:** n54,36217 e12,80610.

DE

⬛€6/night. **Surface:** gravel.
Distance: 🚶500m ⚓on the spot.

| 🍴S | Dalwitz | 6A3 |

Ferien Gut Dalwitz, Dalwitz 46. **GPS:** n53,93484 e12,53830. ⬆.

2 ⬛€10 🚰€1 🚿 WC ⬜ ⬛€3/3 📶. **Surface:** grassy. ⭕ 01/01-31/12
Distance: 🚶15km ⊗on the spot ⚓on the spot.
Remarks: Parking estate.

| 🍴S | Dassow | 5C3 |

Reisemobilplatz Ostseestrand, Straße des Friedens 14, Rosenhagen.
GPS: n53,96195 e10,93944. ⬆.

DE

5 ⬛€10 🚰 🔌 Ch 🚿€3 WC ⬜€3. 🛁 **Location:** Rural, comfortable, quiet.
Surface: grassy. ⭕ 01/01-31/12
Distance: ⚓500m ⊗on the spot.
Remarks: At Café Strandgut.

| 📷S | Dobbertin | 5D4 |

Campingplatz Am Dobbertiner See, Am Zeltplatz 1. **GPS:** n53,61868 e12,06440.
⬆.

10 ⬛€10, 2 pers.incl 🚰 🔌 Ch 🚿 €0,50/kWh.
Surface: grassy.
⭕ 01/04-31/10
Distance: 🚶500m ⚓on the spot ⚓on the spot ⊗500m 💧500m 🚌500m.

| 📷S | Dömitz 🌿 ⚓ | 5C5 |

Campingpark Marina Dömitz, An der Schleuse 1. **GPS:** n53,14078 e11,25908.
⬆.

26 ⬛€10 🚰 🔌 Ch 🚿 WC ⬜included. **Location:** Rural, comfortable, quiet.
Surface: grassy. ⭕ 01/01-31/12
Distance: 🚶400m ⚓20m ⚓20m ⊗100m 💧800m.

| ⚓S | Dömitz 🌿 ⚓ | 5C5 |

Dömitzer Hafen, Hafenplatz 3. **GPS:** n53,13724 e11,26034. ⬆.

22 ⬛€8 🚰 €1/50liter 🔌 Ch 🚿 (10x)€2/day WC ⬜. **Location:** Rural,
comfortable, quiet. **Surface:** grassy. ⭕ 01/01-31/12
Distance: 🚶1km ⚓10m ⚓10m ⊗200m 💧800m 🚌600m.

| 📷S | Dranske/Bakenberg 🏖 | 6B1 |

Küstencamp, Nonnevitz 23. **GPS:** n54,66288 e13,26929. ➡.

18 ⬛€15 🚰 🔌 Ch 🚿 WC ⬜ ⬛.
Distance: ⚓400m ⚓400m ⊗100m 💧800m.
Remarks: Bread-service.

| 📷S | Eldena ⚓🏖 | 5D5 |

Bootshafen und Campingplatz Eldena, Am Bootshafen 1.
GPS: n53,23163 e11,42422.

12 ⬛€10,50 🚰 🔌 Ch 🚿 WC included ⬜€1,10 ⬛€3,50/3,50.
Location: Rural, comfortable, quiet. **Surface:** grassy. ⭕ 01/04-31/10
Distance: 🚶400m ⚓10m ⚓10m ⊗50m 💧400m 🐟on the spot.

| ⚓ | Feldberg | 6B4 |

Weidendamm 1. **GPS:** n53,33583 e13,44176.

10 ⛽€ 10. **Surface:** grassy/metalled. ◻ 01/01-31/12
Distance: 🏊on the spot ⊗150m 🛒400m.

| 🚲S | Fresenbrügge | 5D4 |

Womo & Caravan Stelplatz Eldekrug, Eldeufer 1. **GPS:** n53,26355 e11,54243. ⬆.

20 ⛽€ 10 🚰€1/100liter 🔌Ch ⚡€0,50/kWh WCincluded 🚮€1/pp. 🚿
Location: Rural, comfortable, isolated, quiet. **Surface:** grassy.
◻ 01/01-31/12
Distance: 🏊on the spot 🚣on the spot ⊗2km 🚴2km 🛒on the spot
🚶on the spot.

| 🚲 | Graal-Müritz | 5D2 |

Strandmitte, Buchenkampweg. **GPS:** n54,25663 e12,25005.

15 ⛽€ 15/24h, tourist tax € 2/pp. **Surface:** grassy/metalled.
◻ 01/01-31/12
Distance: 🚲500m 🏊on the spot 🚣on the spot ⊗500m 🛒500m.
Remarks: Max. 3 days.

| ⚓S | Grabow | 5D4 |

Stadthafen, Canalstrasse. **GPS:** n53,27738 e11,55949. ⬆.

18 ⛽free 🚰€0,50/time 🔌Ch€0,50 ⚡ WC€0,50 🚮€1. 🚿
Surface: metalled. ◻ 01/01-31/12, service: 8-9.30h and 18.30-20h
Distance: 🚲200m 🏊10m 🚣10m ⊗100m 🛒50m.

| ⚓S | Greifswald | 6B2 |

Am Museumhafen, Marienstraße 10. **GPS:** n54,09887 e13,38945. ⬆.

20 ⛽€ 11 🚰€2 🔌Ch€2 ⚡€1 WC 🚮.
Surface: metalled.
◻ 01/04-30/11
Distance: 🚶8 min walking ⊗300m.
Tourist information Greifswald:
👁 Fischerdorf Greifswald-Wieck. Fishermen's village worth seeing.

| 👁 | Güstrow | 6A3 |

Gleviner Platz. **GPS:** n53,79117 e12,18054. ⬆.

3 ⛽free. **Surface:** asphalted. ◻ 01/01-31/12
Distance: 🚲400m 🏊5km 🚣5km ⊗100m 🛒100m.

| 🍴S | Güstrow | 6A3 |

Hotel Am Tierpark, Verbindungschaussee 7. **GPS:** n53,79159 e12,21577. ⬆.
30 ⛽€ 10, 2 pers.incl 🚰 🔌Ch ⚡€2,50 WC 🚮use sanitary €2,50/pp.
Surface: grassy. ◻ 01/01-31/12
Distance: 🚲5km ⊗on the spot 🛒5km.

| 🚲S | Gützkow | 6B3 |

Rittergut Schloss Pentin, Zum Bollwerk 11. **GPS:** n53,91824 e13,46763. ➡.

40+10 ⛽€ 8 🚰€0,50/80liter 🔌Ch ⚡€0,50/kWh WC 🚮€1.
Surface: grassy/gravel. ◻ 01/01-31/12
Distance: ⊗1km 🛒400m.
Remarks: Bread-service.

| 🚲S | Heringsdorf | 6C2 |

Blasendorff, Labahnstrasse 10. **GPS:** n53,95940 e14,15680. ⬆.

3 ⛽€ 10 excl. tourist tax 🚰€0,50/40liter 🔌€1,50 ⚡€1,80. **Surface:** grassy.
◻ 01/01-31/12

DE

Distance: 🚶10min ⤴300m ⊗300m 🚰300m.

🏕️S **Heringsdorf** 🌊⛵ 6C2
P An der Kirche, Rudolf-Breitscheid-Straße. **GPS**: n53,95762 e14,16219.
30 🏕️€ 10,50, 2,50 pers.incl, tourist tax € 2,50/pp ⛽ Ch ✏€1,50 🔌€1.
Surface: grassy/sand. 📅 01/01-31/12
Distance: 🚶on the spot ⤴beach 500m ⊗250m.

🏕️S **Heringsdorf** 🌊⛵ 6C2
Pension Ariane, Bülowstrasse 13. **GPS**: n53,95240 e14,16600.⬆️

6 🏕️€ 12 ⛽€1/40liter Ch ✏€2 WC 🔌€2. **Surface**: grassy.
📅 01/04-30/09
Distance: 🚶on the spot ⤴300m ⊗on the spot 🚰on the spot.

🏕️S **Hinrichshagen** 6B2
Reisemobilstellplatz Wöller, Chausseestraße 12. **GPS**: n54,07450 e13,35230.
⬆️

50 🏕️€ 10 ⛽ Ch ✏included WC 🔌use sanitary €5/day. **Surface**: metalled.
📅 01/01-31/12
Distance: 🚶1km ⊗800m 🚰1km.

🏞️S **Hornstorf** 5D3
Gartencenter Offermann, Dorfstraße 1. **GPS**: n53,89473 e11,54159.⬆️

20 🏕️€ 10 ⛽ Ch ✏included. **Surface**: concrete. 📅 01/01-31/12

🏕️S **Insel Poel** ⛵ 5C3
Strandparkplatz Timmendorf, Tau n Lüchttorm. **GPS**: n53,99287 e11,38058.⬆️

60 🏕️€ 5/day, € 4/night ⛽€0,50/80liter Ch ✏(64x)€2/2kWh 🔌€1.🔌
Surface: grassy. 📅 01/01-31/12
Distance: 🚶150m ⤴500m ⊗200m 🚰300m.

🍴🏕️S **Insel Poel** ⛵ 5C3
Poeler Forellenhof, Niendorf 13. **GPS**: n53,99454 e11,44714.

16 🏕️€ 13, 2 pers.incl ⛽€2 ✏ WC included 🚿. **Surface**: concrete.
📅 01/01-31/12
Distance: 🚶1,5km ⤴on the spot 🛒on the spot ⊗on the spot 🚰1,5km.
Remarks: Check in at restaurant, steam bath and sauna, fish smokehouse.

⛪S **Kamminke** 6C3
Ortstraße. **GPS**: n53,86750 e14,20480.⬆️

15 🏕️€ 8. **Surface**: grassy. 📅 01/01-31/12
Distance: 🚶on the spot ⊗on the spot.

🐴S **Karenz** ♨️ 5C5
Reiterhof am Steinberg, Grebserstrasse 1. **GPS**: n53,23638 e11,34836.

3 🏕️€ 10 ⛽€1 Ch ✏€1,50 WC 🔌. **Location**: Rural, simple, isolated.
Surface: grassy. 📅 01/01-31/12
Distance: 🚶1km ⊗1km 🚰300m.
Remarks: Parking at manege.

🏕️S **Kargow** 6A4
Reisemobilstellplatz Ziegenwiese, Schwarzenhof 7.
GPS: n53,46433 e12,79925.⬆️

10 🏕️€ 7,50 ⛽€3 Ch ✏€3. **Surface**: grassy. 📅 01/01-31/12
Distance: ⤴1km 🛒1km ⊗200m 🚰4km.

⛪S **Karnin** 6C3
Hafen, Karnin 14a. **GPS**: n53,84450 e13,85860.⬆️

3 ⌀ € 10 ⊤ €0,50/100liter ⌷ Ch €1 ⚡ €0,50/kWh WC ⌷ €1 ⊙.
Surface: metalled. ▯ 01/01-31/12
Distance: ⊗500m.

⚓ Kühlungsborn 5D2
Am Hafen, Hafenstrasse. **GPS:** n54,15063 e11,77150.

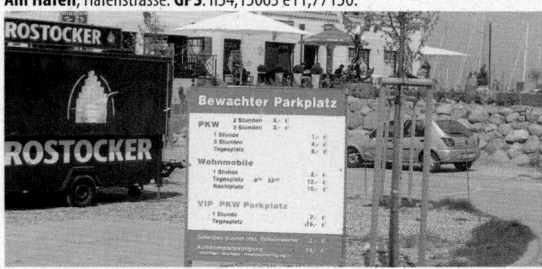

50 ⌀ € 10/night. **Surface:** gravel. ▯ 01/01-31/12
Distance: ⌿800m ⊗on the spot ⚓600m.

⌷S Langen Brütz 5D3
Landhaus Bondzio, Hauptstrasse 21a. **GPS:** n53,65722 e11,55737. ⬆.

6 ⌀ € 12 ⊤ ⚡ WC included ⌷€2. **Surface:** asphalted/grassy.
▯ 01/01-31/12 ⊙ Restaurant: Mo
Distance: ⌿150m ⊗on the spot ⊸50m.

⌷S Lenz über Malchow 6A4
Lenzer Hafen, Zum Hafen 1. **GPS:** n53,46793 e12,34929. ⬆.

25 ⌀ € 8,30- €12,40 ⊤ ⌷ Ch ⚡ WC ⌷€1,30 ⊙€2. **Surface:** grassy.
▯ 01/03-31/10
Distance: ⌿6km ⊗on the spot ⊸on the spot ⊗on the spot ⚓6km.
Remarks: Parking eastern bank Plauersee.

⌷S Lohme 6B1
Knöpfle Dorfladen, Arkonastrasse 4. **GPS:** n54,58300 e13,61150.

35 ⌀ € 12 ⊤ €1/50liter ⌷ Ch ⚡ €1/8h WC €0,50 ⌷€2 ⊙.
Surface: grassy/metalled.
▯ 01/01-31/12
Distance: ⌿on the spot ⊿200m ⊗on the spot ⚓on the spot ⊸on the spot.

⌷S Lohme ⚓ 6B1
Zum Königsstuhl, Stubbenkammerstraße 57, Hagen. **GPS:** n54,56220 e13,62590.
⬆.

40 ⌀ € 10,50 ⊤ €2/100liter ⌷ Ch €2 ⚡ €2,50/24h WC ⌷€1 ⊚.
Surface: metalled. ▯ 01/01-31/12
Distance: ⊗on the spot ⚓600m ⊸on the spot.

⌷S Ludwigslust ⚘⚓ 5D4
Am Schloss, Friedrich-Naumann-Allee. **GPS:** n53,32735 e11,49080. ⬆.

20 ⌀free ⊤€1 ⌷€1 Ch€1 ⚡. **Location:** Rural, simple, quiet.
Surface: gravel/sand. ▯ 01/01-31/12
Distance: ⌿600m ⊿500m ⚓600m.

⌷S Lütow ⚓ 6C2
Yachtlieger Achterwasser, Netzelkow. **GPS:** n54,02690 e13,90950. ➡.

22 ⌀ € 1/meter + € 1/pp ⊤ ⌷ Ch ⚡ (20x)€0,25/kWh WC ⌷€2.
Surface: grassy. ▯ 01/01-31/12
Distance: ⊿on the spot ⊸on the spot ⊗on the spot.
Remarks: Bread-service, bike/car rental.

⌷S Malchin 6A3
Malchiner Kanu-club, Am Kanal 2. **GPS:** n53,74417 e12,76611.

7 🛏 € 9 🚰 ⚡ WC ⤵€0,50 ⊡€1/1. **Surface:** grassy. ⬛ 01/01-31/12
Distance: 🚶500m ⛵on the spot 🛶on the spot ⊗500m 🛒500m.

🛥S | **Malchow** | 6A4

Marina Malchow, Ziegeleiweg 5. **GPS:** n53,46432 e12,42417.⬆.

20 🛏 € 10-20 excl. tourist tax 🚰 🔌 Ch ⚡ €2,50 WC ⤵€2,50 🚿.
Surface: grassy. ⬛ 01/01-31/12
Distance: 🚶2km ⛵on the spot 🛶on the spot ⊗100m 🛒4km 🚏250m.
Remarks: Bread-service.

🛥S | **Malchow** | 6A4

Wohnmobilstellplatz Am Plauer See, Zum Plauer See 1.
GPS: n53,49192 e12,37268.⬆ .

6 🛏 € 8-10, 2 pers.incl 🚰included 🔌 Ch€1,50 ⚡ (5x)€3,30 WC€1
⤵€1/5minutes ⊡ 🚿. **Surface:** gravel. ⬛ 01/01-31/12
Distance: 🚶4km ⛵on the spot 🛶on the spot ⊗on the spot 🛒on the spot.

🛥S | **Mirow** | 6B4

Schloßstraße 1A. **GPS:** n53,27623 e12,81348.

4 🛏guests free. **Surface:** metalled.

⛽S | **Mönkebude** | 6C3

Stettinger Haff, Am Hafen. **GPS:** n53,77174 e13,96868.⬆.

25+15 🛏 € 8,50-10 + € 1/pp tourist tax, dog € 2 🚰€0,50/100liter 🔌
Ch ⚡ €2/24h WC ⤵€1 ⚡€3,50/3 🚿€1,50/h.
Surface: grassy.
⬛ 01/01-31/12
Distance: 🚶50m ⊗nearby 🛒50m.
Remarks: Peak season: sanitary installation, nov/apr service only on demand.

🎡S | **Muess** | 5D4

Feriendorf Muess, Alte Crivitzer Landstrasse 6. **GPS:** n53,59995 e11,47940.⬆.

6 🛏 € 10 31/10-01/03, € 20 01/03-31/10, dog € 1 🚰 🔌
Ch ⚡ WC ⤵included, winter fee no shower. **Surface:** grassy.
⬛ 01/01-31/12
Distance: 🛒100m 🚏100m.
Remarks: At open air museum.

🛥S | **Neu Kaliss** 🎠 🍴 | 5C5

Find's Hier, An der Elde 2. **GPS:** n53,17810 e11,29720.⬆.

13 🛏 € 8 🚰€1 🔌 Ch included ⚡ €2/night WC ⤵€1. 🛶
Location: Rural, simple, isolated, quiet. **Surface:** grassy. ⬛ 01/01-31/12
Distance: ⛵on the spot 🛶on the spot ⊗on the spot 🛒400m 🚏400m.

⛽S | **Neubrandenburg** | 6B4

Wassersportzentrum Tollensesee, Augustastrasse 7.
GPS: n53,53861 e13,25665.➡.

🅿S | **Mistorf** | 5D3

Wohnmobilpark Mistorf, Dorfstrasse 50. **GPS:** n53,88152 e12,14325.⬆.
10 🛏 € 8 🚰 🔌Ch ⚡€2,50 WC ⤵€2,50. **Surface:** grassy. ⬛ 01/01-31/10
Remarks: Check in at Imbiss, bread-service, grill and picknic area.

🍴 | **Mönkebude** | 6C3

Gastätte Kregelin's Bistro, Hauptstrasse. **GPS:** n53,76663 e13,97614.⬆.

8 🛏free 🚰€1 🔌€1 ⚡ (8x)€0,50 WC€0,50. **Surface:** grasstiles/metalled.
⬛ 01/01-31/12
Distance: 🚶400m ⊗200m 🛒400m.

DE

30 🛏€10 🚰€1 🗑 Ch 🔌€0,50/kWh WC 🚽€1 🚿€2/day.
Surface: grassy/metalled. ⬜ 15/03-31/10
Distance: 🏊2km ⛱on the spot 🛒on the spot ⊗on the spot 🚉1km.
Remarks: Water sports centre.

🚻S	**Neuendorf**	6A2

Wohnmobilstellplatz Saal Neuendorf, Am Hafen. **GPS**: n54,33516 e12,52812.

20 🛏€10 🚰 🔌 WC€0,20 🚽€1. **Surface:** grassy. ⬜ 01/04-31/10
Distance: ⛱on the spot ⊗Imbiss 🚉kiosk.

🏕S	**Neuenkirchen**	6B2

Marktkauf, Dorfstrasse. **GPS**: n54,11810 e13,36390.

10 🛏free 🚰€1 🗑 Ch 🔌 (5x)€1. **Surface:** metalled. ⬜ 01/01-31/12
Distance: ⊗on the spot 🚉on the spot.

🏕S	**Neukloster** 🌿 🍴 🐑 🐚	5D3

Wohnmobilpark Neuklostersee, Alte Gärtnerei 3. **GPS**: n53,86121 e11,69536.
⬆.

69 🛏16/3-15/10 €9,50, 16/10-15/3 €8 🚰 🗑 Ch 🔌€1/2kWh WC 🚽€1.
Surface: gravel. ⬜ 01/01-31/12, toilets/showers 8-21h
Distance: 🏊500m ⛱on the spot 🛒50m ⊗500m 🚉1,2km 🚌500m.

🚻S	**Neustrelitz**	6B4

Parkplatz Am Stadthafen, Zierker Nebenstrasse 6. **GPS**: n53,36568 e13,05551.
⬆.

25 🛏€8 🚰€0,50/80liter 🗑€1 Ch€1 🔌 (25x)€0,50/kWh WC€0,20 🚽€0,50
💧€2/2. **Location:** Comfortable, quiet. **Surface:** metalled.
Distance: 🏊on the spot ⛱100m, swimming 1km 🛒200m ⊗100m 🚉200m
🚌200m 🚴on the spot 🚶on the spot.
Remarks: Coins at harbourmaster (200m), historical centre.

🍴S	**Nossentin**	6A4

Am Fleesensee, Am Park 33. **GPS**: n53,51866 e12,46766. ⬆.

4 🛏€8 🚰 🔌 WC included 🚽. **Surface:** grassy. ⬜ 01/04-31/10
Distance: 🏊5km ⛱100m 🛒100m ⊗on the spot 🚉5km.

🏕S	**Ostseebad Sellin/Rügen** 🌿 🏖 🍴	6C1

Reisemobilhafen Sellin, Kiefernweg 4b. **GPS**: n54,37170 e13,70165. ➡.

50 🛏€12 + € 1,40-2,80/pp tourist tax 🚰€0,50/50liter 🗑 Ch€1 🔌
(50x)€0,50/kWh WC 🚽€0,50 💧€2/day. **Surface:** grassy/metalled.
⬜ 15/03-15/11
Distance: 🏊300m ⛱1km 🛒1km ⊗200m 🚉300m 🚌300m.

⛪S	**Ostseebad Sellin/Rügen** 🌿 🏖 🍴	6C1

Hafen Seedorf, Seedorf 8. **GPS**: n54,35410 e13,65359. ⬆.
5 🛏€10 🚰€1/100liter 🔌€0,50/kWh. ⬜ 01/05-15/10
Distance: 🏊250m, Sellin 5km ⊗250m 🚉250m.

🏕S	**Ostseebad Wustrow**	6A2

Surfcenter Wustrow, An der Nebelstation 2. **GPS**: n54,34080 e12,38040.

30 🛏€8 + €3/pp 🚰 🗑 Ch 🔌€2,50 WC 🚽. **Surface:** asphalted.
⬜ 01/04-31/10
Distance: 🏊1km ⛱50m.

DE

Ostseebad Wustrow 6A2

Hafenstraße. **GPS**: n54,34363 e12,40053.

30 ⚑ € 3/day, € 7/night. **Surface**: gravel.
Distance: 📶400m ⚓1,5km ⊗on the spot.
Remarks: Max. 1 night.

Parchim 5D4

Yachthafen, Am Fischerdamm. **GPS**: n53,42594 e11,84494.

8 ⚑ € 5 🔌€0,50 Ch ✎ WC ⏚. **Surface**: asphalted. 🅿 01/01-31/12
Distance: 📶100m ⚓on the spot 🛒on the spot ⊗100m 🍴100m.

Pepelow 5D3

Wohnmobilpark Pepelow, Strandweg 1. **GPS**: n54,03805 e11,58441.

12 ⚑ € 10-12 🔌 Ch ✎€2,50 WC ⏚sanitary€2/pp 🔲€2,50/2,50.
Surface: grassy. 🅿 01/01-31/12
Distance: 📶700m ⚓on the spot 🛒on the spot ⊗200m 🍴200m.

Petersdorf 6A4

Hotel Haus Waldesruh, Lenzerstrasse 19. **GPS**: n53,45892 e12,36060.

10 ⚑ € 7,50 🔌€1 Ch ✎€2 WC ⏚€1,50 🔲€1,50/1,50. **Surface**: grassy.
🅿 01/01-31/12
Distance: 📶7km ⚓600m 🛒600m ⊗on the spot 🍴7km.

Priepert 6B4

Wohnmobilpark Am Großen Priepertsee, An der Freiheit 8.
GPS: n53,22043 e13,04201.

---

22 ⚑ € 7 🔌 Ch ✎€2 WC ⏚€1,50 🔲€5/5. **Surface**: grassy.
🅿 01/01-31/12
Distance: ⚓1,5km 🛒1,5km.

Putbus 6B1

Im-Jaich Wasserferienwelt, Am Yachthafen 1, Lauterbach.
GPS: n54,34278 e13,50167.

20 ⚑ € 7-8, € 1,20/pppd tourist tax 🔌 ✎ WC included ⏚€1 🔲€4/3 .
Surface: gravel. 🅿 01/01-31/12
Distance: 📶500m ⚓on the spot 🛒on the spot ⊗on the spot 🍴800m.
Remarks: Bread kiosk, seaview.

Putgarten 6B1

Kap Arkona, Varnkevitzer Weg. **GPS**: n54,67190 e13,40800.

30 ⚑ € 5, ^3,10m € 15. **Surface**: asphalted. 🅿 01/01-31/12
Distance: 📶100m ⊗Imbiss 🍴6km.

Rerik 5D2

Wohnmobilpark Ostseebad Rerik, Straße am Zeltplatz.
GPS: n54,11332 e11,63037.
35 ⚑ € 13, Jul/Aug € 20 🔌 Ch ✎ WC ⏚ included. 🅿 01/01-31/12
Distance: ⚓sandy beach 600m.

Röbel 6A4

Am Seglerhafen, Müritzpromenade 20. **GPS**: n53,38734 e12,61755.

45 ⚑ € 12 🔌 Ch ✎€1 WC ⏚. **Surface**: grasstiles/metalled.
🅿 01/04-31/10
Distance: ⚓on the spot ⊗300m.

Rüterberg 5C5

Wohmobilparkplatz Dorfrepublik Rüterberg, Ringstraße 2.
GPS: n53,15294 e11,18511.⬆.

10 ⌁ € 5/24h+ € 0,50/pp ⌁€1/50liter ⌁€1 Ch€1 ⚡€1/kWh WC ⌁€1.
Location: Rural, simple, central, quiet. **Surface**: grassy.
◻ 01/01-31/12
Distance: 🚶10m ⊗50m.
Remarks: Bread-service.

Schwerin 5C4

Am Hauptbahnhof, Wismarsche Straße. **GPS**: n53,63692 e11,40893.⬆.
4 ⌁ € 8/24h ⌁€1/80liter ⌁Ch ⚡(4x)€1/2kWh. ⌁
Location: Simple, central. **Surface**: metalled.
Distance: 🚶on the spot.

Schwerin 5C4

Marina-Nord Schwerin, Buchenweg 19. **GPS**: n53,64584 e11,43264.⬆.

20 ⌁ € 10 + € 1/pp ⌁⌁Ch ⚡(14x)€0,50/kWh WC ⌁€1,50.
Surface: grassy. ◻ 15/04-15/10
Distance: 🚶4km ⊗on the spot ⚓1km.

Schwerin 5C4

Altstadt, Schliemannstraße-Werderstraße. **GPS**: n53,62978 e11,41975.
⌁ € 8/24h. ⌁
Location: Simple, central. **Surface**: metalled.
Distance: 🚶on the spot.

Schwerin 5C4

Am Stadthafen, Schliemannstraße. **GPS**: n53,62977 e11,41966.⬆.
10 ⌁ € 8/24h ⚡(8x)€1/2kWh. ⌁ **Surface**: metalled. ◻ 01/01-31/12

Seehof 5C3

Campingplatz Seehof, Am Zeltplatz 1. **GPS**: n53,69676 e11,43658.⬆.
10 ⌁ € 16-22, 2 pers.incl ⌁Ch ⚡ WC included ⌁€1 ⚡€3,50/3,50.
Surface: grassy. ◻ 01/01-31/10
Distance: 🚶1,2km ⚓on the spot ⌁on the spot ⊗on the spot
⚓on the spot.

Sembzin 6A4

An der Müritz, Dorfstrasse 2. **GPS**: n53,46445 e12,60386.

14 ⌁ € 8 ⌁⌁Ch ⚡included WC€1 ⌁€2 ⌁€2/24h.
Surface: grassy/gravel. ◻ 01/01-31/12

Distance: 🚶5km ⊗on the spot.
Remarks: Swimming pool.

Sievershagen 5D2

Ferienhof Dubberke, Alt Sievershagen 16. **GPS**: n54,11480 e12,03481.⬆.

5 ⌁ € 10 ⌁⌁Ch ⚡ WC ⌁included. **Surface**: grassy. ◻ 01/01-31/10
Distance: 🚶500m ⊗800m.

Sommersdorf 6B3

Wohnmobilpark Sommersdorf, Am Kummerower See.
GPS: n53,79824 e12,87576.

23 ⌁ € 8-12, 2 pers.incl ⌁€3 ⌁Ch ⚡€3/night WC€2 ⌁€1/5minutes 📶.
Surface: grassy. ◻ 01/01-31/12
Distance: ⚓on the spot ⌁on the spot ⚓on the spot.

Sternberg 5D3

Sternberger, Maikamp 11. **GPS**: n53,71318 e11,81236.⬆➡.

15 ⌁ € 14-18 ⌁⌁Ch ⚡€2,70/day WC ⌁included 📶.
Surface: grasstiles. ◻ 01/04-31/10
Distance: 🚶1km ⚓on the spot ⌁on the spot ⊗on the spot ⚓500m
🚐500m.

Stralsund 6B2

An der Rügenbrücke, Werftstrasse 16. **GPS**: n54,30190 e13,10110.⬆➡.

40 ⌁ € 15, 2 pers.incl ⌁€1/5minutes ⌁€1 Ch€1 ⚡(40x)€0,50/kWh ⌁€1
⌁. **Surface**: grassy/gravel. ◻ 01/01-31/12
Distance: 🚶1,5km 🚐on the spot.
Remarks: Bread-service.

DE

DE

Ueckermünde 6C3
An der Uecker, Ueckerstrasse 125. **GPS:** n53,73470 e14,04930.⬆.

13 ⬛€8 + €1/pp tourist tax 🚰🔌Ch ⚡included.
Surface: grassy/metalled. ⬛ 01/01-31/12
Distance: 🚶Old city centre 200m ⊗200m 🛒100m.

Usedom 6C3
Gaststätte Haffschänke, Dorfstraße 19, Karnin. **GPS:** n53,84348 e13,86537.⬆.

20 ⬛€7 🚰🔌Ch ⚡€3 WC ⬛€2,50. **Surface:** grassy. ⬛ 01/01-31/12
Distance: 🏊on the spot 🛒on the spot ⊗on the spot.

Usedom 6C3
Am Hafen Usedom, Peenestraße. **GPS:** n53,87099 e13,92679.⬆.

20 ⬛€5 🚰🔌Ch ⚡€5 WC€0,50 ⬛€2. **Surface:** metalled.
⬛ 01/01-31/12
Distance: 🚶600m 🏊on the spot ⊗on the spot.
Remarks: At former fishing-port.

Vielank 5C5
Vielanker Brauhaus, Lindenplatz 1. **GPS:** n53,23443 e11,14023.⬆.

12 ⬛free ⚡€3 WC. **Location:** Rural, simple, quiet. **Surface:** grassy.
⬛ 01/01-31/12
Distance: 🚶20m ⊗20m.
Remarks: Check in at reception.

Waren 6A4
Blumen und Parken, Mecklenburgerstrasse. **GPS:** n53,51363 e12,69431.⬆.

40 ⬛€9 + €1-1,50/pp tourist tax 🚰🔌Ch ⚡€0,50/kWh WC included
⬛€1/5minutes. **Surface:** grassy/gravel. ⬛ 01/01-31/12
Distance: 🚶100m 🏊1km 🛒1km ⊗1km 🛒1km 🚌on the spot.

Waren 6A4
Wohnmobilpark Kamerun, Zur stillen Bucht 3, Müritz.
GPS: n53,51175 e12,65174.⬆.

49 ⬛€8-14, tourist tax excl 🚰🔌Ch ⚡€3,25 WC ⬛sanitary €2/pp 📶.
Surface: grassy. ⬛ 01/01-31/12
Distance: 🚶3km 🏊on the spot 🛒on the spot ⊗on the spot 🛒on the spot
🚌500m.

Waren 6A4
Wohnmobilpark Müritz, Teterower Straße 35, Waren-Müritz.
GPS: n53,52611 e12,67194.⬆➡.

22 ⬛€8/24h, tourist tax €1,50/pp 🚰🔌Ch ⚡€0,40/kWh WC ⬛€1,50.
Surface: grasstiles/grassy. ⬛ 01/01-31/12
Distance: 🚶4km 🏊4km 🛒4km ⊗4km 🛒Edeka 10m.

Waren 6A4
Campingplatz Ecktannen, Fontanestraße 66. **GPS:** n53,49944 e12,66361.⬆➡.

16 ⬛€16 🚰🔌Ch ⚡WC ⬛included 📷€2,60/2,60 📶.
Surface: grasstiles/metalled. ⬛ 01/01-31/12
Distance: 🚶3,5km 🏊500m 🛒500m ⊗Bistro 🛒3km 🚌on the spot.

Waren 6A4
Parkplatz Am Hafen, Strandstrasse 3b. **GPS:** n53,51194 e12,68583.⬆.

20 € 10 Ch . **Surface:** metalled.
01/01-31/12, holidays 16.30-11h
Distance: on the spot on the spot on the spot on the spot on the spot.

S Warnemünde 5D2

Am Bahnhof. **GPS**: n54,17841 e12,09185.

100 € 6/3h, € 12/12h, € 16/24h . **Surface:** metalled.
01/01-31/12

Warnemünde 5D2

Parkplatz Strand-Mitte, Parkstrasse 46. **GPS**: n54,17643 e12,05765.
€ 4. **Surface:** metalled. 01/01-31/12
Distance: 2,5km 100m 400m.

S Wesenberg 6B4

Wohnmobilstellplatz Wesenberg, Ahrensberger weg 11.
GPS: n53,27666 e12,98694.

34 € 14, 2 pers.incl €1/80liter €1 Ch€1 WC included.
Surface: grassy/gravel. 01/01-31/12
Distance: 1km on the spot on the spot on the spot 2,5km 1km.

S Wismar 5C3

Wohnmobilpark Westhafen Wismar, Schiffbauerdamm 12.
GPS: n53,89430 e11,45151.

65 € 7/12h, € 10/24h €1/100liter Ch €1/8h WC €1.
Surface: gravel. 01/01-31/12
Distance: 800m 300m, Burger King 400m 300m 800m 100m.

Remarks: Caution key sanitary € 10.

S Wittenbeck 5D2

Sanddornstrand, Bäderweg. **GPS**: n54,14513 e11,79277.

60 € 12-15 €3 Ch WC. **Surface:** unpaved. 01/01-31/12
Distance: 1,5km on the spot on the spot on the spot.
Remarks: Bread-service.

S Zingst 6A1

Wohnmobilhafen Am Freesenbruch, Seestrasse. **GPS**: n54,44060 e12,66058.

40 € 18-24 incl. 2 pers, dog € 3 Ch €2 WC included.
Surface: grassy. 01/01-31/12
Distance: 1,5km 50m on the spot.
Remarks: Bread-service.

S Zingst 6A1

Strandübergang 6, Straminke. **GPS**: n54,44070 e12,70750.

40 € 15 €1/5minutes €3 WC €1. **Surface:** grassy.
01/01-31/12

S Zurow 5D3

Urlaub am Schloss, Kastanienallee 56, Krassow. **GPS**: n53,87379 e11,56618.

10 € 5 €1 Ch €2 WC €2 . **Surface:** grassy/metalled.
01/01-31/12
Distance: 1,5km 1km 3km.
Remarks: Caution key sanitary € 10.

Saxony Anhalt

S Ahlum 5C6

Fischreihütte Ahlumer See, Am Mühlenberg 63. **GPS**: n52,69541 e11,00583.

DE

100 🏍 € 8 🔌 Ch 🔧 €0,50/kWh WC included. 📷 01/01-31/12
Distance: ⛽ on the spot ⊗ on the spot.
Remarks: Bread-service.

🍴 S | **Allrode** | 10C3
Hotel Harzer Land, Teichstraße 28. **GPS:** n51,67774 e10,96478. 🔼.

25 🏍 € 15,50 🔌 Ch 🔧 WC included. **Surface:** grassy.
📷 01/01-31/12
Distance: ⛽ on the spot ⊗ on the spot.

🍴 | **Altenbrak** 🌲🏕 | 10C2
Bodewiese, Am Bielstein. **GPS:** n51,72569 e10,94196. 🔼.

8 🏍 € 5, overnight stay free. 🅿 **Location:** Rural, simple. **Surface:** metalled.
📷 01/01-31/12
Distance: ⛽100m ⊗100m 🚌200m 🧍 on the spot.

🍴 S | **Altenbrak** 🌲🏕 | 10C2
Hotel Zur Talsperre, Oberbecken 1, Wendefurth. **GPS:** n51,73434 e10,90690. 🔼.

20 🏍 € 10 excl. tourist tax 🔌 (20x)€0,50/kWh WC included. 🚿
Location: Rural, simple, isolated. **Surface:** asphalted/grassy.
📷 01/01-31/12
Distance: ⊗ on the spot.

🍴 S | **Arendsee** | 5D5
Im kleinen Elsebusch, Lüchower strasse 6a. **GPS:** n52,87656 e11,46121. 🔼➡.

20 🏍 € 10 🔌€1 🔌€1 Ch 🔧. **Surface:** grassy. 📷 01/01-31/12
Distance: ⛽2,5km ⊗ on the spot 🍽2,5km.

🍴 S | **Aschersleben** 🌲🏕 | 10D2
Sport- und Freizeitzentrum Ballhaus, Seegraben. **GPS:** n51,76101 e11,45760. 🔼.

8 🏍 free 🔌 €1/15minutes 🔌€2/time Ch €2/time 🔧 (12x)€1/6h.
Location: Urban, comfortable, central, quiet. **Surface:** asphalted.
📷 01/01-31/12
Distance: ⛽1km ⊗200m 🍽200m 🔧 on the spot 🚲 on the spot
🧍 on the spot.
Remarks: Caution key € 15, key at reception desk BallHaus.

🍴 | **Bad Bibra** | 10D4
Parkplatz am Schwimmbad. **GPS:** n51,21214 e11,60002. 🔼.

20 🏍 € 3. 🚿 **Location:** Rural, simple, isolated, quiet. **Surface:** gravel/metalled.
📷 01/01-31/12
Distance: ⛽1,5km ⊗200m 🍽1,5km.
Remarks: At swimming pool.

🍴 | **Bad Bibra** 🏕 | 10D4
Parkplatz Bürgergarten, Haus des Gastes. 🔼. **GPS:** n51,20526 e11,57929

10 🏍 € 3. 🚿 **Location:** Urban, simple, central, quiet. **Surface:** gravel/metalled.
📷 01/01-31/12
Distance: ⛽200m 🍽500m.

🍴 S | **Bad Kösen** 🐾 | 10D4
Am Saalebogen, Stendorf 14. **GPS:** n51,11356 e11,69609. 🔼➡.

DE

15 🗓 € 8 ⌁ 🔌 Ch 🧹 (15x)€2/day WC included 🗑€1/time. 🚐
Location: Rural, comfortable, quiet. **Surface:** grasstiles/metalled.
📅 01/01-31/12
Distance: 🚶3km ⊗200m 🍞bakery 200m 🚲on the spot 🚴on the spot.

🍴🅂 **Bad Suderode** 🌿🍂 **10C2**
Restaurant Am Kurpark, Jägerstrasse 7. **GPS**: n51,72685 e11,12078. ⬆️

4 🗓 € 10, € 13 service incl ⌁ 🔌 Ch 🧹 🗑€5/day. 🚐
Location: Urban, comfortable, central, quiet. **Surface:** grasstiles/grassy.
📅 01/01-31/12
Distance: 🚶100m ⊗on the spot 🍺200m 🚍200m 🚲on the spot
🚴on the spot.

🅂 🅂 **Ballenstedt** 🌿 **10D2**
Verkehrslandeplatz Ballenstedt/Quedlinburg, Asmusstedt 13.
GPS: n51,74190 e11,23427. ⬆️

32 🗓 € 4,50/pppn ⌁ 🔌 Ch 🧹 (16x) WC 🗑 📶 included. 🚐 **Location:** Rural,
simple, quiet. **Surface:** grasstiles/metalled. 📅 01/01-31/12
Distance: 🚶2km ⊗on the spot 🍺2km 🚍200m.

🅲🅂 **Bergwitz** **11B2**
Camping Bergwitzsee, Strandweg. **GPS**: n51,79439 e12,57773. ⬆️

20 🗓 € 6 ⌁€3 🔌 Ch. 🚐 **Location:** Rural, simple, isolated, quiet.
Surface: grassy/sand. 📅 01/01-31/12
Distance: 🚶1km ⊘50m 🛶50m ⊗300m 🍺1,5km.
Remarks: Check in at reception campsite, service on campsite.

🍴 **Berssel** **10C2**
Gasthof Zum Schloß, Am Schloß 1. **GPS**: n51,95266 e10,76027. ⬆️

5 🗓 free ⌁on demand. **Location:** Rural, simple, quiet. **Surface:** metalled.
📅 01/01-31/12
Distance: 🚶200m ⊗on the spot 🚲on the spot 🚴on the spot.

🅂🅂 **Bertingen** **10D1**
Hotel La Porte, Im Wald 2. **GPS**: n52,35994 e11,82264. ⬆️➡️

30 🗓 € 7,50 ⌁ 🔌 Ch 🧹 included. **Surface:** grassy. 📅 01/01-31/12
Distance: ⊗on the spot 🍺5km.
Remarks: Bread-service.

🅂🅂 **Bitterfeld** **11A2**
Spaßbad Woliday, Reudener Straße, Bitterfeld-Wolfen.
GPS: n51,67102 e12,24842. ⬆️

10 🗓 € 13 ⌁ 🧹 WC 🗑included. 🚐
Surface: grasstiles. 📅 01/01-31/12
Distance: 🚶1,2km ⊗on the spot 🍺900m.
Remarks: Incl. access swimming pool.

🅂🅂 **Blankenburg** 🌿 **10C2**
Am Schnappelberg, Schnappelberg 2. **GPS**: n51,78862 e10,96036. ⬆️

4 🗓 € 6 ⌁€1/time 🧹€2/night WC. 🚐 **Location:** Urban, simple, central,
quiet. **Surface:** asphalted. 📅 01/01-31/12
Distance: 🚶500m ⊗300m 🍺on the spot.

🅂🅂 **Blankenburg** 🌿 **10C2**
Busparkplatz, Am Schnappelberg. **GPS**: n51,78884 e10,96076. ⬆️

DE

6 ⌘€4/24h ⚡(6x)€1/kWh. 🏠 **Location:** Urban, simple, quiet. **Surface:** metalled. ☀ 01/01-31/12 **Distance:** 🚃400m ⊗300m 🚲200m 🚌on the spot ⚓on the spot.

🚤S **Blankenburg** 🌿 10C2
Teichwirtschaft, Harzstraße 31a, Timmenrode. **GPS:** n51,76874 e10,99134. ⬆.

10 ⌘€9 🚰€1 Ch ⚡€1 🚽€1. 🧺 **Location:** Rural, simple, quiet. **Surface:** grassy/metalled. ☀ 01/01-31/12 **Distance:** 🚃Blankenburg 5km 🚲on the spot ⊗on the spot. **Remarks:** Fishpond.

⚓S **Brachwitz** 〰 11A3
Marina Saale-Ufer, An der Fähre. **GPS:** n51,53270 e11,87059. ⬆➡.

30 ⌘€5 ⚡(4x)€0,50/kWh WC. 🧺 **Location:** Rural, comfortable, quiet. **Surface:** grassy. ☀ 01/01-31/12 **Distance:** 🚃500m 🚲on the spot ⊗500m.

🍴S **Braunsbedra** 11A3
Mobilpark am Geiseltalsee, Schortauer Weg. **GPS:** n51,29421 e11,85346. ⬆.

25 ⌘€10 🚰🍴Ch ⚡WC included 🚽€2/time 📷against payment. 🧺 **Location:** Urban, comfortable, quiet. **Surface:** grassy/metalled. ☀ 01/01-31/12 **Distance:** 🏊700m 🚲500m.

📷S **Breitenstein** 🎍 10C3
Hauptstrasse, L236. **GPS:** n51,61756 e10,94957. ⬆.

8 ⌘free 🚰stay ⚡(4x)€1/8h. **Location:** Rural, simple, quiet. **Surface:** gravel. ☀ 01/01-31/12 **Distance:** 🚃400m ⊗Sportgaststätte.

🍴S **Burg bei Magdeburg** 🌿 10D1
Eschenhof, Parchauer Chaussee 5. **GPS:** n52,28718 e11,86583. ⬆➡.

15 ⌘€12 2 pers.incl, dog €1 🚰🍴Ch ⚡WC 🚽included. **Surface:** grassy. ☀ 01/01-31/12 **Distance:** 🚃2km ⊗on the spot 🚲1km.

⚓S **Burg bei Magdeburg** 🌿 10D1
Wassersportfreunde Burg, Am Kanal 20a. **GPS:** n52,28329 e11,84808. ⬆.

6 ⌘€18 🚰€1/100liter ⚡WC 🚽included. **Surface:** grassy. ☀ 01/05-30/09 **Distance:** 🚃1km 🚲on the spot.

🍴S **Coswig/Anhalt** 11A2
Hotel Zur Fichtenbreite, Fichtenbreite 5. **GPS:** n51,88723 e12,40749. ⬆➡.

15 ⌘€5 🚰🍴Ch included ⚡(4x)€2,50/day 🚽€3,50/time 🧺🧺🧺 **Location:** Rural, simple, noisy. **Surface:** grassy. ☀ 01/01-31/12 **Distance:** 🚃2km 🚲500m ⊗on the spot 🚲2km. **Remarks:** Bread-service, bicycle rental.

⚓S **Coswig/Anhalt** 11A2
Marina Coswig, Post Elbstrasse 22. **GPS:** n51,88071 e12,43552. ⬆➡.

40 � € 7,50 2 pers.incl, dog € 1 ⌐€1/100liter ⌐Ch ⌐€0,50/ kWh WC ⌐€1,50/time. **Location:** Comfortable, quiet. **Surface:** gravel.
○ 01/01-31/12
Distance: ⌐750m ⌐on the spot ⌐on the spot ⌐150m ⌐on the spot.

| | | Dankerode | | 10C3 |

Campingplatz Panoramablick, Hinterdorf 79. **GPS:** n51,58832 e11,14189.⬆
➡

12 ⌐€ 10 excl. tourist tax ⌐€1 ⌐€1 Ch€1 ⌐(6x)€2,50 WC ⌐ ⌐ ⌐
Location: Rural, simple, isolated, quiet. **Surface:** grassy.
○ 01/04-30/10
Distance: ⌐500m ⌐on the spot ⌐500m ⌐on the spot ⌐on the spot.

| | | Darlingerode | | 10C2 |

Wohnmobilpark Harzblick, Hinter den Gärten 11. **GPS:** n51,85278 e10,73667.
⬆➡

25 ⌐€ 8 ⌐€1/80liter ⌐Ch ⌐(12x)€0,60/kWh ⌐€1/day.⌐
Location: Rural, comfortable, quiet. **Surface:** grassy/gravel. ○ 01/01-31/12
Distance: ⌐600m ⌐500m ⌐500m ⌐500m ⌐on the spot ⌐on the spot.

| | | Dessau-Roßlau | | 11A2 |

Flugplatz Hugo Junkers, Alte Landesbahn 27. **GPS:** n51,83447 e12,18289.⬆

8 ⌐€ 9 ⌐⌐Ch ⌐WC ⌐included. ⌐**Location:** Rural, comfortable, isolated, quiet. **Surface:** grassy/metalled. ○ 01/01-31/12
Distance: ⌐5km.
Remarks: Arrival < 19h, max. 8M.

| | | Drübeck/Harz | | 10C2 |

Zur Waldschänke, Tänntalstraße 6. **GPS:** n51,84564 e10,71415.⬆

8 ⌐first day € 10, then € 5 ⌐⌐Ch ⌐included. ⌐
Location: Rural, simple, quiet. **Surface:** grassy/gravel.
○ 01/01-31/12 ⌐ Restaurant: Mo-Tue
Distance: ⌐1,5km ⌐on the spot.

| | | Elend | | 10C2 |

Waldbad Schenke, Am Waldbad 1. **GPS:** n51,74612 e10,69531.⬆

10 ⌐€ 5 + € 1,50/pp tourist tax ⌐(5x). ⌐**Location:** Rural, simple, quiet.
Surface: grassy/metalled. ○ 01/01-31/12
Distance: ⌐600m ⌐on the spot ⌐500m ⌐on the spot ⌐on the spot.

| | | Freyburg/Unstrut | | 10D4 |

Stellplatz Schleusenblick, Wasserstraße 22. **GPS:** n51,21049 e11,76979.⬆

8 ⌐€ 10 + € 1/pp tourist tax ⌐⌐Ch ⌐WC included ⌐€2/day.
⌐**Location:** Urban, comfortable, central, quiet. **Surface:** metalled.
○ 01/01-31/12
Distance: ⌐100m ⌐50m ⌐300m.
Remarks: Along the Unstrut river.

| | | Gernrode | | 10C2 |

Osterteich, Osterallee. **GPS:** n51,72449 e11,16007.⬆

20 ⌐free. **Location:** Rural, simple, isolated, quiet. **Surface:** metalled.
○ 01/01-31/12
Distance: ⌐1,5km ⌐300m ⌐1,5km ⌐on the spot.
Remarks: Next to train stop Selketalbahn.

| | | Haldensleben | | 10D1 |

Am Stendaler Turm, Bornsche Strasse. **GPS:** n52,29291 e11,41342.⬆

DE

DE

10 🛏free. **Surface:** concrete. ⬛ 01/01-31/12
Distance: 🚶200m ⊗250m 🛒150m Aldi.

⚓S | Haldensleben | 10D1
Am Sportboothafen, Kronesruhe. **GPS:** n52,27933 e11,40240. ⬆.

15 🛏€ 10 🚰 🔌 Ch included 💧€0,50/kWh WC 🗑€1. **Location:** Rural.
Surface: grassy. ⬛ 15/04-31/10
Distance: 🚶2km 🚲14km ⛱on the spot ⊗on the spot 🛒200m.
Remarks: Bread-service.

🛏S | Halle/Saale 💮 | 11A3
Parkplatz, Fährstraße. **GPS:** n51,50210 e11,95397. ⬆.

3 🛏€ 5 🚰€1/80liter 🗑Ch 💧stay WC against payment. 🚐
Location: Urban, simple, central, noisy. **Surface:** metalled.
⬛ 01/01-31/12
Distance: 🚶2km 🚲7km ⊗200m 🛒500m 🚌on the spot.
Remarks: Max. 5 days, green zone: environmental badge obligatory.

🛏 | Halle/Saale 💮 | 11A3
P25, An der Stadtschleuse. **GPS:** n51,48065 e11,96183. ⬆.

10 🛏free. **Location:** Urban, simple, central, noisy. **Surface:** metalled.
⬛ 01/01-31/12
Distance: 🚶Old city centre 500m 🚌on the spot.
Remarks: Along railwayline, green zone: environmental badge obligatory.

🛏 | Harzgerode | 10C3
Parkplatz Wallgarten, Wallstrasse. **GPS:** n51,64210 e11,13983. ⬆.

---

5 🛏free. **Location:** Urban, simple, quiet. **Surface:** metalled.
⬛ 01/01-31/12
Distance: 🚶100m 🏊1km 🚲3km ⊗100m 🛒100m 🚌100m �+1km.

👁 | Hasselfelde ⚓ | 10C3
P Pullman City/Westernstadt, Im Rosentale. **GPS:** n51,70179 e10,86604. ⬆.

10 🛏free. **Location:** Rural, simple, quiet. **Surface:** gravel.
⬛ 15/04-31/10

👁S | Havelberg | 6A6
Campinginsel. GPS: n52,82830 e12,06853.

🛏€ 6 🚰€1 🗑€3 Ch 💧(24x)€1/kWh. **Surface:** metalled.

🛏S | Ilsenburg 💮🏕🏊🌲❄ | 10C2
Wohnmobilstellplatz Ilsetal, Ilsetal 6. **GPS:** n51,85386 e10,67013. ⬆➡.

40 🛏€ 9 🚰€2/120liter 🗑Ch 💧(24x)€3/night,3Amp. 🚐 **Location:** Rural,
simple, quiet. **Surface:** metalled. ⬛ 01/01-31/12
Distance: 🚶700m 🏊500m 🚲2km ⊗300m 🛒800m 🚌50m 🚴15km
�+15km.

👁S | Kelbra ⛵ | 10C3
Seecamping Südharz, L1040. **GPS:** n51,42583 e11,00287. ⬆.

15 🛏€ 10-12 🚰 🔌 Ch 🔋 included 📶 against payment.
Location: Rural. **Surface:** gravel. 🅾 01/01-31/12
Distance: 🚶2,5km ⚓on the spot ⊗on the spot 🚊on the spot.

| P | Lutherstadt Wittenberg 🏍️🎠 | 11B2 |

Platz der Jugend. **GPS:** n51,86712 e12,63120.⬆️.

5 🛏free. **Location:** Urban, simple, noisy. **Surface:** metalled.
🅾 01/01-31/12
Distance: 🚶centre 500m ⊗150m 🚊150m.
Remarks: Max. 8h, overnight stay allowed.

| 🚐S | Magdeburg | 10D1 |

Stellplatz Petriförde, Petriförder 1. **GPS:** n52,13289 e11,64714.

50 🛏€ 8 🚰€1 🔌€1 Ch€1. **Surface:** metalled. 🅾 01/01-31/12
Distance: 🚶on the spot.
Remarks: Along the river Elbe.

| 🚐 | Merseburg ⚓ | 11A3 |

Am Saaleufer, Brühl. **GPS:** n51,35491 e12,00234.⬆️➡️.

6 🛏€ 3, guests free. 🚣 **Location:** Rural, simple, quiet.
Surface: gravel/metalled. 🅾 01/01-31/12
Distance: 🚶1km 🚊1,5km.

| 🚐S | Naumburg/Saale | 11A4 |

Altstadtparkplatz **Vogelwiese**, Luisenstraße. **GPS:** n51,14861 e11,81391.⬆️.

15 🛏€ 5/night 🚰€0,50/80liter 🔌 Ch 🔌 (6x)€0,50/kWh WC.
Surface: gravel. 🅾 01/01-31/12
Distance: 🚶500m ⊗50m 🚊500m 🚌50m.
Remarks: Max. 3 days.

| 🚐S | Oranienbaum-Wörlitz | 11A2 |

Jugendverkehrsschule Oranienbaum, Dessauer Strasse 47.
GPS: n51,80279 e12,39023.⬆️➡️.

6 🛏€ 7,50 🚰 🔌 Ch 🔌 (6x) WC included 📋€1/day. 🚣 **Location:** Rural,
comfortable, quiet. **Surface:** gravel/metalled. 🅾 01/01-31/12
Distance: 🚶1km.

| 🚐S | Oranienbaum-Wörlitz | 11A2 |

Seespitze 25. **GPS:** n51,84729 e12,41301.
24 🛏€ 10 🚰 🔌 (24x)€2. **Surface:** metalled. 🅾 01/01-31/12
Distance: 🚶600m 🚲7,5km 🏊on the spot ⊗600m.

| 🚐S | Prettin | 11B2 |

Bade- und Angelsee, Hinterfährstraße. **GPS:** n51,66485 e12,90551.⬆️.

5 🛏€ 6 + € 2,80/pp 🚰 🔌 Ch included 🔌 €0,30/kWh. **Surface:** gravel.
🅾 01/04-31/10
Distance: 🚶1,2km.

3 🛏free. **Location:** Urban, simple. **Surface:** metalled.
🅾 01/01-31/12
Distance: 🚶500m.

| 🚐 | Merseburg ⚓ | 11A3 |

Luftfahrt und Technik-museum Merseburg, Kastanienpromenade 50.
GPS: n51,36004 e11,97044.⬆️.

DE

🅂 Quedlinburg 10C2

An den Fischteichen. GPS: n51,79308 e11,14863.⬆️➡️

20 free €1/80liter (8x)€1/6h.
Location: Urban, comfortable, central, quiet. **Surface:** grasstiles/metalled.
🗓 01/01-31/12
Distance: 350m 300m 250m 150m.

🅂 Quedlinburg 10C2

Marschlinger Hof. GPS: n51,79138 e11,13965.⬆️➡️

6 €10/24h €1/80liter Ch (4x)€1/6h WC.
Location: Urban, comfortable, central, quiet. **Surface:** metalled.
🗓 01/01-31/12
Distance: 100m 50m 400m 200m.
Remarks: Max. 7m.

🅂 Quedlinburg 10C2

Schloßparkplatz, Schenkgasse. **GPS:** n51,78755 e11,13507.⬆️➡️

6 €6/24h €1/80liter Ch (4x)€1/6h. **Location:** Urban,
comfortable, quiet. **Surface:** metalled. 🗓 01/01-31/12
Distance: on the spot 100m.

🅂 Quedlinburg 10C2

Wohnmobilparkplatz Familie Jahnke, Feldmark links der Bode 17.
GPS: n51,80373 e11,17548.⬆️➡️

10 €10 €2/day WC included. **Location:** Rural, simple, quiet.
Surface: concrete. 🗓 01/01-31/12
Distance: 2,5km.

🅂 Salzwedel 5C6

Stellplatz der Hansestadt Salzwedel, Dämmchenweg 41.
GPS: n52,85049 e11,13911.⬆️

6 €3 Ch €2 WC sanitary €2. **Surface:** metalled.
🗓 01/01-31/12
Distance: historical centre 1km 100m.

🅂 Sangerhausen 10D3

An der Walkmühle, Taubenberg. **GPS:** n51,49056 e11,31127.⬆️

50 free. **Surface:** sand. 🗓 01/01-31/12
Distance: 2km on the spot.

🅂 Sangerhausen 10D3

P7, An der Probstmühle. **GPS:** n51,47707 e11,30798.⬆️

20 free. **Surface:** unpaved. 🗓 01/01-31/12
Distance: 500m 200m 100m.

🅂 Sangerhausen 10D3

Rosarium, Sotterhäuser Weg. **GPS:** n51,47245 e11,31798.⬆️
€2 Ch. 15/04-15/10
Remarks: Check in at shop.

🅂 Schierke 10C2

Campingplatz "Am Schierker Stern", Hagenstrasse. **GPS:** n51,75696 e10,68398.⬆️

6 €10 excl. tourist tax Ch included (6x)against payment.
Location: Rural, simple, quiet. **Surface:** gravel/metalled.
🗓 01/01-31/12
Distance: 1km on the spot on the spot on the spot on the spot

DE

on the spot.

S Seehausen 5D5

Stellplatz Seehausen, Schulstrasse 6. **GPS**: n52,89068 e11,75119.

12 €5 €2 Ch (3x)€2. **Surface:** metalled. 01/01-31/12
Distance: 100m. 200m.
Remarks: Check in at tourist office.

Stassfurt 10D2

Neumarkt, Lehrter Straße. **GPS**: n51,85424 e11,58284.

6 free. **Location:** Urban, simple, central, quiet. **Surface:** gravel.
01/01-31/12
Distance: 500m. 100m.
Remarks: Along the Bode river.

S Stendal 5D6

Nordwall-Schützenplatz. **GPS**: n52,61116 e11,86121.

20 free €1/80liter €1 Ch. **Surface:** grassy/metalled.
01/01-31/12
Distance: on the spot bakery 50m.

Stolberg/Harz 10C3

Am Bahnhof. **GPS**: n51,56727 e10,95696.

5 free. **Location:** Rural, simple, quiet. **Surface:** asphalted.
01/01-31/12
Distance: centre 800m.
Remarks: Max. 2 days.

Stolberg/Harz 10C3

Am Rittertor, Rittergasse. **GPS**: n51,57655 e10,94539.

5 free. **Location:** Rural, simple, quiet. **Surface:** asphalted.
01/01-31/12
Distance: 1km.
Remarks: Max. 2 days.

Stolberg/Harz 10C3

Freizeitbad Thyragrotte, Thyratal 5. **GPS**: n51,56378 e10,95796.

3 free. **Location:** Rural, simple. **Surface:** asphalted.
01/01-31/12
Distance: city centre 1km 1km on the spot.

S Tangermünde 5D6

Tangerplatz, Klosterberg. **GPS**: n52,53774 e11,96803.

30 €5 Ch included. **Surface:** metalled. 01/01-31/12
Distance: 700m 150m.

S Wahrenberg 5D5

Stellplatz Storchenwiese, Eichenwinkel 34. **GPS**: n52,98342 e11,67362.

8 €5 €1/100liter Ch€2 (6x)€3. **Surface:** grassy.
01/01-31/12

S Weissenfels 11A4

Caravan- und Freizeitmarkt Gerth, Drei Wege. **GPS**: n51,19822 e11,99875.

DE

7 🚐 free 🚰 €1/80liter 🔌 Ch 🧹 (4x)€1/stay. **Location:** Urban, simple, noisy.
Surface: asphalted. 🗓 01/01-31/12
Distance: 🚲 4km ⊗ on the spot 🛒 on the spot.

♨️S Wernigerode 🌿🏔 10C2
Am Katzenteich. GPS: n51,83882 e10,78168. ⬆️➡️.

20 🚐 € 5/stay 🚰 €1/40liter 🔌 Ch 🧹 (20x)€1/kWh WC €0,50/time.
Location: Comfortable, quiet. **Surface:** metalled. 🗓 01/01-31/12
Distance: 🚶500m ⊗200m 🛒500m 🏍 on the spot 🚶 on the spot.

♨️S Wernigerode 🌿🏔 10C2
Schlossparkplatz am Anger, Halberstädler strasse 1. **GPS:** n51,83807 e10,79535.
⬆️.

24 🚐 € 5, overnight stay free 🚰 €2/time 🔌 Ch WC €0,50/time. 🚐
Location: Urban, simple, central, quiet. **Surface:** metalled.
🗓 01/01-31/12, service 9-18h
Distance: 🚶300m ⊗200m 🛒600m ⊗ on the spot 🚶 on the spot.

🍴S Wernigerode 🌿🏔 10C2
Harzpension Familie Mann, Mühlental 76, B244. **GPS:** n51,81902 e10,81430.
⬆️.

6 🚐 € 10 excl. tourist tax 🚰 €0,50/time 🔌 Ch included 🧹 €0,50/kWh
WC 🚽€0,50/time. 🚐 **Location:** Rural, simple, quiet. **Surface:** gravel.
🗓 01/04-10/11
Distance: 🚶4km ⊗ on the spot.
Remarks: Arrival <21h, check in at restaurant.

🚐S Wörlitz 🌿🏔 11A2
Seeparke, Seespitze, K2376. **GPS:** n51,84899 e12,41296. ⬆️➡️.

24 🚐 € 5 day/€ 5 night 🚰 free 🧹 (24x)€2 WC €0,50/time 🚽€0,50/time. 🚐
Location: Rural, comfortable, quiet. **Surface:** metalled.
🗓 01/01-31/12
Distance: 🚶800m ⊗500m 🛒800m 🚏800m 🏍 on the spot 🚶 on the spot.
Remarks: Parking at the edge the Wörlitzer park, max. 24h, caution key sanitary
€ 15.

🍴 Wörlitz 🌿🏔 11A2
Hotel Coswiger Elbterrasse, Elbterrasse 1. **GPS:** n51,87750 e12,45097. ⬆️.

10 🚐 € 5, guests free. 🚐 **Location:** Simple, quiet. **Surface:** grassy.
🗓 01/01-31/12
Distance: 🚶1,5km ⊗ on the spot 🛒4km.
Remarks: Check in at hotel, guests free.

🌾S Zeitz 11A4
Obsthof Martin, Kloster Posa 1. **GPS:** n51,05836 e12,15797. ⬆️.

20 🚐 € 5 🚰 🔌 Ch 🧹 (4x)€3/day. 🚐 **Location:** Rural, comfortable, quiet.
Surface: grassy. 🗓 01/01-31/12
Distance: 🚶1,5km ⊗200m 🛒1km.

Brandenburg/Berlin

🍴S Abbendorf 5D5
Gasthaus Dörpkrog an Diek, Am Deich 7. **GPS:** n52,89663 e11,90975. ⬆️.

6 🚐 € 5, guests free 🚰 🔌 Ch 🧹 WC included. 🗓 01/01-31/12
Remarks: Bread-service.

Alt-Zeschdorf 6D6

Reiterhof Blumrich, Falkenhagerweg 11. **GPS**: n52,42649 e14,42328.

30 €10 Ch included. **Surface:** grassy.
01/01-31/12 winter Mo
Distance: 1,5km.
Remarks: At manege, bread-service.

Altdöbern 11D2

Q1 Rasthof Altdöbern, Senftenberger strasse 11. **GPS**: n51,64523 e14,03544.

20 €10 WC included. **Surface:** metalled. 01/01-31/12
Distance: 500m on the spot 500m.

Angermünde 6C5

Parkplatz Am Oberwall, Oberwall 5. **GPS**: n53,01501 e14,00371.

5 free €1/100liter €1/2kWh. **Location:** Urban, simple, central.
Surface: metalled. 01/04-31/10
Distance: on the spot on the spot on the spot
Historische Stadtkerne Märkischer Landweg.
Remarks: Near city wall.

Angermünde 6C5

NABU-Erlebniszentrum Blumberger Mühle, Blumberger Mühle 2.
GPS: n53,03572 e13,96806.

10 free. **Location:** Rural, simple, isolated, quiet. **Surface:** grassy/metalled.
01/01-31/12
Distance: 4km near fish pond on the spot on the spot
on the spot.
Remarks: At biosphere reserve.

Bad Saarow 11D1

Parkplatz Strolin, Silberbergerstrasse. **GPS**: n52,28726 e14,03895.

4 free. **Surface:** metalled. 01/01-31/12
Distance: 100m 100m.

Bad Saarow 11D1

Saarow-Therme, Ringstrasse. **GPS**: n52,29399 e14,06243.

6 free. **Surface:** metalled. 01/01-31/12
Distance: on the spot 300m 400m.

Bad Wilsnack 5D5

Kur- und Gradier-Therme Bad Wilsnack, Am Kähling.
GPS: n52,96316 e11,95007.

43 €13,50 + € 1/pp tourist tax Ch (43x) WC included.
Surface: sand. 01/01-31/12
Distance: 500m 200m 500m.
Remarks: Check in at pay-desk of the Therme, bread-service.

Berlin 6C6

Historisches Fährhaus Berlin, Muggelbergallee 1, Berlin-Köpenick.
GPS: n52,41851 e13,58734.

15 01/03-01/11 € 18, 02/11-28/02 € 14 Ch (15x) €2/24h
WC included €1/time €5/stay. **Location:** Urban, luxurious, quiet.
Surface: grassy/gravel. 01/01-31/12
Distance: on the spot 8km on the spot on the spot on the spot
100m, supermarket 750m 1km tram 100m.
Remarks: Sauna €5.

DE

⊠S Berlin 6C6

WohnmobilPark Berlin, Waidmannsluster Damm 12-14.
GPS: n52,59559 e13,28910.⬆️➡️.

90 € 10-22, 2 pers.incl, tourist tax € 1/pp, dog € 2 €1/100liter
Ch €3,50/24h WC €1, €4/4.
Location: Urban, central. **Surface**: grassy/metalled.
01/01-31/12
Distance: centre Berlin 16km 600m on the spot on the spot metro 1km.
Remarks: Key sanitary building € 4/day, hotline-Nr.: 0176 – 99 55 25 00.

⊠S Berlin 6C6

Reisemobilhafen Berlin Spandau, Askanierring 70. **GPS**: n52,55309 e13,20050.
⬆️.

180 € 15, 2 pers.incl, tourist tax € 1/pp €0,10/10liter
Ch WC included €1/5minutes €2/24h.
Location: Urban, simple, central, noisy. **Surface**: grassy/gravel.
01/01-31/12
Distance: on the spot 100m on the spot 300m.
Remarks: Near approach route of airport, 23-5h quiet, check in at kosk, outside environmental zone. In area of the former English barracks 'Alexander Barracks', A10 exit Berlin-Spandau, follow road till cross roads Heerstraße/Gatowerstraße,here to the left, at Flakenseerplatz straight on, Neuendorferstraße, before Hohenzollernring to the left.

⊠S Berlin 6C6

Int. Reisemobilstation Berlin-Mitte, Chausseestrase 82.
GPS: n52,53817 e13,37304.⬆️.

50 € 20-22, 2 pers.incl Ch WC included.
Location: Urban, comfortable, central, noisy. **Surface**: grassy/metalled.
01/01-31/12
Distance: on the spot 500m 500m 200m.
Remarks: Check in at reception.

⊠S Berlin 6C6

Köpenicker Hof, Stellingdamm 15, Berlin-Köpenick. **GPS**: n52,45929 e13,58532.
⬆️➡️.

40 € 10-14, 2 pers.incl stay Ch €0,50/kWh WC included12h.
Location: Simple, quiet. **Surface**: grassy/metalled.
01/01-31/12
Distance: on the spot on the spot Tram (centre 300m).
Remarks: Caution key sanitary building € 20, bread-service.

⚓S Berlin 6C6

Marina Lanke Berlin, Scharfe Lanke 109-131. GPS: n52,50344 e13,18801.
⬆️.

20 € 1,50/m + € 3,50/pp, dog €2 Ch WC included €3/2.
Location: Urban. **Surface**: asphalted. 01/05-15/10
Distance: centre Berlin 16km on the spot on the spot 1km.
Remarks: Check in at harbourmaster.

⚓S Berlin 6C6

Marina Wendenschloss, Wendenschlossstrasse 350-354.
GPS: n52,42558 e13,58384.⬆️.

10 € 15 Ch WC included €1/time.
Location: Simple, quiet.
Surface: grassy/metalled.
01/04-31/10
Distance: 18km city centre on the spot 100m Tram 200m.
Remarks: Outside environmental zone.

Tourist information Berlin:
ℹ️ Tourist Info, Europacenter, Eingang Budapester strasse 3; Brandenburgertor, Südflügel; Fernsehturm, Alexanderplatz, www.btm.de. Documentation available, via Internet.
👁️M Zeughaus. German historical museum.
👁️ Alexanderplatz. The old historical centre of Berlin.
👁️ Brandenburger Tor. Built in 1791 as a triumphal arch after the construction of the Berlin Wall the arch remained as a symbol of the German separation.
T free.
👁️ Haus am Checkpoint Charly, Friedrichstrasse 44. At the former border crossing. History of the Wall is told with photographs. 9-22h.
👁️ Schloß Charlottenburg, Luisenplatz. Summer residence of the Prussian kings. Tue-Fri 9-17h, Sa-Su 10-17h.
⚘ Arkonaplatz. Flea market. Su 10-16h.
⚘ Ostbahnhof. Antiques and flea market. Su 9-17h.

DE

⚐ Strasse des 17. Juni. Arts and fleamarket. ⏺ Sa-Su 10-17h.
🅿 Zoologischer Garten, Hardenbergplatz 8. City-zoo. ⏺ 01/04-30/09
9-18.30h, 01/10-31/10 9-18h, 01/11-28/02 9-17h.

| 🏕S | Brandenburg 🌿🏞🍽 | 11A1 |

Am Brandenburger Dom, Grillendamm. **GPS**: n52,41724 e12,56576.⬆

60 🛢€ 10 ⛽€1/100liter 🗑 Ch ⚡(26x)€1/kWh WC ⬜€1/4minutes. 🚙
Location: Urban, simple, noisy. **Surface:** asphalted. ⏺ 01/01-31/12
Distance: 🛵Neustadt 15min, Altstadt 15min ⛱on the spot ⊗Imbiss
🚆on the spot 🚲on the spot ⚐on the spot.

| 🏕S | Brandenburg 🌿🏞🍽 | 11A1 |

Wassersportzentrum Alte Feuerwache, Franz Zieglerstrasse 27.
GPS: n52,40485 e12,54868.⬆➡

30 🛢€ 12 ⛽🗑 Ch ⚡€1/day WC ⬜€1/time 🚿included. 🛶
Location: Urban, simple, central, noisy. **Surface:** grassy/metalled.
⏺ 01/01-31/12
Distance: 🛵500m ⛱on the spot ⊗500m 🚆on the spot 🚲on the spot
⚐on the spot.
Remarks: Bread-service, boat rental, bike and e-bike rental.

| 🏕S | Brieske | 11D3 |

Reimann, Brieske Dorf 27. **GPS**: n51,49203 e13,94743.➡

20 🛢€ 6 ⛽🗑 Ch ⚡(12x)€2 WCincluded. **Surface:** grassy.
⏺ 01/01-31/12
Distance: 🛵200m 🚣9,3km 🚂2km.

| 🏕S | Burg/Spreewald | 11D2 |

Hagens Insel - Wasserwanderrastplatz, Weidenweg 4.
GPS: n51,86138 e14,11527.

10 🛢€ 10 ⛽🗑 Ch ⚡ WC ⬜included. **Surface:** grassy.

| 🏕S | Burg/Spreewald | 11D2 |

Landgasthof zur Wildbahn, Wildbahnweg 20. **GPS**: n51,85104 e14,09384.

9 🛢€ 13, 2 pers.incl, tourist tax € 1,50/pp, dog € 2 ⛽🗑 ⚡ WCincluded.
Surface: metalled. ⏺ 01/03-30/10

| 🏕S | Dollenchen | 11D2 |

Gasthaus Stuckatz, Hauptstrasse 29. **GPS**: n51,60745 e13,86226.➡

20 🛢€ 8 ⛽🗑 Ch ⚡ WC ⬜included. **Surface:** grassy. ⏺ 01/01-31/12
Distance: 🛵on the spot ⊗on the spot 🚂3km.

| 🏕S | Dreetz | 6A6 |

Reiterhof Müller, Schulstrasse 61. **GPS**: n52,79796 e12,46874.⬆.

10 🛢€ 12 ⛽🗑 Ch ⚡included WC. 🐴 **Location:** Rural, simple, isolated,
quiet. **Surface:** grassy. ⏺ 01/01-31/12
Distance: 🛵800m ⊗300m 🚂500m 🚆500m.

| 🏕S | Fehrbellin | 6B5 |

FF Freizeitmobile, Gewerbepark 29. **GPS**: n52,79770 e12,78624.⬆➡

DE

10 € 7,50 Ch included €2,50/day free. **Location:** Urban, simple, quiet. **Surface:** grassy. 01/01-31/12
Distance: 1km 2km 1km 1km on the spot on the spot.
Remarks: Accessory shop.

S Fürstenberg/Havel 6B4

Marina Fürstenberg, Ravensbrücker Dorfstrasse 26. **GPS**: n53,19489 e13,14895.

50 € 9 Ch included €2,50/day WC €1,50/time free.
Location: Rural, comfortable, quiet. **Surface:** grassy.
01/01-31/12
Distance: 1km on the spot on the spot on the spot 1km on the spot on the spot.
Remarks: Wifi code at harbour master, boat rental.

S Höhenland 6C6

Das Forsthaus, Bahnhofstraße 13. **GPS**: n52,68433 e13,88171.

8 € 10,50 Ch WC included €5/day.
Location: Rural, comfortable, quiet. **Surface:** grasstiles. 01/01-31/12
Distance: 3km on the spot on the spot.
Remarks: Bread-service.

S Kienitz 6D6

Ferienhaus Marth, Kienitzeroderstrasse 20. **GPS**: n52,67616 e14,39890.

8 €6 Ch €1,50 WC €1,50. **Surface:** grassy. 01/04-30/09
Distance: 3km 3km.

S Klein-Ossnig 11D2

Caravan-Krokor, Haupstrasse 12/a, B169. **GPS**: n51,69962 e14,27917.

15 €7 Ch included. **Surface:** grassy.
01/01-31/12
Distance: on the spot 3km 50m 2km on the spot on the spot.
Remarks: Arrival only during opening hours: Mo-Fr 8-19, Sa 8-13h.

S Kloster Lehnin 11B1

Hotel Seehof, Am See 51. **GPS**: n52,34924 e12,70374.

15 € 10, guests free €2/day WC €2/time.
Location: Rural, simple, comfortable. **Surface:** grassy.
01/01-31/12
Distance: 1,8km on the spot on the spot on the spot on the spot.
Remarks: Check in at hotel.

S Kolkwitz 11D2

Bauernhof Korreng, Papitzerstrasse 48. **GPS**: n51,76676 e14,22410.

3 € 10 Ch WC included. **Surface:** grassy. 01/03-31/10
Distance: 2,5km.

S Kyritz 6A5

Parkplatz Wässering, Graf-von-der-Schulenburg-Straße.
GPS: n52,94044 e12,40053.

15 free €1/100liter Ch €1/8h. **Location:** Urban, simple, noisy.
Surface: grasstiles. 01/01-31/12
Distance: city centre 100m on the spot 250m 250m.

Lindow/Mark 6B5

Am Wutzsee. **GPS**: n52,97205 e12,98924.

DE

3 🛏️ free, tourist tax € 0,50/pp. 🚿 **Location:** Urban, simple, noisy.
Surface: metalled. ☐ 01/01-31/12
Distance: 🚶on the spot ⚓on the spot ⊗150m 🛒150m 🚲on the spot
🚶on the spot.
Remarks: Max. 1 night, pay at tourist office.

Autocamping im Spreewald, Chausseestrasse 17a, Lübbenau-Zerkwitz.
GPS: n51,86559 e13,93324. ⬆️➡️.

6 🛏️ € 14/24h, tourist tax € 1,50/pp, dog € 1 🚰 € 1,50 🔌
Ch 🚿 WC ⌁ included. **Surface:** grasstiles. ☐ Easter-31/10
Distance: 🏊2,5km 🛒500m.

Am Bahnhof, Bahnhofstraße (B115). **GPS**: n51,86139 e13,96361.

10 🛏️ € 8 🚰 € 1/80liter 🔌 Ch 🚿 € 0,50/kWh. ⛽ **Surface:** asphalted.
☐ 01/01-31/12
Distance: 🚶800m 🏊3,3km ⊗350m 🛒50m.
Remarks: Along railwayline, max. 2 days.

Kahnfährhafen Leipe, Dorfstrasse 34, Leipe. **GPS**: n51,85301 e14,05023. ⬆️.

4 🛏️ € 5. **Surface:** metalled. ☐ 01/01-31/12
Distance: 🏊11,6km.

Restaurant Elsthal, Teichwiesenweg, Elsthal. **GPS**: n52,07428 e13,16744. ⬆️.
10 🛏️ € 10 🚰 Ch 🚿 WC ⌁ included. **Surface:** sand. ☐ 01/01-31/12
Distance: ⊗on the spot.

Remarks: Max. <>2.35m.

Marina-Yachthafen Lychensee, Schlüssstrasse 7. **GPS**: n53,21187 e13,29686.
⬆️.

6 🛏️ € 10 🚰 🔌 Ch 🚿 € 2,50/day WC ⌁ € 1/time. 🚿 **Location:** Rural, simple,
quiet. **Surface:** grassy. ☐ 15/04-15/10
Distance: 🚶700m 🛒650m.
Remarks: Check in at harbourmaster, boat rental.

Gaststätte Birkenhof, Segeletzerstrasse 2. **GPS**: n52,82503 e12,56528. ⬆️.

3 🛏️ € 3 🚰 🔌 Ch included. 🚿 € 3/day WC. 🚿 **Location:** Rural, simple,
isolated, quiet. **Surface:** metalled. ☐ 01/01-31/12 ◉ Tue
Distance: 🚶5km ⊗on the spot 🚲on the spot 🚶on the spot.

Sportcenter Neuruppin, Trenckmannstraße 14. **GPS**: n52,91573 e12,80365. ⬆️.

30 🛏️ € 6 WC ⌁ € 2,50/time 📶. 🚿 **Location:** Urban, simple, quiet.
Surface: grasstiles. ☐ 01/01-31/12
Distance: 🚶on the spot ⚓Neuruppiner See 500m ⊗on the spot 🛒200m,
bakery 400m 🚲on the spot 🚶on the spot.
Remarks: Check in at sport centre.

Bäckerei Plentz, Dorfstraße 43. **GPS**: n52,73643 e13,08540. ⬆️➡️.

4 🛏️ € 8 🚰 🔌 Ch 🚿 WC included. 🚿 **Location:** Rural, simple, quiet.
Surface: metalled. ☐ 01/01-31/12
Distance: 🚶on the spot 🚌1km 🛒500m 🚆train 500m 🚲on the spot

DE

⚐on the spot.
Remarks: Along railwayline, in front of bakery.

⳥⳥S **Oranienburg** ◀ **6B6**
Motel Havelidyll, Havelhausener Brücke 1, Havelhausen.
GPS: n52,72161 e13,25047. ⬆ .

10 ⭣ € 15 ⛽ Ch ⚡ WC ⬇ 📶included. 🛁 **Location:** Rural, simple, isolated, quiet. **Surface:** grassy. ◯ 01/04-15/11
Distance: ⛴10km ⚓4km ⤵on the spot ⊗on the spot.

⚓S **Oranienburg** **6B6**
Am Schlosshafen, Rungestrasse 47. **GPS:** n52,75760 e13,23879. ⬆.

26 ⭣ € 10 ⚡€1/80liter ⛽ Ch ⚡ (16x)€1/kWh WC €0,50/time ⬇€1/5minutes ▣€5/time. 🏠 **Location:** Rural, comfortable, central, quiet.
Surface: metalled. ◯ 01/01-31/12
Distance: ⛴600m ⤵on the spot ⊗600m ⚓600m ⚓ on the spot ⚐on the spot.
Remarks: Tallycard: service, electricity, sanitary building, caution € 10.

▣ **Potsdam** 🌿⛵ **6B6**
Am Krongut, Potsdamer Straße 196. **GPS:** n52,41332 e13,02905. ⬆.

11 ⭣ € 10/24h. 🏠 **Location:** Urban, simple. **Surface:** concrete.
◯ 01/01-31/12
Distance: ⛴city centre 2km ⊗100m 🚋Tram 300m.

▣ **Potsdam** 🌿⛵ **6B6**
P historische Mühle, Zur Historischen Mühlen. **GPS:** n52,40562 e13,03453. ⬆.

5 ⭣ € 2/h, max. € 20/24h. 🏠 **Location:** Urban, simple. **Surface:** metalled.
◯ 01/01-31/12

Distance: ⛴2km ⊗on the spot.
Tourist information Potsdam:
◉ Filmpark Babelsberg, August-Bebel-Str. 26-53. Attractions park concerning the film. ◯ 23/03-31/10 10-18h.

⚓S **Rehfelde** **6C6**
Campershof, Alt Werder 8. **GPS:** n52,52093 e13,94080. ⬆➡.

10 ⭣ € 7,50 ⛽ 🔌 Chincluded ⚡€1,50/day WC ⬇. 🛁 **Location:** Rural, comfortable, quiet. **Surface:** grassy. ◯ 01/01-31/12
Distance: ⛴2km ⤵2km ⚓2km ⚓ on the spot ⚐on the spot.
Remarks: Bread-service.

⳥⳥S **Schmergow** **6B6**
Zum fröhlichen Landmann, Ziegeleiweg 17. **GPS:** n52,45416 e12,80553. ⬆➡.

30 ⭣ € 7,50 ⛽ 🔌 Ch ⚡€1/2kWh 📶included. 🛁
Location: Rural, simple, isolated. **Surface:** grassy. ◯ 01/04-31/10
Distance: ⛴500m ⊗on the spot 💧500m ⚓400m.

⚓S **Schwedt/Oder** ◀ **6D5**
Wassersportzentrum Schwedt, Wasserplatz 4. **GPS:** n53,05759 e14,29861. ⬆.

30 ⭣ € 10 ⛽ 🔌 Ch ⚡ WC ⬇included. **Surface:** grassy. ◯ 01/01-31/12
Distance: ⛴1km ⤵on the spot ⊗on the spot 💧500m.
Remarks: Check in at harbourmaster or bar.

▣S **Senftenberg** **11D2**
Wohnmobilstellplatz Buchwalde, Buchwalder Straße 52.
GPS: n51,51256 e14,02278.
12 ⭣ € 11-14 ⛽ 🔌 Chincluded ⚡€2 WC ⬇€0,50. **Surface:** grasstiles.
◯ 01/04-01/11
Distance: ⛴2km ⤵Senftenberger See ⊗on the spot ⚓ on the spot.
Remarks: Max. 4 nights, caution key sanitary € 20.

▣S **Stolzenhagen** 🏘 **6D5**
Am Kietz, Kietz 9. **GPS:** n52,94916 e14,10833. ⬆➡.

20 🛏€ 7,50 🚰 🔌 Ch 🚿 (10x)€2,50/day WC included 🗑€2,50/pp. 🛵
Location: Rural, comfortable, quiet. **Surface:** grassy/metalled.
🔵 01/01-31/12
Distance: 🛒on the spot ⊗Imbiss 🚲 Oder-Neiße-Radweg 🚶on the spot.
Remarks: Directly on the canal, check in at Imbiss, bread-service.

🔵S | **Storkow/Mark** 🌊🏖 | **11C1**

An der Schleuse, Kirchstrasse. **GPS:** n52,25792 e13,93178. ⬆➡.
5 🛏€ 10 🚰 🔌 included. **Surface:** grasstiles. 🔵 01/01-31/12
Distance: 🛒200m ⊗300m 🍴500m.
Remarks: At the Storkower Canal, max. 36h.

🔵S | **Templin** 🌊🏖⚓ | **6C5**

Alter Knehdenerstrasse. **GPS:** n53,12359 e13,49423. ⬆➡.

40 🛏free 🚰€1/60liter 🔌 Ch. **Location:** Urban, simple, quiet.
Surface: asphalted/metalled. 🔵 01/01-31/12
Distance: 🛒300m ⊗300m 🍴300m 🚲 on the spot 🚶 on the spot.

🔵S | **Tiefensee** 🍴🖼 | **6C6**

Reisemobilplatz, Country Camping Tiefensee, Schmiedeweg 1.
GPS: n52,68302 e13,84292. ⬆🖼.

64 🛏€ 14, dog € 1,50 🚰 🔌 Ch 🚿 (51x) WC included 🗑€0,50/time 📷€2,50/h
🛵 **Location:** Rural, comfortable, quiet. **Surface:** grassy.
🔵 01/01-31/12
Distance: 🛒on the spot 🛒on the spot 🎣 on the spot ⊗on the spot
🍴on the spot 🚲on the spot 🚲 on the spot 🚶 on the spot.
Remarks: Check in at reception campsite.

🔵S | **Weisen** | **5D5**

Wohnmobilstellplatz Am Biotop, Heinrich-Heine-Strasse 4.
GPS: n53,02062 e11,78086. ⬆➡.

8 🛏€ 5 🚰 🔌 Ch included. **Surface:** gravel. 🔵 01/01-31/12
Distance: 🛒300m ⊗200m 🍴300m.

🔵S | **Werder/Havel** 🌊🏖 | **11B1**

An der Föhse. **GPS:** n52,37807 e12,93704. ⬆.

25 🛏€ 6,50 + € 1,50/pp tourist tax 🚰€0,50/80liter 🔌 Ch 🚿 (8x)€0,50/
kWh,(8x)€0,50/kWh WC€0,50/time. 🛵 **Location:** Urban, simple.
Surface: gravel. 🔵 01/01-31/12
Distance: 🛒on the spot 🛒on the spot ⊗on the spot 🍴on the spot 🚤100m
🚲 on the spot.
Remarks: Check in at harbourmaster.

🔵S | **Wusterhausen/Dosse** 🌊🏖 | **6A5**

Dossehalle, Zur Dossehalle 6. **GPS:** n52,89337 e12,46537. ⬆.

3 🛏free 🚰 🔌 Ch free 🚿 €1/8h. **Location:** Urban, simple, quiet.
Surface: asphalted. 🔵 01/01-31/12
Distance: 🛒centre 500m 🍴450m.

Saxony

🔺 | **Adorf** | **11A6**

Waldbad, Waldbadstrasse 5. **GPS:** n50,30778 e12,25056.

3 🛏free. **Surface:** metalled. 🔵 01/03-30/11
Distance: 🛒1km 🍴500m.
Remarks: Max. 24h.

🔺S | **Amtsberg** | **11C5**

Waldcamping Erzgebirge, B174, An der Dittersdorfer Höhe, Dittersdorf.
GPS: n50,76583 e13,01444.

60 🛏€ 13-15 🚰🍽 Ch ⚡€2 WC 🚽included. **Surface:** grassy/metalled.
⏰ 01/01-31/12

Im Kurgebiet, Parkstraße 1. **GPS:** n51,60122 e12,58278.⬆️

4 🛏free, tourist tax € 1,20-1,50/pp 🚰€1/80liter 🍽€1 Ch€1. **Location:** Rural.
Surface: metalled. ⏰ 01/04-31/12
Distance: 🚶750m ⊗1,4km. 🛒1,4km.

Albertbad, Austus-Klingner Straße. **GPS:** n50,28545 e12,24034.⬆️
5 🛏€ 8 + € 2,20/pp tourist tax 🚰€1/100liter ⚡included.
Surface: asphalted. ⏰ 01/01-31/12
Distance: 🚶1km ⊗250m.
Remarks: Check in at pay desk swimming pool, caution € 20.

Campingplatz Landidyll, Beuchaer Oberweg 7. **GPS:** n51,15200 e12,62663.
35 🛏€7,50 🚰🍽 WCincluded 🚽€0,50. ⏰ 01/01-31/12
Distance: 🚶on the spot ⚓1km 🛒2km.

Freizetbad Am Riff, Am Riff 3. **GPS:** n51,14321 e12,65383.⬆️
10 🛏free. **Surface:** asphalted.
Distance: ⊗on the spot.
Remarks: At swimming pool.

Am Fürst-Pückler-Park, Heideweg 2. **GPS:** n51,53365 e14,71727.⬆️
25 🛏€ 8-12 + € 1,25/pp tourist tax 🚰🍽 Ch ⚡ WC 🚽.
Surface: asphalted/gravel. ⏰ 01/01-28/12
Distance: 🚶on the spot⚓4km 🛒2km.

Erholungsgebiet Biehainer See'n, Zum Waldsee. **GPS:** n51,28662 e14,92490.
10 🛏€ 5 🚰 Ch ⚡ WC 🚽included 📶€0,75/day.
Distance: 🚶1km ⚓on the spot ⊗on the spot 🛒2km.
Remarks: Max. 48h.

Sportpark Rabenberg, Rabenbergweg. **GPS:** n50,45556 e12,74417.

15 🛏€ 5 + € 5/pp 🚰🍽 Ch ⚡€2/day WC 🚽€0,50. **Surface:** metalled.
⏰ 01/01-31/12

Distance: 🚶5km ⊗5km 🛒5km.
Remarks: Arrival <22h, dog € 2/day.

Caravan Service Bressler, Zwickauerstrasse 78. **GPS:** n50,80889 e12,48667.

6 🛏€ 4/night 🚰€1 ⚡ Ch ⚡€2. **Surface:** metalled. ⏰ 01/01-31/12
Distance: ⚡2,1km.

Parkplatz Am Schloss, An der Weinstraße. **GPS:** n51,24111 e13,41575.
6 🛏€ 4 ⚡ (2x). **Surface:** metalled. ⏰ 01/01-31/12
Distance: ⊗on the spot.

Parkplatz Grosse Meissner, Wiesentor Strasse. **GPS:** n51,05639 e13,74306.

30 🛏€ 14 <6,8m, € 16 6,8m-8m, € 20 > 8m 🚰€2/100liter ⚡ Ch€2 ⚡
(14x)€4/day. **Location:** Urban. **Surface:** asphalted. ⏰ 01/01-31/12
Distance: 🚶100m.

Sachsenplatz Dresden, Johannstadt Käthe-Kollwitz-Ufer 4, Johannstadt.
GPS: n51,05700 e13,75990.⬆️
150 🛏€ 10 ⚡ (25x)€3/24h.
Location: Urban, central.
Distance: 🚶Old city centre 2,2km ⊗300m 🛒Aldi 700m 🚃500m.

Werner Knopf, B6, Meissner Landstrasse. **GPS:** n51,08131 e13,65563.
16 🛏€ 5/6m + € 1/m 🚰€2 ⚡€2 🚽€1,50. **Location:** Urban.
Surface: grasstiles.
Distance: 🚶6km 🚃500m.
Remarks: Gate closes at 22h.

Wohnmobilplatz Dresden, Kesselsdorfer Straße 153. **GPS:** n51,04004 e13,66963.
5 🛏€ 12 🚰🍽 Ch ⚡€2,50 🚽€2.
Location: Urban. **Surface:** gravel.
⏰ 01/01-31/12
Distance: 🚶centre Dresden 4km ⚡4km ⊗on the spot 🛒800m 🚃800m.
Remarks: At Wellnesshotel Landlust.

Wohnmobilstellplatz am Blüherpark, Zinzendorfstraße 7.
GPS: n51,04426 e13,74371.⬆️
50 🛏€ 14 🚰€1 ⚡€1 ⚡€3/night 🚽€2. **Location:** Urban.
Surface: metalled. ⏰ 01/01-31/12
Distance: 🚶1km ⚡5km ⊗500m 🛒450m.
Remarks: Check in at Cityherberge, Lingnerallee 3, 24/24.

CaravaningPark Schaffer, Kötzschenbroderstrasse 125.
GPS: n51,08639 e13,68222.⬆️

DE

100 ⌷ €11 €0,50/60liter €0,50 Ch €0,50 €0,50/kWh WC €0,50 .

Location: Urban, comfortable.
Surface: grassy.
☐ 01/01-31/12
Distance: Dresden 5km 2km 200m 500m 200m 500m.
Remarks: Bread-service, repair possibilities motorhome, access <19h.

Tourist information Dresden:
ℹ Dresden-City-Card. Card gives among other things for free public transport, entrance to many museums, discounts on boat trips, restaurants etc. ☐ 01/01-31/12. ⊤ € 18/48h.
ℹ Tourist Information, Prager strasse; Schinkelwache/Theaterplatz, www.dresden.de. Former residence city with many curiosities.
☀ Striezelmarkt, Altstadt. Christmas fair. ☐ advent season.

Ebersbach/Sachsen 11D6
Fest- und Parkplatz am Freibad, Kottmarsdorfer Strasse.
GPS: n51,00972 e14,59806.

7 ⌷ € 5, € 10 service incl Ch . **Surface:** metalled.
☐ 01/04-30/10
Distance: 1km 500m 1km.

Elsterheide 11D3
Wohnmobilstellplatz Lothar Meusel, Am Hochwald 27, Tätzschwitz.
GPS: n51,48304 e14,10750.

8 ⌷ € 6,50-7,50 Ch WC included €2,25. ☐ 01/04-31/10
Distance: 3km 8-10km.

Freiberg 11C4
Am Johannisbad, Lessingstraße. **GPS:** n50,91513 e13,33334.
10 ⌷ € 10 €1/80liter €1 Ch €1 €0,50/kWh WC . **Surface:** metalled.
☐ 01/01-31/12
Distance: Altstadt 900m 150m Kaufland 500m.

Geierswalde 11D3
Ferien- und Freizeitpark Geierswalde See, Promenadeweg.
GPS: n51,49547 e14,13146.
⌷ € 6 €2 Ch WC . **Surface:** grassy. ☐ 01/04-01/10
Distance: 500m Geierswaldesee 300m 5km.

Grünhain 11B5
Freizeitpark, Auer Strasse 82, Haus des Gastes, Grünhain-Beierfeld.
GPS: n50,58139 e12,79167.

6 ⌷ € 5 €1 €1,customers free Ch €1,50/day WC €1.
Surface: metalled. ☐ 01/01-31/12
Distance: 1km on the spot 3km.

Heidenau 11D4
Wohnmobilplatz Heidenau, Rudolf Breischeidstrasse 23.
GPS: n50,98417 e13,85028.

20 ⌷ € 9 €1,50 Ch €1,50 €1,50. **Surface:** gravel.
☐ 01/04-31/10
Distance: Heidenau 4km 1,5km, Imbiss 50m 2km 1,5km.

Hermsdorf 11D5
Ski- & Sporthotel SWF, Bahnhofstraße 7. **GPS:** n50,73241 e13,66400.
8 ⌷ € 4, tourist tax € 0,50/pp €2 €2 Ch €0,40/kWh. ☐ 01/01-31/12

Königsfeld-Stollsdorf 11B4
Spreer's Ferienhaus, Hauptstrasse 28. **GPS:** n51,04861 e12,74500.

4 ⌷ € 8 Ch €2. ☐ 01/01-31/12
Distance: 4km 4km.

Königstein 11D4
Panoramhotel Lilienstein, Ebenheit 7. **GPS:** n50,92527 e14,07527.
10 ⌷ € 15-20 included €3.
Distance: on the spot.
Remarks: Bread-service and breakfast buffet.

Leipzig 11A3
Campinghof Bartl, Bornaer Chaussee 36, Markkleeberg.
GPS: n51,27000 e12,43194.

26 🗓 € 15 🚰 €2 ⟍ Ch ⟋ €2 WC 🗑 🔲. **Surface:** grassy/metalled.
🅿 01/01-31/12
Distance: 🚶Leipzig 5km ⛵2km 🛒1,5km.

| 🛁S | Leipzig 🌿🚲🛒 | 11A3 |

Reisemobilhafen Leipzig, Im Dölitzer Holz 20. **GPS:** n51,28525 e12,38352.⬆

30 🗓 € 10 🚰 €1 🍴€1 Ch €1 ⟋ (12x)€2,50/day. 🐕 **Location:** Rural,
comfortable, quiet. **Surface:** unpaved. 🅿 01/01-31/12
Distance: 🚶5,5km ⛵2,5km ⊗300m 🚋Tram 850m.
Remarks: Can be reached without environmental: from the direction
Goethesteig.

| 🛁S | Leipzig 🌿🚲🛒 | 11A3 |

Stellplatz Melinenburg, Stöhrerstraße 3. **GPS:** n51,36648 e12,42717.⬆

20 🗓 € 10, 2 pers.incl, extra pers € 1, dog € 1 🚰 €1 🍴€1 Ch €1 ⟋ (8x)€2.
Location: Urban, comfortable, quiet. **Surface:** gravel.
🅿 01/01-31/12
Distance: 🚶4,5km 🛒1,2km 🚌200m.
Remarks: Bread-service, outside environmental zone.

| 🛁S | Marienberg ⛲❄ | 11C5 |

Rätzteich, Geloblland 27c. **GPS:** n50,62417 e13,17861.

3 🗓 € 3 🚰 €1 🍴€1 Ch €1 ⟋ €1. **Surface:** metalled. 🅿 01/01-31/12
Distance: 🚶5km ⛵on the spot ⊗500m 🛒5km 🚴3km ⚓ on the spot.
Remarks: Recreation area.

| 🛁S | Oberwiesenthal 🚲🏔❄ | 11C5 |

OTG Tennishalle, Vieren Strasse 1a. **GPS:** n50,42722 e12,96944.

20 🗓 € 18, 01/11-31/03 € 25, tourist tax excl 🚰 🍴 Ch ⟋ WC included 🗑 €1.
Surface: metalled. 🅿 01/01-31/12
Distance: ⊗on the spot 🚴250m.
Remarks: Check in at reception tennishall < 22h, bread-service.

| 🛁 | Rothersdorf | 11B3 |

Zur-Tabak-Baude, Grimmaische Straße 117. **GPS:** n51,30647 e12,73830.

20 🗓 € 5, guests free. **Surface:** grassy. 🅿 01/01-31/12
Distance: 🚶2km ⊗on the spot 🛒1,5km 🚌on the spot.

| 🍴🛁S | Seiffen | 11C5 |

Berghof, Kurhausstrasse 36. **GPS:** n50,64605 e13,48114.

20 🗓 guests free 🚰 🍴 ⟋ . 🅿 01/01-31/12
Distance: 🚶2,5km ⊗on the spot 🛒300m.

| 🛁S | Zittau | 11D6 |

Zittau Am Dreiländereck, Brückenstrasse 23. **GPS:** n50,89405 e14,82176.⬆➡
100 🗓 € 7 🚰 €1 ⟍ Ch ⟋ (16x)€1/8h WC 🗑. 🚌 **Surface:** metalled.
🅿 01/01-31/12
Distance: 🚶1,5km 🛒200m.
Remarks: Three Countries' Corner Germany-Czech Republic-Poland.

| 🛁S | Zwota | 11B6 |

Natur Camping Platz, Merkneukirchner Strasse 79. **GPS:** n50,35111 e12,38111.
⬆

40 🗓 € 10 🚰 €1,50 🍴€1 Ch ⟋ (16x) WC 🗑included. **Surface:** gravel.
🅿 01/01-31/12
Distance: 🚶Klingenthal 6km 🛒6km.

North Rhine Westphalia

S Aachen 🌿🍴🚻 **8D5**

Aachen-Camping, Branderhofer Weg 11. **GPS:** n50,76111 e6,10306. ⬆️➡️.

46 🛏€ 15/night 🚰🅲h 🔧 WC included 🚽€1. 🚿 **Location:** Urban, luxurious, central, quiet. **Surface:** metalled. 🅾️ 01/01-31/12
Distance: 🚶1,7km 🚌700m 🚉700m 🚏300m.
Remarks: Baker 8.30-09.00.

S Ahaus **9A2**

Krimesplatz, Schlossstrasse. **GPS:** n52,07450 e7,00299. ⬆️.

8 🛏free 🚰€0,50/80liter 🅲h 🔧 (6x)€0,50/kWh WC. **Surface:** metalled. 🅾️ 01/01-31/12 ⭕ during event
Distance: 🚶on the spot.
Remarks: Parking centre, max. 3 nights.

S Ahlen **9B3**

Freizeitbad Berliner Park, Dolbergerstrasse 66. **GPS:** n51,75559 e7,89694. ⬆️.

4 🛏€ 8/24h 🚰🅲h 🔧 included. **Surface:** metalled. 🅾️ 01/01-31/12
Distance: 🚶centre 300m 🚌300m.
Remarks: Max. 3 nights, 50% discount at swimming pool.

S Alpen **8D3**

An der Motte, Burgstrasse 66. **GPS:** n51,57985 e6,51846. ⬆️.

11 🛏€ 7,50 🚰🅲h 🔧 included. 🚆 **Location:** Rural, comfortable. **Surface:** gravel. 🅾️ 01/01-31/12
Distance: 🚶500m 🚲2,5km 🚉500m.

S Altena 🚻 **9B4**

Sauerlandhalle Pragpaul, Hermann Vossstrasse 14. **GPS:** n51,30861 e7,66056. ⬆️➡️.

12 🛏free 🚰€0,50 🅲€0,50 Ch 🔧 (6x)€0,50/kWh. **Location:** Rural, simple, quiet. **Surface:** asphalted/gravel. 🅾️ 01/01-31/12
Distance: 🚶2km 🚲10km 🚌nearby 🚉2km 🚲on the spot 🚶on the spot.

🍴 Altenbeken 🍴🚻 **9D3**

Landhaus Friedenstal, Hüttenstrasse 42. **GPS:** n51,75992 e8,95111. ⬆️.

5 🛏€ 5 🔧 (5x)€2,50/24h WC on demand, at restaurant. 🚿 🚲 **Location:** Simple, central. **Surface:** grassy/gravel. 🅾️ 01/01-31/12
Distance: 🚶200m 🚌on the spot 🚉200m.

S Altenberge 🚻 **9B2**

Sportpark Grosseberg, Bijlenweg. **GPS:** n52,05528 e7,47056. ⬆️.

20 🛏free 🚰€0,50 🅲h. **Surface:** metalled. 🅾️ 01/01-31/12
Distance: 🚶on the spot 🚌nearby 🚉1,5km.
Remarks: Parking sports centre.

S Arnsberg **9C4**

An der Schlacht/Ruhrstrasse. **GPS:** n51,40127 e8,06468. ⬆️.
4 🛏free. **Location:** Simple. **Surface:** gravel.
Distance: 🚲3,3km 🚉Lidl 50m.

S Ascheberg **9B2**

Appelhof, Appelhofstraße. **GPS:** n51,79003 e7,61902.
4 🛏free. **Surface:** metalled. 🅾️ 01/01-31/12
Distance: 🚶on the spot.

🍴S Ascheberg **9B2**

Gasthaus Eickholt, Frieport 22, Davensberg. **GPS:** n51,82619 e7,59391.

DE

6 ⌕ € 5, free with a meal ⚡ ✏ WC 📶. **Surface:** grassy.
⬛ 01/01-31/12 ⚫ Mo
Distance: 🚶800m ⚓5,5km ⊗on the spot 🛒1km 🚗800m.
Remarks: Swingolf.

| 🍴 S | Attendorn | 9C4 |

Land-Hotel-Struck, Repetalstrasse 245, Niederhelden. **GPS:** n51,12073 e7,97284.

6 ⌕ guests free ✏ € 3,50 WC. ⬛ 01/01-31/12
Distance: 🚶on the spot ⊗on the spot 🛒2km ⚽on the spot 🚶on the spot.

| ⊙ S | Attendorn | 9C4 |

Atta Höhle, Finnentroper Straße. **GPS:** n51,12489 e7,91421.↑.
8 ⌕ € 7,50 ⚡🍺Ch ✏ included. ⬛ 01/01-31/12
Distance: 🚶500m 🛒Lidl 400m.

| ⊙ S | Bad Berleburg 🌳❄ | 9C4 |

Bismarckstraße. **GPS:** n51,04986 e8,39406.↑.
3 ⌕ free ⚡€ 2/100liter 🍺Ch ✏€ 1/8h. **Surface:** metalled.
⬛ 01/01-31/12
Distance: 🚶500m 🛒500m.

| 🍴 S | Bad Berleburg 🌳❄ | 9C4 |

Pension-Bauernladen Schmelzhütte, K52 Hoheleye. **GPS:** n51,13874 e8,45742.

6 ⌕ € 10 ⚡🍺Ch ✏€ 2. **Surface:** asphalted. ⬛ 01/01-31/12 ⚫ Mo
Distance: 🚶1km ⊗on the spot 🛒1km.
Remarks: Bread-service.

| 🍴 | Bad Berleburg 🌳❄ | 9C4 |

Hotel-Restaurant Erholung - Laibach, Auf dem Laibach 1.
GPS: n51,06776 e8,44527.

5 ⌕ free with a meal ⚡ ✏ (1x)€ 5/day WC. **Surface:** asphalted.
⬛ 01/01-31/12
Distance: 🚶5km ⊗on the spot 🛒5km 🚗on the spot ⚽on the spot
🚶on the spot ✈1,5km.

| 🍴 S | Bad Driburg 🌳 🌳 | 9D3 |

P Driburg Therme, Georg-Nave-Strasse 24. **GPS:** n51,74194 e9,02542.↑.

10 ⌕ € 5 + tourist tax ✏ (10x)€ 3/24h WC. 🚌 **Location:** Rural, simple, quiet.
Surface: asphalted. ⬛ 01/01-31/12
Distance: 🚶1km ⊗on the spot 🛒1km 🚗on the spot ⚽on the spot
🚶on the spot.
Remarks: Max. 7m, caution € 10, key electricity at pay-desk.

| ⊙ S | Bad Laasphe | 9C5 |

Mühlenstrasse. **GPS:** n50,92412 e8,41146.↑→.

7 ⌕ € 6/day ⚡€ 0,50/80liter 🍺Ch ✏€ 0,50/kWh. **Surface:** asphalted.
⬛ 01/01-31/12
Distance: 🚶500m ⊗500m 🛒500m.
Remarks: Parking at town hall.

| 🍴 S | Bad Laasphe 🌳 | 9C5 |

Hotel Jagdhof Glashütte, Glashütterstrasse 20, Volkholz.
GPS: n50,92008 e8,28070.

6 ⌕ € 13,80, free with a meal ✏ WC 📶. 🚌 **Location:** Rural.
Surface: grassy. ⬛ 01/01-31/12 ⚫ 23-24/12
Distance: 🚶4km ⚓on the spot ⊗on the spot 🛒4km 🚗1,5km.

| ⊙ S | Bad Lippspringe | 9D3 |

Arminiuspark, Burgstraße 10. **GPS:** n51,78124 e8,82447.

DE

11 ⛺ € 2,80/1p +1p € 2/pp ⚡🔌 Ch ✎. **Location:** Urban, quiet.
Surface: metalled. 🅾 01/01-31/12
Distance: 🚶300m ⊗350m 🚲 on the spot 🧍on the spot.
Remarks: Pay at tourist office.

🏕️S	Bad Münstereifel	9A6

Wohnmobilpark Eifel, Dr.Grevestraße 16. **GPS:** n50,54600 e6,76514. ⬆️➡️.

30 ⛺ € 7 + € 1/pp tourist tax ⚡€1/100 🔌€1 Ch ✎ (30x)included
WC 🚾€1,80. 🚿
Location: Rural, comfortable, quiet. **Surface:** grassy/metalled.
🅾 01/01-31/12
Distance: 🚶350m ⊗on the spot 🍴100m.
Remarks: Pay and coins at swimming pool, 20% discount pool.

🏕️	Bad Oeynhausen 🌡️	9D1

Südbahnstraße/Detmolder Straße. **GPS:** n52,19680 e8,80038. ⬆️.
3 ⛺free. **Surface:** asphalted. 🅾 01/01-31/12
Remarks: Max. 2 days.

🏕️	Bad Oeynhausen 🌡️	9D1

Siekmeiers Hof, Volmerdingsener strasse 111. **GPS:** n52,24679 e8,78394.

10 ⛺guests free. **Location:** Urban, quiet. **Surface:** gravel.
🅾 01/01-31/12 🔴 Mon, Tue
Distance: 🚶on the spot ⊗on the spot 🍴1km.

🏕️S	Bad Salzuflen	9D2

Wohnmobil-Park Flachsheide, Forsthausweg. **GPS:** n52,09868 e8,74569. ⬆️.

25 ⛺ € 7/day, tourist tax € 2,90/pp/day ⚡🔌 Ch ✎ WC 🚾included.
Location: Rural, quiet. 🅾 01/01-31/12
Distance: 🚶1,5km ⚓5,5km ⛵on the spot ⊗500m 🍴1,5km 🚌free.

🏕️S	Bad Sassendorf 🌡️	9C3

Kurcamping Rumkerhof, Weslarnerstrasse 30. **GPS:** n51,59581 e8,17909. ⬆️➡️.

93 ⛺ € 8,50 ⚡🔌 Ch ✎ (93x)included. **Surface:** gravel. 🅾 01/01-31/12
Distance: 🚶1,3km ⊗1,3km.
Remarks: Waste dump € 0,50, bread-service.

🏕️S	Bad Waldliesborn	9C3

Wohnmobilstellplatz, Quellenstraße. **GPS:** n51,71759 e8,33587. ⬆️.

10 ⛺ € 4,40 + € 7/pp ⚡€2/100liter 🔌 Ch ✎ (8x)€2/24h.
Location: Rural, quiet. **Surface:** gravel. 🅾 01/01-31/12
Distance: 🚶400m ⊗200m 🍴400m 🚌400m.
Remarks: Discount on access terme.

🌡️S	Bad Westernkotten	9C3

Wohnmobilplatz An den Sole-Thermen, Mühlenweg 1.
GPS: n51,63126 e8,35195. ⬆️.

46 ⛺ € 7, tourist tax € 2/pp ⚡€1/100liter 🔌 Ch ✎ €0,50/kWh. 🔋
Surface: grassy. 🅾 01/01-31/12
Distance: 🍴bakery 300m.
Remarks: Bread-service.

🏕️S	Bad Wünnenberg 🌡️	9D3

Wohnmobilhafen, In den Erlen. **GPS:** n51,52058 e8,70133. ⬆️➡️.

12 ⛺ € 4 ⚡€1/100liter 🔌 Ch ✎ (12x)€1/24h. 🚿
Location: Urban, central. **Surface:** gravel. 🅾 01/01-31/12
Distance: 🚶100m 🚲400m ⊗100m 🍴400m 🚲 on the spot 🧍on the spot.

🏕️S	Balve 🌡️	9B4

Am Hallenbad, In der Murmke 9. **GPS:** n51,32729 e7,86920. ⬆️➡️.

DE

3 🛏 free ⛽ €1/100liter 🚰 💧 €1/kWh. **Location:** Urban, simple.
Surface: metalled. 📅 01/01-31/12
Distance: 🚶600m ⊗600m 🍽600m 🚲 on the spot 🚶 on the spot.

♿🅂 **Barntrup** 9D2
Badeanstaltsweg. **GPS:** n51,98790 e9,10990. ⬆️➡️

50 🛏 € 6 ⛽ €0,50/100liter 🚰 Ch 💧 €2,50/24h 📶. 🏪 **Location:** Rural,
comfortable. **Surface:** grasstiles. 📅 01/01-31/12
Distance: 🚶Kleve-zentrum 8km ⛵2,5km ⊗300m.
Remarks: Golf court 500m, Schloss Moyland 300m.

🍴🅂 **Bedburg-Hau** 📶 8D3
Landgasthaus Schwanenhof, Mühlenstraße 71, Ortsteil Schneppenbaum.
GPS: n51,76096 e6,20404. ⬆️

4 🛏 € 6 ⛽ €1/100liter 🚰 Ch 💧 €0,50/kWh. **Location:** Rural, simple.
Surface: asphalted. 📅 01/01-31/12
Distance: 🚶450m ⊗450m 🍽450m 🚌450m.
Remarks: To be paid at campsite Teutoburger Wald.

🄲🅂 **Barntrup** 9D2
Ferienpark Teutoburger Wald, Badeanstaltsweg 4. **GPS:** n51,98768 e9,11027.
⬆️

25 🛏 € 5 ⛽ 🚰 Ch 💧 (18x). 🚿
Location: Rural, comfortable. **Surface:** grassy. 📅 01/01-31/12
Distance: 🚶500m 🍽on the spot 🍽1km.
Remarks: Bread-service.
Tourist information Bedburg-Hau:
🏛❌ Schloß Moyland, Am Schloss 4. Castle. 📅 Tue-Fri 11-18h, sa-su 10-18h,
1/4-31/3 tue-so 11-17h 🔘 Mon.

🅂 **Bergheim** 9A5
Stellplatz Paffendorf, Königsstrasse/Kastanienallee. **GPS:** n50,96389 e6,61194.
⬆️➡️

9 🛏 € 20,50 ⛽ 🚰 Ch 💧 🍽 📅 €5/5 📶 included. **Location:** Rural, luxurious,
quiet. **Surface:** grassy/metalled. 📅 01/04-31/10
Distance: 🚶450m ⊗450m 🍽 450m 🚌450m 🚲 on the spot 🚶 on the spot.

🅂 **Beckum** 9C3
Am Hallenbad, Paterweg 4. **GPS:** n51,75129 e8,03585. ⬆️➡️

8 🛏 free. **Location:** Rural, simple, quiet. **Surface:** asphalted.
📅 01/01-31/12
Distance: 🚶Bergheim 2km 🚲2,3km ⊗300m 🍽500m.
Remarks: Max. 2 days, castle Paffendorf 100m.

🅂 **Bergkamen** 9B3
Wohnmobilhafen Marina Rünthe, Hafenweg, Rünthe.
GPS: n51,64106 e7,64309.

3 🛏 free ⛽ €0,50/100liter 🚰 Ch 💧 (2x)€0,50/kWh. **Location:** Urban,
simple. **Surface:** metalled. 📅 01/01-31/12
Distance: 🚶1km ⊗1km 🍽1km.

🅂 **Bedburg-Hau** 📶 8D3
Womo-Moyland, Moyländer Allee 3a, Moyland. **GPS:** n51,75562 e6,24381. ⬆️➡️

18 🛏 € 7/24h ⛽ €1/80liter 🚰 Ch 💧 (12x)€0,50/kWh. 🏪

Surface: grassy/gravel. 🔲 01/01-31/12
Distance: 🚶500m 🚲 3,8km.
Remarks: Max. 3 days, only exact change.

Bergkamen 9B3
Freizeitzentrum Im Häupen, Häupenweg 29. **GPS:** n51,61300 e7,63075. ⬆️➡️.

5 🛏️ free. **Surface:** metalled. 🔲 01/01-31/12
Distance: 🚶500m 🚲 3,4km ✖️500m 🚉500m.
Remarks: Max. 72h.

Bestwig 9C4
Besucherbergwerk, Ziegelwiese, Ramsbeck. **GPS:** n51,31821 e8,40318. ⬆️.

6 🛏️ free. **Location:** Simple. **Surface:** metalled. 🔲 01/01-31/12
Distance: ✖️800m.

Bestwig 9C4
Ludwigstrasse. **GPS:** n51,36064 e8,40165. ⬆️.

4 🛏️ free. **Location:** Simple, simple. **Surface:** metalled.
🔲 01/01-31/12
Distance: 🚶on the spot ✖️300m 🚉200m.

Beverungen 10A3
Wohnmobilhafen Weser, Am Hakel. **GPS:** n51,66167 e9,37639. ⬆️➡️.

12 🛏️ free. 🔌€1/100liter 🚰 Ch€1 💧 (12x)€1/6h. **Location:** Urban, simple.
Surface: grassy/metalled. 🔲 01/01-31/12
Distance: 🚶on the spot 🏊on the spot 🛒on the spot ✖️on the spot 🚉on the spot.
Remarks: Next to Festplatz.

Bielefeld 9C2
Am Johannisberg, Dornbergerstrasse. **GPS:** n52,02270 e8,51155. ⬆️➡️.

10 🛏️01/03-01/12 €5/24h 🔌€1/8 🚰 Ch 💧 (10x)€0,50/kWh. 🅿️
Location: Rural, comfortable, quiet. **Surface:** metalled.
🔲 01/01-31/12
Distance: 🚶2km ✖️Imbiss 🚉2km 🚌2km.

Billerbeck 9A2
Am Freibad, Osterwickerstrasse. **GPS:** n51,97928 e7,28190. ⬆️➡️.

10 🛏️free 🔌€1 🚰 Ch 💧 (4x)€1. **Surface:** gravel. 🔲 01/01-31/12
Distance: 🚶500m 🚉500m.
Remarks: At swimming pool.

Blankenheim 9A6
Weiherhalle, Koblenzerstrasse. **GPS:** n50,43499 e6,65439. ⬆️.

15 🛏️ €5/24h 🔌€1/80liter 🚰 Ch 💧 (12x)€2/10h. 🅿️
Location: Rural, simple. **Surface:** metalled. 🔲 01/01-31/12
Distance: 🚶150m.

Bocholt 8D2
WoMo Park am Aasee, Uhlandstraße 39. **GPS:** n51,83496 e6,63146. ⬆️.

37 🛏️ €5 🔌€0,50/50liter 🚰 Ch 💧 (20x)€0,50/kWh WC 🔲 ⚡€3,50/2,50 📶.
💧 **Location:** Urban, central, noisy. **Surface:** metalled.
🔲 01/01-31/12
Distance: ✖️300m 🚉300m.

Bocholt 8D2
Inselbad Bahia, Hemdenerweg 169. **GPS:** n51,86265 e6,61002. ⬆️➡️.

DE

10 free ⚡🅐Ch.
Location: Rural, simple. **Surface:** grasstiles.
🅾 01/01-31/12
Distance: 2,5km ⊗450m 1km on the spot.
Remarks: Max. 48h, coins at swimming pool, first coin € 3, next € 0,50.

| Bocholt | 8D2 |

Euregio-Gymnasium, Unter den Eichen, Blücherstrasse.
GPS: n51,84884 e6,63700.⬆

10 free. **Location:** Urban, simple. **Surface:** metalled.
🅾 01/01-31/12
Distance: 1km ⊗700m on the spot.
Remarks: Parking 'Stadtswald', max. 3 nights.

Tourist information Bocholt:
⚓ Rathaus - Gasthausplatz. 🅾 Thu-evening.

| Bonn | 9A5 |

An der Rheinaue, Ludwig-Erhard-Allee. **GPS:** n50,70981 e7,13904.⬆
18 free. **Surface:** asphalted. 🅾 01/01-31/12
Distance: centre 4km 🚗 A565 4,6km 300m line 66 > Bonn centre.

| Borken | 9A2 |

Aquarius-Bad, Feldmark. **GPS:** n51,83644 e6,86479.⬆➡

20 free ⚡🅐Chfree. **Location:** Rural, simple. **Surface:** grassy.
🅾 01/01-31/12
Distance: 1km ⊗1km 1km.
Remarks: Parking swimming pool, max. 3 nights, service: Kläranlage Borken
Mo-Thu 7-16h, Fri 7-11.30h.

| Borken | 9A2 |

Festplatz Weseke, Borkenwirther strasse, Weseke. **GPS:** n51,90529 e6,85210.⬆

---

5 free. **Location:** Rural, simple. **Surface:** metalled.
🅾 01/01-31/12
Distance: 500m ⊗500m 500m.
Remarks: Max. 3 nights.

| Borken | 9A2 |

Schlossklinik Pröbsting, Pröbstinger Allee. **GPS:** n51,83861 e6,80556.⬆.
10 free. **Surface:** metalled. 🅾 01/01-31/12
Distance: Badesee 150m.

| Borken | 9A2 |

Wasserburg Gemen, Coesfelderstrasse, Gemen. **GPS:** n51,86172 e6,86909.⬆➡

5 free. **Location:** Rural, simple. **Surface:** metalled.
🅾 01/01-31/12
Distance: 1km 500m 500m ⊗1km 1km.
Remarks: Parking sports park, max. 3 nights.

| Borken | 9A2 |

Camping Pröbstingersee, Dirkshof 11, Hoxfeld. **GPS:** n51,83237 e6,78764.

10 free ⚡🅐Ch. **Surface:** metalled.
🅾 01/01-31/12
Distance: 6,5km 100m ⊗100m.
Remarks: Max. 3 nights, service against payment on campsite.

| Borken | 9A2 |

Gestüt Forellenhof Wolter, Zum Homborn 9. **GPS:** n51,86245 e6,89797.⬆
15 € 11 ⚡🅐Ch (7x)included. **Surface:** gravel. 🅾 01/01-31/12
Distance: Borken 3,5km fish pond ⊗on the spot.
Remarks: Check in at Gaststätte, € 5 euro discount coupon.

| Bottrop | 9A3 |

Movie Park, Kirchhellen, Warner Allee 1. **GPS:** n51,62400 e6,97096.⬆

DE

100 ⌇ € 5. **Surface:** metalled. ◻ 01/04-31/10
Distance: 2,7km 100m 2,7km.

Tourist information Bottrop:
 Alpincenter, Prosperstrasse. Indoor ski centre. ◻ 9-24h. day ticket € 25, <18h € 18.

| S | Brakel/Bellersen | 9D2 |

Wohnmobilhafen Mühlengrund, Meinolfussstrasse 6.
GPS: n51,77217 e9,18804.

23 ⌇ € 8,50 €0,50 Ch (23x)included. **Location:** Rural, comfortable, isolated. **Surface:** grasstiles. ◻ 01/01-31/12
Distance: 800m 400m 800m 800m on the spot.

| | Bruchhausen | 10A3 |

Bruchhäuserstrasse. **GPS:** n51,70714 e9,29192.

4 ⌇ free. **Location:** Rural, simple. **Surface:** grassy/gravel.
◻ 01/01-31/12
Distance: 200m 200m 200m.

| S | Brüggen | 8D4 |

Freizeitplatz Brachter Wald, St.-Barbara-Straße 40–42, Bracht.
GPS: n51,25713 e6,17022.
14 ⌇ € 9, 2 pers.incl Ch €2/day WC €1. **Surface:** grasstiles.
◻ 01/01-31/12
Distance: 2km on the spot on the spot.

| S | Brüggen | 8D4 |

Wohnmobilhafen Brüggen, Bornerstraße 48. **GPS:** n51,24264 e6,18955.

30 ⌇ € 4 Ch included €2. **Surface:** metalled. ◻ 01/01-31/12

Distance: 50m 100m 50m 50m.
Remarks: Behind Aldi-süd.

| S | Brühl | 9A5 |

Phantasialand P1, Berggeiststrasse 31-41. **GPS:** n50,79919 e6,87875.

10 ⌇ € 12,50/night WC . **Location:** Comfortable, quiet.
Surface: metalled.
◻ 04/04-31/10
Distance: 100m.

Tourist information Brühl:
 Phantasialand. Large amusement park. ◻ 01/04-31/10 9-18h, winter changing visiting hours.

| | Bünde | 9C1 |

Stadtgarten, Steinmeisterstrasse/Viktoriastrasse. **GPS:** n52,19869 e8,58986.

5 ⌇ free. **Location:** Urban, simple. **Surface:** metalled.
◻ 01/01-31/12
Distance: 50m 50m 50m.
Remarks: Max. 72h.

| S | Büren | 9C3 |

Parkplatz an der Afte, Fürstenberger Strasse. **GPS:** n51,54897 e8,56381.

8 ⌇ free Ch . **Location:** Urban, simple.
◻ 01/01-31/12
Distance: on the spot 500m 200m.
Remarks: Parking nearby swimming pool.

| S | Coesfeld | 9A2 |

Brauhaus Stephanus, Overhagenweg 1. **GPS:** n51,93719 e7,15617.
4 ⌇ customers free . **Surface:** metalled. ◻ 01/01-31/12
Distance: on the spot.

| S | Dahlem | 8D6 |

Flugplatz Dahlemer Binz, Dahlemer Binz. **GPS:** n50,40663 e6,53700.

DE

DE

3 ☷free ⚡€1 🔌Ch. **Location:** Rural, simple. **Surface:** asphalted. 🚻 01/01-31/12
Distance: ⊗on the spot.
Remarks: Airport Dahlemer Binz.

🛉S ‖ **Dahlem** ‖ **8D6**
Wohnmobilstellplatz Kronenburger See, Seeuferstrasse 6.
GPS: n50,35785 e6,46989.⬆️➡️

16 ☷€ 8/24h ⚡€1/120liter 🔌Ch.🚿(12x)included.
Location: Rural, simple, quiet. **Surface:** grassy. 🚻 01/01-31/12
Remarks: At artificial lake.

🛉S ‖ **Delbrück** ‖ **9C3**
Landgasthaus Roseneck, Haselhorster Strasse 3. **GPS:** n51,75770 e8,43441.

10 ☷€ 5, free with a meal 🚿(10x)included. **Location:** Rural, simple.
Surface: metalled. 🚻 01/01-31/12
Distance: 🚶2km ⊗on the spot 🚉2km.

🛉S ‖ **Detmold** 🌼⛲🍴 ‖ **9D2**
Detmolder City Camp, Bahnhofstrasse 8. **GPS:** n51,94055 e8,87123.⬆️➡️

14 ☷€ 8 ⚡€1/100liter 🔌Ch.🚿(14x)€2,16Amp WC 🚻. **Location:** Urban.
Surface: asphalted. 🚻 01/01-31/12
Distance: 🚶500m ⊗500m 🚉200m kiosk 🚌50m.

🛉 ‖ **Dinslaken** ‖ **9A3**
Am Rotbachsee, Am Freibad. **GPS:** n51,56707 e6,77807.⬆️➡️

10 ☷free. **Surface:** sand. 🚻 01/01-31/12
Distance: 🚶100m ⊗100m 🚉100m.

🛉S ‖ **Dormagen** ‖ **9A4**
Parkplatz Flügeldeich, Herrenweg, Feste Zons. **GPS:** n51,12553 e6,85001.⬆️

3 ☷€ 5. **Surface:** metalled. 🚻 01/01-31/12
Distance: 🚶400m ⛵on the spot ⛵on the spot ⊗100m 🚉500m.
Remarks: Near the Rhine river, max. 3 days.

🛉S ‖ **Dorsten** ‖ **9A3**
Reisemobilhafen An der Lippe, Zur Lippe. **GPS:** n51,66550 e6,96744.⬆️➡️

38 ☷€ 5 ⚡🔌Ch.🚿(34x)€1/8h. **Surface:** metalled/sand.
🚻 01/01-31/12
Distance: 🚶300m ⊗300m 🚉300m.

Tourist information Dorsten:
⚑ Marler Str.. Flea market. 🚻 2nd Su of the month, 11-18h.

🛉S ‖ **Dortmund** 🌼🍴 ‖ **9B3**
Mobil-Camp Wischlingen, Wischlinger Weg 50-61, Wischlingen.
GPS: n51,52001 e7,39868.⬆️➡️

50 ☷€ 8, 2 pers.incl ⚡€1/80liter 🔌Ch.🚿(30x)€0,50/kWh WC 🚻€1.
Surface: asphalted. 🚻 01/01-31/12
Distance: 🚶1km 🚉Rewe 1km 🚌200m.
Remarks: Former tennis-court in recreation area.

🛉S ‖ **Drensteinfurt** 🌼 ‖ **9B3**
Am Erlbad, Im Erlfeld 2. **GPS:** n51,78972 e7,74778.
3 ☷€ 3/pp ⚡🔌Ch.🚿WC 🚻included. **Surface:** metalled.
🚻 01/05-01/10

Distance: 🛒800m 🚆9km.
Remarks: Max. 8M, check in at swimming pool, swimming pool incl.

| 🅂 | Duisburg | 9A3 |

Landschaftspark Duisburg-Nord, Emscherstraße 71, Meiderich.
GPS: n51,48413 e6,78077.
5 🆓free 🚰🔌Ch. **Surface:** asphalted. ⬛ 01/01-31/12
Distance: 🚆1,6km.

| 🅂 | Dülmen | 9A2 |

Reisemobilstellplatz Hüttendyk, Ecke Halterner Strasse.
GPS: n51,82606 e7,27228.⬆➡.

6 🆓free 🚰€1/80liter 🔌Ch 💧€1/8h. **Surface:** metalled.
⬛ 01/01-31/12
Distance: 🛒500m 🍴200m 🚍100m.
Remarks: Max. 72h.

| 🅂 | Dülmen | 9A2 |

Reisemobilstellplatz Kapellenweg, Kapellenweg. **GPS:** n51,82331 e7,27945.
⬆.

7 🆓free 🚰🔌Ch. **Surface:** metalled. ⬛ 01/01-31/12
Distance: 🛒500m 🍴600m.
Remarks: Max. 72h.

| 🅂 | Dülmen | 9A2 |

Reisemobilstellplatz düb, Nordlandwehr 99. **GPS:** n51,84408 e7,27300.⬆.
7 🆓free. **Surface:** grasstiles/metalled. ⬛ 01/01-31/12
Distance: 🛒2km 🍴1km.
Remarks: Max. 72h.

| 🅂 | Dülmen | 9A2 |

Reisemobilstellplatz Hausdulmen, Sandstrasse. **GPS:** n51,80707 e7,24746.
⬆➡.

12 🆓free. **Surface:** grassy. ⬛ 01/01-31/12
Distance: 🛒2,5km ⊗500m 🍴400m 🚍on the spot.
Remarks: Max. 72h.

| 🅂 | Düren | 8D5 |

IG Reisemobilhafen Düren, Rurstrasse 188. **GPS:** n50,80861 e6,46556.

20 🆓€7 🚰🔌Chincluded 💧(18x)€2. 🛒 **Location:** Rural, simple, quiet.
Surface: gravel.
Distance: 🛒900m ⊗Bistro 100m 🍴Lidl 500m.
Remarks: Service passerby € 2.

| Düsseldorf 〰🏛🏺 | 9A4 |

P Rheinterasse/Tonhalle, Robert-Lehr-Ufer. **GPS:** n51,23710 e6,77029.⬆.

30 🆓€ 2/h, max. € 12/24h. **Surface:** metalled. ⬛ 01/01-31/12
Distance: 🛒Old city centre 1km ⊗50m 🍴1,3km.

| 🅂 | Düsseldorf 〰🏛🏺 | 9A4 |

Wohnmobilstellplatz Düsseldorf/Erkrath, Heinrich-Hertz-Straße 18,
Unterfeldhaus, Düsseldorf/Erkrath. **GPS:** n51,19825 e6,91679.⬆.

6 🆓€6 🚰€1/100liter 🔌Ch 💧included. 🛒📷
Location: Urban, simple, quiet. **Surface:** metalled.
⬛ 01/01-31/12
Distance: 🛒500m 🚆5,5km ⊗300m 🚍50m.

Tourist information Düsseldorf:
ℹ Tourist Info, Immermannstrasse, Gegenüber Station; Kö-Galerie/Finanzhaus,
Berliner Alee; Burgplatz, Berliner Allee, www.duesseldorf-tourismus.de.
Historical centre, important city of fashion, all large marks established in the
Königsallee, Umweltzone: the green environmental badge is required.
☀ During the Caravan Salon (by the end of August/beginning September) there
is a large area for motorhomes available. Free shuttlebus to the exhibition and
Old city centre. Also several events on the exhibition grounds.

| 🅂 | Eckenhagen 🍴 | 9B5 |

Rodener Festplatz, Rodener Platz. **GPS:** n50,98667 e7,69361.⬆.

DE

20 🛏free 🗑Chfree. **Location:** Urban, simple, quiet.
Surface: asphalted/gravel. 📅 01/01-31/12
Distance: 🚶200m 🚲4km ⊗300m 🚊300m 🚌on the spot 🚶on the spot.

Auf dem Eltenberg, Luitgardisstraße. **GPS:** n51,86559 e6,17265.⬆️➡️

25 🛏free. **Location:** Rural, simple. **Surface:** grasstiles.
📅 01/01-31/12
Distance: 🚶1km ⊗1km 🚊on the spot.

P6, Kleiner Wall, Rheinpromenade. **GPS:** n51,83229 e6,23594.⬆️

6 🛏free. **Location:** Urban, simple, noisy. **Surface:** unpaved.
📅 01/01-31/12
Distance: 🚶on the spot.

Yachthafen, Fackeldeystrasse 15-65. **GPS:** n51,83693 e6,21948.⬆️

75 🛏€ 8,50 🔌🗑Ch 💧 (80x) WC 🗑€0,50 📶€1. 🚿 **Location:** Rural,
comfortable. **Surface:** grassy/metalled. 📅 01/01-31/12
Distance: 🚶2,5km 🏊on the spot ⊗on the spot 🚊on the spot 🚲on the spot
🚶on the spot.

Firma Möller-Elektronic, Königstrasse 17, Oelkinghausen.
GPS: n51,29086 e7,32050.

5 🛏free 🔌€3 🗑Ch 💧. **Location:** Urban, simple, quiet. **Surface:** metalled.
📅 01/01-31/12
Distance: 🚶2km 🚲11km ⊗1km 🚊200m 🚌on the spot 🚶on the spot.

Am Platsch, Mittelstraße 108. **GPS:** n51,29295 e7,37668.⬆️

4 🛏€ 3 💧 included. 🚿 **Surface:** gravel. 📅 01/01-31/12
Distance: 🚲10,8km ⊗5km 🚊5km 🚌on the spot 🚲on the spot
🚶Routes for nordic walking.
Remarks: Check in at pay-desk of swimming pool, on the spot: bistro, pool,
sauna and golf court.

Am Freibad 3. **GPS:** n51,83304 e8,01629.⬆️
2 🛏free 🔌€0,50/50liter 🗑Ch 🔌€0,50/kWh. **Surface:** metalled.
📅 01/01-31/12
Distance: 🚶600m.

Ferienhof Bettmann, Beesen 4. **GPS:** n51,84366 e7,99567.

4 🛏€ 6/pp 🔌🗑Ch 🔌 WC 🗑included.
Distance: 🚶2km ⊗on the spot 🚊3km 🚌on the spot.

Mobilcamp am Ville-Express, Carl-Schurz-strasse 1a, Liblar.
GPS: n50,81781 e6,81986.⬆️➡️

11 🛏€ 6 🔌€1/80liter 🗑Ch 💧 (11x)€0,50/kWh. 🖥
Location: Urban, comfortable. **Surface:** metalled. 📅 01/01-31/12
Distance: 🚶1km 🚲4,4km 🚊500m ⊗200m 🚊1km.

Pension Hofius, Hilchenbacherweg 2, Zinse. **GPS:** n51,00599 e8,21224.➡️

3 🛏€ 7/24h 🔌🗑Ch 💧 WC 🗑. 🚿 📅 01/01-31/12

Distance: 5km on the spot on the spot.

| 🛰️ S | **Everswinkel** | 9B2 |

Vitus-Bad, Alverkirchenerstrasse 29. **GPS:** n51,92309 e7,83776.⬆️.

3 free €0,50/100liter Ch €0,50/kWh. **Surface:** metalled.
01/01-31/12
Distance: 500m on the spot on the spot 100-Schlösser-Route
on the spot.
Remarks: Parking swimming pool.

| 🛰️ | **Freudenberg (NRW)** | 9B5 |

Lohmühle, P5. **GPS:** n50,89625 e7,87636.⬆️.

5 free. **Surface:** metalled. 01/01-31/12
Distance: on the spot 100m 200m.
Remarks: Max. 3 days.

| 🛰️ S | **Gangelt** | 8D5 |

Rodebachtal, Am Freibad 13. **GPS:** n50,98583 e5,99806.⬆️➡️.

40 € 7, weekend € 10 Ch WC €0,50/4minutes.
Location: Rural, luxurious, quiet. **Surface:** metalled. 01/01-31/12
Distance: on the spot on the spot 1,5km.
Remarks: Caution key € 10.

| 🛰️ S | **Geldern** | 8D3 |

Am Holländer See, Am Holländer See 19. **GPS:** n51,51131 e6,32867.⬆️➡️.

50 € 7/24h, 3 days € 17 €1/80liter Ch €0,50/kWh.
Surface: grassy/metalled. 01/01-31/12
Distance: 1km 1km 1km.
Remarks: Parking centre.

| 🛰️ S | **Geldern** | 8D3 |

Reisemobilhafen Am Freibad, Am Freibad 6, Walbeck.
GPS: n51,49461 e6,22666.⬆️➡️.

50 € 7/24h €1/80liter Ch (36x)€0,50/kWh. **Surface:** grassy/sand.
01/01-31/12
Distance: city centre Walbeck 1km, city centre Geldern 6km 1km 1km.
Remarks: At swimming pool.

| 🛰️ S | **Geldern** | 8D3 |

Reisemobilstellplatz Am Sportplatz, Hülspassweg 20, Veert.
GPS: n51,52960 e6,30347.⬆️➡️.

30 free. **Surface:** gravel. 01/01-31/12
Distance: city centre Veert 200m, city centre Geldern 2km 500m.
Remarks: Parking at sports park.

| S | **Geldern** | 8D3 |

Freizeit-Store Diepers, Liebligstrasse 33. **GPS:** n51,52971 e6,35456.
€1 €1 Ch. 01/01-31/12, during opening hours

Tourist information Geldern:
☀️ Internationaler Wettbewerb der strassenmaler und strassenmusikanten und
-theatergruppen, Centrum. International street painting competition, street
musicians and theater groups. beginning Sep.
☀️ Internationales Reisemobilfest. International festival for motorcaravanners
with vast tourist program. Not necessary to book in advance,. last weekend
April. 🆃 free.

| 🛰️ S | **Gelsenkirchen** | 9A3 |

Revierpark Nienhausen, Feldmarkstraße 201. **GPS**: n51,50167 e7,06333.⬆️.

20 € 7, 2 pers.incl. €1/80liter Ch €1/2kWh. **Surface:** metalled.
01/01-31/12
Distance: 2,8km 3,2km 100m 2km Tram 700m.
Remarks: Bread-service.

| 🛰️ S | **Gladbeck** | 9A3 |

Freitzeitstätte Wittringer Wald, Bohmertstrasse 277.
GPS: n51,55912 e6,98403.⬆️➡️.

20 ⬛free ⬛⬛ Ch. **Surface:** grasstiles/grassy. ⬛ 01/01-31/12
Distance: ⬛2km ⬛1km ⬛200m ⬛1km.
Remarks: Green zone: environmental badge obligatory, Wasserschloß
Wittringen 450m.

| ⬛S | **Goch** | 8D3 |

Friedensplatz, Thielenstrasse. **GPS**: n51,67556 e6,16639.⬛⬛.

70 ⬛€ 4/24h ⬛€1/100liter ⬛Ch ⬛ (60x)€0,50/kWh. **Surface:** grassy.
⬛ 01/01-31/12
Distance: ⬛700m ⬛on the spot ⬛700m ⬛700m ⬛100m.
Remarks: Along the Niers river.

| ⬛ | **Goch** | 8D3 |

Reisemobilstellplatz GochNess, Kranenburger Strasse 20, Kessel.
GPS: n51,70291 e6,08915.⬛.

6 ⬛free. **Surface:** grassy. ⬛ 01/01-31/12
Distance: ⬛1km ⬛1km ⬛1km.

Tourist information Goch:
⬛ Pilgrimage for motorhomes. ⬛ last weekend Jun.
⬛ Museumscafé Edison, Museum Goch. Collection of gramophones.
⬛ Su 15-17h.
⬛ Herrensitz-Route. Cycle route along the Meuse and the Niers, available at
Kultourbühne Goch. ⬛ € 5.

| ⬛S | **Grefrath** | 8D4 |

Eissportzentrum Grefrath, Stadionstrasse. **GPS**: n51,34889 e6,33972.
50 ⬛free. **Surface:** grasstiles.
Distance: ⬛2km ⬛500m ⬛300m ⬛2km.
Remarks: Niederrheinisches Freilichtmuseum, Open air museum 650m.

| ⬛S | **Greven** | 9B2 |

Wohnmobilcamp Marina, Alten Fahrt Fuestrup,, Fuestruperstrasse 37,
Fuestrup. **GPS**: n52,04449 e7,68328.⬛.

90 ⬛€ 11 ⬛€0,50/50liter ⬛Ch ⬛€2,50 WC ⬛€1 ⬛€2,50/1,50.
⬛ 01/01-31/12
Distance: ⬛Restaurant/Biergarten ⬛3km.
Remarks: Marina at canal.

| ⬛S | **Gronau** ⬛ | 9A1 |

Erholungsgebiet Dreiländersee, Brechter Weg. **GPS**: n52,23716 e7,08006.⬛
⬛.

80 ⬛€ 8/24, only exact change ⬛€0,50/130liter ⬛Ch ⬛€1/4h WC ⬛.
Surface: grassy/metalled. ⬛ 01/01-31/12
Distance: ⬛3km ⬛100m ⬛on the spot ⬛200m ⬛50m (camping)
⬛on the spot.
Remarks: Near the lake, max. 48h.

| ⬛S | **Haltern am See** | 9A3 |

Reisemobilstellplatz Silbersee II, Zum Vogelsberg. **GPS**: n51,79764 e7,21008.
⬛⬛.

15 ⬛€ 14, 2 pers incl ⬛€1/80liter ⬛Ch ⬛€1/8h. **Surface:** grassy.
⬛ 01/04-31/10
Distance: ⬛Haltern 6km ⬛on the spot ⬛on the spot.
Remarks: At Silbersee, max. 3 nights.

| ⬛S | **Haltern am See** | 9A3 |

Reisemobilstellplatz, Hullerner Straße/West, Lippspieker.
GPS: n51,74278 e7,19525.⬛⬛.

30 ⬛€ 5 ⬛€1 ⬛Ch ⬛ (8x)€1/8h. **Surface:** metalled. ⬛ 01/01-31/12
Distance: ⬛Old city centre 1km ⬛1km ⬛100m.

DE

Haltern am See 9A3

RMS ReisemobileSpezialist, Hellweg 252. **GPS:** n51,75589 e7,20127.⬆️.

4 ⛴€7 🚰€1 🔌 Ch 🚿€3,50. **Surface:** grassy/gravel. ⬛ 01/01-31/12
Distance: 🚶Old city centre 1km ⊗800m 🚋800m.

Hamm 9B3

Maximare, Jürgen-Graef-Allee 2. **GPS:** n51,68840 e7,83535.
5 ⛴€3,80 🚰🚿 included. **Surface:** gravel. ⬛ 01/01-31/12
Distance: 🚶1km.
Remarks: Caution key €35.

Hamm 9B3

Freizeitpark Maximilian Park, Alter Grenzweg 2. **GPS:** n51,68392 e7,88395.
5 ⛴free. **Surface:** asphalted. ⬛ 01/01-31/12

Harsewinkel 9C2

Frei- und Hallenbad, Prozessionsweg 8. **GPS:** n51,96556 e8,21935.⬆️➡️⬆️.

5 ⛴free. **Surface:** grassy. ⬛ 01/01-31/12
Distance: 🚶200m ⊗100m 🚋200m.
Remarks: Parking next to swimming pool, max. 48h.

Hattingen 9A4

Wohnmobilstellplatz Ruhrtal, Ruhrdeich 24. **GPS:** n51,40839 e7,18091.⬆️➡️.

15 ⛴€7 🚰€1/80liter 🔌 Ch 🚿€1/2kWh,12 📶free. **Location:** Rural,
comfortable, quiet. **Surface:** gravel. ⬛ 01/01-31/12
Distance: 🚶2,5km 🚲5km ⊿on the spot 🚌on the spot ⊗500m 🚋1km.
Remarks: Along the Ruhr river, next to midget golf, bread-service.

Hattingen 9A4

August-Bebel strasse. **GPS:** n51,39833 e7,18028.

2 ⛴€3. 🚆 **Location:** Urban, simple, central, noisy. **Surface:** metalled.
⬛ 01/01-31/12
Distance: 🚶on the spot 🚲5km ⊗on the spot 🚋on the spot 🚌on the spot.
Remarks: At shopping centre Carré.

Hattingen 9A4

Roonstrasse. **GPS:** n51,40167 e7,18389.⬆️➡️.

2 ⛴free. **Location:** Urban, simple, quiet. **Surface:** asphalted/metalled.
⬛ 01/01-31/12
Distance: 🚶300m 🚲5km ⊗300m 🚋300m.

Hattingen 9A4

Ruhrgasse, Bahnhofstrasse. **GPS:** n51,40127 e7,17700.➡️.

3 ⛴free. **Location:** Urban, simple, quiet. **Surface:** gravel.
⬛ 01/01-31/12
Distance: 🚶500m 🚲5km ⊗500m 🚋500m.
Remarks: Parking behind the Amtshäusern, only on Sa and Su.

Hattingen 9A4

Wanderparkplatz, Isenbergstrasse. **GPS:** n51,38969 e7,15340.⬆️.

3 ⛴free. **Location:** Rural, simple. **Surface:** gravel.
⬛ Mo-Fri, 01/01-31/12
Distance: 🚶2km 🚲5km ⊗300m 🚋1km 🚌on the spot 🚴on the spot
🚶on the spot.
Remarks: Parking along the Ruhr, max. 2 days.

Havixbeck 9B2

Freibad, Kardinal von Hartmann strasse. **GPS:** n51,97507 e7,42092.⬆️➡️.

4 ⛴free 🚰🔌Ch on demand WC. **Surface:** metalled. ⬛ 01/01-31/12

DE

Remarks: Parking at swimming pool, small pitches.

Havixbeck 9B2

Klute's Historischem Brauhaus, Poppenbeck 28. **GPS**: n51,98938 e7,39291.

15 guests free (8x)€5 . **Surface:** metalled.
01/01-31/12
Distance: 2km on the spot 2km.

Havixbeck 9B2

EDEKA, Blickallee 44. **GPS**: n51,97480 e7,41168.

4 free. **Surface:** metalled. 01/01-31/12
Distance: 100m 100m on the spot 100m.
Remarks: At supermarket, small pitches.

Heiligenhaus 9A4

Westfalenstrasse. **GPS**: n51,32853 e6,97327.
3 free. **Location:** Simple. **Surface:** metalled. 01/01-31/12
Distance: 200m 200m 200m.

Heimbach 8D6

Womohafen Heimbach, An der Laag 4. **GPS**: n50,63683 e6,47265.

19 € 7,50/24h, € 0,45/pp tourist tax €1/100liter Ch (20x)€0,50/kWh. **Location:** Rural, simple, noisy. **Surface:** gravel.
01/01-31/12
Distance: 200m 100m on the spot.
Remarks: Nearby Regioshuttle Rurtallbahn.

Heinsberg 8D4

Heinsberg am Lago, Fritz-Bauer-Strasse 3. **GPS**: n51,07333 e6,09278.

44 P1 € 10/day, P2 € 10/2 days €1/100liter Ch (31x)€0,50/kWh.

Location: Rural, luxurious, quiet. **Surface:** grasstiles.
Distance: 1km Bagger See on the spot 800m.

Hellenthal 8D6

Grenzlandhalle Hellenthal, Aachenerstrasse. **GPS**: n50,49251 e6,43651.

15 free. **Location:** Rural, simple. **Surface:** grasstiles.
01/01-31/12
Distance: 500m 200m.
Remarks: Service on campsite.

Hellenthal 8D6

Wohnmobilhafen Weißer Stein, Am Weissen Stein, Udenbreth, B265.
GPS: n50,40896 e6,37220.

28 € 9 €2 Ch (28x). **Location:** Rural, simple.
Surface: metalled.
Distance: on the spot on the spot.
Remarks: Service on campsite, winter sports area Hellenthal am Wald.

Hellenthal 8D6

Breuerhof, Zum Wilsamtal 39, Udenbreth. **GPS**: n50,41081 e6,38992.

2 € 10 Ch (2x). **Location:** Rural, comfortable, quiet.
Surface: metalled.
Distance: 2km on the spot. **Remarks:** Check in at nr. 35.

Tourist information Hellenthal:
Greifvogelstation. Predatory bird station. 01/11-31/03 9-17h, 01/04-31/10 9-18h.

Hemer 9B4

Wohnmobilstellplatz Hemer, Hönnetalstraße. **GPS**: n51,37841 e7,77151.

DE

20 🗄€ 2/8-20h ⌁€1/100liter 🗄Ch€1 ⚡ (12x)€0,50/kWh. **Location:** Urban, comfortable, quiet. **Surface:** asphalted/grassy. ◻ 01/01-31/12 **Distance:** 🚶1km 🚲6km ⊗300m 🛒bakery 500m 🎣on the spot.

| 🗄S | Herford 🍲🍴 | 9D2 |

Am Stadion, Dennewitzstrasse 15. **GPS**: n52,10474 e8,68931.⬆➡.

3 🗄free. **Location:** Rural, simple. ◻ 01/01-31/12
Distance: 🚶2,5km 🚲1,8km ⛰100m 🚏100m ⊗2,5km 🛒2,5km.

| 🗄S | Herscheid 🍲 | 9B4 |

Am Warmwasserfreibad, Unterdorfstraße. **GPS**: n51,17567 e7,74368.⬆.

3 🗄free ⌁€1/10minutes 🗄Ch ⚡ (4x)€1/8h.
Location: Rural, comfortable, quiet. **Surface:** gravel. ◻ 01/01-31/12
Distance: 🚶1,2km 🚲10km ⊗400m 🛒650m 🎣on the spot.

| 🗄S | Hilchenbach 🍲🍴 | 9C5 |

Hallenbad Dahlbruch, Bernhard-Weiss-Platz, Dahlbruch.
GPS: n50,97792 e8,05343.⬆.

3 🗄free ⌁€1/10minutes 🗄. **Surface:** asphalted/metalled. ◻ 01/01-31/12
Distance: 🚶400m ⊗400m.
Remarks: Parking behind swimming pool, max. 48h.

| 🗄 | Hilchenbach 🍲🍴 | 9C5 |

Bürgerhaus, Merklinghäuser weg, Müsen. **GPS**: n50,99267 e8,04497.⬆.

3 🗄free. **Surface:** asphalted. ◻ 01/01-31/12
Remarks: Max. 48h.

| 🗄 | Hilchenbach 🍲🍴 | 9C5 |

Parkplatz P4, Rothenberger strasse, L728. **GPS**: n50,99702 e8,11103.⬆➡.

3 🗄free. **Surface:** metalled. ◻ 01/01-31/12
Distance: 🚶100m ⊗200m 🛒100m.
Remarks: Parking in front of shopping centre Gerberpark, max. 48h.

| 🍲🍴S | Hilchenbach 🍲🍴 | 9C5 |

Landhotel Steubers Siebelnhof, Siebelnhoferstrasse, Vormwald.
GPS: n50,98658 e8,13173.
6 🗄€ 20,50, use sanitary facilities/swimming pool sauna incl WC 🗄included.
◻ 01/01-31/12
Distance: ⊗on the spot.

| 🗄S | Hille | 9D1 |

Am Marktplatz, Sportplatzweg 31. **GPS**: n52,34205 e8,73017.⬆➡.

8 🗄free ⌁€1 🗄Ch ⚡€1. **Location:** Rural, quiet. **Surface:** gravel.
◻ 01/01-31/12
Distance: 🚶1km ⊗500m.

| 🗄S | Hopsten | 9B1 |

Dreifachturnhalle, Rüschendorfer strasse 4. **GPS**: n52,38900 e7,60230.⬆.

6 🗄free ⌁🗄Ch ⚡free. **Surface:** grasstiles. ◻ 01/01-31/12
Distance: 🚶100m ⊗100m 🛒100m 🚐on the spot.
Remarks: Parking at gymnasium, max. 3 days.

| 🗄 | Horn 🍲 | 9D2 |

Wohnmobilhafen Mein Bad, Wällenweg, Bad Meinberg.
GPS: n51,89818 e8,99249.⬆➡.

35 🗄€ 5 + € 2,60/pp tourist tax ⌁€1/100liter 🗄Ch ⚡€0,50/kWh.
Location: Rural, quiet. **Surface:** grassy/metalled. ◻ 01/01-31/12
Distance: 🚶200m ⊗on the spot 🛒200m 🚐100m.

DE

Remarks: Behind spa, discount at swimming pool.

🏕️Ⓢ **Hörstel** 9B1

Wohnmobilhafen Riesenbeck, Postdamm-Lazarusbrücke. **GPS:** n52,25574 e7,63387.⬆️➡️.

13 🔥free 🚰🗑️Chfree 🔌€1/4kWh. **Surface:** metalled.
📅 01/01-31/12
Distance: 🛁700m ⛱️on the spot 🚤on the spot 🛒300m 🚌on the spot 🚲 100-Schlösser-Route 🚶on the spot.
Remarks: Max. 3 nights.

🏕️Ⓢ **Hövelhof** 👪 9D2

P Bahnhof, Westfalenstrasse. **GPS:** n51,82417 e8,66099.⬆️.

6 🔥free 🚰free 🔌(6x)€1/kWh. **Location:** Urban. **Surface:** gravel.
📅 01/01-31/12
Distance: 🛁500m 🚣4,2km ⊗500m 🛒500m 🚌50m 🚲on the spot 🚶on the spot.

🏕️Ⓢ **Höxter** 🌿⛱️🍰👪 10A2

Freizeitanlage Godelheimer See, Godelheimer Strasse, Höxter-Godelheim. **GPS:** n51,75787 e9,37557.⬆️➡️.

50 🔥€6 🚰Ch WC 🗑️included. 🏠 **Location:** Comfortable. **Surface:** grasstiles.
📅 01/01-31/12 🔵 service: 01/10-01/04
Distance: 🛁2km ⛱️on the spot 🚤river 500m ⊗on the spot 🛒2km 🚲on the spot 🚶on the spot.
Remarks: Bread-service, recreation area.

🏕️Ⓢ **Höxter** 🌿⛱️🍰👪 10A2

Wohnmobilhafen Flossplatz, Milchweg. **GPS:** n51,77325 e9,38781.⬆️➡️.

---

50 🔥€6, only overnight stay € 4 🚰€1/100liter 🗑️Ch 🔌(18x)€0,50/kWh. 🏠 **Location:** Rural, comfortable, central, quiet. **Surface:** grassy/gravel.
📅 01/01-31/12
Distance: 🛁300m ⛱️on the spot 🚤fishing permit available ⊗100m 🛒300m 🚌500m on camp site 🚲50m.
Remarks: Parking beside river Weser.

🏕️Ⓢ **Hückelhoven** 8D4

Hückelhovener Ruraue, Rheinstraße 4b. **GPS:** n51,05111 e6,21306.⬆️.

6 🔥€4,50 🚰€0,50/100liter 🗑️Ch 🔌€0,50/kWh.🐕
Location: Rural, simple, isolated, quiet. **Surface:** metalled.
📅 01/01-31/12 🔵 With snow
Distance: 🛁1,5km.

🏕️Ⓢ **Hürtgenwald** 👪 8D5

Einmünding Kall-Rur, Zerkall. **GPS:** n50,69156 e6,45212.⬆️.

10 🔥free. **Location:** Rural, simple. **Surface:** gravel.
📅 01/01-31/12
Distance: 🛁100m ⛱️on the spot 🚤on the spot 🚌200m.
Remarks: Along the river Kall/Rur.

🏕️ **Hürtgenwald** 👪 8D5

Parkplatz Burgstrasse, Burgstrasse, Bergstein. **GPS:** n50,69582 e6,43848.⬆️.

5 🔥free. **Location:** Simple. **Surface:** metalled. 📅 01/01-31/12

🏕️ **Hürtgenwald** 👪 8D5

Soldatenfriedhof, Höhenstrasse, Hürtgen. **GPS:** n50,70552 e6,36063.⬆️.

9 🔥free. **Location:** Rural, simple, noisy. **Surface:** asphalted. 📅 01/01-31/12

ⅢⅢS | **Hürtgenwald** 👥 | 8D5
Simonskall 20, Kallweg. **GPS:** n50,66716 e6,35395.

5 🍴free. **Location:** Rural, comfortable, quiet. **Surface:** metalled.
🚰 01/01-31/12
Distance: ⬛200m ⊗on the spot.

🏕 | **Hüsten** | 9C3
Parkplatz Große Wiese. **GPS:** n51,43151 e8,00475.⬆.
4 🍴free. **Surface:** asphalted.
Distance: ⬛2km.
Remarks: Next to the Sole-Bad.

🏕 | **Ibbenbüren** | 9B1
Aseebad, An der Umfluth 99. **GPS:** n52,26181 e7,73171.

30 🍴€3. **Surface:** grassy/metalled.
Distance: ⬛2,3km.
Remarks: Parking next to swimming pool, max. 4 nights.

🏕 | **Ibbenbüren** | 9B1
Dorenthe, Hafenstrasse. **GPS:** n52,22056 e7,67944.
3 🍴free. **Location:** Simple. **Surface:** asphalted. 🚰 01/01-31/12
Distance: ⬛7km ⬛on the spot.
Remarks: At the Dortmund-Ems Canal.

🏕 | **Ibbenbüren** | 9B1
Sommerrodelbahn, Münsterstrasse 265. **GPS:** n52,24977 e7,70292.

10 🍴free. **Surface:** metalled. 🚰 01/04-31/10
Distance: ⬛1,2km ⊗on the spot.

ⅢⅢS | **Iserlohn** 👥 | 9B4
Parkplatz Seilerblick, Friesenstraße. **GPS:** n51,38456 e7,71128.⬆➡.

5 🍴free ⬛€1 ⬛Ch€1 ⬛ (4x)€0,50. **Location:** Urban, simple, noisy.
Surface: asphalted. 🚰 01/01-31/12
Distance: ⬛2km ⬛2,5km ⬛on the spot ⬛on the spot.
Remarks: Next to tennis-court.

🏕 | **Isselburg** 👥 | 8D3
Hotel Restaurant Brüggenhütte, Hahnerfeld 23, Anholt.
GPS: n51,85301 e6,47187.⬆.

5 🍴free. **Location:** Rural, simple. **Surface:** grassy.
🚰 01/01-31/12
Distance: ⬛200m ⊗on the spot.
Remarks: Along through road, behind restaurant.

🏕 | **Isselburg** 👥 | 8D3
Parkplatz Zentrum, Münsterdeich. **GPS:** n51,83452 e6,46477.⬆.

3 🍴free. **Location:** Simple. **Surface:** grassy. 🚰 01/01-31/12
Distance: ⬛on the spot ⬛on the spot ⊗300m ⬛100m.
Remarks: At the Issel, parking centre, max. 72h.

🏕 | **Isselburg** 👥 | 8D3
Spargelhof Mäteling, Buchenallee 4, Anholt. **GPS:** n51,84120 e6,41597.⬆.

5 🍴free. **Location:** Rural, simple. **Surface:** asphalted.
🚰 01/01-31/12
Distance: ⊗on the spot.
Remarks: Max. 72h.

Ⅲ | **Isselburg** 👥 | 8D3
Bürgerhaus, Anholter strasse, Vehlingen. **GPS:** n51,83089 e6,42297.⬆.

DE

3 🛏 free. **Location:** Rural, simple. **Surface:** gravel.
🔲 01/01-31/12 ◖ May
Distance: ⊗on the spot.
Remarks: Max. 2 nights.

35 🛏 € 4/24h ⚡€2/100liter ⚑Ch ⚡€1/5kWh. ▯🚻
Location: Rural, comfortable. **Surface:** grassy. 🔲 01/01-31/12
Distance: ⟿500m ⊗400m ⚑700m.
Remarks: Max. 3 nights.
Tourist information Kalkar:
😊 KernWasser Wunderland. Amusement park.

| Isselburg | 8D3 |

Ponyhof Leiting, Alte Bundesstrasse 3, Werth. **GPS:** n51,81332 e6,49258. ⬆➡

| ▦S | Kall | 8D6 |

Im Kallbachtal, Kapellenstrasse 25, Golbach. **GPS:** n50,52784 e6,53681. ⬆➡

10 🛏 free. **Location:** Simple. **Surface:** grassy. 🔲 01/01-31/12
Distance: ⊗on the spot.
Remarks: Max. 72h.

| ▦S | Issum-Sevelen | 8D3 |

Wohnmobilpark Hexenland-Sevelen, Koetherdyck 18.
GPS: n51,49926 e6,43676. ⬆➡

6 🛏 € 6 ⚡€1 ⚑Ch ⚡(8x)€0,50/kWh. ⚒ **Location:** Rural, simple, quiet.
Surface: gravel. 🔲 01/01-31/12

| ⚓ | Kamp-Lintfort | 8D3 |

Pappelsee, Berthastraße 74. **GPS:** n51,50026 e6,53861. ⬆➡

20 🛏 € 9 ⚡ ⚑Ch ⚡€3/24h WC. **Surface:** gravel. 🔲 01/01-31/12
Distance: ⟿Sevelen 1km ⌂200m ⊗100m ⚑1km.

| ◖S | Jülich | 8D5 |

Brückenkopf-Park, Rurauenstrasse 11. **GPS:** n50,92345 e6,34029. ⬆

20 🛏 free. **Surface:** asphalted.
🔲 01/01-31/12
Distance: ⟿1,5km ⊗1km ⚑1,5km.
Remarks: Caution € 2,50 to pay-desk of the park.
Tourist information Kamp-Lintfort:
⚐ Marktplatz, Eberstrasse. 🔲 Thu, Sa.
⚐ Rathausplatz. 🔲 Tue 7.30-13h.
☀ Mittelalterlicher Markt, Abteiplatz. Medieval market. 🔲 3rd weekend Sep.

| ▦S | Kempen | 8D4 |

Reisemobilpark Kempen am Aqua-sol, Berliner Allee.
GPS: n51,36719 e6,40910. ⬆

22 🛏 € 8,50 ⚡€1/100liter ⚑Ch ⚡WC ⚑. ⚒ **Location:** Simple, noisy.
Surface: grassy. 🔲 01/01-31/12 ◖ sanitary building: 1/11-31/3
Remarks: Parking at the Rur.
Tourist information Jülich:
ℹ Old fortress city.

| ▦S | Kalkar | 8D3 |

Reisemobilstellplatz Kalkar, Waysche strasse. **GPS:** n51,74008 e6,30101. ⬆➡

29 🛏 € 7 ⚡€1/100liter ⚑Ch ⚡€0,50/kWh. **Surface:** metalled.

◘ 01/01-31/12
Distance: 1,5km ⊗on the spot 1,5km.

Kerken 8D4

Wohnmobilpark Aldekerker Platte, Kempener Straße 9, Aldekerk.
GPS: n51,43551 e6,41902. ⬆️➡️.

30 €9 ⌁ Ch €3. **Surface:** grassy/gravel. ◘ 01/01-31/12
Distance: 600m ⊗600m 600m.

Kevelaer 8D3

Den Heyberg, Im Auwelt 45, Twisteden. **GPS:** n51,56345 e6,19418. ⬆️.

150 € 8,50 ⌁ Ch (150x)included. **Surface:** asphalted/metalled.
◘ 01/01-31/12
Distance: 2km ⊗100m 2km 100m.
Remarks: Bread-service (weekend), barbecue place.

Kevelaer 8D3

Sporthotel Schravelsche Heide, Grotendonkerstrasse 54-58.
GPS: n51,59556 e6,25306. ⬆️➡️.

80 € 7 ⌁ Ch WC included. **Surface:** grassy.
◘ 01/01-31/12
Distance: 1,5km ⊗100m 1km.
Remarks: To pay at sanitary building tennis-courts.

Kevelaer 8D3

Europaplatz, Bahnhof/Geldernstrasse, B9. **GPS:** n51,57904 e6,25192. ⬆️.

3 free. **Surface:** asphalted.
Distance: 500m ⊗500m on the spot.
Tourist information Kevelaer:

⌂ ◘ Fr 14-18h.

Kirchhundem 9C4

Restaurant Rhein-Wester-Turm, Alfons Kleffmann, Rhein-Weser-Turm.
GPS: n51,07109 e8,19791.

10 € 10 ⌁ Ch included. ◘ 01/01-31/12
Distance: ⊗on the spot.

Kirchhundem 9C4

Panorama-Park, Rinsecker Straße 100. **GPS:** n51,06972 e8,17417. ⬆️.
10 free. ◘ 01/01-31/12

Kleve 8D3

Van-den-Bergh-Straße. GPS: n51,78917 e6,14836. ⬆️.

60 € 4 ⌁ Ch (30x)€0,50/kWh. **Location:** Urban, simple.
Surface: metalled. ◘ 01/01-31/12
Distance: 500m.

Kleve 8D3

Reisemobilpark Kleve, Landwehr/Spyckstraße. **GPS:** n51,80083 e6,13222. ⬆️.

75 € 6,50, 2 pers.incl ⌁€1 Ch (45x)€2,50 WC €0,50 €1.
Location: Comfortable. **Surface:** grassy/metalled. ◘ 01/01-31/12
Distance: Kleve-zentrum 1,5km ⊗300m 400m.

Kleve 8D3

Parkplatz Bürgerhaus, Drususdeich, Rindern. **GPS:** n51,81212 e6,12884. ⬆️.

5 free. **Location:** Simple. **Surface:** asphalted. ◘ 01/01-31/12
Distance: Kleve-zentrum 2,3km ⊗450m 400m.
Remarks: Behind church.

DE

Kleve 🧁 🍴 〰 **8D3**

Parkplatz Sporthalle Kleve-Kellen, Postdeich, Kellen.
GPS: n51,80463 e6,16378.⬆.

20 🚐 free. **Location**: Rural, simple. **Surface**: metalled.
Distance: 🚶2,5km ⊗Steakhaus 350m 🚐on the spot.

Kleve 🧁 🍴 〰 **8D3**

Parkplatz Sportplatz Reichswalde, Dorfanger, Reichswalde.
GPS: n51,75985 e6,10243.⬆.

10 🚐 free. **Location**: Urban, simple. **Surface**: metalled.
Distance: 🚶5km 🚌500m.

Kleve 🧁 🍴 〰 **8D3**

Schenkenschanz. **GPS**: n51,83526 e6,11205.⬆.

5 🚐 free. **Location**: Simple. **Surface**: metalled. ☐ 01/01-31/12
Distance: 🚌2,5km.

Kleve 🧁 🍴 〰 **8D3**

Tiergarten, Tiergartenstrasse, B9 dir Nijmegen. **GPS**: n51,79784 e6,12059.⬆.

5 🚐 free. **Location**: Highway, simple. **Surface**: metalled.
☐ 01/01-31/12
Distance: 🚶800m ⊗250m.

Kleve 🧁 🍴 〰 **8D3**

Wehrpöhl, Griethausen. **GPS**: n51,82476 e6,16448.⬆.

5 🚐 free. **Location**: Rural, simple. **Surface**: asphalted.
☐ 01/01-31/12
Distance: 🚶2,5km ⊗300m. 🚌300m.
Remarks: Access via Brienen.
Tourist information Kleve:
🕷 Lichterfest. City celebration. ☐ 2nd Sa of the month.
🐾 Tiergarten Kleve, Tiergartenstrasse. Animal park.

S **Köln** **9A5**

P+R-Terminals Haus Vorst, Emmy-Noether-Straße, Marsdorf, Cologne (Köln).
GPS: n50,91666 e6,84693.⬆➡.

21 🚐 free ⛽€0,50/100liter 🚰 Ch ⚡€1/12h. **Location**: Urban, simple, noisy.
Surface: metalled. ☐ 01/01-31/12
Distance: 🚶Old city centre 8km 🚲450m ⊗250m 🚌on the spot
🚋Tram centre 50m.
Remarks: Max. 24h.

S **Köln** **9A5**

Reisemobilhafen Köln, An der Schanz, Cologne (Köln).
GPS: n50,96265 e6,98254.⬆➡.

65 🚐 €10/24h ⛽€0,50 🚰 Ch ⚡(30x)€0,50/kWh. 🚿
Location: Urban, comfortable, quiet. **Surface**: asphalted.
Distance: 🚶on the spot 🚲5km 🚇metro 10 min walking.
Remarks: Along the Rhine river.

Königswinter **9A5**

Hauptstrasse, Niederdollendorf. **GPS**: n50,69697 e7,17641.⬆.

30 🚐 free. **Location**: Urban, simple. **Surface**: asphalted/metalled.

◻ 01/01-31/12
Distance: 🚶400m 🚲9km 🚌800m on the spot 🚶on the spot.

🏕🅂 Kranenburg 🛝 8D3
Am Sportzentrum, Großen Haag. **GPS**: n51,79242 e6,01033.⬆➡.

30 🛏€4 🚰€0,20/liter 🗑 Ch 🔌(12x)€0,50/kWh.🚐
Location: Rural, simple. **Surface:** grassy. ◻ 01/01-31/12
Distance: 🚶500m 🏊1km 🚲1km ⊗500m 🛒500m.
Remarks: Service 500m.

🏕🅂 Kreuztal 9C5
Heugraben. GPS: n50,95778 e7,99167.⬆.

2 🛏free 🚰€1/100liter 🗑 Ch 🔌€1/2kWh. **Surface:** metalled.
Distance: 🚶300m 🚲7,5km ⊗300m 🛒300m 🚐station 100m.
Remarks: Max. 3 days.

🏕🅂 Kürten 🛝 9B4
Wohnmobil Park - Kürten, Broch 8. **GPS**: n51,05586 e7,28943.⬆.

20 🛏€8 🚰€2 🗑 Ch included 🔌€3. **Location:** Rural, simple, quiet.
Surface: gravel. ◻ 01/01-31/12
Distance: 🚶2km 🚲17km ⊗on the spot 🚴on the spot 🚶on the spot.
Remarks: Behind Sauna-/Badeland Splash.

🏕🅂 Ladbergen 9B2
Rathauspark, Jahnstrasse. **GPS**: n52,13652 e7,74009.⬆.

10 🛏free. **Surface:** grassy. ◻ 01/01-31/12
Distance: 🚶200m ⊗200m 🛒200m.
Remarks: Parking behind town hall.

🏕🅂 Lennestadt 9C4
Parkplatz P4, An der Sauerlandhalle. **GPS**: n51,10557 e8,08017.⬆.

4 🛏free 🔌(4x)€0,50/4h. **Surface:** asphalted. ◻ 01/01-31/12
Distance: 🚶700m ⊗700m 🛒100m.

🏕🅂 Leverkusen 9A4
Camping-Caravaning Meier, Adolf-Kaschny-Straße 9, Küppersteg.
GPS: n51,05211 e7,00003.⬆.

10 🛏free 🚰€0,50 🗑 Ch€0,50. **Location:** Urban. **Surface:** gravel.
◻ 01/01-31/12
Distance: 🚲3,2km.
Remarks: Motorhome dealer, accessory shop, repairs.

🏕🅂 Lienen 9C2
Hallenfreibad, Holperdorperstrasse 37/39. **GPS**: n52,15575 e7,97392.⬆➡.

3 🛏free 🚰€5 🗑 WC. **Surface:** metalled. ◻ 01/01-31/12
Distance: 🚶1km.
Remarks: Parking next to swimming pool, max. 3 nights, service to be paid at swimming pool.

🏕🅂 Lindlar 🛝 9B5
Am Freizeitpark, Brionner Straße. **GPS**: n51,01550 e7,36645.⬆➡.

2 🛏free 🚰€1 🗑 Ch 🔌(4x)€1/6h. **Location:** Urban, simple.
Surface: metalled. ◻ 01/01-31/12
Distance: 🚶1km 🚲16km ⊗1km 🛒1km 🚴on the spot 🚶on the spot.

🏕🅂 Lippstadt 9C3
Campingoase Lange, Dorfstraße 47, Benninghausen. **GPS**: n51,66103 e8,24435.

15 🛏 € 10, 2 pers.incl 🚰🗑Ch 🚿 included. **Location:** Rural, simple.
Surface: metalled. 📷 01/01-31/12
Distance: 🚶300m 🛒on the spot.
🛁S **Löhne** 9D1
Reisemobilstellplatz, Albert-Schweitzer-strasse 12. **GPS**: n52,20399 e8,71892.
⬆️➡️.

18 🛏 € 8 🚰🗑Ch included. 🚿 (18x)€ 1/2kWh. **Location:** Rural, quiet.
Surface: metalled. 📷 01/01-31/12
Distance: 🚶500m 🚲1km 🚌100m ⊗500m 🛒500m.
🛁S **Lotte** 9B1
Fam. Arendröwer, Am Nordberg 4. **GPS**: n52,26306 e7,89833. ⬆️➡️.
4 🛏 € 6 🚰🗑Ch 🚿 included. 🐕 **Surface:** grassy/metalled.
📷 01/03-01/10
Distance: 🚶3km 🚲500m 🛒3km.
🛁 **Lotte** 9B1
Tennishalle Lotte, Kornweg 3. **GPS**: n52,27192 e7,92275. ⬆️.
10 🛏 free. **Surface:** grasstiles. 📷 01/01-31/12
Distance: 🚶900m 🚲3,5km 🛒1km.
🛁S **Lübbecke** 9C1
Stellplatz Lübbecke, Rahdener Straße. **GPS**: n52,31019 e8,61839.

4 🛏 € 6 🚰€3 🗑Ch 🚿 €3. 🐕 **Location:** Urban, central. **Surface:** metalled.
📷 01/01-31/12
Distance: 🚶600m 🛒500m.
Remarks: Max. 3 days.
🛁S **Lüdenscheid** 👣 9B4
Familienbad Nattenberg, Talstraße 59. **GPS**: n51,21042 e7,61803. ⬆️➡️.

4 🛏 free 🚰€1 🗑Ch 🚿€1/6h. **Location:** Urban, simple. **Surface:** metalled.
📷 01/01-31/12
Distance: 🚶city centre 1,6km 🚲4km ⊗Burger King 450m 🛒Aldi 900m
🚶on the spot.
🛁 **Lüdinghausen** 9B3
Parkplatz Aqua-See, Rohrkamp 23. **GPS**: n51,77229 e7,42731. ⬆️.

2 🛏 free. **Surface:** metalled. 📷 01/01-31/12
Distance: 🚶1,5km 🚐on the spot.
Remarks: Parking swimming pool.
🛁S **Lüdinghausen** 9B3
Parkplatz Rosengarten, Am Rosengarten, Seppenrade.
GPS: n51,76407 e7,39728. ⬆️.

2 🛏 free. **Surface:** asphalted. 📷 01/01-31/12
Distance: 🚶200m.
🛁S **Marsberg** 👣 9D3
Wohnmobilhafen, Am Sportplatz. **GPS**: n51,45974 e8,84864. ⬆️➡️.

4 🛏 € 5 🚰🗑Ch 🚿 (4x)included. 🐕
Location: Urban. **Surface:** asphalted.
📷 01/01-31/12
Distance: 🚶100m ⊗200m 🛒200m.
Remarks: Max. 5 days, caution key € 20 (pay-desk of theTherme).
🛁S **Mechernich** 9A6
Parkplatz Essensgasse, Am Kirchberg, Kommern. **GPS**: n50,61376 e6,64479.

8 ⌂free. **Location:** Rural, simple, noisy. **Surface:** metalled.
⬛ 01/01-31/12
Distance: historical centre 200m.
Remarks: Via B266.

| | Mechernich | 9A6 |

Mühlental, Elisabethhütte, B477. **GPS:** n50,59686 e6,63207. ⬆.

40 ⌂free. **Location:** Rural, simple, noisy. **Surface:** asphalted.
⬛ 01/01-31/12
Distance: 500m.

| | Meinerzhagen | 9B4 |

An der Musikschule, Schulplatz. **GPS:** n51,10865 e7,64329. ⬆.

3 ⌂free ⚡ (4x)€0,50/kWh. **Location:** Urban, simple, quiet.
Surface: asphalted. ⬛ 01/01-31/12
Distance: 400m 3km 400m 400m on the spot on the spot.

| | Meschede | 9C4 |

Am Wofibad, Im Ohl 13, Freienohl. **GPS:** n51,37574 e8,17664. ⬆.

3 ⌂free ⟻ against payment. **Location:** Simple. **Surface:** metalled.
⬛ 01/01-31/12

| | Meschede | 9C4 |

P Hallenbad, Arnsberger Strasse. **GPS:** n51,34897 e8,27356. ⬆ ➡.

3 ⌂free. **Location:** Simple. **Surface:** metalled. ⬛ 18.30-9.30h
Distance: 500m on the spot on the spot 500m 500m.

| | Meschede | 9C4 |

Knaus Campingpark Hennesee, Mielinghausen 7. **GPS:** n51,29846 e8,26366. ⬆.

16 ⌂€ 8-10 ⟻€1/60liter €0,50 Ch€0,50 (16x)€0,70/kWh
WC sanitary€2,30-3,50. **Surface:** grassy/metalled. ⬛ 01/01-31/12
Distance: 5km 100m 100m on the spot on the spot
on the spot on the spot.

| | Mettingen | 9B1 |

Hallenbad, Bahnhofstrasse 18-20. **GPS:** n52,31679 e7,78337. ⬆.

3 ⌂free ⟻ ⚡ WC. **Surface:** metalled. ⬛ 01/01-31/12
Distance: on the spot 200m 200m.
Remarks: Parking swimming pool, service: Kläranlage, Neuenkirchenerstrasse
208, bicycle rental.

| | Minden | 9D1 |

Reisemobilstellplatz Kanzlers Weide, Hausbergerstrasse.
GPS: n52,28750 e8,92551. ⬆.

100 ⌂free ⟻€1/120liter €0,50 Ch (18x)€0,50/kWh,6Amp.
Location: Urban, simple, quiet. **Surface:** metalled. ⬛ 01/01-31/12
Distance: 200m 50m 50m 200m 200m 200m.
Remarks: Max. 3 nights, not during big events.

| | Moers | 8D3 |

Freizeitpark Schoßpark, Krefelder straße. **GPS:** n51,44659 e6,61642. ⬆ ➡.

4 🚐 free. **Surface:** grasstiles. 🅿 01/01-31/12
Distance: 🚶700m ⊗700m 🚊500m.

📷S **Möhnesee** 🚻🛶 9C3
Freizeitanlage Möhnesee-Körbecke, Börnigeweg. **GPS:** n51,49160 e8,12555. ⬆.

20 🚐 € 6/24h 🛢(8x)€2/24h. 🅿 **Location:** Simple. **Surface:** metalled. 🅿 01/01-31/12
Distance: 🚶1km 🛶on the spot ⊗on the spot 🚊1km 🚲on the spot 🏃on the spot.
Remarks: Max. 24h.

📷S **Möhnesee** 🚻🛶 9C3
Strandbad, Linkstraße 20, Delecke. **GPS:** n51,49177 e8,08255. ⬆.
50 🚐 € 12 🚰🍺Ch 🛢(16x)WC 🚽included. 🅿 **Location:** Rural, comfortable, quiet. **Surface:** gravel. 🅿 01/03-01/11
Distance: 🚶Möhnesee 3,5km 🚗7,3km A44 ⛴Möhnesee.

📷 **Möhnesee** 🚻 9C3
Völlinghausen, Kettelbötel. **GPS:** n51,47360 e8,19831. ⬆➡.

10 🚐 free. **Surface:** grassy/gravel. 🅿 01/01-31/12
Distance: 🛶1,5km ⊗on the spot 🏃on the spot.

📷 **Mönchengladbach** 8D4
Schloß Wickrath, Neukircherweg, Wickrath. **GPS:** n51,12889 e6,42258. ⬆.

10 🚐 free. **Surface:** asphalted. 🅿 01/01-31/12
Distance: 🚶2km ⊗2km 🚊500m.
Remarks: Parking behind castle (500m), max. 2 days.

📷S **Mönchengladbach** 8D4
Camping-Center Krings, Monschauerstrasse 10/32. **GPS:** n51,19454 e6,40884. ⬆➡.

15 🚐 free 🚰🍺Ch free. **Surface:** metalled. 🅿 01/01-31/12
Distance: 🚶3km ⊗1km 🚊500m.
Remarks: Max. 2 nights, service during opening hours.

📷S **Monschau** 🚲🛶🚻🍴 8D6
Biesweg, B258. **GPS:** n50,55389 e6,23194. ⬆➡.

4 🚐 € 5/19-10h 🚰€5/7minutes 🍺Ch 🛢(4x)€5/10h. 🅿
Location: Simple, noisy. **Surface:** asphalted. 🅿 01/01-31/12
Distance: 🚶600m ⊗600m 🚊600m.
Remarks: Max. 1 night.

🍴 **Monschau** 🚲🛶🚻🍴 8D6
Haus Vennblick, Hauptstrasse 24, Höfen. **GPS:** n50,53934 e6,25292. ⬆.

6 🚐 guests free. **Location:** Rural, simple, noisy. **Surface:** gravel. 🔴 Wed
Distance: 🚶300m ⊗on the spot 🚲4km 🏃on the spot 🎿4km.

📷 **Mülheim/Ruhr** 🛶 9A4
Mintarder Straße 4. **GPS:** n51,41462 e6,86934. ⬆.

6 🚐 free. **Surface:** metalled. 🅿 01/01-31/12
Distance: 🚶2,7km ⊗50m 🚊100m 🚲on the spot 🏃on the spot.
Remarks: Max. 72h.

S **Mülheim/Ruhr** 🛶 9A4
Hymer Zentrum, Kölner Strasse 35-37. **GPS:** n51,39985 e6,87700. 🚰€0,50/80liter 🍺Ch.

Münster 9B2
Hafenstraße/Albersloher Weg. **GPS**: n51,95199 e7,63600.
6 🛏️€ 2/h, overnight stay free. **Location**: Noisy. **Surface**: asphalted.
📅 01/01-31/12
Distance: Old city centre 1km.
Remarks: Along railwayline.

Münster 9B2
Campingplatz Münster, Laerer Werseufer. **GPS**: n51,94583 e7,69082.⬆️

24 🛏️€ 15 2 pers.incl, dog € 3,50 ⛽€0,50 🚰€1 Ch ♿ WC included 🚿€0,50
📶 📅 01/01-31/12
Distance: Münster 4,5km ⊗100m 🛒on the spot 🚏100m.

Netphen 9C5
Freitzeitpark Netphen, P3, Brauersdorferstrasse. **GPS**: n50,91250 e8,12567.➡️

3 🛏️€ 3,50/day ⛽€1/70liter 🚰Ch. **Surface**: metalled. 📅 01/01-31/12
Distance: 2km 🛒2km.
Remarks: Max. 48h, coins at swimming pool.

Nettersheim 9A6
Wohnmobilhafen Nettersheim, Urftstraße. **GPS**: n50,48591 e6,62597.⬆️➡️

30 🛏️€ 8/24h ⛽€1 🚰Ch ♿included. 🏪
Location: Rural, simple, quiet. **Surface**: metalled. 📅 01/01-31/12
Distance: on the spot 🚶on the spot.
Remarks: Bread-service.

Nettetal 8D4
Am Nettebruch, Flothender straße/Flothend. **GPS**: n51,30188 e6,26715.⬆️➡️

5 🛏️free. **Surface**: grassy/gravel. 📅 01/01-31/12

Distance: 1km ⚓on the spot ⊗on the spot 🛒1km.

Nettetal 8D4
Am Krickenbeck See, Krickenbecker Allee 38. **GPS**: n51,34460 e6,25793.

50 🛏️Free, use of a meal desired. **Surface**: asphalted. 📅 01/01-31/12
Distance: 2km ⊗on the spot 🛒2km.

Neuss 9A4
Allrounder Winterworld/Skihalle, An der Skihalle 1. **GPS**: n51,17316 e6,64862.

30 🛏️free. **Surface**: metalled. 📅 01/01-31/12
Distance: ⊗on the spot ⛷️indoor ski.

Nideggen 8D5
Parkplatz Danzley, Bahnhofstrasse. **GPS**: n50,69247 e6,47952.⬆️

14 🛏️free. **Location**: Rural, simple. **Surface**: metalled.
📅 01/01-31/12
Distance: 500m 🛒500m.

Nordkirchen 9B3
Hotel Plettenberger Hof, Schlossstrasse 28. **GPS**: n51,73659 e7,52819.⬆️

2 🛏️guests free. **Surface**: asphalted. 📅 01/01-31/12
Distance: 200m ⊗on the spot.

Nottuln 9B2
Wellenfreibad/Hallenbad, Rudolf-Harbigstrasse. **GPS**: n51,92410 e7,34514.

DE

5 ⛺free ⛲. **Surface:** metalled. 🅿 01/01-31/12
Distance: 🚃on the spot.
Remarks: Parking swimming pool, service during opening hours.

| | Oberhausen | 9A3 |

Am Kaisergarten. GPS: n51,48690 e6,85551. ⬆➡.

60 ⛺€7 ⛲€1 Ch €0,50/3h. **Surface:** grassy.
🅿 01/01-31/12
Distance: 🚶Oberhausen City 30 min walking 🚲1,6km ⊗1,7km 🚉1,7km.

| | Oberhausen | 9A3 |

Parking 10 - CentrO, Arenastraße. **GPS:** n51,48930 e6,87063. ⬆➡.

40 ⛺free. **Surface:** metalled.
🅿 01/01-31/12
Distance: 🚶100m ⊗on the spot 🚉on the spot.
Remarks: At CentrO.

Tourist information Oberhausen:
😊 CentrO Park, Promenade 10. Amusement park. 🅿 01/04-31/10 11-18/19h.
🏠 CentrO. Large shopping centre, 300 shops, 100 restaurants/bars and a market. 🅿 Mo-Thu 10-20h restaurant 10-22h, Fri-Sa 10-22h restaurant 10-24h.

| | Oedt | 8D4 |

Wohnmobile-Stellplatz Niers-Perle-Oedt, Mühlengasse.
GPS: n51,32327 e6,37650. ⬆.

7 ⛺free. **Surface:** asphalted. 🅿 01/01-31/12
Distance: 🚶800m ⊗500m 🚉500m.

| | Oelde | 9C2 |

Pott's Brau und Backhaus, In der Geist 120. **GPS:** n51,81126 e8,13255. ⬆.

---

6 ⛺€5 ⛲€1/60liter Ch included. **Location:** Simple.
Surface: grassy/metalled. 🅿 02/01-23/12
Distance: ⊗on the spot.

| | Olpe | 9B4 |

Freizeitbad Olpe, Seeweg 5. **GPS:** n51,03242 e7,84163. ⬆➡.

10 ⛺€5 ⛲€0,20/liter Ch (4x)€1/2kWh WC included, at swimming pool 7-22h. **Location:** Urban. **Surface:** asphalted. 🅿 01/01-31/12
Distance: 🚶500m 🚲2km ⊗250m.
Remarks: On the banks of the Biggesee, max. 3 days.

| | Ostbevern | 9B2 |

Bever Bad, Am Hanfgarten 22. **GPS:** n52,03673 e7,84392. ➡.

6+10 ⛺€ 10, overnight stay only 20-9h free ⛲ Ch WC included.
Surface: grassy. 🅿 01/01-31/12
Distance: 🚶400m ⊗300m 🚉300m.
Remarks: Parking swimming pool, incl. access swimming pool.

| | Overhetfeld | 8D4 |

Camp Graskamp, Graskamp 19. **GPS:** n51,22259 e6,13977. ⬆.

5 ⛺€8 ⛲ Ch WC included. **Surface:** grassy. 🅿 01/01-31/12
Distance: 🚶200m ⊗200m 🚉on the spot.

| | Paderborn | 9D3 |

Maspernplatz, P4, Hathumarstrasse. **GPS:** n51,72278 e8,75417. ⬆➡.

8 ⛺€5/24h (4x)€0,50/h. **Location:** Urban, central, noisy.
Surface: metalled. 🅿 01/01-31/12
Distance: 🚶on the spot 🚲4km ⊗100m 🚉500m 🚃on the spot.

Paderborn 9D3

Wilhelm-Kaufmann-Allee/Fürstenweg. **GPS**: n51,72825 e8,74509.

16 € 5/24h €0,50/60liter Ch free (16x)€0,50/kWh.
Surface: asphalted. 01/01-31/12
Distance: 1,5km on the spot.
Remarks: Max. 72h.

Paderborn 9D3

Liboriberg, Liboriberg. **GPS**: n51,71543 e8,75529.

4 € 3,50/24h. **Location:** Urban, noisy.
01/01-31/12
Distance: on the spot on the spot on the spot on the spot.
Remarks: Small pitches.

Paderborn 9D3

Lippesee-Nordufer, Sennelagerstraße 58, Sande. **GPS**: n51,76087 e8,67756.

20 free. **Location:** Rural, simple. **Surface:** grassy.
01/01-31/12
Distance: 1km 150m 150m 1km 500m on the spot
on the spot.

Petershagen 9D1

Stellplatz Petershagen, Hohoffstrasse. **GPS**: n52,37532 e8,96875.

10 free €1/90liter (8x)€1/kWh. **Location:** Urban, quiet.
Surface: metalled. 01/01-31/12
Distance: 100m 100m 100m.
Remarks: Nearby football ground, max. 3 days.

Plettenberg 9B4

Aqua Magis, Albert Schweizerstrasse, Böddinghausen. **GPS**: n51,23220 e7,85308.

10 free €1/40liter Ch (8x)€0,50. **Location:** Rural, comfortable,
quiet. **Surface:** metalled. 01/01-31/12
Distance: on the spot 11km on the spot 200m on the spot
on the spot.
Remarks: At paradise pool, max. 48h.

Raesfeld 9A3

Wohnmobilstellplatz Graf Alexander, Südring. **GPS**: n51,76523 e6,83035.
8 € 8 €1 Ch €1/12h WC . **Surface:** gravel.
01/01-31/12
Distance: 1km 150m.
Remarks: At historic moated castle, max. 2 nights.

Recke 9B1

Yackthafen Marina Recke, Auf der Haar 23. **GPS**: n52,35082 e7,71174.

40 € 5 Ch (10x)€1,50 WC €1,50 . **Surface:** grassy/metalled.
01/01-31/12
Distance: 1km, Recke 3,5km on the spot on the spot on the spot
900m 400m.
Remarks: At the Mittelland canal, check in at harbourmaster.

Rees 8D3

Wohnmobilstellplatz, Ebentalstrasse. **GPS**: n51,76428 e6,38829.

31 € 6/day Ch included €1. **Location:** Urban, comfortable.
Surface: grassy. 01/01-31/12
Distance: 400m.
Remarks: Behind swimming pool.

Reken 9A2

Wohnmobilstellplatz Reken, Bergen 2a. **GPS**: n51,82864 e7,05895.

20 ⌁€6 ⚡€1/200liter ⚑Ch ⚒(10x)€0,50/kWh. **Surface:** grassy. ◘ 01/01-31/12
Distance: ⛟1km ⊗1km ⛢1km.
Remarks: Max. 2 days.

4 ⌁free. **Location:** Urban, quiet. **Surface:** metalled. ◘ 01/01-31/12
Distance: ⛟1km ⊗200m ⛢bakery 200m ⛲ on the spot ⚶ on the spot.
Remarks: Parking swimming pool.

| ⛺ | Remscheid | 9A4 |

| ⛺S | Rhede | 9A2 |

Brückenpark Müngsten, Mügstener Brückenweg. **GPS:** n51,16833 e7,13750.⬆.

Reisemobilstellplatz Kettelerplatz, Kettelerstrasse 9. **GPS:** n51,83677 e6,69346.⬆.

4 ⌁free. **Location:** Rural, simple, quiet. **Surface:** gravel. ◘ 01/01-31/12
Distance: ⛟5km ⚓4km ⚲100m ⛵100m ⚶ on the spot.

15 ⌁free ⚡€1/75liter ⚑Ch ⚒(6x)€1/2kWh. **Location:** Urban, simple.
Surface: grassy. ◘ 01/01-31/12
Distance: ⛟750m ⊗750m ⛢500m.

| ⛺ | Remscheid | 9A4 |

| ⛺ | Rhede | 9A2 |

Dörperhöhe, Bei Haus nr. 15, Lennep. **GPS:** n51,17986 e7,30205.
4 ⌁free. **Surface:** asphalted.

Hallen- und Freibad, Heideweg 59. **GPS:** n51,83164 e6,68635.⬆.

| ⛺ | Remscheid | 9A4 |

Jahnplatz, Am Stadion, Lennep. **GPS:** n51,19052 e7,26110.
4 ⌁free. **Surface:** asphalted. ◘ 01/01-31/12
Distance: ⛟historical centre of Lennep 300m.

| S | Remscheid | 9A4 |

Garage Pauli GmbH, Lenneperstrasse 152 (Bundesstrasse 229).
GPS: n51,18020 e7,22591.
⚡⚑Chfree. ◘ 01/01-31/12

| ⛺S | Rheda-Wiedenbrück | 9C2 |

Am Werl, Gütersloherstrasse. **GPS:** n51,85456 e8,29768.

2 ⌁free. **Location:** Urban, simple. **Surface:** metalled.
◘ 01/01-31/12
Distance: ⛟1,5km.
Remarks: Parking swimming pool, max. 3 days.

| ⛺ | Rheinbach | 9A6 |

Parkplatz Freizeitpark/Erlebnisbad Monte Mare, Münstereifelerstraße 69.
GPS: n50,61883 e6,93262. ⬆➡.

4 ⌁free ⚡⚑Ch ⚒WC free. **Location:** Urban. **Surface:** metalled.
◘ 01/01-31/12
Distance: ⛟300m ⛢300m.
Remarks: Max. 3 days.

| ⛺ | Rheda-Wiedenbrück | 9C2 |

P Hallenbad, Ostring/Am Hallenbad, Wiederbrück. **GPS:** n51,83188 e8,32350.
⬆➡.

4 ⌁free. **Location:** Rural, simple. **Surface:** metalled.
◘ 01/01-31/12
Distance: ⛟1,5km ⛙1,5km.
Remarks: Max. 3 days.

| ⛺ | Rheine | 9B1 |

Am Walshagenpark, Liobastrasse/Walshagenstrasse. **GPS:** n52,29562 e7,43580.
2 ⌁free. ◘ 01/01-31/12

DE

Distance: 300m 300m 300m 300m.

Rheine 9B1

Im Stadtpark, Kopernikusstrasse. **GPS:** n52,28137 e7,45478.

2 free. **Surface:** metalled. 01/01-31/12

Rheurdt 8D3

Wohnmobilhafen Ökodorf, St. Nikolausweg 15. **GPS:** n51,46382 e6,46780.

21 €9 Ch €3/24h WC. **Surface:** metalled. 01/01-31/12
Distance: 500m 500m 500m.

Rietberg 9C2

Jakobistrasse, Mastholte. **GPS:** n51,75667 e8,39111.

4 free €0,50/80liter Ch. **Location:** Rural, central. **Surface:** asphalted. 01/01-31/12
Distance: 100m 100m 100m.

Rietberg 9C2

Am Heimathaus, Langenberger Strasse, Mastholte. **GPS:** n51,75765 e8,38945.

2 free. **Location:** Urban. **Surface:** asphalted. 01/01-31/12
Distance: 100m 100m 100m.

Rietberg 9C2

Schulzentrum, Torfweg. **GPS:** n51,80724 e8,43295.

2 free. **Location:** Urban, simple. **Surface:** metalled.
01/01-31/12
Distance: 200m 100m 200m 200m on the spot.

Roetgen 8D5

Am Bahnhof, Bahnhofstrasse. **GPS:** n50,64868 e6,18506.

10 free. **Location:** Rural, simple, noisy. **Surface:** gravel/metalled.
01/01-31/12
Distance: 300m 300m.

Rosendahl 9A2

Wohnmobilplatz Darfeld, Sudetenstrasse, Darfeld. **GPS:** n52,02696 e7,26501.

20 free €1/100liter Ch €0,50/kWh. **Surface:** grassy/metalled.
01/01-31/12
Distance: 500m on the spot 500m.

Rüthen 9C3

Am Hachtor, Hachtorstrasse. **GPS:** n51,49405 e8,43119.

4 free. **Surface:** metalled. 01/01-31/12
Distance: 50m 50m 50m, Aldi 200m.

Sassenberg 9C2

Parkplatz Feldmark, Feldmark. **GPS:** n52,00172 e8,06546.

3 free €1/80liter Ch.
Distance: 4km on the spot on the spot.

Schieder 9D2

Freizeitzentrum Schiedersee, Kronenbruch. **GPS:** n51,92073 e9,16471.

DE

300 🗲 € 10 🚰€1/100liter 🗑 Ch ⚡€0,50/kWh WC 🚽€0,50 🔌€2 📶.
Location: Rural, comfortable, quiet. **Surface:** grassy/metalled.
📅 01/01-31/12
Distance: 🛒1,3km 🏊50m 🚰50m ⊗on the spot 🚉on the spot
🎣on the spot 🚶on the spot.

Wohnmobilhafen am Nationalpark-Eifel, Pfarrer-Kneipp-strasse, Gemünd.
GPS: n50,57855 e6,49107.⬆️➡️.

40 🗲€ 7 + € 1/pp tourist tax 🚰€0,50/50liter 🗑 Ch ⚡€0,50/kWh
📶100m. 🐾 **Location:** Rural, comfortable, quiet. **Surface:** gravel/metalled.
📅 01/01-31/12
Distance: 🛒within walking distance ⊗500m 🚉500m.
Remarks: Bread-service.

Am Freibad, Im Wiesengrund. **GPS:** n50,52993 e6,47022.⬆️.

8 🗲free. **Location:** Rural, simple, quiet. **Surface:** asphalted.

Reisemobilstellplatz Am Sennebach, Liemkerstrasse 27, Liemke.
GPS: n51,86979 e8,61531.⬆️.

20 🗲€ 5 🚰€2 🗑 Ch ⚡(18x)included. **Location:** Rural, isolated, quiet.
Surface: grasstiles. 📅 01/01-31/12 🔵 service: sa/su
Distance: ⊗1km 🚉1km.
Remarks: Behind Froli Kunstoffwerk Fromme.

Im Sorpetal, Winkhausen 21. **GPS:** n51,16083 e8,34056.➡️.

12 🗲€ 9 🚰€0,50/80liter Ch ⚡(12x)€0,50/kWh. 📅 01/01-31/12
Distance: 🛒on the spot ⊗100m 🚉2km 🚰500m 🚶1km 🏃on the spot.
Remarks: Trout pond, golf court 500m, playground.

Schulze Althoff, Heven 48. **GPS:** n52,07361 e7,22361.⬆️.

30 🗲€ 14/night, 3 pers. Incl. 4th pers. € 4 🚰🗑 Ch ⚡included WC 🚽sanitary
€2/pp 🔌€4. **Surface:** grassy.
Distance: 🛒2,5km 🏊on the spot 🛒on the spot 🚉2,5km 🚰on the spot.
Remarks: Swimming pool available.

Sportpark Senden, Buldenerstrasse. **GPS:** n51,85419 e7,47433.⬆️.

10 🗲free. **Surface:** grasstiles. 📅 01/01-31/12
Distance: 🛒on the spot ⊗200m 🚉300m 🚰on the spot.
Remarks: Parking swimming pool.

Wohnmobilstellplatz Steinhoff, Gettrup 37. **GPS:** n51,83305 e7,46878.⬆️➡️.

10 🗲€ 6 🚰🗑 Ch ⚡€0,50/kWh. **Surface:** grassy/metalled.
📅 01/01-31/12
Distance: 🛒Senden 4km ⊗2,5km 🚉2,5km.

Westor 31. **GPS:** n51,84286 e7,81849.⬆️➡️.

DE

4 🅕free 🚰€0,50/40liter 🅲Ch 🚿€0,50. **Surface:** metalled.
🅾 01/01-31/12
Distance: 🚶on the spot ⊗300m 🏪1km 🚌on the spot.
Remarks: Max. 3 nights.

| 🅢 | Siegen | 9C5 |

Am Hallenbad, Poststraße. **GPS:** n50,89463 e8,02405.➡️.

3 🅕free 🚰€1/10minutes 🅲Ch 🚿(2x)€1/8h. **Location:** Urban.
Surface: metalled. 🅾 01/01-31/12
Distance: 🚶200m ⊗200m 🏪200m 🚌250m 🚲on the spot 🚶on the spot.
Remarks: Max. 3 days.

| 🅢 | Siegen | 9C5 |

An der Alche, Freudenbergerstraße 67. **GPS:** n50,88073 e8,00764.⬆️.
4 🅕free 🚰€0,50/50liter 🅲Ch 🚿€0,50/kWh. 🅾 01/01-31/12
Distance: 🚶1km 🚲5km ⊗200m 🏪1km.
Remarks: Max. 3 days.

| 🅢 | Simmerath | 8D6 |

Wohnmobilhafen Rurseezentrum, Seeufer 1, Rurberg.
GPS: n50,60658 e6,38177.⬆️.

10 🅕€ 8/24h 🚰€2 🅲Ch. 🖥 **Location:** Rural, comfortable.
Surface: grasstiles. 🅾 01/01-31/12
Distance: 🚲100m ⊗50m.

| 🅢 | Soest | 9C3 |

City Motel, Altes Stellwerk 9. **GPS:** n51,57503 e8,11478.⬆️.

14 🅕€ 8 🚰🅲Ch 🚿(14x) WC 🅲€2 🖥€3 📶included.
Location: Urban, comfortable, central, quiet. **Surface:** gravel.

🅾 01/01-31/12
Distance: 🚶200m ⊗200m 🏪200m 🚌200m 🚲on the spot 🚶on the spot.

| 🅢 | Solingen | 9A4 |

Am Brandteich, Gräfrath. **GPS:** n51,21151 e7,07217.⬆️.

10 🅕free. **Location:** Urban, simple, quiet. **Surface:** concrete.
🅾 01/01-31/12
Distance: 🚶on the spot 🚂2,7km ⊗on the spot 🏪300m.
Remarks: Parking fire-station.

| 🅢 | Stadtlohn | 9A2 |

Freizeit- und Hallenbad, Uferstrasse 29. **GPS:** n51,99792 e6,93019.⬆️➡️.

4 🅕free 🚰€0,50/100liter 🅲Ch 🚿(4x)€1 WC 🅲. **Surface:** metalled.
🅾 01/01-31/12
Distance: 🚶800m.
Remarks: Parking swimming pool.

| 🅢 | Steinfurt | 9B2 |

Wohnmobilstellplatz Steinfurt, Liedekerkerstrasse 70, Burgsteinfurt.
GPS: n52,14738 e7,34746.⬆️➡️.

20 🅕free 🚰€1/100liter 🅲Ch 🚿€1/2kWh. **Surface:** gravel.
🅾 01/01-31/12
Distance: 🚶1km ⊗500m 🏪200m.
Remarks: Parking behind police station, max. 3 nights.

| 🅢 | Steinfurt | 9B2 |

Am Rathaus, Emsdettener Strasse 40. **GPS:** n52,12822 e7,39356.
8 🅕free. **Surface:** asphalted. 🅾 01/01-31/12
Distance: 🚶400m.

| 🅢 | Steinhagen | 9C2 |

Am Cronsbach. **GPS:** n51,99998 e8,42351.⬆️➡️.

DE

2 ⛺free. **Location:** Urban, simple. **Surface:** metalled.
🗓 01/01-31/12
Distance: 🚶100m ⊗100m 🚊100m.

| 🏭 | Stemwede 👬 | 9C1 |

Fest- und Schiesshalle, Schrottinghauserstrasse, Levern.
GPS: n52,37217 e8,44552.⬆➡.

2 ⛺free. **Location:** Rural, simple, isolated. **Surface:** metalled.
🗓 01/01-31/12
Distance: 🚶1,5km ⊗1,5km 🚊1,4km.

| 🏭 | Stemwede 👬 | 9C1 |

Park Stemwederberg, Stemwederbergstrasse/Freudeneck, Westrup.
GPS: n52,43246 e8,43973.⬆➡.

8 ⛺free. **Location:** Rural, comfortable. **Surface:** grassy.
🗓 01/01-31/12
Distance: 🚶2km ⊗2km 🚊2km 🚶on the spot.

| 🍴S | Stemwede 👬 | 9C1 |

Hotel-Gasthof Moorhof, Wagenfelderstrasse 34, Oppenwehe.
GPS: n52,49979 e8,53507.⬆.

20 ⛺€ 7, free with a meal 🚰 ⚡included ⚡€2,16Amp.
Location: Rural, quiet. **Surface:** grassy. 🗓 01/01-31/12 🔘 Thu
Distance: ⊗on the spot.

| 🏭S | Stemwede 👬 | 9C1 |

Rila Feinkost-Importe, Schröttinghauser Strasse/Hinterm Teich 3, Levern.
GPS: n52,36783 e8,43833.

50 ⛺€ 15 🚰 ⚡Ch ⚡ WC ⬜included. **Location:** Rural, comfortable.
Surface: grassy/gravel. 🗓 01/01-31/12
Distance: ⊗on the spot.
Remarks: Voucher incl. € 6 for 'Rila erleben': restaurant, Tapas bar, food, garden, playground.

| 🏭S | Straelen 🌿🚲👬 | 8D3 |

Fitnessbad Wasserstraelen, Lingsforterstraße 100. **GPS:** n51,45201 e6,25708.
⬆.

27 ⛺€ 7 🚰€1/80liter ⚡Ch ⚡(8x)€0,50/8kWh. **Surface:** asphalted.
🗓 01/01-31/12
Distance: 🚶1,2km ⊗1km 🚊1km.
Remarks: Max. 3 days.

| 🏭 | Tecklenburg | 9B1 |

Parkplatz Bismarckturm, Am Weingarten. **GPS:** n52,22129 e7,79905.⬆➡.

5 ⛺free. **Surface:** asphalted. 🗓 01/01-31/12
Distance: 🚶800m.

| ©S | Tecklenburg | 9B1 |

Regenbogen-Camp, Grafenstraße. **GPS:** n52,22941 e7,89052.⬆.
20 ⛺€ 10 🚰 ⚡Ch ⚡included. 🗓 01/01-31/12
Distance: 🚶Tecklenburg 7km.

| 🏭S | Telgte | 9B2 |

Am Dümmert, Emstor. **GPS:** n51,98497 e7,79151.⬆➡.
3 ⛺free 🚰€1/100liter ⚡Ch ⚡€1/kWh. **Location:** Simple. **Surface:** gravel.
🗓 01/01-31/12
Distance: 🚶600m.

| 🏭S | Telgte | 9B2 |

Waldschwimmbad Klatenberge, Waldweg. **GPS:** n51,99459 e7,78328.⬆.

20 🛏free ⚡🔌 Ch 🚿. **Surface:** asphalted. ⬛ 01/01-31/12
Distance: 🚶1km.
Remarks: Parking swimming pool, recreation area.

| 🍴S | Telgte | 9B2 |

Altes Gasthaus Lauheide, Lauheide 3, K17. **GPS:** n51,99862 e7,75319.⬆.

60 🛏€7,50 ⚡🔌 Ch 🚿 included. **Surface:** grassy.
⬛ 01/01-31/12 ⬤ Restaurant: Wed
Distance: 🚶4km ❌on the spot 🚌Bus 300m.

| 🛏S | Uedem | 8D3 |

Reisemobilstellplatz Uedem, Bergstraße. **GPS:** n51,66173 e6,28734.⬆.

26 🛏€8 ⚡🔌 Ch 🚿 (24x)€2/24h WC. **Surface:** grassy.
⬛ 01/01-31/12
Distance: 🚶1,5km.

| 🛏S | Velbert 👥 | 9A4 |

Unter der Saubrücke, Parkstraße, Velbert-Mitte. **GPS:** n51,34097 e7,03050.⬆.
➡.

8 🛏€3 ⚡€1/100liter 🔌 Ch 🚿 €0,50/kWh. **Location:** Urban, simple, quiet.
Surface: gravel. ⬛ 01/01-31/12
Distance: 🚶800m 🚲1,6km ❌250m 🏃on the spot.

| 🛏S | Velbert 👥 | 9A4 |

Panoramabad Velbert-Neviges, Wiesenweg. **GPS:** n51,30582 e7,08546.⬆.

5 🛏free ⚡€1/80liter 🔌 Ch. **Location:** Urban, simple, quiet.
Surface: concrete. ⬛ 01/01-31/12
Distance: 🚶800m ❌nearby 🚲500m.
Remarks: Parking swimming pool, max. 3 nights.

| 🛏 | Velbert 👥 | 9A4 |

Domparkplatz, Bernsaustrasse Schloss Hardenberg. **GPS:** n51,31565 e7,08724.
⬆.

5 🛏€2.🚿💦 **Location:** Urban. **Surface:** gravel. ⬛ 01/01-31/12
Distance: 🚶600m ❌on the spot.

| 🛏 | Velbert 👥 | 9A4 |

Nizzabad, Kalversiepen, Langenberg. **GPS:** n51,34362 e7,13766.⬆➡.

4 🛏free. **Location:** Simple, quiet. **Surface:** gravel. ⬛ 01/01-31/12
Distance: 🚶Langenberg 2,5km ❌on the spot.

| 🛏S | Velen 👥 | 9A2 |

Erholungsgebiet Waldvelen, ven der Buss, Klyer Damm 8-10.
GPS: n51,90167 e7,01167.⬆➡.

30 🛏€ 15, 2 pers.incl ⚡🔌 Ch 🚿 (50x). **Location:** Rural, luxurious.
Surface: gravel. ⬛ 01/01-31/12
Distance: 🚶2km 🚲8,5km.

| 🛏S | Velen 👥 | 9A2 |

Freibad Ramsdorf, Velener Straße, Ramsdorf. **GPS:** n51,88955 e6,92503.⬆.

DE

5 ⛟free. **Surface:** asphalted. ▢ 01/01-31/12
Distance: Ramsdorf 300m.
Remarks: At swimming pool.

| | Viersen | 8D4 |

Am Familienbad Ransberg, Heesstraße 80, Viersen-Dülken.
GPS: n51,25083 e6,35291.⬆

9 ⛟free €0,50/100liter Ch (6x)€1/2kWh. **Surface:** metalled.
▢ 01/01-31/12
Distance: Dülken 400m, Viersen 3km 400m 2km 100m.
Remarks: Max. 3 days.

| | Vreden | 9A2 |

Hotel Zum Möwenparadies, Zwillbrockstrasse 39. **GPS:** n52,05305 e6,70733.⬆

10 ⛟€ 10 Ch WC included. **Surface:** grassy. ▢ 01/01-31/12
Distance: on the spot on the spot 200m.

| | Vreden | 9A2 |

Wohnmobilpark Vreden, Ottensteiner Strasse 59. **GPS:** n52,03962 e6,84136.⬆

24 ⛟€ 5 €0,50/80liter €0,50 Ch (12x)€0,50/kWh. **Surface:** gravel.
▢ 01/01-31/12
Distance: 400m 100m 400m.

| | Wadersloh | 9C3 |

Im Klostergarten 18, Liesborn. **GPS:** n51,71414 e8,25960.⬆➡

4 ⛟free €0,50/80liter Ch (4x)€0,50/12h. **Location:** Rural.
Surface: metalled. ▢ 01/01-31/12
Distance: 400m 100m 400m on the spot on the spot.
Remarks: Behind gymnasium.

| | Waldbröl | 9B5 |

Am Hallenbad, Vennstrasse. **GPS:** n50,87511 e7,60987.⬆

5 ⛟free. **Location:** Rural, simple, quiet. **Surface:** metalled.
▢ 01/01-31/12
Distance: on the spot 18km on the spot on the spot.
Remarks: Max. 2 days.

| | Waldfeucht-Brüggelchen | 8D4 |

Reisemobilstellplatz "Tilder Weg", Tilderweg. **GPS:** n51,07076 e5,99454.⬆

50 ⛟€ 8, 4 pers.incl Ch (14x)included WC €2 €3/h .
Surface: grassy. ▢ 01/01-31/12
Distance: 500m on the spot.
Remarks: Breakfast-service, swimming pool € 2/pp.

| | Wachtendonk | 8D4 |

Bleiche P4, Achter de Stadt. **GPS:** n51,40601 e6,33170.⬆➡

18 ⛟€ 4 €0,50/80liter Ch (8x)€0,50/kWh.
Location: Rural, simple, quiet. **Surface:** metalled. ▢ 01/01-31/12
Distance: 1km on the spot 500m 100m.
Remarks: Max. 4 nights.

| | Waltrop | 9B3 |

Restaurant Zur Lohburg, Lohburgerstrass 105, A2 Ausfahrt henreichenburg,
Schiffshebewerk. **GPS:** n51,60613 e7,34882.

DE

10 ⌇€5 ⚡ ⚡€3. **Surface:** grassy. ◘ 01/01-31/12
Distance: 1km ⊗on the spot 1km.

Warburg   9D3
Schützenplatz, Paderborner Tor. **GPS:** n51,48993 e9,13810.
5 ⌇€5 ⚡ Ch ⚡included. **Surface:** metalled. ◘ 15/09-15/10
Distance: 500m.

Warendorf   9C2
Parkplatz Emssee, Sassenberger Strasse 26. **GPS:** n51,95514 e7,99797.⬆

15 ⌇free ⚡€1/50liter ⚡Ch ⚡€1/kWh. **Surface:** metalled.
◘ 01/01-31/12
Distance: 1km ⟶on the spot ⊗on the spot.
Remarks: Max. 3 days.

Warendorf   9C2
Am Wörden 4, Freckenhorst. **GPS:** n51,91727 e7,97019.⬆
5 ⌇free. **Surface:** metalled. ◘ 01/01-31/12
Distance: 500m.
Remarks: At sports grounds.

Warendorf   9C2
Parkplatz Zwischen den Emsbrücken, Am Emswehr. **GPS:** n51,95426 e7,99164.
⬆

2 ⌇free. ◘ 01/01-31/12
Distance: 100m.

Warstein 〰🍴🍦   9C3
Camperpark zum Bayernstadl, Enkerbruch 12a. **GPS:** n51,43041 e8,37432.⬆
➡

18+22 ⌇€8 ⚡€1/100liter ⚡Ch ⚡(18x)€2/16,€1 summer,€2 winter.
Surface: gravel. ◘ 01/01-31/12
Distance: 1,5km ⊗on the spot 1,5km 1,5km.
Remarks: Bread-service.

Warstein 〰🍴🍦   9C3
Vans in Paradise, Zu Hause im Waldpark. **GPS:** n51,42615 e8,35525.⬆

60 ⌇€15 ⚡ ⚡Ch ⚡(76x),16Amp WC ⚡included ◙€2/2.
Location: Isolated, quiet. **Surface:** grassy/gravel. ◘ 01/01-31/12
Distance: 2km ⊗small menu 2km 2km.
Remarks: At Warstein brewery, bread-service + breakfast-service.

Warstein 〰🍴🍦   9C3
Wohnmobilstellplatz, Dammweg. **GPS:** n51,45103 e8,34750.⬆➡

5 ⌇free. **Location:** Simple. **Surface:** gravel/metalled.
◘ 01/01-31/12
Distance: 2km ⊗500m 1km 1km.
Remarks: At sports park.

Tourist information Warstein:
👁 Warsteiner Brauerei, Zu Hause im Waldpark. Guided tour 1.45h, 2 drinks
included. ◘ daily 12-17, Su 13-15h.

Wassenberg   8D4
Parkbad Wassenberg, Auf dem Taubenkamp 2. **GPS:** n51,09833 e6,14364.⬆➡

11 ⌇€5/day, €20/week ⚡€1/100 ⚡€1 Ch ⚡€0,50/kWh.
Location: Rural, comfortable, quiet. **Surface:** metalled. ◘ 01/01-31/12
Distance: 1,5km.
Remarks: To be paid at swimming pool.

Weeze   8D3
Tierpark Fährsteg, L5 Fährsteg. **GPS:** n51,63074 e6,20086.⬆

DE

13 ⛺€5 ⚡€0,50/kWh. 🅾 01/01-31/12
Distance: 🚶500m 🚊500m.

| S | **Weeze** | 8D3 |

Aral, Industriestraße. **GPS:** n51,62029 e6,20972.⬆.
⚡€1 🚰Ch.

| S | **Wegberg** | 8D4 |

Wegberger Reisemobilstellplatz, Schul- und Sportzentrum, Maaseiker
Strasse 67. **GPS:** n51,13389 e6,28266.⬆➡.

10 ⛺€8 ⚡ 🚰Ch ✂ included. **Surface:** gravel/sand. 🅾 01/01-31/12
Distance: 🚶400m ⊗400m 🚊400m 🚌on the spot.
Remarks: Caution key € 20.

| S | **Werne** 🛁 | 9B3 |

Natur Solebad, Am Hagen. **GPS:** n51,65910 e7,63414.⬆➡.

12 ⛺€5/24h ⚡€1/80liter 🚰Ch ✂€0,50/kWh. **Surface:** metalled.
🅾 01/01-31/12
Distance: 🚶400m ⊗200m 🚊400m.
Remarks: Tuesday and Friday market.

| S | **Wesel** 🚢 | 8D3 |

Reisemobilstellplatz Römerwardt, Rheinpromenade.
GPS: n51,66116 e6,59256.⬆➡.

48 ⛺€6-8 ⚡€1/80liter 🚰Ch ✂€1/kWh. **Surface:** grassy/metalled.
🅾 01/01-31/12
Distance: 🚶1,5km ⊗100m 🚲on the spot 🚶on the spot.

| S | **Wiehl** | 9B5 |

Freizeitpark Wiehl, Brüchnerstrasse. **GPS:** n50,94716 e7,54585.⬆➡.

3 ⛺free ⚡€1/80liter 🚰Ch.
Location: Simple, central.
Surface: metalled.
Distance: 🚶300m 🚶5,4km 🚊400m.
Remarks: Parking next to recreation park and disco, max. 2 days.

Tourist information Wiehl:
🛈 www.wiehl.de. Small town in the green hills. 180 kilometres marked hiking
routes.
👁 Wiehler Dahlienschau. 400 varieties of dahlias. 🅾 15/08-15/10 daily 8-18h.
🎫 free.
👁 Wiehler Trofsteinhöhle. Caves Temperature is approx. 8ºC. 🅾 15/03-31/10
9-17h, 01/11-14/03 Sa-Su 11-16h.
🚣 Bergische Postkutsche, Nümrecht Post. Ride by mail-coach between Wiehl
and Nümbrecht. 🅾 01/05-30/09 Fri-Su 10-16h.

| S | **Wilnsdorf** | 9C5 |

Wielandshof, Bauhofstraße 5. **GPS:** n50,80692 e8,10896.⬆.

5 ⛺€5 ⚡€0,50/60liter 🚰Ch ✂(4x)€1/12h. 🚿 **Surface:** gravel.
🅾 01/01-31/12
Distance: 🚶900m ⊗900m.
Remarks: Check in at farm.

| S | **Windeck** 🌳 | 9B5 |

Am Sportplatz, Im Bungert, Herchen. **GPS:** n50,78025 e7,51308.➡.

8 ⛺free ⚡ ✂(10x)€0,50/kWh. **Location:** Rural, simple, quiet.
Surface: gravel. 🅾 01/01-31/12
Distance: 🚶200m 🚶8,5km ⊗200m 🚊200m 🚲on the spot 🚶on the spot.
Remarks: Parking sports park.

| S | **Windeck** 🌳 | 9B5 |

Hallenbad, Bergische strasse 21, Dattenfeld. **GPS:** n50,80754 e7,56105.⬆➡.

DE

4 ⌁free €1,50 €1,50 Ch 1,50. **Location:** Rural, simple, quiet.
Surface: metalled. ☐ 01/01-31/12
Distance: 8,5km on the spot on the spot.

Museumsdorf Altwindeck, Im Thal Windeck 17, Alt-Windeck.
GPS: n50,81276 e7,57554.

4 ⌁free. **Location:** Rural, simple, quiet. **Surface:** gravel.
☐ 01/01-31/12
Distance: 2km 8,5km on the spot 2km on the spot
on the spot.
Remarks: Parking museum, max. 3 days.

Windeck 9B5
Auf dem Greent, Dattenfeld. **GPS:** n50,80697 e7,55495.

50 ⌁free. **Location:** Rural, simple, quiet. **Surface:** asphalted/grassy.
☐ 01/01-31/12
Distance: 500m 8,5km 500m 500m.
Remarks: Fair ground.

Windeck 9B5
Brunnenweg, Dattenfeld. **GPS:** n50,80486 e7,56087.

5 ⌁free. **Location:** Simple, quiet. **Surface:** grassy/gravel.
☐ 01/01-31/12
Distance: 200m 8km 200m 150m on the spot on the spot.
Remarks: Recreation park.

Winterberg 9C4
Wohnmobilpark Winterberg, Neuastenberger Straße 4a, OT Neuastenberg.
GPS: n51,15974 e8,48383.
70 ⌁€ 11,50 + tourist tax € 1,75/pp €1/100liter Ch €0,50/kWh €1
€2,50/2,50 . **Surface:** gravel. ☐ 01/01-31/12 on the spot
on the spot.
Remarks: Bread-service.

Winterberg 9C4
Parkplatz Stadthalle, Schulstrasse. **GPS:** n51,19163 e8,53810.

20 ⌁€ 8/24h €0,50/50liter Ch (10x)€0,50/3h. **Surface:** metalled.
☐ 01/01-31/12
Distance: 1km 1km.

Winterberg 9C4
Campingplatz Winterberg. **GPS:** n51,18632 e8,50445.

⌁€ 7,50-8 + € 5,50-6/pp, dog € 2 Ch (25x)€0,55/kWh WC €1
€0,50. **Location:** Rural, luxurious. **Surface:** metalled.
Distance: 2km on the spot 2km 20m on the spot on the spot
on the spot on the spot.
Remarks: Parking at skipistes.

Winterberg 9C4
Kirchmeier Sporthotel, Renauweg 54, Altastenberg. **GPS:** n51,19391 e8,46844.

10 ⌁€ 26 + € 1,75/pp tourist tax (10x) WC
Surface: asphalted. ☐ 01/01-31/12
Distance: Winterberg 5km on the spot on the spot 800m
on the spot. **Remarks:** Free entrance swimming pool, Dampfbad, sauna,
shuttle-bus, cross-country skiing piste.

Winterberg 9C4
Bergrestaurant Bobhaus, Auf der Kappe 1. **GPS:** n51,18493 e8,50559.

DE

8 ⚒ € 12, free with a meal. 🛁
Location: Rural. **Surface:** asphalted.
Distance: 🎿2km ⊗on the spot 🚲on the spot 🚶on the spot 🚴on the spot 🛷on the spot.
Remarks: Parking ski-lift, check in at restaurant.

| 🏕 S | Witten | 9B3 |

Reisemobil-Center, Pferdebachstrasse 150. **GPS**: n51,45411 e7,35246. ⬆.

8 ⚒free 🚿€1/80liter 🚰 Ch. **Surface:** gravel. 📅 01/01-31/12
Distance: 🎿3km ⊗3km 🚉3km.

| 🏕 | Wülfrath 🍽 | 9A4 |

Parkplatz, Mettmanner strasse 42. **GPS**: n51,28188 e7,02741. ⬆.

10 ⚒free. **Location:** Urban, simple, quiet. **Surface:** concrete.
📅 01/01-31/12
Distance: 🎿on the spot ⊗500m 🚉800m.

| 🏕 S | Xanten | 8D3 |

Womopark Xanten, Fürstenberg 6. **GPS**: n51,65413 e6,46389. ⬆➡.

60+20 ⚒€ 10 🚿🚰 Ch included 🔌€2 ⚒€1. **Surface:** grassy.
📅 01/01-31/12
Distance: 🎿1,7km ⊗300m 🚉200m.

| 🏕 S | Zülpich | 9A5 |

Wohnmobilhafen am Zülpicher See, Am Wassersportsee.
GPS: n50,67592 e6,65795. ⬆➡.

40 ⚒€5 🚿€1 🚰 Ch 🔌 (4x)€1. 📮 **Location:** Rural, simple, isolated.
Surface: grassy/metalled. 📅 01/01-31/12
Distance: ⛵100m.
Remarks: Service nearby tenniscourt 100m.

Rhineland-Palatinate/Saarland

| 🏕 S | Alf 🍇🚡 | 16D1 |

Freizeitbad Arrastal, Mühlenstraße. **GPS**: n50,05273 e7,11326.

100 ⚒€ 6,00 🚿🚰 Ch included 🔌€2,50/day ⚒. 🛁 **Location:** Rural, simple.
Surface: asphalted/grassy. 📅 01/01-31/12
Distance: 🎿800m.

| 🏕 | Alken 🚡 | 9B6 |

P2, Moselstraße. **GPS**: n50,24525 e7,44573.

6 ⚒free. **Surface:** metalled. 📅 01/01-31/12
Distance: 🎿500m ⊗on the spot 🚊200m 🚲on the spot 🚶on the spot.

| 🏕 S | Alsheim | 17B2 |

Weingut Elisabethenhof, In den Weingärten 10. **GPS**: n49,76563 e8,34748. ⬆.

4 ⚒€ 10 🚿🚰 included 🔌€2/24h. 🛁 **Location:** Rural, simple, quiet.
Surface: concrete. 📅 01/01-31/12
Distance: 🎿300m 🚉500m.

| 🏕 S | Altdorf | 17A3 |

Spelzenhof, Hauptstrasse 77. **GPS**: n49,28869 e8,22028. ⬆.

DE

6 ⛶€7,50 ⛽ 🔌 included. **Location:** Simple. **Surface:** grassy.
🅿 01/01-31/12 ⊙ Mon, Tue
Distance: 🚂nearby 🏊7km ⊗150m 🛒400m 🚌nearby.

⛩S | **Altendiez** | 9C6
Restaurant Bimbes-Stubb, Lahnblick 4. **GPS:** n50,36612 e7,98041.⬆➡.

6 ⛶€8 ⛽ 🔌€2. **Location:** Simple. **Surface:** gravel.
🅿 01/01-31/12 ⊙ Mo
Distance: 🚂on the spot ⊗on the spot 🛒500m.

📷S | **Altenglan** 🎡 | 16D2
Draisine, Austrasse. **GPS:** n49,55001 e7,46465.⬆.

3 ⛶free ⛽€1/80liter 🚰Ch 🔌(4x). **Surface:** gravel. 🅿 01/04-31/10
Distance: ⊗100m 🛒100m.

📷S | **Andernach** | 9B6
Wohnmobilstellplatz Andernach, Scheidsgasse/Uferstrasse.
GPS: n50,44176 e7,40796.⬆.

70 ⛶€7 ⛽€1/100liter 🚰Ch 🔌(40x)€1/2kWh WC€0,50/time.🚿
Surface: metalled. 🅿 01/01-31/12
Distance: 🚂on the spot ⚓Rhine river ⊗200m 🛒400m.
Remarks: Max. 3 nights.

⛩S | **Andernach** | 9B6
Wohnmobilstellplatz Monte Mare, Klingelswiese 1. **GPS:** n50,42633 e7,38492.
⬆.

---

12 ⛶€3 ⛽€1/100liter 🚰Ch 🔌(12x)€0,50/kWh WC🚽📶.
Surface: concrete. 🅿 01/01-31/12
Distance: 🚂2km.
Remarks: Bread-service.

📷S | **Annweiler** | 17A3
Am Kurpark, Bindersbacherstrasse. **GPS:** n49,19624 e7,96817.⬆➡.

10 ⛶free ⛽€1/80liter 🚰Chfree. **Location:** Rural, quiet. **Surface:** asphalted.
🅿 01/01-31/12
Distance: 🚂1km 🛒600m.
Remarks: Max. 3 days.

📷S | **Bacharach** | 17A1
Reisemobilplatz Sonnenstrand, B9 Leinpfad. **GPS:** n50,05487 e7,77123.⬆.

30 ⛶€8 ⛽€1 🚰Ch 🔌(12x)€2,50/24h 🚽€1 ⊙€3/3 📶.
Location: Comfortable, central, quiet. **Surface:** gravel.
🅿 01/01-31/12 ⊙ high water
Distance: 🚂on the spot ⚓Rhine river ⊗300m 🛒300m.

📷S | **Bad Bergzabern** | 17A3
Schloßgärten, Weinbergstrasse. **GPS:** n49,10322 e7,99737.⬆➡.

7 ⛶€4 ⛽€1/80liter 🚰€1 Ch 🔌€1.🍴
Location: Urban, simple, central, noisy. **Surface:** metalled.
🅿 01/01-31/12 ⊙ water disconnected in winter
Distance: 🚂on the spot ⊗on the spot 🛒200m.

⛩S | **Bad Bergzabern** | 17A3
Weingut Hitziger, Liebrauenbergweg 3. **GPS:** n49,10667 e7,99611.⬆.

DE

8 🛏€5 🚐🔌 Ⓒincluded 🔌€1/kWh. 🚌 **Location:** Rural, simple, quiet.
Surface: grassy. 🗓 01/01-31/12
Distance: 🚶1km ⊗2km 🚲2km.

S **Bad Dürkheim** 🏊🎾 **17A2**
In der Silz, Leistadterstrasse. **GPS:** n49,46944 e8,16722.⬆️➡️

170 🛏€6 🚐€1/80liter Ⓒ Ch 🔌€1/kWh. 🚌 **Location:** Urban, simple.
Surface: grassy/gravel. 🗓 01/01-31/12
Distance: 🚶300m ⊗100m 🚲300m 🚃200m.
Remarks: Servicepoint at Knaus Park.

Ⓒ**S** **Bad Dürkheim** 🏊🎾 **17A2**
Knaus park, In den Almen 3. **GPS:** n49,47472 e8,19167.⬆️

16 🛏€9,50 🚐€1/70liter Ⓒ Ch 🔌€0,70/kWh 🚿€3,30/pp 📶.
Surface: gravel/metalled. 🗓 01/01-31/12

S **Bad Dürkheim** 🏊🎾 **17A2**
Katharinenhof, In den Kornwiesen 1. **GPS:** n49,46633 e8,20144.
10 🛏€10 🚐Ⓒ Ch 🔌. **Surface:** grassy. 🗓 01/01-31/12
Remarks: Bread-service.

⚓**S** **Bad Ems** 〰 **9B6**
Yachthafen Kutscher's Marina, Nievernerstrasse 20. **GPS:** n50,33278 e7,70167.
⬆️➡️.

16 🛏€10 🚐Ⓒ Ch 🔌€1/kWh WC 🚿€1. 🚌 **Location:** Comfortable, quiet.
Surface: gravel. 🗓 01/03-15/11
Distance: 🚶on the spot 🔌on the spot ⊗1km 🚲300m.

S **Bad Kreuznach** 🏊🎾 **17A1**
Wohnmobilstellplatz Salinental, Karlshalle 11, Saline.
GPS: n49,82778 e7,85001.⬆️➡️.

35 🛏€12 🚐€0,50/60liter Ⓒ Ch 🔌€2,50/night WC 🚿€1. **Surface:** gravel.
🗓 01/01-31/12
Distance: 🚶2km 🏊on the spot 🔌on the spot ⊗200m 🚲2km
🚃on the spot.

S **Bad Kreuznach** 🏊🎾 **17A1**
Weingut Desoi, Am Darmstädter Hof. **GPS:** n49,82803 e7,88934.⬆️.

3 🛏€5 🚐🔌 included. 🚌 **Location:** Rural, simple, quiet. **Surface:** concrete.
🗓 01/01-31/12
Distance: 🚶1,5km 🚲10km 🚲500m.

S **Bad Kreuznach** 🏊🎾 **17A1**
Weingut Gut Neuhof, Gut Neuhof. **GPS:** n49,86923 e7,85924.⬆️.

4 🛏€10 🚐🔌 included. 🚌 **Location:** Rural, simple, quiet. **Surface:** grassy.
🗓 01/01-31/12
Distance: 🚶3km 🚲2,5km.

S **Bad Marienberg** 🎯🎾 **9C5**
Marienbad, Bismarckstrasse 65. **GPS:** n50,64321 e7,93515.➡️.

40 🛏€10 🚐€1/80liter Ⓒ Ch 🔌(40x)€0,50/kWh 🚿included.
Location: Luxurious, quiet. **Surface:** metalled. 🗓 01/01-31/12
Distance: 🚶2km ⊗Bistro.
Remarks: 10 days € 78, bread-service, free use of sun beds and beach chairs.

Bad Münster a. St.-Ebernburg 17A2

Reisemobilstellplatz Weingut Rapp, Schlossgartenstrasse 74. **GPS:** n49,80800 e7,83208.

3 €9,50 €1/100liter **Location:** Rural, simple, quiet.
Surface: gravel. 01/01-31/12
Distance: 15km.

Bad Neuenahr 9A6

Am Schwimmbad. **GPS:** n50,53806 e7,10139.

25 €7 €0,50 Ch €1/2kWh €0,50. **Location:** Urban, central.
Surface: metalled. 01/01-31/12
Distance: 400m 300m bakery 500m.
Remarks: Along the Ahr river, max. 24h.

Bad Neuenahr 9A6

Apolinaris-Stadion, Kreuzstrasse. **GPS:** n50,54456 e7,15132.

50 €5/24h €1/80liter Ch. **Surface:** asphalted.
01/01-31/12
Distance: 3km.

Bad Neuenahr 9A6

St Piusstrasse. **GPS:** n50,53962 e7,10775.

20 €5/24h. **Location:** Urban, simple. **Surface:** asphalted.
01/01-31/12
Distance: 700m 700m.
Remarks: Parking at the Ahr.

Bad Sobernheim 17A2

Reisemobilstellplatz am Nohfels - Bad Sobernheim

Am_Nohfels@web.de - www.amnohfels.de

**Ideal base for walking and cycling
Nearby things of interest
Located in a quit location**

Reisemobilstellplatz am Nohfels, Hömigweg 1. **GPS:** n49,77993 e7,65702.
39 €8 €0,10/10liter Ch (39x)€2/day,16Amp WC included.
Location: Rural, comfortable, quiet. **Surface:** metalled.
01/01-31/12
Distance: 500m 100m 100m 200m 500m 300m
on the spot on the spot.
Remarks: Bread-service.

Battweiler 16D3

Flugplatz Pottschütthöhe, Pottschütthöhe. **GPS:** n49,26761 e7,49096.

10 €15 Ch (10x)included. **Location:** Simple, isolated, quiet.
Surface: grassy/gravel. 01/01-31/12 Mo
Distance: 2km 10km on the spot.
Remarks: At airfield.

Baumholder 16D2

Freizeitzentrum Am Weiher, Ringstrasse. **GPS:** n49,61111 e7,33917.

3 free . **Surface:** asphalted. 01/03-31/10
Distance: 2km on the spot on the spot 250m.

Bechel 9B6

Restaurant Zum Wolfsbusch, Emser strasse 1. **GPS:** n50,29609 e7,71503.

DE

5 ⌷€ 2, guests free ⌁€2.
Location: Simple, quiet. **Surface:** gravel/metalled.
Distance: on the spot on the spot 300m.

| ⌷S | **Beckingen** | 16C3 |

Wohnmobilstellplatz Düppenweiler, Brunnenstrasse 11, Düppenweiler.
GPS: n49,41414 e6,76973.

30 ⌷€4 ⌁€1/100liter ◌Ch ◌€1/8h. **Surface:** metalled.
☐ 01/03-31/10
Distance: on the spot.

| ⌷S | **Beckingen** | 16C3 |

Landgasthaus Wilscheider Hof, Zum Wilscheider Hof, Düppenweiler.
GPS: n49,42585 e6,76431.

15 ⌷€5 ⌁◌Ch ◌€1 WC ◌€1,50 ◌. **Surface:** grassy.
☐ 01/01-31/12
Distance: 1,5km on the spot 1,5km.

| S | **Bellheim** | 17B3 |

Wohnmobilstellplatz Bellheim, Auchtweide. **GPS:** n49,19552 e8,27466.⬆

8 ⌷€5 ⌁WCincluded ◌€1/pp. ◌ **Location:** Simple, isolated, quiet.
Surface: grassy/gravel. ☐ 01/05-31/10
Distance: 700m 3km 750m 1km 200m.
Remarks: At tennis-courts, max. 24h.

| ⌷ | **Bendorf** | 9B6 |

Wohnmobilstellplatz Bendorf, Koblenz Olper Strasse.
GPS: n50,43998 e7,57486.
6 ⌷free. ☐ 01/01-31/12

Distance: 4km.

| ⌷S | **Bernkastel** | 16D1 |

Weingut Studert-Prüm im Maximin Hof, Hauptstrasse 150, Wehlen.
GPS: n49,93771 e7,04811.⬆

43 ⌷€ 10 ⌁◌Ch ◌WC included. ◌ **Location:** Rural, comfortable, quiet.
Surface: grassy. ☐ 01/04-31/10
Distance: on the spot on the spot on the spot on the spot
2km, bakery 300m on the spot on the spot.

| PS | **Bernkastel** | 16D1 |

Nikolausufer. **GPS:** n49,91119 e7,06721.⬆

40 ⌷10-18h ⌁◌Ch. ◌ **Location:** Urban. **Surface:** grasstiles.
☐ 01/01-31/12
Remarks: Max. 6h.

| ⌷ | **Betzdorf** | 9B5 |

Friedrichstrasse. **GPS:** n50,78636 e7,87781.⬆

1 ⌷free. **Location:** Urban, simple, noisy. **Surface:** asphalted.
☐ 01/01-31/12
Distance: 500m.
Remarks: Max. 24h.

| ⌷ | **Betzdorf** | 9B5 |

Schützenplatz, Martin-Luther-Strasse. **GPS:** n50,79323 e7,86793.⬆

1 ⌷free. **Location:** Urban, simple. **Surface:** gravel. ☐ 01/01-31/12
Distance: on the spot on the spot.
Remarks: Max. 1 night.

DE

Betzdorf 9B5

Vor dem Stadion, Eberhardystrasse. GPS: n50,78524 e7,86507. ✈.

1 ⌁free. **Location:** Urban, simple, central. **Surface:** gravel.
◻ 01/01-31/12
Distance: 1km 50m on the spot on the spot.
Remarks: Max. 1 night.

Bexbach 16D3

Bexbacher Reisemobilhafen, Im Blumengarten. GPS: n49,34161 e7,25698.↑
➡.

35 ⌁€ 7 €1/80liter Ch (36x)€2,50/night WC. **Surface:** grassy.
◻ 01/01-31/12
Distance: 900m 5km on the spot 500m 200m.
Remarks: Bread-service.

Biebelnheim 17A2

Wohnmobilpark am Petersberg, Flonheimer Strasse 34.
GPS: n49,79432 e8,16236.

20 ⌁€ 5 €2 Ch €2. **Surface:** metalled. ◻ 01/01-31/12
Distance: 1km 1,5km Bistro Am Petersberg 1km.
Remarks: Max. 2 nights.

Biebernheim 17A1

Reiterhof Pabst, Auf dem Flürchen. GPS: n50,14127 e7,70828.↑➡.

20 ⌁€ 6, 2 pers.incl €1 Ch (6x)€2. **Location:** Rural, simple,
isolated, quiet. **Surface:** grassy. ◻ 01/01-31/12
Distance: 10km.
Remarks: Bread-service.

Bingen/Rhein 17A1

Wohnmobilpark Bingen, Mainzer Straße, Bingen/Kempten.
GPS: n49,96860 e7,94417.↑➡.

39 ⌁€ 6,50/night Chincluded €2,50/24h €3/3 €2/h,€0,50/
every next hour. **Location:** Comfortable, quiet. **Surface:** grassy/metalled.
◻ 01/01-31/12
Distance: 2,5km 1,5km 800m 2,7km.
Remarks: Bread-service.

Birgel 9A6

Historische Wassermühle, Bahnhofstrasse 16. GPS: n50,32033 e6,61764.↑.

10 ⌁€ 15, free with a meal > € 15 Ch (2x)included.
Location: Simple, quiet. **Surface:** gravel. ◻ 01/01-31/12
Distance: 500m 25km on the spot 1km.

Blieskastel 16D3

Freizeitanlage Würzbacher Weiher, Marxstraße, Niederwürzbach.
GPS: n49,24674 e7,19226.↑➡.

10 ⌁€ 4,50 €1/10minutes €1 Ch €1/4h.
Surface: grassy/gravel.
◻ 01/01-31/12
Distance: 500m on the spot on the spot 100m 600m 600m.
Remarks: At lake, Würzbacher Weiher.

Blieskastel 16D3

Hotel Restaurant Hubertushof, Kirschendell 32. GPS: n49,24456 e7,21573.↑
✈.

8 ⌁€ 5, free with a meal . **Surface:** asphalted. ◻ 01/01-31/12

DE

Distance: 🚶on the spot ⊗on the spot 🛒1km.
Remarks: Arrival < 19h, max. 2 nights, bread-service.

Blieskastel 16D3
Freizeitzentrum Blieskastel, Bliesaue 1, Webenheim. **GPS:** n49,23527 e7,26946. ⬆.

3 🏕free. **Location:** Urban, simple, noisy. **Surface:** metalled.
🅿 01/01-31/12
Distance: 🚶on the spot 🚲5km 🛒on the spot.

Bobenthal/Bornich 17A3
Hotel-Restaurant St. Germanshof, Hauptstrasse 10. **GPS:** n49,04749 e7,89985.

4 🏕guests free. **Surface:** metalled. 🅿 01/01-31/12 🅿 Mo
Distance: 🚶5km ⊗on the spot 🛒7km.

Bockenheim 17A2
Weingut Benss, Am Spiegelpfad 10. **GPS:** n49,59959 e8,17823.⬆.

6 🏕free 🚰free 🚿(6x)€2,50/24h WC ▯. **Location:** Rural, simple, quiet.
Surface: grassy. 🅿 01/01-31/12
Distance: 🚲7km ⊗500m 🛒3km.

Bockenheim 17A2
Weingut W. Kohl, Am Sonnenberg 3. **GPS:** n49,59902 e8,17925.⬆.

6 🏕€8/night 🚰🚿WC ▯included. **Surface:** metalled. 🅿 01/01-31/12
Distance: 🚶500m ⊗500m 🛒3km.

Braubach 9B6
Braubacher Rheintreff, Rheinuferstrasse, B42. **GPS:** n50,26972 e7,64750.⬆.

30 🏕€8 🚰€1/80liter 🏕€1 Ch€1 🚿€0,50/kWh WC ▯included ▣€3.
Location: Comfortable, quiet. **Surface:** asphalted.
🅿 01/01-31/12
Distance: 🚶300m ⊘on the spot 🎣on the spot ⊗300m 🛒300m 🚌300m.
Remarks: Bread-service.

Brauneberg 16C1
Wohnmobilplatz Juffer, Moselweinstrasse. **GPS:** n49,90518 e6,97760.➡.

25 🏕€8 🚰🏕Ch 🚿.🛥 **Surface:** metalled. 🅿 01/01-31/12
Distance: 🚶100m ⊘on the spot ⊗300m 🛒300m 🚌100m.

Bremm 16D1
Weingut Oster-Franzen, Calmontstrasse 96. **GPS:** n50,09593 e7,12383.⬆➡.

16 🏕€14, 2 pers incl 🚰€0,50/60liter 🏕Ch 🚿€0,60/kWh
WC ▯€2/6minutes ▣€3,50 🛜. **Location:** Rural, comfortable. **Surface:** gravel.
🅿 01/03-30/11
Distance: 🚶on the spot ⊗800m 🚴on the spot 🧍on the spot.

Briedern 16D1
Wohnmobilstellplatz Briedern, Birkenweg. **GPS:** n50,11165 e7,20867.➡.

15 🏕€4,50. 🛥 **Location:** Rural, simple. **Surface:** grassy/gravel.
Distance: 🚶on the spot ⊗300m 🛒200m 🚴on the spot.

Brodenbach 16D1
Historische Mühle Vogelsang, Rhein-Mosel-strasse 63.
GPS: n50,22142 e7,44573.
🏕€4,80 + €5/pp 🚿€2 WC ▯€1,30/6minutes ▣€3. 🅿 01/01-31/12
Distance: ⊗on the spot.

Brodenbach 16D1
Moselufer. **GPS:** n50,22471 e7,43930. ⬆️.

2 🛏 free. **Location:** Urban, simple. **Surface:** metalled.
◻ 01/01-31/12
Distance: 🚶500m ⊗500m 🏃 on the spot.

Brodenbach 16D1
Salzwiese 9. **GPS:** n50,22519 e7,44291. ⬆️ ➡️.

4 🛏 free. **Location:** Urban. **Surface:** concrete. ◻ 01/01-31/12
Distance: 🚶400m ⌇Moselle river 200m ⊗400m.

🍴 S Burgen 🍴 16D1
Hotel Schmause Mühle, Baybachstrasse 50. **GPS:** n50,20859 e7,39365. ⬆️.

20 🛏 €8 🚰 ⚡Ch 🔌€2,50/day WC 🚽€1. **Location:** Quiet.
◻ 01/01-31/12
Distance: 🚶on the spot ⊗on the spot 🛒300m.

S Burgen bei Bernkastel-Kues 16C1
Weingut Bohn-Leimbrock, Lindenstrasse 6. **GPS:** n49,87986 e6,99967. ⬆️.

4 🛏 €8 🚰 🔌 WC 🚽. 🚲 **Surface:** grassy. ◻ 01/01-31/12
Distance: 🚶150m ⊗50m 🛒2km 🚲50m 🚴on the spot 🏃on the spot.

🚲 S Burrweiler 17A3
Wein- und Sektgut Hermann-Bruno Eberle, Böchingerstrasse 1a.
GPS: n49,24649 e8,07989. ⬆️.

3 🛏 €6 🚰 🔌 WC included. 🚲 **Location:** Rural, quiet. **Surface:** metalled.
◻ 01/01-31/12
Distance: 🚶100m 🛒200m.
Remarks: Arrival <21h.

🚲 S Burrweiler 17A3
Weingut Diether Bauer, Weinstrasse 52. **GPS:** n49,21982 e8,03059. ⬆️.

3 🛏 €5 🚰 🔌 WC included. 🚲 **Location:** Rural, quiet. **Surface:** metalled.
◻ 01/01-31/12
Distance: 🚶on the spot 🛒300m.

🚲 S Burrweiler 17A3
Weingut Hertel, Raiffeisenstrasse 2. **GPS:** n49,24861 e8,07705. ✈️.

3 🛏 €5 🚰 free 🔌 WC 🚽on demand. **Location:** Rural, simple, quiet.
Surface: metalled. ◻ 01/04-31/10

🚲 S Burrweiler 17A3
Weingut Winzerhof, Am Schlossberg 3. **GPS:** n49,25147 e8,07902. ⬆️.

4 🛏 €8 🚰 🔌 WC included. 🚲 **Location:** Rural, quiet. **Surface:** metalled.
◻ 01/01-31/12
Distance: 🚶1km 🛒300m.

🍴 Busenberg 17A3
Weißensteiner Hof, An der B427. **GPS:** n49,12152 e7,83943. ⬆️.

3 ⟐guests free ⟐on demand. **Location:** Rural, simple. **Surface:** asphalted. ⬛ 01/01-31/12 ⬤ Mon + Fri

| 🗓 | Cochem ⚓⛵ | 16D1 |

Bergstrasse, K59. **GPS:** n50,15028 e7,17083.

⟐€ 5 9-19h, overnight stay free.
Surface: grasstiles/metalled.
Distance: 🚶300m ⊗300m.

| 🗓 | Cochem ⚓⛵ | 16D1 |

Moselpromenade, B49. **GPS:** n50,14108 e7,16936.⬆.

4 ⟐€ 1/h 8-19h, overnight stay free. **Surface:** metalled.
⬛ 01/01-31/12

| 🗓 | Cochem ⚓⛵ | 16D1 |

Wohnmobil-Stellplatz am Freizeitzentrum, Stadionstrasse.
GPS: n50,16051 e7,17956.
50 ⟐€ 0,50/h. ⬛ 01/01-31/12

| 🗓 | Cochem ⚓⛵ | 16D1 |

Wohnmobil-Stellplatz an der Nordbrücke, Moselstrasse, B49.
GPS: n50,15329 e7,16828.⬆.

16 ⟐€ 1/h 8-19h, overnight stay free. 🚆 **Location:** Urban, simple.
Surface: metalled. ⬛ 01/01-31/12
Distance: 🚶700m ⊗200m ⟐200m 🚍on the spot.

| 🗓 S | Dahn/Reichenbach | 17A3 |

Altes Bahnhöf'l, An der Reichenbahn 6. **GPS:** n49,13890 e7,79908.⬆.

10 ⟐free. **Location:** Rural, simple, quiet. **Surface:** gravel. ⬛ 01/01-31/12 ⬤ Mo
Distance: 🚶on the spot ⊗on the spot ⟐100m.

| 🍴 S | Darscheid/Vulkaneifel | 16C1 |

Kucher's Landhotel, Karl-Kaufmann-Strasse 2. **GPS:** n50,21060 e6,88270.
3 ⟐guests free ⟐. ⬛ 01/01-31/12 ⬤ Tue

| 🗓 S | Deidesheim | 17A3 |

Weinhaus Villa Giessen, Weinstrasse 3. **GPS:** n49,41210 e8,19105.
3 ⟐€ 7,50 ⟐⟐. ⬛ 01/01-31/12
Distance: 🚲5km.

| 🗓 | Deudesfeld | 16C1 |

Meisburgerstrasse. **GPS:** n50,10084 e6,72932.
8 ⟐free ⟐€1/120liter ⟐€1 Ch ⟐€0,50/kWh. **Location:** Rural.
⬛ 01/01-31/12
Distance: 🚲13km.

| 🗓 | Deudesfeld | 16C1 |

Leyendecker Platz, Mandertscheider Strasse. **GPS:** n50,10164 e6,73217.
4 ⟐free. ⬛ 01/01-31/12
Distance: 🚲13km.

| 🗓 S | Deuselbach | 16D2 |

Wohnmobilstellplatz Erbeskopf, K130. **GPS:** n49,73589 e7,08327.
50 ⟐€ 4,00 ⟐⟐ Ch ⟐ (5x)€3/day WC ⟐. **Surface:** metalled.
⬛ 01/01-31/12
Distance: 🚶10km.

| 🍴 | Dexheim | 17B1 |

Weingut Bacchushof, Wörrstädter Strasse 14. **GPS:** n49,84812 e8,31144.⬆.

5 ⟐free. **Location:** Rural, simple. **Surface:** concrete.
⬛ 01/01-31/12
Distance: 🚲12km.

| 🗓 S | Dierbach | 17A3 |

Jahnstrasse. **GPS:** n49,08177 e8,06201.⬆.

10 ⟐€ 5 ⟐⟐Ch ⟐ (5x)free. 🚆 **Location:** Simple, quiet.
Surface: asphalted. ⬛ 01/01-31/12
Distance: 🚶700m 🚲12km ⊗1km ⟐3km 🚍50m.
Remarks: At sports centre.

DE

⚷S | **Dohm** | **9A6**

Am Heidberghof, Heidberghof 1, Dohm-Lammersdorf. **GPS**: n50,26696 e6,67366.

6 ⛺€10 ⛽ 🚰 Ch 🚿 (6x)€2 WC 🚽 🚽€3,50. **Surface**: grassy/gravel.
◯ Ascension-31/09
Distance: 🏊15km.
Remarks: Bread-service, incl. swimming pool (summer).

⚷S | **Dolgesheim** | **17A2**

Weingut Seck, Weinolsheimer Strasse 12. **GPS**: n49,79752 e8,26154.⬆

3 ⛺€5 ⛽ 🚿 🚽 📶included. 🐕 **Location**: Rural, simple, quiet.
Surface: grassy. ◯ 01/01-31/12
Distance: 🏊200m 🚲13km ⊗300m 🛒2km.

⚷S | **Dörrenbach** | **17A3**

Übergasse. **GPS**: n49,08840 e7,96921.⬆

10 ⛺€6 ⛽ 🚰 Ch 🚿 included. 🐕 **Location**: Rural, quiet.
Surface: gravel/sand. ◯ 01/01-31/12
Distance: 🏊500m 🛒700m.
Remarks: Next to sports fields.

⚷ | **Eckersweiler** | **16D2**

Am Sportplatz. **GPS**: n49,55646 e7,30577.⬆

4 ⛺free. **Location**: Rural, simple, isolated. **Surface**: grassy.
◯ 01/01-31/12
Distance: 🏊1,3km 🚴on the spot 🏃on the spot.

⚷ | **Edenkoben** | **17A3**

Wohnmobilstellplatz Kirchbergplatz, Bahnhofstraße.
GPS: n49,28234 e8,13116.⬆

40 ⛺€5/24h ⛽€1/100liter 🚰Ch 🚿 (8x)€1/kWh. **Surface**: asphalted.
◯ 01/01-31/12
Distance: 🏊on the spot 🚲2km ⊗300m 🛒Aldi 800m.
Remarks: Max. 3 nights.

⚷S | **Edenkoben** | **17A3**

Obstgut & Brennerei Göring, Blücherstrasse 45. **GPS**: n49,27792 e8,13487.

5 ⛺€10 ⛽ 🚰Ch 🚿 included WC 🚽. **Surface**: grassy. ◯ 01/01-31/12
Distance: 🏊3km.

⚷S | **Edenkoben** | **17A3**

Weingut Bernd und Herbert Schäfer, Rhodter Strasse 24.
GPS: n49,27844 e8,12572.
3 ⛺free ⛽ 🚿€5. ◯ 01/01-31/12
Distance: 🏊3,5km.

⚷S | **Edenkoben** | **17A3**

Weingut Edel Brauch, St.-Martiner-Strasse 30. **GPS**: n49,28901 e8,12236.
4 ⛺free ⛽€2 🚰Ch 🚿€2. ◯ 01/01-31/12
Distance: 🏊3km.

⚷S | **Edenkoben** | **17A3**

Gasthof Ziegelhütte, Luitpoldstrasse 75-79. **GPS**: n49,28539 e8,13872.

3 ⛺€5/night 🚿. **Surface**: metalled. ◯ 01/01-31/12
Distance: 🏊on the spot ⊗1km ⊗on the spot 🛒on the spot.

⚷S | **Edesheim** | **17A3**

Weingut Boos, Ludwigstrasse 150. **GPS**: n49,25785 e8,11673.⬆

3 ⛺€6 ⛽ 🚰Ch 🚿 (3x)included. **Location**: Rural, simple, quiet.
Surface: grassy. ◯ 01/01-31/12

DE

Distance: 500m ⊗300m 1km.

S Edesheim 17A3
Weingut Braun & Sohn, Ludwigsstrasse 151. **GPS:** n49,25761 e8,11587.

3 €5 Ch included. **Location:** Rural, simple, quiet.
Surface: grassy. 01/01-31/12
Distance: 300m ⊗300m.

S Edesheim 17A3
Weingut Rehm, Ludwigstrasse 36. **GPS:** n49,26015 e8,12734.

6 €5 included (6x)€2,50/day WC €2,50. **Location:** Rural,
simple, quiet. **Surface:** grassy. 01/01-31/12

Edesheim 17A3
Weingut Erlenmühle, Erlenmühle 1. **GPS:** n49,25865 e8,11417.

5 €5 Ch included on demand. **Location:** Rural, simple,
quiet. **Surface:** gravel. 01/01-31/12
Distance: 500m on the spot 1km.
Remarks: Arrival <22h.

S Ediger/Eller 16D1
Stellplatz Ediger, Moselweinstrasse. **GPS:** n50,09320 e7,15942.

18 €5 Ch included. **Location:** Rural, simple.
Surface: gravel/metalled. 01/04-30/11
Distance: 100m on the spot on the spot ⊗on the spot on the spot
on the spot.
Remarks: Along the Moselle river in Ediger.

S Ediger/Eller 16D1
Stellplatz Moselufer, Eller. **GPS:** n50,09915 e7,14370.

10 €5. **Location:** Rural, simple. **Surface:** metalled.
01/04-30/11
Distance: on the spot on the spot ⊗on the spot 200m
on the spot.
Remarks: Along the Moselle river in Eller.

S Eisenschmitt 16C1
Hotel-Restaurant Molitors Mühle, Eichelhütte. **GPS:** n50,03681 e6,73766.

5 guests free WC included. **Location:** Rural, simple. **Surface:** gravel.
01/01-31/12
Distance: 1km 6km on the spot on the spot ⊗on the spot 1km
300m on the spot.
Remarks: Arrival <23h.

Ellenz/Poltersdorf 16D1
Weingut Loosen, Im Goldbäumchen 4. **GPS:** n50,11389 e7,23528.

12 €9 WC included. **Location:** Rural, comfortable. **Surface:** gravel.
01/01-31/12
Distance: on the spot 150m ⊗500m 1km on the spot.

Tourist information Ellenz/Poltersdorf:
Strassenweinfest. Wine-growers and - houses open their doors, wine-tastery.
end Sep.
Wein- und Heimatfeste. Traditional wine celebration. last weekend Jul,
1st weekend Aug.

S Elmstein 17A3
NaturFreundeHaus Elmstein, Esthaler Strasse 63. **GPS:** n49,36133 e7,95123.

12 €3 €1 €2 €1/pp. **Location:** Rural, simple, central, quiet.

Surface: gravel. ◻ 01/01-31/12
Remarks: Bread-service.

🖪🅂 Elmstein 🖼 17A3
Stellplatz Elmstein, Bahnhofstrasse 88. **GPS:** n49,34803 e7,94337. 🖼🖼.

4 🖥free 🔌 (4x)€0,50/kWh. **Location:** Rural. **Surface:** gravel.
◻ 01/01-31/12
Distance: 🚶500m ⊗100m 🗑500m.

🍴 Elmstein 🖼 17A3
Wohnmobilplatz Waldesruhe, Schwarzbach 36. **GPS:** n49,34037 e7,83397. 🖼.

10 🖥€5, free with a meal. **Location:** Rural, simple, isolated, quiet.
Surface: grassy. ◻ 01/01-31/12
Remarks: To be paid at restaurant.

🖪🅂 Elzweiler 16D2
Stellplatz Elzweiler, Hauptstraße 7. **GPS:** n49,58036 e7,51393. 🖼🖼.

2 🖥free ⊏€1 🗑Ch 🔌€1. **Location:** Rural. **Surface:** metalled.
◻ 01/01-31/12
Distance: 🚶on the spot 🚌on the spot 🚲on the spot 🅿on the spot.
Remarks: Small pitches.

🖪🅂 Enkirch 🌿 16D1
Wohnmobilplatz an der Mosel, Moselvorgelände, B53.
GPS: n49,98396 e7,12157. 🖼🖼.

200 🖥€7 ⊏€1/80liter 🗑Ch 🔌 (90x)€2/day WC 🗑€1
📷🌊€1,50/30minutes ♻🚿 **Location:** Rural, comfortable, quiet.
Surface: grassy. ◻ Easter-31/10
Distance: 🚶on the spot 🛍on the spot.

Remarks: Along ther Moselle river.

🖪🅂 Ensch 16C2
Reisemobilplatz An den 2 Pappeln, Am Moselufer/ B53.
GPS: n49,82760 e6,83549. 🖼🖼.

45 🖥€5 ⊏🗑Ch 🔌 (45x)€2. 🐕 **Surface:** grassy. ◻ 01/04-31/10
Distance: 🚶200m ⊗300m 🗑500m 🚌100m.
Remarks: Bread-service.

🖪🅂 Eppelborn 16D3
Wohnmobilstellplatz Finkenrech, L303. **GPS:** n49,43285 e6,99986.
🖥€5 🔌€0,50. ◻ 01/01-31/12
Distance: ⛵3km.

🖪 Eppenbrunn 16D3
Im Sportzentrum. **GPS:** n49,11179 e7,56512. 🖼.

6 🖥free. **Location:** Rural, simple, quiet. **Surface:** metalled.
◻ 01/01-31/12
Distance: 🚶500m ⊗on the spot 🗑1km.
Remarks: Parking sports centre in nature reserve Pfälzer Wald.

🖪 Eppenbrunn 16D3
Neudorfstrasse. **GPS:** n49,11531 e7,55360. 🖼.

5 🖥free. **Location:** Rural, simple, noisy. **Surface:** metalled.
◻ 01/01-31/12
Distance: 🚶on the spot ⛲on the spot 🛍on the spot ⊗on the spot.

🖪🅂 Erden 16D1
Wohnmobilstellplatz Erden, An Moselufer 1. **GPS:** n49,97989 e7,02120.
21 🖥€8 ⊏🗑Ch 🔌 (21x)€2,50 🗑€0,30/minutes 📶. ◻ 01/04-31/10
Distance: ⛵15km 🗑300m.

🖪🅂 Ernst 🌿🍇 16D1
Winzergenossenschaft der Kreises Cochem-Zell, Weingartenstrasse 106.
GPS: n50,14339 e7,23237. 🖼.

DE

30 🛏 8 🚰 €1/80liter 🗑 Ch 🔌 📶 €5/10h. **Location:** Rural, comfortable.
Surface: gravel. 🔲 01/01-31/12
Distance: 🚶300m ⊗ on the spot 🛒200m 🚌100m.

⟦⟧S ⟨⟩ **Ernst** 🌿 **16D1**
Mosella Schinkenstube, Weingatenstrasse 97. **GPS:** n50,14382 e7,23071. ⬆.

18 🛏 8 🚰 🔌 included. **Surface:** grassy.
⟦⟧S **Eschbach** **17A3**
Weingut Wind, Weinstrasse 3-5. **GPS:** n49,17594 e8,02171. ✈.

3 🛏 € 5, discount for clients 🚰 €1/100liter 🔌 €3 WC included. 🚽
Location: Rural, simple, quiet. **Surface:** gravel. 🔲 01/01-31/12
Distance: 🚶 on the spot ⊗ on the spot 🛒250m.
Remarks: Check in on arrival.
⟦⟧S **Essingen** **17A3**
Weingut Schweikart Dalberghof, Kirchstrasse 16. **GPS:** n49,23478 e8,17524. ✈.

3 🛏 € 5 🚰 €1/100liter 🔌 (3x)€1/night WC €1. **Location:** Simple, quiet.
Surface: grassy. 🔲 01/01-31/12
Distance: 🚶 on the spot 🚲3km ⊗1km 🛒3km 🍴7km 🚌30m.
Remarks: Sale of wines.
⟦⟧S **Fell** **16C2**
Besucherbergwerk, Auf den Schiefergruben, K82. **GPS:** n49,75440 e6,79731. ⬆.

30 🛏 4 🔌 €2. **Location:** Isolated, quiet. **Surface:** concrete.
🔲 01/01-31/12
⟦⟧S **Fischbach** 🛖 **16D2**
Wohnmobilpark, Marktstraße 1. **GPS:** n49,74046 e7,40444. ⬆➡.

40 🛏 € 6,50/night 🚰 🗑 Ch included 🔌 (40x)€2,. 🚽
Location: Rural, simple, central. **Surface:** grassy. 🔲 01/01-31/12
Distance: 🚶800m ⊗300m 🛒1,5km.
Remarks: Bread-service.
⟦⟧S **Fischbach** 🛖 **16D2**
Historisches Kupferbergwerk, Hosenbachstraße. **GPS:** n49,75398 e7,38287.
✈ .

10 🛏 free. **Location:** Rural, simple, isolated, quiet. **Surface:** gravel.
🔲 01/01-31/12
Distance: 🚶1,7km ⊗ on the spot.
Remarks: Visitors' center former copper mine.
⟦⟧S **Flemlingen** **17A3**
Weingut Eichhorn, Maxstrasse 21. **GPS:** n49,24122 e8,09341. ⬆.

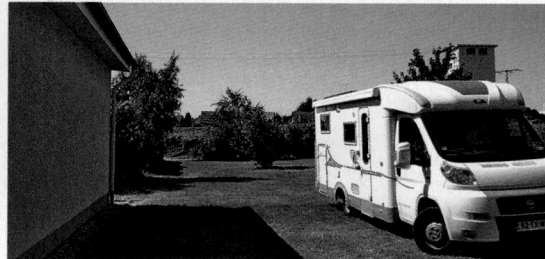

10 🛏 € 5 🔌 (10x)€2 WC included 🚿€2/pp. 🚽
Location: Rural, simple, quiet. **Surface:** grassy. 🔲 01/01-31/12
Distance: 🚲6km 🛒400m.
⟦⟧S **Flonheim** **17A2**
Weingut Meyerhof, Aussiedlerhof. **GPS:** n49,78836 e8,04531. ✈.

4 🛏 € 8 ⚡ ✦ (4x)included. 🚿 **Location:** Rural, simple, quiet.
Surface: concrete. 🅾 01/01-31/12
Distance: 🚰700m 🚲4km ✪100m 🚆100m.
Remarks: Bread-service.

Föckelberg 🍴 16D2
Wildpark Potzberg, Auf dem Potzberg. **GPS:** n49,52240 e7,48079.⬆

4 🛏 free. **Location:** Rural, simple, quiet. **Surface:** asphalted/sand.
🅾 01/01-31/12
Distance: 🚰1km.

🚐S Forst an der Weinstrasse 17A2
Weingut Margarethenhof, Wiesenweg 4. **GPS:** n49,42814 e8,19219.
3 🛏 € 8 ⚡ ✦ WC ⬆. 🅾 01/01-31/12
Distance: 🚰1km 🚲7km 🚆1km.

🚐S Freisen 16D2
Weiselbergbad, Zum Schwimmbad. **GPS:** n49,53324 e7,26048.⬆

3 🛏 € 5 ✦ €2/day. **Location:** Rural, simple, noisy. **Surface:** metalled.
🅾 01/01-31/12
Distance: 🚰1km 🚲3km.
Remarks: Check in at swimming pool.

🚐S Gau-Algesheim 17A1
Reimo Gau-Algesheim, Bingerstrasse 8. **GPS:** n49,96331 e8,01213.⬆➡

40 🛏 € 4/night ⚡ 🍱 Ⓒincluded ✦ (40x)€2 📶.
Location: Comfortable, quiet. **Surface:** metalled. 🅾 01/01-31/12
Distance: 🚰800m 🚲2,5km ✪500m 🚆200m.

🚐S Gau-Bickelheim 17A1
Winzerhof Schnabel, Bahnhofstrasse 31. **GPS:** n49,83941 e8,02116.✈ .

15 🛏 € 5 ⚡included ✦ (8x)€3/day. **Location:** Rural. **Surface:** grassy.
🅾 01/01-31/12
Distance: 🚲3km ✪5km 🚆1km.

🍴 Gau-Bickelheim 17A1
Am Autohof, B50. **GPS:** n49,83461 e7,99664.✈ .

15 🛏 free. **Location:** Rural, simple, noisy. **Surface:** asphalted.
🅾 01/01-31/12
Distance: 🚲 on the spot.

🚐S Gau-Heppenheim 17A2
Weingut Gustavshof, Hauptstrasse 53. **GPS:** n49,74138 e8,17082.⬆.

3 🛏 € 8 ⚡ ✦ (3x)included. 🚿 **Location:** Rural, simple, quiet.
Surface: concrete. 🅾 01/04-31/10
Distance: 🚲4km ✪2km 🚆3km.

🚐 Gau-Odernheim 17A2
Petersberghalle, Mühlstraße. **GPS:** n49,78528 e8,19575.⬆➡

3 🛏 free. **Surface:** metalled. 🅾 01/01-31/12
Distance: 🚰200m 🚆200m.

🚐 Gebhardshain 9B5
Festwiese, Steinebacherstrasse. **GPS:** n50,74412 e7,82079.⬆.

5 ⌒free. **Location:** Urban, simple, central, quiet. **Surface:** asphalted.
◻ 01/01-31/12
Distance: 500m ⊗500m ⌁500m.

Geiselberg 17A3
Grillplatz Geiselberg, Hauptstrasse, K31. **GPS:** n49,32381 e7,70957.

10 ⌒free. **Location:** Rural, simple, quiet. **Surface:** gravel.
◻ 01/01-31/12
Remarks: Max. 2 days.

Germersheim 17B3
Carnot'sche Mauer, Rüdolf von Habsburgstrasse. **GPS:** n49,22004 e8,37906.

8 ⌒€ 3/24h €1/100liter Ch (8x)€1/5kWh.
Location: Simple, central. **Surface:** grassy. ◻ 01/01-31/12
Distance: 300m 2km ⊗500m ⌁300m 100m on the spot.

Gerolstein 16C1
Wohnmobilplatz Gerolstein, Raderstrasse 22. **GPS:** n50,22096 e6,65387.

20 ⌒€ 10/24h €1/100liter Ch (12x)€1/day.
Location: Urban, simple. **Surface:** grassy/metalled. ◻ 15/03-15/11
Distance: nearby 25km ⊗500m ⌁1km.
Remarks: At swimming pool.

Gevenich 16D1
Am Sportplatz. GPS: n50,14727 e7,08385.
7 ⌒free. ◻ 01/01-31/12
Distance: 1km ⊗on the spot.

Gillenfeld 16C1
Wohnmobilhafen Pulvermaar, K14. **GPS:** n50,13294 e6,93218.

30 ⌒€ 7 €1/100liter Ch €0,50/kWh WC €2/time.
Location: Simple. **Surface:** gravel. ◻ 01/01-31/12
Distance: 3km on the spot on the spot ⊗200m ⌁200m 300m.

Gillenfeld 16C1
Feriendorf Pulvermaar, Vulkanstrasse. **GPS:** n50,13000 e6,93194.

12 ⌒€ 7, 2 pers.incl €1/100liter Ch included €0,50/kWh
WC €1/7minutes. **Surface:** grassy. ◻ 01/03-30/11
Distance: 3km 7km on the spot on the spot ⊗150m ⌁150m
200m.

Gimbsheim 17B2
Schwimbadstrasse. GPS: n49,77806 e8,38278.

8 ⌒€ 4/night. **Surface:** asphalted/grassy. ◻ 15/05-15/09
Distance: 500m ⌁300m.

Gimbsheim 17B2
Weingut Falger-Baier, Alsheimerstrasse 25. **GPS:** n49,77733 e8,36959.
3 ⌒€ 5 ◻ 01/01-31/12
Distance: 3km ⊗Pizzeria 50m ⌁500m.

Glan-Münchweiler 16D2
Am Bahnhof, Bahnhofstraße. **GPS:** n49,46935 e7,44420.

3 ⌒free €1 Ch (4x)€1/2h. **Location:** Urban, simple, central, noisy.
Surface: metalled. ◻ 01/01-31/12
Distance: 750m ⊗150m ⌁on the spot.

DE

S Gleisweiler 17A3

Weingut Kost, Hainbachtalstrasse 3. **GPS**: n49,23862 e8,06737.

3 free free. **Location:** Rural, quiet. **Surface:** grassy.
01/01-31/12
Distance: 8km on the spot.

S Gleiszellen-Gleishorbach 17A3

Weingut Schoenlaub, Bergstrasse 14. **GPS**: n49,13131 e8,00465.

2 free free. **Location:** Rural, simple, quiet. **Surface:** grassy.
01/01-31/12
Distance: 15km 500m.
Remarks: Check in at Weingut.

Graach/Mosel 16D1

Wohnmobilpark Sun-Park, Gestade 16a. **GPS**: n49,93322 e7,06249.

140 €10/day liter Ch (132x)€3/day WC included €1,50/pp
€2,50. **Location:** Rural, simple. **Surface:** grassy. 27/03-03/11
Distance: 200m on the spot 200m 2km on the spot
on the spot on the spot.
Remarks: Bread-service.

Grafschaft 9A6

Panorama Sauna, Panoramaweg 2. **GPS**: n50,56029 e7,05368.

20 free. **Surface:** gravel. 01/01-31/12
Distance: 5km 300m 300m.

Gries 16D3

Seestube am Ohmbachsee, Bahnhofstrasse 17b. **GPS**: n49,41664 e7,40377.

12 €6 €1/80liter Ch (12x)€0,60/kWh.
Location: Rural, simple, quiet. **Surface:** grassy. 01/01-31/12
Distance: 6km on the spot on the spot.
Remarks: Bread-service.

S Gundersheim 17A2

Huppert's Wohnmobile Wingert, Untere Grabenstraße 21.
GPS: n49,69499 e8,20465.

12 €5 €3. **Surface:** gravel/sand. 01/01-31/12
Distance: 1km on the spot 300m.
Remarks: Max. 3 nights.

S Guntersblum 17B2

Am Sportanlage, Alsheimerstrasse 85. **GPS**: n49,78974 e8,34373.

16 €5 €1/80liter Ch (12x)€0,50/kWh. **Location:** Rural.
Surface: gravel. 01/01-31/12
Distance: 500m 500m 500m.

S Guntersblum 17B2

Weingut Katharinenhof, Alsheimerstrasse 95. **GPS**: n49,78667 e8,34324.

10 €5 included (7x)€2/24h. **Location:** Rural, simple, quiet.
Surface: grassy. 01/01-31/12
Distance: 1km 1km 1km.

S Hachenburg 9B5

P4 - Burggarten, Alexanderring. **GPS**: n50,66250 e7,82694.

DE

8 free €1/70liter Ch €1/6h WC. **Location:** Urban, simple, quiet.
Surface: grasstiles. 01/01-31/12
Distance: 300m 300m 300m on the spot on the spot.
Remarks: June 2014 during inspection service out of order, just electricity, historical centre.

Hagenbach 17B4

Stadtbrauhaus Hagenbach, Stixwörthstrasse 2-4. **GPS**: n49,00884 e8,25902.

10 free. 01/01-31/12 Mon, Tue
Distance: 5km on the spot.

Hassloch 17B3

Hotel Sägmühle, Sägmühlweg 140. **GPS**: n49,34674 e8,25491.

2 € 12, guests free (2x) WC included.
Location: Simple, isolated, quiet. 01/01-31/12
Distance: 10km.
Remarks: Bicycle rental.

Hassloch 17B3

Magin Reisemobile, Hans-Böckler-Strasse 52. **GPS**: n49,34968 e8,23935.

8 € 12,50, 2 pers.incl Ch (8x)included.
Location: Urban, simple, quiet. **Surface:** gravel/metalled. 01/01-31/12
Distance: 2km 7km 50m 200m.

Hassloch 17B3

Badepark Hassloch, Lachener Weg 175. **GPS**: n49,34804 e8,24677.

9 free free. **Location:** Simple, quiet.
01/01-31/12
Distance: 2km 10km 50m 200m 100m.

Tourist information Hassloch:
Holiday Park. Attractions park with shows. 01/04-30/09 10h, summer 9h, Oct weekend. € 21.

Hauenstein 17A3

Stellplatz am Deutschen Schumuseum Hauenstein, Turnstrasse.
GPS: n49,18896 e7,85669.

12 € 7 80liter Chfree €0,55/kWh. **Location:** Rural, simple, quiet.
Surface: gravel. 01/01-31/12
Distance: on the spot 200m 300m.
Remarks: Check in on arrival, pay at pay-desk of the museum.

Heimborn 9B5

Gasthaus zum Nisterstrand, Vor der Hardt. **GPS**: n50,71609 e7,75322.

6 guests free Ch. **Location:** Rural, simple, quiet.
Surface: asphalted. 01/01-31/12
Distance: on the spot on the spot on the spot.

Heltersberg 17A3

Am Bergbad, Bergstrasse. **GPS**: n49,31654 e7,70380.

5 free. **Location:** Rural, simple, quiet. **Surface:** grassy.
01/01-31/12
Distance: 900m.
Remarks: Parking swimming pool.

DE

🍴 Hemmelzen   9B5
Hotel Im Heisterholz, Heisterholzstrasse 10. **GPS**: n50,69579 e7,58456. 🔼 .

4 🛏€ 12 🔌 included. **Location:** Rural, quiet. **Surface:** gravel.
🅿 01/01-31/12 🅿 Mo
Distance: 🚶200m ⊗on the spot 🚌100m ♨ on the spot 🧍on the spot.
Remarks: € 2 reduction in restaurant.

🔲S Herrstein 🌿🏕   16D2
Wohnmobilstellplatz Herrstein, Brühlstrasse. **GPS**: n49,77963 e7,33569. 🔼 .

3 🛏free 🚰€1/80liter 🔌€0,50/kWh WC.
Surface: metalled.
🅿 01/01-31/12
Distance: 🚶300m ⊗on the spot.
Remarks: Max. 48h.

Tourist information Herrstein:
ℹ Touristinformation Deutsche Edelsteinstraße, Brühlstrasse 16. Renovated mall half-timbered city. 🅿 01/05-01/10.

🔲S Herxheim ⛲   17A3
Festhalle, Bonifatiusstraße. **GPS**: n49,14463 e8,21656. 🔼➡ .

8 🛏free 🚰 🔲Chfree. **Location:** Simple, central. **Surface:** grasstiles.
🅿 01/01-31/12
Distance: 🚶on the spot 🚲4km 🚏150m 🚊200m 🚌75m.

🔲S Heuchelheim-Klingen   17A3
Gästehaus am Fürstweg, Hauptstrasse 2. **GPS**: n49,14511 e8,05788.
3 🛏€5 🚰 🔲Ch. 🅿 01/01-31/12
Distance: 🚲14km.

🔲S Heuchelheim-Klingen   17A3
Weingut Junghof, Hauptstrasse 21. **GPS**: n49,14572 e8,05580.

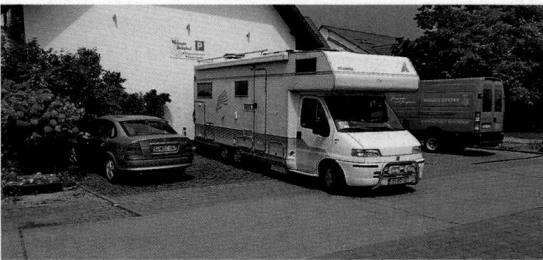

4 🛏€ 5, free with a meal 🚰€2/100liter 🔌€2/night. **Location:** Simple.
Surface: grassy/metalled. 🅿 01/01-31/12
Distance: 🚶on the spot 🚲14km ⊗500m 🚊2km 🚌500m.

🔲S Hillesheim ⛲   9A6
Markt- und Messeplatz, Am Viehmarkt. **GPS**: n50,28895 e6,67239. 🔼➡ .

6 🛏€4 🚰 🔲Ch 🔌(6x) WCincluded. **Location:** Urban, simple, central.
Surface: gravel. 🅿 01/01-31/12
Distance: 🚶on the spot ⊗on the spot 🚊200m.

🔲S Hillesheim ⛲   9A6
Wohnmobilstellplatz Birkenhof, Birkenhof 1. **GPS**: n50,28639 e6,69083. 🔼 .

8 🛏€ 10 🚰 🔌(4x)included 📶free. **Location:** Rural, simple, quiet.
Surface: gravel. 🅿 01/01-31/12
Distance: 🚶1,5km ⊗1,5km.
Remarks: Bread-service.

🔲S Hillesheim ⛲   9A6
Wohnmobile Theres, Prümer Straße 20. **GPS**: n50,28957 e6,66310.

15 🛏€5 🚰 🔲Ch 🔌included. **Surface:** asphalted. 🅿 01/01/31/12
Distance: 🚶750m ⊗750m 🚊750m.
Remarks: Motorhome dealer, accessory shop, repairs.

🔲S Hochspeyer   17A2
Am Schwimmbad, Mühlhofstraße. **GPS**: n49,44108 e7,89333. 🔼 .

6 🛏€5 ⛽€1/80liter 🗑 Ch ⚡(12x)€0,50/kWh. 💧
Location: Simple, central, quiet. **Surface:** asphalted.
⏲ 01/01-31/12 ◉ 01/08-15/08
Distance: 🛒400m 🏊5km 🍞400m bakery.
Remarks: Max. 3 days.

| 🏕 | **Höheinöd** | 16D3 |

Am Haus des Bürgers, Hauptstrasse 24. **GPS:** n49,28691 e7,60468. ⬆

3 🛏free. **Location:** Rural, simple, quiet. **Surface:** metalled.
⏲ 01/01-31/12
Distance: 🛒on the spot 🏊8km.
Remarks: Max. 2 nights.

| 🏕 | **Höhr-Grenzhausen** | 9B6 |

Ferbachstraße. **GPS:** n50,43330 e7,66833. ⬆

8 🛏free. ⏲ 01/01-31/12
Distance: 🛒on the spot 🏊2km 🍴100m.

| 🏕S | **Holzappel** | 9C6 |

Stellplatz am Herthasee, Am Herthasee. **GPS:** n50,36135 e7,90274. ➡

12 🛏€6/24h, €11/48h, €15/72h ⛽€1/90liter 🗑 Ch ⚡(12x)€1/2kWh. 🚐
Location: Rural, comfortable, quiet. **Surface:** grassy.
⏲ 01/01-31/12
Distance: 🛒1km 🏊on the spot 🚲on the spot 🍴on the spot.

| 🏕S | **Hornbach** | 16D3 |

Wohnmobilpark Hornbach, Bahnhofstraße. **GPS:** n49,18382 e7,36560. ⬆

26 🛏€6 ⛽€1/60liter 🗑 Ch ⚡(30x)€1/2kWh. **Surface:** gravel.
⏲ 01/01-31/12
Distance: 🛒on the spot 🏊8km 🍴on the spot.

| 🏕S | **Hörschhausen** | 9A6 |

Mechels Hof, Dauner Straße 24. **GPS:** n50,24248 e6,92770.
3 🛏€5 🚰 🗑 Ch ⚡water and electricity €2.
Location: Rural. ⏲ 01/01-31/12
Distance: 🏊9km.
Remarks: Bread-service.

| 🏕 | **Idar/Oberstein** | 16D2 |

Edelsteinbörse, Hauptstrasse 100. **GPS:** n49,71932 e7,30313. ⬆

12 🛏€6/day, first 24h free ⛽€1/100liter 🗑 Ch WC.
Surface: asphalted.
⏲ 01/01-31/12
Distance: 🛒on the spot 🍴on the spot 🍺300m.
Tourist information Idar/Oberstein:
👁 Edelsteinminen des Steinkaulenberges. Gem mine. ⏲ 15/03-15/11 9-17h.
Ⓜ Deutsches Edelsteinmuseum. Gem museum. ⏲ 01/05-31/10 9-18h, 01/11-30/04 9-17h.

| 🏕 | **Impflingen** 🍴 | 17A3 |

Weingut Junker, Sonnenberghof 1. **GPS:** n49,16242 e8,10728. ⬆➡

3 🛏€5 🚰 ⚡(4x)€2 WC. 💧 **Location:** Simple, quiet. **Surface:** gravel.
⏲ 01/01-31/12
Distance: 🛒1km 🏊7km 🍴on the spot 🍺3km 🚌200m 🚲on the spot ⛰on the spot.

| 🏕S | **Ingelheim am Rhein** | 17A1 |

Weingut Menk, Außenliegend 143. **GPS:** n49,97190 e8,09295. ⬆

6 ⬛ € 10 🔌🔧 Ch ⚡ WC included. **Location:** Rural, comfortable, quiet.
Surface: grassy. ⬜ 01/01-31/12
Distance: 🚶2km 🚲9km 🛒 on the spot.

🚿S   **Jettenbach** 🌳   **16D2**

Freizeitgelände Schwimmbad, Austrasse. **GPS:** n49,52919 e7,56453. ⬆️➡️

6 ⬛ free 🔌🔧 Ch ⚡. **Surface:** asphalted. ⬜ 01/01-31/12
Distance: 🚶500m 🛒800m.

🚿   **Kaisersesch**   **16D1**

Am Markt. **GPS:** n50,23223 e7,14044.
4 ⬛ free. ⬜ 01/01-31/12
Distance: 🚲1km.

🍴S   **Kaiserslautern**   **17A2**

Gasthaus Licht Luft, Enterweilerstraße 51. **GPS:** n49,43828 e7,80338. ⬆️

14 ⬛ free 🔌🔧 Ch on demand. **Location:** Urban, central, quiet.
Surface: gravel. ⬜ 01/01-31/12
Distance: 🚲5km ⊗on the spot 🛒on the spot 🛁on the spot 🏃on the spot.

🛁   **Kaiserslautern** 🛒   **17A2**

Am Monte Mare, Mailänder Straße 6. **GPS:** n49,45387 e7,81203. ⬆️.

10 ⬛ free. **Location:** Rural, simple, quiet. **Surface:** metalled.
⬜ 01/01-31/12
Distance: 🚲1km.

🍴S   **Kamp-Bornhofen** 🚢   **16D1**

Bistro Rheinufer, Rheinuferstrasse 66 A. **GPS:** n50,22305 e7,61888. ⬆️➡️
7 ⬛ € 7,50 🔌€1 ⚡ € 2,50 WC. **Surface:** metalled.
⬜ 01/01-31/12

Distance: 🚶on the spot ⊗on the spot 🛒300m 🛍on the spot.
Remarks: Along the Rhine river, toilets only during opening hours restaurant.

🍴S   **Kandel** 〰️🌳   **17A3**

Adams Hof, Rheinzaberner Strasse 1. **GPS:** n49,08902 e8,22194. ⬆️.

30 ⬛ € 10/night 🔌€2,50 ⚡ (20x)€2,50/12h WC.
Location: Simple, quiet. **Surface:** grassy. ⬜ 01/01-31/12
Distance: 🚶1,5km 🛍on the spot ⊗on the spot 🛒1,5km 🛍1,5km.
Remarks: € 5 voucher Biergarten.

🍇S   **Kapellen-Drusweiler** 🌳   **17A3**

Weingut Manderschied, Dorfstrasse 4. **GPS:** n49,10482 e8,03723. ⬆️.

10 ⬛ free 🔌 ⚡ (3x)free. **Location:** Rural, simple, quiet. **Surface:** grassy.
⬜ 01/01-31/12
Distance: 🚶500m ⊗500m 🛒2km.

🏠S   **Kelberg**   **9A6**

Maß-Schneider, Schulstrasse 14. **GPS:** n50,28453 e6,91594.
7 ⬛ free 🔌🔧 Ch ⚡. ⬜ 01/01-31/12
Remarks: Producer of cushions and upholstery for motorhomes.

⬛S   **Kell am See**   **16C2**

Am Camping Hochwald, L 143. **GPS:** n49,63800 e6,80140.
10 ⬛ €6 + € 6/pp 🚶 Ch ⚡ €0,50/kWh. ⬜ 01/05-31/08

🍴   **Kempenich**   **9A6**

Eifel-Gasthof Kleefuß, In der Hardt 1. **GPS:** n50,42209 e7,10951.

4 ⬛ guests free. **Location:** Rural. **Surface:** gravel.
⬜ 01/01-31/12 ⬛ Mon, Tue
Distance: 🚶500m.

🚿   **Kempfeld** 〰️🌳   **16D2**

An der Wildenburg, Wildenburgstraße. **GPS:** n49,77588 e7,25423. ⬆️➡️

DE

3 🅿free. **Surface:** metalled. ⏻ 01/01-31/12
Distance: ⊗2km ⛴2km.

| 🏕S | Kesten 🎣 ⛲ ⛵ | 16C1 |

Wohnmobilpark Kesten - Kesten

info@wohnmobilpark-kesten.de - www.wohnmobilpark-kesten.de

Flat motorhome pitches
Located directly at the river
Located in a quit location

Wohnmobilpark Kesten/Mosel, Urmetzgasse/K134.
GPS: n49,90306 e6,96232.➡️
100 🅿 € 6/24h 🚰 €0,50/50liter 🔌Cincluded ⚡ (100x)€2/24h,6Amp. 🚿
Surface: grassy/metalled. ⏻ 01/04-31/10
Distance: 🏪300m ⛱10m 🚲10m ⊗300m ⛴1km 🏍300m 🚶 on the spot 🏊 on the spot.
Remarks: Parking at the Moselle River, bread-service.

| 🏕S | Kinheim ⛵ | 16D1 |

Am Moselufer, Moselweinstraße, B53. **GPS:** n49,97218 e7,05706.⬆️➡️

50 🅿 € 7 🚰 🔌Cincluded ⚡€2/day. 🚿 **Location:** Rural, simple, quiet.
Surface: grassy. ⏻ 01/01-31/12
Distance: 🏪100m ⛱on the spot ⊗on the spot ⛴150m 🏍 on the spot 🏊 on the spot.
Remarks: Parking at the Moselle River.

Tourist information Kinheim:
🍷 Tag den offenen Weinkeller. Open wine-cellars. ⏻ 2nd Thu after Whitsuntide.
🍷 Wein- und Frülingsfest. Wine and spring celebration. ⏻ Whitsuntide.
🍷 Winzerfest. Wine festival. ⏻ 2nd weekend Sep.

| 🏞S | Kirchberg | 16D1 |

AMB-Reisemobile, Herbert-Kühn-Straße 10. **GPS:** n49,95349 e7,40759.
15 🅿 € 6 🚰 🔌Ch ⚡ included. ⏻ 01/01-31/12

| | Kirchheimbolanden 🏰 | 17A2 |

Festplatz Herrengarten, Hitzfeldstrasse. **GPS:** n49,66667 e8,01501.⬆️

20 🅿free 🚰€1/70liter 🔌Ch ⚡€0,50. **Surface:** metalled.
⏻ 01/01-31/12 🎡 2nd weekend May-Aug-Oct
Distance: 🏪300m ⊗300m ⛴on the spot.

| 🏕S | Kirn ⛲ | 16D2 |

Wohnmobilstellplatz "Auf der Kiesel", Fontaine-les-Dijon-Strasse.
GPS: n49,78406 e7,45798.

3 🅿 € 1,25/day. 🏙Location: Urban, comfortable, quiet, noisy.
Surface: concrete. ⏻ 01/01-31/12
Distance: 🏪300m ⛴on the spot ⛴on the spot.
Remarks: Monday market.

| ⛲ | Klausen | 16C1 |

Zentralparkplatz, Eberhardstrasse/ K51. **GPS:** n49,90550 e6,88104.➡️

5 🅿free. ⏻ 01/01-31/12
Distance: 🚴2km.

| ⛲S | Kleinbundenbach ⛲ | 16D3 |

Auf der Stampermühle, Stampermühle 1. **GPS:** n49,31778 e7,45694.⬆️

10 🅿 € 7 🚰 ⚡ 📶included. **Location:** Rural, simple, isolated.
Surface: gravel.
Distance: ⊗on the spot.

| 🏕S | Klüsserath ⛵ | 16C2 |

Reisemobilpark Klüsserath, B53. **GPS:** n49,84170 e6,85475.✈️ .

DE

400 🛏€6,50 ⛽€1/90liter 🚰Ch🚿€1,50/24h. 🚲
Surface: grassy. ⬛ Easter-31/10
Remarks: Along ther Moselle river, bread-service.

| 🛁S | Kobern 🌊 | 9B6 |

Am Kalkofen B416, Kobern-Gondorf. **GPS:** n50,30524 e7,46064. ✈ .

50 🛏€5 ⛽€1/80liter 🚿€0,10/time Ch€0,10/time. 🚐
Surface: metalled. ⬛ 01/01-31/12
Distance: 🚶300m ⛵8km 🏊on the spot 🛒on the spot ✕300m 🍴300m.

| 🛁 | Koblenz 🍂🌿🌊 | 9B6 |

Busparkplatz, Pastor-Klein-Straße. **GPS:** n50,36557 e7,57417. ⬆ .

50 🛏free. **Location:** Simple. **Surface:** gravel. ⬛ 01/01-31/12
Distance: 🚶Old city centre 2km ✕600m 🍴Aldi 500m.

| ⚓ | Konz | 16C2 |

An der Saarmündung, Am Moselufer 1. **GPS:** n49,70550 e6,57597. ➡
3 🛏€8 ⛽🚰ChWC 📶against payment 📶. **Surface:** grassy.
⬛ 01/03-31/10
Distance: 🏊on the spot 🛒on the spot ✕100m 🍴1km 🚴on the spot
🚶 on the spot.
Remarks: Service 100m.

| 🛁S | Köwerich 🌊 | 16C2 |

Weingut Hans Klären-Maringer 'Off'm Herrach', Beethovenstrasse 40.
GPS: n49,84123 e6,86287. ⬆➡

20 🛏€7 ⛽🚰Ch 🚿€0,50/kWh WC 🚽€1 💧€4/time. 🚲 **Surface:** grassy.
⬛ 01/01-31/12
Distance: 🚶500m ⛵500m 🚵500m 🏊on the spot 🍴2km 🚌100m.

Remarks: Check in at restaurant, bread-service.

| 🛁S | Kusel 🎣🍞 | 16D2 |

Parkplatz der Tuchfabriken, Trierer Straße 61. **GPS:** n49,54016 e7,39626. ⬆➡

3 🛏free ⛽🚿. **Surface:** asphalted. ⬛ 01/04-31/10
Distance: 🚶500m 🍴300m.
Remarks: Max. 3 days, key service at Touristinformation (300m).

| 🛁 | Lahnstein | 9B6 |

Wohnmobilstellplatz Blücherstraße, Blücherstraße 20.
GPS: n50,31335 e7,59331. ➡

10 🛏free. **Location:** Urban, simple, central. **Surface:** gravel.
⬛ 01/01-31/12
Distance: 🚶2km 🏊on the spot 🛒on the spot ✕on the spot.
Remarks: Max. 3 days.

| 🛁 | Lahnstein | 9B6 |

Wohnmobilstellplatz Kränchen, Johannesstraße. **GPS:** n50,30939 e7,59833.
➡

40 🛏free. **Location:** Simple. **Surface:** gravel. ⬛ 01/01-31/12
Distance: 🚶1km ✕600m 🍴600m.
Remarks: Max. 3 days.

| 🛁S | Landau ♈ | 17A3 |

Wellnessoase La Ola, Horstring 2. **GPS:** n49,20230 e8,14270. ⬆➡

5 🛏€10/24h ⛽€4 🚰Ch 🚿. 🚲 **Location:** Simple, quiet.
Surface: metalled. ⬛ 01/01-31/12
Distance: 🚶3km 🚵1km ✕500m 🚌100m.

DE

DE

Landstuhl · 16D3

Bahnstraße. **GPS:** n49,41595 e7,57092.⬆️➡️.

2 🛏free 🚰 Ch 🧹 free. **Location:** Urban, simple, noisy.
Surface: metalled. 🅿️ 01/01-31/12
Distance: 🚶on the spot 🚲1,3km ⊗350m 🛒Aldi 100m.
Remarks: Max. 3 days.

Langenlonsheim · 17A1

Weingut Im Zwölberich, Schützenstrasse 14. **GPS:** n49,89672 e7,89466.⬆️.

5 🛏€ 10 🚰 🧹 included. **Location:** Rural, simple, central, quiet.
Surface: asphalted/grassy. 🅿️ 01/01-31/12
Distance: 🚲7km.

Lauterecken · 16D2

Wohnmobilstellplatz Villa Toskana, Friedhofweg 3a. **GPS:** n49,65056 e7,58806. ⬆️➡️.

30 🛏€ 8 🚰€1/80liter Ch (18x)€1/8h WC €1/5minutes.
Surface: grassy/gravel. 🅿️ 01/01-31/12
Distance: 🚶300m ⊗on the spot 🛒100m.
Remarks: Bread-service.

Leimersheim · 17B3

Sport- und Freizeithalle, Rheinstraße 42. **GPS:** n49,12534 e8,35457.⬆️.

5 🛏free. **Location:** Rural, simple, quiet. **Surface:** gravel.
🅿️ 01/01-31/12
Distance: 🚶500m 🚲4km ⚓100m 🚊100m ⊗on the spot 🛒1km.
Remarks: At tennis-courts.

Leinsweiler · 17A3

Weingut Erlenswein, Wacholderhof. **GPS:** n49,18747 e8,03323.⬆️.

8 🛏€ 10 🚰 Ch 🧹 included. **Location:** Rural, simple, quiet.
Surface: grassy. 🅿️ 01/03-31/11
Distance: 🚶1km.
Remarks: Check in at Weingut.

Leiwen · 16C2

Weingut Heinz Spieles, Schulstrasse 20. **GPS:** n49,82331 e6,87524.⬆️.

4 🛏€ 8 🚰€1 Ch 🧹€1 included. **Surface:** grassy/gravel.
🅿️ 01/01-31/12
Distance: ⚓400m 🚊400m.

Leiwen · 16C2

Moselblick, Flurgartenstrasse 2/ Weinallee. **GPS:** n49,82611 e6,88057.⬆️.

12 🛏€ 8 🚰 Ch 🧹 WC €1 🚗. **Surface:** grassy/gravel.
🅿️ 01/01-31/12
Distance: 🚶500m ⚓on the spot 🚊on the spot ⊗on the spot 🛒300m
🚆500m.

Lemberg · 17A3

Lemberger Weiher, Weiherstraße. **GPS:** n49,17284 e7,64731.⬆️.

5 🛏free, service/electricity incl. € 7 🚰🧹.
Location: Rural. **Surface:** grasstiles. 🅿️ 01/01-31/12
Distance: 🚶400m ⊗600m 🏊on the spot 🎣on the spot.
Remarks: Max. 3 days.

Linz am Rhein · 9B6

B42 Linzhausenstrasse. **GPS:** n50,56291 e7,27982.⬆️.

6 🛏free. **Surface:** asphalted. ☐ 01/01-31/12
Distance: 🚶500m ⚓on the spot ⊗50m.
Remarks: Along the Rhine river, max. 3 days.

| 🏕 S | **Löf** | 9B6 |

SOG Dahmann, In der Mark 2. **GPS:** n50,23194 e7,43750.⬆

9 🛏free 🚰🗑Ch 🔌(4x)€0,50/kWh WC. **Location:** Rural.
Surface: metalled. ☐ 01/01-31/12
Distance: 🚲13km ⊗1km.

| 🚲 S | **Longuich/Mosel** | 16C2 |

Feiten, Rioler weg 2. **GPS:** n49,80417 e6,77899.⬆➡

40 🛏€5 🚰€0,50/70liter 🗑Ch 🔌€3 WC 🗑€1. 🚿 **Surface:** grassy.
☐ 01/01-31/12
Distance: 🚶300m 🚲2km ⚓on the spot 🚣on the spot ⊗on the spot
🍺1km.
Remarks: Playground.

| 🍴 S | **Longuich/Mosel** | 16C2 |

WeinKulturgut Longen Schlöder, Kirchenweg 9. **GPS:** n49,81023 e6,76427.⬆

8 🛏€7 🚰€2 🔌(3x)€2,50 WC 🗑€3. 🚿 **Surface:** gravel/metalled.
☐ 01/01-31/12 🔘 Tue
Distance: 🚲1km 🚶150m 🚣150m ⊗on the spot 🍺500m.

| 🚲 S | **Losheim am See** | 16C2 |

Reisemobilplatz am Stausee, Zum Stausee. **GPS:** n49,51999 e6,74123.➡

20 🛏€6 🚰🗑Ch 🔌WC 🗑included. **Surface:** asphalted/grassy.
☐ 01/01-31/12
Distance: 🚶1km ⚓200m 🚣200m ⊗100m 🍺1km.
Remarks: Parking at lake, in front of tourist office, incl. use sanitary and service
on campsite 1km.

| 🚲 S | **Lösnich** 🌿🍇 | 16D1 |

Stellplatz am Moselufer, Gestade. **GPS:** n49,97560 e7,04276.⬆

96 🛏€6 🚰🗑Chincluded 🔌€2/day. 🚿 **Location:** Rural, simple, quiet.
Surface: grassy. ☐ 01/03-01/11
Distance: 🚶on the spot ⚓on the spot 🚣on the spot ⊗on the spot 🍺3km
🚴on the spot 🎣on the spot.
Remarks: Along ther Moselle river, baker every morning.

| 🚲 S | **Lutzerath** 🍴 | 16C1 |

Trierer Strasse. **GPS:** n50,13015 e7,01002.⬆

10 🛏€5/day 🚰€0,50 🗑Ch 🔌(6x)€0,50/kWh.
Location: Urban, simple. **Surface:** asphalted. ☐ 01/01-31/12
Distance: 🚶on the spot ⊗on the spot 🍺on the spot.
Remarks: Check in at Hotel Restaurant Maas, Trierer Str. 30.

| 🚲 S | **Maikammer** | 17A3 |

Sporthalle Kalmit, Johannes Dammstrasse. **GPS:** n49,30307 e8,13219.⬆➡

🛏€4/day 🚰🔌included. **Surface:** asphalted. ☐ 01/01-31/12
Distance: 🚶100m ⊗nearby 🍺nearby.

| 🚲 S | **Maikammer** | 17A3 |

Weingut Hubert Müller, Raiffeisenstrasse 59. **GPS:** n49,30737 e8,13646.
3 🛏€13 🚰🗑 🔌WC 🗑included. **Surface:** gravel. ☐ 01/01-31/12

DE

Distance: 🛒 on the spot 🏖 7km.

🚲⛽ **Maikammer** `17A3`

Weingut Schädler, Dieterwiesenstraße. **GPS**: n49,30848 e8,12530.
3 🛏 €7 🚰 💧 WC included. ⬛ 01/01-31/12
Distance: 🛒 500m 🍴 1km 🚲 on the spot 🎿 on the spot.

🚲⛽ **Maikammer** `17A3`

Weingut Ziegler-Ullrich, Weinstraße Nord 46. **GPS**: n49,30659 e8,13369.
2 🛏 €5 🚰 💧 included. ⬛ 01/01-31/12
Distance: 🏖 4km.

⛽ **Mainz** 🚤 `17A1`

Wohnmobilstellplatz Mainz, Dr.-Martin-Luther-King-Weg 21.
GPS: n49,99849 e8,24638.
50 🛏 🚰 💧 Ch 💧. ⬛ 01/01-31/12
Distance: 🛒 Old city centre 1,7km 🍴 50m 🍴 Aldi 200m 🚌 Bus 160m.

⛽ **Mandelbachtal** 👫 `16D3`

Ommersheimer Weiher, L107. **GPS**: n49,21899 e7,16766. ⬆️

2 🛏 free 🚰 💧 (2x)€1/12h. **Location:** Rural, simple, isolated, quiet.
Surface: asphalted. ⬛ 01/01-31/12
Distance: 🏊 on the spot 🚣 on the spot.

🏕 **Mandelbachtal** 👫 `16D3`

Kloster Gräfinthal, Gräfinthal. **GPS**: n49,15975 e7,11924. ⬆️

2 🛏 free. **Location:** Rural, simple, noisy. **Surface:** metalled.
⬛ 01/01-31/12
Distance: 🛑 100m.

🅲⛽ **Manderscheid** 🏰 `16C1`

Campingplatz Vulkaneifel, Herbstwiese. **GPS**: n50,09713 e6,79969. ➡️

8 🛏 € 6/pp, dog € 1,50 🚰 €0,50/100liter 🍴 Ch 💧 €2,50 WC included 🛜.
Location: Rural, simple, quiet. **Surface:** metalled. ⬛ 15/03-31/10
Distance: 🛒 800m 🛑 800m 🍴 800m 🍽 on camp site 🚲 on the spot
🎿 on the spot.
Remarks: Bread-service.

🏨⛽ **Manderscheid** 🏰 `16C1`

Hotel Heidsmühle, Mosenbergstrasse 22. **GPS**: n50,08504 e6,80021. ⬆️.

20 🛏 free 🚰 💧 (4x)€2,50/day. **Location:** Rural, simple, isolated, quiet.
Surface: grassy/gravel. ⬛ 01/01-31/12
Distance: 🛒 2km 🏖 6km 🚤 on the spot ⊗ on the spot 🚲 on the spot
🎿 on the spot.

⛽ **Mayen** 🚤 `9B6`

Wohnmobilstellplatz am Viehmarkt, Polcherstrasse. **GPS**: n50,32194 e7,22806.
⬆️

6 🛏 free 🚰 €1/80liter 🍴 Ch WC. **Location:** Simple. **Surface:** gravel.
⬛ 01/01-31/12
Distance: 🛒 100m 🏖 4km ⊗ 100m 🍴 100m.
Remarks: Next to event ground.

⛽ **Mayschoss** ⚓ 🚤 `9A6`

Ahruferplatz, Ahr-Rotweinstraße 46. **GPS**: n50,51736 e7,01948. ⬆️.

60 🛏 € 6 🚰 €1/100liter 🍴 Ch 💧 (15x)€2,50/day WC. 🚿
Location: Rural, central. **Surface:** asphalted/gravel. ⬛ 01/01-31/12
Distance: 🛒 on the spot ⊗ 100m 🍴 250m bakery 🚌 50m.
Remarks: Along the Ahr river, parking at station.

⛽ **Meckenheim** `17A3`

Sporthalle Meckenheim, Rödersheimerstraße. **GPS**: n49,41167 e8,24056. ⬆️.
10 🛏 free 💧 €0,50/kWh. **Surface:** gravel. ⬛ 01/01-31/12
Distance: 🛒 1km.

⛽ **Meddersheim** 🍇 `16D2`

Winzergenossenschaft, Naheweinstrasse 63. **GPS**: n49,77988 e7,61347.
10 🛏 free 🚰 🍴 free 💧 €3/day. **Location:** Rural, simple, quiet.
Surface: gravel. ⬛ 01/01-31/12
Distance: 🛒 800m.
Remarks: Max. 2 nights, gate can be opened manually.

🚲⛽ **Mehring** 🚤 `16C2`

Weingut Zellerhof, Zellerhof 1. **GPS**: n49,79369 e6,81944. ⬆️➡️.

DE

43 ⌁ € 6 ⌁ €0,50/70liter ▣ Ch ⌁ (43x)€0,50/kWh WC ▤ € 1.
Surface: grassy/metalled. ▣ 01/01-31/12
Distance: ⌁100m ⊗on the spot ⌁on the spot ⊗on the spot ⌁100m.

| S | Mehring ⌁ | 16C2 |

Wohnmobilstellplatz del Mosel, Moselweinstrasse 2. **GPS:** n49,79423 e6,81726. ⬆.

72 ⌁ € 6 + € 1,50/pp ⌁ €1,50/100liter ▣ Ch ⌁ (60x)€2 WC ▤ €1,50. ⌁
Surface: grassy. ▣ 01/01-31/12
Distance: ⌁100m ⊗on the spot ⌁200m.
Remarks: Bread-service.

| S | Meisenheim | 17A2 |

Schwimmbad Meisenheim, In der Heimbach. **GPS:** n49,71472 e7,65750. ⬆.

12 ⌁ € 5 ⌁ €1/100liter ▣ €1 Ch ⌁ (12x)€1/kWh. **Surface:** gravel.
▣ 01/01-31/12 ▣ 01/07-09/07
Distance: ⌁1,6km ⊗on the spot ⌁500m.

| S | Mendig ⌁ | 9B6 |

Brauerstraße. **GPS:** n50,37678 e7,28404. ⬆.

20 ⌁ free ⌁ €1/80liter ▣ Ch ⌁ (12x)€0,50/kWh. **Location:** Rural, quiet.
Surface: gravel. ▣ 01/01-31/12
Distance: ⌁200m ⊗Vulkanbrauhaus&Felsenkeller.
Remarks: In front of football ground, Vulkanmuseum Lava-Dome 100m.

| S | Merzig | 16C3 |

Das Bad, Saarwiesenring 3. **GPS:** n49,44541 e6,62418. ⬆➡.

12 ⌁ € 6,50 ⌁ €1/100liter ▣ Ch ⌁ included ⌁. **Surface:** grassy/gravel.
▣ 01/01-31/12
Distance: ⌁2km ⊗on the spot ⌁2km.
Remarks: Check in at swimming pool, caution key € 50.

| ⌁ S | Merzig | 16C3 |

Yachthafen Merzig, Saarwiesenring 10. **GPS:** n49,44205 e6,63566. ➡.

15 ⌁ € 7 ⌁ ▣ Ch ⌁ €0,50/kWh WC ▤. **Surface:** metalled.
▣ 01/04-31/10
Distance: ⌁1km ⊗on the spot ⌁800m.

| S | Mettlach | 16C2 |

Cloef-Atrium, Alfred-Backer-strasse, Mettlach-Orscholz.
GPS: n49,50394 e6,53225. ⬆➡.

10 ⌁ € 5 ⌁ ▣ WC. **Surface:** gravel. ⌁on the spot.
Remarks: Pay with SMS, max. 24h.

| ⌁ S | Mettlach | 16C2 |

Mettlacher Abtei-Bräu, P6, Bahnhofstrasse 32. **GPS:** n49,49847 e6,59612. ⬆.

10 ⌁ € 5 ⌁ ▣ Chfree. **Surface:** gravel. ▣ 01/01-31/12
Distance: ⌁500m ⌁7km ⌁on the spot ⌁on the spot ⊗on the spot.
Remarks: Along the Saar River, pay with SMS.

| ⌁ S | Mettlach | 16C2 |

Restaurant zum Kaltenborn, Zur Großwies 21, Orscholz.
GPS: n49,50916 e6,53030. ⌁.

DE

10 ⌁ € 5. 🔌 ⬛ 01/01-31/12 ⬤ Thu
Distance: ⊗on the spot.
Tourist information Mettlach:
👁 Ⓜ Erlebniszentrum Villeroy&Boch. ⬛ Mo-Fr: 9.30-19h, Sa 9.30-18h.
🍴 Villeroy&Boch Outletcenter, Freiherr-vom-Stein-Strasse 4-6. ⬛ Mo-Fr: 9.30-19h, Sa 9.30-18h.

Minheim | 16C1
Reisemobilpark Sonneninsel, K53. **GPS:** n49,86500 e6,94111. ⬆➡.

90 ⌁ € 6,50 🚰 €1/100liter 🗑 Ch ⚡ €1/2kWh. 🔌
Surface: grassy/gravel. ⬛ 01/01-31/12
Distance: 🏊 10km ⊗400m 🚉3km.
Remarks: Along the Moselle river, next to football ground.

Minheim | 16C1
Weinhaus Moselblick, In der Olk 9. **GPS:** n49,86428 e6,93294. ⬆ .

10 ⌁ € 9 🚰 🗑 Ch ⚡ €1,50/day. 🔌 **Surface:** grassy/gravel.
⬛ 01/01-31/12
Distance: 🏊200m 🚶200m.

Monzernheim | 17A2
Weingut Helmut Geil, Am Römer 26. **GPS:** n49,72376 e8,22715. ⬆.

3 ⌁ € 6 🚰 🗑 ⚡ (3x)included. 🔌 **Location:** Rural, simple, quiet.
Surface: grassy. ⬛ 01/01-31/12
Distance: 🏊8km ⊗4km 🚉4km.
Remarks: Check in at Weingut.

Monzingen | 16D2
Parkplatz Festhalle, Rosengartenstrasse 11. **GPS:** n49,79438 e7,59075. ⬆.

3 ⌁free. **Location:** Rural, simple, noisy. **Surface:** asphalted.
⬛ 01/01-31/12
Distance: ⊗on the spot 🚉1km.

Monzingen | 16D2
Weingut Axel Schramm, Soonwaldstrasse 49. **GPS:** n49,81088 e7,48058.⬆.

3 ⌁free 🚰 ⚡ free. **Location:** Rural, simple, isolated, quiet.
Surface: concrete. ⬛ 01/01-31/12
Distance: 🚶1,2km.

Monzingen | 16D2
Weingut Holger Alt, Hauptstrasse 67. **GPS:** n49,00000 e7,59144.

5 ⌁free. **Location:** Rural, simple, isolated, quiet. **Surface:** grassy.
⬛ 01/01-31/12
Distance: 🚉800m.

Morbach | 16D2
Reisemobilhafen Morbach, Zum Camping 15, Hoxel. **GPS:** n49,77855 e7,10695. ⬆➡.

40 ⌁ € 5/night 🚰 €1/80liter 🗑 Ch ⚡ (40x)€2/night. **Surface:** grassy.
⬛ 16/03-15/11
Distance: ⊗300m 🚉300m.

Neef | 16D1
Wohnmobilstellplatz Zum Frauenberg. **GPS:** n50,09455 e7,13730.⬆.

DE

100 🛏€6 🚰⚡ Ch included ✎ (42x)€2/24h,4Amp. ♿
Location: Rural, simple. **Surface:** grassy. ☀ 01/04-01/11
Distance: ⚓on the spot ⛵on the spot ☒200m.
Remarks: Along ther Moselle river, nearby sports fields.

20 🛏€14 🚰⚡€2,50 Ch ✎ WC ⚡ included. **Surface:** grassy.
☀ 01/03-31/10
Distance: ⚓3km ⛵1,7km ☒1,4km.
Remarks: Next to campsite.

🅿S **Neuhäusel** 9B6
Wohnmobilstellplatz Efferz, Im Feldchen. **GPS:** n50,38271 e7,70331.

🅿S **Neustadt/Weinstrasse** 17A3
Dammstrasse-Ost, Hambach. **GPS:** n49,33083 e8,13139. ⬆

20 🛏€8 🚰€1/80liter ⚡ Ch ✎ (12x)€1/2kWh WC ⚡.
Surface: metalled. ☀ 01/01-31/12
Distance: ⚓250m ☒250m ⛵250m 🚍100m > Koblenz.
Remarks: Bread-service.

20 🛏free 🚰€1/100liter ⚡€1 Ch. **Surface:** grassy. ☀ 01/01-31/12
Distance: ⚓nearby ☒nearby ⛵nearby.

🅿S **Neumagen-Dhron** 16C1
Gaststatte Beim Ketsch, In der Zeil. **GPS:** n49,86449 e6,90321. ⬆➡

🅿S **Neustadt/Weinstrasse** 17A3
Reisemobilstellpatz Martin-Luther-Kirche, Martin-Luther-Strasse.
GPS: n49,35485 e8,15255. ⬆

100 🛏€6 🚰⚡ Ch included ✎€1,50/day WC ⚡€2 🚿€3 against
payment. ♿ **Surface:** grassy/gravel. ☀ 01/01-31/12
Distance: ⚓200m ⛵on the spot ⛵500m.
Remarks: Bread-service.

30 🛏€4/24h 🚰⚡ Ch included ✎ (8x)€1/2kWh. **Surface:** asphalted.
☀ 01/01-31/12
Distance: ⚓300m ☒250m ⛵Aldimarkt 50m.

🅿S **Neumagen-Dhron** 16C1
Yachthafen Neumagen, Moselstrasse 21. **GPS:** n49,85188 e6,89232. ⬆➡

🅿 **Neustadt/Weinstrasse** 17A3
Festplatz Neustadt-Haardt, Am Mandelring, Haardt. **GPS:** n49,36731 e8,13917.
2 🛏free. ☀ 01/01-31/12
Distance: ⛵5km.

🅿 **Neustadt/Weinstrasse** 17A3
Parkplatz am Rebenmeer, Am Falltor, Duttweiler. **GPS:** n49,30148 e8,21192. ⬆

40 🛏<9m €6, >9m €8 + €2,50/pp 🚰€0,50/40liter ⚡ Ch ✎€0,60/kWh
WC ⚡ included 🚿 ⚡€3/24h. ♿ **Surface:** gravel. ☀ 01/01-31/12
Distance: ⚓100m ⛵on the spot ⛵on the spot ☒on the spot ⛵1,3km.
Remarks: Check in at harbourmaster.

10 🛏free. **Location:** Rural, simple, quiet. **Surface:** gravel/metalled.
☀ 01/01-31/12
Distance: ⛵5km ☒300m ⛵250m bakery.

🅿S **Neunkirchen/Saar** 16D3
Prießnitz, Zweibrücker Straße 148. **GPS:** n49,32766 e7,19375. ⬆

DE

| | Neustadt/Weinstrasse | 17A3 |

Wohnmobilstellplatz Gimmeldingen, Peter-Koch-Strasse.
GPS: n49,37771 e8,15448.
2 free. 01/01-31/12
Distance: 500m 5km on the spot on the spot.

| | Neustadt/Weinstrasse | 17A3 |

Altes Weingut Steigelmann, Lauterbachstrasse 33, Mussbach.
GPS: n49,37285 e8,17230.
5 €5 Ch €1,50. 01/01-31/12
Distance: 3km.

| | Neustadt/Weinstrasse | 17A3 |

Rebenhof Wein- und Sektgut, Andergasse 93, Hambach.
GPS: n49,32157 e8,12241.
5 €8 included. 01/01-31/12
Distance: 5km.

| | Neustadt/Weinstrasse | 17A3 |

Weingut & Weinschenke Hans Abel, Weinstrasse 103, Hambach.
GPS: n49,33784 e8,13157.
3 free €2,50. 01/01-31/12 Thu
Distance: 4,5km.

| | Neustadt/Weinstrasse | 17A3 |

Weingut Andres, Langensteinstrasse 22, Lachen-Speyersdorf.
GPS: n49,33631 e8,20579.
3 free . 01/01-31/12

| | Neustadt/Weinstrasse | 17A3 |

Weingut Carl Disson, Andergasse 96, Diedesfeld. **GPS**: n49,32123 e8,12220.
4 €7 WC . 01/01-31/12
Distance: 5km.
Remarks: Bread-service.

| | Neustadt/Weinstrasse | 17A3 |

Weingut Hammer, Zum Klausental 29. **GPS**: n49,32109 e8,13251.
3 €5 . 01/01-31/12
Distance: 5km.

| | Neustadt/Weinstrasse | 17A3 |

Weingut Klohr, An der Eselshaut 67, Mussbach. **GPS**: n49,36931 e8,17414.
2 . 01/01-31/12
Distance: 2km.

| | Neustadt/Weinstrasse | 17A3 |

Weingut Kreiselmaier, Goethestrasse 77, Lachen. **GPS**: n49,32215 e8,20071.

3 €5 €2/100liter €2/night. **Location**: Simple, quiet. **Surface**: grassy.
01/03-31/10
Distance: on the spot 4,5km 250m 3km 150m.
Remarks: Sale of wines.

| | Neustadt/Weinstrasse | 17A3 |

Weingut Müller-Kern, Andergasse 38, Hambach. **GPS**: n49,32266 e8,12681.
3 €12 WC . 01/01-31/12
Distance: 4,5km.

| | Neustadt/Weinstrasse | 17A3 |

Weingut Rumsauer, Von-Dalheim-Strasse 11, Diedesfeld.
GPS: n49,31978 e8,14028.
2 free . 01/01-31/12
Distance: 5km.

| | Neustadt/Weinstrasse | 17A3 |

Weingut Schäfer, Schiessmauer 56, Mussbach. **GPS**: n49,36335 e8,17111.

5 €15 Ch WC included free. 01/03-31/10
Distance: 2km.

| | Neustadt/Weinstrasse | 17A3 |

Weingut Völcker, An der Eselshaut 15, Mussbach. **GPS**: n49,36825 e8,16805.
3 €5 . **Surface**: grassy. 01/01-31/12
Distance: 3km.

| | Neustadt/Weinstrasse | 17A3 |

Weinhaus Am Herzog, Mandelring 195, Haardt. **GPS**: n49,36889 e8,14583.
2 €15 WC included. 01/01-31/12
Distance: 4km.

| | Neustadt/Weinstrasse | 17A3 |

Weinland Königsbach-Neustadt, Deidesheimer Strasse 12, Königsbach.
GPS: n49,38712 e8,16239.
5 . 01/01-31/12
Distance: 6,5km.

| | Neustadt/Weinstrasse | 17A3 |

Weinland Meckenheim, An der Eselshaut 76, Mussbach.
GPS: n49,37037 e8,17479.
3 €5 €2,50. 01/01-31/12
Distance: 2,3km.

| | Neustadt/Weinstrasse | 17A3 |

Weingut Helbighof, Andergasse 40, Hambach. **GPS**: n49,32256 e8,12657.
3 . 01/01-31/12
Distance: 4,5km.

| | Neustadt/Weinstrasse | 17A3 |

Hambacher Schloss, Weinstrasse 110, Hambach. **GPS**: n49,33706 e8,13155.
2 free. 01/01-31/12 01/10-31/10
Distance: 4,5km.

| | Neuwied | 9B6 |

Yachthafen Neuwied, Rheinstrasse 180. **GPS**: n50,41413 e7,47946.

40 €7, 2 pers.incl. Ch €0,50/kWh WC included.
Surface: metalled. 01/01-31/12
Distance: 2km on the spot 2km.
Remarks: Cash payment.

| | Niederbreitbach | 9B6 |

Campingplatz Neuerburg, Im Freizeitpark 1. **GPS**: n50,52969 e7,41414.

8 ⬛€6 🚰80liter 🔲Ch 💧€1,50/day ☀️€1 🔲€3,50. ♻️
Location: Rural, comfortable. **Surface:** gravel. ⬛ 01/01-31/12
Distance: 🚶250m ⬅️13km ⬇️on the spot ⊗on the spot 🍽️on the spot
🐾on the spot ☀️on the spot.
Remarks: Bread-service.

| 📷S | Niederkirchen bei Deidesheim | 17A3 |

Wohnmobilstellplatz Niederkirchen, An de Sportanlage 1.
GPS: n49,40891 e8,22141.
6 ⬛free 💧€1. **Surface:** gravel. ⬛ 01/01-31/12
Distance: 🚶1km ⬅️4,5km.

| 📷S | Nierstein | 17B1 |

Mobilstellplatz auf dem Weingut Gehring, Ausserhalb 17.
GPS: n49,85621 e8,32520.⬆️

30 ⬛€8 🚰🔲Chincluded 💧(25x)€3/day ⬛€5/time. ♻️
Location: Rural, comfortable, quiet. **Surface:** grassy. ⬛ 01/01-31/12
Distance: 🚶2km 🐾on the spot ☀️on the spot.
Remarks: Bread-service.

| 📷S | Nohfelden | 16D2 |

Campingplatz Bostalsee, P6, L325, Bosen. **GPS:** n49,56039 e7,06113.⬆️➡️

10 ⬛€8/24h 🚰€0,50/50liter 🔲Ch 💧€1/2kWh. **Surface:** metalled.
⬛ 01/01-31/12
Distance: 🚶500m ⬅️6km ⬇️200m ⊗on the spot 🍽️800m.

| 📷 | Nonnweiler | 16C2 |

Stellplatz Am Hallenbad, Triererstrasse 2. **GPS:** n49,60686 e6,97216.⬆️

5 ⬛free. **Surface:** grassy/metalled. ⬛ 01/01-31/12
Distance: 🚶on the spot ⬅️1km ⊗on the spot 🍽️800m.
Remarks: Parking swimming pool, max. 48h.

| 📷S | Nürburg | 9A6 |

Wohnmobilpark Motorsporthotel, Hauptstrasse 34. **GPS:** n50,33982 e6,95131.
12 ⬛€10 🚰🔲💧📶. ⬛ 01/01-31/12
Distance: ⊗on the spot.
Remarks: At racing circuit.

| 📷S | Ober-Hilbersheim | 17A1 |

Napoleonshöhe, Sprendlingers Straße. **GPS:** n49,89785 e8,02421.⬆️

40 ⬛free 🚰🔲Ch. **Surface:** grassy. ⬛ 01/01-31/12
Distance: 🚶500m 🍽️300m.

| 📷S | Oberbrombach | 16D2 |

Wohnmobilstellplatz Höhenblick, Sonnenberger Strasse.
GPS: n49,69481 e7,25960.
75 ⬛€7 🚰🔲Ch 💧(45x)€2/4kWh. **Surface:** grassy/gravel.
⬛ 01/01-31/12
Distance: 🚶400m ⊗600m.

| 📷S | Oberwesel/Rhein | 17A1 |

Stellplatz am Schiffsanleger, B9. **GPS:** n50,10816 e7,72758.⬆️
10 ⬛€8. ⬛ 01/01-31/12
Distance: ⬅️10km ⬇️on the spot 🍽️on the spot.

| 📷S | Oberwesel/Rhein | 17A1 |

Camping Schönburgblick, Am Hafendamm / B9. **GPS:** n50,10294 e7,73663.⬆️

20 ⬛€8,50/24h 🚰🔲Chincluded 💧€0,60/kWh WC⬛€2,50 📶€2.
Location: Comfortable, quiet. **Surface:** grassy. ⬛ 15/03-31/10
Distance: 🚶800m ⬇️on the spot 🍽️on the spot ⊗on the spot 🍽️200m
🚌400m.

| 📷 | Offenbach an der Queich | 17A3 |

Am Queichtalzentrum, Konrad-Lerch-Ring. **GPS:** n49,20056 e8,19478.⬆️➡️

2 ⬛free. **Location:** Simple. **Surface:** metalled. ⬛ 01/01-31/12
Distance: 🚶100m ⬅️6km ⊗500m 🍽️1km 🚌400m.
Remarks: Max. 3 days.

| 📷S | Oppenheim 🍴 | 17B1 |

Womoland Oppenheim, An der Festwiese. **GPS:** n49,85673 e8,36502.⬆️➡️

DE

20 🚐€7 🚰€1/50liter ⚡Ch ♨€3/24h. **Surface:** grassy.
🅿 01/01-31/12 ⬛ week before/after Whitsuntide
Distance: 🚶500m 🚲500m 🚉500m.

🍴🚿 **Osann-Monzel** 16C1

Wohnmobilstellplatz Panorama, Moselstrasse 16. **GPS**: n49,90904 e6,95624. ⬆.

8 🚐€5 ♨€2 📶against payment. ♿ **Surface:** gravel. 🅿 01/06-31/10
Distance: 🚶9km 🚉50m.
Remarks: Key at aparthotel Panorama (50m).

🚿 **Osthofen** 17B2

Festplatz Wonnegauhalle, Herrnsheimer Strasse. **GPS**: n49,69913 e8,32691. ⬆➡.

50 🚐free 🚰⚡Chfree. **Surface:** gravel. 🅿 01/01-31/12
Distance: 🚶500m 🚲7km 🚉500m.
Remarks: Max. 48h.

🚿 **Osthofen** 17B2

Sommerried Stadion, L439. **GPS**: n49,69222 e8,32805. ⬆.

10 🚐free. **Surface:** grassy/sand. 🅿 01/01-31/12
Distance: 🚲6km 🚉800m.
Remarks: Max. 48h.

🚿 **Osthofen** 17B2

Weingut Borntaler Hof, Alter Westhofer Weg. **GPS**: n49,69985 e8,29860. ⬆➡.

4 🚐€5 🚰⚡♨ WCincluded. **Surface:** metalled. 🅿 01/01-31/12
Distance: 🚲9km.

🚿 **Ottweiler** 16D3

Stellplatz Wingertsweiher, Am Wingertsweiher. **GPS**: n49,41134 e7,18076. ⬆➡.

12 🚐€5/24h 🚰€1/150liter ⚡€1 Ch ♨(6x)€3/8h.
Surface: grassy/metalled. 🅿 01/01-31/12
Distance: 🚶1,5km 🏊on the spot 🛒on the spot 🛒on the spot 🚉1,5km 🚲1km.
Remarks: Max. 7 days.

🚿 **Palzem** 16B2

Weingut E. Pauly, Obermoselstrasse 5. **GPS**: n49,56402 e6,37581. ⬆➡.

3 🚐€7 🚰⚡♨ WC. **Surface:** gravel/metalled. 🅿 01/01-31/12
Distance: 🛒50m 🚉4km.
Remarks: Not suitable for big motorhomes, beautiful view.

🚿 **Perl** 16C2

Am Perlbach, Auf dem Sabel 4. **GPS**: n49,47900 e6,38493. ⬆➡.

6 🚐€8, winter €5 🚰€1/6minutes ⚡Ch ♨€1/8h. **Surface:** metalled. 🅿 01/01-31/12
Distance: 🚶500m 🚲3,5km 🛒500m 🚉500m.

🚿 **Pfaffen-Schwabenheim** 17A1

Pferdepension am Sonnenhof, Brühlstraße. **GPS**: n49,85224 e7,95951. ⬆.
10 🚐€10 🚰⚡♨ WCincluded. ♿
Location: Rural, simple, isolated, quiet. **Surface:** concrete. 🅿 01/01-31/12
Distance: 🚲7km.

🚿 **Piesport** 16C1

Piesporter Goldtröpfchen, Moselstrasse. **GPS**: n49,87199 e6,92703. ➡.

30 ⌃€6 🚰€1/80liter ⚡Ch 🚿€2. 🗑 **Surface:** gravel.
🔲 01/01-31/12
Distance: 🚶100m ✈11km ⛵on the spot 🛒on the spot ✕on the spot 🍴500m.
Remarks: Bread-service mo-sa.

⚑S **Piesport** 16C1
Altes Kelterhaus, St. Martinstrasse 33. **GPS:** n49,87872 e6,92590. ➡.

6 ⌃€7,50, guests free 🚰€2,50 ⚡Ch 🚿€2,50. 🗑 **Surface:** gravel.
🔲 01/01-31/12
Distance: ✈10km ✕on the spot 🍴on the spot.

⚑S **Piesport** 16C1
Weingut Heinz Kirsten, In der Noo. **GPS:** n49,88017 e6,92597. ⬆.

6 ⌃€6 🚰 🚿€1. 🗑 **Surface:** gravel. 🔲 01/01-31/12
Distance: ✈7,5km ✕on the spot 🍴on the spot.
Remarks: Check in at Bahnhofstrasse 28.

⚑S **Piesport** 16C1
Weingut Spang, Reisemobilplatz Rebengarten, In den Dur 11.
GPS: n49,88287 e6,92781. ⬆ ➡.

3 ⌃€8 🚰 🚿€0,70/kWh WC ⌃€2,50. 🗑 **Surface:** gravel.
🔲 01/01-31/12
Distance: 🚶on the spot ✈8km ⛵100m ✕100m 🍴500m 🚌500m.
Remarks: Bread-service.

⚑S **Piesport** 16C1
Wohnmobilstellplatz Loreleyblick, Loreleyblick 20. **GPS:** n49,87323 e6,92535. ⬆.

5 ⌃€8 🚰 ⚡Ch 🚿(10x) ⌃€1. 🗑 **Surface:** gravel. 🔲 01/01-31/12
Distance: 🚶on the spot ✈11km ✕1km 🍴300m.
Remarks: Bread-service.

⚑S **Pirmasens** 16D3
Am Messegelände, Zeppelinstraße. **GPS:** n49,20446 e7,60885. ⬆.

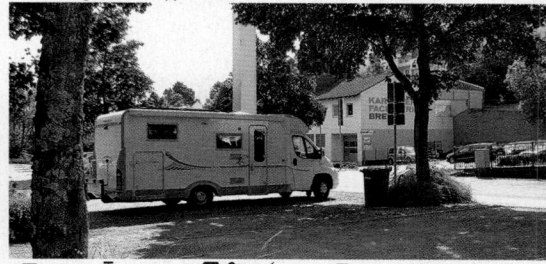

8 ⌃€5/24h 🚰€1/100liter ⚡Ch 🚿€1/6h. 🏠**Location:** Urban, simple, noisy. **Surface:** gravel. 🔲 01/01-31/12
Distance: 🚶450m ✈6km ✕450m 🍴450m.

🍴 **Pirmasens** 16D3
Forsthaus Beckenhof, Beckenhofer Strasse. **GPS:** n49,19604 e7,65635. ⬆.

10 ⌃guests free. **Location:** Rural, simple, quiet. **Surface:** gravel.
🔲 01/01-31/12

⊕ **Plaidt** 9B6
Wohnmobilstellplatz am Vulkanpark, Rauschermühle 6.
GPS: n50,38790 e7,40444. ⬆.

10 ⌃free. **Location:** Rural. **Surface:** metalled. 🔲 01/01-31/12
Distance: ✈5km.

🍴 **Plein** 16C1
Hotel-Restaurant Waldschlößchen Plein, Zum Waldschlößchen 3.
GPS: n50,03223 e6,88074.
3 ⌃guests free. 🔲 01/01-31/12
Distance: ✈4km ✕on the spot.

⚑S **Polch** 9B6
Niesmann&Bisschof, Clou-strasse 1. **GPS:** n50,30680 e7,30684. ⬆.

25 ⌃free 🚰€0,50/80liter ⚡Ch 🚿(12x)€0,50/kWh. **Surface:** metalled.

DE

🔲 01/01-31/12
Distance: ⊗on the spot 🍺on the spot.

🏕S   **Pronsfeld** 🌿🍽   **16B1**
Am Alten Bahnhof, Bahnhofstrasse. **GPS:** n50,16343 e6,33669. ⬆➡.

50 🚐€5 🚰€0,50/60liter 🚽Ch ⚡(12x)€0,50/kWh. **Location:** Rural, comfortable, quiet. **Surface:** grassy/gravel. 🔲 01/01-31/12
Distance: 🚶600m 🚲7,5km ⊗600m 🍺700m 🚌500m 🚴on the spot 🚶on the spot.

🏕   **Prüm**   **16C1**
Wohnmobilstellplatz Prüm, Monthermeerstrasse. **GPS:** n50,20956 e6,42715. ⬆.

4 🚐free. **Surface:** gravel. 🔲 01/01-31/12
Distance: 🚶600m.

🏕S   **Pünderich** 🌿🌊   **16D1**
Wohnmobilstellplatz Pünderich, Moselallee. **GPS:** n50,04355 e7,12548. ⬆➡.

80 🚐€6 🚰🚽Chincluded ⚡(12x)€2/24h. 🚿 **Location:** Rural, simple, quiet. **Surface:** grassy. 🔲 01/04-31/10
Distance: 🚶on the spot 🛒on the spot 🚤on the spot ⊗300m 🍺500m.

🏕   **Ramstein-Miesenbach** 🍽   **16D2**
City Parkplatz, Talstrasse. **GPS:** n49,45103 e7,55557. ⬆➡.

3 🚐free. **Location:** Urban, simple, noisy. **Surface:** gravel.
🔲 01/01-31/12
Distance: 🚲3,7km.

🏊   **Ramstein-Miesenbach** 🍽   **16D2**
Freizeitbad Azur, Schernauer Strasse 5. **GPS:** n49,44578 e7,56971. ⬆.

30 🚐free. **Location:** Rural, simple, noisy. **Surface:** metalled.
🔲 01/01-31/12
Distance: 🚲5,5km.

🏕   **Rech**   **9A6**
Wohnmobilstellpark "Alt Bodendorf", Rotweinstraße 13.
GPS: n50,51458 e7,03738.

15 🚐€4. 🚿 🔲 01/01-31/12
Distance: 🚲11km.

🏕   **Rech**   **9A6**
Im Bungert. GPS: n50,51343 e7,03865. ⬆.
10 🚐€4. 🚿 **Location:** Rural, simple. **Surface:** gravel.
🔲 01/01-31/12
Distance: 🚶on the spot ⊗on the spot 🚤on the spot 🚶on the spot.

🏕S   **Reil/Mosel** 🌿🌊   **16D1**
Am Moselufer, Moselstrasse. **GPS:** n50,02566 e7,11493. ⬆.

70 🚐€6 🚰🚽Ch ⚡(48x)€2 WCincluded. 🚿 **Location:** Rural, comfortable, quiet. **Surface:** grassy. 🔲 01/03-31/10
Distance: 🚶500m 🛒on the spot ⊗450m.
Remarks: Along ther Moselle river.

🏕S   **Reipoltskirchen**   **17A2**
Wasserburg, Kegelbahnstrasse. **GPS:** n49,63448 e7,66373. ⬆.

7 🚐free 🚰€1/4minutes 🚽Ch ⚡€1/12h. **Surface:** metalled.
🔲 01/01-31/12
Distance: 🚶150m ⊗on the spot 🍺bakery 100m.

DE

Reipoltskirchen 17A2

Stellplatz Ausbacherhof, K42, Ausbacherhof. **GPS:** n49,61210 e7,65630.⬆️.

4 🚐free. **Surface:** gravel. ⬜ 01/01-31/12

Remagen 9B6

Wohnmobilhafen Goldene Meile, Simrockweg 9–13. **GPS:** n50,57667 e7,24750.➡️.

30 🚐 € 12 🚰€1/90liter 🔌 Ch 💧 (18x)€1/6h. 🚾 **Surface:** grassy. ⬜ 01/04-31/10
Distance: 🛫10km 🛒on the spot 🍴on the spot.

Rengsdorf 9B6

Monte Mare, Monte-Mare-Weg 1. **GPS:** n50,50803 e7,48388.⬆️.

4 🚐free. **Location:** Rural. **Surface:** gravel. ⬜ 01/01-31/12
Distance: 🚆600m 🛒600m.

Rheinbreitbach 9A6

Wohnmobilstellplatz Siebengebirgsblick, Rolandsecker Weg 8.
GPS: n50,62193 e7,22812.⬆️.

14 🚐 € 8 🚰€1/90liter 🔌 Ch 💧 (12x)€1/2kWh. **Location:** Simple.
Surface: grassy/gravel. ⬜ 01/01-31/12
Distance: 🛒500m.
Remarks: To be paid at Rolandsecker Weg 8.

Rhodt unter Rietburg 17A3

Theresienstraße. **GPS:** n49,27464 e8,09917.⬆️.

20 🚐 € 4. 🚾 **Location:** Rural, simple. **Surface:** gravel.
⬜ 01/01-31/12
Distance: 🚆100m 🛫5km.

Rhodt unter Rietburg 17A3

Meyer Karl Herman, Edesheimerstrasse 17. **GPS:** n49,26883 e8,10868.⬆️.

6 🚐 € 9 🚰 💧 (6x)included. 🛜 **Location:** Rural, simple, quiet.
Surface: gravel. ⬜ 01/01-31/12
Distance: 🚆200m 🛒200m 🍴200m.

Rhodt unter Rietburg 17A3

Weingut Fader, Traminerweg 1. **GPS:** n49,26972 e8,11057.⬆️➡️.

12 🚐 € 10 🚰 🔌 Ch 💧 (12x)included. 🛜 **Location:** Rural, simple, quiet.
Surface: gravel. ⬜ 01/04-31/10
Distance: 🚆300m 🛒200m 🍴200m.

Rhodt unter Rietburg 17A3

Weingut Krieger, Edesheimerstrasse 7. **GPS:** n49,26961 e8,10803.⬆️.

2 🚐 € 5 🚰free 💧 on demand. 🛜 **Location:** Rural, simple, quiet.
Surface: grassy. ⬜ 01/01-31/12
Distance: 🚆100m 🛫6km 🛒200m 🍴200m.

Rhodt unter Rietburg 17A3

Weingut Nichterlein, Mühlgasse 15. **GPS:** n49,27349 e8,10802.⬆️.

3 🅿€6 🚰💧 on demand WC free. 🚐 **Location:** Quiet. **Surface:** metalled. ⭘ 01/01-31/12
Distance: 🚶300m 🚲5km.

Rhodt unter Rietburg — 17A3
Weingut Jürgen Heußler, Weyherer Strasse 34/35. **GPS:** n49,27052 e8,10386. ⬆.

20 🅿€6 + reduction swimming pool 🚰🗑Ch💧 (4x)€1/24h.
Surface: metalled. ⭘ 01/01-31/12
Distance: on the spot ⊗ on the spot 🛒500m.
Remarks: To pay at swimming pool.

Saarburg — 16C2
Reisemobilpark Saarburg, Am Saarufer. **GPS:** n49,60158 e6,55442. ⬆➡.

3 🅿€3. 🚐 **Location:** Simple. ⭘ 01/01-31/12
Distance: 🚶300m 🚲6km ⊗100m.

Rockenhausen — 17A2
Reisemobilhafen Rockenhausen, Obermühle. **GPS:** n49,62136 e7,82146. ⬆.

70 🅿€8, winter €5 🚰€1🗑Ch💧 (70x)€0,50/kWh WC 📶€4/day. 🚐
Surface: grassy/metalled. ⭘ 01/01-31/12 ⭘ Service: winter
Distance: 🚶850m 🍴on the spot 🛒on the spot 🛒200m.
Remarks: Bread-service.

Saarburg — 16C2
Reisemobilstellplatz Leukbachtal, Leukbachtal 1. **GPS:** n49,59921 e6,54130.
20 🅿€15 🚰€1🗑Ch💧WC🗑 ⭘ 01/03-31/10
Distance: 🚶1km 🛒150m.

Saarlouis — 16C3
In den Fliesen, Sankt Nazairer Allee. **GPS:** n49,32146 e6,74267. ⬆.

5 🅿free 🚰€1/80liter🗑Ch💧 (6x)€1/6h. **Location:** Rural, simple.
Surface: gravel. ⭘ 01/01-31/12
Distance: 🚶800m 🛒on the spot.
Remarks: At swimming pool.

Roschbach — 17A3
Weingut Koch, Am Rosenkränzel 13. **GPS:** n49,24736 e8,11532. ➡.

30 🅿free 🚰€1/80liter🗑Ch. **Location:** Urban, simple, quiet.
Surface: metalled. ⭘ 01/01-31/12
Distance: 🚶500m 🚲1,5km 🍴on the spot 🛒on the spot.
Remarks: At sports centre, bread-service.

Saarlouis — 16C3
Hotellerie Waldesruh, Siersburger Strasse 8, Wallerfangen.
GPS: n49,34440 e6,67614. ⬆.

3 🅿€5 🚰included 💧€2/night. 🚐 **Location:** Rural, quiet. **Surface:** grassy.
⭘ 01/01-31/12
Distance: 🚲5km.

Ruppertsberg — 17A3
Winzerhaus "Im Linsenbusch", Hauptstrasse 70. **GPS:** n49,39944 e8,20044.
2 🅿€8 🚰included WC🗑€7/day. ⭘ 01/01-31/12
Distance: 🚲3km.

Saarbrücken — 16C3
Reisemobilhafen Calypso, Deutschmühlental 7. **GPS:** n49,23027 e6,96222. ⬆.

2 🅿€10, guests free. 🚐 **Location:** Rural, simple, noisy. **Surface:** metalled.
⭘ 01/01-31/12

Distance: 10km on the spot.

S Sankt Aldegund 16D1

Am Moselstausee. **GPS**: n50,07899 e7,13119.

40 € 6 Ch included (28x)€ 1,50/day. **Location:** Rural, simple.
Surface: grassy/metalled. 01/04-01/12
Distance: 250m on the spot 250m.
Remarks: Bread-service.

Sankt Goarshausen 17A1

Loreley Besucherzentrum, Auf der Loreley 7. **GPS**: n50,14191 e7,73303.

25 € 8. **Location:** Simple, isolated.
Distance: 600m 600m.

S Sankt Ingbert 16D3

Reisemobilplatz 'Das Blau', Spieser Landstraße. **GPS**: n49,28652 e7,13194.

8 free € 1/80liter Ch. **Surface:** grassy. 01/01-31/12
Distance: 1,5km 3,5km 100m 1,7km.
Remarks: Next to parking swimming pool.

S Sankt Julian 16D2

An der Ölmühle, An der Lenschbach. **GPS**: n49,60758 e7,51480.

10 € 5 € 1 Ch € 1/kWh. **Location:** Rural, simple, quiet.
Surface: grassy. 01/04-31/10
Distance: on the spot 300m.

Sankt Martin 17A3

Edenkoperstrasse. **GPS**: n49,29702 e8,10838.

14 € 6/day. **Surface:** asphalted. 01/01-31/12
Distance: 5km.
Remarks: Max. 1 night.

S Sankt Martin 17A3

Weingut Schreieck, Friedhofstrasse 8. **GPS**: n49,30113 e8,10560.
17 € 12 Ch WC included. 01/01-31/12
Distance: 5km.

S Sankt Martin 17A3

Weinkellerei Ziegler, Mühlstrasse 26. **GPS**: n49,29921 e8,10028.
3 € 10 . 01/01-31/12
Distance: 5km.

Sankt Martin 17A3

Consulat des Weines, Maikammerer strasse 44. **GPS**: n49,29934 e8,10826.
10 € 1 pp. 01/01-31/12
Distance: 4,5km.

Sankt Martin 17A3

Winzer Holger Schneider, Riedweg. **GPS**: n49,29814 e8,10824.

free for clients. **Surface:** gravel.
Distance: on the spot.

S Sankt Martin 17A3

Riedweg. **GPS**: n49,29814 e8,10824.
€ 1 Ch.

S Sankt Wendel 16D2

Am Wendelinuspark, Tholeyer Straße. **GPS**: n49,46907 e7,14267.

12 € 5 Ch free. **Surface:** metalled. 01/01-31/12
Distance: 1km on the spot 100m 20m.
Remarks: Tickets Wendelinusbad.

S Schiersfeld 17A2

Sulzbachtal, Bismarkstraße. **GPS**: n49,69274 e7,76895.

DE

8-12 ⌇free ⌁€1 ⚡(8x)€1/4kWh. **Location:** Rural, simple, quiet. **Surface:** gravel. ☐ 01/01-31/12 **Distance:** ⚓500m ⚑bakery 500m ⚒Moscheltalradweg ⚐on the spot.

40 ⌇< 6m € 11 incl. 2 pers, + € 1/m, dog € 2,10 ⌁⚐Ch ⚡€0,60/kWh,+ €1 ⚐€0,50 ☒€3 ⚐against payment. ⚒ **Surface:** grassy. ☐ 01/04-31/10 **Distance:** ⚓on the spot ⚑on the spot ⚒on the spot ⚑on the spot ⚒50m ⚒on the spot ⚐on the spot. **Remarks:** Boat rental.

| ⚑S | Schleich | 16C2 |

Zum Moselufer, Am Moselufer. **GPS:** n49,81335 e6,84228.⬆➡

| ⚑S | Selzen | 17A1 |

Weingut Kapellenhof, Kapellenstrasse 18. **GPS:** n49,86484 e8,25528.⬆

6 ⌇€5 ⌁⚐Ch ⚡€2 WC.⚒ **Surface:** grassy. ☐ 01/01-31/12 **Distance:** ⚓on the spot ⚑on the spot ⚒on the spot ⚒200m.

| ⚑S | Schwabenheim/Selz | 17A1 |

Reisemobilstellplatz Schwabenheim, Ingelheimer Straße. **GPS:** n49,93284 e8,09430.⬆➡

4 ⌇€5 ⌁⚡(4x)included. ⚒ **Location:** Rural, simple, quiet. **Surface:** grasstiles. ☐ 01/01-31/12 **Distance:** ⚓on the spot ⚒100m ⚒2km.

| ⚑S | Siefersheim | 17A2 |

Weingut Sommer, Mühlweg 19. **GPS:** n49,79850 e7,95245.⬆

10 ⌇free ⚡(12x)free. **Location:** Rural, comfortable, quiet. **Surface:** grasstiles. ☐ 01/01-31/12 **Distance:** ⚓200m ⚓8,5km ⚒200m ⚒on the spot ⚐on the spot. **Remarks:** Max. 96h free, then € 3/24h.

| ⚑S | Schwabenheim/Selz | 17A1 |

Weingut Schuck Sonnenhof, Ausserhalb 6. **GPS:** n49,93130 e8,09117.⬆

6 ⌇€5 ⌁⚡(6x)included. ⚒ **Location:** Rural, simple. **Surface:** grassy. ☐ 01/04-31/10 **Distance:** ⚓8km ⚒2km ⚒2km.

| ⚑S | Simmern/Hunsrück | 16D1 |

Wohnmobilstellplatz Simmern, Gemündener Straß. **GPS:** n49,98011 e7,52283. ⬆➡ 3 ⌇free ⌁⚐Ch. **Surface:** metalled. ⚐ water disconnected in winter **Distance:** ⚓on the spot ⚒250m ⚒200m.

| ⚑S | Sinzig | 9A6 |

Wohnmobilhafen am Sportplatz, Bäderstrasse. **GPS:** n50,55128 e7,21731.⬆

3 ⌇€5 ⌁⚡(3x)included WC. **Location:** Rural, comfortable, quiet. **Surface:** grassy/gravel. ☐ 01/01-31/12 **Distance:** ⚓500m ⚓9km.

| ⚓S | Schweich/Mosel bei Trier | 16C2 |

Wohnmobilpark zum Fahrturm, Am Yachthafen. **GPS:** n49,81455 e6,75038.➡

10 ⌇€5/24h ⌁€1 ⚐Ch ⚡(12x)€0,50/kWh WC ⚐€1/1time,at Freibad. ⚐ **Location:** Rural, simple. **Surface:** gravel. ☐ 01/01-31/12 **Distance:** ⚓7km ⚒800m ⚒on the spot ⚐on the spot.

DE

Sinzig 9A6

Sinziger Schloß, Jahnstrasse. **GPS**: n50,54684 e7,24844.

20 free. **Location:** Urban, simple. **Surface:** metalled.
01/01-31/12
Distance: 100m on the spot.

Sinzig 9A6

Wohnmobilhafen am Thermalfreibad, Bäderstrasse. **GPS**: n50,54912 e7,21749.

50 € 5/24h, electricity incl €1 Ch (18x)€0,50/kWh €1/pp.
Location: Rural, simple. **Surface:** metalled. 01/01-31/12
Distance: 50m on the spot on the spot.

Speyer 17B3

Techniek Museum Speyer, Geibstrasse. **GPS**: n49,31222 e8,45009.

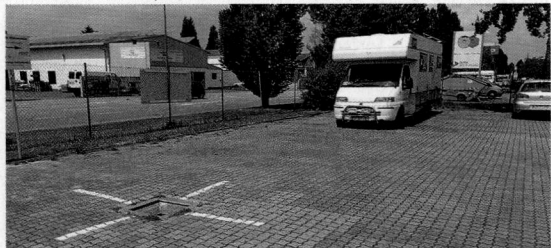

90 € 22 Ch WC included. **Location:** Comfortable, central, noisy. **Surface:** grassy. 01/01-31/12
Distance: 8,5km 150m 200m on the spot on the spot on the spot.
Remarks: Bread-service, discount museum and theater.

Speyer 17B3

An den Stadtwerken, Industriestraße 21. **GPS**: n49,30329 e8,44817.

10 € 5 €1 €1 Ch €1 included. **Location:** Simple.
Surface: asphalted.
Distance: 1,5km 6km 1,5km 1,6km 500m on the spot.
Remarks: Check in at Stadwerke.
Tourist information Speyer:

Technik Museum Speyer/Imax Filmtheater, Geibstrasse. Mo-Fr 9-18h, Sa-Su 9-17h.

Spirkelbach 17A3

Grillplatz Spirkelbach. **GPS**: n49,19454 e7,88208.

4 € 7 Ch WC included.
Location: Rural, simple, quiet. **Surface:** gravel.
01/01-31/12
Distance: 500m 500m on the spot on the spot.
Remarks: Check in on arrival, tel: 0171 3355971, nature reserve Pfalzer Wald.

Sprendlingen 17A1

Wiesbach, Bachgasse/Bleichstrasse. **GPS**: n49,85424 e7,98538.

24 € 4 €2/10minutes Ch (24x)€2/day. **Location:** Rural, comfortable, quiet. **Surface:** asphalted. 01/01-31/12
Distance: 700m 3,4km 500m 900m on the spot.
Remarks: Parking at swimming pool, bread-service, swimming pool € 2/day.

Sprendlingen 17A1

Weingut Annenhof, Außerhalb 13. **GPS**: n49,85778 e7,99278.

4 free WC free. **Location:** Rural, simple. **Surface:** concrete.
01/01-31/12
Distance: 3km 500m 800m.

Sprendlingen 17A1

Weingut Hembd, Karlstrasse 24a. **GPS**: n49,86422 e7,98811.

10 € 10 included. **Location:** Rural, simple. **Surface:** grassy.
01/01-31/12
Distance: 4km 500m 500m.

DE

🚐S Sprendlingen 17A1
Eura Mobil Stellplatz, Graf-von-Sponheimstrasse. **GPS**: n49,86297 e7,97612.⬆️

38 🚐free 🚰€1 🗑️Ch 💧 (38x)free. **Location:** Rural, simple, quiet.
Surface: asphalted/metalled. 🅾️ 01/01-31/12
Distance: 🚶600m 🚲4,4km 🛒300m.
Remarks: Workdays from 9h guided tours (free).

🚐S Stadecken-Elsheim 17A1
Weingut Mengel-Eppelmann, Mühlstrasse 16. **GPS**: n49,91575 e8,12107.⬆️

5 🚐€5, free for clients 🚰 💧 included. **Location:** Comfortable, quiet.
Surface: asphalted. 🅾️ 01/01-31/12
Distance: 🚶on the spot 🚲6km ⊗on the spot.

🚐S Stromberg 17A1
Reisemobilplatz Michels Land, Königsberger Straße. **GPS**: n49,94709 e7,78818.
⬆️➡️

6 🚐€5 🚰🗑️Ch included 💧 (6x)€0,50/kWh. 🐕 **Location:** Comfortable, quiet. **Surface:** grassy. 🅾️ 01/01-31/12
Distance: 🚶500m 🚲500m 🛒50m Lidl.

🚐S Thalfang 16C2
Festplatz Thalfang, Talstrasse 2. **GPS**: n49,75103 e6,99902.⬆️

40 🚐€5 🚰🗑️Ch 💧 (6x)free. **Surface:** gravel. 🅾️ 01/01-31/12 ⬛ 21/09-30/09
Distance: 🚶200m 🏊on the spot 🚴on the spot ⊗on the spot 🛒200m.
Remarks: Max. 4 nights, check in at swimming pool.

Thalfang 16C2
Ferienpark Himmelberg, Birkenweg 73. **GPS**: n49,74835 e6,98721.

---

2 🚐free. 🅾️ 01/01-31/12

🚐 Thallichtenberg 16D2
Burg Lichtenberg, K23. **GPS**: n49,55716 e7,35975.⬆️➡️

4 🚐free. **Surface:** asphalted. 🅾️ 01/01-31/12
Distance: 🚲7km ⊗300m 🛒1km.
Remarks: Max. 3 days.

🚐 Tholey 16D2
Parkplatz Am Schaumburg, Am Schaumberg. **GPS**: n49,48965 e7,03804.⬆️➡️

±20 🚐free. **Surface:** metalled. 🅾️ 01/01-31/12
Distance: ⊗100m.

🚐S Traben-Trarbach 16D1

Wohnmobilstellplatz am Mosel - Traben Trarbach

info@moselcampingplatz.de - www.moselstellplatz.de

Located directly at the river
Ideal base for walking and cycling
Restaurant with regional specialties

Wohnmobilstellplatz am Mosel, Rissbacherstraße 155.
GPS: n49,96583 e7,10583.⬆️.
45 🚐€10 🚰💧Ch 💧 (45x),6Amp WC 🚿 included. 🚐
Location: Comfortable. **Surface:** grassy/gravel. 🅾️ 01/04-31/12
Distance: 🚶500m 🏊on the spot 🚴on the spot ⊗500m 🛒200m 🚌100m
🚲on the spot 🚶on the spot.
Remarks: Along ther Moselle river.

©S Trechtinghausen 17A1
Camping Marienort, Mainzer Straße. **GPS**: n50,00426 e7,85516.⬆️➡️

DE

20 ⌷7 🔌 🗑 C included 🚿€2/24h WC 🚽€1. **Location:** Comfortable, quiet. **Surface:** grassy. ⬛ 01/01-31/12
Distance: 🛒on the spot 🍴on the spot ⊗on the spot.
Remarks: Bread-service, sanitary at campsite, narrow entrance.

| 🏕️S | Trier | 16C2 |

Reisemobilpark Treviris, In den Moselauen. **GPS:** n49,74092 e6,62502.⬆️➡️.

110 ⌷€ 0,20/h 10-18h, € 8/18-10h 🔌€1/100liter 🗑 Ch 🚿(62x)€0,70/kWh WC 🚽€1. 🚻 **Surface:** grasstiles. ⬛ 01/01-31/12
Distance: 🚉3km 🚲6km ⊗400m McDonald's 🚌on the spot.
Remarks: Along ther Moselle river, bread-service.

| 🍷S | Trier | 16C2 |

Weingut Vonnell, Im Tiergarten 12. **GPS:** n49,73840 e6,65914.⬆️➡️.

15 ⌷€ 10 🔌🚿 included. **Surface:** grassy/gravel.
⬛ 01/01-31/12
Distance: 🚉3km 🚲7km.

Tourist information Trier:
ℹ️ Tourist Information, An der Porta Nigra, www.trier.de. Old Roman city with the best kept and also largest Roman gate in Europe: Porta Nigra.
ℹ️ Triercard. Free city bus and discount at museums, boat trips, swimming pool etc. 🎫 € 9,90, family card € 21, 3 days.

| 🏕️S | Trittenheim | 16C2 |

Moselpromenade Reisemobilplatz Trittenheim, Moselstrasse.
GPS: n49,82436 e6,90295.⬆️➡️.

50 ⌷€ 6,50 🔌€0,50/100liter 🗑 Ch 🚿(30x)€3/24h.
Surface: grassy/metalled. ⬛ 01/01-31/12

Distance: 🚉500m 🍴on the spot 🚌on the spot ⊗300m 🚰400m.
Remarks: Bread-service.

| 🏕️S | Unkel | 9A6 |

P3, Parkplatz Hallenbad, Kamenerstrasse. **GPS:** n50,59776 e7,21962.⬆️.

6 ⌷free 🔌€1/80liter 🗑 Ch WC. **Location:** Urban. **Surface:** asphalted.
⬛ 01/01-31/12
Distance: 🚉100m 🍴100m 🚰150m 🚌on the spot.

| 🏕️S | Urmitz/Rhein | 9B6 |

Wohnmobilhafen am Rhein, Kaltenengerser Straße 3.
GPS: n50,41849 e7,52448.⬆️.

24 ⌷€ 5 🔌€1/4minutes 🗑 Ch 🚿€1/8h. 🚻 **Surface:** metalled.
⬛ 01/01-31/12
Distance: 🚉on the spot 🚲5km 🍴on the spot 🛒on the spot ⊗350m 🚌300m.
Remarks: Along the Rhine river, bread-service.

| 🏕️S | Ürzig | 16C1 |

Panorama-Mobilstellplatz Ürzig, Moselufer B53. **GPS:** n49,97837 e7,00700.⬆️.

25 ⌷€ 9,50 🔌🗑 Ch included 🚿€1,50/day. 🚲 **Location:** Rural, comfortable, quiet. **Surface:** grassy. ⬛ 01/04-31/10
Distance: 🚲9km 🍴on the spot ⊗on the spot 🚰bakery 150m 🚉on the spot 🏃on the spot.
Remarks: Along ther Moselle river.

| 🏕️S | Vallendar | 9B6 |

Rheinufer. GPS: n50,39749 e7,61277.⬆️.

3 ⌷free 🔌🗑. **Location:** Urban, simple. **Surface:** asphalted/metalled.

01/01-31/12
Distance: centre 500m 3km on the spot 200m Aldi 200m.
Remarks: Along railwayline.

Valwig 16D1
Moselweinstrasse. **GPS:** n50,14271 e7,21292.

40 €5. **Surface:** grassy. 01/01-31/12
Distance: 100m on the spot 100m.

Veldenz 16D1
Wohnmobilpark Veldenz, Hauptstrasse, K88. **GPS:** n49,89222 e7,01944.

40 €6 Ch (24x)included €2. **Surface:** grassy.
01/01-31/12
Distance: 300m 300m 300m 200m.

Völklingen 16C3
Weltkulturerbe Völklinger Hütte, Rathausstraße. **GPS:** n49,24730 e6,84492.

10 free €1/80liter Ch (6x)€0,25/h.
Location: Urban, simple, central, noisy. **Surface:** asphalted.
01/01-31/12
Distance: 500m 1,1km 400m 850m on the spot on the spot.
Remarks: Visitors centre Industrial Heritage.

Wachenheim 17A2
Weingut Rudolf Hein, Hauptstrasse 38. **GPS:** n49,63860 e8,16832.

8 €6 included (6x)€2/24h. **Location:** Rural, simple, quiet.
Surface: grassy. 01/01-31/12
Distance: 10km 1km 3km.

Wadern 16C2
An der Stadthalle. **GPS:** n49,54188 e6,89232.

10 free €1,50/day. **Surface:** metalled. 01/01-31/12
Distance: on the spot 3km on the spot 100m.
Remarks: Parking in centre.

Wadern 16C2
Noswendeler See, Seestrasse. **GPS:** n49,52021 e6,86387.

5 free. 01/01-31/12
Distance: on the spot on the spot on the spot on the spot 3km.

Wadern 16C2
Zum Wiesental, Nunkirchen. **GPS:** n49,48905 e6,83679.

5 free. 01/01-31/12
Distance: on the spot on the spot on the spot.

Wadern 16C2
Hotel Pension Steil, Schlossstrasse 2, Lockweiler. **GPS:** n49,52765 e6,90158.

4 guests free. **Surface:** metalled. 01/01-31/12
Distance: 1km on the spot 500m.

Wadern 16C2
Hotel Restaurant Reidelbacher Hof, Reidelbach 5, Reidelbach.
GPS: n49,57706 e6,86808.
5 €5, guests free. 01/01-31/12
Distance: 3km 9km on the spot 3km.

Tourist information Wadern:
Tourist Information, Marktplatz 13, www.wadern.de. Nature reserve Saar Hunsrück, many signposted cycle and hiking routes.

S | Waldalgesheim | 17A1

An der Keltenhalle, Niedergasse. **GPS:** n49,95371 e7,83614. ⬆ .

8 ⬆free ⛽€1/100liter Ch ✦ (8x)€1/6h. **Location:** Simple, quiet. **Surface:** metalled. ⬜ 01/01-31/12
Distance: 🚶400m 🚲4km 🛒200m 🛒500m.

10 ⬆free. **Location:** Rural, simple, quiet. **Surface:** metalled.
⬜ 01/01-31/12
Distance: 🚶250m 🏊on the spot 🛒on the spot ⊗250m.

S | Westhofen | 17A2

Parkplatz Nickelgarten, Am Nickelgarten. **GPS:** n49,70559 e8,24672. ⬆ .

S | Waldfischbach-Burgalben 🍴 | 17A3

In den Bruchwiesen, Carentaner Platz. **GPS:** n49,28155 e7,64772.

6 ⬆free ⛽€1/80liter Ch ✦€1/8h. **Surface:** asphalted.
⬜ 01/01-31/12
Distance: 🚶600m ⊗100m.

15 ⬆free ✦ (12x)€1/8h. **Surface:** metalled. ⬜ 01/01-31/12
Distance: 🚶100m 🚲4km ⊗100m.
Remarks: Max. 3 days.

S | Westhofen | 17A2

Weingut Dreihornmühle, An der Brennerei. **GPS:** n49,70375 e8,25288. ⬆ .

S | Waxweiler 🌿 | 16B1

Wohnmobilplatz Waxweiler, Bahnhofstrasse. **GPS:** n50,09401 e6,35669. ➡

30 ⬆€5 ⛽€1 Ch ✦€2. 🍴 **Location:** Rural, simple, quiet. **Surface:** metalled. ⬜ 01/01-31/12
Distance: 🚶on the spot ⊗1km 🛒500m.

3 ⬆€5, guests free ✦€1/day. **Surface:** grassy. ⬜ 01/01-31/12
Distance: 🚶600m ⊗600m 🛒150m.
Remarks: Max. 24h.

S | Westhofen | 17A2

Tankstelle Raiffeisen. **GPS:** n49,70039 e8,24699. ⬆ .
⛽Ch. ⬜ 01/01-31/12
Remarks: Coins at petrol station.

⛲ | Weyher 🌿 | 17A3

Weingut Möwes, Hübühl 10. **GPS:** n49,26982 e8,08663. ⬆ .

S | Weiskirchen | 16C2

Am Kurpark, Burgstrasse. **GPS:** n49,55868 e6,81810.

6 ⬆€1,40/pp ⛽€0,50 🛒€0,50 Ch ✦€0,50. **Surface:** metalled.
⬜ 01/01-31/12
Distance: 🚶on the spot ⊗500m 🛒300m.
Remarks: Parking at the health resort, max. 2-3 days, pay at tourist office.

2 ⬆€8 ⛽✦ included. **Location:** Rural, quiet. **Surface:** metalled.
⬜ 01/01-31/12
Distance: 🚶200m 🚲7km.

⛲ | Westerburg | 9C6

Am Segelhafen, Seestrasse, Pottum. **GPS:** n50,59526 e7,99860. ⬆ .

⛲ | Weyher 🌿 | 17A3

Weingut Valentin Ziegler Sohn, Hübühl 9. **GPS:** n49,26937 e8,08609. ⬆ .

DE

2 ⛺ €5 🔌 included 💧 on demand. 🏕 **Location:** Rural, quiet.
Surface: grassy. 📅 01/01-31/12
Distance: 🚶200m 🚲7km.

| 🚿 S | Willroth | 9B6 |

Steiger-Mühle, Steinstrasse. **GPS:** n50,57176 e7,52995. 🔼 .

15 ⛺ €6 💧 €2,50. **Location:** Rural. 📅 01/01-31/12
Distance: 🚲2km ⊗on the spot.
Remarks: To be paid at Biergarten.

| 🚿 S | Wintrich 🍷 | 16C1 |

Mosel Stellplatz Wintrich - Wintrich

info@moselcampingplatz.de - www.moselstellplatz.de

Located directly at the river
Located in a quit location
Restaurant with regional specialties

Mosel Stellplatz Wintrich, Moselstrasse. **GPS:** n49,88417 e6,94833. 🔼➡
90 ⛺ €9 🔌€1/100liter 🔋 Ch 💧(90x) WC €0,50 🚿€1 📶included. 🛒
Surface: grassy/gravel. 📅 01/04-31/10
Distance: 🚶on the spot ⊘on the spot 🛒on the spot ⊗100m ⛽200m
🚌200m 🚲on the spot 🚶on the spot.
Remarks: Along the Moselle river.

| 🚿 S | Wintrich 🍷 | 16C1 |

Weingut Clemens, Kurfürstenstrasse 11. **GPS:** n49,89000 e6,95416. 🔼➡

20 ⛺ €5 🔌€2 🔋 Ch 💧€2 WC. 🏕 **Surface:** gravel/metalled.

📅 01/01-31/12
Distance: 🚶on the spot ⊗on the spot ⛽1km.

| 🍴 S | Wissen 🍴 🍷 | 9B5 |

Hahnhof, Nistertalstraße. **GPS:** n50,76106 e7,72083. 🔼 .

25 ⛺ €5 🔌 🔋 Ch 💧€1/kWh WC 🚿€1,50. **Location:** Rural, isolated, quiet.
Surface: gravel. 📅 01/01-31/12
Distance: 🚶2,5km ⊗on the spot 🚲on the spot.

| 🚿 S | Wittlich 🍷 | 16C1 |

Zweibächen, Hasenmühlenweg. **GPS:** n49,99470 e6,87595. 🔼➡

30 ⛺ €5/24h 🔌€1/80liter 🔋 Ch. **Location:** Rural, simple. **Surface:** grassy.
📅 01/01-31/12
Distance: 🚶1km 🚲4km ⊗1km ⛽1km.
Remarks: Max. 3 days, to be paid at swimming pool, service 50m.

| 🚿 S | Worms | 17B2 |

Wohnmobilhafen, Kastanienallee. **GPS:** n49,63458 e8,37513. 🔼➡

30 ⛺ €4/24h 🔌€1 🔋 Ch 💧(12x)€1/6h. 🛒
Surface: gravel.
📅 01/01-31/12
Distance: 🚶15 min walking 🚲7km ⚓Rhine promenade ⊗300m ⛽500m
🚌on the spot.
Remarks: Along river, service at Gaststätte Hagenbräu 300m from the parking.

| 🚿 S | Wörrstadt | 17A1 |

Spargelhof Weinmann, Rommersheimer Strasse 105. **GPS:** n49,83446 e8,10673.
🔼 .

3 ⛺ €6 🔌 💧(6x)included. 🏕 **Location:** Rural, simple, central, quiet.

Surface: gravel. 🅾 01/01-31/12
Distance: 🚶4km ⊗300m 🚰300m.

| 🅢 | Zell/Mosel | 16D1 |

Wohnmobilstellplatz Römerquelle, Am Freizeitzentrum, Kaimt.
GPS: n50,01632 e7,17662.⬆️➡️.

70 🚐€6 🚰€1/100liter 🅒Ch 🔌€1/2kWh. 🅛 **Location:** Rural,
comfortable. **Surface:** grassy/metalled. 🅾 01/01-31/12
Distance: 🚶1km ⊘on the spot 🚲on the spot ⊗500m 🚰1km.
Remarks: Along ther Moselle river, bread-service.

| 🅢 | Zell/Mosel | 16D1 |

Am Fussgängerbrücke. GPS: n50,02991 e7,17754.⬆️.

23 🚐€6 🚰€0,50/90liter 🅒Ch 🔌€2,at camp site. 🅛 **Location:** Simple, quiet.
Surface: asphalted. 🅾 Easter-31/10
Distance: 🚶300m ⊘on the spot 🚲on the spot ⊗200m 🚰300m.

| 🅢 | Zweibrücken | 16D3 |

Eitel's Wohnmobil-Stellplatz, Californiastraße. **GPS:** n49,26477 e7,36112.➡️.

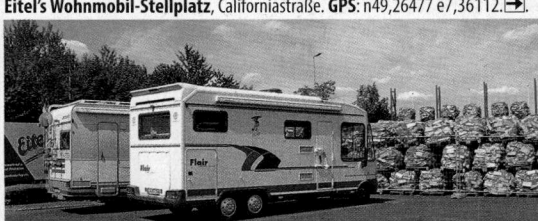

2 🚐€7 🚰€0,50/3minutes 🅒Ch 🔌included. 🅛 **Location:** Rural, simple,
noisy. **Surface:** asphalted. 🅾 01/01-31/12
Distance: 🚶2 km 🚲3 km 🚌100m.
Remarks: Check in on arrival.

Hesse

| 🅢 | Aarbergen | 9C6 |

Im Brührl, Hauptstraße 58, Michelbach. **GPS:** n50,23099 e8,05988.⬆️➡️.
10 🚐€5 🚰🅒Ch 🔌included. **Surface:** metalled. 🅾 01/01-31/12

| 🅢 | Alsfeld | 10A5 |

Erlenstadion, Fulder Weg. **GPS:** n50,74844 e9,27947.⬆️➡️.

20 🚐€7 🚰€0,50 🔌€0,50 Ch 🔌€0,50/kWh. **Surface:** metalled.
🅾 01/01-31/12
Distance: 🚶200m 🚲1,8km.

| 🅢 | Alsfeld | 10A5 |

Hotel zum Schäferhof, A20 dir Eudorf. **GPS:** n50,76742 e9,29048.

20 🚐free 🔌€6. **Surface:** metalled. 🅾 01/01-31/12
Distance: 🚶2km ⊗on the spot 🚰500m.

| 🅢 | Alsfeld | 10A5 |

Fina-tankstelle, Pfefferhöhe. **GPS:** n50,73366 e9,24128.⬆️.

5 🚐free 🚰€0,50 🔌€0,50 WC 🔌€2,50. **Location:** Highway.
Surface: metalled. 🅾 01/01-31/12
Distance: 🚶300m ⊗on the spot.

| 🚐 | Amöneburg | 9D5 |

In den Lückeäckern. **GPS:** n50,79554 e8,93135.⬆️.
4 🚐free. 🅾 01/01-31/12
Distance: 🚶Old city centre 1km ⊗500m 🚰500m.
Remarks: Parking tennishall.

| 🅢 | Bad Arolsen | 9D3 |

DE

Reisemobilhafen Twistesee, Bericher Seeweg 1, Wetterburg. **GPS**: n51,38396 e9,06546.⬆➡.
130 🛏 € 10, tourist tax incl 🚰€1/100liter 🔌 Ch ⚡(120x)€0,50/kWh,16Amp WC included ⬜€1/time. 🏠 **Location**: Rural, comfortable, isolated.
Surface: grassy/gravel. 📅 01/01-31/12
Distance: 🚶500m ⚓50m ⊗50m ⊗800m 🚌800m 🛒 on the spot ⚹ on the spot.
Remarks: Directly at lake, bread-service, dogs beach.

| 🚻S | **Bad Camberg** ♨ | 9C6 |
Jahnstraße. **GPS**: n50,29650 e8,26660.
8 🛏free 🚰€1 🔌€1 Ch ⚡€1/kWh. **Surface**: grassy. 📅 01/01-31/12
💧 water: 01/12-31/03
Distance: 🚶350m ⚓2,5km ⊗250m.

| 🚻S | **Bad Emstal** ♨ | 10A4 |
Erzeberg, Birkenstraße, Balhorn. **GPS**: n51,26927 e9,25147.⬆.
20 🛏€ 9, 4 pers incl., 1 pers + € 4 🚰 Ch ⚡€0,50 📶 included.
Surface: metalled. 📅 01/01-31/12
Distance: ⊗100m.
Remarks: Check in at campsite (100m), use pool incl.

| 🚻S | **Bad Emstal** ♨ | 10A4 |
Am Mineral-Thermalbad, Karlsbader Straße 4, Sand. **GPS**: n51,24858 e9,24952.⬆➡.

8 🛏€ 7, tourist tax incl 🚰€1/100liter 🔌 Ch ⚡(12x)€1/kWh.🛒
Location: Comfortable. **Surface**: gravel/metalled. 📅 01/01-31/12
Distance: 🚶1km ⊗on the spot 🛒on the spot ⚹on the spot.

| 🚻S | **Bad Endbach** ♨ | 9C5 |
Kultur-, Sport- und Freizeitzentrum, Am Bewegungsbad 4.
GPS: n50,75669 e8,47875.⬆.

18 🛏€ 5 + tourist tax 🚰🔌 ⚡WC ⬜included,sanitary at spa resort.
Surface: grasstiles. 📅 01/01-31/12
Distance: 🚶1km ⊗on the spot 🍽100m.
Remarks: Check in at Lahn-Dill-Bergland-Therme 200m.

| 🚻 | **Bad Hersfeld** | 10A5 |
Geistalbad, Am Schwimmbad. **GPS**: n50,87485 e9,70025.⬆➡.

20 🛏€ 5 🚰€1/80liter 🔌 Ch ⚡(6x)€0,50/kWh.
Surface: asphalted/metalled. 📅 01/01-31/12 💧 Lullusfest (Oct)

Distance: 🚶50m ⚓3,9km.

| 🚻 | **Bad Hersfeld** | 10A5 |
Acqua-fit, Kolpingstraße 6. **GPS**: n50,86771 e9,72951.
5 🛏free. **Surface**: asphalted. 📅 01/01-31/12
Distance: ⚓2km.
Remarks: At swimming pool.

| 🚻 | **Bad Hersfeld** | 10A5 |
Auf der Unteraue. **GPS**: n50,86231 e9,70340.⬆.

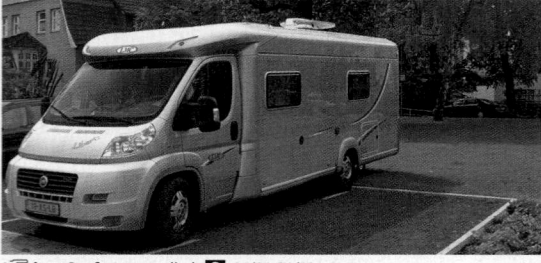

3 🛏free. **Surface**: metalled. 📅 01/01-31/12
Remarks: At tennis-court.

| 🍽🚻S | **Bad Hersfeld** | 10A5 |
Waldhotel Glimmesmühle, Hombergerstraße. **GPS**: n50,88420 e9,66984.⬆.

10 🛏free with a meal 🚰included ⚡against payment. **Surface**: metalled.
📅 01/01-31/12
Distance: ⊗on the spot.

Tourist information Bad Hersfeld:
🎭 Lullusfest. Traditional folk festival for the honour of the founder of the city.
💧 week 16/10.

| 🚻S | **Bad Karlshafen** 🌿⚓🍽 | 10A3 |
Am Rechten Weserufer, Am rechten Weserufer 2. **GPS**: n51,64508 e9,44953.⬆.

24 🛏€ 11 🚰🔌 Ch ⚡(12x)€1/2kWh.🛒 **Location**: Central.
Surface: grasstiles/grassy. 📅 01/01-31/12
Distance: 🚶on the spot 🚌on the spot ⊗on the spot 🍽on the spot 🛒 on the spot ⚹ on the spot.
Remarks: Max. 4 days.

| 🚻S | **Bad König** ♨ | 17C2 |
P3, Am Bahndamm. **GPS**: n49,74312 e9,00320.⬆.
5 🛏€ 5 ⚡ included. **Surface**: metalled.
Distance: 🚶400m ⊗400m 🥖bakery 300m.

| 🚻 | **Bad Nauheim** | 9D6 |
Usa-Wellenbad, Friedberger Strasse 16-20. **GPS**: n50,35352 e8,74305.⬆.

DE

40 ⌘ € 5. ☐ 01/01-31/12
Distance: 🚶1km ⊗on the spot 🚰300m 🚌on the spot.
Remarks: Check in at Wellenbad, 8-20h.

| � S | **Bad Orb** ♒ | 10A6 |

Am Busbahnhof, Austraße. **GPS:** n50,23014 e9,34659.⬆.
4 ⌘ € 7, tourist tax incl 🚰 Ch ⚡ (4x)included. 🅿 **Surface:** metalled.
☐ 01/01-31/12
Distance: ⊗450m 🚰300m.

| 🗆🗆 S | **Bad Orb** ♒ | 10A6 |

Am Kurpark, Spessartstraße. **GPS:** n50,21700 e9,35477.⬆.
9 ⌘ € 7 + tourist tax € 2,50/pp 🚰€1/90liter ⚡€1/8h. **Surface:** asphalted.
☐ 01/01-31/12
Distance: 🚶1,1km 🚲6km ⊗200m 🚶on the spot.

| 🗆 S | **Bad Salzschlirf** ♒ | 10A5 |

Riedstraße. **GPS:** n50,62090 e9,50304.⬆.

3 ⌘free 🚰€1 🗆 Ch. **Surface:** asphalted. ☐ 01/01-31/12
Distance: 🚶100m.

| 🗆🗆 S | **Bad Schwalbach** ♒ | 17A1 |

Am Kurpark, Reitallee 21. **GPS:** n50,13988 e8,06362.⬆.
4 ⌘free 🚰€0,50/50liter 🗆 Ch ⚡€0,50/kWh. **Surface:** metalled.
☐ 01/01-31/12
Distance: 🚶500m ⊗400m.

| 🗆🗆 S | **Bad Soden-Salmünster** | 10A6 |

Spessart Therme, Parkstraße 12, Bad Soden. **GPS:** n50,28544 e9,35917.⬆➡.

33 ⌘ € 6, tourist tax incl 🚰€1/70liter 🗆 Ch ⚡€1/2kWh. **Surface:** metalled.
☐ 01/01-31/12
Distance: 🚶on the spot ⊗on the spot 🚰on the spot.
Remarks: Pay and coins at Spessart Therme.

| 🗆 S | **Bad Soden-Allendorf** � | 10B4 |

Reisemobilhafen Franzrasen, Am Alten Festplatz, Allendorf.
GPS: n51,27149 e9,97209.⬆➡.

100 ⌘ € 8 🚰€1/5minutes 🗆€0,50 Ch ⚡ (40x)€0,50/kWh,16Amp
🗆€2,50/30minutes. 🗆 **Location:** Rural, simple, isolated, quiet.
Surface: grassy/metalled. ☐ 01/01-31/12
Distance: 🚶200m 🚲on the spot 🚶on the spot.
Remarks: Price including tourist taxes and public transport.

| 🗆 S | **Bad Wildungen** ♒ | 9D4 |

Wohnmobilstellplatz Bad Wildungen, Bahnhofstrasse.
GPS: n51,12008 e9,13631.⬆➡.

16 ⌘ € 5 🚰€1/45liter 🗆 Ch ⚡ (14x)€1/10h. 🅿 **Surface:** metalled.
☐ 01/01-31/12
Distance: 🚶1,5km.
Remarks: Max. 7 days.

| 🗆🗆 S | **Bad Wildungen** ♒ | 9D4 |

Wohnmobilstellplatz Frekot, Wiesenweg 23. **GPS:** n51,11134 e9,06677.
5 ⌘ € 6 🚰 Chincluded ⚡ according consumption. **Surface:** grassy.
☐ 01/01-31/12
Distance: 🚰300m.
Remarks: Bread-service.

| 🗆 S | **Bad Zwesten** ♒ | 9D4 |

Reisemobilstellplatz, Hardtstr./Kasseler Straße. **GPS:** n51,05706 e9,17748.⬆
➡.

2 ⌘free. **Surface:** metalled. ☐ 01/01-31/12
Distance: 🚶400m ⊗on the spot 🚰300m.

| 🗆 S | **Battenberg** ❄ | 9D4 |

Festhalle Battenberg, Festplatzweg. **GPS:** n51,00915 e8,63643.⬆.

3 ⌧free ⌧🏕 Ch. **Surface:** gravel/metalled. ⬛ 01/01-31/12
Remarks: At community centre, service: Esso-station, Battenfelderstr. 6.

Battenberg ☀ 9D4
Hallen- und Freibad, Senonchesstraße. **GPS:** n51,01233 e8,63532.

3 ⌧free ⌧🏕 Ch. **Surface:** asphalted. ⬛ 01/01-31/12
Distance: on the spot 100m on the spot on the spot.
Remarks: Parking swimming pool, service: Esso-station, Battenfelderstr. 6.

Tourist information Battenberg:
Besucherbergwerk Burgbergstollen. 150 years old mine shaft, can be reached from Marktplatz. ⬛ 01/05-30/09 1st Su of the month 14-17h.

Baunatal 10A4
Parkstadion. GPS: n51,25865 e9,39956.

16 ⌧€ 5/24h ⌧€1/100liter Ch. (16x)€0,50/kWh.
Location: Rural, simple, quiet. **Surface:** gravel. ⬛ 01/01-31/12
Distance: 500m 4km on the spot on the spot.
Remarks: Max. 3 days.

Bebra 10A4
Natur- und Freizeitpark Fuldaaue Breitenbachen Seen, Hersfelder Straße.
GPS: n50,95899 e9,78764.

30 ⌧€ 3, € 18/week ⌧€1/100liter Ch. (18x)€0,50/kWh.
Surface: grassy. ⬛ 01/01-31/12
Distance: 1km on the spot on the spot on the spot on the spot.

Bebra 10A4
Annastrasse 17. **GPS:** n50,97464 e9,79836.

4 ⌧free. **Surface:** asphalted. ⬛ 01/01-31/12

Distance: 400m.
Remarks: Parking swimming pool.

Bebra 10A4
Mehrzweckparkplatz, Bei der Laupfütze/Rathausstrasse.
GPS: n50,97000 e9,79000.

10 ⌧free. **Surface:** metalled. ⬛ 01/01-31/12
Distance: on the spot.

Beerfelden 17C2
Parkplatz NordicCenter, Seeweg. **GPS:** n49,56034 e8,97557.
4 ⌧free ⌧€0,50/50liter Ch. (4x)€0,50/kWh. **Surface:** asphalted.
⬛ 01/01-31/12
Distance: 1km.

Berkatal 10B4
Am Sportplatz. **GPS:** n51,23763 e9,91504.

3 ⌧free. **Location:** Rural, simple, isolated, quiet. **Surface:** asphalted.
⬛ 01/01-31/12
Distance: 800m 500m on the spot.

Biedenkopf ❄ 9D5
Freizeitzentrum Sackpfeife, An der Berggaststätte. **GPS:** n50,94735 e8,53317.

6 ⌧€ 2, overnight stay free . **Surface:** concrete. ⬛ 01/01-31/12
Distance: on the spot on the spot on the spot.
Remarks: Max. 3 days.

Biedenkopf ❄ 9D5
Parkplatz Stadtwerke, Mühlweg. **GPS:** n50,90925 e8,52687.

4 🍳€ 5/24h 🧹 €1/12h. **Surface:** asphalted. ◻ 01/01-31/12
Distance: 🚶200m.
Remarks: Max. 3 days.

| 🍴 | Biedenkopf 🌿♨⛲❄ | 9D5 |

Parkhotel Bürgerhaus, Auf dem Radeköppel 2. **GPS:** n50,91183 e8,53515.

5 🍳free with a meal. ◻ 01/01-31/12
Distance: 🚶on the spot ⊗on the spot 🍺500m 🎾12km 🏊12km.

| 🍳 | Bischoffen | 9C5 |

P Aartalsee, Am See. **GPS:** n50,70172 e8,46726.⬆
10 🍳€ 3/day, € 5,50/night. **Surface:** grassy/gravel. ◻ 01/01-31/12
Distance: 🚶1,5km.

| | Braunfels | 9C6 |

Wohnmobilstation Schloss Braunfels, Jahnplatz. **GPS:** n50,51478 e8,38609.
4 🍳€ 5, € 7,50 service incl 🚰Ch🧹.
Surface: metalled.
◻ 01/01-31/12
Distance: 🚶on the spot ⊗350m.
Remarks: Pay and key service: Gasthof am Turm, Marktplatz 11, caution € 15.

| 🍳 S | Breuberg | 17C1 |

Bahnhofstraße 4, Neustadt. **GPS:** n49,81576 e9,04063.
4 🍳free 🚰€1/60liter 🍽€1 Ch🧹€0,50/kWh. **Surface:** asphalted.
◻ 01/01-31/12
Distance: 🚶on the spot ⊗300m 🍺550m.

| 🍳 S | Breuna 🌳 | 9D3 |

Märchenlandtherme, Schulstraße. **GPS:** n51,41875 e9,18612.⬆
3 🍳free 🧹 €3. **Surface:** gravel. ◻ 01/01-31/12
Distance: 🚶500m ⊗50m.

| 🏊 | Büdingen 🌿 | 9D6 |

Hinter der Meisterei 20. **GPS:** n50,29094 e9,12587.
8 🍳free. **Surface:** metalled.
Distance: 🚶Old city centre 750m ⊗500m.
Remarks: At swimming pool.

| 🏊 | Büdingen 🌿 | 9D6 |

Mühltorbrücke. GPS: n50,29051 e9,11581.
2 🍳€ 5/5h. 🚐 **Surface:** metalled. ◻ 01/01-31/12
Distance: 🚶Old city centre 50m.

| 🍳 S | Burghaun | 10A5 |

Oberste Straße. **GPS:** n50,69179 e9,73203.
4 🍳free 🚰€1/100liter 🍽Ch🧹€0,50/kWh. **Surface:** asphalted.
◻ 01/01-31/12
Distance: 🚶500m ⊗on the spot 🍺on the spot.

| 🏊 | Calden | 10A3 |

Waldschwimmbad Calden, Zum Lindenrondell. **GPS:** n51,39420 e9,40064.⬆

3 🍳free. **Location:** Rural, simple, isolated. **Surface:** grassy.
◻ 01/01-31/12
Distance: 🚶1km ⊗1,5km 🍺2km.

| © | Diemelsee | 9D4 |

Terrassenparkplatz Hohes Rad, Hohes Rad 1. **GPS:** n51,33533 e8,75319.⬆

30 🍳€ 5 + € 1/pp tourist tax. **Surface:** metalled. ◻ 01/01-31/12
Distance: ⊿Diemelsee.

| 🍳 S | Diemelstadt | 9D3 |

Autohof, Kupferkuhle. **GPS:** n51,49034 e9,00885.⬆
10 🍳free 🚰€1 🍽€1 Ch🧹€1. **Location:** Highway. **Surface:** asphalted.
◻ 01/01-31/12
Distance: ⫽500m ⊗250m McDonalds.

| 🍳 S | Dillenburg | 9C5 |

Aquarena-Bad, Stadionstrasse. **GPS:** n50,73994 e8,27815.⬆➡

8 🍳free 🚰€1/90liter 🍽Ch🧹 (6x)€1/8h. **Surface:** asphalted.
◻ 01/01-31/12
Distance: 🚶300m.

| 🍳 S | Edermünde 〰 | 10A4 |

Aueweg, Grifte. **GPS:** n51,21252 e9,44905.⬆➡

12 🍳€ 5 🚰€1/100liter 🍽Ch🧹(6x)included15h. 🚐
Location: Rural, simple, comfortable, isolated, noisy. **Surface:** asphalted.
◻ 01/01-31/12
Distance: 🚶300m ⫽1,7km ⊗300m 🍺100m 🚲Premium-Radweg R1
🚶on the spot.

| | Edertal | 9D4 |

Wohnmobilstellplatz Hemfurth/Edersee, Kraftwerkstrasse.
GPS: n51,17022 e9,05096.⬆➡

30 🍳< 8m € 6, >8m € 10 🚰€1/100liter 🍽Ch€1. **Surface:** metalled.

DE

◻ 01/01-31/12
Distance: 🚶500m ⛱on the spot ⊗100m 🚰500m.

| 🏕 | Edertal | 9D4 |

Wohnmobilstellplatz Rehbach, Am Rechbachteich. **GPS**: n51,18394 e9,02618. ⬆.
20 🛏< 8m € 6, >8m € 10. **Surface:** gravel. ◻ 01/01-31/12
Distance: ⛱beach 200m.

| 🏕 S | Eltville am Rhein | 17A1 |

Parkplatz Weinhohle, Weinhohle. **GPS**: n50,02832 e8,12406.
+20 🛏€ 5 🚰€1/60liter 🗑€1 Ch. **Surface:** metalled.
Distance: 🚶200m ⊗400m 🚰50m.

| 🏕 S | Erbach | 17C2 |

Alexanderbad, In der Stadtwiese. **GPS**: n49,66349 e8,98863. ⬆.

11 🛏free 🚰€1/70liter 🗑Ch 💡(6x)€ 0,50/kWh. **Surface:** metalled.
◻ 01/01-31/12
Distance: 🚶800m ⊗500m 🚰100m 🚌100m.
Remarks: Max. 72h.

| 🏕 S | Eschwege ❄ | 10B4 |

Reisemobilhafen Werratalsee, Am werratalsee 2. **GPS**: n51,19196 e10,06728. ⬆➡.

20 🛏€ 9-15 🚰€1/80liter 🗑Ch 💡(18x)€ 2/5kWh WC 🚽use sanitary €3,30/pp. 🚿 **Location:** Rural, simple, central, noisy. **Surface:** metalled.
◻ 01/01-31/12
Distance: 🚶2km 🚲 on the spot 🚶 on the spot.
Remarks: Pay at bistro.

Tourist information Eschwege:
👁 Besuchbergwerk Grube Gustav, Höllethal, Meissner, Abterode. Slate mine.
◻ 15/03-31/10 Tue -Su 13-16h.

| 🏕 S | Flörsbachtal-Lohrhaupten | 17C1 |

Am Schwimbad, Mühlweg. **GPS**: n50,12453 e9,47830. ⬆➡.

20 🛏€ 8 🚰€1,50 🗑Ch 💡€1,50. **Surface:** grassy.
◻ 01/01-31/12 ◉ Service: winter
Distance: 🚶1km ⊗100m 🚰1km 🚲 on the spot 🚶 on the spot.
Remarks: Check in at Gartenstrasse 10a.

| 🏕 S | Frankenberg/Eder 〰 | 9D4 |

Ederberglandhalle, Teichweg 3. **GPS**: n51,05613 e8,80195. ⬆.

10 🛏free 🚰€1 🗑Ch 💡€ 0,50/kWh. **Surface:** grassy/gravel.
◻ 01/01-31/12 ◉ water disconnected in winter
Distance: 🚶500m ⊗200m 🚰1,5km.

| 🏕 S | Friedberg | 9D6 |

Engel Caravaning, Dieselstraße 4. **GPS**: n50,34646 e8,75685.
3 🛏voluntary contribution is appreciated 🚰🗑Ch 💡. **Surface:** metalled.
◻ 01/01-31/12
Distance: 🚶800m ⊗800m 🚰800m.
Remarks: Motorhome dealer, accessory shop, closed at night.

| 🏕 S | Frielendorf | 10A4 |

Wohnmobilpark Silbersee, Zum Silbersee. **GPS**: n50,98389 e9,34667. ⬆➡.

50 🛏€ 10 🚰🗑Ch 💡€ 2/day. **Location:** Rural, comfortable, quiet.
Surface: grassy/metalled. ◻ 01/04-01/11
Distance: 🚶250m ⛱250m.

| 🏕 S | Fritzlar | 10A4 |

Grauen Turm. **GPS**: n51,13221 e9,26974. ⬆➡.

10 🛏€ 7 🚰€1/60liter 🗑Ch 💡€1/2kWh. **Surface:** metalled.
◻ 01/01-31/12
Distance: 🚶100m ⊗100m.

Tourist information Fritzlar:
✦ Stadtführingen. Guided tour around the historic city center.
◻ 01/04-31/10 Tue-Sa 10.30h, Su 11h. 🎫 € 2,50.

| 🏕 S | Fulda | 10A6 |

Weimarerstrasse. **GPS**: n50,55685 e9,66663. ⬆.

30 🛏€ 0,10/1h, € 5/24h 🚰€1 🗑Ch 💡€1/2kWh WC 🚽. **Surface:** asphalted.
◻ 01/01-31/12
Distance: 🚶400m 🚰200m.

| 🏕 S | Gelnhausen | 10A6 |

Am Hallenbad. **GPS**: n50,20125 e9,17795. ⬆.

4 🛏free. ⏻ 01/01-31/12
Distance: 🚶100m 🚰on the spot.
Remarks: Parking at swimming pool.

🛏S **Gießen** 9D6
Badezentrum Ringallee, Gutfleischstraße. **GPS:** n50,58947 e8,68406.⬆.
6 🛏free 🔌(6x)€0,50/kWh. **Surface:** metalled. ⏻ 01/01-31/12
Distance: 🚶600m 🚲1,5km.

🍴S **Gilserberg** 9D5
Landgasthof Steller, Marburgerstrasse 3. **GPS:** n50,95047 e9,06220.⬆.

4 🛏€ 5, clients € 2,50 🚰€2,50 🗑 🔌€2,50 WC. **Surface:** asphalted.
⏻ 01/01-31/12 ⦿ Wed

🏕S **Gilserberg** 9D5
Rasthof Gilserberg Hochland, B3. **GPS:** n50,95242 e9,06923.
10 🛏free 🚰🗑 Ch 🔌€5. **Surface:** asphalted. ⏻ 01/01-31/12

🍴S **Gladenbach** 9D5
Restaurant Rosengarten, Hoherainstrasse 45. **GPS:** n50,77462 e8,57952.⬆➡.

3 🛏€ 5,50 🚰🗑🔌. **Surface:** grassy. ⏻ 01/01-31/12
Distance: ⊗on the spot.
Remarks: Pay and key at restaurant.

🛏S **Grebenau** 10A5
Borngasse 20. **GPS:** n50,74134 e9,47212.
4 🛏free 🚰🗑free. **Surface:** asphalted. ⏻ 01/01-31/12
Distance: 🚶on the spot ⊗200m.
Remarks: At fire-station.

🛏S **Grebenhain** 10A6
Reisemobilstellplatz am Kurpark, Hindenburgstraße, Hochwaldhausen.
GPS: n50,51910 e9,31756.⬆.
🛏€ 7,50 🚰🗑 Ch 🔌. **Surface:** gravel. ⏻ 01/01-31/12
Distance: 🚌bike-bus 200m 🚴Vulkanradweg 200m 🚶on the spot.

🛏S **Großalmerode** 10A4
Am Mühlgraben, Oststraße. **GPS:** n51,25841 e9,79349.⬆.
20 🛏free 🚰🗑 Ch 🔌. **Location:** Rural. **Surface:** grassy.
⏻ 01/01-31/12
Distance: 🚶700m ⊗150m.

🛏S **Grünberg** 9D5
Gallusplatz, Gerichtsstraße. **GPS:** n50,59477 e8,95439.⬆.

10 🛏free 🚰€0,50 🗑 Ch 🔌€0,50/kWh. **Surface:** gravel.
⏻ 01/01-31/12
Distance: 🚶Old city centre 300m ⊗100m 🛒Aldi 400m.

🛏S **Habichtswald** 10A4
Am Kressenborn, Bergweg, Dörnberg. **GPS:** n51,34361 e9,34389.⬆.

4 🛏free 🔌(2x)€2/24h WC. **Location:** Simple, quiet. **Surface:** gravel.
⏻ 01/01-31/12
Distance: 🚶200m 🚲5,5km ⊗200m.
Remarks: Caution € 20, key electricity/toilet at petrol station.

🛏S **Habichtswald** 10A4
Hasenbreite, Ehlen. **GPS:** n51,32291 e9,31961.⬆➡.

6 🛏free 🔌€2/24h WC. **Location:** Rural, simple, isolated, quiet.
Surface: grassy/metalled. ⏻ 01/01-31/12
Distance: 🚶400m 🚲2,5km ⊗400m 🛒400m.
Remarks: Caution € 20, key electricity/toilet at swimming pool.

🛏 **Helsa** 10A4
Sportplatzweg. **GPS:** n51,25444 e9,68638.⬆➡.

4 🛏free. **Surface:** metalled. ⏻ 01/01-31/12
Distance: 🚶800m ⊗800m 🛒700m 🚰400m.

🛏S **Herborn** 9C5
Herborner Schießplatz, Sinner Landstraße. **GPS:** n50,67950 e8,30672.⬆➡.
6 🛏free 🚰€1/90liter 🗑 Ch ⬕€1/90minutes 🔌(6x). **Surface:** metalled.
⏻ 01/01-31/12
Distance: 🚶200m 🚲1,8km.

🍴S **Herbstein** ♨ 10A6
VulkanTherme Herbstein, Zum Thermalbad 1. **GPS:** n50,56883 e9,34647.⬆.
11 🛏€ 6 + € 0,80/pp tourist tax 🚰🗑 Ch 🔌🗑€1,50,at spa resort.
Surface: metalled. ⏻ 01/01-31/12
Distance: 🚶1,1km ⊗800m 🛒300m.
Remarks: Coins available at pay-desk of theTherme.

🛏S **Hessisch Lichtenau** 🌿🏊🏕🎡 10A4
Sportcenter Fürstenhagen, Breslauer strasse 18. **GPS:** n51,20672 e9,69443.⬆
➡.

DE

10 🛏 € 5/24h 🚰 €1/80liter 🔌 Ch 🔧 €0,50/kWh ⟙ ♨

Location: Rural, simple, quiet. **Surface:** metalled. ⬛ 01/01-31/12
Distance: 🚶3km ⊗1km 🚲2km.
Remarks: Check in at sport centre.

🛏	Hessisch Lichtenau ❄🏕🏛👪	10A4

Alter Bahnhof/Western Rail Station, Bahnhofstrasse 5, Warlburg.
GPS: n51,20055 e9,77833. ⬆➡.

10 🛏 € 10. ♨ **Location:** Rural, isolated, quiet. **Surface:** asphalted.
⬛ 01/01-31/12
Distance: 🚶5km ⊗700m 🚌1km 🚶on the spot.

🛏	Hessisch Lichtenau ❄🏕🏛👪	10A4

Hopfelderstrasse. **GPS:** n51,19417 e9,72389. ⬆➡.

14 🛏 free. **Location:** Urban, simple, isolated, quiet. **Surface:** metalled.
⬛ 01/01-31/12
Distance: 🚶500m ⊗400m 🚌500m.

🛏	Hessisch Lichtenau ❄🏕🏛👪	10A4

Wohnmobilstellplatz am Hallenbad, Freiherr vom Stein strasse 12.
GPS: n51,20445 e9,72655. ⬆.

6 🛏 free. **Location:** Rural, simple, isolated, quiet. **Surface:** metalled.
⬛ 01/01-31/12
Distance: 🚶600m.
Remarks: Parking swimming pool.

🚻🛏	Hessisch Lichtenau ❄🏕🏛👪	10A4

Berggasthof Hohe Meissner, Hoher Meissner 1. **GPS:** n51,20376 e9,84852. ⬆.

10 🛏 free 🚰🔌 🔧 WC.
Location: Rural, simple, isolated, quiet. **Surface:** metalled.
⬛ 01/01-31/12
Distance: 🚶10km ⊗on the spot 🚌on the spot 🚲on the spot 🚶on the spot.

🛏	Hilders	10B5

Ulsterwelle, Heideweg 19. **GPS:** n50,56909 e9,99351.
5 🛏 free. **Surface:** gravel. ⬛ 01/01-31/12
Distance: 🚶750m ⊗50m.

🛏S	Hirschhorn	17C2

Beim Ätsche, Jahnstraße 22. **GPS:** n49,44214 e8,89804. ⬆.
18 🛏 € 7 🚰 €0,20/40liter 🔌 Ch 🔧 €2. **Surface:** grassy. ⬛ 01/01-31/12
Distance: 🚶500m ⊗on the spot 🚌train 400m.
Remarks: Along the Neckar river.

🛏	Hirzenhain	10A6

Festplatz Hirzenhain, Robert-Eichenauerweg. **GPS:** n50,39259 e9,13593. ⬆➡.

6 🛏 free. **Surface:** metalled. ⬛ 01/01-31/12
Distance: 🚶100m.

🛏S	Hirzenhain	10A6

Müller-Mobil, Junkerwiese 2. **GPS:** n50,40004 e9,14744.

5 🛏 free 🚰 €1/130liter 🔌 🔧. **Surface:** metalled. ⬛ 01/01-31/12
Distance: 🚶1,5km.

🛏S	Hofgeismar 🛁	10A3

Am Sälber Tor. GPS: n51,49521 e9,37547. ⬆.

100 🛏 free 🚰 €1/80liter 🔌 Ch 🔧 (18x)€1/2kWh. **Location:** Rural,
comfortable, central, quiet. **Surface:** gravel. ⬛ 01/01-31/12

DE

Distance: 🚰on the spot 🚽300m 🚿 on the spot 🧍on the spot.

♨S Homberg/Efze 10A4
Wassmuthshäuserstrasse, Dresdener Alee. **GPS:** n51,02757 e9,41470. ⬆️➡️.

7 🚐free 🚰€1/80liter 🚽 Ch 🚿free. **Surface:** metalled.
🅿 01/01-31/12
Distance: 🚰on the spot ⊗1km 🚽500m.

♨ Homberg/Ohm 9D5
An der Stadthalle, Stadthallenweg. **GPS:** n50,72626 e8,99439. ⬆️.
4 🚐free. 🅿 01/01-31/12
Distance: 🚰400m.

♨S Hünfeld 🏕🏘❄ 10A5
Hessisches Kegelspiel, Zu den Unaben. **GPS:** n50,67626 e9,77622. ⬆️➡️.

18 🚐€5 🚰€1/120liter 🚽 Ch 🚿 (16x)€1/kWh. 🚿🅿 01/01-31/12
Distance: 🚰500m ⊗250m 🚽500m.

♨S Hungen 9D6
Inheiden, Am Köstgraben. **GPS:** n50,45509 e8,90049. ⬆️.
6 🚐free 🚰€1/100liter 🚽 Ch 🚿€1/4h. **Surface:** grasstiles.
🅿 01/01-31/12 🚰 water: 01/11-31/03
Distance: 🏊Trais-Horloffer See ⊗3km 🚽3km 🚲bike-bus 1km.

♨S Idstein 〰 9C6
Wohnmobilhafen Idstein, Himmelsbornweg. **GPS:** n50,21775 e8,27923. ⬆️.
12 🚐€10 🚰€1/80liter 🚽 Ch 🚿€1/8h. **Surface:** gravel/metalled.
🅿 01/01-31/12 🚰 water disconnected in winter
Distance: 🚰500m Altstadt 🏊3,3km.

♨S Kassel 🍺🏊 10A4
Wohnmobilplatz Kassel, Am Sportzentrum/Giessenallee, Kassel-süd.
GPS: n51,29250 e9,48750. ⬆️➡️.

12 🚐€12,50/day 🚰€1/100liter 🚽€0,50 Ch€0,50 🚿 (8x)€0,50/kWh.
Location: Rural, simple, isolated, quiet.
🅿 01/01-31/12
Distance: 🏊1,4km ⊗500m 🚌50m 🚿 on the spot 🧍on the spot.
Remarks: With parking ticket free public transport, max. 3 nights.

Tourist information Kassel:
👁🏛 Treppenstrasse, shopping promenade, modern architecture.

♨S Kaufungen 🏘 10A4
Festplatz, Am Steckkopf. **GPS:** n51,28525 e9,61956. ⬆️➡️.

4 🚐free 🚰€2 🚽Ch. **Location:** Rural, simple, quiet. **Surface:** metalled.
🅿 01/01-31/12
Distance: 🏊800m Steinersee ⊗300m 🚽500m.
Remarks: 2013: during inspection service out of order.

©S Kirchheim 10A5
Campingplatz Seepark, Brunnenstrasse 20. **GPS:** n50,81400 e9,52000. ⬆️➡️.

50 🚐€10, dog €2/day 🚰€1 🚽Ch 🚿 (30x)€3/day 🚽€1,50.
Surface: metalled. 🅿 01/01-31/12
Distance: 🚰5km 🏊4,9km 🏊20m 🍺on the spot ⊗20m.

♨ Korbach 9D4
Westring. **GPS:** n51,27260 e8,85509. ⬆️.
5 🚐free. **Surface:** grasstiles/metalled. 🅿 01/01-31/12
Distance: 🚰1km 🚽Lidl 200m.
Remarks: Max. 3 nights.

©S Laubach 9D6
Quick Camp Caravanpark Laubach, Kurze Hohl. **GPS:** n50,55021 e9,00806. ⬆️.
65 🚐€6, 2 pers.incl 🚰€2 🚽€2 Ch WC 🚿🔌. **Surface:** grasstiles/grassy.
🅿 01/01-31/12
Distance: 🚰1,5km.

♨ Lauterbach 10A5
Auf der Bleiche, Bleichstrasse. **GPS:** n50,63849 e9,40444. ⬆️.

5 🚐free. **Surface:** gravel. 🅿 01/01-31/12
Distance: 🚰100m 🍺on the spot.

♨ Lauterbach 10A5
Freizeitzentrum, Am Sportfeld. **GPS:** n50,62758 e9,39288. ⬆️.

DE

8 �》free. **Surface:** metalled. ◘ 01/01-31/12
Distance: 800m ⊗50m ⚘on the spot ⚘on the spot.

| ⑤ | Lauterbach | 10A5 |

David-Eifertstrasse. **GPS:** n50,64288 e9,39393.
⚷€1 ⚏Ch. ◘ 01/01-31/12

| ⑤ | Leun | 9C6 |

Lahnwiese, Limburger Straße. **GPS:** n50,55089 e8,35346.⬆.
5 ⌋€6 ⚷€2 WC. **Surface:** grassy. ◘ 01/01-31/12
Distance: 400m ⊗400m 🛒400m.
Remarks: Along the Lahn river, max. 4 days.

| ⑤ | Lich 🌿 | 9D6 |

P6, Ringstraße. **GPS:** n50,51816 e8,82257.⬆.

3 ⌋free. **Surface:** grassy/metalled. ◘ 01/01-31/12
Distance: 300m ⊗400m 🛒Lidl 50m ⚌100m.
Remarks: Max. 3 days.

| ⓒⓈ | Limburg | 9C6 |

Lahncamping, Schleusenweg 16. **GPS:** n50,38902 e8,07387.⬆.
8 ⌋max. € 12-15/24h ⚷€0,50/50liter ⚏Ch ⚡€0,50/kWh ⚲€1/day.
◘ 01/01-31/12
Distance: 900m ⚓1,5km ⊗Gaststätte.
Remarks: Along the Lahn river, summer: bread-service, biergarten.

| ⑤ | Limburg | 9C6 |

Freizeitfalzeuge Singhof, Hoenbergstraße 2. **GPS:** n50,40312 e8,07148.
3 ⌋free ⚷€3 ⚏free. **Surface:** metalled. ◘ 01/01-31/12

| ⑤ | Lindenfels | 17B2 |

Parkplatz Kappstraße, Kappstraße. **GPS:** n49,68018 e8,78294.⬆➡.

10 ⌋€5 ⚷€1/80liter ⚏Ch ⚡(4x)€0,50/6h WC.⚏ **Surface:** grassy.
◘ 01/01-31/12
Distance: on the spot ⊗on the spot.

| ⑤ | Lorsch | 17B2 |

Odenwaldallee. **GPS:** n49,65206 e8,57855.
16 ⌋€10 ⚷⚏Ch ⚡. **Surface:** metalled. ◘ 01/01-31/12

| ⑤ | Maintal | 17B1 |

Wohmobilstellplatz Maintal, Uferpromenade, Dörnigheim.
GPS: n50,13067 e8,83920.⬆.
4 ⌋free. **Surface:** grasstiles. ◘ 01/01-31/12

Distance: ⚘on the spot ⚘on the spot ⚘on the spot.
Remarks: Along Main river.

| ⑤ | Maintal | 17B1 |

Manfred Hüttl Wohnwagen und Reisemobile, Wilhelm-Röntgenstrasse 12.
GPS: n50,13047 e8,86256.
⚷⚏⚡. ◘ 01/01-31/12

| ⑤ | Marburg 🌿⛲☕ | 9D5 |

Jahnstraße. **GPS:** n50,80354 e8,77544.⬆➡.

8 ⌋€ 10/24h ⚷€1/100liter ⚡(4x)€1/4h. ⚏ **Surface:** gravel.
◘ 01/01-31/12
Distance: 300m 🛒500m.

| ⑤ | Melsungen | 10A4 |

Am Sand, Sandstraße. **GPS:** n51,13280 e9,54502.
10 ⌋€0,30/h, overnight stay free. **Surface:** metalled. ◘ 01/01-31/12
Distance: 200m ⚓5km ⚘on the spot ⚘on the spot.
Remarks: Along the Fulda river.

| ⑤ | Melsungen | 10A4 |

Waldparkplatz, Dreuxallee. **GPS:** n51,12352 e9,55169.
5 ⌋free. **Surface:** asphalted. ◘ 01/01-31/12
Distance: centre 1,1km ⚓5km.

| ⑤ | Mernes | 10A6 |

Wohnmobilstellplatz Mernes, Jossastraße, Mernes. **GPS:** n50,24109 e9,47700.
6 ⌋€5 ⚷€1 ⚏Ch ⚡€0,50. ◘ 01/01-31/12
Distance: 200m ⊗250m.
Remarks: To be paid at Gasthaus Zum Jossatal, Salmünsterer Straße 15.

| ⑤ | Michelstadt 🌿 | 17C2 |

Parkplatz Altstadt, Wiesenweg. **GPS:** n49,68038 e9,00143.⬆.

10 ⌋free ⚷€1/70liter ⚏Ch ⚡€1/2kWh. **Surface:** gravel.
◘ 01/01-31/12
Distance: 200m ⊗200m 🛒50m.

| ⑤ | Münzenberg | 9D6 |

Sporthallenparkplatz, Am Viehtrieb. **GPS:** n50,45712 e8,77171.⬆.
5 ⌋free. **Surface:** gravel. ◘ 01/01-31/12
Distance: 800m ⚓2,6km ⊗500m.
Remarks: Max. 3 days.

| ⑤ | Münzenberg | 9D6 |

Sportplatz, Butzbacher Straße, Gambach. **GPS:** n50,45770 e8,73412.⬆.
5 ⌋free. **Surface:** asphalted. ◘ 01/01-31/12
Distance: ⚓2,4km ⊗400m 🛒350m.
Remarks: Max. 3 days.

| ⓒⓈ | Neuental | 10A4 |

Neuenhainer See, Seeblick 14, Neuenhain. **GPS:** n50,99533 e9,26652.
8 ⌋€4 ⚷€1 ⚏Ch ⚡€1/12h WC ⚡€0,50 ⚲. **Surface:** asphalted.
◘ 01/01-31/12
Distance: Neuental 6km ⚓on the spot ⊗250m.

| ⑤ | Neukirchen | 10A5 |

Birkenallee, Knüllgebirge. **GPS:** n50,86567 e9,34478.

DE

5 🛏free 🚰 ♻free. **Surface:** asphalted. ⬛ 01/01-31/12
Distance: 🛒500m ⊗200m.

| 🅂 | Niedenstein | 10A4 |

Am Hallenbad, Schulstraße. **GPS:** n51,22739 e9,31657.⬆.
2 🛏free. **Surface:** gravel. ⬛ 01/01-31/12
Distance: 🚊300m.

| 🅂 | Niestetal | 10A4 |

Spiekershäuser Straße/Fuldablick. **GPS:** n51,32686 e9,55490.⬆.
3 🛏free 🚰€1/100liter 🅲h ♻€1/2kWh. **Surface:** asphalted.
⬛ 01/01-31/12
Distance: 🛒1,1km 🚲on the spot 🎣on the spot.
Remarks: Along the Fulda river, Kassel centre 6km.

| 🅂 | Oberaula | 10A5 |

Sportplatz, Schwimbadstraße. **GPS:** n50,85421 e9,45908.⬆➡.

5 🛏free 🚰 🅲hfree. **Surface:** asphalted. ⬛ 01/01-31/12
Distance: 🛒800m 🛒Rewe 300m.

| 🅂 | Oberaula | 10A5 |

Golfplatz, Am Golfplatz 1. **GPS:** n50,83590 e9,46211.⬆➡.

3 🛏free. **Surface:** grassy.
⬛ 01/01-31/12
Distance: 🛒2,5km.
Remarks: Max. 4 days, follow the signs 'Golfplatz', 18-holes golf course.

| 🅂 | Oberaula | 10A5 |

Teichstrasse. **GPS:** n50,86116 e9,47353.⬆➡.

10 🛏free. **Surface:** metalled. ⬛ 01/01-31/12
Distance: 🛒500m ⊗500m 🛒Edeka 500m.
Remarks: Parking tennis-court, max. 4 days.

| 🅂 | Oberursel | 9D6 |

Wanderparkplatz Taunus, Alfred-Lechler-Straße. **GPS:** n50,21533 e8,53606.
5 🛏€7. **Surface:** metalled. ⬛ 01/01-31/12
Distance: 🛒4km ⊗100m 🚇metro 100m 🚲on the spot 🎣on the spot.

| 🅂 | Oestrich-Winkel | 17A1 |

Am Sportzentrum, Kirchstraße 125. **GPS:** n50,00470 e7,99904.⬆➡.
12 🛏free. **Surface:** metalled. ⬛ 01/01-31/12
Distance: 🛒1km.
Remarks: Max. 2 days.

| 🅂 | Ottrau | 10A5 |

Am Schwimmbad 10. **GPS:** n50,80400 e9,38500.⬆.

4 🛏€6 🚰🛒 ♻ WC🛒. **Surface:** asphalted. ⬛ 01/01-31/12
Distance: 🛒on the spot.

| 🅂 | Poppenhausen 🍴 | 10B6 |

Sport- und Freizeitgelände Lüttergrund, Sebastian-Kneippweg, Wasserkuppe.
GPS: n50,49012 e9,87689.⬆➡.

10 🛏€6 🚰€1 🅲h ♻€1/6h. 🔌 **Surface:** metalled.
⬛ 01/01-31/12
Distance: 🛒300m ⊗300m 🛒300m.

| 🅂 | Rasdorf | 10B5 |

Sport- und Freizeitgelände, Setzelbacher Straße. **GPS:** n50,71422 e9,90306.
4 🛏€4 🚰€1/120liter 🅲h ♻€1/12h. **Surface:** metalled.
⬛ 01/01-31/12
Distance: 🛒850m 🛒500m.
Remarks: Max. 3 days.

| 🅂 | Reichelsheim/Odenwald | 17B2 |

Reichenbergschule, Beerfurhterstrasse. **GPS:** n49,71507 e8,84234.⬆➡.

20 🛏free 🚰€1 🛒🅲h ♻(8x)€0,50/kWh. **Surface:** asphalted.
⬛ 01/01-31/12
Distance: 🛒500m ⊗100m.

| 🅂 | Reinhardshagen 🍴 | 10A3 |

Freibad, Klinkersweg. **GPS:** n51,48694 e9,59194.⬆.

4 🛏free. **Location:** Rural, simple, isolated. **Surface:** asphalted.
⬛ 01/01-31/12

DE

Distance: 2km on the spot ⊗2km 2km on the spot on the spot on the spot.
Remarks: Parking swimming pool, OT Veckerhagen.

| S | **Ringgau** | 10B4 |

Am Festplatz, In der Röste, Gandenborn. **GPS:** n51,08139 e10,04239.⬆.

20 free, service/electricity incl. € 7 Ch.
Location: Rural, simple, quiet. **Surface:** gravel. 01/01-31/12
Distance: 100m ⊗200m.

| S | **Rosenthal** | 9D5 |

Fischewosse, Willershäuser Straße 2. **GPS:** n50,97561 e8,86884.⬆.
5 free € 2. **Surface:** metalled. 01/01-31/12
Distance: 400m 800m.
Remarks: Max. 48h.

| S | **Rotenburg a/d Fulda** | 10A4 |

Wohnmobilpark Am Wittlich, Braacher Straße 14. **GPS:** n51,00049 e9,72074.
50 € 6,50 €1 Ch €0,50/kWh. **Surface:** grassy.
01/01-31/12
Distance: Old city centre 650m 200m.
Remarks: Along the Fulda river.

| S | **Rotenburg a/d Fulda** | 10A4 |

Am Kuckucksmarktgelände, Braach. **GPS:** n51,00583 e9,69361.➡.

15 free €1/80liter Ch. **Surface:** unpaved. 01/01-31/12
Distance: 200m on the spot on the spot ⊗200m.

| | **Rotenburg a/d Fulda** | 10A4 |

Im Heienbach. **GPS:** n51,00223 e9,74141.⬆➡.

10 free. 01/01-31/12
Remarks: Parking swimming pool.

| S | **Rotenburg a/d Fulda** | 10A4 |

Biergarten Hof Hafermas, Rotenburgerstrasse 13, Braach.
GPS: n51,00316 e9,69085.

3 free €1 Ch. **Surface:** gravel. 01/01-31/12
Distance: on the spot ⊗on the spot.
Tourist information Rotenburg a/d Fulda:
Kuckucksmarkt, Braach. Farmers market. 01/05-30/09 last weekend of the month 10-18h.

| S | **Schlitz** | 10A5 |

Damenweg. **GPS:** n50,66909 e9,56908.
3 free. **Surface:** gravel. 01/01-31/12
Remarks: At swimming pool.

| S | **Schlüchtern** | 10A6 |

Ludovica-von-Stumm-Straße. **GPS:** n50,34935 e9,53023.⬆.
5 free. **Surface:** metalled. 01/01-31/12
Distance: 300m 4,3km.

| S | **Schwalmstadt** | 10A5 |

Altstad Schwalmstadt-Treysa. **GPS:** n50,91447 e9,19327.

10 free Ch. 01/01-31/12
Distance: 100m.
Remarks: Service nearby, indicated.

| S | **Schwalmstadt** | 10A5 |

Fünftenweg, Ziegenhain. **GPS:** n50,91753 e9,24633.⬆.

10 free Ch. **Surface:** metalled. 01/01-31/12
Distance: on the spot.
Remarks: Parking swimming pool, service nearby, indicated.

| S | **Schwalmtal** | 10A5 |

Reisemobilplatz, Friedenstrasse, Storndorf. **GPS:** n50,65579 e9,26935.⬆➡.

15 ⌇free ⚡€1/50liter ⚐Ch ✎(6x)€0,50/kWh. **Surface:** asphalted.
◻ 01/01-31/12
Distance: 👟300m.
Remarks: Nearby sports park.

| 🛏S | Sontra | 10B4 |

Langhelle/Jahnstrasse. **GPS:** n51,07227 e9,94673.

14 ⌇€5 ⚡€1/80liter ⚐Ch ✎(6x)€0,50/kWh. 🚲 **Surface:** asphalted.
◻ 01/01-31/12
Distance: 👟1km ⊗1km 🍴1km.
Remarks: Beautiful view.

| 🛏 | Villmar | 9C6 |

P3, König-Konrad-Straße. **GPS:** n50,39102 e8,18625. ⬆➡.

5 ⌇free ⚡€0,50/80liter ⚐Ch ✎€1/12h WC. **Location:** Rural, simple,
isolated, quiet. **Surface:** asphalted/metalled. ◻ 01/01-31/12
Distance: 👟600m 🚐on the spot.
Remarks: Parking behind swimming pool.

| 🛏S | Sontra | 10B4 |

Vimoutiersstrasse. **GPS:** n51,07139 e9,93306. ⬆.
8 ⌇free. **Location:** Urban, simple. **Surface:** gravel/metalled.
◻ 01/01-31/12
Distance: 👟400m ⊗300m 🍴50m.

| 🛏S | Steinau/Strasse | 10A6 |

Am Steines. **GPS:** n50,31605 e9,46029.

10 ⌇free. **Surface:** metalled. ◻ 01/01-31/12
Distance: ⊗on the spot.
Remarks: Parking at the river.

| ⏚ | Vöhl | 9D4 |

Camping-und Ferienpark Teichmann, Herzhausen. **GPS:** n51,17472 e8,89103.
3 ⌇€ 10-14. **Surface:** metalled. ◻ 01/01-31/12
Distance: ⊗on the spot.
Remarks: Max. 1 night.

| 🛏 | Volkmarsen | 9D3 |

Schulstraße. **GPS:** n51,41249 e9,11058. ⬆.
4 ⌇free. **Surface:** asphalted. ◻ 01/01-31/12
Distance: 👟200m 🚗7,8km 🍴Aldi 650m.

| 🛏S | Wahlsburg 🌳 | 10A3 |

Landhotel "Zum Anker", Weserstrasse 14. **GPS:** n51,62447 e9,55212. ⬆➡.

5 ⌇free ⚡€1 ⚐Ch. **Surface:** asphalted. ◻ 01/01-31/12
Distance: 👟1km 🍴150m.
Remarks: Parking near sports centre, max. 2 days.

| 🛏S | Tann/Rhön | 10B5 |

Festplatz Tann, Am Unsbach. **GPS:** n50,64264 e10,01948.
10 ⌇€5 ⚡€1/120liter ⚐Ch ✎€1/2kWh. **Surface:** gravel.
◻ 01/01-31/12
Remarks: Max. 3 days.

| 🛏S | Ulrichstein | 10A6 |

Reisemobilstellplatz Panoramablick, Erlenweg. **GPS:** n50,57588 e9,20619.
⬆➡.

60 ⌇€7 ⚡€0,50/50liter ⚐Ch ✎(60x)€0,50/kWh WC 📶 🚲
Location: Rural, comfortable, quiet. **Surface:** grassy. ◻ 01/01-31/12
Distance: 👟200m 🚲on the spot ⊗on the spot 🍴500m 🚴on the spot
🏊on the spot.
Remarks: Along the Weser river, bread-service.

| 🍴S | Waldeck | 9D4 |

Seeblick Wohnmobil, Güldener Ort 12. **GPS:** n51,20309 e9,05004.
⌇€ 11 2 pers.incl, dog € 1 ⚡⚐Ch ✎€3 WC ⌐included.
Surface: grasstiles. ◻ 01/01-31/12
Distance: ⚓50m ⊗on the spot.
Remarks: At Edersee.

| 🛏S | Waldkappel 🌳 | 10B4 |

Am Sportplatz. **GPS:** n51,14177 e9,87278. ⬆➡.

4 🛏free ⛽€1/100liter. **Location:** Rural, simple, isolated, quiet.
Surface: gravel. ☐ 01/03-31/10
Distance: 🛒400m ⊗400m 🍴400m bakery 🏃Waldpark 500m.
Remarks: At sports park.

| 🏕🅂 | **Wanfried** 👫 | 10B4 |

In der Werraaue, Eschweger Straße. **GPS:** n51,18722 e10,16528. ⬆➡.

30 🛏€ 7 + € 1,50/pp, dog € 1 ⛽€1/20liter 🔌Ch ⚡€0,50/kWh
WC ⬜included. **Surface:** metalled. ☐ 01/01-31/12
Distance: 🛒500m ⊗300m 🍴6km.

| 🛏 | **Weilrod** 👫 | 9C6 |

Golfclub Taunus, Merzhäuser Straße 29. **GPS:** n50,32082 e8,42694.
2 🛏free, only guest players. **Surface:** asphalted. ☐ 01/05-30/09
Distance: ⊗on the spot.

| 🏕🅂 | **Wetzlar** 🌿 | 9C6 |

Parkplatz Lahninsel, Lahninsel. **GPS:** n50,55506 e8,49794. ⬆.
5 🛏€ 8 (8-19h), overnight stay free ⛽🔌Ch ⚡included WC.
Surface: asphalted. ☐ 01/01-31/12
Distance: 🛒300m 🚶1,5km ⊗250m.

| 🏕🅂 | **Wiesbaden** 🦌 | 17A1 |

Reisemobilhafen Wiesbaden, Wörther-See-Strasse/Saarstrasse.
GPS: n50,05583 e8,20972. ⬆.

+40 🛏€ 7, overnight stay 21-9h € 3,50 ⛽1/80liter 🔌Ch ⚡(40x)€0,50/
kWh WC⬜€ 1. ☐ 01/01-31/12
Distance: 🛒150m ⊗800m 🍴800m 🚌150m.
Remarks: Can be reached without environmental: A643 exit Wiesbaden
Dotzheim.

| 🛏 | **Wiesbaden** 🦌 | 17A1 |

Alfred-Delp-Strasse, Frauenstein. **GPS:** n50,06755 e8,16526.

12 🛏€ 5 ⛽€2/100liter 🔌Ch ⚡(12x)€ 1/24h. 👨‍👩‍👧
Location: Rural, simple, quiet. **Surface:** metalled. ☐ 01/01-31/12
Distance: 🛒50m 🍴50m 🛝on the spot 🏃on the spot.

| 🏕🅂 | **Weilburg** | 9C6 |

Wohnmobilstation, Hainallee. **GPS:** n50,48385 e8,25848. ⬆➡.

80 🛏€ 7,50 ⛽🔌⚡included WC 10-17h. 👨‍👩‍👧 **Surface:** metalled.
☐ 01/01-31/12 ⬤ events
Distance: 🛒on the spot ⊗on the spot.
Remarks: Caution key € 15.

| 🏕🅂 | **Weilmünster** | 9C6 |

In der Au, Am Froschgraben, L3054. **GPS:** n50,43345 e8,37343. ⬆➡.

10 🛏free. **Surface:** gravel. ☐ 01/01-31/12
Distance: 🛒4km.
Remarks: Parking in front of sports ground.

| 🏕🅂 | **Willingen** | 9D4 |

Wohnmobilpark Willingen, Am Hagen. **GPS:** n51,29050 e8,61278. ⬆.

8-10 🛏free ⛽🔌Chfree ⚡€2/16h. **Surface:** metalled.
☐ 01/01-31/12
Distance: 🛒on the spot ⊗100m 🍴100m.

| 🏕🅂 | **Weilrod** 👫 | 9C6 |

Taunus Mobilcamp, Hochtaunusstrasse. **GPS:** n50,31138 e8,42581. ⬆.

DE

55 ⌱€ 12, 2 pers.incl ⚡€1/10minutes ⛽Ch ⚡€1/6h WC ⌱€2,50,at swimming pool. **Surface:** metalled. ◻ 01/01-31/12
Distance: 🚶1km ⊗1km 🛒1km ⚲500m ⚓500m.
Remarks: Discount at subtropical swimming pool and indoor skating rink.

Witzenhausen 10A4
Reisemobilplatz Diebesturm, Oberburgstrasse. **GPS:** n51,34110 e9,85435.⬆️ ➡️.

4 ⌱€ 2,50 ⚡€0,50/100liter ⛽Ch ⚡(4x)€0,50. 🔌
Location: Urban, simple, central, noisy. **Surface:** gravel. ◻ 01/01-31/12
Distance: 🚶500m ⊗on the spot 🛒500m.

Witzenhausen 10A4
Reisemobilplatz Josef-Pott-Platz, Laubenweg. **GPS:** n51,34477 e9,85503.⬆️

10 ⌱€ 5 ⚡€1/100liter ⛽Ch ⚡(10x)€0,50/6h. 🔌
Location: Rural, simple, quiet. **Surface:** metalled. ◻ 01/01-31/12
Distance: 🚶800m ⊗9km 🛒800m 🛒Aldi 100m 🚲on the spot 🚶on the spot.

Witzenhausen 10A4
Haus des Gastes, Ringkopfstrasse, Dohrenbach. **GPS:** n51,31061 e9,83372.⬆️➡️.

8 ⌱€ 4 ⚡⛽Chfree ⚡€2/24h WC . 🛁 **Location:** Rural, simple, isolated, quiet. **Surface:** metalled. ◻ 01/01-31/12
Distance: 🚶on the spot ⊗on the spot 🛒300m 🚶on the spot.
Tourist information Witzenhausen:
🎆 Kesperkirmes. Village fair. ◻ beginning Jul.

Wolfhagen 9D4
Freizeitanlange Bruchwiesen, Siemensstrasse. **GPS:** n51,32944 e9,17083.⬆️ ➡️.

35 ⌱€ 3/24h ⚡€1/80liter ⛽Ch ⚡(12x)€1/8h. 🔌
Location: Rural, simple, isolated, quiet. **Surface:** grassy/gravel.
◻ 01/01-31/12
Distance: 🚶on the spot ⊗500m 🛒200m 🚲on the spot 🚶on the spot.

Ziegenhagen 10A3
Erlebnispark Ziegenhagen, Ziegenberg 3. **GPS:** n51,37191 e9,76472.➡️.

30 ⌱€ 5 ⚡€1 ⛽Ch. 🛁 **Location:** Simple, isolated, quiet.
◻ 01/03-31/10
Distance: 🚶6km.

Thuringia

Asbach/Sickenberg 10B4
Grenzmuseum Schifflersgrund, Sickenberger Straße 1.
GPS: n51,28667 e10,01052.
6 ⌱€ 3 ⚡⛽Ch ⚡. **Surface:** gravel.

Bad Berka 10D4
P2, Bleichstrasse. **GPS:** n50,89969 e11,28528. ⬆️➡️.

3 ⌱free ⚡€1/3minutes ⛽€1 Ch ⚡(3x)€1/3h. **Surface:** asphalted.
◻ 01/01-31/12
Distance: 🚶200m ⚲on the spot ⊗200m 🛒200m.
Remarks: 10/7/10 during inspection service out of order.

Bad Colberg/Heldburg 10C6
Rainbrünnlein. **GPS:** n50,27967 e10,73063.⬆️.

5 🛏free ⛽€1/60liter 🚽Ch 🚿€1/8h. **Location:** Simple. **Surface:** grasstiles. ⬛ 01/01-31/12
Distance: 🚶100m ⊗200m 🛒200m.
Remarks: At sports park.

6 🛏€8 ⛽€1/100liter 🚽Ch 🚿€2 WC. **Location:** Comfortable, quiet.
Surface: gravel. ⬛ 01/01-31/12 ⬤ Tuesday
Distance: 🚶500m ⊗on the spot 🛒800m 🏃on the spot.

♨️S Bad Frankenhausen/Kyffhäuser ♨️ 10C3
Bornstraße, B85. **GPS:** n51,35550 e11,10333. ⬆️➡️.

♨️S Bad Lobenstein 10D6
Ardesia Therme, Parkstrasse 8. **GPS:** n50,44981 e11,64294. ⬆️➡️.

6 🛏€12 ⛽🚽🚿 included. **Location:** Rural. **Surface:** metalled.
⬛ 01/01-31/12
Distance: 🚶500m ⊗200m 🛒300m.
Remarks: Check in at pay-desk of the Therme.

11 🛏€2,50 + €1/pp tourist tax, free with use of spa ⛽€2 🚽Ch 🚿€0,50/kWh WC 🍴€3. **Surface:** metalled. ⬛ 01/01-31/12
Distance: 🚶200m ⊗on the spot 🛒200m 🚌on the spot.

♨️S Bad Klosterlausnitz 11A4
Kristall Sauna-Wellnesspark/Soletherme, Köstritzerstrasse 16.
GPS: n50,91190 e11,87242. ⬆️➡️.

♨️S Bad Salzungen 🌿⛲♨️ 10B5
ErlebisINSEL Flößrasen, Flössrasen 1. **GPS:** n50,81541 e10,23748. ⬆️.

15 🛏€10 + €1,30/pp Kurtaxe ⛽€1/80liter 🚽Ch 🚿€1/2kWh WC 🍴.
Surface: gravel. ⬛ 01/01-31/12
Distance: 🚶800m 🏊2,8km ⊗on the spot.

88 🛏€7,50 + €1,50/pp tourist tax ⛽€1/60liter 🚿(88x)€1/2kWh 🍴against payment. 🚌🚻 **Location:** Urban, comfortable. **Surface:** metalled.
⬛ 01/01-31/12
Distance: 🚶500m ⊗400m 🛒400m 🚌on the spot 🏃on the spot.

♨️S Bad Langensalza ♨️ 10C4
Friederiken Therme, Böhmenstrasse. **GPS:** n51,11535 e10,64440. ⬆️➡️.

🍴S Breitungen 10B5
Hotel Jagdhaus Seeblick, Seeblick. **GPS:** n50,74250 e10,32306. ⬆️➡️.

8 🛏€4 + €1,20/pp tourist tax ⛽€1 🚽Ch 🚿(8x)€1/10h.
Surface: metalled. ⬛ 01/01-31/12
Distance: 🚶1km ⊗1km 🛒200m.
Remarks: Parking spa resort, pay at pay-desk of theTherme.

15 🛏€5 ⛽voluntary contribution 🚿€2/day WC 🚽.
Location: Rural, simple, quiet. **Surface:** grassy. ⬛ 01/01-31/12 ⬤ Mon
Distance: 🚶2km ⛰️1km ⊗on the spot 🛒2km 🏃on the spot.

🍴S Bad Liebenstein 🌿⛲ 10B5
Villa Georg, Friedensallee 12. **GPS:** n50,81876 e10,35517. ⬆️.

Brotterode 10C5
Inselbergbad, Am Bad 1. **GPS:** n50,82290 e10,45302. ⬆️.

DE

10 ♨ € 5. Location: Rural, simple. **Surface:** gravel.
◻ 01/01-31/12
Distance: 500m ⊗on the spot Edeka 250m 50m.
Remarks: To be paid at swimming pool.

🏕S **Dorndorf** 10B5
Kultur- und Freizeitzentrum, Hardtstraße 3a. **GPS:** n50,83453 e10,09087. ⬆

8 ♨ € 4 €1/90liter €1 Ch €0,50/kWh. Location: Urban, simple.
Surface: grasstiles. ◻ 01/01-31/12
Distance: 1km ⊗50m.
Remarks: Next to Fahrradherberge.

🏕 **Eisenach** 10B4
Automobilmuseum, Heinrich-Erhardt-Platz. **GPS:** n50,98122 e10,32342. ⬆

3 ♨free. **Location:** Simple. **Surface:** metalled. ◻ 01/01-31/12
Distance: 1km ⊗400m 100m.

🏕 **Eisenach** 10B4
Burg Wartburg, Auf der Wartburg. **GPS:** n50,96775 e10,30989. ⬆ .

3 ♨9-17h max. € 6, free overnight stay. **Surface:** gravel.
◻ 01/01-31/12
Distance: 500m ⊗100m 100m.

🏞S **Eisenach** 10B4
Wohnmobile A. Waldhelm, Ringstrasse 27. **GPS:** n51,00194 e10,32667. ⬆ .

20 ♨ € 10 Chincluded €3/day WC €0,50.
Location: Urban, simple. **Surface:** grasstiles. ◻ 01/01-31/12
Distance: 1km ⊗1km 1km Shuttle bus.
Remarks: Motorhome dealer, accessory shop, check in on arrival, bread-service.

🏕 **Eisfeld** 10C6
Festplatz, Am Volkshaus. **GPS:** n50,42615 e10,90992. ➡ .

5 ♨free. **Location:** Simple. **Surface:** grasstiles.
◻ 01/01-31/12 ◉ Whitsuntide
Distance: 200m ⊗200m 300m on the spot.

🏕S **Eisfeld** 10C6
Waldhotel Hubertus, Coburgerstrasse 501. **GPS:** n50,39680 e10,92269. ⬆ .

20 ♨free, use of a meal desired €2 €2. **Location:** Rural, simple.
Surface: asphalted/grassy. ◻ 01/01-31/12
Distance: 3km ⊗on the spot 2km on the spot.

🏕 **Eisenach** 10B4
Karl Marxstrasse. **GPS:** n50,97861 e10,32083. ⬆ .

5 ♨ € 5. Location: Urban. **Surface:** metalled. ◻ 01/01-31/12
Distance: on the spot.
Remarks: Nearby castle Wartburg.

DE

Am Saunabad Trautmann - Erfurt

S | Erfurt 🌿⛲🏺 | 10C4

info@sauna-trautmann.de - www.caravan-erfurt.de

Bread-service
Comfortable motorhome stopover
Open all year

Am Saunabad Trautmann, Rottenbacherweg 11, Melchendorf.
GPS: n50,95404 e11,06654.
15 🗲€ 7,50 ⛽€1,50/150liter 🔌€1,50 Ch€1,50 ⚡(15x)€1,50/5kWh,16Amp
WC⬜€1,50 💧€3,50/1,50 included. **Surface:** gravel. 🕐 01/01-31/12
Distance: 🚶on the spot 🚲1,2km 🚉300m 🚌200m 🚊300m.
Remarks: Discount on access sauna/wellness.

S | Erfurt 🌿⛲🏺 | 10C4
Domplatz, An den Graden. **GPS:** n50,97591 e11,02455.

4 🗲€ 15 ⛽⚡(3x)€2. **Surface:** gravel. 🕐 01/01-31/12
Distance: 🚶on the spot ⊗on the spot 🚉on the spot 🚌on the spot.

S | Erfurt 🌿⛲🏺 | 10C4
P&R, Am Urbicher Kreuz. **GPS:** n50,94992 e11,09456.➡️.

15 🗲free ⛽🔌Ch. **Surface:** asphalted. 🕐 01/01-31/12
Distance: 🚶7km 🚉Total-shop 🚌Tram till 24am.
Remarks: Service at petrol station.

S | Erfurt 🌿⛲🏺 | 10C4
Am kleinen Ring, Juri-Gagarin-Ring. **GPS:** n50,98111 e11,03472.⬆️.

---

4 🗲free. **Surface:** asphalted. 🕐 01/01-31/12
Distance: 🚶Old city centre 1km ⊗500m 🚉500m.
Remarks: Max. 48h.

S | Erfurt 🌿⛲🏺 | 10C4
Eichenstrasse. **GPS:** n50,97327 e11,02737.⬆️➡️.

4 🗲€ 5. **Surface:** asphalted. 🕐 01/01-31/12
Distance: 🚶200m ⊗200m 🚉300m 🚌on the spot.
Remarks: Max. 48h.

S | Erfurt 🌿⛲🏺 | 10C4
P&R Parkplatz Messe, Gothaerstrasse. **GPS:** n50,95818 e10,98296.⬆️.

4 🗲free. **Surface:** asphalted. 🕐 01/01-31/12
Distance: 🚶centre 4km 🚌Bus <23.00h.
Remarks: Parking exhibition ground.

S | Erfurt 🌿⛲🏺 | 10C4
P&R Parkplatz Thüringerhalle, Werner-Seelenbinderstrasse.
GPS: n50,95771 e11,03605.⬆️.

7 🗲free. **Surface:** gravel. 🕐 01/01-31/12
Distance: 🚶2,6km 🚌Tram till 23am.
Remarks: Nearby B4, south edge of the city.

Tourist information Erfurt:
ℹ️ Erfurt-Card. Card gives for free entrance on among other things public transport and city museums, and discount on a lot of curiosities, guided tours, swimming pools, theater, souvernirs. 🎫 € 14,90.
🖊️ Stadtführung, Tourist Information, Benediktsplatz 1. Guided tour around the historic city center. 🕐 01/04-31/12 Mo-Fri 13h, Sa-Su 11h, 13h, 01/01-31/03 Sa-Su 11h, 13h. 🎫 € 5,50.

S | Ichtershausen | 10C5
Autohof, Thöreyerstrasse. **GPS:** n50,88824 e10,93478.⬆️.

20 �')€6,50/24h, first hour free ⌐€0,50 ⌐Ch€0,50 WC. **Location:** Highway.
Surface: asphalted. ◙ 01/01-31/12
Distance: ⌐4km ⊗on the spot ⌐Esso-shop.

| ⌐S | **Ichtershausen** | 10C5 |

Freizeitfahrzeuge Mobilease, Feldstrasse 1. **GPS:** n50,86907 e10,96563.⬆.

5 ⌐)€5 ⌐⌐Ch ⌐(4x)€2,50 WC during opening hours. **Surface:** gravel.
◙ 01/01-31/12
Distance: ⌐3km ⊗500m ⌐bakery 500m.

| ⌐⌐S | **Ilfeld** 🏠🌳 | 10C3 |

Gasthof Brauner Hirsch, Dorfstrasse 42, Sophienhof. **GPS:** n51,63467 e10,79223.
⬆.

15 ⌐)€5 ⌐⌐Ch ⌐(3x)€0,30/kWh WC ⌐€2 ⌐. **Surface:** metalled.
◙ 01/01-31/12
Distance: ⊗on the spot ⌐3km ⌐on the spot ⌐on the spot.

| ⌐S | **Ilmenau** | 10C5 |

Festhalle, Naumannstraße. **GPS:** n50,68139 e10,90472.⬆.

4 ⌐free ⌐€2/80liter ⌐Ch. **Surface:** asphalted. ◙ 01/01-31/12
Distance: ⌐1km ⊗100m ⌐500m.
Remarks: Max. 24h.

| ⌐S | **Kühndorf** | 10C5 |

Flugschule Dolmar, Am Flugplatz 1. **GPS:** n50,61198 e10,47079.➡.

20 ⌐)€6 ⌐€1 ⌐Ch€1,50/time ⌐€2/day WC ⌐€1,50/time. ⌐
Location: Rural, isolated. **Surface:** grassy/gravel. ◙ 01/01-31/12
Distance: ⌐2km ⊗on the spot ⌐on the spot.
Remarks: Bread-service, parking behind the hangar.

| ⌐ | **Lauscha** ❄ | 10D6 |

Parkplatz Obermühle. GPS: n50,48026 e11,16795. ⬆.

10 ⌐free. **Location:** Simple. **Surface:** asphalted. ◙ 01/01-31/12
Distance: ⌐300m ⊗100m ⌐1km ⌐on the spot ⌐on the spot.

| ⌐ | **Lauscha** ❄ | 10D6 |

Sommerrodelbahn, Lauschaer Straße, Ernstthal. **GPS:** n50,48726 e11,17243.
⬆.

10 ⌐free. **Location:** Simple. **Surface:** asphalted. ◙ 01/01-31/12
Distance: ⌐650m ⊗50m ⌐50m.

| ⌐S | **Linda** | 11A5 |

Knappmühle, Ortsstraße. **GPS:** n50,68473 e11,78324.⬆.

10 ⌐)€6 ⌐⌐Ch ⌐(6x)€1/kWh. **Surface:** grassy/gravel.
◙ 01/03-31/10
Distance: ⌐300m ⌐5km ⌐3km ⌐5km.

| ⌐S | **Meiningen** | 10B5 |

Rohrer Stirn, Frankental. **GPS:** n50,56976 e10,43477.⬆.

DE

10 🛏free ⚡ (6x)€0,50/kWh. **Location:** Urban, simple, quiet.
Surface: asphalted. 📷 01/01-31/12
Distance: 🚶2km.
Remarks: Parking at swimming pool.

| 🛏 | **Meiningen** | 10B5 |

Grossmutterwiesen, Werrastrasse. **GPS:** n50,56172 e10,41266. ⬆️➡️

5 🛏free. **Location:** Simple. **Surface:** concrete. 📷 01/01-31/12
Distance: 🚶on the spot ⊗200m 🚰100m.
Remarks: Service possible at Kläranlage.

| 🛏 | **Meiningen** | 10B5 |

Volkshausplatz, Landsbergerstrasse. **GPS:** n50,57427 e10,41369. ⬆️➡️

10 🛏guests free ⚡ (6x)€0,50/kWh. **Surface:** grassy/gravel.
📷 01/01-31/12 🍽️ Restaurant: Mo
Distance: 🚶2,6km 🚲12,2km ⊗on the spot 🚰2,6km.

| 🛏 S | **Nimritz** | 10D5 |

Wohnmobilstellplatz Nimritz, Ortsstrasse 29. **GPS:** n50,70079 e11,64858. ⬆️
➡️

10 🛏voluntary contribution 🚰€0,50 🍽️Ch ⚡ (7x)€0,50/kWh.
Surface: grasstiles.
Distance: 🚶300m 🚰300m.

| 🛏 S | **Nordhausen** | 10C3 |

Am Badehaus, Grimmelallee 40. **GPS:** n51,50450 e10,78508. ⬆️➡️

2 🛏€ 5, € 10 service and swimming pool incl 🚰€2 🍽️€1 Ch€1 ⚡€1 🚰€3.
Location: Simple. **Surface:** metalled.
Distance: 🚶800m ⊗500m 🚰300m.

| 🛏 S | **Nordhausen** | 10C3 |

Am Kuhberg, Parkallee. **GPS:** n51,51502 e10,78492. ⬆️

10 🛏free. **Surface:** asphalted. 📷 01/01-31/12
Distance: 🚶2km ⊗on the spot 🚰500m.

| 🛏 S | **Oberhof** 🍴 ❄️ | 10C5 |

Wohnmobilstellplatz Oberhof, Jahnstrasse 7. **GPS:** n50,70278 e10,72694. ⬆️
➡️

| 🛏 S | **Mihla** | 10B4 |

Graues Schloss, Thomas-Münztzer-Straße 4. **GPS:** n51,07854 e10,33166. ⬆️➡️

15 🛏€ 8, guests free. **Location:** Rural, simple, quiet. **Surface:** unpaved.
📷 01/01-31/12 🍽️ Whitsuntide
Distance: 🚶on the spot ⚓fishing permit obligatory ⊗on the spot 🚰500 m
🚲on the spot 🚶on the spot.

| 🛏 S | **Neustadt/Orla** 🚻 | 11A5 |

Gaststätte & Pension Heinrichs-Ruhe, Heinrichsruhe 1, Rodaer Strasse.
GPS: n50,75545 e11,75595. ⬆️

DE

+60 🛏€ 10 + € 2/pp tourist tax 🚰€1/80liter 🗑 Ch 🔌(50x)€0,50/kWh. 🛁
Location: Urban, simple. **Surface:** asphalted.
🅿 01/01-31/12
Distance: 🚶400m ⊗200m 🚉500m 🏊on the spot.
Remarks: Bread-service.

Tourist information Oberhof:
👁 Rennsteiggarten Oberhof. Botanical garden. 🅿 01/05-30/09 9-18, 01/10-31/10 9-17h.
Ⓜ Thüringer Wintersportausstellung, Crawinkler strasse 1 / Oberer Hof. Winter sport museum. 🅿 10-13h, 14-17h.
😊 Rennsteig Thermen. Swimming pool complex. 🅿 daily 10-22h.

🏕 S	Reichenbach	11A4

Holzland Freizeitcenter, Rodaer Landstrasse. **GPS:** n50,86118 e11,87607. ⬆

50 🛏€ 8, guests free 🚰€1 🗑 Ch 🔌(15x)€2/day WC 🗑€2/pp.
Surface: concrete. 🅿 01/01-31/12
Distance: 🚶2km ⊗on the spot 🚉bakery 500m.

🏕 S	Rudolstadt	10D5

Freizeit- und Erlebnisbad Saalemaxx, Hugo-Trinckler-Straße 6.
GPS: n50,70635 e11,31659.
9 🛏€ 7/24h 🚰€1/80liter 🗑€1 Ch 🔌€0,50/kWh. **Surface:** gravel.
🅿 01/01-31/12
Distance: 🚶2km 🚉100m.
Remarks: Discount at swimming pool.

🏕	Saalfeld	10D5

Reschwitzerstrasse, B281. **GPS:** n50,63720 e11,36751. ⬆➡

10 🛏free. **Surface:** gravel. 🅿 01/01-31/12
Distance: 🚶2,8km.
Remarks: Parking at swimming pool.

👁 S	Saalfeld	10D5

Saalfelder Feengrotten, Feengrottenweg 2. **GPS:** n50,63468 e11,33982. ⬆➡

30 🛏free 🚰€3/5minutes 🗑€3 Ch 🔌(6x)€0,50/kWh WC 🗑.
Surface: grassy. 🅿 01/01-31/12
Distance: 🚶2,3km ⊗on the spot 🚉bakery 500m 🚌500m.

🏕 S	Schleiz	11A5

Spitzbergs Zollhaus, Burgkerstrasse 25. **GPS:** n50,55507 e11,73438. ⬆➡

5 🛏€ 5, free with a meal 🚰 🗑 Ch 🔌(7x)€2/24h. **Surface:** gravel/metalled.
🅿 01/01-31/12 🅿 Mo
Distance: 🚶7km 🚲5,4km ⊗on the spot 🚉7km.

🏕 S	Schleiz	11A5

HEM-Großtankstelle, Saalburgerstrasse. **GPS:** n50,55717 e11,78706. ⬆

8 🛏€ 2 🚰€1 🗑€1 Ch WC. **Location:** Highway. **Surface:** asphalted.
🅿 01/01-31/12
Distance: 🚶5km ⊗on the spot 🚉shop.
Remarks: Industrial area, max. 24h.

🏕 S	Schmiedefeld 🚻	10C5

Sportplatz, Sportplatzstraße. **GPS:** n50,60324 e10,81491. ⬆

20 🛏€ 3 + € 1/pp tourist tax. **Location:** Rural, simple, quiet.
Surface: grasstiles/metalled. 🅿 01/01-31/12
Distance: 🚶500m ⊗400m 🚶‍♂on the spot 🏊on the spot.
Remarks: Pay at tourist office or Gasthaus Thüringer Hof.

🏕	Sitzendorf	10D5

Sitzendorfer Porzellanmanufaktur, Hauptstrasse 26.
GPS: n50,63174 e11,16788. ⬆
5 🛏free. **Surface:** asphalted. 🅿 01/01-31/12
Distance: 🚶on the spot ⊗200m 🚉200m.

S Sondershausen 10C3

P7 zur Windleite, Hospitalstrasse. **GPS**: n51,37824 e10,86234. ↑→.

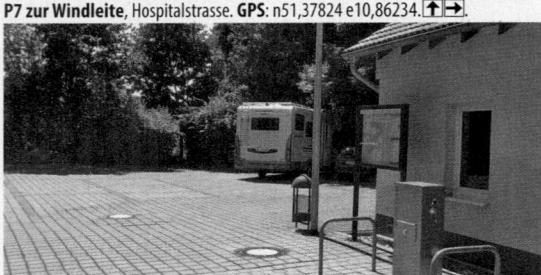

5 free €1 Ch (4x)€1/2h. **Surface:** metalled.
01/01-31/12
Distance: 2,5km 500m 100m.

Sondershausen 10C3

Freizeitpark Possen, Possen 1. **GPS**: n51,33800 e10,86265.

10 € 2/stay. **Surface:** metalled. 01/01-31/12
Distance: 5km on the spot.

S Stadtlengsfeld 10B5

Am Schwimmbad, Eisenacher Straße. **GPS**: n50,79065 e10,11373.

6 free €1/80liter against payment. **Location:** Rural, simple.
Surface: asphalted. 01/01-31/12
Distance: 1,5km.

Steinheid 10D6

Am Rennsteig, Eisfelder Straße, Limbach. **GPS**: n50,47568 e11,06937. ⛶.

4 free. **Location:** Rural, simple, noisy. **Surface:** gravel.
01/01-31/12
Distance: 150m 10km on the spot.

S Steinheid 10D6

Thüringer Baumschmuck, Neuhäuser Strasse 8-10. **GPS**: n50,47302 e11,08672.
⛶.

8 € 5, free for clients €2/90liter included. **Location:** Simple.
Surface: unpaved. 01/01-31/12
Distance: 3km, bakery 50m on the spot on the spot on the spot.
Remarks: At Christmas Balls manufacturer.

Tabarz 10C5

Karl-Kornhaß-Straße. **GPS**: n50,87782 e10,52038. ↑.

8 free, tourist tax € 1,50/pp. **Location:** Rural, simple, quiet.
Surface: metalled. 01/01-31/12
Distance: 200m Rewe 400m.
Remarks: To be paid at TABBS sports centre.

S Tambach-Dietharz 10C5

Festplatz, Burgstallstraße. **GPS**: n50,78902 e10,60897. ↑.

4 free, tourist tax € 1/pp Ch service €6.
Location: Urban, simple. **Surface:** gravel. 01/01-31/12
Distance: on the spot on the spot.
Remarks: Key service at town hall.

S Tambach-Dietharz 10C5

Freigelande Lohmühle, Lohmühle 1-5. **GPS**: n50,81056 e10,62778. ↑.

30 € 6 + € 4/pp Ch €2 WC €1 €1.
Location: Rural, simple, quiet. **Surface:** grassy. 01/02 -31/12 Mon
Distance: on the spot 3km on the spot on the spot.
Remarks: Check in on arrival, barefoot park, museum.

S Themar 10C6

Am Hexenturm, Mauerstrasse. **GPS**: n50,50512 e10,61194. ↑→.

5 ⌁free ⛽€1/50liter 🚻Ch 💧€1/kWh. **Location:** Urban, simple, quiet.
Surface: grasstiles. 📅 01/01-31/12
Distance: 🚶100m ⊗300m 🚊400m 🚲on the spot 🧍on the spot.
Remarks: Along the Werra river, 01/11-31/03 water disconnected.

| 🚻S | Tiefenort | 10B5 |

Freizeitanlage Heerstatt, Auf der Heerstatt. **GPS:** n50,83444 e10,16306.⬆️➡️

6 ⌁free 💧€2/day. **Location:** Rural, simple. **Surface:** concrete.
📅 01/03-31/10
Distance: 🚶on the spot ⊗50m 🚊bakery 900m 🧍on the spot.
Remarks: On island in the Werra river.

| 🚻S | Treffurt | 10B4 |

Unter den Linden. **GPS:** n51,13398 e10,23659.⬆️➡️

20 ⌁free ⛽€0,50/80liter 🚻Ch 💧(8x)€0,50/kWh.
Location: Rural, simple, quiet.
Surface: grasstiles/grassy.
📅 01/01-31/12 📷 15/07-31/07
Distance: 🚶300m 🏊on the spot ⊗50m 🚊500m 🚲on the spot
🧍on the spot.
Remarks: Along river, water closed during wintertime.

Tourist information Treffurt:
ℹ️ Small town with half-timbered houses and medieval castle Normannstein.

| 🚻S | Weimar | 10D4 |

Hermann Brill-Platz. **GPS:** n50,98501 e11,31701.⬆️➡️

20 ⌁€10/24h ⛽€1 🚻Ch 💧(6x)€1/6h. **Surface:** metalled.
📅 01/01-31/12

Distance: 🚶Weimar centre 1,2km ⊗on the spot 🚊500m.

| 🍴S | Zella-Mehlis | 10C5 |

Toschis Station, An der Quelle 5. **GPS:** n50,64375 e10,68436.⬆️
10 ⌁€5 ⛽🚻Ch 💧(20x). 🏍️**Location:** Simple, central.
Surface: grassy/gravel. 📅 01/01-31/12
Distance: ⊗on the spot 🚊300m.
Remarks: Check in at reception.

| 🚻S | Zeulenroda | 11A5 |

Badewelt Waikiki, Am Birkenwege 1. **GPS:** n50,66543 e11,99355.
6 ⌁free ⛽🚻Ch 💧water and electricity€10/day. **Surface:** metalled.
📅 01/01-31/12

Baden Württemberg

| 🚻S | Aalen | 18A4 |

Hirschbach, Hirschbachstrasse 68. **GPS:** n48,84524 e10,10712.⬆️➡️

10 ⌁free ⛽€1/80liter 🚻Ch. **Location:** Rural. **Surface:** asphalted.
📅 01/01-31/12
Distance: 🚶800m ⊗100m 🚏200m.
Remarks: At swimming pool, max. 3 days.

| 🏕️ | Aalen | 18A4 |

Limes-Thermen, P1, Osterbucher Steige. **GPS:** n48,82047 e10,07918.⬆️

12 ⌁free. **Location:** Rural. **Surface:** grasstiles. 📅 01/01-31/12
Distance: ⊗100m.

| 🚻S | Achern | 17A5 |

Wohnmobilstellplatz Achern, Kapellenstrasse/Badstrasse.
GPS: n48,62436 e8,07359.⬆️

12 ⌁€4 ⛽€1/100liter 🚻Ch 💧(12x)€1/16h. 🏧**Location:** Urban, simple,
quiet. **Surface:** gravel/metalled. 📅 01/01-31/12
Distance: 🚶500m 🚴4,8km 🚊650m 🚲on the spot 🧍on the spot.

| 🚻S | Albstadt | 17C5 |

Badkap. GPS: n48,21402 e8,97844.⬆️

DE

25 ⌇free 🚰🔌Chfree 🚿€2,50/day. **Surface:** metalled.
◻ 01/01-31/12
Distance: 🚶1km ⊗200m 🚉500m.
Remarks: Parking swimming and sauna centre, max. 3 days.

🍴 | **Allensbach** | 24C1
Landgasthaus Mindelsee, Gemeinmärk 7. **GPS:** n47,74279 e9,04411.⬆

15 ⌇€ 8, guests free. **Surface:** metalled. ◻ 01/01-31/12 ◼ Tue
Distance: 🚶5km ⊗on the spot.
Remarks: Max. 1 night, max 3,5t.

🍴S | **Amtzell** | 24D1
Wohnmobilanlage Büchelweisen, Haus 3. **GPS:** n47,70871 e9,76684.⬆➡

25 ⌇€ 9 🚰🔌Ch 🚿(24x)€0,50/kWh WC ⌇€3/day. **Surface:** grasstiles.
◻ 01/01-31/12
Distance: 🚶1,5km ⊿1km 🚶1km ⊗on the spot 🚉1,5km.
Remarks: Bread-service.

🚌 | **Aspach** | 17C3
Wanderparkplatz Fautenhau, Im Fautenhau, Hohrot. **GPS:** n48,97823 e9,39483.
⬆

 (top right first)

5 ⌇free. **Location:** Rural, quiet. **Surface:** asphalted/grassy. ◻ 01/01-31/12
Distance: 🚶on the spot.
Remarks: Max. 1 night.

🚌 | **Aspach** | 17C3
Wanderparkplatz Kelter, Kelterstrasse, Allmersbach. **GPS:** n48,99543 e9,39006.
⬆

5 ⌇free. **Location:** Rural, isolated. **Surface:** asphalted. ◻ 01/01-31/12
Distance: 🚶on the spot.
Remarks: Max. 1 night.

🚌 | **Aspach** | 17C3
Wanderparkplatz Lapidarium, Ortsstrasse, Kleinaspach.
GPS: n48,99738 e9,35711.⬆

2 ⌇free. **Location:** Simple. ◻ 01/01-31/12
Distance: 🚶on the spot ⊗1km 🚉1,5km 🚶on the spot.
Remarks: Max. 1 night.

🚐S | **Aulendorf** | 17D6
Carthago City, Carthago ring 1. **GPS:** n47,93156 e9,65429.
6 ⌇free 🔌€0,50 🚰Ch 🚿€0,50/kWh. **Surface:** metalled.
◻ 01/01-31/12
Distance: 🚶2,5km.
Remarks: At motohome manufacturer.

♨ | **Aulendorf** | 17D6
Schwaben-Therme, Ebisweilerstrasse 5. **GPS:** n47,95797 e9,63728.➡

🚌 | **Aspach** | 17C3
Wanderparkplatz Heiligental, Heiligentalstrasse, Rietenau.
GPS: n48,99158 e9,40519.⬆

5 ⌇free. **Location:** Rural. **Surface:** metalled. ◻ 01/01-31/12
Remarks: Max. 1 night, parking P0.

20 (P3) ⌇free. **Location:** Rural. **Surface:** metalled. ◻ 01/01-31/12
Distance: 🚶500m ⊗on the spot 🚉500m.

Remarks: Parking swimming pool, max. 2 nights.

Backnang 🏕 17D4

Gartenstrasse. **GPS:** n48,95041 e9,45281. ⬆

4 🛏 free ⚡ €1/90liter 🚰 Ch. **Location:** Rural, simple. **Surface:** gravel.
🅿 01/01-31/12
Distance: 🚶1km 🛒400m 🚶 on the spot 🚶 on the spot.

Bad Bellingen ♨ 24A1

Balinea Thermen, Badstrasse 14. **GPS:** n47,72963 e7,55233. ⬆

31 🛏 €10 + €1,45-2,25 tourist tax ⚡ €1/80liter 🚰 Ch ⚡(24x)€1/kWh
WC 🚿 €1,50. **Location:** Urban, noisy. **Surface:** asphalted/metalled.
🅿 01/01-31/12
Distance: 🚶500m 🚴5,5km 🚫on the spot 🚶on the spot.

Bad Buchau 17D6

Adelindis Therme, Am Kurpark. **GPS:** n48,06865 e9,60653. ⬆

21 🛏 €9,50 XL-pitch €11 ⚡ €1/80liter 🚰 Ch ⚡€0,50/kWh WC €1.
Surface: metalled. 🅿 01/01-31/12
Distance: 🚶500m.

Bad Buchau 17D6

Seegasse. **GPS:** n48,06801 e9,60977.

17 🛏 €9,50 ⚡ €1/80liter 🚰 Ch ⚡(17x)€0,50/kWh.
Surface: metalled. 🅿 01/01-31/12
Distance: 🚶500m.
Remarks: Adelindis Therme 300m.

Bad Buchau 17D6

Federseemuseum, Wellerstraße. **GPS:** n48,07051 e9,60949. ➡

12 🛏 €9 ⚡(12x)€0,50/kWh WC 🚿. Location: Rural. **Surface:** asphalted.
🅿 01/01-31/12
Distance: 🚶800m.
Remarks: Adelindis Therme 500m.

Bad Buchau 17D6

Am Freibad, Friedhofstrasse. **GPS:** n48,06292 e9,61714. ⬆

10 🛏 €9. **Surface:** asphalted. 🅿 01/01-31/12
Distance: 🚶700m.

Bad Ditzenbach ♨ 17D4

Vinzenz Therme, Badstraße 20. **GPS:** n48,59003 e9,70553. ⬆

10 🛏 €5, winter €6 ⚡ 🚰 Ch ⚡. **Surface:** asphalted. 🅿 01/01-31/12

Bad Dürrheim 17B6

Reisemobilhafen Bad Dürrheim, Huberstraße 34/2. **GPS:** n48,01204 e8,53506.
⬆➡.

300 🛏 €9 ⚡ €1/100liter 🚰 Ch ⚡€2,50/night WC €2 🚿.
Location: Rural, comfortable. **Surface:** gravel.
🅿 01/01-31/12
Distance: 🚫on the spot.
Remarks: Pay at reception, bread-service, special health arrangement possible.

Bad Herrenalb ♨ 17B4

Therme Siebentäler, Schweizer Wiese. **GPS:** n48,80334 e8,44067. ⬆

10 🛏 € 4,10 + € 2,50/pp ⛽€1 🚰€1 Ch€1 ♨ (4x)€1.
Location: Rural, simple. **Surface:** asphalted.
📅 01/01-31/12
Distance: 🚶500m ⛽100m 🛒200m 🚂200m 🚲on the spot 🚶on the spot.
Remarks: Max. 2 nights, discount on access terme.

Tourist information Bad Herrenalb:
✒ Quellenerlebnispfad, Kurpark Herrenalb. Hiking trails past 60 fountains.

20 🛏 € 5 ⛽€1/80liter 🚰Chfree ♨ (16x)€1/8h. **Location:** Rural, simple.
Surface: gravel. 📅 01/01-31/12
Distance: 🚶Old city centre 1km ⊗200m 🛒Lidl 800m 🚂100m.
Remarks: Max. 3 nights, check in at restaurant tennispark.

Bad Niedernau · 17C5
Wohnmobilparkplatz Bad Niedernau, Blaue Brücke. **GPS:** n48,45931 e8,89959.
5 🛏free. **Location:** Rural. **Surface:** unpaved. 📅 01/01-31/12
Distance: 🚶500m 🛒3km.
Remarks: Along the Neckar river, max. 3 nights.

Bad Krozingen · 17A6

Vita Classica Therme - Bad Krozingen

tourist.info@bad-krozingen.info - www.bad-krozingen.info

Reservations possible
Rural location
Open all year

Vita Classica Therme, Thürachstraße. **GPS:** n47,91763 e7,68821. ⬆️➡️.
80 🛏 € 11, from 7th night € 9,50 ♨ 🚰 Ch ♨€3,50/day,16Amp WC ⬜€3
📶 included 📷.🚿.📹 🚙
Location: Rural, comfortable. **Surface:** asphalted/metalled. 📅 01/01-31/12
Distance: 🚶600m 🚲3km ⊗50m 🛒600m 🚂800m 🚂on the spot
🚲on the spot 🚶on the spot.
Remarks: Bread-service, trailer € 2,50/night.

Bad Liebenzell · 17B4
Campingpark Bad Liebenzell, Pforzheimer strasse 34.
GPS: n48,77850 e8,73120.⬆️.

Bad Rappenau · 17C3
Weinbrennerstrasse. **GPS:** n49,23517 e9,11396.⬆️➡️.

30 🛏 € 3/pp, child € 2 ⛽€1/80liter 🚰 Ch ♨ (16x)€1/4h.
Location: Comfortable. **Surface:** metalled. 📅 01/01-31/12
Distance: 🚶1km ⊗50m 🛒1km.
Remarks: Therme 400m.

Bad Rappenau · 17C3
Autohof Bad Rappenau, A6, Wilhelm-Hauff-Straße 43, Fürfeld.
GPS: n49,21043 e9,06927.⬆️.
15 🛏 € 10, free for clients ⛽ 🚰 Ch 📅. **Location:** Highway, simple.
Surface: metalled. 📅 01/01-31/12
Distance: ✒300m ⊗on the spot 🛒on the spot.
Remarks: Breakfest-service.

Bad Säckingen · 24A1
Reisemobilplatz Am Rheinufer, Ausstrasse. **GPS:** n47,54903 e7,94765.⬆️➡️.

16 🛏 € 8 + € 2/pp tourist tax ⛽ 🚰 Ch ♨ (16x) WC ⬜included 📷€3 📶 📷.
🚙 **Location:** Rural, simple, noisy. **Surface:** metalled/sand.
📅 01/01-31/12
Distance: 🚶on the spot ✒17km ⊗500m 🛒100m 🚂on the spot
🚲on the spot 🚶on the spot.

Bad Mergentheim · 17D2
Festplatz beim Freibad, Erlenbachweg. **GPS:** n49,49194 e9,79167.⬆️➡️.

30 🛏 € 10/24h ⛽€0,50/100liter 🚰€0,20 Ch ♨ (39x) WC. 🛢
Location: Urban, comfortable, quiet. **Surface:** gravel.
📅 01/01-31/12 📅 beginning Mar, end Oct
Distance: 🚶300m ✒6km 🛒50m 🚂on the spot 🚲on the spot.
Remarks: Several offers, i.e. free public transport.

Tourist information Bad Säckingen:
✒ Nachtwächterführungen. Evening tour guided by night watch in historical
cloths and with lantern. Information and booking: Kurverwaltung. 📞 € 2.

Bad Saulgau · 17D6
GolfPark Bad Saulgau, Koppelweg 103. **GPS:** n47,97928 e9,48623.⬆️.

DE

30 ⌧€ 10, golfers free ⛽€1/100liter 🗑 Ch 🚿€1/6h 📶 🚐🛢 ♻
Location: Rural, quiet. **Surface:** metalled. ☀ 01/03-31/10
Distance: 🚶4km ⊗on the spot 🛒4km.

🚻🅂 **Bad Saulgau** ⚓ 17D6
Wonhmobilstellplatz Sonnenhof-Therme, Am Schönen Moos.
GPS: n48,01703 e9,48838.⬆.

30 ⌧free ⛽ 🗑 Ch 🚿€5,reduction for guests WC.
Location: Quiet. **Surface:** metalled.
☀ 01/01-31/12
Distance: 🚶on the spot ⊗150m 🛒250m.
Remarks: Brewery and brewery museum.
Tourist information Bad Schussenried:
Ⓜ Kloster Schussenried. History of the monastry. ☀ Easter-Oct 13.30-17.30h.

🚻🅂 **Bad Teinach** 🏔👪 17B4
Zavelsteiner strasse. **GPS:** n48,68890 e8,69440.

53 ⌧€ 11 + € 1,50/pp tourist tax ⛽stay 🗑 Ch 🚿 (69x)included 📷 🛒
Location: Rural. **Surface:** metalled. ☀ 01/01-31/12
Distance: 🚶on the spot ⊗on the spot 🛒on the spot.
Remarks: Bread-service, discount on access terme.

🚻🅂 **Bad Schönborn** ⚓ 17B3
Reisemobilhafen WellMobilPark, Kraichgaustraße 16.
GPS: n49,21839 e8,67144.⬆➡.

20 ⌧free. **Location:** Rural, simple. **Surface:** asphalted.
☀ 01/01-31/12
Distance: 🚶50m ⊗100m 🛒100m 🚌on the spot 🚲on the spot
🚶on the spot.
Remarks: Parking swimming pool, max. 24h.

🚻🅂 **Bad Urach** 🏖🏔❄ ⚓ 17C5
Wohnmobilstellplatz Bad Urach, Bäderstraße. **GPS:** n48,50060 e9,37713.⬆.

86 ⌧€ 9, >10m € 13 ⛽€1/100liter 🗑 Ch 🚿 (112x)€0,50/kWh 🛢€1,50
📷 📶. **Location:** Rural, luxurious. **Surface:** metalled. ☀ 01/01-31/12
Distance: 🚶500m ⊗on the spot 🛒1km 🚌200m.
Remarks: Bread-service, swimming pool available.

🚻🅂 **Bad Schussenried** 17D6
Am Zellersee, Zellerseeweg. **GPS:** n48,00160 e9,64724.⬆.

26 ⌧€ 8 ⛽€0,50/60liter 🗑€0,50 Ch 🚿 included. 🛒 **Surface:** asphalted.
☀ 01/01-31/12
Distance: 🚶on the spot 🚲5km ⊗200m 🛒800m 🚌200m 🎿10km
⛷10km.

🚻🅂 **Bad Waldsee** ⚓ 17D6
Bauernhof Lott, Mattenhaus 4. **GPS:** n47,95113 e9,75838.

12 ⌧€ 5 + € 1,20/pp tourist tax ⛽ 🗑 Ch 🚿 🚐 **Surface:** asphalted.
☀ 01/01-31/12
Distance: 🚶900m 🏊on the spot ⊗on the spot.

🚻🅂 **Bad Schussenried** 17D6
Bierkrugmuseum, Wilhelm Schussenstrasse 12. **GPS:** n48,00325 e9,65902.⬆.

10 ⌧€ 10, 2 pers.incl, tourist tax € 2/pp ⛽ 🗑 Ch 🚿 (10x)€0,50/kWh
WC 📷🛢€4. ☀ 01/03-30/11
Distance: 🚶3,5km 🏊3km 🚲3km ⊗200m 🛒3km.

DE

Remarks: Bread-service.

🛈S **Bad Waldsee** ⚓ 17D6

Waldsee-Therme, Unterurbacher weg. **GPS**: n47,91441 e9,76047. ⬆➡.

40 🛏 € 5 + € 2/pp tourist tax 🚰€1 🔌€1 Ch 🔌 €0,50/kWh. 🗑
Surface: metalled. 🕐 01/01-31/12
Distance: 🚶1km 🚲1km 🚇1km ⊗500m 🚋1km 🚌500m.
Remarks: Bread-service.

🏔S **Bad Wildbad** ⚓ ⚓ 17B4

Kernerstrasse. **GPS**: n48,74132 e8,54740. ⬆.

16 🛏 € 5, tourist tax € 2,90/pp 🚰€1/60liter 🔌 Ch 🔌 (16x)€2/8h. 🗑
Location: Rural, simple, noisy. **Surface:** asphalted.
🕐 01/01-31/12
Distance: 🚶500m ⊗500m 🚇300m 🚌on the spot 🚲on the spot
🚶on the spot.
Remarks: Max. 3 days.

🏔 **Bad Wimpfen** ⚓ 17C3

Am alter Bahnhof, Carl Ulrichstrasse 1. **GPS**: n49,22942 e9,16745. ⬆.

10 🛏 € 2, overnight stay free. **Location:** Urban, simple. **Surface:** gravel.
🕐 01/01-31/12
Distance: ⊗400m 🚇400m 🚌50m 🚲on the spot.

🛈S **Bad Wimpfen** ⚓ 17C3

An der Alten Saline 2. **GPS**: n49,23604 e9,15630. ⬆.

8 🛏 € 8, tourist tax excl 🚰€1/70liter 🔌 Ch 🔌 (8x)€1/12h WC.
Location: Rural, comfortable, quiet. **Surface:** asphalted. 🕐 01/01-31/12
Distance: 🚶800m.

Remarks: Parking at health resort.

🛈S **Bad Wurzach** ⚓ 17D6

Wohnmobilstellplatz Vitalium, Riedhalde. **GPS**: n47,91437 e9,90363. ⬆➡.

17 🛏 € 5,50 + € 1,50/pp tourist tax 🚰€0,50 🔌€0,50 Ch 🔌 WC 🗑.
Location: Rural, quiet. **Surface:** asphalted. 🕐 01/01-31/12
Distance: 🚶500m ⊗300m 🚇500m.
Remarks: Check in at pay-desk of Vitalum.

🛈S **Baden-Baden** ⚓ 17B4

Wohnmobilparkplatz, Hubertusstraße 2, Badenscheunern.
GPS: n48,78193 e8,20388. ⬆➡.

28 🛏 € 12 🚰€1/100liter 🔌 Ch 🔌 (28x)€0,50/kWh. 🗑
Location: Urban, comfortable, noisy. **Surface:** metalled. 🕐 01/01-31/12
Distance: 🚶Baden-Baden 4km 🚲1km ⊗100m 🚇150m 🚌on the spot
🚲on the spot 🚶on the spot.
Remarks: Max. 4 days, video surveillance.

🛈S **Baiersbronn** ⚓ ⚓ 17B5

Schelklewiesen, Neumühleweg/Lochweg. **GPS**: n48,51016 e8,37272. ⬆➡.

15 🛏 € 6 🚰€1/80liter 🔌 Ch 🔌 (12x)€0,50/kWh. 🚲
Location: Rural, simple, quiet. **Surface:** metalled. 🕐 01/01-31/12
Distance: 🚶300m 🚌on the spot 🚇100m 🚌200m 🚲on the spot
🚶on the spot.

🛈S **Balingen** 🌿 ⚓ 🍺 🍴 17C5

Wohnmobilstellplatz an der Eyach, Heinzlerstrasse. **GPS**: n48,27028 e8,85222.
➡.

10 🛏 free 🚰€1 🔌 Ch 🔌 (8x)€0,50/kWh. **Surface:** asphalted.

🔲 01/01-31/12

Distance: 🚶on the spot ⚓500m ⊗300m 🚊 300m.

Remarks: Max. 4 days.

| 🏕 | Benningen am Neckar | 17C4 |

Parkplatz Gemeindehalle, Max-Eyth Strasse. **GPS:** n48,94574 e9,23363.

4 ⌇free. **Location:** Rural, simple. **Surface:** metalled.

🔲 01/01-31/12

Distance: 🚶on the spot ⊗50m 🚊 1km.

| 🏕 S | Bernau im Schwarzwald 🏔❄ | 24A1 |

Sportzentrum Spitzenberg, Sportplatzstraße. **GPS:** n47,80614 e8,02803. ⬆➡.

15 ⌇16/04-30/09 free, 01/10-15/04 € 3,50 + € 2,20/pp tourist tax
🚰€1/100liter ♨ Ch ⚡€1/8h WC 🚻. **Location:** Rural, simple, quiet.

Surface: grassy/gravel. 🔲 01/01-31/12

Distance: 🚶500m ⊗1km 🚊500m.

Remarks: Pay at tourist office.

| 🏕 S | Besigheim 🏊⛵🎣🍴🍽 | 17C3 |

Wohnmobilstellplatz bei der Minigolfanlage, Auf dem Kies 32.
GPS: n48,99771 e9,14863. ⬆➡.

6 ⌇€ 5 🚰€1/80liter ♨ Ch ⚡(6x)€0,50/kWh.

Location: Rural, comfortable, quiet. **Surface:** metalled. 🔲 01/01-31/12

Distance: 🚶500m ⚓500m ⊗200m 🚊500m 🚆200m 🚲on the spot
🚶on the spot.

Remarks: After 2 nights € 20/night.

| 🏕 S | Beuron | 17C6 |

Kloster Beuron, Abteistraße. **GPS:** n48,05306 e8,96704. ⬆.

± 4 ⌇free. **Location:** Simple. **Surface:** gravel. 🔲 01/01-31/12

Remarks: Parking monastery.

| 🏕 S | Beuron | 17C6 |

Besi-Kanu-Sport, Bahnhofstrasse 29. **GPS:** n48,08597 e9,09559. ⬆.

10 ⌇€ 5 🚰 ♨ Ch ⚡WC included. **Surface:** gravel.

Distance: 🚶1km ⊗200m 🚊5km.

Remarks: Canoe rental.

| 🏕 S | Biberach/Riss | 17D6 |

Rissstrasse. GPS: n48,10401 e9,79582. ⬆.

10 ⌇free, voluntary contribution 🚰 ♨ Ch free. **Surface:** gravel.

🔲 01/01-31/12 ⬤ service: 01/11-28/02

Distance: 🚶700m.

Remarks: Max. 3 days.

| 🏕 S | Bietigheim-Bissingen | 17C4 |

Wohnmobilstellplatz an der Enz, Mühlwiesenstrasse.
GPS: n48,96110 e9,13329. ⬆.

9 ⌇€ 5 🚰€0,50/80liter ♨ Ch ⚡(8x)€0,50/kWh. **Location:** Urban.

Surface: metalled. 🔲 01/01-31/12

Distance: 🚶200m ⚓1km 🚲1km ⊗100m 🚊100m 🚆100m.

Remarks: Max. 4 days, check in at Lama Bar.

| 🏕 S | Blaubeuren | 17D5 |

Parkplatz P6, Dodelweg. **GPS:** n48,41351 e9,79102. ➡.

20 ⌇€ 5 🚰€1/5minutes ♨ Ch €1. **Surface:** metalled. 🔲 01/01-31/12

Distance: 🚶1km ⊗1km 🚊1km 🚆800m.

Remarks: Parking at swimming pool, max. 2 days.

DE

Blaustein 17D5

Freizeitbad Bad Blau, Boschstraße. **GPS:** n48,41757 e9,91630. ⬆️
3 🛁free. **Location:** Simple. **Surface:** gravel.
Distance: 🚲6,5km ⊗200m 🚊500m.

Blumberg 17B6

P1, Festplatz, Oberes Ried. **GPS:** n47,83943 e8,54226. ⬆️➡️

48 🛁€ 6,50-7,50 🚰€1/50liter 🔲Ch 🔌(36x)€1/24h. ♨️
Location: Comfortable, quiet. **Surface:** gravel/metalled. 🅿️ 01/01-31/12
Distance: 🚶800m ⊗100m 🚊80m.
Remarks: With payment: KONUS guest card with many advantages.

Blumberg 17B6

P2, Parkplatz Bahnhof Zollhaus, Achdorf. **GPS:** n47,83767 e8,55777. ⬆️

10 🛁€ 6,50-7,50 🚰. **Location:** Urban, noisy. **Surface:** gravel.
🅿️ 01/01-31/12
Distance: 🚶1,5km.

Blumberg 17B6

P3, Achdorfer Tal. **GPS:** n47,83528 e8,49833. ⬆️

10 🛁€ 6,50-7,50 🚰€1 🔲Ch 🔌(12x)€1/night,winter€1,50. ♨️
Location: Rural, simple, isolated, quiet. **Surface:** gravel. 🅿️ 01/01-31/12
Distance: 🚶4km.
Remarks: With payment: KONUS guest card with many advantages, caution key
€ 10 (connection electricity), service at Kläranlage 800m.

Böblingen 17C4

Im Zimmerschlag. **GPS:** n48,67000 e9,03272.
4 🛁free 🚰🔲Chfree. **Surface:** grasstiles/metalled. 🅿️ 01/01-31/10
Distance: 🚶3km ⊗100m 🚊1,5km ⚓on the spot.

Bodman-Ludwigshafen 17C6

Am Sportplatz. **GPS:** n47,82369 e9,05153. ⬆️

20 🛁€ 8 🚰🔲Ch 🔌(4x)€2. **Location:** Simple. **Surface:** grassy/metalled.
🅿️ 01/01-31/12
Distance: 🚶1km 🚲3,2km ⛱1,4km.

Bonndorf 17B6

Wohnmobilstellplatz Holzschlag, Schulstrasse/Bonndorfer Strasse, Bonndorf-
Holzschlag. **GPS:** n47,84970 e8,26784. ⬆️.

🛁€ 5 🚰🔲Chincluded. **Location:** Simple, noisy.
Distance: ⊗100m.

Bönnigheim 17C3

Mineralfreibad Bönnigheim, Bachstrasse 40. **GPS:** n49,03910 e9,08439. ⬆️

4 🛁free 🚰🔲. **Location:** Rural, simple. **Surface:** grasstiles/metalled.
🅿️ 01/01-31/12
Distance: 🚶500m ⊗500m 🚊1km.
Remarks: Caution key € 10 (water).

Bopfingen 18A4

Gasthof zum Bären, Nördlinger strasse 3. **GPS:** n48,85715 e10,35508. ⬆️

🛁€ 6 🚰€1 🔲€1 Ch 🔌€1. **Surface:** asphalted. 🅿️ 01/01-31/12
Distance: 🚶on the spot 🚲16km ⊗500m 🚊100m.

Boxberg 17D2

Gasthof Hagenmühle, Uiffinger strasse 74. **GPS:** n49,48710 e9,61299. ⬆️

12 🛏€5 🚰 💧 (12x)€2,50. **Location:** Rural, simple. **Surface:** grassy/gravel.
⭕ 01/01-31/12 🍽 Restaurant: Mo
Distance: 🚶2km 🎣trout pond ⊗on the spot 🛒1km 🚌200m.

5 🛏free. **Location:** Simple. **Surface:** metalled. ⭕ 01/01-31/12
Distance: 🚶2km ⊗on the spot 🛒500m.
Remarks: Along the Rhine river, guests only.

Tourist information Breisach/Rhein:
✦ Weinfest Kaiserstuhl Tuniberg. Wine festivals. ⭕ end Aug.

🏷🅂	**Brackenheim**	17C3

Weingut und Besenwirtschaft 'Zum Alten Pflug', Seebergweg.
GPS: n49,10261 e9,04994.⬆.

🅂	**Bretten**	17B3

Reisemobil-Stellplatz Bretten, Willi-Hesselbacher-Weg.
GPS: n49,02980 e8,71914.
4 🛏free 🚰€1/100liter 💧€1/10h. **Surface:** metalled.
Distance: 🚶city centre 1,5km.
Remarks: Max. 2 days.

🅂	**Bruchsal**	17B3

Giesgrabenweg. **GPS:** n49,13227 e8,58981.⬆.

3 🛏€6, free for clients 🚰 🗑 Ch 💧 (3x)€2 WC 🗑€2. **Surface:** metalled.
⭕ 01/01-31/12
Distance: 🚶3km 🛒3km.
Remarks: Sunday on demand.

🏷🅂	**Brackenheim**	17C3

Weingut Winkler, Stockheimer strasse 13. **GPS:** n49,08001 e9,06270.⬆.

2 🛏free. **Location:** Urban, simple, central. **Surface:** metalled.
⭕ 01/01-31/12
Distance: 🚶1km 🚣4km ⊗100m 🛒1km 🚌on the spot.
Remarks: At sports centre, max. 48h.

🅂	**Bruchsal**	17B3

Autohaus Konrad, Murgstrasse 9-13, Gewerbegebiet Stegwiesen.
GPS: n49,13700 e8,59437.⬆.

5 🛏€5 🚰 🗑 💧 included. **Location:** Rural, simple.
Surface: grassy/metalled. ⭕ 01/01-31/12
Distance: 🚶on the spot ⚓10km 🛒10km ⊗300m 🛒1km 🚌300m.

3 🛏free 🚰€1/80liter 🗑 Ch 💧 (4x) WC 🗑.
Location: Urban. **Surface:** metalled. ⭕ 01/01-31/12
Distance: 🚶2km ⚓3km ⊗2km 🛒200m 🚌300m.
Remarks: Max. 3 nights, service during opening hours.

🅂	**Breisach/Rhein** 🚤 🛥	16D4

Wohnmobil-Parkplatz, Josef-Buebstrasse. **GPS:** n48,02944 e7,57576.⬆➡.

🅂	**Buchen/Odenwald** 🍴	17C2

Wohnmobilhafen Morretal, Mühltalstraße. **GPS:** n49,52888 e9,31020.

80 🛏free 8-20h, € 6/night, 2 nights € 10, 3 nights € 13, winter free
🚰€1/100liter 🗑€1 Ch€1. 🏠 **Location:** Urban, simple. **Surface:** asphalted.
⭕ 01/01-31/12 🍽 Other parking in case of festivities
Distance: 🚶300m ⚓on the spot 🎣on the spot ⊗300m 🛒1,5km.
Remarks: Ground of wine festival, bread-service.

🍴	**Breisach/Rhein** 🚤 🛥	16D4

Restaurant Am Rhein, Hafenstrasse 11. **GPS:** n48,04292 e7,57378.⬆.

DE

12 🛏 € 5/24h, 3 days € 20 🚰 €1/100liter ⚡Ch included ♨ (12x)€0,50/kWh WC ᵂ€0,20/time 📶€3/day. 📶 **Location:** Rural, comfortable, quiet.
Surface: grassy. ⬛ 01/01-31/12
Distance: 🚶800m on the spot.
Remarks: Parking Waldbad, use sanitary only during opening hours swimming pool.

🛏S Buchenbach 17A6
Wanglerhof, Vogtweg 1. **GPS:** n47,96820 e7,99269.⬆

10 🛏€ 10 + € 1,20/pp tourist tax 🚰 ⚡Ch included ♨€2/day. 🚿
Location: Rural, simple. **Surface:** grassy.
Distance: 🚶1km ⊗100m 🛒1km. ⬛ 01/01-31/12

🛏S Bühl 17A4
Wohnmobilstellplatz am Schwarzwaldbad, Ludwig-Jahn-strasse 8.
GPS: n48,68862 e8,12995.⬆➡

50 🛏€ 5 🚰 €2/100liter ⚡€2 Ch 🚿. 📶 **Location:** Urban, simple, noisy.
Surface: metalled. ⬛ 01/01-31/12
Distance: 🚶1km 🚲6km ⊗500m 🛒1km ♿on the spot 🏊on the spot.
Remarks: Bread-service.

🛏S Calw 🏰❄ 17B4
Wohnmobilstellplatz Am Alten Bahnhof, Bahnhofstrasse.
GPS: n48,70592 e8,73808.⬆➡

6 🛏free 🚰€1/80liter ⚡€1 Ch€1 ♨ (4x)€0,50/kWh.
Location: Rural, simple, noisy. **Surface:** asphalted. ⬛ 01/01-31/12
Distance: 🚶1km 🛒100m 🚌200m ♿on the spot 🏊on the spot.

Erlebnispark Tripsdrill - Cleebronn

info@tripsdrill.de - www.tripsdrill.de
Located near amusement park
Located in a quit location
BBQ area

Erlebnispark Tripsdrill. GPS: n49,03102 e9,05096.⬆➡
100 🛏free.
Location: Rural, isolated, quiet.
Surface: grassy.
⬛ 28/03/2015-08/11/2015
Distance: 🚶1km ⊗on the spot 🛒3km 🚌400m.
Remarks: Max. 3 days.

Tourist information Cleebronn/Tripsdrill:
😊 Erlebnispark Tripsdrill. Amusement park. ⬛ 8/03/2015-08/11/2015, 9-18h.

🛏S Crailsheim 17D3
Autohof Euro Rastpark, Marco-Polo-Straße 1, Satteldorf.
GPS: n49,18146 e10,06889.
10 🛏€ 5, free with a meal 🚰🔴. **Surface:** metalled. ⬛ 01/01-31/12
Distance: 🚲600m ⊗on the spot.

🛏S Dettenheim 🌊 17B3
Kartbahn Liedolsheim, Kartbahnring 1. **GPS:** n49,14326 e8,43118.

20 🛏free 🚰⚡Ch ♨ (8x)€3 WC ᵂ€2,50. **Location:** Rural, simple, isolated.
Surface: grassy/metalled. ⬛ 01/01-31/12
Distance: 🚶2km 🏊2km 🚌2km ⊗on the spot 🛒5km.
Remarks: Parking at Karting.

🛏S Donaueschingen 🌊🚤🍺 17B6
Prinz Fritz Allee. GPS: n47,94746 e8,51183.⬆➡

10 🛏free ♨ (14x)€1. **Location:** Rural, simple, quiet. **Surface:** grassy.
⬛ 01/01-31/12
Distance: 🚶1,5km 🚲Danube Bike Trail.
Remarks: Max. 2 days, service 300m.

S Donaueschingen 🌊🚤🍺 17B6
Kläranlage, Haberfeld. **GPS:** n47,94931 e8,52209.⬆➡

⌐€1/50liter 🗲 Ch.
🕐 01/01-31/12

Tourist information Donaueschingen:
ℹ️ Tourismus- und Sportamt, Karlstrasse 58, www.donaueschingen.de. Horse city, named after the source of the River danube.
🚲 Der Donau Radweg. Signposted cycle route along the Donau.

| 🏞️ S | **Durbach** ⚓ | **17A5** |

Grol/Festplatz, Almstrasse. **GPS**: n48,49407 e8,01105. ⬆️ ➡️.

15 🛏️€6 🛠️ (8x)€1/8h. 📶 **Location:** Simple. **Surface:** gravel.
🕐 01/01-31/12 💡 festivities
Distance: 🚶500m 🚲10km 🚆50m.

| 🏞️ S | **Durbach** ⚓ | **17A5** |

Halle am Durbach, Wiesenstraße, Ebersweier. **GPS**: n48,50122 e7,98940. ⬆️ ➡️.

6 🛏️€6 ⌐€1/80liter 🗲 Ch 🛠️ (6x)4h. 📶 **Location:** Rural, simple.
Surface: grasstiles. 🕐 01/01-31/12
Distance: 🚶500m 🚲10km 🚆750m 🚆200m.

| 🏞️ S | **Eberbach** 🌿⚓🏞️ | **17C2** |

Wohnmobilstellplatz In der Au, In der Au. **GPS**: n49,46162 e8,97812. ⬆️.

7 🛏️free 🛠️ (6x)€1/2kWh WC. **Location:** Simple, isolated. **Surface:** gravel.
🕐 01/01-31/12 💡 16/08-31/08
Distance: 🚶1km 🏊on the spot.
Remarks: Max. 2 nights.

| 🏞️ S | **Eberbach** 🌿⚓🏞️ | **17C2** |

Wohnmobilstellplatz Neckarlauer, B37, Uferstrasse. **GPS**: n49,46012 e8,98652.
⬆️.

10 🛏️free. **Location:** Central. **Surface:** metalled.
🕐 01/01-31/12 💡 high water
Distance: 🚶300m ⊗300m 🚆500m.

| 🏞️ S | **Eberbach** 🌿⚓🏞️ | **17C2** |

In der Au. **GPS**: n49,46217 e8,97351. ⬆️.
⌐€1/80liter 🗲 Ch.

| 🏞️ S | **Ebringen** | **17A6** |

An der Schönberghalle, Schulstraße 8. **GPS**: n47,95639 e7,77667. ⬆️ ➡️.

3 🛏️free. **Location:** Simple. **Surface:** grasstiles. 🕐 01/01-31/12
Distance: 🚴7,6km 🏊on the spot
Remarks: Max. 2 days, max. 6,5m.

| 🏞️ S | **Ehingen** 🌿⚓🏞️🍺 | **17D5** |

Wohnmobilstellplatz, Am Stadion. **GPS**: n48,28053 e9,73571. ⬆️.

10 🛏️free ⌐€1/100liter 🗲 Ch 🛠️ (4x)€1/4h. **Surface:** metalled.
🕐 01/01-31/12
Distance: 🚶1km 🚶1km ⊗on the spot 🚆500m 🚆10m
🚲 Danube Bike Trail.

| 🍷 S | **Eichstetten** | **17A6** |

Weingut Köbelin, Altweg 131. **GPS**: n48,09472 e7,72083.

5 🛏️€13 🚰 🗲 Ch 🛠️ included. 🐕
Location: Rural, comfortable, isolated, quiet. **Surface:** gravel/sand.

| 🍴 S | **Eigeltingen** | **17C6** |

Landgasthof Mönchhof, Mönchhof. **GPS**: n47,88094 e8,95278.

4 🛏️guests free 🚰 🗲 Ch 🛠️. **Surface:** metalled. 🕐 01/01-31/12
Distance: 🚶6km ⊗on the spot 🏊4km 🚆on the spot.

DE

Eisenbach 🏔 ❄ 17B6

Reisemobilpark Höchstberg. GPS: n47,94938 e8,25441. 🔼.

20 🛏 € 8 + Kurtaxe € 1,60/pp 🚰 €1/100liter 🗑 Ch 💧 (20x) 🔌 included, only in summer. 🛒 **Location:** Rural, comfortable, quiet. **Surface:** grassy/gravel.
🅿 01/01-31/12
Distance: ⊗ on the spot 🧍 on the spot.
Remarks: Altitude 1033m, at sports park.

Ellwangen 18A3

Maxi-Autohof Ellwangen, Max-Eyth-Strasse 1. **GPS:** n48,95628 e10,18319. 🔼.

15 🛏 € 5/night 🚰 🗑 Ch WC 🔌 🔘 🛜 against payment. **Location:** Highway.
Surface: asphalted. 🅿 01/01-31/12
Distance: ⛽3km ⊗ on the spot 🛒1km.

Emmendingen 17A6

Wohnmobilstellplatz am Sportfeld, Am Sportfeld. **GPS:** n48,11869 e7,84154.
🔼.

20 🛏 free 🚰 €1/80liter 🗑 Ch. **Location:** Urban, simple. **Surface:** asphalted.
🅿 01/01-31/12
Distance: ⛽1km ⊗400m 🛒600m.
Remarks: In front of swimmingpool, max. 3 days.

Endingen am Kaiserstuhl 17A6

P2 Stadthalle, Freiburger Weg. **GPS:** n48,13830 e7,70321. 🔼 ➡.

20 🛏 free. **Location:** Urban, simple, central.
Surface: asphalted/metalled.
Distance: ⛽200m ⊗200m.

Eppingen 🌿 ⛲ 17C3

Wohnmobilhalt am Parkweg, Am Altstadring. **GPS:** n49,13793 e8,91402. 🔼.

4 🛏 free 🚰 €1/80liter 🗑 €1 Ch €1 💧 (4x)€1. **Location:** Rural, comfortable.
Surface: metalled. 🅿 01/01-31/12
Distance: ⛽500m ⊗ on the spot 🚰500m 🧺 on the spot 🧍 on the spot.

Esslingen am Neckar 🌿 ⛲ 🍽 🏛 17C4

Äußerer Burgplatz, Mülbergerstraße. **GPS:** n48,74713 e9,31064. 🔼.

2 🛏 free. **Location:** Urban, simple. **Surface:** metalled.
🅿 01/01-31/12
Distance: ⛽1km ⛰1km ⊗ on the spot 🛒1km 🚰300m.
Remarks: Max. 48h.

Ettenheim 17A5

Ernst Caravan und Freizeit Center, Rudolf Hell Straße 32-44.
GPS: n48,27431 e7,78161. 🔼.

30 🛏 free 🚰 €1 🗑 €1 Ch €1 💧 (12x)€0,50/kWh.
Location: Highway, simple. **Surface:** metalled. 🅿 01/01-31/12
Distance: 🚤500m.
Remarks: Motorhome dealer, accessory shop, repairs.

Ettlingen 17B4

Wohnmobilstellplatz Am Freibad, Schöllbronner strasse.
GPS: n48,93561 e8,41747. 🔼 ➡.

14 🛏 free 🚰 €1 🗑 Ch 💧 (8x)€1/kWh. **Location:** Urban, simple.
Surface: asphalted. 🅿 01/01-31/12
Distance: ⛽100m 🚲3,3km ⊗100m 🛒700m 🧺 on the spot 🚲 on the spot 🧍 on the spot.

DE

Remarks: Parking swimming pool, max. 48h.

🏕S **Filderstadt** 17C4

Parkplatz P2, Tübinger Strasse 40. **GPS**: n48,67347 e9,21456.⬆️↑

8 🍴€7/24h 🚰€1/80liter 🗑Ch 🔌(8x)€0,50/kWh,16Amp. 🏠
⬛ 01/01-31/12
Distance: 🚶500m ⊗500m 🛒500m 🚲500m.

🏕S **Freiburg** 🚣⛴❄🎿 17A6

Reisemobilplatz Freiburg, Bissierstrasse / Am Eschholzpark.
GPS: n47,99915 e7,82643.⬆️➡️

80 🍴€ 8, motorhome >7m + € 0,50/50cm 🚰€1/100liter 🗑Ch 🔌
(20x)€0,50/kWh 🚿free.🛁
Location: Urban, comfortable. **Surface:** asphalted/gravel.
⬛ 01/01-31/12
Distance: 🚶Old city centre 1,5km 🚴4,3km ⊗450m.
Remarks: Max. 72h, green zone: environmental badge obligatory.

🏕S **Freiburg** 🚣⛴❄🎿 17A6

WV-Südcaravan, Hanferstrasse 30, Hochdorf. **GPS**: n48,04146 e7,81473.⬆️

6 🍴free 🚰€1/80liter 🗑Ch. **Location:** Urban, simple.
Surface: asphalted/metalled. ⬛ 01/01-31/12
Distance: 🚶Old city centre 10km 🚴3km ⊗300m 🛒3km.
Remarks: During opening hours.

🏕S **Freudenberg** 🌊 17C2

P. Freudenberg-Süd, Hauptstrasse. **GPS**: n49,74001 e9,31938.⬆️

10 🍴€ 5/night 🚰€1/15minutes 🗑Ch 🔌(6x)€1/8h,16Amp.🛁
Location: Rural, comfortable. **Surface:** metalled. ⬛ 01/01-31/12

Distance: 🚶50m 🏊20m 🚤20m ⊗300m 🛒500m.

🏕S **Friedrichshafen** 24D1

Stellplatz Friedrichshafen, Lindauerstrasse 2. **GPS**: n47,65025 e9,49597.⬆️➡️

20 🍴free, 01/04-31/10 € 12 🚰€1/80liter 🗑Ch WC 🚿.🏠
Surface: asphalted/metalled. ⬛ 01/01-31/12
Distance: 🏊200m 🚤200m 🛒on the spot.
Remarks: Max. 3 nights, payment only with coins.

🏕S **Gaildorf** 17D3

Bleichgärten. **GPS**: n49,00224 e9,76587.⬆️➡️

7 🍴free 🚰🗑Ch 🔌(4x)free,16Amp. **Location:** Simple. **Surface:** metalled.
⬛ 01/01-31/12
Distance: 🚶500m ⊗400m 🛒500m 🚲500m.

🏕 **Gailingen am Hochrhein** 🌊 24C1

Rheinuferpark, Strandweg. **GPS**: n47,69051 e8,75621.⬆️➡️
20 🍴€ 15. 🏠 ⬛ 01/04-31/10
Distance: 🚶1km 🏊on the spot.

🏕S **Gammertingen** 17C5

Reutlingerstrasse. **GPS**: n48,25611 e9,21056.

8 🍴free 🔌(6x)€2/12h. **Surface:** grassy/gravel. ⬛ 01/01-31/12
Distance: 🚶1km 🏊on the spot 🚤on the spot ⊗1km 🛒700m.

DE

Geisingen 17B6

Reisemobilstellplatz Geisingen - Geisingen

info@geisingen.de - www.geisingen.de

**Located in a quit location
Ideal base for walking and cycling
Flat motorhome pitches**

Reisemobilstellplatz Geisingen, Am Espen 8. **GPS:** n47,92016 e8,65153.
37 €7 €1/80liter Ch included (37x)€1/4kWh. **Surface:** gravel.
01/01-31/12
Distance: 300m 2km 50m 300m 300m 500m 100m
100m.

Gernsbach 17B4

Parkplatz Murginsel, Schlossstrasse/Klingelstrasse. **GPS:** n48,75934 e8,33900.

8 €5 €1/100liter Ch (8x)€1/12h WC. **Location:** Rural, simple.
Surface: asphalted. 01/01-31/12
Distance: 500m on the spot 500m 1km on the spot
on the spot on the spot.
Remarks: Max. 7 days.

Gernsbach 17B4

Am Schwimmbad 1, Oberstrot. **GPS:** n48,74239 e8,34186.

5 free. **Location:** Rural, simple. **Surface:** grassy.
01/01-31/12
Distance: 200m 200m on the spot on the spot.
Remarks: At swimming pool.

Giengen 18A4

Reisemobilstation Charlottenhöhle, Lonetalstrasse 60, Hürben.
GPS: n48,58412 e10,21203.

15 €7 €2 Ch (6x)€2/12h,16Amp WC €2. **Location:** Rural, quiet.
Surface: gravel. 01/01-31/12
Remarks: At prehistoric cave, coins at Hölenhaus.

Giengen 18A4

Am Schießberg, Auf dem Schießberg. **GPS:** n48,62975 e10,25159.

8 free. **Location:** Simple. **Surface:** gravel.
01/01-31/12
Distance: 1,5km 4,3km 1,5km 1,5km.
Tourist information Giengen:
Charlottenhöhle. Caves. 8.30-11.30h, 13.30-16.30h, Su 8.30-16.30h.

Göppingen 17D4

Hohen Staufenhalle, P1, Lorcherstrasse. **GPS:** n48,71176 e9,64816.

10 free €1/80liter Ch. **Location:** Urban. **Surface:** asphalted.
01/01-31/12
Distance: 1km 1km 1km.
Remarks: Max. 2 nights.

Grossbottwar 17C3

Parkplatz an der Wunnensteinhalle, In den Frauengärten.
GPS: n49,00363 e9,28739.

3 free. **Surface:** metalled. 01/01-31/12
Distance: 400m 400m 200m.
Remarks: Max. 3 nights.

Gschwend 17D4

Naturbadesee, Frickenhofer Strasse. **GPS:** n48,93603 e9,75143.

DE

3 🛏free. **Location:** Rural. **Surface:** forest soil. ⬛ 01/01-31/12
Distance: 🚶1,5km.

| S | Gschwend | 17D4 |

Joosenhofer Sägmühle. **GPS:** n48,92312 e9,77393. ⬆➡.

free ⛽€1/80liter 🚽Ch. **Surface:** asphalted. ⬛ 01/01-31/12

| S | Güglingen | 17C3 |

Oberes Tal. **GPS:** n49,06492 e8,99489. ⬆➡.

6 🛏free ⛽€1 🚽Ch. **Location:** Rural, simple. **Surface:** metalled.
⬛ 01/01-31/12
Distance: 🚶700m ⊗500m 🏪Aldi-Lidl 500m 🚴on the spot 🚶on the spot.
Remarks: At swimming pool, max. 5 nights.

| S | Haigerloch | 17C5 |

Wohnmobilstellplatz Haigerloch, Weildorfer Kreuz 1. **GPS:** n48,36875 e8,79384.
10 🛏free ⛽🚽Ch✍. **Surface:** asphalted.
⬛ 01/01-31/12
Distance: 🚶300m.
Remarks: Max. 4 days.

| S | Hardheim | 17C2 |

Am Alten Bahnhof, Bretzinger Straße. **GPS:** n49,60245 e9,47126. ⬆➡.

12 🛏free ⛽€1/80liter 🚽Ch free ⚡(8x)€1/2kWh.
Location: Rural, comfortable, noisy. **Surface:** gravel. ⬛ 01/01-31/12
Distance: 🚶1km ⊗1km 🏪1km.

| S | Haslach/Kinzigtal | 17A5 |

Klosterplatz, Ringstraße. **GPS:** n48,27572 e8,08509. ⬆.

20 🛏free. **Location:** Urban, simple. **Surface:** metalled.
⬛ 01/01-31/12
Distance: 🚶50m ⊗150m 🏪500m 🚉100m.

| S | Haslach/Kinzigtal | 17A5 |

Parkplatz Eichenbach-sporthalle, Strickerweg. **GPS:** n48,27854 e8,07968. ⬆.

10 🛏free. **Location:** Simple. **Surface:** metalled. ⬛ 01/01-31/12
Distance: 🚶500m 🏪300m.

| S | Haslach/Kinzigtal | 17A5 |

Waldseeparkplatz, Waldseeweg. **GPS:** n48,27161 e8,09148. ⬆.

10 🛏free. **Location:** Rural, simple. **Surface:** asphalted.
⬛ 01/01-31/12
Distance: 🚶1km ⊗200m 🏪1km.

| S | Hausach | 17A5 |

Waldstadion, Waldstraße. **GPS:** n48,28058 e8,17829. ⬆➡.

4 🛏free ⛽WC. **Location:** Rural, simple, simple, quiet, noisy.
Surface: gravel/sand. ⬛ 01/01-31/12
Distance: 🚶500m ⊗100m.

| S | Hausach | 17A5 |

Badepark, Schanze 3. **GPS:** n48,28620 e8,16589. ⬆➡.

6 ⏃free. **Location:** Simple. **Surface:** metalled. ▢ 01/01-31/12
Distance: ⊗on the spot 🛒500m.
Remarks: Nearby swimming pool.

⏃S Hechingen 17C5
Freizeitanlage Domäne Areal, Brielhof 1. **GPS:** n48,33773 e8,94966.
18 ⏃€18 🔌included. **Surface:** metalled. ▢ 01/01-31/12
Distance: 🚶2km ⊗on the spot.
Remarks: Reduction at restaurants and Golf Park.

⏃S Hechingen 17C5
Zollernalbcamping, Niederhechingerstrasse. **GPS:** n48,35797 e8,96093.
20 ⏃€6 🚰€1 ⏃Ch 🔌€1/kWh WC€2 ⏃€2. **Surface:** metalled.
▢ 01/01-31/12 ▢ sanitary building: 01/11-01/04
Distance: 🚲on the spot 🚶on the spot. **Remarks:** Waste dump € 2/day.

⏃S Heidenheim 18A4
In den Seewiesen. **GPS:** n48,69455 e10,16410. ⬆️➡️

22 ⏃€ 2/day 🚰€1/70liter ⏃€1 Ch 🔌(18x)€1/6h,16Amp. 🚮
Location: Rural, simple. **Surface:** asphalted/gravel. ▢ 01/01-31/12
Distance: 🚲5km 🛒1km.

⏃S Heilbronn 🌼🍴☕ 17C3
Wertwiesenpark, Neckarhalde. **GPS:** n49,13047 e9,20469. ⬆️➡️

20 ⏃free 🚰€1/100liter ⏃Ch 🔌(12x)€0,50/kWh. **Location:** Comfortable.
Surface: metalled. ▢ 01/01-31/12
Distance: 🚶2km 🚲7km ⊗100m 🚌500m.

⏃S Heiligenberg 🌼 17C6
Sennerei Schläge, Betenbrunner strasse. **GPS:** n47,81892 e9,31445. ⬆️➡️

---

10 ⏃€5/16-09h 🚰€0,50 ⏃€0,50 Ch. 🚮 **Surface:** grassy/metalled.
▢ 01/01-31/12
Distance: 🚶300m 🏊300m ⛵300m ⊗200m 🛒bakery 200m.
Remarks: Max. 2 nights.

⏃S Herbrechtingen 🌼 18A4
P7 Eselstalparkplatz, Baumschulenweg. **GPS:** n48,61758 e10,17411. ⬆️➡️

15 ⏃€7 🚰€2 ⏃Ch 🔌€2/24h. **Location:** Rural, quiet. **Surface:** asphalted.
▢ 01/01-31/12
Remarks: Check in at Hölenhaus.

⏃S Hessigheim 17C3
Fasanenhof, Römerweg 1. **GPS:** n49,00939 e9,18877. ⬆️
15 ⏃€5 🚰. **Location:** Rural, simple. ▢ 01/01-31/12
Distance: 🚲3,5km ⊗on the spot 🛒shop with farm products 🚲on the spot 🚶on the spot.
Remarks: Farm/restaurant/Biergarten/shop.

⏃S Hessigheim 17C3
Felsengarten Kellerei Besigheim e.G., Am Felsengarten 1.
GPS: n48,99612 e9,18068. ⬆️

5 ⏃guests free 🚰🔌. **Surface:** asphalted. ▢ 01/01-31/12
Distance: 🚶1km ⊗on the spot 🛒1km.
Remarks: Max. 2 nights.

⏃S Heubach 17D4
Am Freibad, Mögglinger Strasse. **GPS:** n48,79802 e9,93831.

6 ⏃€6 🚰€1/90liter ⏃Ch€0,50. **Surface:** grasstiles. ▢ 01/01-31/12
Distance: ⊗200m 🛒Lidl 400m.

⏃S Höchenschwand ☕ 24B1
Natursportzentrum. **GPS:** n47,73652 e8,15990. ⬆️➡️

DE

12 🛏 € 7 🚰 ⚡ Ch 💧 (12x) € 1/6h WC. **Location:** Rural, comfortable.
Surface: gravel. 🕐 01/01-31/12
Distance: 🚶400m ⊗100m 🚌600m 🛒on the spot.

| 📷 | Holzmaden | 17D4 |

Urwelt-Museum Hauff, Aichelbergerstrasse 75/90. **GPS:** n48,63482 e9,52771.
6 🛏 free. **Surface:** metalled. 🕐 01/01-31/12
Distance: 🚶3km 🚲2,2km.
Remarks: Max. 1 night.

| 🍴 S | Hornberg 🎡 🚣 ❄ | 17B6 |

Hotel Schöne Aussicht, Schöne Aussicht 1, Niederwasser.
GPS: n48,19443 e8,18494.
4 🛏 € 8 🚰 💧 included.
Distance: ⊗on the spot.

| 📷 S | Hüfingen | 17B6 |

Bräunlinger Straße. **GPS:** n47,92361 e8,48707. ⬆➡.

22 🛏 € 5 🚰 € 1 ⚡ Ch 💧 € 1. **Location:** Urban, comfortable, noisy.
Surface: grasstiles. 🕐 01/01-31/12
Distance: 🚶300m ⊗300m.
Remarks: Thursday market.

| 📷 S | Hülben 🎡 | 17D5 |

Phoenix Wohnmobihafen, Kaltentalstrasse. **GPS:** n48,52620 e9,41227. ⬆➡.

10 🛏 free 🚰 € 0,50/80liter ⚡ Ch 💧 (6x) € 0,50/kWh. **Surface:** gravel.
🕐 01/01-31/12
Distance: 🚶400m 🛒400m 🚌500m 🚲Vordere-Alb-Radweg 🚶on the spot.
🛒on the spot.
Remarks: Max. 4 days.

| 📷 S | Ihringen | 17A6 |

Kaiserstuhl Camping, Nachtwaid 5. **GPS:** n48,03083 e7,65778. ⬆➡.

6 🛏 € 14,60 + tourist tax 🚰 ⚡ Ch 💧 € 1,80/3kWh WC 🚿 included. 🚻
Location: Rural, comfortable. **Surface:** asphalted/metalled.
🕐 31/03-30/10
Distance: 🚶600m ⊗200m.

| 📷 S | Isny | 25A1 |

Parkplatz An der Untere Mühle, Seidenstrasse 43. **GPS:** n47,69457 e10,03780.
⬆➡.

10 🛏 € 7,50 + € 1,50/pp tourist tax 🚰 € 1/80liter ⚡ Ch 💧 (8x) € 0,50/kWh
WC. 🚻 **Location:** Urban. **Surface:** asphalted/gravel. 🕐 01/01-31/12
Distance: 🚶300m ⊗100m 🛒300m 🚌200m.
Remarks: Max. 2 nights.

| 📷 S | Isny | 25A1 |

Caravans Dethleffs, Rangenbergweg. **GPS:** n47,69938 e10,05490. ⬆.

9 🛏 € 5 + € 1,50/pp tourist tax, clients Dethleffs free 🚰 ⚡ Ch 💧 (9x)
included. **Surface:** metalled. 🕐 01/01-31/12
Distance: 🚶1km 🛒1km 🚌1km ⊗1,4km 🛒500m.
Remarks: Max. 3 nights.

| 😊 | Kaisersbach | 17D4 |

Schwaben-Park, Hofwiesen 11, Gmeinweiler. **GPS:** n48,90304 e9,65484. ⬆.

10 🛏 free. 🕐 01/04-31/10
Remarks: Inclining pitches.
Tourist information Kaisersbach:
🎡 Schwaben-Park. Amusement park. 🕐 Easter-Oct 9-18h.

DE

Kappelrodeck — 17A5

Wohnmobileck am Heidenhof, Grüner Winkel. GPS: n48,58370 e8,12650.

18 € 5/day, 3 days € 10, 7 days € 20 €1/100liter Ch (8x)€1/2kWh. **Location:** Rural, simple, quiet. **Surface:** gravel/metalled. 01/01-31/12
Distance: 800m 150m 500m on the spot on the spot.
Remarks: Max. 6 nights.

Karlsruhe — 17B3

Ettlinger Allee. GPS: n48,98761 e8,40412.
5 free. **Surface:** asphalted. 01/01-31/12
Distance: centre 2,5km metro 400m.

Karlsruhe — 17B3

Am Yachthafen Maxau, Maxau am Rhein. GPS: n49,03720 e8,30583.

12 . 01/01-31/12
Distance: Karlsruhe 9km on the spot 2km.
Remarks: Along the Rhine river.

Kehl — 17A5

Reisemobilstellplatz Hurst, An den Sportanlagen 1, Kehl-Auenheim. GPS: n48,60653 e7,83146.

18 €6 €1 Ch (12x)€2/2kWh WC €1.
Location: Rural, simple, quiet. **Surface:** asphalted/grassy. 01/01-31/12
Distance: 500m on the spot 500m on the spot on the spot.
Remarks: Check in at cafe zum Ganz.

Kehl — 17A5

Am Wasserturm, Schwimbadstrasse. GPS: n48,56381 e7,81498.

40 €6 €1/100liter Ch (16x)€0,50/kWh. **Location:** Urban, comfortable, quiet. **Surface:** grassy/metalled. 01/01-31/12
Distance: 100m 500m on the spot on the spot on the spot.
Remarks: Max. 3 days.

Kehl — 17A5

Bürstner-Service-Centrum, Elsässer strasse 80, Kehl-Neumühl. GPS: n48,57010 e7,84042.

6 free €1/100liter Ch (6x)€1/kWh WC . **Location:** Rural. **Surface:** asphalted. 01/01-31/12
Distance: 1km 100m 600m on the spot on the spot.

Kenzingen — 17A6

Ritter's Weingut, Rossleiteweg 1. GPS: n48,18739 e7,78343.

15 € 10, 2 pers.incl. € 2/pp €2,50/day WC included.
Location: Comfortable. **Surface:** grassy/gravel. 01/01-31/12
Distance: 7,5km on the spot.

Kirchberg/Jagst — 17D3

Wanderparkplatz Kirchberg-Tal, Hohen Loher Strasse. GPS: n49,20367 e9,98344.

10 free. **Surface:** gravel. 01/01-31/12

Kisslegg — 17D6

Wohnmobilhafen Kißlegg, Strandbadweg. GPS: n47,79602 e9,87950.
24 € 5-7 €1/100liter (5x)€0,50/kWh WC .
Surface: metalled. 01/01-31/12
Distance: 800m 100m 100m 100m 1km 400m.

Kisslegg — 17D6

Familiefreizeitgelände St Anna, Le Pouliguenstrasse. **GPS:** n47,79119 e9,87229.

3 free. **Surface:** grassy/metalled. 01/01-31/12
Distance: 800m 500m 500m.
Remarks: Max. 2 nights.

Kisslegg — 17D6

Hotel Sonnenstrahl, Sebastian Kneipp strasse 1. **GPS:** n47,78421 e9,87973.
3 free. **Surface:** asphalted/metalled. 01/01-31/12
Distance: 800m on the spot 800m.
Remarks: Max. 2 nights.

Königschaffhausen — 17A6

Wohnmobilgarten im Kirschenhof Schmidt, Königsweg 5.
GPS: n48,14277 e7,66273.

16 € 11 + tourist tax € 1/pp Ch WC included € 1 in Café.
Location: Rural, comfortable. **Surface:** gravel/metalled. 01/01-31/12
Distance: 500m on the spot.
Remarks: Wifi in café.

Königsfeld — 17B6

Reisemobilpark Bregnitzhof, Buchenberger Strasse 34.
GPS: n48,14028 e8,40583.

21 € 8/night €0,50 Ch €1/8h.
Location: Rural, luxurious, quiet. **Surface:** gravel. 01/01-31/12
Distance: 1km 10 min walking.
Remarks: Check in between 14-19h, 18-holes golf course, Saunalandschaft Bregnitzhof.

Konstanz — 24C1

Parkplatz Döbele, Döbeleplatz. **GPS:** n47,65794 e9,16933.

12 € 1/h, € 15/24h Ch WC included. **Surface:** asphalted/metalled.
01/01-31/12
Distance: 1km 800m 800m 200m 800m 500m.
Remarks: Max. 24h.

Korb — 17C4

Reisemobilstellplatz Unterm Korber Kopf, Brucknerstrasse 14.
GPS: n48,84597 e9,35544.

6 € 3 €0,50/80liter Ch (6x)€0,50/kWh. **Surface:** metalled.
01/01-31/12
Distance: 400m Gaststätte 300m 500m.
Remarks: Coins at restaurant.

Kressbronn — 24D1

Wohnmobilstellplatz Tunau, Tunauerweg 4. **GPS:** n47,58999 e9,57512.

40 € 17,50-21 Ch (40x) WC €1,50/pp included.
Surface: asphalted/grassy. 01/04-31/10
Distance: 1km 1km 1km on the spot 1km.

Kressbronn — 24D1

Gohren am See. **GPS:** n47,58818 e9,56256.
11 € 12 Ch €3/12h WC €1/day. **Surface:** grassy/gravel.
01/04-15/10
Distance: Bodensee.

Külsheim — 17D2

Am Schloss Külsheim, Kirchbergweg. **GPS:** n49,67123 e9,52255.

12 free €0,50/80liter Ch (12x)€0,50/kWh. **Location:** Rural.
Surface: grasstiles. 01/01-31/12 10/09-25/09

DE

Distance: 300m.

Ladenburg ⬏ 17B2

Wohnmobilstellplatz Ladenburg, Heidelberger Straße.
GPS: n49,46596 e8,61460. ⬆.

34 €10 €1/80liter Ch €1/2kWh. Location: Urban, comfortable, central, quiet. **Surface**: grassy. 01/01-31/12
Distance: Altstadt 500m, Heidelberg 10km 3km 200m 200m.

Langenau 18A5

Karlstraße. **GPS**: n48,50193 e10,12203. ⬆.
4 €5 €0,50/70liter €0,50/kWh. **Location**: Simple. **Surface**: metalled.
01/01-31/12
Distance: 500m 3,2km 300m 1,2km.

Langenbrettach 17C3

Freibad Langenbeutingen, Schwabbacker Strasse 24, Langenbeutingen.
GPS: n49,21227 e9,40767. ⬆.

3 free. **Location**: Rural. **Surface**: asphalted.
Remarks: Parking swimming pool.

Langenburg 17D3

Am Freibad, In der Strut 5. **GPS**: n49,24973 e9,86681. ⬆. 01/01-31/12
2 free. **Surface**: gravel. 01/01-31/12
Distance: 1km.
Remarks: Not accessible coming from the west.

Lauchringen ⬏ 24B1

An der Wutach, Badstrasse. **GPS**: n47,62556 e8,31361. ➡.

20 free, 01/04-01/11 €5 Ch included (16x)€2/24h.
Location: Rural, comfortable, quiet. **Surface**: gravel.
01/01-31/12 service: 01/11-01/04
Distance: on the spot on the spot.
Remarks: Pay at town hall or swimming pool, caution € 20, key electricity at pool.

Lauda-Königshofen 17D2

Badstrasse, Lauda. **GPS**: n49,55886 e9,70099. ⬆.

4 free. **Location**: Rural, simple. **Surface**: asphalted.
01/01-31/12
Distance: 1km 500m.
Remarks: Parking at swimming pool.

Lauda-Königshofen 17D2

Gasthaus Zur Lamm, St. Josefstrasse 30-32, Marbach. **GPS**: n49,56568 e9,72834.
⬆ ➡.

12 €5/24h (12x)included WC free, at restaurant.
Location: Rural, simple, quiet. **Surface**: asphalted.
01/01-31/12 Restaurant: Mo
Distance: on the spot on the spot.

Laufenburg 24A1

Laufenburg Baden P6, Andelsbachstraße. **GPS**: n47,56585 e8,06677. ⬆ ➡.

6 €5 €2/5minutes Ch €2 (6x)€0,50/kWh. **Location**: Urban, quiet.
Surface: concrete. 01/01-31/12
Remarks: Along the Rhine river.

Laupheim 17D5

Schloß Grosslaupheim, Klaus-Graf-Stauffenberg-Strasse.
GPS: n48,23128 e9,88872. ⬆ ➡.

7 €8 €0,50 €0,50 Ch €0,50. **Location**: Rural. **Surface**: metalled.
01/01-31/12
Distance: on the spot.

Leonberg 17C4

Parkplatz Steinstrasse, Steinstrasse. **GPS**: n48,79705 e9,01751. ⬆.

5 🛏free, Mo-Fr 8-18h € 2,50. 🚻 **Surface:** metalled.
⚪ 01/01-31/12 ⚫ Sa 5-13h
Distance: 🏪400m ⊗150m 🚉300m 🚏on the spot.

🛏S **Leutkirch im Allgäu** 18A6
Wohnmobilstellplatz Leutkirch, Kemptener Straße. **GPS:** n47,82228 e10,03939.
⬆.

14 🛏€6 🚰€1/100liter 🗑Ch 🔌€0,50/kWh. **Surface:** asphalted.
⚪ 01/01-31/12
Distance: 🏪1km ⊗300m.

🛏S **Löffingen** 🏊 17B6
Waldbad Löffingen, Am Waldbad. **GPS:** n47,90017 e8,33287.⬆➡.

7 🛏€ 8 + € 2/pp tourist tax, 01/10-31/05 free 🚰🗑🔌(4x)included
🗑€0,50,At swimming pool. **Location:** Comfortable. **Surface:** concrete.
⚪ 01/01-31/12 ⚫ service 01/10-01/05
Distance: 🏊Swimming pool ⊗on the spot.
Remarks: Check in at pay-desk of swimming pool.
Tourist information Löffingen:
🌐 Schwarzwaldpark. Game preserve and summer toboggan slide (€ 1.02 a time). ⚪ Easter-Oct 9-18h.

🛏S **Malsch** 17B4
Gast Caravanning, Daimlerstr. 20b. **GPS:** n48,89079 e8,30747.⬆.

6 🛏free 🚰€1/80liter 🗑Ch. **Location:** Simple. **Surface:** asphalted/metalled.
⚪ 01/01-31/12
Distance: 🚗7,6km.
Remarks: Motorhome dealer, accessory shop.

🛏S **Mannheim/Friedrichsfeld** 17B2
Güma Reisemobile, Steinzeugstrasse 21. **GPS:** n49,44570 e8,56780.⬆.

3 🛏free 🚰🗑Ch 🔌WCfree.
Location: Simple, noisy. **Surface:** metalled.
⚪ 01/01-31/12
Distance: 🏪10km 🚲1km 🚉1km 🚏300m.
Remarks: Max. 3 nights, sanitary use during shop opening hours.

🛏S **Marbach am Neckar** 🌐 17C4
Parkplatz Bolzplatz, Poppenweiler/Weimarstrasse. **GPS:** n48,93389 e9,26278.
⬆.

5 🛏€5 🚰🗑Ch.🚾 **Location:** Rural, simple. **Surface:** metalled.
⚪ 01/01-31/12
Distance: 🏪1km 🚲6,2km ⊗100m 🚉600m 🚏500m.
Remarks: Max. 2 nights, service: Gruppenklärwerk Häldenmühle, L1100.

🛏 **Markelsheim** 17D2
Engelbergparkplatz, Engelsbergstrasse. **GPS:** n49,47537 e9,83474.⬆➡.

2 🛏free. **Location:** Urban. **Surface:** asphalted.
⚪ 01/01-31/12 ⚫ week of Whitsuntide
Distance: 🏪300m ⊗300m.
Remarks: At fire-station, max. 2 nights.

🛏S **Meckenbeuren** 24D1
Wohnmobilplatz Besenwirtschaft Georgshof, Pfingstweiderstrasse 10-12/1, Reute. **GPS:** n47,68022 e9,55308.⬆➡.

9 🛏€9 🚰🗑Ch 🔌(9x)€0,50/kWh WC 🗑€1. **Surface:** grassy/gravel.
⚪ 01/01-31/12

DE

Distance: ⚡on the spot ⚓Bodensee 5km ⊗200m �
100m.

⬛S   **Meersburg/Bodensee** 🌿🏕🛶   **24C1**
Ergeten, Allmendweg. **GPS:** n47,70160 e9,26898.⬆.

35+60 🍴€ 10/24h 🚰€1/100liter 🔌€1 Ch 🔌€0,50/kWh WC.🚮🚐
Surface: metalled. ⬛ 01/01-31/12
Distance: ⚡1km ⊗100m 🚍50m 🚌shuttle to centre.
Remarks: At edge of city, + 2x parking Allmendweg P1 n47.70211, o 9.26983,
P2 n47,70159, o 9,27172.

⬛S   **Meißenheim**   **17A5**
Wohnmobilpark Ortenau, Winkelstrasse 36. **GPS:** n48,41616 e7,77736.⬆➡.

24+24 🍴€ 5/day 🚰€1/120liter 🔌🔌(24x)€1/kWh.🚐
Location: Rural, comfortable. **Surface:** gravel/metalled. ⬛ 01/01-31/12
Distance: ⚡500m 🚍800m.

⬛S   **Memmingen** 👄   **18A6**
Wohnmobilstellplatz Memmingen, Colmarer Straße/Hemmerlestraße.
GPS: n47,99531 e10,18245.⬆➡.

20 🍴€ 1/2h, € 5/24h 🚰€1/100liter 🔌Ch 🔌(18x)€0,50/kWh.🚮🚐
Location: Urban, simple. **Surface:** metalled. ⬛ 01/01-31/12
Distance: ⚡900m 🚲2,2km ⊗700m 🚍Lidl 600m.
Remarks: Max. 3 days.

⬛S   **Mengen** 🍴🍽   **17C6**
Südsee III, Uferweg 25. **GPS:** n48,03117 e9,28265.⬆.

50 🍴€ 9,50 🚰€1/80liter 🔌Ch 🔌(16x)€0,50/kWh WC ⬛included 📶.
Surface: gravel. ⬛ 01/01-31/12
Distance: ⚡500m ⚓on the spot 🛶on the spot 🚍500m.

Remarks: Incl. access Badesee.

⬛S   **Messkirch** 🌿   **17C6**
Messplatz P2, Am Stachus. **GPS:** n47,99381 e9,11514.⬆.

5 🍴free 🚰€1/80liter 🔌Ch WC. **Surface:** metalled.
⬛ 01/01-31/12, service 01/04-30/09
Distance: ⚡500m ⊗400m 🚍200m 🚌500m.

⬛S   **Metzingen** 🏕👄   **17C5**
Reisemobilplatz Outletcity Metzingen, Stetterstrasse 4.
GPS: n48,53241 e9,27574.⬆.

20 🍴€ 10 🚰🔌Chincluded 🔌(6x)€3,16Amp. **Surface:** gravel.
⬛ 01/01-31/12
Distance: ⚡800m ⚓800m ⊗800m 🚍800m 🚌shuttle every 15 min.

⬛S   **Mosbach** 🌿🍴👄   **17C3**
Wasemweg. **GPS:** n49,36139 e9,14833.⬆.

10 🍴free 🚰€1/150liter 🔌Ch 🔌(10x)€1/12h.
Location: Rural, comfortable, quiet. **Surface:** concrete. ⬛ 01/01-31/12
Distance: ⚡800m.

⬛S   **Mössingen**   **17C5**
Wohnmobilstellplatz Firstwald, Firstwaldstraße, Kernstadt.
GPS: n48,41348 e9,06915.⬆.

10 🍴free 🚰€1 🔌€1 Ch 🔌(10x)€0,50/kWh,16Amp. **Surface:** grasstiles.
⬛ 01/01-31/12
Distance: ⚡1,5km ⊗500m 🚍1km 🚌100m.

⬛   **Muggensturm**   **17B4**
Muggensturm, Vogesenstraße. **GPS:** n48,87946 e8,28721.⬆.

3 🛏free. **Location:** Urban, simple. **Surface:** gravel.
🅾 01/01-31/12
Distance: 🚶1,5km 🚲4,4km ⛱beach 100m.

| 🐾S | | Mühlberg 🏰 | 18A6 |

Ferienhof Musch, Unterer weg 7. **GPS:** n47,98534 e9,98697.⬆

3 🛏€ 10, 2 pers.incl 🔌🍽 Ch 🚿 (3x)included WC 🚽💧€3 📶€2,50/day.
Surface: grassy/metalled. 🅾 01/01-31/12
Distance: 🚶10km ⛱100m 🎣100m ⊗10km 🛒10km.
Remarks: Bread-service.

| 🛏 | | Müllheim 🏛 | 24A1 |

Am Engelberg, Hügelheim. **GPS:** n47,83282 e7,62320.⬆➡

2 🛏free. **Location:** Rural, simple, isolated, quiet.
🅾 01/01-31/12
Distance: 🚶500m 🛒1,5km.

| 🛏 | | Müllheim 🏛 | 24A1 |

Am Nüsslegarten, Am Nüsslegarten, Britzingen. **GPS:** n47,82891 e7,67336.⬆

2 🛏free. **Location:** Rural, simple, quiet.
🅾 01/01-31/12

| 🛏 | | Müllheim 🏛 | 24A1 |

Freibad Müllheim, Ziegleweg 7. **GPS:** n47,80237 e7,63403.⬆

3 🛏free. **Location:** Urban, simple. **Surface:** asphalted.
🅾 01/01-31/12
Remarks: Next to swimming pool.

| 🛏 | | Müllheim 🏛 | 24A1 |

Parkplatz Nußbaumallee, Nußbaumallee. **GPS:** n47,80942 e7,62985.⬆

3 🛏free. **Location:** Urban, simple. **Surface:** asphalted.
🅾 01/01-31/12
Remarks: Max. 2 days.

| 🛏S | | Müllheim 🏛 | 24A1 |

Markgräfler Kräuterhof, Im Käppeleacker 3, Hügelheim.
GPS: n47,83237 e7,62045.

4 🛏free 🚿 free. **Location:** Urban, simple. **Surface:** grasstiles.
🅾 01/01-31/12
Distance: 🚶500m 🛒1km.
Remarks: Herbery, herb-Stube.

| 🛏S | | Münsingen | 17D5 |

Wiesentalstadion, Grafenecker Straße. **GPS:** n48,40939 e9,48580.⬆
18 🛏€ 5/24h, 3 days € 12 🔌€1/100liter 🚿 Ch 🚿 €1/6h. **Surface:** gravel.
🅾 01/01-31/12
Distance: 🚶1km 🛒within walking distance 🏊on the spot.

| 🛏S | | Murg 🏳 | 24A1 |

Am Freibad. **GPS:** n47,55196 e8,02403.⬆➡

15 🛏€ 10 🔌€1/100liter 🔌€0,50/kWh. 🐕
Location: Rural, comfortable, quiet. **Surface:** metalled. 🅾 01/01-31/12
Distance: 🚶500m 🚴on the spot.

DE

DE

Murrhardt 17D3
Parkplatz Festhalle, Kaiser-Ludwig-Straße 25. **GPS:** n48,97960 e9,57461.⬆️➡️

3 🛏free 🚰€1/90liter 🚽 Ch. **Location:** Rural, simple. **Surface:** asphalted.
◻ 01/01-31/12
Distance: 🚶400m 💧100m.

Nagold 17B5
Wohnmobilhafen, Am Glockenrain. **GPS:** n48,56389 e8,72306.⬆️➡️

12 🛏free 🚰€1/80liter 🔌€1 Ch€1 💧(12x)€1/kWh. **Location:** Rural,
simple, quiet. **Surface:** gravel/metalled. ◻ 01/01-31/12
Distance: 🚶1km 🚲25m 🚉900m 🚌400m 🛒on the spot 🎣on the spot.

Nagold 17B5
Am Bahnhof, Bahnhofstraße. **GPS:** n48,55791 e8,72748.⬆️

4 🛏free. **Location:** Rural, simple, noisy. **Surface:** asphalted.
◻ 01/01-31/12
Distance: 🚶700m 💧100m 🚌on the spot 🛒on the spot 🎣on the spot.
Remarks: Max. 4 nights.

Nattheim 18A4
Ramensteinbad, Dieselstrasse 22. **GPS:** n48,70261 e10,23745.⬆️➡️

50 🛏free 🚰€2/60liter 🚽 Ch. **Location:** Rural, simple.
Surface: asphalted/gravel. ◻ 01/01-31/12
Distance: 🚲4km.
Remarks: Parking swimming pool, max. 24h.

Neckarwestheim 17C3
Wohnmobilstellplätze Im Bühl, Liebensteiner Strasse.
GPS: n49,04186 e9,18797.⬆️

2 🛏free 🚰€2 🚽 Ch 💧(4x)€2/8h. **Surface:** metalled.
◻ 01/01-31/12
Distance: 🚶500m 💧200m 🚉500m.
Remarks: From 4th night € 25/night.

Neresheim 18A4
Stellplatz Alter Bahnhof, Dischinger Straße 11. **GPS:** n48,75102 e10,33957.⬆️

5 🛏free 🚰€1 🚽 Ch 💧(4x)€1/4h. **Location:** Noisy. **Surface:** metalled.
◻ 01/01-31/12
Distance: 🚶on the spot 🚲12km 💧on the spot.
Remarks: Service during opening hours.

Neuhausen ob Eck 17C6
Beim Friedhof. **GPS:** n47,97473 e8,92397.⬆️

8 🛏voluntary contribution 🚰€1 🔌€1 Ch 💧(9x). **Surface:** metalled.
◻ 01/01-31/12
Distance: 🚶300m 💧500m 🚉1km 🚌300m 🚲2km 🚶2km.
Remarks: Max. 3 nights.

Neckarsulm 17C3
Aquatoll, Reisachmühlweg. **GPS:** n49,18802 e9,24302.⬆️

4 🛏free 🚰€1/100liter 🚽 Chfree 💧€1/2kWh. **Location:** Urban, quiet.
Surface: metalled. ◻ 01/01-31/12 ◉ 25/04-07/05
Distance: 🚶500m 💧300m 🚉200m Lidl.
Remarks: Parking swimming pool, max. 3 days.

Neunkirchen 17C3
Festplatz, Zwingenbergerstrasse. **GPS:** n49,38818 e9,01531.⬆️

8 ⌂free ⟍€1/90liter ⬚Ch. **Location:** Simple, quiet. **Surface:** asphalted. ▢ 01/01-31/12

Distance: ⚲300m.

Remarks: Service next to: Autohaus Weishaupt, Industriestrasse 3 (200m).

| ⬚S | **Nordheim** | 17C3 |

Lauffener Straße. **GPS:** n49,10461 e9,13552. ⬆.

2 ⌂€ 5/3 days ⟍⬚Ch✎ included. **Location:** Simple. **Surface:** asphalted. ▢ 01/01-31/12 ⚙on the spot ☗on the spot.

Remarks: In front of swimmingpool, max. 3 days.

| ⬚S | **Nordheim** | 17C3 |

Müllers Weingut unf Weinstube, Im Auerberg 3. **GPS:** n49,10236 e9,13810.

2 ⌂€ 5,with electricity and water € 8 ⟍⬚Ch✎.

Location: Rural.

Distance: ⚲800m ⊗on the spot ⇌on the spot ⚙on the spot ☗on the spot.

| ⬚S | **Nordrach** ⛲ | 17A5 |

Schwarzwald-Panorama Wohnmobilstellplatz, Im Dorf 29.

GPS: n48,39873 e8,07927. ⬆➡.

8 ⌂free ⟍€1/10liter ⬚Ch ✎ (8x)6h. **Location:** Rural, simple, central.

Surface: metalled. ▢ 01/01-31/12

Distance: ⚲100m ⬚100m.

| ⬚S | **Nürtingen** | 17C4 |

Stellplatz Plätschwiesen, B313, Plätschwiesen, Oberensingen.

GPS: n48,63645 e9,33051. ⬆.

12 ⌂€ 5/24h ⟍€1 ⬚Ch ✎ (8x)€1. **Surface:** metalled. ▢ 01/01-31/12

Distance: ⚲1km ⊗on the spot ⬚500m.

Remarks: Max. 7 days.

| ⬚S | **Oberkirch** | 17A5 |

Am Renchtalstadion, Renchallee. **GPS:** n48,52972 e8,07250. ⬆➡.

21 ⌂€ 5, € 7/2 days + €2 tourist tax ⟍€1/80liter ⬚€1 Ch ✎ (30x)€0,50/kWh. ▯ **Location:** Rural, simple, quiet. **Surface:** grassy/gravel. ▢ 01/01-31/12 ◉ week before and week after 1st weekend Sep

Distance: ⚲100m ⊗100m ⬚100m ⚙on the spot ☗on the spot.

| ⏮S | **Oberkirch** | 17A5 |

Waldparkplatz Schauenburg, Burgstraße 29. **GPS:** n48,53812 e8,09452. ⬆.

4 ⌂€ 8 ✎ (4x)€2 ⬚. ⚙ **Location:** Simple, isolated, quiet.

Surface: grassy/sand. ▢ 01/01-31/12

Distance: ⊗500m.

Remarks: Max. 4 days, € 8 voucher restaurant.

| ⬚S | **Oberndorf/Neckar** | 17B5 |

Neckarhalle, Austrasse 12. **GPS:** n48,28222 e8,58472. ⬆➡.

8 ⌂free ⟍€1/70liter ⬚Ch ✎ (4x)€1/kWh. **Location:** Rural, simple, noisy. **Surface:** asphalted. ▢ 01/01-31/12

Distance: ⚲2km ⊗300m ⬚200m ⇌50m ⚙on the spot ☗on the spot.

| ⬚ | **Oberstenfeld** | 17C3 |

Mineralfreibad, Beilsteiner Strasse 100. **GPS:** n49,03160 e9,31890. ⬆.

DE

4 🛏free. **Surface:** asphalted. 🔲 01/01-31/12

〚⚥〛S **Oberteuringen** 24D1

Ferienhof Kramer, St. Georg strasse 8. **GPS:** n47,73948 e9,47278. ⬆➡.

8 🛏€ 16, 2 pers.incl ⟿ ⚏Ch ⚘ (8x)€2 WC ◉€4. **Surface:** gravel/metalled. 🔲 15/04-15/09
Distance: 🚶2km ⛱on the spot ⊗300m 🛒300m.

〚⚥〛S **Offenburg** 17A5

Strandbad Gifizsee, Platanenallee 15. **GPS:** n48,45785 e7,93663.
11 🛏€ 12 + € 3 /pp (peak season) ⟿€1/80liter ⚏Ch ⚘(11x)€0,50/kWh
WC 🛎🚿. 🦮 **Location:** Simple. **Surface:** grasstiles. 🔲 01/04-31/10
Distance: 🚶2,5km ⚓3,8km ⛱100m ⊗on the spot 🛒150m.
Remarks: Bread-service, dog € 1,50/night.

〚⚥〛S **Offenburg** 17A5

Bürgerpark, Stegermattstraße 26a. **GPS:** n48,46565 e7,94566. ⬆.

2 🛏free. **Location:** Urban, simple, quiet. **Surface:** asphalted/metalled.
🔲 01/01-31/12
Distance: 🚶500m ⊗300m.
Remarks: In front of swimmingpool.

〚⚥〛S **Offenburg** 17A5

Camping Kuhn, Im Drachenacker 4. **GPS:** n48,48039 e7,92776. ⬆.

10 🛏free ⟿€0,50/50liter ⚏Ch ⚘(8x)free. **Location:** Urban, simple.
Surface: metalled. 🔲 01/01-31/12
Distance: 🚶2km ⚓3,7km 🛒500m.
Remarks: Service during opening hours.

〚⚥〛S **Öhringen** 17D3

P Frei- und Hallenbad, Pfaffenmühlweg. **GPS:** n49,19771 e9,51137. ⬆➡.

15 🛏€ 8 ⟿Ch ⚘included. **Location:** Rural, simple. **Surface:** gravel.
🔲 01/01-31/12
Distance: 🚶1km 🚌100m.
Remarks: Max. 3 days, to be paid at swimming pool.

Tourist information Öhringen:
⚘ RADius. Cycle route, 18km.

〚⚥〛S **Öllingen** 18A5

Parking Rathaus, Hauptstrasse. **GPS:** n48,52816 e10,14813. ⬆.

5 🛏free ⟿€4 ⚏Ch ⚘. **Surface:** grasstiles. 🔲 01/01-31/12

〚⚥〛S **Oppenau** 🏔 17A5

Hauptstrasse. **GPS:** n48,47639 e8,16972. ⬆.

6 🛏free ⟿€1/100liter ⚏Ch ⚘(6x)€1/8h. **Location:** Rural, simple, quiet.
Surface: gravel. 🔲 01/01-31/12
Distance: 🚶300m ⊗150m 🛒bakery 300m 🚴on the spot 🚶on the spot.

〚⚥〛S **Oppenweiler** 17D3

Caravanstation, Murrwiesenstraße 15. **GPS:** n48,97999 e9,45898. ⬆➡.

2 🛏free ⟿€1/80liter ⚏Ch. **Surface:** asphalted. 🔲 01/01-31/12
Distance: 🚶600m.
Remarks: Max. 2 days.

〚⚥〛S **Ottenhöfen im Schwarzwald** 🏔🏕👥 17A5

Bauernhof Murhof, Murhof 1. **GPS:** n48,56005 e8,15350. ⬆➡.

15 🅂 € 10, 2 pers.incl 🚰€1/100liter 🅒 Ch ⚡ (15x)€0,50/kWh WC 🚾€0,50.
🛁 **Location:** Rural, simple, quiet. **Surface:** grassy/metalled.
⭕ 01/04-31/10
Distance: 🚶1km ⊗500m 🚮500m 🧗on the spot.
Remarks: Swimming pool 200m.

| 🅂 | **Pforzheim** | 17B4 |

Reisemobilplatz Oststadt am Enzauenpark, Wildersinnstraße.
GPS: n48,89784 e8,72232. ⬆️.

15 🅂free 🚰€1/80liter ⚡ (4x)€1/kWh. **Location:** Urban, simple, noisy.
Surface: metalled. ⭕ 01/01-31/12
Distance: 🚶1,5km ⊗200m 🚮100m 🚏on the spot 🚲on the spot
🧗on the spot.
Remarks: Max. 7 days, service 200m.

| 🅂 | **Pforzheim** | 17B4 |

Parkplatz 2 Wildpark, Tiefenbronnerstraße. **GPS:** n48,87651 e8,71749.
🅂€ 2-4/24h. **Location:** Urban.
Remarks: Max. 1 night.

| S | **Pforzheim** | 17B4 |

Hohwiesenweg. **GPS:** n48,89750 e8,72674. ⬆️.
4 🚰€1/80liter 🅒€1 Ch€1 ⚡ (2x)€1/kWh. **Location:** Simple, noisy.
Surface: metalled.
Distance: 🚶1,5km ⊗50m 🚮100m 🚏on the spot 🚲on the spot
🧗on the spot.

| 🅂 | **Pfullendorf** | 17C6 |

Seepark Linzgau, P-Ost, Bannholzerweg 18. **GPS:** n47,93097 e9,23728.

15 🅂 € 4/24h 🚰. **Surface:** unpaved. ⭕ 01/01-31/12

| 🅂 | **Pfullingen** | 17C5 |

Wohnmobilplatz Schönbergbad, Klosterstraße. **GPS:** n48,45537 e9,22812.
7 🅂free 🚰€1 🅒 Ch ⚡€1/2kWh. **Surface:** grassy. ⭕ 01/01-31/12
Distance: 🚶1,5km ⊗nearby.
Remarks: Max. 4 days.

| 🅂 | **Radolfzell** | 24C1 |

Wohnmobilstellplatz in den Herzen, Zeppelinstraße. **GPS:** n47,73888 e8,95331.

15 🅂€ 8/24h 🚰€1/80liter 🅒 Ch ⚡ (12x)€0,50/kWh. **Surface:** metalled.
⭕ 01/01-31/12
Distance: 🚶1km ⊗500m 🚮1km 🚲BodenseeRadweg
🧗Bodensee-Rundwanderweg.
Remarks: Max. 2 nights.

| 🅂 | **Radolfzell** | 24C1 |

Wohnmobilstellplatz Halbinsel Mettnau, Strandbadstrasse.
GPS: n47,73784 e8,98007. ⬆️.

12 🅂€ 8/24h 🚰€1/50liter 🅒 Ch ⚡ (6x)€0,50/kWh. **Surface:** asphalted.
⭕ 01/01-31/12
Distance: 🚶500m ⛵700m 🚤700m ⊗500m 🚮700m 🚏100m.
Remarks: Max. 2 nights.

| 🅲 🅂 | **Radolfzell** | 24C1 |

Campingplatz Böhringer See, Hindenburgstrasse. **GPS:** n47,76176 e8,93488.
⬆️.

10 🅂€ 10-13 🚰 🅒 Ch ⚡ (5x)€0,50/kWh WC 🚾€1. **Surface:** metalled.
⭕ 01/01-31/12
Distance: 🚶1km ⊗on the spot 🚮1km.

| 🅂 | **Rastatt** 🌿⛲ | 17A4 |

Leopoldring. **GPS:** n48,85409 e8,19970. ⬆️➡️.

5 🅂€ 5 🚰€1/10minutes 🅒 Ch ⚡ (8x)€1/6h. 🛁 **Location:** Simple.
Surface: metalled. ⭕ 01/01-31/12
Distance: 🚶500m ⛵3,8km.
Remarks: Check in at pay-desk of swimming pool, discount at swimming pool
and sauna.

DE

Ravensburg 17D6

Wohnmobilstellplatz Ravensburg, Mühlbruckstrasse. **GPS**: n47,78196 e9,60001.⬆️➡️.

19 ⛺€ 8 ⛽€1/80liter ♻️Ch ⚡€0,50/kWh. **Surface**: metalled.
📅 01/01-31/12
Distance: 🚶centre 800m ⚓500m 🛒200m 🚊250m 🚴 Donau-Bodensee Radweg.
Remarks: Max. 3 nights.

Tourist information Ravensburg:

ℹ️ Bodensee-Erlebniskarte. Card gives free access to all boats, telpher carriers, beaches etc. Around the Lake Constance in Germany, Switzerland and Austria.
🎫 € 57/3 days.
ℹ️ Tourist Information, Kirchstrasse 16. City of the Tore und Turme, gates and towers.

Rechberghausen 17D4

Sportpark Lindach, Am Desenbach. **GPS**: n48,72405 e9,63594.⬆️➡️.

6 ⛺free ⛽€0,50/80liter ♻️Ch ⚡(6x)€0,50/kWh. **Location**: Rural, simple. **Surface**: grassy. 📅 01/04-01/10
Distance: 🚶1km ⚓500m ⊗1km 🛒1km 🚊500m.

Reichenau 24C1

Zum Sandseele. **GPS**: n47,69887 e9,04711.⬆️.

12 ⛺€ 12/24h ⛽€1/80liter ♻️Ch ⚡(8x)€1/2kWh.
Surface: asphalted/metalled. 📅 01/01-31/12
Distance: 🚶1,5km ⚓on the spot 🛒on the spot ⊗100m 🚊2km.
Remarks: Max. 1 night.

Reutlingen 17C5

P&R Parkplatz, Am Südbahnhof/Marktstrasse. **GPS**: n48,48280 e9,22982.

3 ⛺free ⛽♻️Ch. **Location**: Noisy. **Surface**: gravel.
📅 01/01-31/12
Distance: 🚶3km ⊗on the spot 🛒on the spot.
Remarks: In front of motorhome dealer Berger, max. 48h.

Reutlingen 17C5

Sportpark Markwasen, Hermann-Hesse-Straße. **GPS**: n48,47536 e9,19377.⬆️.
10 ⛺€ 8 ⛽€0,50 ♻️Ch ⚡€0,50/kWh. **Surface**: gravel.
📅 01/01-31/12
Distance: 🚶3km.
Remarks: Public transport included.

Rheinmünster 17A4

Freizeit Center Oberrhein, Am Campingpark 1. **GPS**: n48,77312 e8,04044.⬆️.

20 ⛺€ 8 ⛽€1/80liter ♻️Ch ⚡(20x)€0,50/kWh. 🏠
Location: Rural, comfortable, quiet. **Surface**: grassy. 📅 01/01-31/12
Distance: ⚓on the spot ⊗200m 🚴on the spot 🏊on the spot.

Riedlingen 17D6

Stadthalle, Hindenburgstraße. **GPS**: n48,15189 e9,47766.➡️.

3 ⛺free ⛽€1/100liter ♻️Ch ⚡€1/4h. **Location**: Urban.
Surface: asphalted. 📅 01/01-31/12
Distance: 🚶300m ⊗200m 🛒100m.

Rielasingen-Worblingen 24C1

Naturbad Aachtal, Herdweg. **GPS**: n47,72127 e8,86332.⬆️.
⛺free, May-Sep € 4,50/day ⛽€1/100liter ♻️Ch ⚡€0,50/kWh 📅01/05-30/09. **Location**: Rural. **Surface**: gravel. 📅 01/01-31/12
Distance: 🚶600m.

Rottenburg/Neckar 17C5

Wohnmobilhafen Neckarufer, Ulmenweg 4. **GPS**: n48,47213 e8,95010.⬆️➡️.

DE

12 ⬛€5 🚰€1/80liter 🗑Ch 🔌(8x)€0,50/kWh. **Surface:** asphalted. ⬛ 01/01-31/12
Distance: 🚿800m 🏊800m ⊗800m 🍴800m.
Remarks: Max. 3 days.

| 🅂 | **Rottweil** | 17B6 |

Parkplatz, Stadionstrasse. **GPS:** n48,15556 e8,62861.

€5 ⬛free 🚰€1 🗑Ch 🔌(16x)€1/8h. **Surface:** gravel.
⬛ 01/01-31/12
Distance: 🚿1km ⊗1km 🍴1km 🚌500m.
Remarks: Parking stadium.

| 🅂 | **Rust** 🚂 | 17A5 |

Europapark Rust, Europa-Parkstrasse. **GPS:** n48,27189 e7,71745.⬆➡

200 ⬛8-20h € 2/h (max. € 6), 20-8h € 2/h (max. € 22) 🚰€1 🗑
Ch 🔌 WC ⬜included.🏳
Location: Simple. **Surface:** asphalted.
⬛ 03/04-07/11, 27/11-09/01 9-18
Distance: ⊗on the spot.

Tourist information Rust:
☺ Europa-park, Europa-Park-Straße 2. Large amusement and theme park with Europe as theme. ⬛ 03/04-07/11, 27/11-09/01 9-18h.

| 🅂 | **Sankt Blasien** 🏔 | 24A1 |

Rehbach in Menzenschwand, Rehbachweg, Sankt Blasien.
GPS: n47,81306 e8,06933.⬆

20 ⬛€6 🚰🗑Ch 🔌(16x)€3/24h. **Location:** Rural, simple, quiet.
Surface: gravel. ⬛ 01/01-31/12

Distance: 🚿St Blasien 8km 🛒bakery 500m 🚴on the spot 🚶on the spot 🎿on the spot.
Remarks: At ski-lift Rehbach, in winter time not always easy to reach.

| 🅂 | **Sasbachwalden** 🍂🚠🍷 | 17A5 |

Wohnmobilstellplatz "Alde Gott", Talstraße 2. **GPS:** n48,61945 e8,12094.⬆➡

30 ⬛€7 🚰€1/100liter 🗑Ch 🔌(20x)€2/24h. 🏳
Location: Rural, comfortable, quiet. **Surface:** gravel/metalled. ⬛ 01/01-31/12
Distance: 🚿centre 300m 🚲9km 🏊9km ⊗100m 🍴250m 🍽250m 🚌100m 🚴on the spot 🚶on the spot.
Remarks: Waterfall 1km, swimming pool 800m.

| 🅂 | **Schiltach** ⚓🏔🍷 | 17B5 |

P1, Lehewiese. **GPS:** n48,29111 e8,34250.⬆➡

10 ⬛free 🚰 🔌(3x). **Location:** Simple, quiet. **Surface:** gravel.
⬛ 01/01-31/12
Distance: 🚿200m ⊗50m 🍴50m 🚌on the spot 🚴on the spot 🚶on the spot.
Remarks: Busy parking during the day.

| 🅂 | **Schluchsee** 🏔 | 24B1 |

P Aqua Fun, Faulenfürster Straße. **GPS:** n47,81569 e8,18113.⬆

20 ⬛€8 🚰€1/100liter 🔌€1/8h. 🏳 **Location:** Rural, comfortable, central, quiet. **Surface:** asphalted. ⬛ 01/01-31/12
Distance: 🏊200m.
Remarks: Max. 1 night.

| 🅂 | **Schonach im Schwarzwald** 🏔❄ | 17B6 |

Parkplatz Obertal, Schwimmbadweg. **GPS:** n48,14573 e8,18872.⬆

10 ⛺€7 ⛽€1 🚰€0,50 Ch ⚡(8x)€1/8h. **Location:** Rural, comfortable. **Surface:** grasstiles. 🅿 01/01-31/12 **Distance:** 🚶1km 🍺650m 🏊on the spot 🎣on the spot. **Remarks:** Max. 3 nights, coins at tourist info, free entrance swimming pool, ski-lift and public transport.

4 ⛺8-18h max. € 5, 18-8h max. € 2 ⚡(4x)€0,10/18minutes. 🚐 **Location:** Urban, simple. **Surface:** asphalted. 🅿 01/01-31/12 **Distance:** 🚶200m. **Remarks:** Max. 24h.

🅂 Schwaigern 17C3

🅂 Schorndorf 17D4
Gmünder Straße 84/1. **GPS:** n48,80539 e9,54187.⬆.

Wohnmobilstellplatz Schaigern, Gemminger Straße 91. **GPS:** n49,14576 e9,04529.⬆.

7 ⛺€5 + €4/pp ⛽€2 🚰Ch€2 ⚡WC 🚽€2 💡€2 📶€1.🚿 **Location:** Simple. **Surface:** metalled. 🅿 01/01-31/12 **Distance:** 🚶10min.

2 ⛺free ⛽€1 🚰Ch ⚡free. **Surface:** asphalted. 🅿 01/01-31/12 **Distance:** 🚶1km ⊗300m 🚲on the spot 🚶on the spot.

🅂 Schramberg ⬇ 17B5
Bahnhofstraße, B462. **GPS:** n48,23017 e8,38323.⬆.

🅂 Schwetzingen ⛩ 17B3
Ketscher Landstrasse. **GPS:** n49,37803 e8,55820.⬆.

2 ⛺free ⛽€1/80liter 🚰€1 Ch€1. **Location:** Rural, simple, noisy. **Surface:** metalled. 🅿 01/01-31/12 **Distance:** 🚶on the spot ⊗100m 🍺50m 🚗10m 🚲on the spot 🚶on the spot.

12 ⛺free ⛽€3/80liter 🚰Ch. **Location:** Simple. **Surface:** grasstiles/metalled. 🅿 01/01-31/12 **Distance:** 🚶500m ⊗on the spot 🍺on the spot 🚲on the spot 🚶on the spot. **Remarks:** Max. 3 nights, noisy place.

🅂 Seelbach 17A5
Reisemobil-Wellness-Stellplatz Schwarzwälder Hof, Am Tretenbach. **GPS:** n48,30042 e7,94497.⬆.

🅂 Schwäbisch Gmünd 17D4
Schiesstalplatz, Schiesstalstraße. **GPS:** n48,80543 e9,81308.⬆.

8 ⛺free ⛽€1/50liter 🚰Ch ⚡(8x)€0,50/kWh. **Location:** Rural, simple. **Surface:** gravel. 🅿 01/01-31/12 **Distance:** 🚶1km ⊗50m 🚗500m. **Remarks:** Motorhome < 7m, max. 5 days a month.

16 ⛺€18 ⛽€1/90liter 🚰Ch ⚡(16x)kWh WC 💡 📶. 🚐 **Location:** Rural, comfortable. **Surface:** metalled. 🅿 01/01-31/12 **Distance:** 🚶600m ⊗100m. **Remarks:** Including access to swimming pool, use sanitary facilities, entrance 1p wellness/sauna.

🅂 Schwäbisch Hall 17D3
P5 Weilerwiese, Johanniterstrasse. **GPS:** n49,11666 e9,73269.⬆.

🅂 Seewald 🍴⛏♨⛩ 17B5
P4, L362. **GPS:** n48,55131 e8,49522.⬆➡.

17 free WC free. **Location:** Rural, simple, quiet. **Surface:** asphalted.
01/01-31/12 service 01/11-31/03
Distance: 1,5km 25m 600m.

15 € 9 €1 €1 Ch (6x)€0,50/kWh. **Surface:** grassy/gravel.
01/01-31/12
Distance: 300m 2km 2km 300m 300m 300m.

| | Sigmaringen | 17C6 |
Wohnmobilplatz Sigmaringen, Georg Zimmerer Straße 4.
GPS: n48,08545 e9,21029.
20 € 5 Ch . **Surface:** metalled. 01/01-31/12

| | Stockach/Bodensee | 17C6 |
Reisemobilhafen 'Papiermühle', Johann-Glatt-strasse 3.
GPS: n47,84169 e8,99945.

| | Sindelfingen | 17C4 |
Badezentrum Sindelfingen, Hohenzollernstrasse. **GPS:** n48,71993 e9,01779.
10 free. **Surface:** asphalted. 01/01-31/12
Distance: on the spot.

| | Singen | 24C1 |
P Landesgartenschau, Schaffhauserstrasse. **GPS:** n47,75992 e8,82766.

85 € 10 €0,50/50liter Ch (118x) WC . **Surface:** gravel/metalled.
01/01-31/12
Distance: 1,5km on the spot 700m.

| | Sulz am Neckar | 17B5 |
Stellplatz Wöhrd, Ludwigstraße. **GPS:** n48,36427 e8,63681.

20 free Ch free (16x)€1/6h. **Surface:** grassy/gravel.
01/01-31/12, service 15/03-15/11
Distance: 1km on the spot 200m.
Remarks: Max. 72h.

| | Singen | 24C1 |
Hallenbad, Waldeckstraße 4. **GPS:** n47,76472 e8,84781.
3 free. **Surface:** asphalted. 01/01-31/12
Distance: 500m.
Remarks: At swimming pool.

| | Sinsheim | 17C3 |
Schwimmbadweg 11b. **GPS:** n49,24778 e8,88667.

6 free €1/80liter €1 Ch (4x)€0,50/kWh.
Location: Rural, simple, quiet. **Surface:** metalled. 01/01-31/12
Distance: 300m 100m 100m on the spot on the spot on the spot.

| | Sulzburg | 17A6 |
Camping Sulzbachtal, Sonnmatt 4. **GPS:** n47,84773 e7,69868.

5 free. **Location:** Rural, comfortable, quiet. **Surface:** asphalted.
01/01-31/12
Distance: 1,5km 1,5km.
Remarks: Max. 48h.

| | Stetten | 24C1 |
Alte Brennerei, Riedetsweilerstrasse 5. **GPS:** n47,69326 e9,29788.

10 € 15 + tourist tax + Ecotaxe Ch (10x)€0,70/kWh
WC included. **Location:** Comfortable. **Surface:** grassy/gravel.
01/01-31/12
Distance: 500m on the spot.

| | Tauberbischofsheim | 17D2 |
P Freibad, Vittryallee. **GPS:** n49,62155 e9,66632.

3 🅿 free 🔌🚰 Ch WC free 🚽€0,50,during opening hours. **Location:** Simple.
Surface: asphalted. 🅾 01/01-31/12
Distance: 🚶500m ⊗300m 🚆100m 🚍500m.
Remarks: Service at Kläranlage ma-do 7-16 uur.

| 📷S | Tettnang | 24D1 |

Loretostrasse. **GPS:** n47,66425 e9,59175.⬆➡

14 🅿 €5 🔌€1 🚰€1 Ch€1 🚿 (8x)€1/8h. 📶 **Surface:** grassy/metalled.
🅾 01/01-31/12
Distance: 🚶800m ⊗200m 🚆200m 🚍200m.

| ©S | Tettnang | 24D1 |

Gutshof Camping Badhütten, Badhütten, Laimnau. **GPS:** n47,63370 e9,64668.
⬆.

70 🅿 €20 🔌€1 🚰 Ch 🚿€1/3kWh WC 🚽€1. **Surface:** grassy.
🅾 01/01-31/12

| ©S | Titisee | 17A6 |

Camping Bankenhof, Bruderhalde 31a. **GPS:** n47,88643 e8,13046.⬆.

8 🅿 €13, 2 pers.incl 🔌🚰 Ch 🚿 WC 🚽included 🔲€2,60/time 📶€2/2h.
Location: Rural, comfortable, quiet. **Surface:** gravel/sand.
🅾 01/01-31/12
Distance: 🏊Titisee 600m.
Remarks: Pay at reception.

| 📷S | Todtmoos 🍴🎿 | 24A1 |

Jägermatt, Vordertodtmoos. **GPS:** n47,73390 e8,00285.⬆➡

30 🅿 €5 🔌🚰 Ch included. 📶 **Location:** Rural, simple, noisy.
Surface: gravel/metalled. 🅾 01/01-31/12
Distance: 🚶1km 🚆50m.

| 📷 | Triberg im Schwarzwald | 17B6 |

Sommerauer Strasse, Nußberg. **GPS:** n48,13161 e8,25294.⬆➡.

20 🅿 free. **Location:** Rural, simple. **Surface:** gravel.
🅾 01/01-31/12
Distance: 🚶2km ⊗on the spot.

| 📷S | Trochtelfingen 🌿🏖🍦 | 17C5 |

Eberhard-von Werderberg-Halle, Siemensstrasse. **GPS:** n48,30811 e9,23546.
➡.

20 🅿 €3 🔌€1/80liter 🚰 Ch 🚿 (4x)free,16Amp. **Surface:** gravel.
🅾 01/01-31/12
Distance: 🚶Old city centre 🚆500m 🚍500m.

| 📷S | Trochtelfingen 🌿🏖🍦 | 17C5 |

Kräuter- und Erlebnisgarten Alb-Gold Nudelfabrik, Grindel 1.
GPS: n48,32838 e9,24001.

4 🅿 free. **Surface:** metalled. 🅾 01/01-31/12
Distance: 🚶3km ⊗on the spot 🚆on the spot.

| 📷S | Trossingen | 17B6 |

Reisemobilplatz am Naturbad Troase, Steppach 5. **GPS:** n48,07703 e8,62192.
⬆➡.

DE

8 ⌁ € 4 ⛽ €1/100liter 🗑 Ch ♨ €1/12h. **Surface:** gravel.
⭘ 01/01-31/12

Tuttlingen ⚓ 17C6
Stellplatz Donaupark, Stuttgarter strasse. **GPS:** n47,98490 e8,81316. ⬆.

10 ⌁ free ⛽ €1/5minutes 🗑 €1 Ch 📶. **Surface:** metalled.
⭘ 01/01-31/12
Distance: 🚶500m ⊗500m 🛒500m 🚌500m 🚲 Donauradweg.
Remarks: Max. 3 nights.

Überlingen ⚓ 24C1
Reisemobilhafen Überlingen, Kurt-Hahn-strasse. **GPS:** n47,77617 e9,15046.

20 ⌁ € 6-10 ⛽ €0,50/70liter 🗑€0,50 Ch ⚡ (30x)€0,50/2kWh WC . ⛟
Surface: asphalted/gravel.
⭘ 01/01-31/12
Distance: 🚶1km 🚲1km 🛒1km ⊗200m 🛒1,5km 🚌200m.
Remarks: Max. 3 days, price incl. bus transport (max. 5 pers) to the city centre.

Uhldingen-Mühlhofen 24C1
Ehbachstrasse. **GPS:** n47,72535 e9,23649. ⬆.

21 ⌁ 8-18h € 1,50/h, max. € 5, night € 10 ⛽ €1 🗑€1 Ch WC .
Surface: grasstiles/metalled. ⭘ 01/03-31/10
Distance: 🚶1km 🚲2km 🛒2km ⊗kiosk on the spot 🛒300m.
Remarks: Max. 24h.

Ulm 17D5
P+R Friedrichsau, Wielandstrasse. **GPS:** n48,40774 e10,00929. ⬆➡.

50 ⌁ free ⛽ €1 🗑 Ch. **Location:** Urban, simple, central. **Surface:** metalled.
⭘ 01/01-31/12
Distance: ⊗175m 🚌on the spot.
Remarks: Max. 3 days, green zone: environmental badge obligatory.

Ummendorf 🌾 17D6
Bräuhaus Ummendorf, Bachstrasse 10. **GPS:** n48,06340 e9,83252. ⬆➡.

5 ⌁ free ⛽ ♨ (5x)€3/day WC 🗑€3 📶. **Surface:** metalled.
⭘ 01/01-31/12
Distance: 🚶300m ⊗on the spot 🛒800m 🚌100m.
Remarks: 3 days free stay.

Unterkirnach 🌿 ⚓ 🏔 🐑 17B6
Reisemobilhafen Am Rathaus, Rathausplatz. **GPS:** n48,07719 e8,36707. ⬆➡.

16 ⌁ €9 ⛽ 🗑 Ch ♨ included. **Location:** Urban, luxurious, quiet.
Surface: gravel. ⭘ 01/01-31/12
Distance: 🚶on the spot 🏊400m 🚲500m ⊗200m 🛒300m 🚌200m
🚴150m 🛒400m.
Remarks: Pay at tourist office, alternative arrangement if full.

Unterkirnach 🌿 ⚓ 🌲 🐑 17B6
Ackerloch-Grillschopf, Unteres Ackerloch 2. **GPS:** n48,08473 e8,36573. ⬆.

20 ⌁ € 4 + € 2,10/pp tourist tax ⛽ 🗑 Ch ♨ WC included. 🚿
Location: Rural, simple. **Surface:** unpaved. ⭘ Nov
Distance: 🚶1,5km ⊗on the spot 🎿on the spot 🚴on the spot 🐑on the spot.

Untermünkheim 17D3
Wohnmobilpark Ostertag, Kupfer Straße 20, Übrigshausen.
GPS: n49,17603 e9,71321. ⬆.

10 ⌷€8 ⌷Ch ✍€0,50 ⌷€1. **Location:** Rural, comfortable.
Surface: grassy/gravel. ⌷ 01/03-30/11
Distance: ⊗50m.
Remarks: At manege.

10 ⌷free ⌷€1/80liter ⌷€1 Ch€1. **Location:** Urban, simple, central.
Surface: asphalted. ⌷ 01/01-31/12
Distance: ⌷500m.
Remarks: Max. 2 days.

Villingen/Schwenningen	17B6

Messegelände VS-Schwenningen, Waldeckweg. **GPS:** n48,05028 e8,54056.⬆

Waldshut-Tiengen	24B1

Wohmobil-Park Waldshut-Tiengen, Jahnweg 22, Waldshut.
GPS: n47,61121 e8,22513.⬆➡

4 ⌷free ⌷€1 ⌷Ch. **Location:** Urban, simple, noisy. **Surface:** asphalted.
⌷ 01/01-31/12
Distance: ⌷1km ⌷500m.

44 ⌷€10 ⌷€1/100liter ⌷Ch ✍€1/kWh ⌷€0,50.⌷
Location: Urban, luxurious, quiet. **Surface:** metalled. ⌷ 01/01-31/12
Distance: ⊗on the spot.
Remarks: Along the Rhine river, bread-service.

Vogtsburg im Kaiserstuhl	17A6

Hauptstraße/L115, Oberrotweil. **GPS:** n48,09000 e7,64361.

Walldürn	17C2

Basilikaplatz, Hauptstrasse. **GPS:** n49,58637 e9,36726.⬆

8 ⌷free. **Location:** Rural, simple, isolated, quiet.
⌷ 01/01-31/12
Distance: ⌷800m.

8 ⌷free ⌷€1/80liter ✍ (4x)€0,50/kWh. **Location:** Rural, simple.
Surface: gravel. ⌷ 01/01-31/12
Distance: ⌷250m ⊗400m.
Remarks: Pilgrimage site.

Waiblingen	17C4

Parkplatz Hallenbad, An der Talaue. **GPS:** n48,83029 e9,32540.⬆

Walldürn	17C2

Goldschmitt Technik-Center, Industrieparkstrasse. **GPS:** n49,58977 e9,39339.
⬆

20 ⌷€ 6/24h, 19-9h €2 ⌷€1/80liter ⌷Ch ✍(6x)€1/kWh WC.
Location: Urban. **Surface:** gravel. ⌷ 01/01-31/12
Distance: ⌷500m ⌷500m ⊗50m ⌷300m ⌷600m.
Remarks: Parking swimming pool, max. 3 nights, during congresses special
tariff.

30 ⌷free ⌷€1/80liter ⌷Ch ✍(18x)€0,50/kWh.
Location: Rural, comfortable. **Surface:** asphalted/gravel. ⌷ 01/01-31/12
Distance: ⌷2,6km ⊗100m.
Remarks: Baker every morning.

Waldkirch	17A6

Reisemobilstellplatz Am Stadpark, Am Stadtrain. **GPS:** n48,09023 e7,95833.
⬆

Wangen im Allgäu 24D1

P17, Am Klösterle. **GPS:** n47,68160 e9,83401. ⬆➡.

40 €7 + € 1,30/pp tourist tax €0,50/120liter Ch (46x) WC.
Surface: metalled. 01/01-31/12
Distance: on the spot 500m 500m on the spot on the spot on the spot.
Remarks: Tourist tax € 1.

Tourist information Wangen im Allgäu:
ℹ️ Tourist Information, Parkplatz 1, Rathaus. Traditional small Bavarian town. Every Thursday city walk through historical city centre, 15.30-17. free. Wed.

Wehr 24A1

Ludingarten. **GPS:** n47,62515 e7,90582. ⬆➡.

10 €10 €1/100liter Ch (8x)€1/8h WC.
Location: Simple, quiet. **Surface:** metalled.
01/01-31/12
Distance: nearby.
Remarks: Pay at tourist office, Hauptstr. 14 or Bistro Gleis 13, Bahnhofplatz.

Weikersheim 17D2

Parkplatz Tauberwiesen, August-Laukhuff-Straße 15. **GPS:** n49,48364 e9,89706. ⬆.

30 free. **Location:** Rural, simple. **Surface:** gravel.
01/01-31/12
Distance: 300m 400m.

Weikersheim 17D2

Campingplatz Schwabenmühle, Weikersheimer Strasse 21, Laudenbach. **GPS:** n49,45795 e9,92691. ⬆.

6 €5/night €2/100liter Ch (6x)€4/12h. **Location:** Simple. **Surface:** gravel. Easter-15/10
Distance: 300m 200m.

Weil der Stadt 17C4

Festplatz, Jahnstrasse. **GPS:** n48,75268 e8,87453. ⬆➡.

4 free €1/80liter €1 Ch€1 (4x)€1/kWh.
Location: Urban, simple, noisy. **Surface:** asphalted. 01/01-31/12
Distance: 300m 300m 250m on the spot on the spot.
Remarks: Max. 3 days.

Weingarten 17D6

Festplatz, Abt Hyller Strasse 55. **GPS:** n47,81009 e9,63041. ⬆.
8 €5 €1 €1 Ch €2. **Surface:** metalled. 01/01-31/12
Distance: 1km 500m on the spot on the spot.
Remarks: Max. 3 nights.

Weinsberg 17C3

Eugen-Diez-Straße 2. **GPS:** n49,14846 e9,28464. ⬆➡.
6 free €1 Ch (6x)€0,50/kWh. **Location:** Rural, quiet.
Surface: grasstiles. 01/01-31/12
Distance: 500m 2km on the spot on the spot.

Welzheim 17D4

Aichstruter Stausee, Seiboldsweiler, Aichstrut. **GPS:** n48,90020 e9,63719. ⬆.

12 €5 €1/80liter Ch WC. **Surface:** gravel. 01/01-31/12
Distance: 5km on the spot on the spot on the spot.
Remarks: At artificial lake, max. 1 week.

Wertheim 17D1

Wohnmobilstellplatz An der Taubermündung, Linke Tauberstrasse. **GPS:** n49,76501 e9,51213. ⬆➡.

DE

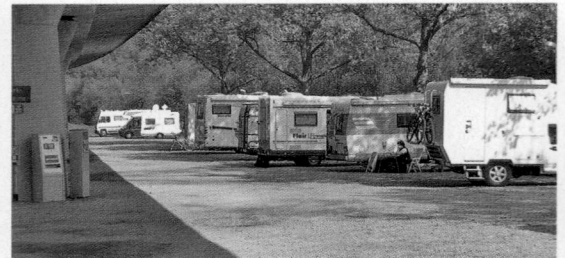

54 ⌁ € 7/24h ⚡€1/90liter ⬛ Ch. **Location:** Simple, noisy. **Surface:** gravel.
◯ 01/01-31/12 ◉ 2nd sa of the month + high water
Distance: 500m on the spot.
Remarks: Along the Tauber river, max. 3 days.

Wertheim — 17D1
Expocamp, Wertheim Caravaning & Freizeit, Hymerring 1.
GPS: n49,77368 e9,58034.

90 ⌁ free ⚡€1/90liter ⬛ Ch ⚡€1/3h WC during opening hours.
Location: Rural, comfortable. **Surface:** asphalted. ◯ 01/01-31/12
Distance: ⊗400m ⚑3,7km.
Remarks: Baker at 8am, Wertheim Outletcentrum 100m.

Tourist information Wertheim:
Wertheim Village, Almosenberg. Outlet-shopping.

Wildberg — 17B4
Wohnmobilstellplatz Wildberg, Klosterhof 4. **GPS:** n48,62055 e8,74485.

4 ⌁ free ⚡€1/100liter ⬛ Ch ⚡€1/kWh. **Location:** Quiet.
Surface: asphalted/metalled. ◯ 01/01-31/12 ◉ service 01/11-31/03
Distance: historical centre 500m ⊗700m ⚑1km on the spot.
Remarks: Along river, nearby monastery.

Wolfach — 17B5
Trendcamping Schwarzwald, Schiltacher Straße 80, Halbmeil.
GPS: n48,29053 e8,27763.

6 ⌁ € 15 + tourist tax ⚡⬛ Ch WC included ◉€3 €2
Location: Rural, simple, quiet. **Surface:** grassy/sand. ◯ 10/04-15/10
Distance: ⊗on the spot.

Wolfach — 17B5
Ferienhof Bartleshof, Ippichen 6, Ippichen. **GPS:** n48,30183 e8,26264.

5 ⌁€ 15 ⚡⬛ Ch (4x) €2 ◉€2. **Location:** Rural, simple, quiet.
Surface: grassy/gravel. ◯ 01/01-31/12
Distance: ⊗on the spot on the spot.
Remarks: € 10, reduction at restaurant.

Wolfegg/Allgäu — 17D6
Reisemobilhafen Loretopark, Rötenbacher Straße. **GPS:** n47,81489 e9,79802.
12 ⌁€ 5 ⚡€1/80liter ⬛ Ch ⚡€0,50/kWh. ◯ 01/01-31/12
Distance: 500m.

Wolfegg/Allgäu — 17D6
Hofgarten, Alttaner strasse. **GPS:** n47,82105 e9,79487.

2 ⌁€ 5. **Surface:** gravel/metalled.
◯ 01/01-31/12
Distance: on the spot.
Remarks: Max. 2 nights.

Tourist information Wolfegg/Allgäu:
Automobilmuseum. 200 oldtimers. ◯ 01/04-31/10 9.30-18h, 01/11-31/03 Su 10-17h.
Bauernhaus-museum. Open air museum. ◯ 01/04-31/10 Tue-Su 10-18/17h ◉ Mo Apr Oct.

Wutöschingen — 24B1

Wohnmobilplatz Degernau - Wutöschingen

h-aberle@t-online.de - www.wohnmobilplatz-degernau.de

Ideal base for walking and cycling
Comfortable motorhome stopover
Convenient for longer stays

Wohnmobilplatz Degernau, Ofteringer Strasse 1, Degernau.
GPS: n47,66639 e8,37917.
17 ⌁€ 8/day, 2 pers.incl ⚡€1/100liter ⬛ Ch ⚡(17x)€0,50/kWh,16Amp
WC €1 ◉€3/3 included. **Location:** Rural, comfortable, quiet.
Surface: grassy/gravel. ◯ 01/04-30/09

Distance: 🛒on the spot 🏊200m ⊗1km 🚲500m 🚐on the spot 🚶on the spot 🏃on the spot.
Remarks: Sauna, solarium.

🏕️S **Zell am Harmersbach** 17A5

Stellplatz am Schwimmbad, Nordracher Strasse. **GPS:** n48,35146 e8,05942. ⬆️ ➡️

14 🚐€ 3/20-12h 🚰€1/10minutes 🍴Ch 🧹 (8x)€1/10h. 🗑️
Location: Rural, simple, quiet. **Surface:** gravel. ⬛ 01/01-31/12
Distance: 🛒2km 🚲2km.

Bavaria

🏕️S **Absberg** 18B3

Badehalbinsel Brombachsee, Gunzenhausen-Pleinfeld Ausfart Absberg.
GPS: n49,13770 e10,87389.

150 🚐€ 8/24h 🚰€0,20/60liter 🍴Ch 🧹 (80x)€0,50/kWh WC 🗑️€0,50. 🗑️
Location: Rural, comfortable, quiet. **Surface:** grassy. ⬛ 01/04-01/10
Distance: 🛒1km 🏊on the spot ⊗on the spot 🚲1km 🚶on the spot 🏃on the spot.

🍴S **Adelsdorf** 18B2

Gasthof Niebler, Neuhauser Hauptstrasse 30. **GPS:** n49,70017 e10,90221.

4 🚐€ 15, guests free 🚰 🧹. **Surface:** metalled. ⬛ 01/01-31/12
Distance: 🛒on the spot ⊗on the spot.

🏕️ **Ahorn** 10C6

Freizeitzentrum Wittmannsberg, Badstrasse 20, Eicha.
GPS: n50,22537 e10,90252.

4 🚐free. **Surface:** metalled. ⬛ 01/01-31/12
Distance: 🛒on the spot 🚲5km.

🏕️S **Aichach** 18B5

Reisemobilplatz, Franz-Beck-Strasse. **GPS:** n48,45889 e11,12611. ⬆️

4 🚐€ 5 🚰🍴Ch free. 🚐 **Location:** Urban, simple, quiet.
Surface: grassy/gravel. ⬛ 01/01-31/12
Distance: 🛒500m ⊗500m 🚲100m.

🏕️S **Albertshofen** 18A1

An der Fähre Mainstockheim-Albertshofen, Mainstraße.
GPS: n49,77254 e10,15749. ⬆️

10 🚐€5 🚰🍴Ch 🧹 included. **Surface:** gravel. ⬛ 01/01-31/12
Distance: 🛒on the spot 🏊on the spot ⊗50m.
Remarks: Along Main river, closed when high water.

🍴S **Altmannstein** 18C3

Gasthof Forster, Schulstrasse 9. **GPS:** n48,90125 e11,69559.

20 🚐guests free 🚰 🧹 (4x)€2/night. **Surface:** asphalted.
⬛ 01/01-31/12
Distance: 🛒on the spot ⊗on the spot 🚲3km.
Remarks: Bread-service, check in before 19h (Mo-Tue 16h).

🏕️S **Altötting** 19A5

Griesstraße. GPS: n48,22946 e12,67493. ⬆️

8 🚐free 🚰€1/80liter 🍴Ch 🧹 (8x)€1/4h WC.
Location: Urban, simple, noisy. **Surface:** grasstiles. ⬛ 01/01-31/12
Distance: 🛒5 min ⊗on the spot 🚲on the spot.
Remarks: Max. 3 days.

DE

Altötting 19A5

P2 Dultplatz, Traunsteinerstrasse. **GPS:** n48,22287 e12,67921. ⬆

7 ⌕free ⛽€1/10liter 🚰 ✦ (8x)€1/4h. **Location:** Urban, simple, central. **Surface:** gravel. 🅿 01/01-31/12
Distance: 🚶700m.
Remarks: Max. 3 days.

Altusried 18A6

Am Freibad, Im Tal 4. **GPS:** n47,79915 e10,21934. ⬆ ➡

10 ⌕€5 ⛽€1 Ch ✦ €0,50/kWh. **Location:** Rural, simple, quiet.
Surface: grassy/gravel. 🅿 01/01-31/12
Distance: 🚶500m 🛒700m.
Remarks: Parking at swimming pool.

Amberg 18C2

Gasfabrikstraße. **GPS:** n49,44139 e11,86222. ⬆ ➡

10 ⌕free ⛽€1/80liter 🚰 Ch ✦ (12x)€1/12h. **Surface:** asphalted.
🅿 01/01-31/12
Distance: 🚶500m 🛒1km ⛽1km.

Amorbach 17C2

P Altstadt, Dr.F.A.Freundt-Straße. **GPS:** n49,64683 e9,22115.

5 ⌕free. **Location:** Urban, simple. **Surface:** asphalted.
🅿 01/01-31/12
Distance: 🚶500m ⊗400m ⛽Lidl.

Ansbach 18A3

Freizeitbad Aquella, Am Stadion 2. **GPS:** n49,30459 e10,55852. ⬆ ➡

12 ⌕free ⛽€0,50/50liter 🚰Ch ✦ (12x)€0,50/kWh.
Location: Simple, central. **Surface:** metalled. 🅿 01/01-31/12
Distance: 🚶1km ⚡7,7km ⊗on the spot ⛽1km 🚌on the spot.
Remarks: At swimming pool.

Arnbruck 19A3

Landhotel Rappenhof, Rappendorf 5. **GPS:** n49,13517 e12,95069.

5 ⌕€15 ⛽🚰Ch ✦WC ⌐included. **Surface:** grassy. 🅿 01/01-31/12
Distance: 🚶2km ⊗on the spot ⛽2km 🚴10km ⛷8km.
Remarks: Use of sauna against payment.

Arnstein 17D1

Badesee, Am Alten Schwimmbad. **GPS:** n49,97667 e9,95917. ⬆

6 ⌕free ⛽€1/80liter 🚰Ch ✦ (4x)€1/2kWh. **Surface:** grassy/metalled.
🅿 01/01-31/12, service 01/04-31/10
Distance: 🚶100m ⊗snack 100m.
Remarks: At the old swimming pool.

Arnstein 17D1

Cancale Platz. **GPS:** n49,97625 e9,96564.

5 ⌕free. **Surface:** metalled. 🅿 01/01-31/12
Distance: 🚶100m ⊗100m ⛽100m.
Remarks: Max. 1 night.

Arzberg 11A6

Am Rathausplatz. **GPS:** n50,05528 e12,18870. ⬆.
2 ⌕free. **Surface:** metalled. 🅿 01/01-31/12
Distance: 🚶250m ⊗300m ⛽250m.

DE

Aschaffenburg 17C1

Willigesbrücke, Grossostheimerstrasse. **GPS:** n49,97139 e9,13722.

25 € 3/24h (18x)€0,50/kWh. **Location:** Simple, quiet.
Surface: grassy/gravel. 01/01-31/12
Distance: historical centre 500m 8km on the spot.
Remarks: Parking along the Main, near Altstadt, being indicated with small signs, max. 3 days.

Aschheim 18C5

Gasthof Zur Post, Ismaningerstrasse 11. **GPS:** n48,17433 e11,71490.

2 € 10. **Surface:** asphalted. 01/01-31/12
Distance: on the spot on the spot 300m.

Aufseß 18B1

Brauerei-Gasthof Reichold, Hochstahl 24. **GPS:** n49,88389 e11,26855.

38 € 6 €1/90liter Ch (38x)€1,50 WC .
Surface: grassy/metalled. 01/01-31/12
Distance: on the spot Brauereienweg.
Remarks: Bread-service, breakfast buffet € 6/pp.

Augsburg 18B5

Schillstraße 109, Lechhausen. **GPS:** n48,38914 e10,90435.

4 € 5 Ch €1/2kWh WC . **Location:** Urban. **Surface:** gravel.
01/01-31/12
Distance: 3,2km Sportgaststätte 200m on the spot on the spot.
Remarks: At sports centre.

Augsburg 18B5

Wohnmobilstellplatz Wertach, Bürgermeister Ackermann strasse 1.
GPS: n48,36944 e10,87750.

12 € 8 €1/90liter Ch €1/6h. **Location:** Urban, simple.
Surface: gravel. 01/01-31/12
Distance: on the spot 4,5km on the spot on the spot 500m
500m.

Bad Abbach 18D3

Kaiser-Therme, Kurallee 4. **GPS:** n48,92712 e12,04044.

34 € 8 + € 1,80/pp €1/4minutes Ch (16x) WC .
Surface: grasstiles/grassy. 01/01-31/12
Distance: 2km.
Remarks: Check in at pay-desk of the Therme.

Bad Aibling 18D6

Stellplatz an der Therme P13, Lindenstrasse/Heubergstrasse.
GPS: n47,85639 e12,00583.

25 € 7 Ch €0,50/kWh. **Location:** Comfortable.
Surface: grasstiles/metalled. 01/01-31/12
Distance: 500m 400m 500m 600m 100m.

Bad Bayersoien 25B1

Wohnmobilstellplatz Bad Bayersoien, Am Bahnhof 6.
GPS: n47,68798 e10,99820.

12 € 9/24h €1/90liter Ch €1/2kWh. **Location:** Rural, simple,
quiet. **Surface:** gravel. 01/01-31/12
Distance: 400m 300m 300m 400m 400m.

DE

© S **Bad Birnbach** ☿ 19B4
Camping Arterhof, Hauptstraße 3, Lengham. **GPS**: n48,43512 e13,10939. 🔼.

10 🛏 € 10 🚰 🔌 Ch WC 🚿 📶 included. **Location:** Rural, simple, quiet. **Surface:** gravel. ◪ 01/01-31/12
Distance: ⊗on the spot.

🛏 S **Bad Bocklet** ☿ 10B6
Kurgarten, Aschacherstrasse. **GPS**: n50,26490 e10,07486. 🔼 ➡️.

13 🛏 € 8, tourist tax incl 🚰 € 1/80liter 🔌 Ch 🔌 (13x)€0,50/kWh.
Surface: metalled. ◪ 01/01-31/12
Distance: 🚶500m 🚌 Free bus to Bad Kissingen.

🛏 S **Bad Brückenau** ☿ 10B6
Schlosspark König Ludwig I, Schlüchterner Straße. **GPS**: n50,30556 e9,74861.
🔼 ➡️.

10 🛏 € 8 + € 2,50/pp Gästekarte 🚰 € 1/100liter 🔌 Ch 🔌 €0,50/kWh.
Surface: asphalted. ◪ 01/01-31/12
Distance: 🚶4km 🚌50m.

🛏 S **Bad Brückenau** ☿ 10B6
Sinnflut, Industriestrasse P5. **GPS**: n50,31212 e9,79607. 🔼 ➡️.

8 🛏 € 3 🚰 🔌 Ch 🔌 (8x)€1. **Surface:** gravel. ◪ 01/01-31/12
Distance: 🚶250m ⊗250m 🔌250m.
Remarks: Parking swimming pool.

🛏 S **Bad Brückenau** ☿ 10B6
Stellplatz Bahnhofstrasse, Buchwaldstrasse. **GPS**: n50,30667 e9,78556. 🔼.

20 🛏 € 3 🔌 € 1/8h. **Surface:** metalled. ◪ 01/01-31/12
Distance: 🚶300m ⊗on the spot 🔌 on the spot 🚌on the spot.

🍴 **Bad Feilnbach** 18D6
Gasthof Tiroler Hof, Aiblinger strasse 95. **GPS**: n47,76476 e12,03857. 🔼 🔼.

3 🛏 guests free. **Location:** Simple, isolated. **Surface:** gravel.
◪ 01/01-31/12
Distance: 🚶on the spot ⊗on the spot 🔌1km.

© S **Bad Füssing** ☿ 19B5
Campingplatz Holmerhof, Am Tennispark 10. **GPS**: n48,35798 e13,30658. 🔼.

9 🛏 € 9,10 🚰 € 1/30liter 🔌 Ch 🔌 (9x)€2/kWh WC 🚿 📶 €2.
Location: Rural, simple. **Surface:** metalled. ◪ 01/01-31/12
Distance: 🚶1km ⊗on the spot 🔌1km.
Remarks: Max. 3 days, use sanitary € 5/motorhome, swimming pool available.

🛏 S **Bad Gögging** ☿ 18C4
Limes-Therme, Am Brunnenforum 1. **GPS**: n48,81857 e11,78868. 🔼.

+20 🛏 € 8, tourist tax excl 🚰 € 1 🔌 Ch. **Surface:** asphalted. ◪ 01/01-31/12
Distance: 🚶150m ⊗150m 🔌150m.
Remarks: Check in at pay-desk of the Therme.

🛏 S **Bad Griesbach** ☿ 19B4
Mobilhafen Dreiquellenbad, Singham 40. **GPS**: n48,42023 e13,19261. 🔼.

29 🚐 € 16,50, incl tourist tax 🚰 €1/80liter 🔲 Ch 🔌 (29x)€0,60/kWh ⬜included 🚿€5. **Location:** Rural, simple, quiet. **Surface:** metalled. ⬛ 01/01-31/12
Distance: 🚶2km ⊗on the spot.
Remarks: Max. 3 days, thermal-Vital-Oase incl.

🔲🆂 **Bad Hindelang** 🏔❄ **25A1**
Wiesengrund Wohnmobilpark, Parkplatz Wiesengrund 1.
GPS: n47,49931 e10,37218. ⬆➡.

30 🚐 € 8-10 + tourist tax € 2,10/pp, 7><16 € 1,60, <7 € 0,90 🚰 €1/100liter 🔲 Ch 🔌€0,50/kWh WC⬜€1 🚿. 🚲 **Location:** Rural, luxurious, quiet.
Surface: grassy/gravel. ⬛ 01/01-31/12
Distance: ⊗on the spot 🚰1km 🚶on the spot.

🅒🆂 **Bad Hindelang** 🏔❄ **25A1**
Wohnmobilplatz Bergheimat, Passstraße 60, Oberjoch.
GPS: n47,51791 e10,42142. ⬆ .

10 🚐 € 15, dog € 3,50 🚰 🔲 Ch 🔌 WC⬜€1 🚿. 🛉
Location: Rural, simple, noisy. **Surface:** grassy/gravel. ⬛ 01/01-31/12
Distance: 🎣on the spot ⛵on the spot.

🔲🆂 **Bad Kissingen** 🌿⛱♨ **10B6**
KissSalis Therme, Heiligenfelder Allee 16. **GPS:** n50,18861 e10,06139. ⬆➡.

18 🚐 € 4 + € 3,40/pp tourist tax 🚰 €1/90liter 🔲 Ch 🔌€1/8h.
Surface: asphalted. ⬛ 01/01-31/12
Distance: 🚶500m ⊗on the spot 🚰on the spot.

🅒🆂 **Bad Kohlgrub** **25B1**
Kur-Camping Waldruh, Sonnen 93. **GPS:** n47,65789 e11,04393. ⬆.

16 🚐 € 10,40 + € 2,50/pp 🚰🔲Ch 🔌€0,40/kWh WC⬜🔲€2,50 🚿 📷.
Surface: gravel. ⬛ 01/01-31/12
Distance: 🚶1,5km 🚰1,5km.

🔲🆂 **Bad Kohlgrub** **25B1**
Sanatorium Kurhaus Dr. Lauter, Kurhausstrasse 81. **GPS:** n47,66412 e11,04315. ⬆ .

4 🚐 € 12 🚰 🔌. **Location:** Rural, simple, quiet. **Surface:** gravel. ⬛ 01/01-31/12
Distance: 🚶1,5km ⊗on the spot 🛒1,5km 🚲1km 🚲1km.

🔲🆂 **Bad Königshofen** **10C6**
Frankentherme, Am Kurzentrum 1. **GPS:** n50,30003 e10,47503. ⬆➡.

77 🚐 € 9 🚰€1 🔲Ch 🔌€0,50/kWh WC⬜. **Surface:** grasstiles/metalled. ⬛ 01/01-31/12
Remarks: Washing-machine/dryer available, if full 2 alternatives will be given, special health arrangement possible.

Tourist information Bad Königshofen:
ℹ Kurverwaltung Königshofen, Am Kurzentrum 1, www.bad-koenigshofen.de. Traditional small town with half-timbered houses, cycle and hiking routes in the surroundings.

🍴🆂 **Bad Kötzting** 🏔💒❄ **19A3**
Kaitersbacher Hof, Kaitersbach 40. **GPS:** n49,15520 e12,89467.

10 🚐 € 5, free with a meal 🚰 🔲 🔌€2,50. **Surface:** grassy/gravel.
⬛ 01/12-31/10
Distance: 🚶4km ⊗on the spot 🚰Aldi 2km 🚲10km 🚲8km.

⌂Ⓢ | **Bad Neustadt** | 10B6
Parkplatz An der Saale. GPS: n50,31637 e10,22205.⬆➡.

30 ⌁€ 8/24h ⌐€1/50liter ⌷Ch. **Location**: Rural. **Surface**: asphalted.
◻ 01/01-31/12
Distance: 🚰1km ⊗500m ⚉500m 🚌500m.
Remarks: Max. 48h, incl. Kurkarte.

Tourist information Bad Tölz:
☺ Alpamare. Large swimming pool complex with wave machine, Alpa, slides, sauna etc. ◻ Su-Thu 8-21h, Fri-Sa 8-22h, 24/12-01/01 8-16h.

60 ⌁€ 8 ⌐€1/50liter ⌷Ch ⚡(48x)included. 🚽 **Surface**: grasstiles.
◻ 01/01-31/12
Distance: 🚰500m.

⌂ⓈS | **Bad Reichenhall** ♨ | 19A6
Wohnmobilpark Rupertus Therme, Hammerschmiedweg.
GPS: n47,73466 e12,87536.⬆➡.

25 ⌁€ 13, 2 pers.incl ⌐€1/80liter ⌷Ch ⚡included.
Location: Comfortable. **Surface**: gravel. ◻ 01/01-31/12
Distance: 🚰500m ⊗on the spot.

⌂ⓈS | **Bad Windsheim** ♨ | 18A2
Phoenix Reisemobilhafen, Bad Windsheimer Strasse 7.
GPS: n49,51361 e10,41722.⬆➡.

100 ⌁€ 10,90 ⌐€1/100liter ⌷Ch ⚡(80x)€0,50/kWh WC ⌷€1
⚉€2,50/2,50 📶. **Surface**: gravel. ◻ 01/01-31/12
Distance: 🚰1km ⊗100m ⚉500m.
Remarks: Bread-service.

⌂ⓈS | **Bad Rodach** | 10C6
ThermeNatur Bad Rodach, Thermalbadstrasse. **GPS**: n50,33452 e10,77499.

24 ⌁€ 4,50 + € 2/pp tourist tax ⌐€1,50 ⌷Ch ⚡(16x)€1,50 WC ⌷.
Surface: metalled. ◻ 01/01-31/12, water: 01/04-30/09
Distance: 🚰on the spot ⊗on the spot ⚉500m.
Remarks: Caution key service € 10, caution key electricity € 20, key service at swimming pool.

○ | **Bad Windsheim** ♨ | 18A2
Fränkisches Freilandmuseum, Eisweiherweg. **GPS**: n49,49705 e10,41667.⬆➡.

20 ⌁€ 5 + € 1,60/pp tourist tax. **Surface**: grassy. ◻ 01/01-31/12
Distance: 🚰1km ⊗500m ⚉500m.
Remarks: Open air museum.

⌂ⓈS | **Bad Steben** ♨ | 10D6
An der Therme, P3, Steinbacher Straße. **GPS**: n50,36250 e11,63239.⬆.

⌂ⓈS | **Bad Wörishofen** ♨ | 18B6
Therme Bad Wörishofen, Thermenallee 1. **GPS**: n48,02120 e10,59100.⬆.

12 ⌁€ 5 + €0,50/pp tourist tax ⌐€0,50/80liter ⌷Ch ⚡€0,50/kWh.
Surface: metalled. ◻ 01/01-31/12
Distance: 🚰500m ⊗200m ⚉500m.

25 ⌁€ 9 ⌐€1/100liter ⌷Ch ⚡included WC. 🛁 **Location**: Urban, simple.
Surface: asphalted. ◻ 01/01-31/12
Distance: 🚰1,5km 🚲4,3km ⊗on the spot ⚉500m 🚌on the spot.

⌂ⓈS | **Bad Tölz** 🌿♨❄ | 18C6
Bürgermeister Stohlreiterpromenade. **GPS**: n47,76252 e11,55142.⬆➡.

Remarks: Check in at pay-desk of the Therme, max. 3 nights, max. 8M, bread-service.

Balderschwang 🏔❄ 25A1

Wohnmobilplatz Schwabenhof, Schwabenhof 23. **GPS:** n47,45745 e10,12963.

50 € 11-16 Ch €3,50/day WC €0,50. **Location:** Rural, comfortable, luxurious. **Surface:** grassy/gravel. 01/01-31/12
Distance: 3km on the spot 3km 100m 100m.
Remarks: Bread-service, drying room for skis.

Bamberg 18B1

Wohnmobilplatz, Am Heinrichsdamm. **GPS:** n49,88583 e10,90221.

25 € 12 €1/100liter Ch €0,50/kWh. **Surface:** gravel. 01/01-31/12
Distance: 10 min walking.
Remarks: Max. 24h.

Bärnau 🏔🌳❄ 18D1

Gasthof und Wald-Pension Blei, Altglashütte 4. **GPS:** n49,77222 e12,38880.

30 € 10, guests free Ch WC included, customers free.
Surface: asphalted/grassy. 01/01-31/12
Distance: 6km on the spot 6km 100m.

Baunach 18B1

Sportplatz-Festplatz, Bahnhofstrasse 14-4. **GPS:** n49,98750 e10,85444.

5 free €1 Ch €1/12h. **Surface:** grassy/metalled. 01/01-31/12
Distance: 200m 200m 200m.

Remarks: Parking at the edge of nature reserve Haßberge, in the old part of the city, max. 2 nights.

Bayerbach 19B4

Wohnmobilhafen Vital, Huckenham 11. **GPS:** n48,41537 e13,13010.

10 € 12,50 2 pers.incl, dog € 2,50 Ch (8x)€0,50/kWh
WC included €1. **Location:** Rural, simple, quiet. **Surface:** metalled. 01/01-31/12
Distance: 500m on the spot.
Remarks: Max. 3 nights, use sanitary facilities at campsite.

Bayreuth 18C1

Lohengrin Therme Bayreuth, Kurpromenade 5. **GPS:** n49,94319 e11,62861.

24 € 6 €1/50liter Ch €1 €1/6h WC €1,50.
Surface: metalled. 01/01-31/12
Distance: 1,5km 3,5km 500m 1km on the spot.
Remarks: Bread-service.

Bayrischzell 🏔🌳❄ 18D6

Wohnmobilstellplatz Bayrischzell, Seebergstraße. **GPS:** n47,67189 e12,01023.

20 € 10 €0,50/80liter Ch (12x)€0,50/kWh.
Location: Comfortable, central. **Surface:** gravel. 01/01-31/12
Distance: 400m 400m 400m 400m bus 5min on the spot.

Beilngries 18C3

An der Altmühl, An der Altmühl. **GPS:** n49,02655 e11,47121.

20 € 10 Ch WC included.
Location: Urban, comfortable, central, quiet. **Surface:** grassy.

DE

Remarks: Check in at reception campsite.

ⅈ S ‖ Beilngries ‖ 18C3

Landgasthof Euringer, Dorfstrasse 23. **GPS:** n49,01054 e11,50261. 🔼 .

6 🚐 guests free 🚰 🍴 Ch 💦. **Location:** Urban, simple, central.
Surface: metalled. 🔲 01/01-31/12
Distance: 🚶4km ⊗on the spot 🛒4km.

S ‖ Benediktbeuern ⛵ 🏕 ⛳ ‖ 18C6

Wohnmobilstellplatz Benediktbeuern, Schwimmbadstraße 37.
GPS: n47,69920 e11,41556. 🔼➡️ .

8 🚐 €7 🚰 🍴 Ch included 💦€1/6h. **Location:** Rural, comfortable, quiet.
Surface: asphalted. 🔲 15/03-01/11
Distance: 🚶1km.
Remarks: Max. 3 nights, Alpenwarmbad 01/05-01/09 (swimming pool).

ⅈ S ‖ Beratzhausen ‖ 18C3

Landgasthof Friesenmühle, Friesenmühle 1. **GPS:** n49,08534 e11,81176. 🔼 .

10 🚐 free, use of a meal desired 🚰 💦 (2x) WC. **Surface:** grassy/gravel.
🔲 01/01-31/12
Distance: 🚶1km ⊗on the spot 🛒1km.
Remarks: Apply< 22h.

S ‖ Berching ‖ 18C3

Stellplatz Schiffsanleger, Uferpromenade. **GPS:** n49,10972 e11,43910. 🔼 .
12 🚐 €5 🚰€1 🍴 Ch 💦€1/8h. **Surface:** grasstiles/metalled.
🔲 01/01-31/12
Distance: 🚶200m ⛴50m ⊗on the spot 🛒300m 🚌100m.

S ‖ Berchtesgaden 🎿 🏕 ⛳ ‖ 19B6

Reisemobilplatz Rasp, Renothenweg 15, Oberau. **GPS:** n47,65172 e13,07038.
🔼➡️ .

20 🚐 € 8 + € 2,10/pp tourist tax 🚰€2 🍴 Ch 💦€2 WC.
Location: Central, quiet. **Surface:** gravel. 🔲 Easter-30/11
Distance: 🚶500m 🛒500m.

S ‖ Bergen/Chiemgau ❄ ‖ 19A6

Parkplatz Hochfelln-Seilbahn, Maria-Eck-Straße 8. **GPS:** n47,79710 e12,59079.
🔼 .

10 🚐 €5. 🛏 **Location:** Simple. **Surface:** metalled. 🔲 01/01-31/12
Distance: 🚶1,2km ⊗on the spot 🎿on the spot.
Remarks: Parking ski-lift, max. 1 night.

ⅈ S ‖ Bernried ‖ 19A3

Altes Gasthaus Artmeier, Innenstetten 45. **GPS:** n48,89675 e12,90262. 🔼 .

10 🚐 €5 🚰€1/100liter 🍴 💦 (4x)€1/day. **Location:** Rural, simple, quiet.
Surface: gravel/sand. 🔲 Tue, water: 01/11-31/03
Distance: 🚶3km ⊗on the spot 🛒on the spot.

ⅈ S ‖ Biesenhofen ‖ 18B6

Gasthof Stegmühle, Stegmühle 2. **GPS:** n47,82437 e10,64428. 🔼 .

4 🚐 €5, free with a meal 🚰 🍴 Ch 💦 WC 🍴. 🍴 **Location:** Simple.
Surface: gravel/metalled. 🔲 01/01-31/12
Distance: 🚶1km ⛴1km ⊗on the spot 🛒1km.

S ‖ Bischofsgrün 🏕 🎿 ❄ ‖ 18C1

Rangenweg. GPS: n50,05407 e11,79292. 🔼➡️ .

DE

6 � free, tourist tax € 1,50 to be paid at tourist office ⌐€1/40liter ⌐Ch ⌐ (6x)€1/12h. **Surface:** metalled. ▣ 01/01-31/12
Distance: ⌐250m ⌐500m ⌐nearby.

🏕 S | **Bischofsheim an der Rhön** | **10B6**

Viehweg 1, Haselbach. **GPS:** n50,39506 e9,99593. ⬆➡.

12 ⌐ € 5 ⌐€1/80liter ⌐Ch. **Surface:** asphalted. ▣ 01/01-31/12
Distance: ⌐on the spot ⌐on the spot ⌐on the spot.
Remarks: Parking swimming pool in Haselbach.

🍴 | **Bischofswiesen** | **19A6**

Götschen Alm, Kollertradte 21, Loipl. **GPS:** n47,64817 e12,93631.

20 ⌐guests free. **Surface:** gravel. ▣ 01/04-30/11
Distance: ⌐2km ⌐on the spot ⌐2km ⌐on the spot ⌐on the spot.

🏃 S | **Blaichach** | **25A1**

Alpen-Rundblick Mobil Camping, Am Eichbichl 1. **GPS:** n47,54615 e10,25917. ⬆➡.

60 ⌐ € 10,50/12,50 + € 1,70 pp ⌐€1/80liter ⌐Ch ⌐ (54x)€0,60/kWh WC ⌐€1,60 ▣€2,50. **Location:** Luxurious. **Surface:** grassy/gravel.
▣ 01/01-31/12
Distance: ⌐300m ⌐3,3km ⌐on the spot ⌐on the spot ⌐500m ⌐500m ⌐5km ⌐1km.

🏕 S | **Bodenmais** | **19A3**

Concorde-Reisemobil-Stellplatz, Kötztinger Straße. **GPS:** n49,07147 e13,09273. ⬆.

12 ⌐€ 7 + tourist tax ⌐€0,50/100liter ⌐Ch ⌐€0,50/kWh.
Surface: asphalted.
▣ 01/01-31/12
Distance: ⌐800m ⌐200m ⌐200m.
Remarks: Use swimming pool, sauna, fitness-studio incl.

🍴 S | **Bodenwöhr** | **18D2**

Gasthof zum Troidlwirt, Bodenwöhrer strasse 6. **GPS:** n49,28305 e12,26272. ⬆.

40 ⌐€ 10/24h, guests free ⌐Ch ⌐ (12x)€1 WC ⌐€1.
Surface: grassy/metalled. ▣ 01/01-31/12 ▣ Restaurant: Sa
Distance: ⌐on the spot ⌐on the spot ⌐bakery 300m.

🏕 S | **Bogen** | **19A3**

Volksfestplatz, Kotaustraße 12. **GPS:** n48,90744 e12,68877. ⬆.

5 ⌐€ 10 ⌐€2 ⌐Ch ⌐ (5x)€2/8h. **Surface:** grassy/metalled.
▣ 01/01-31/12
Distance: ⌐300m ⌐Edeka 100m.
Remarks: Check in at pay-desk of swiming pool.

🏕 S | **Burgbernheim** | **18A2**

Wohnmobilstellplatz im Gründlein, Freibadstrasse. **GPS:** n49,44627 e10,31869. ⬆➡.

12 ⌐free ⌐€1/100liter ⌐Ch ⌐ (10x)€0,50/kWh. **Surface:** grasstiles.
▣ 01/01-31/12
Distance: ⌐500m ⌐500m ⌐500m ⌐500m.

🍴 | **Burghaslach** | **18A2**

Hotel-Restaurant Steigerwaldhaus, Oberrimbach 2. **GPS:** n49,72764 e10,53542. ⬆.

DE

10 🛌 € 6, guests free. **Surface:** grassy. 🅿 01/01-31/12
Distance: 🚶500m ⊗on the spot 🛒5km.

🛌S | **Burghausen** 🌿 | 19A5

Waldpark Lindach, Berghamer Strasse 1. **GPS:** n48,15443 e12,80859. ⬆➡.

16 🛌 € 5/24h 🚰€1/80liter 🗑 Ch 🧹 (16x)€0,50/kWh WC 🚽 . 🚗
Location: Rural, comfortable, quiet.
Surface: gravel.
🅿 01/01-31/12 ◉ sanitary 01/11-31/03
Distance: 🚶1,5km ⊗500m 🛒1,5km.
Remarks: Check in at Bürgerhaus Marktlerstr. 15a, caution key sanitary € 20.

🛌S | **Burgkirchen** | 19A5

Peterhof, Peterhof 24. **GPS:** n48,15096 e12,75025. ⬆ .

3 🛌 € 12,50, 2 pers.incl 🚰 🗑 🧹 WC included ◉ 📶 .
Location: Rural, simple, quiet. **Surface:** grassy. 🅿 01/01-31/12
Distance: 🚶2km ⊗2km 🛒2km.

🛌S | **Burgkunstadt** 🎭 | 10D6

Alter Postweg. **GPS:** n50,13965 e11,25017. ⬆.

4 🛌free 🚰€1 Ch. **Location:** Rural. **Surface:** gravel.
🅿 01/01-31/12
Distance: 🚶100m 🏊15km 🚂100m ⊗300m 🛒300m 🚲on the spot
🥾on the spot.
Remarks: Max. 48h.

🛌S | **Bürgstadt** 🍷 | 17C2

Winzerfestplatz, Josef-Ullrich-Straße. **GPS:** n49,71356 e9,26405. ⬆.

25 🛌free 🚰€1/80liter 🗑 Ch 🧹 (12x)€1/6h. **Location:** Rural, comfortable.
Surface: asphalted. 🅿 01/01-31/12
Distance: 🚶500m ⊗200m 🛒200m.

🛌S | **Cadolzburg** 🌿 | 18B2

Parkplatz Am Höhbuck, Am Höhbuck. **GPS:** n49,46123 e10,85188.
8 🛌free 🚰 🗑 Ch 🧹 . **Surface:** metalled. 🅿 01/01-31/12
Distance: 🚶on the spot.

🛌S | **Coburg** | 10C6

Ketschenanger, Schutzenstrasse. **GPS:** n50,25306 e10,96417. ⬆.

9 🛌free. **Surface:** asphalted.
Distance: 🚶on the spot ⊗on the spot.
Remarks: Parking next to gymnasium, max. 48h.

🛌S | **Coburg** | 10C6

Aral-station, Bambergerstrasse. **GPS:** n50,24833 e10,96639.

3 🛌free 🚰€1 🗑 Ch.
Surface: metalled.
🅿 01/01-31/12
Distance: 🚶on the spot.

Tourist information Coburg:
🏛 Die Veste Coburg. Medieval fortress.
⚔ Schloß Ehrenburg. 🎫 guided tour Tue-Su.

🛌S | **Deggendorf** | 19A3

Konstantin-Bader-Strasse, Konstantin-Bader-Straße.
GPS: n48,82656 e12,96367. ⬆.

3 🛌free. **Location:** Simple. **Surface:** asphalted. 🅿 01/01-31/12

DE

Distance: centre 500m ⊗250m.

🔲S   **Deiningen**   **18A4**

Cowabanga, Am Sportpark. **GPS**: n48,86292 e10,58042. ➡️

10 ⛺free ⛽ 🚿€2,50 WC 🗑. **Location:** Urban, simple. **Surface:** asphalted. ⚡ 01/01-31/12

Distance: 2km ⊗on the spot.

Remarks: Parking sports centre.

🍴S   **Denkendorf**   **18C3**

Gasthof Lindenwirt, Hauptstrasse 43. **GPS**: n48,92806 e11,45568. ⬆️

10 ⛺€4 ⛽ 🚿 included. 🏖 **Location:** Urban. **Surface:** gravel/sand. ⚡ 01/01-31/12

Distance: on the spot 🏊700m ⊗on the spot 🍺200m 🚴on the spot 🏃on the spot.

🔲S   **Dettelbach**   **18A1**

Zur Mainfähre, Mainsondheimerstrasse. **GPS**: n49,80076 e10,16751. ⬆️➡️

35 ⛺€7 ⛽€1/60liter 🔌Ch 🚿(24x)€0,50/kWh. 🏧 **Surface:** grassy. ⚡ 01/01-31/12 ⚪ Service: winter

Distance: 100m 🚲100m 🍺100m.

🔲S   **Dießen**   **18B6**

Seestraße. **GPS**: n47,95220 e11,10598. ⬆️

12 ⛺€8 ⛽€1 🔌Ch 🚿(12x)€4/8h. 🏧 **Surface:** gravel. ⚡ 01/01-31/12

Distance: 🏊200m 🚲200m ⊗150m 🍺150m.

Remarks: Max. 3 days.

🔲S   **Dingolfing**   **19A4**

Wohnmobilstellplatz Dingolfing, Wollanger/Prasserweg. **GPS**: n48,62827 e12,50206. ⬆️➡️

12 ⛺free ⛽€1/80liter 🔌Ch 🚿(12x)€1/12h.

Location: Rural, comfortable, quiet. **Surface:** gravel. ⚡ 01/01-31/12

Distance: 400m 🚲4,6km ⊗250m.

Remarks: Nearby swimming pool.

🔲S   **Dinkelsbühl** 🌼   **18A3**

Park- & Campanlage, Dürrwanger Straße. **GPS**: n49,07812 e10,32906. ⬆️

12 ⛺€12 ⛽ 🔌Ch 🚿 included 🗑€1,50. **Surface:** metalled. ⚡ 01/01-31/12

Distance: 1,5km 🏊100m 🍺500m.

Remarks: To be paid at campsite (500m).

🍴   **Dittelbrunn**   **18A1**

Gasthaus Goldene Flasche, Strohgasse 1, Hambach. **GPS**: n50,09787 e10,20763. ⬆️

3 ⛺€1. **Surface:** metalled. ⚡ 01/01-31/12

Distance: on the spot ⊗on the spot 🍺200m.

🔲S   **Donauwörth**   **18B4**

Wohnmobilstellplatz am Festplatz, Neue Obermayerstrasse. **GPS**: n48,71490 e10,77874. ⬆️➡️

20 ⛺free ⛽€1/80liter 🔌Ch 🚿€1/8h. **Location:** Urban, simple. **Surface:** asphalted. ⚡ 01/01-31/12

Distance: on the spot ⊗on the spot 🍺500m.

Remarks: Max. 1 night.

🔲   **Ebermannstadt**   **18B1**

P2, Oberes Tor. **GPS**: n49,78222 e11,18946. ⬆️➡️

DE

10 🛌 free. **Surface:** metalled. 🅾 01/01-31/12
Distance: 🚶750m ⊗450m 🛒100m.
Remarks: Max. 1 night.

🛥 **S**   **Ebern**   **18A1**
Wohnmobilhafen Ebern, Walk-Strasser-Anlage. **GPS**: n50,09312 e10,79496.

20 🛌 € 6 ⛽ Ch 🔌 €1/2kWh WC ⌐ included. **Surface:** metalled.
🅾 01/01-31/12
Distance: 🚶 on the spot ⛱1km 🛒2km ⊗100m 🛒200m 🚌100m.

🛥 **S**   **Ebern**   **18A1**
Dietz, Bahnhofstrasse. **GPS**: n50,10167 e10,78917.

10 🛌 € 5 ⛽ €1/100liter 🛒 Ch 🔌 WC ⌐. **Surface:** asphalted/grassy.
🅾 01/01-31/12
Distance: 🛒400m.

🛥 **S**   **Ebrach**   **18A1**
Naturbad, Schwimmbadweg. **GPS**: n49,84639 e10,48306. ⬆➡.

5 🛌 free ⛽ €1/80liter 🛒 Ch WC. **Surface:** metalled. 🅾 01/01-31/12
Distance: 🚶2km ⊗2km 🛒2km 🛒500m.
Remarks: Parking swimming pool.

🛥 **S**   **Eggenfelden**   **19A5**
P2, Birkenallee. **GPS**: n48,40185 e12,77579. ⬆.

5 🛌 free. **Location:** Simple, quiet. **Surface:** grassy/metalled.
🅾 01/01-31/12
Distance: 🚶1km.
Remarks: Max. 3 days.

🛥 **S**   **Eggenfelden**   **19A5**
Tankstelle Breitner Shell, Tiefstadt 10. **GPS**: n48,39591 e12,76621.

🛌 € 3 ⛽ 🛒. **Location:** Simple. **Surface:** asphalted.
Remarks: Max. 1 night.

© **S**   **Eging am See**   **19B4**
Bavaria Kur-Sport Camping Park, Grafenauer Str. 31.
GPS: n48,72120 e13,26519. ⬆➡.

10 🛌 € 15 ⛽ 🛒 Ch 🔌 (10x)included. **Location:** Rural, simple, quiet.
Surface: asphalted. 🅾 01/01-31/12
Remarks: Max. 2 days, check in at reception campsite, use sanitary facilities at campsite.

🛥 **S**   **Eibelstadt** 〰   **17D2**
Wassersportclub Eibelstadt, Mainparkring. **GPS**: n49,73146 e9,98701. ⬆.

35 🛌 € 10 ⛽ €1/5minutes 🛒 Ch 🔌,6Amp WC included ⌐€1/time ⊡€5.
Surface: grassy/gravel. 🅾 01/01-31/12
Distance: 🚶2km 🛒50m ⊗50m 🚌1km.
Remarks: Along Main river.

🛥 **S**   **Eichstätt**   **18B4**
Schottenwiese/Volkfestplatz. **GPS**: n48,88400 e11,19816. ➡.

50 ⬛€8 ⛽ 🚽 Ch ⚡(30x)€0,50/kWh WC 🚿€0,50. 🚿
Location: Urban, simple, central, quiet. **Surface:** metalled.
🅿 01/01-31/12 ◉ Eichstätter Volksfest
Distance: 🚶500m 🛒500m 🚲 on the spot 🅰 on the spot.
Tourist information Eichstätt:
🎪 Volksfestplatz. Flea market. 🅿 10/05, 14/06, 12/07, 13/09, 04/10.
🎊 Altstadtfest, Innenstad. City celebration. 🅿 28/08-06/09.
🎊 Eichstätter Volksfest, Volksfestplatz. Folk festival. 🅿 02/09-11/09.
🌿 Informationszentrum Naturpark Altmühltal, Notre Dame 1, former monastry.
Information centre nature reserve. 🅿 01/04-31/10 Mo-Sa 9-17h, Su 10-17h,
01/11-31/03 Mo-Thu 8-12h, 14-17h, Fri 8-12h. 🅣 free.

📷S | **Einsiedl** 🏖🎣❄ | 25C1
Wohnmobilstellplatz, B11. **GPS:** n47,57000 e11,30389. ⬆➡.

80 ⬛€5 ⛽€1/70liter ⚡€1/6h. **Location:** Rural, comfortable, quiet.
Surface: asphalted/gravel. 🅿 01/01-31/12
Distance: 🚶500m 🛒on the spot 🚲on the spot ⊗500m 🚰3,5km 🎿1,5km
⛷1,5km.
Remarks: Max. 3 nights.

📷S | **Eisenheim** | 18A1
Weingut Herbert Schuler, An der Mainaue, Obereisenheim.
GPS: n49,88883 e10,17942.

60 ⬛€5 ⛽€1/80liter ⚡ Ch ⚡€0,50. **Surface:** grassy/metalled.
🅿 01/01-31/12
Distance: 🚶on the spot 🛒on the spot ⊗on the spot.
Remarks: Along Main river.

📷S | **Eltmann am Main** 🚢 | 18A1
Parkplatz, Mainlände. **GPS:** n49,97306 e10,66250. ⬆➡.

10 ⬛free ⛽€1/80liter ⚡€1/6h. **Surface:** metalled. 🅿 01/01-31/12
Distance: 🚶500m 🛒on the spot 🚲on the spot ⊗100m 🚰300m.

📷S | **Enderndorf** 🏖🎣🍴🚲🎣 | 18B3
Wohnmobilstellplatz Panorama, Kreisstraße, Spalt-Enderndorf.
GPS: n49,15028 e10,91083. ⬆.

60 ⬛€8,00 ⛽€0,20/10liter ⚡ Ch ⚡(60x)€1/kWh 🚿. **Surface:** metalled.
🅿 01/04-31/10
Distance: 🚶400m 🛒400m 🚲400m ⊗400m 🚰3km 🚌150m.

📷S | **Enderndorf** 🏖🎣🍴🚲🎣 | 18B3
Reisemobil-Stellplatz Enderndorf-West, Zum Hafen.
GPS: n49,14777 e10,91126. ⬆.

25 ⬛€8/24h ⛽€0,20/100liter ⚡ Ch ⚡€0,50/kWh. 🚐
Location: Rural, simple, isolated, quiet. **Surface:** grasstiles.
🅿 01/01-31/12
Distance: 🚶200m 🛒150m ⊗200m 🚰200m 🚲on the spot 🅰on the spot.

📷S | **Erbendorf** | 18C1
Am Stadtpark, Bahnhofstraße 21. **GPS:** n49,84144 e12,04769. ⬆➡.

10 ⬛free ⛽€1 ⚡ Ch. **Surface:** gravel. 🅿 01/01-31/12
Distance: 🚶100m ⊗200m 🚰200m.
Remarks: Max. 3 days.

📷S | **Erding** 🎿 | 18D5
Wohnmobilpark Erding, Thermenallee 1. **GPS:** n48,29332 e11,88707. ⬆➡.

DE

55 ⬛ € 10/day ⬝€1/80liter ⬝Ch ⬝€1/2kWh WC.
Surface: grasstiles/metalled. ⬛ 01/01-31/12
Distance: 2km 2km 2km 50m.
Remarks: Max. 7 nights.

Escherndorf — 18A1
Campingplatz Escherndorf, An der Güß 9a. **GPS:** n49,85996 e10,17632.⬆.

22 ⬛ € 8 ⬝Ch ⬝. **Surface:** grassy. ⬛ 01/04-31/10
Distance: 300m 300m.

Ettenbeuren — 18A5
Wohnmobilpark Kammelaue, Zum Sportplatz 12. **GPS:** n48,37565 e10,36021.➡.

40 ⬛ € 7, € 13 service incl ⬝Ch ⬝ WC. **Location:** Rural, comfortable, quiet. **Surface:** grasstiles/metalled. ⬛ 01/04-31/10
Distance: 500m on the spot 500m on the spot on the spot.

Feucht — 18B2
Am Freibad Feuchtasia, Chormantelweg. **GPS:** n49,37848 e11,22495.

9 ⬛ € 7 ⬝€1/80liter ⬝Ch ⬝ (8x)€1/2kWh. **Surface:** grasstiles.
⬛ 01/01-31/12
Distance: 1km 900m.

Fichtelberg — 18C1
Automobilmuseum, Eckert Naglerweg 9. **GPS:** n49,99760 e11,85820.⬆.

15 ⬛ free. **Surface:** asphalted/metalled. ⬛ 01/01-31/12
Distance: 100m.
Remarks: Parking museum.

Fischen — 25A1
Wohnmobil-Stellplatz Fischen, Mühlenstraße. **GPS:** n47,44950 e10,26946.⬆.

12 ⬛ € 8 + € 1,95/pp tourist tax ⬝€1 ⬝Ch ⬝ (12x)€1/12h.
Location: Rural, simple. **Surface:** asphalted.
Distance: 1,2km on the spot on the spot.
Remarks: Pay at Sportpark, Mühlenstraße 55.

Forchheim — 18B1
Sportinsel, An der Regnitzbrücke. **GPS:** n49,72120 e11,04939.⬆➡.

12 ⬛ € 3 ⬝€3 ⬝Ch WC ⬝€1. **Surface:** grasstiles.
⬛ 01/01-31/12 sanitary building: 01/11-28/02
Distance: 600m on the spot on the spot.

Frasdorf — 18D6
Bauernhof Lederstube, Lederstube 3. **GPS:** n47,79521 e12,28774.⬆⬆.

6 ⬛ € 7 ⬝€1,50 ⬝Ch ⬝ €3. **Location:** Rural, simple, isolated, quiet.
Surface: grassy/gravel. ⬛ 01/03-30/09
Distance: 500m 800m 800m 800m.

Freilassing — 19B6
Stellplatz Freilassing, Salzburgerstrasse. **GPS:** n47,84031 e12,98599.⬆.

5 ⌂free. **Surface:** asphalted. ◙ 01/01-31/12
Distance: 6km 100m.
Tourist information Freilassing:
⚐ Flea market.

4 ⌂free. **Location:** Rural, simple, quiet. **Surface:** asphalted.
◙ 01/01-31/12
Distance: 1,8km 5km on the spot 400m on the spot
on the spot.

⌂S	Freyung	19B3

Freizeitpark Solla, Solla. **GPS:** n48,80104 e13,54125. ⬆➡.

S	Friedberg	18B5

Marquardtstrasse 2/A. **GPS:** n48,34825 e10,99757.
Ch free.
Distance: on the spot.

⌂S	Friedenfels	18D1

Freibad, Badstrasse. **GPS:** n49,88639 e12,10417. ⬆.

12 ⌂€5 €1/80liter Ch (12x)€0,50/kWh.
Location: Rural, simple, quiet. **Surface:** grasstiles. ◙ 01/01-31/12
Distance: 2km 500m on the spot on the spot.

⌂	Freyung	19B3

Parking Freibad, Zuppinger Straße. **GPS:** n48,80515 e13,54102. ⬆.

15 ⌂€3,50 €1. **Surface:** metalled. ◙ 01/01-31/12
Distance: 1,5km.
Remarks: Max. 3 days, service during opening hours.

⌂S	Friedenfels	18D1

Zentral, Gemmingenstraße. **GPS:** n49,88102 e12,10297. ⬆.

10 ⌂free. **Location:** Urban, simple, quiet. **Surface:** metalled.
◙ 01/01-31/12
Distance: 1km 1km 1km.

⌂	Friedberg	18B5

Herrgottsruhstrasse. **GPS:** n48,35765 e10,99095.

15 ⌂€3,50 . **Surface:** metalled. ◙ 01/01-31/12
Distance: on the spot 25m.
Remarks: Max. 3 days, pay at tourist office, Café Am Steinwald, Gemmingenstr. 19.

⌂	Friedenfels	18D1

Stellplatz 'Ruhig', Weißensteiner Weg, Frauenreuth. **GPS:** n49,89278 e12,08556. ⬆.

4 ⌂free. **Surface:** gravel.
Distance: 600m 600m 600m.

⌂	Friedberg	18B5

Seestraße. **GPS:** n48,36540 e10,96529. ⬆➡.

5 ⌂€3,50. **Surface:** metalled. ◙ 01/01-31/12
Distance: 1,5km Frauenreuther Weiher.
Remarks: Max. 3 days.

⛺ⓈᏚ **Füssen** ❄ ⚓ 🍳 🏔 🍴 ❄ ♈ **25B1**
Camper's Stop, Abt Hafnerstrasse 9. **GPS**: n47,58186 e10,70080. ⬆️➡️.

120 ⬛€ 13, trailer € 5 ⛽€0,50/150liter ♨Ch ⚡€1/kWh WC 🚽€0,50
💧€2. **Location:** Urban, comfortable, noisy. **Surface:** gravel/metalled.
📷 01/01-31/12
Distance: 🚲1,5km 🏊600m ⛽600m ⊗terrace 🛒50m 🚆250m 🚴4km
🏊400m.

⛺ⓈᏚ **Füssen** ❄ ⚓ 🍳 🏔 🍴 ❄ ♈ **25B1**
Wohnmobilstellplatz Füssen, Abt Hafnerstrasse 1. **GPS**: n47,58224 e10,70355.
⬆️.

30 ⬛€ 13,50 ⛽ ♨Ch ⚡(6x)€2,50 WC 🚽€0,50 💧€2. 🧺 **Location:** Noisy.
Surface: metalled. 📷 01/01-31/12
Distance: 🚲1,8km 🏊1km ⊗200m ⛽300m 🚆500m 🚴 on the spot
🏃 on the spot 🚴 on the spot 🏊 on the spot.

⛺Ⓢ **Garmisch-Partenkirchen** ⚓ 🏔 🎠 ❄ **25B1**
Alpencamp am Wank, Wankbahnstraße 2. **GPS**: n47,50573 e11,10802. ⬆️.

110 ⬛€ 10 + € 2/pp tourist tax, € 1 Umwelttaxe ⛽€1/50liter ♨
Ch ⚡(110x)€1/kWh WC 🚽€1 💧. 🧺 **Location:** Rural, comfortable.
Surface: asphalted. 📷 01/01-31/12
Distance: 🚲1km 🏊2km ⊗50m 🛒700m 🚆50m 🚴2,5km 🏊1,5km.

⛺Ⓢ **Gerolzhofen** **18A1**
P3 Zur Volkach, Schallfelderstrasse. **GPS**: n49,89808 e10,35169. ⬆️➡️.

6 ⬛€5 ⛽€1 ♨Ch ⚡(4x)€0,50/kWh WC. **Surface:** metalled.
📷 01/01-31/12
Distance: 🚲100m.

Remarks: Max. 3 days.

⛺Ⓢ **Gerolzhofen** **18A1**
P1 Geomaris, Dingolshäuser Straße 2. **GPS**: n49,89980 e10,36035. ⬆️.

6 ⬛free. **Surface:** asphalted. 📷 01/01-31/12
Distance: 🚲750m.
Remarks: Parking swimming pool.

⛺Ⓢ **Geslau** **18A2**
Bauernhof Mohrenhof, Lauterbach 3. **GPS**: n49,34630 e10,32500. ⬆️➡️.

20 ⬛€ 10-12 ⛽ ♨Ch ⚡€0,50/kWh WC 🚽€0,50 🔲€3 💧€2,50/2h.
Surface: grassy. 📷 Easter-31/10
Distance: 🚲500m 🏊on the spot.
Remarks: Bread-service.

⛺Ⓢ **Goldkronach** ❄ ⚓ ❄ **18C1**
Festplatz, Schulstrasse. **GPS**: n50,01265 e11,68276. ⬆️➡️.

4 ⬛free ⛽€1/10minutes ♨Ch ⚡(4x)€1/10h. **Surface:** gravel.
📷 01/01-31/12
Distance: 🚲50m 🛒500m 🚴2km.

⛺Ⓢ **Grafenau** **19B3**
Grafenauer Kurpark, Freyunger Straße. **GPS**: n48,85605 e13,40456. ⬆️➡️.

10 ⬛€ 5 Kurtaxe incl ⛽€1/80liter ♨Ch ⚡included 💧free.
Location: Urban, simple, quiet. **Surface:** gravel. 📷 01/01-31/12
Distance: 🚲500m ⊗600m 🛒550m ReWe 🏃on the spot.
Remarks: Wifi in Touristinformation + 1/2h free internet in Stadtbücherei.

DE

Gräfendorf 17D1

Volkert an der Roßmühle, Roßmühle, Weickersgrüben.
GPS: n50,10660 e9,78309.

5 🛏 €5 🚰 €2/100liter 🔌 Ch 🧹 (5x)included.
🅿 01/04-31/10
Distance: 🏊 on the spot 🛒 on the spot ⊗ on the spot.
Remarks: At motorhome dealer, accessory shop, max. 24h, check in at shop.

Greding 18C3

Am Hallenbad. **GPS:** n49,04409 e11,35551.⬆

20 🛏 free. **Location:** Urban. **Surface:** metalled.
🅿 01/01-31/12
Distance: 🛒Old city centre 300m 🚲 500m ⊗250m 🚮250m 🚿 on the spot
🚶 on the spot.
Remarks: Parking at city wall in front of swimming pool.
Tourist information Greding:
ℹ City wall and towers.

Großheubach 17C2

Weingut Gasthaus "Zur Bretzel", Kirchstraße 1. **GPS:** n49,72620 e9,22083.

25 🛏 €17 🚰 🔌 Ch 🧹 WC included 🚽 €1/time.
Location: Rural, comfortable, quiet. **Surface:** grassy/gravel.
🅿 01/11-15/11
Distance: 🛒100 m ⊗on the spot 🚶 on the spot.
Remarks: To be paid at Gasthaus, € 10 euro discount coupon (restaurant, wine).

Großweil 25C1

Aplengasthof Kreut-Alm, Kreut 1. **GPS:** n47,66184 e11,28286.⬆

15 🛏 customers free 🚰 🧹. **Location:** Rural, simple, isolated, quiet.
Surface: asphalted. 🅿 01/03-31/10
Distance: 🚲 3,2km ⊗on the spot.

Großweil 25C1

Freilichtmuseum Glentleiten, An der Glentleiten 4. **GPS:** n47,66495 e11,28506.
⬆➡

10 🛏 free. **Surface:** gravel.
Distance: 🛒2km 🚲 3,5km ⊗Gaststätte - Biergarten 🚮1km.
Remarks: Open air museum, only overnight stays.

Günzburg 18A5

Waldbad, Heidenheimerstrasse. **GPS:** n48,46287 e10,26944.➡

24 🛏 €5/24h 🚰 €1/100liter 🔌 🧹 (24x)€0,50/kWh. 🏠 **Location:** Simple.
Surface: gravel. 🅿 01/01-31/12 🚲 Danube Bike Trail.
Remarks: Parking swimming pool.

Gunzenhausen 18B3

Surfzentrum Schlungenhof. GPS: n49,12790 e10,74559.⬆

80 🛏 €10/24h 🚰 €1 🔌 Ch 🧹 included WC 🚽 €1 🚿. 🚗 🅿 01/04-30/10
Location: Rural, comfortable, quiet. **Surface:** grassy/gravel. 🅿 01/04-30/10
Distance: 🏊100m ⊗on the spot 🚮1,8km.

Gunzenhausen 18B3

Altmühlsee, Seezentrum Mühr. GPS: n49,13145 e10,73534.

40 🛏 €3 day/€6 night. 🏠 **Location:** Rural, comfortable, isolated, quiet.
Surface: grassy. 🅿 01/01-31/12
Distance: 🏊 on the spot ⊗200m 🚮 on the spot 🚶 on the spot.
Remarks: Max. 3 days.

DE

Hammelburg 17D1

Am Bleichrasen, P2, Am Weiher. **GPS:** n50,11390 e9,88820.

25 € 6/24h Ch included (18x)€0,50/kWh WC. **Surface:** asphalted. 01/01-31/12
Distance: 200m 200m 300m.

Hammelburg 17D1

Forellenhof Reuss, Am Erlich 30, Diebach. **GPS:** n50,13310 e9,81917.

20 € 7 Ch included €2 €2. **Location:** Rural. **Surface:** grasstiles. 01/04-31/10
Distance: Hammelburg 7km on the spot.
Remarks: Bread-service, weekend: Gaststätte/Biergarten.

Hammelburg 17D1

Schloß Saaleck, Am Schlossberg. **GPS:** n50,10998 e9,87281.
3 free WC. **Surface:** asphalted/metalled. 01/01-31/12
Distance: on the spot.

Hammelburg 17D1

Restaurant Nöth, Morlesauer Strasse 3. **GPS:** n50,11707 e9,80313.
5 free. **Surface:** gravel. 01/01-31/12
Distance: on the spot on the spot.
Remarks: Check in at restaurant, use of a meal desired.

Hassfurt 18A1

Festplatz am Gries, Ringstrasse. **GPS:** n50,03068 e10,50094.

22 € 5/night €1 Ch €1 WC. **Surface:** asphalted. 01/01-31/12
Distance: 200m 10m 200m 200m.
Remarks: Along Main river.

Herrieden 18A3

Volksfestplatz an der Altmühl, Staatsstrasse 2248. **GPS:** n49,23191 e10,49588.

10 free. **Surface:** asphalted. 01/01-31/12
Distance: 100m 200m 200m.
Remarks: Parking at the old mill bridge.

Hersbruck 18C2

Fackelmanntherme Hersbruck, Badestraße. **GPS:** n49,51142 e11,44267.

6 € 6 €1 Ch €1/6h. **Surface:** gravel. 01/01-31/12
Distance: on the spot 200m 200m.
Remarks: Check in at pay-desk of the Therme.

Herzogenaurach 18B2

Freizeitbad Atlantis, Würzburger Straße 35. **GPS:** n49,57251 e10,86641.
12 € 6/24h Ch (12x). **Surface:** gravel. 01/01-31/12
Distance: on the spot.
Remarks: € 2 reduction swimming pool.

Hilpoltstein 18B3

Seezentrum Heuberg am Rothsee, Heuberg. **GPS:** n49,20954 e11,18595.

50 € 7,50 Ch. **Surface:** metalled. 01/01-31/12 Service: winter
Distance: 200m 200m.

Hilpoltstein 18B3

Am Main-Donau Kanal. GPS: n49,20455 e11,18813.

30 € 6. **Surface:** grassy. 15/04-30/10
Distance: 1,9km Canal 1,9km 1km on the spot on the spot.
Tourist information Hilpoltstein:
Burgfeste. Festival with events. beginning Aug.

Hof/Saale 11A6

Park Theresienstein, Plauener Straße. **GPS**: n50,32956 e11,92041. ⬆️

10 🛏free. **Surface:** metalled. 🔲 01/01-31/12
Distance: 🚶2,5km 🚲1km.
Remarks: Max. 24h.

Hof/Saale 11A6

Utreusee, Wilhelm Löhe strasse. **GPS**: n50,28583 e11,91361. ⬆️

10 🛏free. **Surface:** asphalted/metalled. 🔲 01/01-31/12
Distance: 🏊100m ⊗50m 🚲500m.
Remarks: Max. 24h.

Hof/Saale 11A6

Clean Park, Ernst Reuterstrasse. **GPS**: n50,32641 e11,89248. ⬆️

4 🛏€5 🚰€1 🅲h 🧹. **Surface:** metalled. 🔲 01/01-31/12
Distance: 🚶2km ⊗800m.
Remarks: Max. 72h.

Tourist information Hof/Saale:
👁 Bürgerpark Theresienstein. Landscape park according English example.
🔲 9-18h, winter 9-16h.
😊 Untreusee. Lake with water sports.

Hofheim in Unterfranken 10C6

Wohnmobilplatz Hofheim, Johannisstraße 28. **GPS**: n50,14185 e10,51957. ⬆️ ➡️

30 🛏€7 🚰€1/80liter 🅲h 🧹€0,50/kWh WC 🔲. **Surface:** grasstiles.
🔲 01/01-31/12
Distance: 🚶750m 🚲750m.

Remarks: Bread-service.

Hohenberg/Eger 11A6

Wiesenfestplatz, Selberstrasse. **GPS**: n50,09762 e12,22085.

10-20 🛏voluntary contribution 🚰 🅲h 🧹 free WC. **Surface:** metalled.
🔲 01/01-31/12
Distance: 🚶200m ⊗50m.
Remarks: Beautiful view, porcelain museum.

Hohenburg 18C2

Sportplatz, Sportplatzweg 1. **GPS**: n49,29194 e11,80917. ⬆️

6 🛏€7 🧹€2 WC. **Surface:** metalled. 🔲 01/01-31/12
Distance: 🚶1km.
Remarks: Parking at sports park.

Huisheim 18B4

Waldparkplatz im Schwalbtal, Waldschenke 1, Gosheim.
GPS: n48,84932 e10,71530. ⬆️ ➡️

10 🛏€5, guests free 🚰. **Location:** Rural, simple, quiet. **Surface:** asphalted.
🔲 01/01-31/12
Distance: ⊗on the spot.

Immenstadt 25A1

P 3 Viehmarktplatz, Badeweg. **GPS**: n47,56192 e10,20857. ⬆️ ➡️

6 🛏free 🚰 Ch WC. **Location:** Urban, simple, comfortable. **Surface:** asphalted.
🔲 01/01-31/12
Distance: 🚲700m.

Ingolstadt 18C4

Parkplatz Hallenbad, Jahnstrasse. **GPS**: n48,76025 e11,42038. ⬆️ ➡️

DE

8 ⌂ € 5 (9-17h), overnight stay free ⛽€1/80liter 🚰 Ch ✍ included 🚽. 🚐
Location: Urban, comfortable. **Surface:** metalled. 🅾 01/01-31/12
Distance: 🚶on the spot 🚲1,6km ✖on the spot ▼on the spot 🐾on the spot 🏃on the spot
Remarks: Parking at sports park, max. 3 days.

Inzell 🐚 19A6
Camping Lindlbauer, Kreuzfeldstraße 44. **GPS:** n47,76717 e12,75417.

12 ⌂ € 16 ⛽ 🚰 Ch ✍ WC 🚽 📶 included. **Location:** Rural.
Surface: metalled. 🅾 01/01-31/12
Distance: ▼1km.
Remarks: Max. 1 night, health resort 500m.

Iphofen 18A2
Einesheimer Tor, Birklinger Straße. **GPS:** n49,70260 e10,26459. ⬆

8 ⌂ free ⛽€1 🚰 Ch ✍ (6x)€1 WC. **Surface:** gravel. 🅾 01/01-31/12
Distance: 🚶200m.
Remarks: Parking at city wall.

Ippesheim 18A2
Kempe's Autohof Gollhofen, Industriestraße 1. **GPS:** n49,58546 e10,17579.
25 ⌂ € 5 ⛽ WC 🚽. **Surface:** asphalted. 🅾 01/01-31/12
Distance: ✖on the spot.

Kastl/Oberpfalz 🌿 🏰 18C2
Wanderparkplatz Am Alten Bahnhof, Amberger Straße.
GPS: n49,36657 e11,68388. ⬆

5 ⌂ free ⛽ 🚰 Ch WC free. **Surface:** gravel. 🅾 01/01-31/12
Distance: 🚶200m ✖200m ▼100m 🚂50m.

Kaufbeuren 18B6
Wohnmobilplatz Kaufbeuren, Buronstraße. **GPS:** n47,89885 e10,61650. ⬆
8 ⌂ free ⛽ 🚰 Chfree ✍ (6x)€0,50/2kWh. **Location:** Urban.
Surface: gravel.
Distance: 🚶historical centre 3km.
Remarks: Max. 3 days.

Kelheim ⛵ 18C3
Volksfestplatz, Am Pflegerspitz. **GPS:** n48,91331 e11,87657. ⬆➡

50 ⌂ € 6 ⛽ 🚰 Ch ✍ (18x)€1/2kWh WC. 🚐 **Surface:** metalled.
🅾 01/01-31/12 ⚫ service 01/11-31/03
Distance: 🚶500m ✖500m.
Remarks: Max. 3 nights, hindmost part.

Kemnath 18C1
Wohnmobilstellplatz Kemnath, Am Eisweier 8. **GPS:** n49,87219 e11,88774.

5 ⌂ free ⛽€1 🚰 Ch ✍ (6x)€1/6h WC. **Surface:** concrete.
🅾 01/01-31/12
Distance: 🚶650m ✖650m ▼650m.

Kempten 25A1
Illerstadion, Illerdamm/Jahnstrasse. **GPS:** n47,72915 e10,31940. ⬆➡

6 ⌂ € 5 ⛽€1 🚰 🚽. 🚐 **Location:** Urban, simple, noisy. **Surface:** metalled.
🅾 01/01-31/12
Distance: 🚶500m 🚲2,7km.

Kiefersfelden 🏔 ❄ 25D1
Hödenauer See, Wasserstrasse. **GPS:** n47,62881 e12,18949. ⬆➡

10 ⌂ € 5 WC 🚽€0,50. **Location:** Simple. **Surface:** gravel/sand.

DE

☐ 01/01-31/12
Distance: 🚶2km 🚲3km 🏊on the spot ⊗50m 🚌300m.
Remarks: Max. 3 days.

Kiefersfelden 🏔🌲❄ 25D1
Rathausplatz. **GPS:** n47,61303 e12,18981.⬆

20 🅿€10. **Location:** Simple. **Surface:** asphalted. ☐ 01/01-31/12
Distance: 🚶on the spot 🚲2km ⊗100m.
Remarks: Max. 3 days.

Kirchenlamitz 11A6
REWE-Markt, Weißenstädter Straße. **GPS:** n50,14905 e11,94055.⬆➡

12 🅿free 🔌 Ch. free, voluntary contribution.
Location: Comfortable. **Surface:** asphalted. ☐ 01/01-31/12
Distance: 🚶500m 🚰10m.

Kirchham 19B5
Erlebnispark Haslinger Hof, Ed 1. **GPS:** n48,34947 e13,29115.⬆.

25-30 🅿Overnight stay € 17 (incl. € 9 voucher) 🔌 Ch.
Location: Rural, simple, quiet. **Surface:** gravel. ☐ 01/01-31/12
Distance: ⊗on the spot.

Kitzingen 18A2
Wohnmobilpark Am Main, Bleichwasen, Etwashausen.
GPS: n49,74274 e10,16491.⬆

70 🅿€7/24h 🔌€1/60liter Ch. €0,50/kWh WC. **Surface:** asphalted.
☐ 01/01-31/12
Distance: 🚶300m 🏊on the spot.
Remarks: Between Alter Mainbrücke and Nordbrücke.

Klingenberg 17C2
Sonja's Wohnmobilhafen, Zur Einladung. **GPS:** n49,78370 e9,17805.⬆.

55 🅿€7,50 🔌€1 Ch. (50x)€2. **Location:** Rural, comfortable, quiet.
Surface: grassy/gravel. ☐ 01/01-31/12
Distance: 🚶500m on the spot ⊗500m 🚰2km.

Königsberg 18A1
Buchweg. **GPS:** n50,08472 e10,57028.⬆➡

6 🅿€2 Ch. **Surface:** metalled. ☐ 01/01-31/12
Distance: 🚶300m ⊗300m 🚰300m.
Remarks: Parking sports park.

Königsbrunn 18B5
Königsallee. **GPS:** n48,27243 e10,88283.

12 🅿€6/24h 🔌€1/100liter Ch. (12x)€0,50. **Surface:** metalled.

Kreuzwertheim 17C2
Am Mainufer, Fährgasse. **GPS:** n49,76251 e9,51840.⬆.

10 🅿€5. **Location:** Simple, quiet. **Surface:** gravel.
☐ 01/01-31/12
Distance: 🚶Wertheim centre 1,2km 🏊on the spot ⊗600m.
Remarks: Along Main river, max. 1 night.

Kronach 10D6
Hammermühle, Am Sand. **GPS:** n50,23195 e11,32735.⬆➡

DE

10 ☶€5/24h ☷€1 ☷Ch ☷(12x)€0,50/kWh. **Surface:** asphalted. ☐ 01/01-31/12
Distance: ☷10min ☷on the spot ☷200m ☷300m.

| ☷S | Kronach | 10D6 |

Lucky Stable Ranch, Mostrach 1. **GPS:** n50,21840 e11,34012.☷
5 ☶€5, 2 pers.incl ☷☷ ☷WC included ☷€1,50 ☷€1,50 ☷.
Surface: grassy/metalled. ☐ 01/01-31/12
Distance: ☷2km ☷on the spot ☷on the spot.
Remarks: At manege.

| ☷S | Krün 🌨🏔🏕🌿⛲❄ | 25C1 |

Tennsee Reisemobilhafen, Am Tennsee 1. **GPS:** n47,49083 e11,25444.☷☷

37 ☶€12,50-18,50 + tourist tax €1,50/pp, Umwelttaxe €0,60/pp ☷☷ ☷Ch ☷€0,70/kWh WC ☷ ☷€3 ☷€3/h ☷. ☷
Location: Rural, comfortable, luxurious, quiet. **Surface:** grassy/gravel.
☐ 01/01-31/12 ☐ 07/11-15/12
Distance: ☷2,5km ☷800m ☷3km ☷on the spot ☷on the spot ☷100m ☷on the spot ☷on the spot ☷5km ☷300m.

| ☷S | Kulmbach 🌨 | 10D6 |

Wohnmobilstellplatz Kulmbach, Am Schwedensteg.
GPS: n50,11063 e11,45698.☷☷

25 ☶€3 ☷€1/100liter ☷Ch ☷(25x)€1/2kWh. **Surface:** gravel.
☐ 01/01-31/12 ☐ water disconnected in winter
Distance: ☷on the spot.

| ☷ | Kümmersbruck | 18C2 |

Wohnmobilstellplatz Kümmersbruck, Am Butzenweg.
GPS: n49,41978 e11,89651.☷

8 ☶free. **Surface:** metalled. ☐ 01/01-31/12
Distance: ☷1km ☷1km.
Remarks: At sports centre.

| ☷S | Lalling | 19A3 |

Wohnmobilstellplatz Weber, Euschertsfurth 34. **GPS:** n48,83222 e13,14444.☷

8 ☶€8 ☷ ☷Ch included ☷(10x)€0,30/kWh ☷€1,50.☷
Location: Rural, comfortable, quiet. **Surface:** grassy/metalled. ☐ 01/04-30/11
Distance: ☷1,5km ☷100m.
Remarks: Swimming pool incl.

| ☷S | Lalling | 19A3 |

Lalling-Freizeitgelände, Waldstrasse. **GPS:** n48,84139 e13,13778.☷

2 ☶free ☷€1/80liter ☷Ch ☷€3/day. **Location:** Rural, simple, quiet.
Surface: metalled/sand. ☐ 01/01-31/12
Distance: ☷2km.
Remarks: At tennis-courts.

| ☷S | Lalling | 19A3 |

Familie Stelzer, Euschertsfurth 141. **GPS:** n48,83222 e13,13917.☷

4 ☶€4 ☷Service €1 ☷. **Location:** Rural, simple, quiet.
Surface: asphalted/grassy. ☐ winter
Distance: ☷1km ☷1km.

| ☷S | Lalling | 19A3 |

Lallinger Hof, Hauptstrasse 23. **GPS:** n48,84560 e13,13851.☷ .

DE

4-5 🛏guests free ⚓ against payment. **Location:** Rural, simple, quiet.
📷 01/04-31/10
Distance: 🚶250m ⊗250m.
Remarks: Check in at restaurant.

📶 S | Lalling | 19A3

Sieglinde, Obstgarten 13, Hunding. **GPS:** n48,84502 e13,14939. ⬆ .

3 🛏€ 5 ⛽🚰 Ch included ⚓ (2x)€2/day WC ⅃. **Location:** Rural, simple,
quiet. **Surface:** grassy. 📷 01/04-31/12
Distance: ⊗700m.

🎎 | Lalling | 19A3

Gasthof zur Post, Pfarrweg. **GPS:** n48,84405 e13,14064. ⬆ .

15 🛏free. **Location:** Rural, simple, quiet. **Surface:** metalled. ⊙ winter
Distance: 🚶200m ⊗200m.

📶 S | Lalling | 19A3

Erikas Wohlfühlplatz, Kleinfeld 6, Hunding. **GPS:** n48,84333 e13,17944. ⬆ .

10 🛏€ 5 + €0,50/pp ⛽ ⚓ (10x)€1/day WC ⅃€3.
Location: Rural, simple, quiet. **Surface:** grassy/sand. 📷 01/04-31/10
Distance: ⚓on the spot 🛒on the spot ⊗3km 🍴200m 🚴on the spot
🏊on the spot.
Remarks: Check in at Kleinfeld 6.

📶 | Lalling | 19A3

Feng Shui Kurpark, Euschertsfurther Straße. **GPS:** n48,84137 e13,13952. ⬆ .

🛏€ 1. **Surface:** gravel. 📷 01/01-31/12
Remarks: Not indicated.

📶 S | Landau/Isar | 19A4

Am Festplatz, Harburger Straße 20/B20. **GPS:** n48,67712 e12,68323. ⬆➡ .

± 20 🛏free ⛽€1/100liter 🍴Ch ⚓ (6x)€0,50/kWh. **Surface:** grassy/gravel.
📷 01/01-31/12
Distance: 🚶1,5km 🚲2,3km ⊗McDonalds 200m 🍴bakery 200m.

📶 S | Landsberg am Lech ☕ | 18B6

Waitzinger Wiese, Gottesackerangerweg. **GPS:** n48,05534 e10,87371. ⬆ .

8 🛏€ 1/24h ⛽€1/100liter 🍴Ch ⚓ (8x)€0,50/6h WC€0,50. 🚽
Location: Urban, simple. **Surface:** metalled. 📷 01/01-31/12
Distance: 🚶400m ⊗300m.

📶 S | Lechbruck am See 🌿🏕🌸🍃❄ | 25B1

Wohnmobilpark via Claudia, Via Claudia 6. **GPS:** n47,71556 e10,82139. ⬆➡ .

52 🛏€ 12,50-13,30 2 pers.incl, dog € 3-3,50 ⛽ 🍴Ch ⚓ WC ⅃€1,50
📷€2,50 📶. 🔌 🚿 **Location:** Rural, comfortable, luxurious. **Surface:** gravel.
📷 01/01-31/12
Distance: 🚶5km ⚓on the spot 🛒on the spot ⊗on the spot 🍴on the spot
🚌on the spot 🚴10km 🏊on the spot.

📶 S | Lenggries 🏔🍃❄ | 25C1

Dürrachstrasse, Fall. **GPS:** n47,57039 e11,53380. ⬆➡ .

DE

25 🖅 € 0,50/h, € 4/24h ⟶€2 🔌 WC. **Location:** Isolated, quiet.
Surface: metalled. ⬛ 01/01-31/12
Distance: ⟶250m ⟶250m ⊗150m ⬛8km ⟶on the spot ⟶on the spot.
Remarks: Max. 7 days.

🏕 S ⟶ Lindau 🏔 ⟶ 24D1
Blauwiese, P1. GPS: n47,55869 e9,70130. ⬆➡

34 🖅 € 1/h, € 20/24h ⟶€0,50 🔌€0,50 Ch WC. **Surface:** metalled.
⬛ 01/01-31/12
Distance: ⟶on the spot ⟶1km ⟶1km ⊗500m ⬛500m ⟶on the spot.
Remarks: Max. 24h.

C S ⟶ Lindau 🏔 ⟶ 24D1
Park Camping, Frauenhoferstrasse, Lindau-Zech. **GPS:** n47,53764 e9,73148.

15 🖅 € 12/24h ⟶🔌Ch ⟶ WC ⟶included, on camp site. **Surface:** gravel.
⬛ 15/03-31/10
Remarks: Max. 24h.

Tourist information Lindau:
👁 Lindau Insel. Promenade along the lake with Mangturm, 700 years old lighthouse.

🏕 S ⟶ Lohr/Main ⚓ ⟶ 17D1
Lohrer Mainlände, Osttangente. **GPS:** n49,99429 e9,58053.

20 🖅 € 5 ⟶€1/100liter 🔌Ch ⟶ (22x)€2/8h ⟶€2/h. ⟶
Location: Urban, noisy. **Surface:** metalled. ⬛ 01/04-31/10
Distance: ⟶300m ⟶on the spot ⬛Aldi 800m.
Remarks: Along Main river, max. 3 days.

🏕 ⟶ Mainbernheim 🌿 18A2
Goldgrubenweg. **GPS:** n49,71484 e10,22028. ⬆➡

10 🖅free. **Surface:** metalled. ⬛ 01/01-31/12
Distance: ⟶on the spot.

🏕 S ⟶ Mainstockheim ⟶ 18A1
Wohnmobilhafen Mainstockheim, Albertshöfer straße.
GPS: n49,77173 e10,15595. ⬆➡

37 🖅€ 7 ⟶🔌Ch ⟶ included. ⟶ **Surface:** gravel. ⬛ 01/01-31/12
Distance: ⟶on the spot ⟶5km ⟶on the spot ⊗100m ⬛100m.
Remarks: Along Main river.

🏕 S ⟶ Manching 18C4
Am Braunweiher. GPS: n48,71078 e11,49602. ⬆

50 🖅free ⟶€1/80liter 🔌Ch. **Surface:** grasstiles/metalled.
⬛ 01/01-31/12
Distance: ⟶1,5km ⟶1,3km ⬛Edeka 1km.

🏕 S ⟶ Markt Wald 🌳 ⟶ 18A5
Wohnmobilpark Markt Wald, Bürgle 1a. **GPS:** n48,14602 e10,57517. ⬆➡

20 🖅€ 7 ⟶€1/100liter 🔌Ch ⟶ €0,50/kWh WC ⟶€2. ⟶
Location: Rural, comfortable, quiet. **Surface:** grassy/gravel. ⬛ 01/01-31/12
Distance: ⟶1km ⟶on the spot ⟶on the spot ⊗on the spot ⬛1km ⟶on the spot ⟶on the spot ⟶on the spot.
Remarks: At small lake, bread-service, use sanitary facilities at campsite.

🏕 ⟶ Marktbreit 18A2
Am Kranen, Staatsraße. **GPS:** n49,66878 e10,14241. ⬆

3 🅿free. **Surface:** metalled. ◻ 01/01-31/12
Distance: 🚲on the spot ⊗on the spot.
Remarks: Max. 1 day.

🚐S | **Marktheidenfeld** | 17D1
Martinswiese, Georg-Mayr-Straße. **GPS:** n49,84918 e9,59887. ⬆️➡️.

30 🅿€ 5/24h 🚰€1/100liter 🚽Ch 🔌(8x)€1/4h WC included.
Location: Rural, comfortable, quiet. **Surface:** gravel.
◻ 01/01-31/12 ⦿ during event
Distance: 🚲600m 🏊on the spot 🚌on the spot ⊗200m 🛒Lidl 650m.
Remarks: Along Main river, max. 3 days.

🚐 | **Marktheidenfeld** | 17D1
Georg-Mayr-Straße. **GPS:** n49,85364 e9,60025. ⬆️.

20 🅿free. **Location:** Rural, simple, noisy. **Surface:** gravel.
◻ 01/01-31/12
Distance: 🚲1km ⊗50m 🛒Lidl 50m.
Remarks: Max. 3 days.

🚐S | **Marktleuthen** | 11A6
Am Angerparkplatz. **GPS:** n50,12946 e11,99483. ⬆️.

10 🅿free 🚰 🚽Ch 🔌(10x)free 🚿€0,50. **Surface:** metalled.
◻ 01/01-31/12
Distance: 🚲250m ⊗150m 🛒200m.
Remarks: Max. 7 days, bread-service.

🚐S | **Marktredwitz** | 18D1
Wohnmobilstellplatz am Auenpark, Dörflaser Platz, Fabrikstraße.
GPS: n49,99710 e12,08640. ⬆️➡️.

20 🅿free 🚰€0,50 🚽€0,50 Ch€0,50 🔌(6x)€0,50/kWh.
Surface: asphalted/gravel. ◻ 01/01-31/12
Distance: 🚲300m ⊗50m 🛒150m.

🚐 | **Marktredwitz** | 18D1
Angerplatz, Egerland-Kulturhaus, Fikentscherstrasse.
GPS: n50,00379 e12,09506. ⬆️➡️.

6 🅿free. **Surface:** asphalted. ◻ 01/01-31/12
Distance: 🚲1km 🛒500m.

⊙S | **Massing** | 19A5
Am Freilichtmuseum, Spirknerstraße. **GPS:** n48,39528 e12,60056.
10 🅿free 🚰 🔌 on demand. **Surface:** asphalted.
Distance: ⊗Museumstüberl.
Remarks: Open air museum, busy parking during the day.

🚐 | **Mehlmeisel** | 18C1
Parkplatz Am Park. **GPS:** n49,97615 e11,85471. ⬆️.

🅿free. **Surface:** metalled. ◻ 01/01-31/12
Distance: ⊗250m 🛒bakery 100m.
Remarks: Max. 3 nights.

🚐S | **Mellrichstadt** | 10B6
Malbachweg. **GPS:** n50,43139 e10,30972. ⬆️.

7 🅿free 🚰€1/80liter 🚽Ch 🔌€0,50/kWh. **Surface:** asphalted.
◻ 01/01-31/12
Distance: 🚲500m ⊗750m 🛒750m.

🚐S | **Miltenberg** 🏞️⛲🌊 | 17C2
Linkes Mainufer, Jahnstrasse/Luitpoldstrasse. **GPS:** n49,70464 e9,25860. ⬆️➡️.

DE

20 🛏free ⚓🗑 Ch WC free. **Location:** Central. **Surface:** asphalted.
📅 01/01-31/12
Distance: 🚶200m ⊗200m 🚏200m.

🛈 Miltenberg 🌿🚣🏄 17C2
Am Yachthafen, Steingässerstrasse. **GPS:** n49,70446 e9,25435. ⬆.

20 🛏free. **Location:** Rural, simple. **Surface:** grassy/gravel.
📅 01/01-31/12
Distance: 🚶800m ⚓on the spot ⊗800m 🚏500m 🚌on the spot.
Remarks: Along Main river.

♨S Mistelgau 18B1
Therme Obernsees, An der Therme 1, Obernsees. **GPS:** n49,91630 e11,37831. ⬆.

20 🛏€8 ⚓€1/50liter 🗑 Ch ⚡€1/12h. **Surface:** grasstiles/metalled.
📅 01/01-31/12
Distance: 🚶1km ⊗Therme-Bistro.
Remarks: Discount on access terme.

♨S Mittenwald 🏺 25C1
Wohnmobil-Stellplatz Karwendel, Albert-Schott-Straße.
GPS: n47,43792 e11,26411. ⬆➡.

23 🛏€ 12, 2 pers.incl ⚓🗑 Ch ⚡ WC 🧺🔌♨against payment.
📅 01/01-31/12
Distance: ⊗200m.
Remarks: Bread-service.

🛈S Monheim 🌿🚣🧺 18B4
An der Stadthalle, Schulstraße. **GPS:** n48,84503 e10,85329. ⬆➡.

7 🛏free ⚓€1 🗑 Ch ⚡€1/10h. **Location:** Simple, central.
Surface: grasstiles. 📅 01/01-31/12
Distance: 🚶400m ⊗500m 🚏500m.

🛈S Moosbach 🏔🎡 18D2
Am Badeweiher Tröbes, Friedhofgasse. **GPS:** n49,59076 e12,41193. ⬆➡.

6 🛏€5 ⚓🗑 Ch ⚡. **Surface:** gravel. 📅 01/01-31/12
Distance: 🚶250m ⊗250m 🚏250m.
Remarks: Check in at Gästeinformation.

🛈S Mörnsheim 18B4
Wohnmobilstellplatz Hammermühle, Altendorf. **GPS:** n48,87455 e11,02948.
⬆.

21 🛏€ 10, dog € 1 ⚓🗑 Ch included ⚡€0,60/kWh 🧺€2.
Location: Rural. **Surface:** unpaved.
📅 01/04-31/10
Distance: 🚶Altendorf 2km ⊗Imbiss, Biergarten 🚲on the spot 🚶on the spot.
Remarks: Nature reserve Altmühltal, bread-service.

🛈S München 18C5
Allianz-Arena Wohnmobilstellplätze, Werner-Heisenberg-Allee 25, Munich
(München). **GPS:** n48,22089 e11,62505. ⬆.

30 🛏€ 7/24h + € 4/pp tourist tax ⚓€1/80liter 🗑 Ch ⚡(30x)€0,80/kWh.
Location: Simple, noisy. **Surface:** asphalted/gravel. 📅 01/01-31/12
Distance: 🚶250m 🚌on the spot.
Remarks: Along railwayline.

©S Mitterteich 18D1
Freizeithugl Großbüchlberg, Großbüchlberg 32. **GPS:** n49,97286 e12,22496.

110 Ⓢ€ 15 €0,20/20liter (10x)€1/kWh. **Surface:** asphalted.
during event. **Distance:** Bistro-Biergarten on the spot.
Remarks: FC Bayern Erlebniswelt (Fanmuseum).

München 18C5
Messe Riem, De-Gasperi-Bogen, MÜnchen-Riem, Munich (München).
GPS: n48,13342 e11,70746.
1000 Ⓢ€ 35/incl. 2 pers, € 15/pers Ch WC included.
Surface: metalled. Oktoberfest
Distance: metro 300m. **Remarks:** Opened 2 days before Oktoberfest.

München 18C5
Wohnmobilstellplatz Oktoberfest, Siegenburger Straße 58, Laim, Munich (München). **GPS:** n48,12788 e11,52190.
250 Ⓢ€ 18 + € 3/pp Ch WC included.
Surface: metalled.
Oktoberfest
Distance: 100m 500m.
Remarks: Opened 2 days before Oktoberfest.

Tourist information Munich (München):
München Welcome Card. Card gives for free entrance on among other things public transport and 50% discounts on curiosities. € 11/day 2 pers.
Agustinerbräu, Neuhauserstrasse 16. Brewery from 1644.
Schloß Nymphenburg. Former summer residence of the Witelbacher monarchs. Tue-Su 9-12.30h, 13.30-17h.
Neumarkt. Ruins of citadel dominating the city.
Oktoberfest. Beer festival, special motorhome parking.

Münnerstadt 10B6
Lache, P1, Seminarstrasse. **GPS:** n50,24957 e10,19086.

5 Ⓢfree €1/90liter Ch €0,50 WC. **Surface:** metalled.
01/01-31/12
Distance: 350m.

Murnau am Staffelsee 25C1
Am Bahnhof Murnau, Am Bahnhof. **GPS:** n47,68005 e11,19447.

6 Ⓢ€ 1/day €1/100liter Ch €1/2kWh.
Location: Rural, comfortable, central, quiet. **Surface:** grasstiles/metalled.
01/01-31/12

Distance: 500m 10km 400m 300m on the spot.
Remarks: Max. 72h.

Naila 11A6
Christian-Schlicht-strasse. **GPS:** n50,33071 e11,71127.

4 Ⓢfree €1 €1 Ch€1. **Surface:** metalled. 01/01-31/12
Distance: 100m 300m.
Remarks: Parking left side of the station.

Naila 11A6
Badstraße. **GPS:** n50,32965 e11,70108.
2 Ⓢfree. **Surface:** asphalted. 01/01-31/12
Distance: 650m.

Nesselwang 25A1
An der Riese, Altspitzbahn. **GPS:** n47,61995 e10,49830.

70 Ⓢ€ 8 €1 Ch (62x)€1/kWh. **Location:** Rural, comfortable.
Surface: gravel/metalled. 01/01-31/12
Distance: 500m 3,8km 1km 3km 200m 500m 500m
on the spot 200m 200m.
Remarks: Baker every morning, code internet at tourist office.

Neualbenreuth 18D1
Reisemobilhafen Sibyllenbad, Parkplatz P2, Kurallee.
GPS: n49,98099 e12,42406.

21 Ⓢ€ 8 + € 1/pp tourist tax Ch (20x)€0,50/kWh WC.
Surface: metalled. 01/01-31/12
Distance: 1,5km.
Remarks: Bread-service.

Neuburg/Donau 18B4
Parkplatz P1, Schlösslwiese, Zur Ringmeierbucht. **GPS:** n48,74022 e11,18434.

DE

30 ⛺free ⛽€1 🚻 Ch. **Location:** Urban, simple, central, quiet.
Surface: gravel/sand. 🅿 01/01-31/12
Distance: ⊗100m ✉400m 🚲 on the spot 🚶 on the spot.
Remarks: On the Danube river.

5 ⛺free. **Location:** Urban, simple, central, quiet. **Surface:** metalled.
🅿 01/01-31/12
Distance: 🚂1,2km ✈3km ✉1,2km 🚲 on the spot 🚶 on the spot.

🏕️🅂	Neuhaus/Inn	19B4

Rast & More, Straßfeld 7. **GPS:** n48,46228 e13,40720.⬆️.

🏕️🅂	Neustadt/Aisch	18A2

Am Festplatz, Bei den Sommerkeller. **GPS:** n49,58187 e10,60271.⬆️.

20 ⛺€ 12 ⛽🚻 Ch ✂(17x)€2/day WC 🚽 📶.
Location: Rural, comfortable, quiet. **Surface:** gravel. 🅿 01/02-30/11
Distance: 🚂700m ✈5,2km 🚴8km ⊗500m ✉700m 🚌700m.

8 ⛺free ⛽€1 🚻 Ch ✂€1. **Surface:** gravel. 🅿 01/01-31/12
Distance: 🚂500m 🚆500m ⊗500m ✉500m 🚌 on the spot.

🏕️	Neumarkt/Oberpfalz	18C2

Volksfestplatz, Woffenbacherstrasse. **GPS:** n49,28118 e11,44528.⬆️.

🏕️🅂	Neustadt/Aisch	18A2

Am Waldwad, Eilersweg. **GPS:** n49,57462 e10,62993.⬆️➡️.

30 ⛺free. **Surface:** grassy. 🅿 01/01-31/12
Distance: 🚂600m.
Remarks: At sports centre.

🏕️🅂	Neumarkt/Oberpfalz	18C2

Fritz Berger, Fritz-Berger-Str. 1. **GPS:** n49,30500 e11,48444.⬆️.

6 ⛺free. **Surface:** grasstiles. 🅿 01/01-31/12
Distance: 🚂3,5km ⊗4km ✉4km 🚌1km.

🏕️🅂	Niederwerrn	17D1

Jahnstrasse. GPS: n50,06073 e10,17526.⬆️.

⛺free ⛽🚻Chfree. **Surface:** grassy. 🅿 01/01-31/12
Distance: 🚂2km ✉2km.

🛁	Neusäß	18B5

Titania-Therme, Birkenallee 1. **GPS:** n48,40089 e10,82508.

30 ⛺free ⛽€3 🚻 Ch WC 🚽. **Surface:** asphalted. 🅿 01/01-31/12
Distance: 🚂on the spot ⊗on the spot.
Remarks: Near sports fields, max. 3 nights.

🏕️🅂	Nordheim am Main	18A1

Zehnthofstrasse. GPS: n49,85952 e10,17909.⬆️.

30 ⌁voluntary contribution ⌁ ⌁ Ch free. **Surface:** metalled.
⬤ 01/01-31/12
Distance: ⌁200m.
Remarks: Along Main river.

| ⌁ S | Nördlingen | 18A4 |

Kaiserwiese. **GPS:** n48,85488 e10,48445.⬆.

30 ⌁free ⌁€2 ⌁€2 Ch ⌁€2/kWh WC. **Location:** Urban, simple, quiet.
Surface: asphalted. ⬤ 01/01-31/12
Distance: ⌁on the spot ⊗McDonalds.
Remarks: Max. 48h.

| ⌁ | Nürnberg | 18B2 |

Volkspark Dutzendteich, Munchener Strasse. **GPS:** n49,42403 e11,10586.⬆→.

10 ⌁free. **Location:** Urban. **Surface:** asphalted. ⬤ 01/01-31/12
Distance: ⌁4km ⌁700m.
Remarks: Max. 3 nights.

| ⌁ | Nürnberg | 18B2 |

Volkspark Marienburg, Kilianstrasse. **GPS:** n49,47495 e11,09606.⬆→.

8 ⌁free. **Location:** Urban. **Surface:** grasstiles/metalled.
⬤ 01/01-31/12
Distance: ⌁centre 4km ⊗800m ⌁800m ⌁on the spot.
Remarks: Max. 3 nights.

| ⌁ | Nürnberg | 18B2 |

Wöhrder See, Rechenberganlage, Dr Gustav Heinemannstrasse.
GPS: n49,46041 e11,11548.⬆.

8 ⌁free. **Location:** Urban. **Surface:** metalled. ⬤ 01/01-31/12
Distance: ⌁3km ⌁500m.
Remarks: Max. 3 nights.

Tourist information Nürnberg:
ℹ City walk through old city centre, daily from Tourist Information, Hauptmarkt.
⬤ 14.30h.
ℹ Nürnberg Card. Card gives for free entrance on among other things public
transport and museums, discounts on purchases, boat trips, city walks etc.
Ⓜ Spielzeugmuseum, Karlstrasse 13-15. Toy museum. ⬤ Tue-Su 10-17h, Wed
10-21h.
⚔ Die Burg. Palace. ⬤ 01/04-30/09 9-12h, 12.45-17h, 01/10-31/03 9.30-12h,
12.45-16h. Ⓣ €3.
⊙ Tiergarten. Zoo. ⬤ 01/04-30/09 8-19.30h, 01/10-31/03 9-17h.

| ⓒ S | Oberammergau | 25B1 |

Campingpark Oberammergau, Ettalerstrasse 56B. **GPS:** n47,59040 e11,07157.
⬆→.

20 ⌁€8 ⌁ ⌁ Ch ⌁ WC ⌁ ⌁against payment. ⌁ **Location:** Simple.
Surface: gravel. ⬤ 01/01-31/12
Distance: ⌁1,2km ⌁400m ⊗100m ⌁1,2km ⌁1km.
Remarks: Max. 24h.

| ⌁ S | Oberaudorf | 18D6 |

Pechler Hof, Tatzlwurmstrasse 5. **GPS:** n47,66132 e12,16890.⬆→.

5 ⌁€9 ⌁ ⌁ ⌁ included. **Location:** Simple, central, quiet. **Surface:** grassy.
⬤ 01/01-31/12
Distance: ⌁1km ⊗500m ⌁200m ⌁100m.

| ⌁ S | Oberaudorf | 18D6 |

Hotel Feuriger Tatzlwurm, Tatzlwurm, B307. **GPS:** n47,67223 e12,08448.

DE

10 ⏚guests free ⛟. **Location:** Rural, simple. **Surface:** gravel/metalled.
▢ 01/01-31/12
Distance: ⤴on the spot ⊗on the spot.

150 ⏚€ 12, tourist tax € 2,60/pp ⛟ ⏚Ch ⚡€2,50/24h WC ⏚. ⚒
Location: Rural, luxurious. **Surface:** grassy/metalled.
▢ 01/01-31/12
Distance: ⤴on the spot ⊗250m 🚰100m 🚌on the spot 🚲500m 🚶800m.

⏚S | **Oberelsbach** | 10B6
Wohnmobilstellplatz Oberelsbach, Gangolfstrasse. **GPS:** n50,44234 e10,11412. ⬆️

⏚S | **Oberthulba** | 10B6
Reisemobilstellplatz Thulbatal. GPS: n50,17419 e9,92499. ⬆️

6 ⏚€ 5 ⛟€1/80liter ⏚Ch ⚡(6x)€0,50/kWh. ▢ 01/01-31/12
Distance: ⤴500m ⊗on the spot.
Remarks: Max. 3 days.

25 ⏚€ 6,50, 2 pers.incl ⛟ ⏚Ch ⚡€2 WC ⏚€0,80 ▣€2,30.
Surface: grasstiles. ▢ 15/03-15/11
Distance: ⤴1km ⤴on the spot ⊗150m.

⏚S | **Obermaiselstein** 🏔❄ | 25A1
Wohnmobilplatz Allgäu, Am Goldbach 3, Niederdorf. **GPS:** n47,44422 e10,24288. ⬆️➡️

⏚S | **Oberviechtach** | 18D2
Am Freibad, Im Wiesengrund. **GPS:** n49,45296 e12,42458. ⬆️➡️

30 ⏚€ 10 + € 1,30/pp Kurtaxe ⛟ ⏚Ch ⚡(25x)€2/day WC ⏚€ 1 ▣.
⚒ **Location:** Rural, comfortable, luxurious. **Surface:** asphalted/gravel.
▢ 01/01-31/12
Distance: ⊗on the spot.

+5 ⏚free ⛟ ⏚Ch ⚡(3x)free. **Surface:** asphalted. ▢ 01/01-31/12
Distance: ⤴1km ⊗600m.
Remarks: Max. 3 days.

⏚S | **Oberstdorf** 🌿⛵🏔❄🌸 | 25A1
Rubi-Camp, Rubinger Straße 34. **GPS:** n47,42340 e10,27772. ⬆️

⏚S | **Oettingen** | 18A3
Schießwasen. GPS: n48,95690 e10,60894. ⬆️

80 ⏚€ 10 + € 2,60/pp Kurtaxe, dog € 3 ⛟ ⏚Ch ⚡€0,70/kWh WC ⏚ ▣ 🔊
⚒ ⚡**Surface:** grassy. ▢ 01/01-31/12
Distance: 🚌150m (skibus) ⛷on the spot ⛰on the spot.
Remarks: Bread-service.

4 ⏚free ⛟€1/10minutes ⏚Ch ⚡(4x)€1/8h.
Location: Simple, quiet. **Surface:** metalled.
▢ 01/01-31/12 ▣ last weekend Jul, 1st weekend Aug
Distance: ⤴10 min walking 🚰500m.

⏚S | **Ostheim** 🌿⛵🏔 | 10B6
Streuwiesenparkplatz, Nordheimer Straße/Alexander Straße.
GPS: n50,45820 e10,22656. ⬆️

⏚S | **Oberstdorf** 🌿⛵🏔❄🌸 | 25A1
Wohnmobilstellplatz Oberstdorf, Enzenspergerweg 10.
GPS: n47,40856 e10,28625. ⬆️

6 ⛺€3 ⛽€1/80liter ⚡Ch 🚿€0,50. **Surface:** metalled.
🅿 01/01-31/12
Distance: 🚶300m ⊗300m 🚉300m.
♿S   **Ottobeuren** ❦   18A6
Parking Sportwelt, Galgenberg 4. **GPS:** n47,94907 e10,29649.⬆.

13 ⛺€ 1/h, max. € 8/day ⛽€1/50liter ⚡Ch 🚿€0,50/kWh.
Location: Urban, comfortable, central. **Surface:** metalled.
🅿 01/01-31/12 🔲 high water
Distance: 🚶centre 500m ⊗500m 🚉500m 🚲on the spot.
Remarks: Max. 24h.
♿   **Passau**   19B4
Winterhafen, Regensburgerstrasse/Racklau. **GPS:** n48,57412 e13,42690.⬆➡.

10 ⛺free ⛽€0,50/100liter ⚡Ch 🚿(6x)€0,50/kWh.
Location: Urban, comfortable. **Surface:** metalled.
🅿 01/01-31/12
Distance: 🚶1km.
Remarks: Coins at Sportwelt (9-23h).
♿   **Parkstein** 🏰🍴   18D1
Basaltkegel von Parkstein, Basaltstrasse 16. **GPS:** n49,73179 e12,07127.

60 ⛺free. **Surface:** gravel. 🅿 01/01-31/12 🔲 high water
Distance: 🚶2km ⛵On the Danube river 🚣on the spot ⊗500m 🚉500m
🚌300m.
♿   **Peiting**   18B6
Wellenfreibad, Ammergauer Strasse 22/A. **GPS:** n47,79317 e10,92227.

20 ⛺free. **Surface:** metalled. 🅿 01/01-31/12
Distance: 🚶200m ⊗50m.
Remarks: Nearbij Gasthof Bergstüberl, beautiful view.
♿S   **Passau**   19B4
Güterbahnhof, Regensburger strasse. **GPS:** n48,57406 e13,44495.⬆.

3 ⛺free. 🅿 01/01-31/12
Distance: 🚶100m.
Remarks: Parking at swimming pool, max. 48h.
♿S   **Petting**   19A6
Stellplatz Schneiderhof, Seestrasse 11a. **GPS:** n47,91375 e12,81120.

15 ⛺€ 3/h, max. € 13/day ⛽⚡Ch.🚽 **Location:** Urban, simple, noisy.
Surface: metalled. 🅿 01/01-31/12
Distance: 🚶500m ⊗500m 🚉500m 🚌100m.
Remarks: Price incl. bus transport to the city centre.
♿S   **Passau**   19B4
Halser Straße. **GPS:** n48,57895 e13,47437.⬆.

4 ⛺€ 14 incl. 2 pers., tourist tax incl ⛽⚡Ch 🚿€0,50/kWh WC 🅯included.
Surface: grassy.
Distance: 🚶300m ⛰1km ⊗300m 🚉300m 🚌500m.
♿S   **Petting**   19A6
Wolferstätte, Stubern 1. **GPS:** n47,88988 e12,78455.

DE

3 ⓢ € 12, 2 pers.incl 🚰€2/100liter 🗑Ch 💧 WC 🚿. **Surface:** grassy. 🅿 01/05-30/10
Distance: 🚶4km 🚲5km 🚉2km.

Pfronten ❄ 25B1
Wohnmobilstellplatz Wohlfahrt, Am Wiesele 7, Weißbach.
GPS: n47,59829 e10,55240.⬆➡.

45 ⓢ € 10, 2 pers.incl 🚰€0,50 🗑Ch 💧 (48x) WC included 🗑€0,50 🔌€3.🏪
Surface: gravel. 🅿 01/01-31/12
Distance: 🚌Skibus 🚲5km 🎿on the spot.

Plattling 19A4
Freizeit- und Sportzentrum Plattling, Georg-Ecklstrasse.
GPS: n48,77226 e12,87331.⬆➡.

20 ⓢ free 🚰€1/80liter 🗑Ch 💧(4x)€0,50/kWh. **Location:** Rural, simple.
Surface: metalled. 🅿 01/01-31/12
Distance: 🚶500m 🚉500m.

Plech 18C2
Freizeitpark Fränkisches Wunderland, Zum Herrlesgrund 13.
GPS: n49,65929 e11,46552.⬆.

10 ⓢ free. **Surface:** gravel.
Distance: 🚶1km 🚉1km.
Tourist information Plech:
😀 Freizeitpark Fränkisches Wunderland, Zum Herrlesgrund 13. Amusement park. 🅿 01/05-30/09. 🎫 € 12,50.

Pleystein 18D1
Reisemobilplatz Pleystein, Vohenstraußer Straße/Galgenbergweg.
GPS: n49,64429 e12,40548.⬆.

10 ⓢ free 🚰 🗑 WC free. **Surface:** gravel. 🅿 01/01-31/12
Distance: 🚶350m.

Poppenricht 18C2
Wohnmobilstellplatz an der Vils, Vilsstrasse. **GPS:** n49,48184 e11,83119.⬆.

20 ⓢ free. **Surface:** gravel. 🅿 01/01-31/12
Distance: 🚶1km 🚲on the spot ⊗2km 🚉1km.
Remarks: Along the historic "Goldenen Straße" from Nürnberg to Prague, at sports centre.

Pottenstein 18C1
Wohnmobilpark Pottenstein, Am langen Berg. **GPS:** n49,76294 e11,40826.➡.

25 ⓢ € 7 🚰€1/100liter 🗑 💧(6x)€1/kWh. **Surface:** gravel. 🅿 01/01-31/12
🅿 Service: winter
Distance: 🚶1km 🚉Aldi 200m.

Tourist information Pottenstein:
👁 Teufelshöhle. Caves, constant temperature 9ºC and atmospheric humidity 98%. 🅿 01/04-31/10 9-17h.
⚔ Burg Pottenstein. 1000 Jaar oude burcht. 🅿 Tue-Su 10-17h.

Prichsenstadt 18A1
Wohnmobilstellplatz Schützengesellschaft 1752, Wiesentheider Straße 3.
GPS: n49,81649 e10,34981.⬆.

5 ⓢ € 5 🚰€1 💧€2,50. **Surface:** gravel. 🅿 01/01-31/12
Distance: 🚶300m ⊗on the spot.

S **Prien am Chiemsee** **18D6**

Wohnmobilstellplatz Strandbad Schraml, Harrasser Strasse 39. **GPS**: n47,85400 e12,36679.↑→

30 €9/night, € 2,50/day Ch€3 WC. **Location:** Rural, simple, isolated. **Surface:** grassy/sand. 01/04-15/10
Distance: 1,5km 6km on the spot 500m on the spot.
Remarks: Steep ramp.

S **Rain/Lech** **18B4**

Wohnmobilstellplatz Rain, Fasanenweg. **GPS**: n48,69195 e10,90699.↑

8 free €1 Ch €1/6h. **Surface:** metalled. 01/01-31/12
Distance: 1km on the spot on the spot.

S **Ramsthal** **17D1**

Festplatz, Hauptstrasse, K6-4. **GPS**: n50,13750 e10,06111.↑

12 free €1/100liter Ch €0,50/kWh WC.
Surface: metalled.
01/01-31/12
Distance: on the spot Gasthof Wahler, Gaststätte zum Beck on the spot.

S **Reit im Winkl** **19A6**

Wohnmobilpark Reit im Winkl, Am Waldbahnhof 7, Groissenbach. **GPS**: n47,67013 e12,48358.↑→

250 €8-12 €0,20/10liter Ch €0,75/kWh WC.
Location: Rural, quiet. **Surface:** grassy/metalled. 01/01-31/12
Distance: 1km 200m on the spot on the spot.
Remarks: Use sanitary € 4,50-6/pppn, shuttle bus to ski-piste.

S **Reit im Winkl** **19A6**

Wohnmobilpark Seegatterl, Seegatterl 7. **GPS**: n47,65898 e12,54213.↑→

100 € 8-10, tourist tax excl €0,20/10liter Ch €0,75/kWh WC.
Location: Rural, quiet. **Surface:** grassy/gravel.
17/12-10/04, 01/06-15/10
Distance: 4km 1,5km 150m on the spot.

S **Reit im Winkl** **19A6**

Gasthof Stoaner, Birnbacher Straße 34. **GPS**: n47,67900 e12,44930.
15 € 10, 2 pers.incl., winter € 12 Ch WC included.
Surface: unpaved. 01/11-20/12, Easter-30/04
Remarks: At golf court.

S **Riedenburg** **18C3**

Volksfestplatz, Austraße. **GPS**: n48,96446 e11,68181.↑

40 €6 Ch €1/8h. **Surface:** gravel/metalled. 01/01-31/12
last week of Aug
Distance: 450m 300m 20m.
Remarks: At the Main-Danube Canal.

S **Roßhaupten** **25B1**

Wohnmobilstellplatz Miller, Augsburger Strasse 23. **GPS**: n47,65889 e10,71944.↑

25 € 9, 4 pers.incl Ch (3x)€2 WC €1. **Location:** Simple.
Surface: metalled. 01/01-31/12
Distance: 50m 1,2km 1,2km 200m 150m 150m 1km 500m.
Remarks: Next to Camping- und Freizeitmarkt, reparation work.

S **Rothenbuch** **17C1**

Freizeitanlage, Heigenbrücker Weg. **GPS**: n49,97460 e9,39475.↑

DE

10 🛏 € 7 ⛽ €1/80liter 🗑 Ch 🔌 €0,50/kWh. 🚿
Location: Rural, simple, quiet. **Surface:** grasstiles. 🅿 01/01-31/12
Distance: 🚶250m.

⛟ S — Rothenburg ob der Tauber 🌱 — 18A2
Parkplatz P2, Bensen Strasse. **GPS:** n49,37048 e10,18324.

25 🛏 € 10 ⛽ €1/45liter 🗑 Ch 🔌 €0,50/kWh WC. **Surface:** metalled.
🅿 01/01-31/12
Distance: 🚶700m.

⛟ S — Rothenburg ob der Tauber 🌱 — 18A2
Parkplatz P3, Weinsdorfer Strasse. **GPS:** n49,38222 e10,18889. ⬆.

30 🛏 € 10 ⛽ €1/45liter 🗑 Ch WC.
Surface: metalled.
🅿 01/01-31/12
Distance: 🚶on the spot.

Tourist information Rothenburg ob der Tauber:
Ⓜ Mittelalterliches Kriminalmuseum, Burggasse 3. History of 1000 years of
jurisdiction. 🅿 01/04-31/10 9.30-18h, 01/11-28/02 14-16h, 01/12-31/12,
01/03-31/03 10-16h.
🎭 Schäfertanz. Traditional celebration. 🅿 27/03, 15/05, 04/09.

⛟ S — Rothenkirchen — 10D6
Waldschwimmbad. GPS: n50,37389 e11,31583.

40 🛏 € 5 ⛽ €0,50 🗑 Ch €1 🔌 (16x) WC 🚰included. **Surface:** metalled.
🅿 01/04-31/10
Distance: 🚶1,5km.
Remarks: Parking swimming pool.

⛟ — Röthlein — 18A1
Sportanlage TSV/Bundeskegelbahn, Friedhofstrasse.
GPS: n49,98694 e10,21583. ⬆.

10 🛏free. **Surface:** unpaved.
Distance: 🚶on the spot.

⛟ S — Röttingen 🌱 — 17D2
Wohnmobilplatz an der Tauber, Neubronner Straße. **GPS:** n49,50724 e9,96995.

20 🛏 € 5 ⛽ €1/70liter 🗑 Ch free 🔌 €2/24h WC €0,20/time 🚰€1,20.
Location: Rural, simple. **Surface:** gravel.
🅿 01/04-31/10 🅾 last 2 weeks of August
Distance: 🚶300m 🏊on the spot ⊗500m.
Remarks: Along the Tauber river.

⛟ — Röttingen 🌱 — 17D2
Bach, KlingerStrabe 1. **GPS:** n49,50731 e9,97368. ⬆➡.
10 🛏 🔌 €2,50/day WC 🚰€2,50/day. **Location:** Rural, simple.
Surface: gravel. 🅿 01/01-31/12
Distance: 🚶500m 🎣on the spot ⊗on the spot.
Remarks: Fishing permit available at town hall.

⛟ — Röttingen 🌱 — 17D2
Bach, KlingerStrabe 1. **GPS:** n49,50731 e9,97368. ⬆➡.

10 🛏free 🔌 €2,50/day WC 🚰€2,50/day. **Location:** Rural, simple.
Surface: gravel. 🅿 01/01-31/12
Distance: 🚶500m 🎣on the spot ⊗on the spot.
Remarks: Fishing permit available at town hall.

⛟ S — Ruhpolding — 19A6
Campingplatz Ortnerhof, Ortsstraße 5. **GPS:** n47,74260 e12,66303. ⬆➡.

DE

16 🅿€9 ⛽ 🗑Ch 💧€1,50 + €0,60/kWh WC 🚰◉€3 🚿€3/24h.
Location: Rural. **Surface:** gravel. 🕐 01/01-31/12
Distance: 🚶3km ⊗on the spot 🚰2km 🏊on the spot.
Remarks: At golf court, max. 1 night.

	Scheidegg	24D1

Wohnmobilpark am Kurhaus, Am Hammerweiher 1. **GPS:** n47,57351 e9,84545. ⬆.

20 🅿€6, €1,70/pp tourist tax ⛽ 🗑Ch included 💧€3 🚰€1,50 🚿.
Surface: gravel/metalled. 🕐 01/01-31/12
Distance: 🚰Minishop.
Remarks: Bread-service.

	Scheinfeld	18A2

Freibad Scheinfeld, Badstrasse 5. **GPS:** n49,67434 e10,46173.

2 🅿€6 ⛽🗑Ch 💧. **Surface:** gravel. 🕐 01/01-31/12
Remarks: At swimming pool.

	Schliersee	18D6

Am Spitzingsee, Spitzingstraße. **GPS:** n47,66648 e11,88851. ⬆.

+10 🅿summer €12, winter €9 (no service) ⛽ 🗑Ch.
Location: Rural, simple, isolated, quiet. **Surface:** gravel.
🕐 01/01-31/12 ◉ Service: winter
Distance: 🚶5,4km 🚣on the spot ⊗500m 🚴on the spot 🎿on the spot 🏊on the spot.
Remarks: Altitude 1085m, at lake.

	Schlüsselfeld	18A1

Bambergerstrasse. **GPS:** n49,75878 e10,62104. ⬆.
5 🅿free ⛽€1/80liter. **Surface:** gravel. 🕐 01/01-31/12
Distance: 🚶on the spot.

	Schlüsselfeld	18A1

Concorde, Concorde-Straße 2–4. **GPS:** n49,76745 e10,56478. ⬆.

20 🅿free ⛽€1/100liter 🗑Ch 💧€0,50/kWh. **Surface:** metalled.
🕐 01/01-31/12
Distance: 🚶1km ⊗1km 🚰1km.
Remarks: At motohome manufacturer.

	Schnelldorf	18A3

BP-Truckstop Feuchtwangen, Rudolph Dieselstrasse 1.
GPS: n49,17149 e10,24124. ⬆.

20 🅿€7 ⛽€1/80liter 🗑Ch 💧(3x) WC 🚰€2. **Surface:** metalled.
🕐 01/01-31/12
Distance: 🚲300m ⊗on the spot 🚰on the spot.
Remarks: Reduction at restaurant €5, special part for motor homes.

	Schöllkrippen	17C1

Naturerlebnisbad, Häfner-Ohnhaus-Straße. **GPS:** n50,08484 e9,25247. ⬆.

35 🅿€7/24h ⛽€1/80liter 🗑Ch 💧(24x)€0,50/kWh. 🚰
Location: Rural, comfortable, quiet. **Surface:** grassy. 🕐 01/01-31/12
Distance: 🚶500m.

	Schongau	18B6

Festplatz, Lechuferstrasse. **GPS:** n47,80906 e10,89815. ⬆.

70 🅿€5 ⛽€1/5liter 🗑Ch WC 💧
Location: Urban, simple. **Surface:** asphalted.
🕐 service: 20/03-05/11 ◉ 25/07-08/08
Distance: 🚶400m 🛒100m 🚰400m 🚌on the spot.
Remarks: Caution key sanitary €30, guests free.

Schonungen — 18A1
Behr Reisemobile, An der Kemenate 6, Abersfeld, B303.
GPS: n50,07352 e10,39366.

5 free Ch free. **Surface:** metalled. 01/01-31/12
Distance: 8km.
Remarks: Motorhome dealer, accessory shop.

Schrobenhausen — 18C4
Am Klostergarten, Rot-Kreuz-Straße. **GPS:** n48,55835 e11,26234.

4 free. **Surface:** metalled. 01/01-31/12
Distance: 400m 400m 400m.

Schrobenhausen — 18C4
Kläranlage, Köningslachenerweg 12. **GPS:** n48,57420 e11,26930. Ch.
Remarks: Mo-Thu 7-12h, 13-16h, Fr 7-12h.

Schwandorf — 18D2
Festplatz, Angerring, Krondorf. **GPS:** n49,33230 e12,10247.

30 free Ch free. **Surface:** asphalted/grassy.
01/01-31/12 week before/after Whitsuntide
Distance: 500m 200m 500m.
Remarks: Along the Naab river.

Schwangau — 25B1
Wohnmobilpark Schwangau, Münchenerstrasse 151.
GPS: n47,59167 e10,77250.

24 € 12,50-17,50, dog € 2 Ch (24x)€2,50 WC
Location: Urban, comfortable. **Surface:** grassy/gravel. 01/01-31/12

Distance: 2km on the spot on the spot on the spot on the spot
on the spot 1km on the spot.

Segnitz — 18A2
Mainstraße. **GPS:** n49,67012 e10,14242.

4 free. **Surface:** metalled.
Distance: on the spot on the spot.
Remarks: Max. 1 day.

Segnitz — 18A2
Gasthaus zum Goldenen Anker, Mainstraße 8. **GPS:** n49,67063 e10,14344.

17 € 7,50 Ch . **Surface:** grassy/gravel. 01/01-31/12
Restaurant: Thu
Distance: on the spot on the spot.
Remarks: Along Main river.

Selb — 11A4
Wundsiedler Weiher. **GPS:** n51,15581 e12,13455.

20 free. **Surface:** gravel. 01/01-31/12
Distance: 2km 200m.
Remarks: Hiking trails.

Siegsdorf — 19A6
Gasthof Hörterer der Hammerwirt, Schmiedstrasse, B306, Hammer.
GPS: n47,80096 e12,70392.

10 guests free WC . **Location:** Rural. **Surface:** metalled.
01/01-31/12 Wed
Distance: on the spot 100m 100m 2,5km 300m.
Remarks: Max. 3 nights.

Sonthofen 25A1
Erlebnisbad Wonnemar, Stadionweg 5. **GPS:** n47,50344 e10,27883. ⬆➡

12 free. **Location:** Urban, simple. **Surface:** gravel.
☐ 01/01-31/12
Distance: 2,3km ⊗on the spot on the spot on the spot.
Remarks: Max. 1 night.

Steinach/Straubing 19A3
Firma Hubert Brandl Caravantastic, Gewerbering 11.
GPS: n48,95639 e12,62250. ⬆

3 free €1 . **Surface:** grassy. ☐ 01/01-31/12
Distance: 1,5km ⊗2km 1km.
Remarks: Connection electricity < 18h.

Steinberg am See 18D2
Movin'G'round, Am Steinberger See. **GPS:** n49,28247 e12,17357. ⬆

10 free, use of a meal desired €Ch . **Surface:** grassy.
☐ Whitsuntide-30/09
Distance: 500m on the spot ⊗on the spot.

Steinhausen 17D6
Parkplatz, Am Reiterhof 1. **GPS:** n48,02746 e9,69476.

5 free. **Surface:** gravel. ☐ 01/01-31/12
Distance: ⊗180m.

Sulzbach-Rosenberg 18C2
Großparkplatz, Bayreuther Straße. **GPS:** n49,50583 e11,74500. ⬆➡

4 free €1/80liter Ch (4x)€0,50/kWh. **Surface:** metalled.
☐ 01/01-31/12
Distance: 300m ⊗500m 500m.

Sulzemoos 18C5
Der Freistaat Caravaning, Ohmstrasse. **GPS:** n48,28267 e11,26084. ⬆

40 free €1/80liter Ch (20x)€1/kWh WC. **Surface:** gravel.
☐ 01/01-31/12
Distance: 800m 800m ⊗McDonalds 800m 800m 600m.
Remarks: Motorhome dealer.

Tauberrettersheim 17D2
Brunnenstrasse. **GPS:** n49,49635 e9,93720.

6 free. **Location:** Rural, simple. **Surface:** grassy.
☐ 01/01-31/12
Distance: on the spot on the spot.

Thierstein 11A6
Kaiserstein, Hirtweg. **GPS:** n50,10610 e12,10490. ⬆➡

10 €4 Ch included voluntary contribution.
Surface: metalled. ☐ 01/01-31/12 01/10-31/03 water disconnected
Distance: 500m ⊗500m 500m.
Remarks: Max. 2 nights, beautiful view.

Thüngersheim 17D1
Parkplatz Main-Aue, Am Schwimbad. **GPS:** n49,88084 e9,83717.

20 🛏free 🔌🍴Ch free 🔧 (16x)€0,50/kWh.
Location: Rural, comfortable, noisy. **Surface:** grassy. ⬛ 01/04–31/10
Distance: 🚶500m ⛽on the spot.
Remarks: Along Main river.

| 🏕🅂 | **Traunstein** | 19A6 |

Gasthaus Jobst, Balthasar Permoserstrasse 64, Rettenbach.
GPS: n47,91188 e12,64899. ⬆ .

10 🛏€ 3, guests free 🔌€2 🍴Ch 🔧€2,50. **Surface:** metalled.
⬛ 01/01–31/12 ⬤ Wed

| 🚐🅂 | **Traunstein** | 19A6 |

Firma Grüaugl, Schmidhamerstrasse 31. **GPS:** n47,88227 e12,59941.

12 🛏€ 5 🔌€2 🍴€2 Ch 🔧€0,50/kWh. **Location:** Isolated.
Surface: metalled. ⬛ 01/01–31/12
Distance: ⊗on the spot.
Remarks: Camping equipment store.

| 🔼🅂 | **Treuchtlingen** 🌿⛲🎡 | 18B3 |

Reisemobilstellplatz am Kurpark, Kästleinmühlenstrasse 20.
GPS: n48,96028 e10,91778. ⬆➡ .

56 🛏€ 9,50 🔌€1/80liter 🍴Ch 🔧€1/8h WC 🚽included.
Location: Urban, comfortable, quiet. **Surface:** grasstiles. ⬛ 01/01–31/12
Distance: 🚶800m 🚲on the spot.
Remarks: Bread-service.

| 🔼🅂 | **Übersee/Chiemsee** | 19A6 |

Bauernhof Steiner, Almfischer 11, Stegen. **GPS:** n47,80963 e12,49136. ⬆➡ .

25 🛏€ 11, 2 pers.incl 🔌🍴Ch 🔧€0,40/kWh WC 🚽€1,50. **Surface:** gravel.
⬛ 01/01–31/12
Distance: 🚶Übersee 2km 🚲4,6km ⛵Chiemsee 6km 🏊1km.

| 🔼🅂 | **Übersee/Chiemsee** | 19A6 |

Wohmobilstellplatz Dusenhof, Stegen 4. **GPS:** n47,81237 e12,48843. ⬆➡ .

28 🛏€ 11, 2 pers.incl 🔌🍴Ch 🔧€0,50/kWh 🚽€1. **Surface:** grassy/gravel.
⬛ 01/01–31/12
Distance: 🚶Übersee 1km 🚲4km ⛵Chiemsee 5km.
Remarks: Bread-service.

| 🚐 | **Veitshöchheim** 〰 | 17D1 |

Parkplatz am Fußgängersteg, Am Güßgraben. **GPS:** n49,83623 e9,86916. ⬆➡ .

5 🛏free. **Location:** Rural, simple. **Surface:** metalled.
⬛ 01/01–31/12
Distance: 🚶500m ⛽on the spot.
Remarks: Along Main river, max. 24h.

| 🚐 | **Viechtach** 🏕🏔❄ | 19A3 |

P1, Stadtmitte, Bierfeldstraße. **GPS:** n49,07876 e12,88235. ⬆ .

6 🛏free. **Surface:** metalled. ⬛ 01/01–31/12
Distance: 🚶400m ⊗150m 🏊50m.
Remarks: In front of supermarket Edeka, max. 3 nights.

| 🚐 | **Viechtach** 🏕🏔❄ | 19A3 |

P2, Stadthalle, Friedhofstrasse. **GPS:** n49,07722 e12,88528. ⬆ .

DE

3 ⛺free. **Surface:** metalled. ⬛ 01/01-31/12
Remarks: Max. 3 nights.

| 🏕 | Viechtach 🏖🏔❄ | 19A3 |

P5, TÜV, Karl-Gareis-Straße. **GPS:** n49,08222 e12,88306. ⬆ .

⛺free. **Surface:** asphalted. ⬛ 01/01-31/12
Distance: 🚶500m 🚲500m.
Remarks: Max. 3 nights, small pitches.

| 🏕S | Viechtach 🏖🏔❄ | 19A3 |

Fam. Reisinger, Eging 1. **GPS:** n49,05417 e12,91333. ⬆ .

3 ⛺free 🚰🔌. **Surface:** grassy. ⬛ 01/01-31/12
Distance: 🚶Viechtach 4,5km.

| 🏕S | Viechtach 🏖🏔❄ | 19A3 |

Johann Ebner, Lohmühlweg 2, Pirka. **GPS:** n49,10694 e12,87583. ⬆➡.

3 ⛺€ 8,50, electricity incl 🚰🔌. **Surface:** grassy. ⬛ 01/04-01/10
Distance: 🚶8km.

| 🍴S | Viechtach 🏖🏔❄ | 19A3 |

Landhotel Miethaner, Höllenstein 13. **GPS:** n49,12917 e12,87667. ⬆.

4 ⛺free 🔌€1/12h. **Surface:** asphalted. ⬛ 01/01-31/12
Distance: 🚶7lkm 🚲1km ❌on the spot 🚌on the spot 🚲10km 🚤2km.

| 🍴 | Viechtach 🏖🏔❄ | 19A3 |

Berghütte 'Zum Pröller', Hinterviechtach 3, Kollnburg.
GPS: n49,02939 e12,83892. ⬆.

3 ⛺free. **Surface:** gravel. ⬛ 01/01-31/12
Distance: 🚶Viechtach 7km 🚲20m.
Remarks: Parking at skipistes.

| S | Viechtach 🏖🏔❄ | 19A3 |

Am Regenufer 1. **GPS:** n49,08303 e12,88824. ⬆.
🚰€1 🚿€1 Ch. ⬛ 01/01-31/12

Tourist information Viechtach:
🏛 Stadtplatz. Week market. 🛒 Wed 7-17h.

| | Vilshofen 🏖 | 19B4 |

Schiffanleger, Donaukade. **GPS:** n48,63833 e13,18000. ⬆➡.

12 ⛺free. **Location:** Simple, noisy. **Surface:** asphalted.
⬛ 01/01-31/12
Distance: 🚶500m 🛶On the Danube river 🚲on the spot ❌500m 🚲500m.
Remarks: Max. 1 night.

| 🚻S | Vilshofen 🏖🏔 | 19B4 |

Yachthafen Vilshofen, Am Bootshafen. **GPS:** n48,63870 e13,18785. ⬆➡.

10 ⛺€ 12 🚰🚿Ch.🔌(10x)€3/day WC 🚽€1. **Location:** Comfortable, quiet.
Surface: gravel. ⬛ 01/04-30/11
Distance: 🚶500m 🛶On the Danube river.

DE

S **Vohenstrauß** 18D2
Stadthalle, Neuwirtshauser Weg 11. **GPS:** n49,61872 e12,34523.⬆

15 🏕free ⛽🔲Ch 💧free WC 🔲. **Surface:** gravel. ⬛ 01/01-31/12
Distance: 🚶100m 🚲800m 🛒50m 🚉100m.
Remarks: Caution key sanitary € 50.

Volkach 🐚⛲ 18A1
Mainschleife, Am Main. **GPS:** n49,86389 e10,22139.⬆➡.

40 🏕€ 5,50. **Surface:** gravel. ⬛ 01/01-31/12
Distance: 🚶500m 🏊on the spot 🛒on the spot 🚲500m 🚉500m.

S **Wackersberg** 🐚⛲🏕🌳 18C6
Camping Demmelhof, Stallau 148. **GPS:** n47,75056 e11,49992.⬆.

12 🏕€ 15, 2 pers.incl ⛽🔲Ch 💧€0,60/kWh WC 🔲€0,50 🔲€3.
Surface: grassy. ⬛ 01/01-31/12
Distance: 🚶5km 🚲500m 🚌600m.

S **Wald** 25B1
Walder Badeweiher, Am Sportplatz. **GPS:** n47,72294 e10,56348.⬆➡.

10 🏕€5 ⛽🔲Ch 🐕 **Location:** Rural, quiet. **Surface:** gravel.
⬛ 01/01-31/12
Distance: 🚶500m 🏊on the spot 🚲250m 🐕on the spot 🚶on the spot.

S **Waldkirchen** 🌳❄ 19B4
Karoli-Badepark, VDK Heimstrasse 1. **GPS:** n48,72222 e13,60278.⬆.

16 🏕free ⛽€1/50liter 🔲Ch 💧(10x)€0,50/kWh WC 🔲. **Location:** Rural,
simple, quiet. **Surface:** gravel. ⬛ 01/01-31/12
Distance: 🚶1km 🚲25m 🚉2km 🚌on the spot 🐕on the spot.
Remarks: Parking skating rink-swimming pool, use sanitary only during opening
hours swimming pool, against payment.

Waldsassen ⛲🍺 18D1
P2 Schwanenwiese, Schwanengasse. **GPS:** n50,00526 e12,30739.⬆.

4 🏕€ 5 💧(2x)€2/10h WC. **Surface:** metalled. ⬛ 01/01-31/12
Distance: 🚶500m 🚲500m 🚉500m.
Remarks: Max. 3 days, pay at tourist office.

Waldsassen ⛲🍺 18D1
P1, Joseph-Wiesnetstrasse. **GPS:** n50,00250 e12,30361.⬆.

2 🏕free. **Surface:** metalled. ⬛ 01/01-31/12
Distance: 🚶100m 🚲100m 🚉100m.
Remarks: Max. 3 days.

S **Wassertrüdingen** 18A3
Parkplatz Entengraben. **GPS:** n49,03926 e10,59494.⬆➡.

12 🏕voluntary contribution ⛽€1/80liter 🔲Ch 💧(6x)€1/8h.
Location: Urban, simple, quiet. **Surface:** metalled. ⬛ 01/01-31/12
Distance: 🚶on the spot 🏊on the spot 🛒on the spot 🚉1km.

Weidenberg 18C1
Am Sportpark, In der Au. **GPS:** n49,93781 e11,73068.⬆ .

DE

2-3 ⌇free. **Surface:** gravel. ☐ 01/01-31/12
Distance: ⚲750m ⊗Chinese restaurant 100m ⚑1,5km.

🔲Ⓢ **Weilheim in Oberbayern** 🌱🍴🧁 **18B6**
Reisemobilplatz, Lohgasse. **GPS**: n47,84012 e11,13583.⬆️

8 ⌇€4/24h ⛽€0,50/50liter 🔲Ch ⚡€0,50/kWh WC.🚐
Location: Urban, simple, central. **Surface:** asphalted. ☐ 01/01-31/12
Distance: ⚲Old city centre 500m ⚲100m 🛒200m.
Remarks: Along the Ammer river.

🔲Ⓢ **Weismain** **18B1**
Bauhof, Burgkunstadterstrasse. **GPS**: n50,08639 e11,23872.⬆️

4 ⌇free ⛽€1 🔲€0,50 Ch€0,50 ⚡(6x)€0,50. **Surface:** asphalted.
☐ 01/01-31/12
Distance: ⚲on the spot.
Remarks: Parking in centre.

🔲Ⓢ **Weissenburg** **18B3**
Kirchweihplatz, Limesbad, Badstrasse 5. **GPS**: n49,02476 e10,97180.⬆️

⌇free ⛽€1/80liter 🔲Ch. **Location:** Urban. **Surface:** metalled.
☐ 01/04-31/10
Distance: ⚲Old city centre 300m ⊗La Fattoria, Frauentorstrasse 11; Mai Tai, Bismarckanlage 16; Wittelsbacher Hof, Fr.Ebertstrasse 21 🛒on the spot.

🔲Ⓢ **Wertach** 🌱🍴🏕🎣❄️🌀🏊 **25A1**
Camping Grüntensee, Grüntenseestraße 41. **GPS**: n47,61003 e10,44704.⬆️➡️

12 ⌇€15 + tourist tax €1/pp ⛽🔲Ch ⚡(12x)€0,50/kWh.🚌📷🧹
Location: Rural, luxurious, quiet. **Surface:** gravel. ☐ 01/01-31/12
Distance: ⚲2,5km 🚲600m 🏊on the spot 🎣on the spot ⊗on the spot ⚑1,5km 🚌1,5km 🏃on the spot 🥾on the spot 🚴on the spot 🎿on the spot.

🔲Ⓢ **Wertingen** **18B4**
Wohnmobilpark Wertingen, Am Bahnhof 4. **GPS**: n48,55948 e10,69065.

12 ⌇€7 ⛽€1 🔲Ch ⚡€2/day. 🚌 **Location:** Urban, comfortable, central, quiet. **Surface:** grassy/gravel. ☐ 01/01-31/12
Distance: ⚲800m 🛒300m.

🔲Ⓢ **Wiesenttal** **18B1**
Wohnmobilstellplatz Streitberg, Bahnhofstrasse, B470.
GPS: n49,80782 e11,21636.⬆️

7 ⌇€2 ⛽🔲Chfree. **Surface:** gravel. ☐ 01/01-31/12
Distance: ⚲500m 🚲500m ⊗500m 🛒500m 🚌300m.

🔲Ⓢ **Wolnzach** **18C4**
Schwimm- & Erlebnisbad Wolnzach, Hanslmühlweg 6.
GPS: n48,59718 e11,62792.⬆️

4 ⌇free ⛽€1/80liter 🔲Ch ⚡(4x)€0,50/kWh. **Surface:** metalled.
☐ 01/01-31/12
Distance: ⚲600m 🚲500m 🛒600m.

🍴 **Wonneberg** **19A6**
Gasthof Alpenblick, Traunsteiner Straße 21, Weibhausen.
GPS: n47,89880 e12,69123.

5 🍴 free, use of a meal desired. **Location:** Simple. **Surface:** gravel.
Distance: ⊗on the spot.

🚐Ⓢ **Wunsiedel** 18C1

Wohnmobilstellplatz Festspielstadt Wunsiedel, Ludwigstraße.
GPS: n50,03638 e11,99351.⬆️.

6 🍴 € 5/24h ⛽🔌Ch 🔧 included. **Surface:** gravel.
🅾️ 01/01-31/12 🅾️ water: Nov-March
Distance: 🚶600m ⊗300m 🛒1km.
Remarks: Pay at tourist office.

🚐 **Würzburg** 🌿⚓ 17D1

Viehmarktplatz, Dreikronenstra. **GPS:** n49,79782 e9,92319.⬆️.

🍴6-20h € 5, overnight stay free. **Location:** Urban, simple, noisy.
Surface: asphalted. 🅾️ 01/01-31/12
Distance: 🚶800m ⚓on the spot ⊗50m.

Tourist information Würzburg:
👁 Würzburger Residenz, Residenzplatz. Baroque castle, Unesco World Heritage
Site. 🅾️ 01/04-31/10 9-18h, 01/11-31/03 10-16h. 🎫 € 4.

🚐 **Zeil am Main** 18A1

Altstadtparkplatz, Mittelweg. **GPS:** n50,00667 e10,59583.⬆️.

20 🍴 free. **Surface:** metalled. 🅾️ 01/01-31/12
Distance: 🚶1km ⊗1km 🛒1km.
Remarks: Parking gymnasium.

Tourist information Zeil am Main:
⊗ Brauereigasthof Göller "Zum alten Freyung". Brewery restaurant with regional
specialities and Göller-beer. 🅾️ Mo-Su 9.30-01h.
🍷 Altstadt Weinfest. Wine festivals. 🅾️ 06/08-08/08.
🚶 Wein-Wander-Weg. Hiking trail through wine region.

🚐Ⓢ **Zellingen** ⚓ 17D1

Am Freibad, Badstraße. **GPS:** n49,89476 e9,82680.⬆️.

5 🍴 free ⛽free 🔧€3/day. **Location:** Rural, simple. **Surface:** grassy.
🅾️ 01/01-31/12
Remarks: Check in at swimming pool (service).

🅾️ **Zirndorf** 18B2

Playmobil Funpark, Brandstätterstrasse. **GPS:** n49,43087 e10,93935.
40 🍴 € 4. **Surface:** metalled.
Distance: ⊗on the spot.

5 🍴 free. **Surface:** metalled. 🅾️ 01/01-31/12

🚐 **Zeil am Main** 18A1

Parkplatz Tuchanger, Oskar Winkler strasse. **GPS:** n50,01083 e10,59056.⬆️➡️.

DE

SWITZERLAND

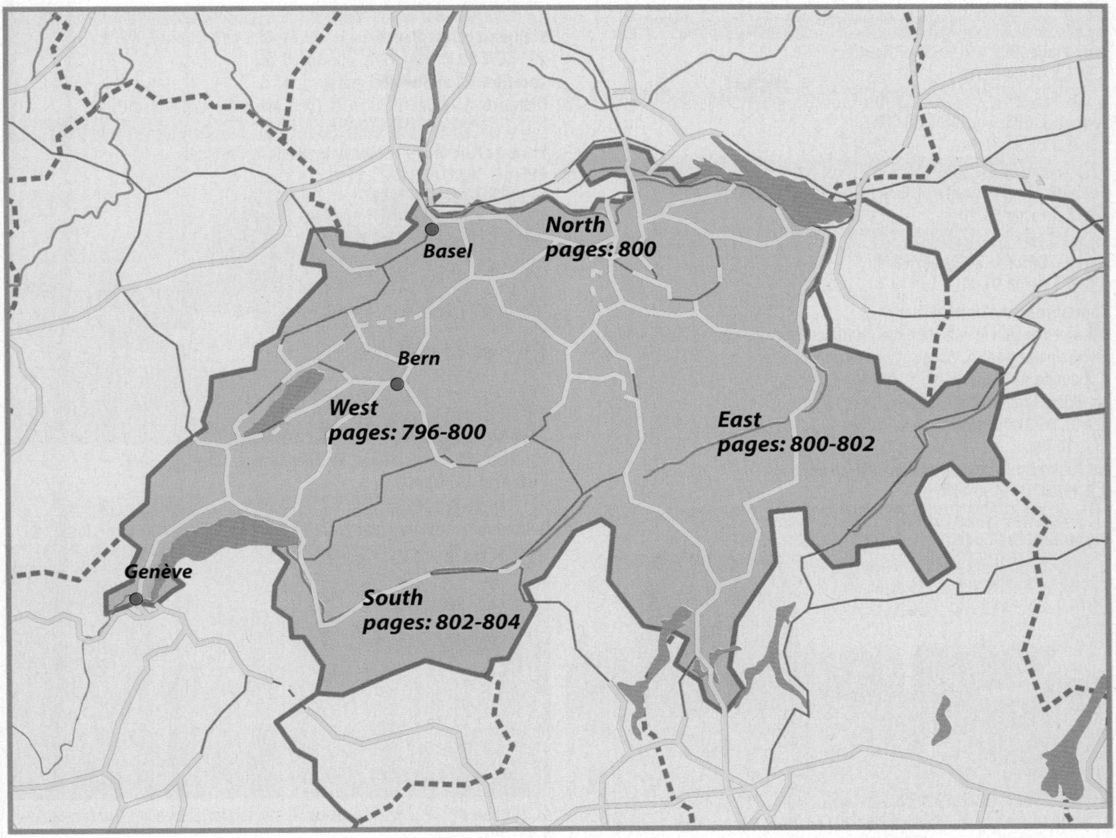

North
pages: 800

Basel

Bern

West
pages: 796-800

East
pages: 800-802

Genève

South
pages: 802-804

Capital: Bern
Government: Direct democracy, Federal republic
Official Language: German, French, Italian, Romansh
Population: 8,000,000 (2014)
Area: 41,284 km²

General information
Dialling code: 0041.
General emergency: 112
Currency: Swiss franc (CHF)
1 CHF = € 0,83, € 1 = CHF 1,21 (October 2014)
1 CHF = £ 0,65, £ 1 = CHF 1,54 (October 2014)

Regulations for overnight stays
Overnight parking is allowed, max 15 hours.

Additional public holidays 2015
August 1National Day

Switzerland

Switzerland West

△ Aeschi 24A3
Panorama, Scheidgasse 272. **GPS:** n46,65399 e7,70070.
🚐. ⬛ 15/05-15/10

△ Avenches 23D3
Port-Plage. GPS: n46,90351 e7,04918.
🚐. ⬛ 01/04-01/10

△ Boltigen 23D4
Jaunpass. GPS: n46,59208 e7,33758.
🚐. ⬛ 01/01-31/12

△ Böningen 24A3
Seeblick, Campingstrasse 14. **GPS:** n46,68987 e7,89398.
🚐. ⬛ Easter-01/10

△ Brienz 🏔❄❋ 24A3
Aaregg. GPS: n46,74634 e8,04844.
🚐. ⬛ 01/04-01/11
Tourist information Brienz:
ℹ Alpen Region Brienz-Meiringen-Hasliberg, Bahnhofstrasse 22, Meiringen, www.alpenregion.ch. Village of wood-cutters.
⬛ during school hours ⬤ 01/07-31/08.
👁 Brienz Rothorn Bahn. Steam rack-railway.
⬛ 01/06-31/10 8.45h.
🚂 CHF 46.
Ⓜ Freilichtmuseum Ballenberg. Open air museum.
⬛ 15/04-31/10 10-17h.

🍴S Bullet 🏔 23C3
Restaurant Les Cluds, Les Cluds. **GPS:** n46,84248 e6,55991.⬆➡

4 🚐CHF 10 🚰🍽Ch🧹(4x)included. **Location:** Rural, simple, isolated, quiet. **Surface:** asphalted. ⬛ 01/01-31/12 ⬤ Restaurant: Mo
Distance: ⊗on the spot.
Remarks: Max. 2 nights, pay at restaurant.

△ Burgdorf 24A2
Waldegg, Waldeggweg. **GPS:** n47,05407 e7,62895.
🚐. ⬛ 01/04-31/10

△ Château-d'Oex 23D4
Le Berceau. GPS: n46,46673 e7,12529.
🚐. ⬛ 01/01-31/12

🚐S Cheyres 🛶 23C3
Route de Crevel. **GPS:** n46,81651 e6,78501.⬆.

12 🚐free 🚰10minutes 🍽Ch🧹(2x)against paymenth. **Location:** Rural, simple. **Surface:** asphalted. ⬛ 01/01-31/12
Distance: ⬇400m ⊗400m 🚲on the spot.
Remarks: Parking at station.
Tourist information Cheyres:
🍇 Fête de vendanges. Wine festivals. ⬛ beginning Oct.

S Cudrefin 23D3
Route de Neuchâtel. **GPS:** n46,96000 e7,02750.⬆.
🚰🍽Chfree.
Remarks: In front of camping Le Chablais.

🐴S Damphreux 23D1
Stellplatz Forest-Ranch, Sur la Côte 21. **GPS:** n47,47588 e7,09978.
20 ⬛CHF 20 🚰🍽ChWC🍽included. 🐴
Location: Rural. **Surface:** grassy.
Distance: ⬇300m ⊗300m 🛒300m 🚲on the spot 🚶on the spot.

🚐S Delémont 23D2
Place de Parc Gros-Pré Monsieur, Route de Porrentruy.
GPS: n47,36289 e7,34008.⬆⬆➡.

10 🚐free 🚰🍽Ch🚻free. **Surface:** gravel. ⬛ 01/01-31/12
Distance: ⬇200m.

🚐S Dürrenroth 🏔🎋 24A2
Reisemobilstellplatz Blueberry Hill, Brunnen. **GPS:** n47,06563 e7,76553.⬆.

4 🚐CHF 10 🚰🧹CHF 2. **Location:** Rural, comfortable, quiet. **Surface:** gravel.
⬛ 01/01-31/12
Distance: ⬇Dürrenroth 3,5km 🚲on the spot 🚶on the spot.
Remarks: Panoramic view.

🚐S Echallens 23C4
Chemin du Pont. **GPS:** n46,63945 e6,64096.⬆➡.

5 🚐free 🚰🍽Chfree. **Location:** Rural, simple. **Surface:** asphalted.
⬛ 01/01-31/12
Distance: ⬇700m ⊗300m 🛒700m.

△ Estavayer-le-Lac 23C3
Nouvelle-Plage. GPS: n46,85602 e6,84801.
🚐. ⬛ 01/04-01/10

△ Frutigen 24A4
Grassi. GPS: n46,58178 e7,64213.
🚐. ⬛ 01/01-31/12

Gampelen 23D3
Fanel, Seestraße. **GPS:** n47,00702 e7,05973.
🚐. ⬛ Easter-01/10

△S Grandson 23C3
Le Pécos, Rue du Pécos. **GPS:** n46,80371 e6,63575.

4 🔥 ⚡🗨Ch. ⚪ 01/04-01/10
Remarks: Next to campsite.

△ **Grindelwald** ⚡🏔❄ 24A4
Eigernordwand. GPS: n46,62135 e8,01683.
🔥. ⚪ 01/01-31/12

Tourist information Grindelwald:
👁 Jungfraubahn. Train journey to the highest train station of Europe.

🗨S **Gryon** 🏔 23D4
Place de la Barboleuse. **GPS:** n46,28222 e7,07028.⬆.

4 🔥CHF 2,80/pp, Summer CHF 5,30/pp ⚡🗨Ch ⚡ (4x)CHF 5. **Location:**
Rural, simple, quiet. **Surface:** asphalted.
Distance: 🚶200m 🚂3,5km 🚌on the spot 🏊100m.
Remarks: To be paid at office de tourisme.

△ **Gstaad** 23D4
Bellerive. GPS: n46,48106 e7,27328.
🔥. ⚪ 01/01-31/12

🍴S **Gündlischwand** 🏔🍽 24A4
Säumertaverne, Am Chienbach 96. **GPS:** n46,63692 e7,92636.
🔥guests free ⚡. **Location:** Rural, central. **Surface:** asphalted.
🍽 Restaurant: Mo
Distance: 🚴7km 🚂on the spot 🚐on the spot ⊗on the spot 🍺on the spot
🏊6km 🚶on the spot.

△ **Gwatt-Thun** 24A3
Betllereiche. GPS: n46,72749 e7,62760.
🔥. ⚪ 01/04-01/10

△ **Hinterkappelen** 23D3
Kappelenbrucke, Wohlenstrasse 62. **GPS:** n46,96433 e7,38361.
🔥. ⚪ 01/01-31/12

🚐S **Huttwil** 🏔🍽 24A2
Firma Flyer E-Bike, Luzernstrasse 89. **GPS:** n47,11527 e7,86795.⬆.

20 🔥free ⚡🗨Ch ⚡ free. **Location:** Rural. **Surface:** gravel.
⚪ 01/01-31/12
Distance: 🚶500m.
Remarks: E-bike factory, guided tour Tuesdays 14.30h.

△ **Interlaken** ❄🏔🏔🐚❄ 24A3
Hobby, Lehnweg 16. **GPS:** n46,68079 e7,82793.
🔥. ⚪ 01/04-01/10

△ **Interlaken** ❄🏔🏔🐚❄ 24A3
Jungfraublick, Gsteigstraße 80. **GPS:** n46,67581 e7,86597.
🔥. ⚪ 01/05-01/10

△ **Interlaken** ❄🏔🏔🐚❄ 24A3
Lazy-Rancho, Lehnweg 6. **GPS:** n46,68090 e7,82793.
🔥. ⚪ 01/04-01/10

Tourist information Interlaken:
👁 Heimwehfluhbahn. Telpher carrier from 1906. ⚪ 01/04-31/10.
🎡 Mistery Park. Attractions and themepark. ⚪ 10-18h ⚫ 25/12-01/01.

🔥S **La Brévine** 🐚 23C3
Les Varodes. **GPS:** n46,97195 e6,58860. 🔼.

10 🔥free ⚡🗨Ch ⚡ (2x)WCfree. **Location:** Rural, simple, isolated, quiet.
Surface: asphalted. ⚪ 01/01-31/12
Distance: 🚶3km 🚂on the spot ⊗1,5km 🚴on the spot 🏊on the spot
🌊on the spot.
Remarks: Parking at Lac des Tailleres.

🔥S **La Chaux-de-Fonds** ❄ 23C2
Bois du Couvent. **GPS:** n47,09334 e6,83593.🔼.

2 🔥free ⚡🗨Ch ⚡ (4x)free. **Location:** Rural, simple. **Surface:** gravel.
⚪ 01/05-30-09
Distance: 🚶1,3km ⊗350m 🚂700m 🏊on the spot.
Remarks: In front of campsite du Bois du Couvent.

Tourist information La Chaux-de-Fonds:
ℹ Tourisme neuchâtelois - Montagnes, Espacité 1, Place Le Corbusier. Capital of the clock industry.
🅼 Musée International d'Horlogerie, Rue des Musée 29. Watch museum.
⚪ 10-17h ⚫ Mo, 25/12-01/01.

🚐S **Langenthal** 24A2
Lexa-Wohnmobile, Bern-Zürichstrasse 49b. **GPS:** n47,22461 e7,77944. 🔼.

5 🔥free ⚡🗨Ch ⚡ free. **Surface:** asphalted. ⚪ 01/01-31/12
Distance: 🚶2km.
Remarks: At motorhome dealer.

🔥S **Lausanne** ❄🏔🏔🐚 23C4
Vidy, Chemin du Camping 3. **GPS:** n46,51734 e6,59777.🔼➡.

CH

10 CHF 23,10 or € 20 Ch WC included CHF 4,35/4h.
Location: Urban, simple, central.
Surface: grassy/metalled.
01/01-31/12
Distance: on the spot on the spot.
Remarks: Next to campsite the Vidy, pay at reception, service passerby CHF 3, free bus to centre.

Tourist information Lausanne:
Lausanne Tourisme, Avenue de Rhodanie 2, www.lausanne-tourisme.ch. Parking at the port, rack-railway to city centre.
M Musée Olympique, Quai d'Ouchy 1. All about the Olympic games. 01/05-14/10 9-18h, 14/10-30/04 10-18h Mo, 01/10-30/04.

| | Lauterbrunnen | 24A4 |
Jungfrau. GPS: n46,58834 e7,90882.
01/01-31/12

| | Lauterbrunnen | 24A4 |
Schützenbach. GPS: n46,59047 e7,91194.
01/01-31/12

Tourist information Lauterbrunnen:
Jungfraubahn, Grindelwald. Train journey to the highest train station of Europe.
Klöppelstube, Altes Schulhaus. Making of bobbin lace. Tue 14-17h. free.
Trümmelbachfälle, Lauterbrunnen dir Stechelberg. Underground waterfalls. 01/04-30/11 9-17h.

| | Le Landeron | 23D3 |
Camp des Pêches. GPS: n47,05257 e7,06993.
01/04-15/10

Tourist information Le Landeron:
Restaurant Le Carnotzet, Rue de la Gare 22. Restaurant with regional specialities. Tue-Sa 11-14h, 17-23h Mo, Su.

| S | Les Brenets | 23C3 |
Champ de la Fontaine. GPS: n47,06588 e6,69898.

CHF5 Ch. 01/01-31/12
Remarks: Nearby campsite Lac de Brenets.

| S | Les Ponts-de-Martel | 23C3 |
Rue du Bugnon. **GPS:** n46,99644 e6,73065.

3 free Ch (2x)free.
Location: Rural, simple. **Surface:** asphalted.
Distance: 600m 700m.
Remarks: At community centre.

| S | Malvilliers | 23C3 |
Hotel-Restaurant La Croisée, Route de Neuchâtel. **GPS:** n47,03200 e6,86779.

5 CHF5 Ch (4x)included. **Location:** Simple, noisy.
Surface: asphalted. 01/01-31/12
Distance: 100m on the spot.

| S | Meiringen | 24B3 |
Alpencamping, Brüningstrasse 46. **GPS:** n46,73448 e8,17122.
8 CHF 27,90 Ch WC included. **Surface:** grassy.
Distance: 1km 1km.
Remarks: Max. 3 nights.

| | Morges | 23C4 |
Le Petit Bois. GPS: n46,50446 e6,48894.
Ch against payment. 01/04-01/10
Remarks: Service at entrance campsite.

| S | Moutier | 23D2 |
Chemin de la Piscine. **GPS:** n47,27365 e7,37923.

5 free Ch free.
Location: Urban, simple, quiet. **Surface:** asphalted.
Distance: 1km.
Remarks: At swimming pool.

| | Murten | 23D3 |
Lac de Morat, Ryf. **GPS:** n46,93240 e7,11967.

30 CHF 1/h, overnight stay free. **Location:** Urban, simple, central.
Surface: grasstiles. 01/01-31/12
Distance: on the spot on the spot on the spot.

| S | Neuchâtel | 23D3 |
Route des Falaises. **GPS:** n47,00145 e6,95735.

CH

8 🛆free 🚰🔧Ch 🛴(4x)free.
Location: Simple, noisy. **Surface:** grasstiles.
Distance: 🚶city centre 2km 🏊300m 🚌100m.
Remarks: Max. 2 days.
Tourist information Neuchâtel:
🚶 Le Creux-du-Van, Val-de-Travers. Nature reserve.
⬛ 01/01-31/12.

| 🛆S | Nyon 🌿⛵🐚 | 23B4 |

Piscine de Colovray, Chemin de la Piscine. **GPS:** n46,36989 e6,22842.

10 🛆free 🚰🔧Ch 🛴WC free. **Surface:** asphalted. ⬛ 01/01-31/12
Distance: 🚶1km 🏊150m ⊗1km 🍴1km.
Remarks: Max. 15h.

| 🛆S | Oberburg | 24A3 |

Reisemobilstellplätze Kürbishof, Krauchthalstrasse 40.
GPS: n47,03807 e7,62079.
5 🛆CHF 13 or € 9 🚰🔧Ch 🛴WC against payment. ⬛ 01/01-31/12
Distance: 🚶600m ⊗300m.
Remarks: Payment also in euros.

| 🛆S | Oron-la-Ville | 23C4 |

Chemin de Botollie. **GPS:** n46,57191 e6,82199. ⬆️

3 🛆free 🚰🔧Ch. **Surface:** gravel/metalled. ⬛ 01/01-31/12
Distance: 🚶on the spot ⊗on the spot 🍴on the spot.

| 🛆S | Payerne 🍴 | 23D3 |

Place de la Concorde. **GPS:** n46,81976 e6,93757. ⬆️

2 🛆free 🚰🔧Ch 🛴(2x)free. **Location:** Urban, simple, central, noisy.
Surface: asphalted. ⬛ 01/01-31/12
Distance: 🚶on the spot ⊗on the spot 🍴on the spot.

| 🛆S | Portalban 🌿⛵🐚 | 23D3 |

Route du Port. **GPS:** n46,92131 e6,95614. ⬆️

26 🛆CHF 20, 2 pers.incl 🚰🔧Ch 🛴(30x)WC included. **Location:** Rural,
simple. **Surface:** grasstiles. ⬛ 01/01-31/12
Distance: 🚶on the spot 🏊200m ⊗on the spot 🍴on the spot.
Remarks: In harbour, near campsite, check in at reception.

| 🔺 | Prêles | 23D2 |

Prêles, Route de la Neuveville 61. **GPS:** n47,08404 e7,11262.
🛆. ⬛ 01/04-15/10

| C S | Rolle | 23C4 |

Camping de Rolle Aux Vernes, Chemin de la Plage. **GPS:** n46,46191 e6,34630.
5 🛆CHF 18-30 + CHF 8,50-10/pp tourist tax 🛴CHF 3. **Surface:** asphalted.
⬛ 01/03-01/10
Distance: 🚶500m.
Remarks: Max. 48h.

| 🛆S | Romont 🌿⛵ | 23D3 |

Promenade des Avoines. **GPS:** n46,69753 e6,91774. ⬆️➡️

2 🛆free 🚰🔧Ch 🛴(4x)free. **Location:** Rural, simple, noisy.
Surface: grasstiles. ⬛ 01/01-31/12
Distance: 🚶on the spot ⊗100m 🍴700m.
Remarks: Max. 24h.

| 🛆S | Saignelégier | 23D2 |

Chemin de la Tuilerie. **GPS:** n47,25223 e7,00347. ⬆️

10 🛆free 🚰🔧Ch ➕free. **Location:** Rural, simple, noisy. **Surface:** grasstiles.
⬛ 01/01-31/12
Distance: 🚶700m ⊗on the spot 🍴200m.

| 🔺 | Satigny | 23B5 |

Bois de Bay, Route du Bois-de-Bay 19. **GPS:** n46,19856 e6,04724.
🛆. ⬛ 01/01-31/12

| 🛆S | St.Aubin 🐚 | 23C3 |

Port de St-Aubin-Sauges. GPS: n46,89181 e6,77427. ⬆️➡️

CH

CH

10 ☐CHF 20 ⚡ ▢ Ch ⚡ (6x)WC ☐included. ⚓ **Location:** Simple, quiet.
Surface: asphalted. ▢ 01/01-31/12
Distance: ⚓600m ⚓on the spot ⚓on the spot ⊗400m ⚓400m.
Remarks: Parking port, nearby the capitainerie.

| ⚓⚓ | St.Blaise ⚓ | 23D3 |

Chemin des Pêcheurs. **GPS:** n47,01139 e6,98778. ⬆➡.

12 ☐CHF 16/24h ⚡ ▢ Ch ⚡ (4x)WC ☐ 📶included. ▢ ⚓ **Location:**
Urban, simple, central, noisy. **Surface:** asphalted.
Distance: ⚓Neuchâtel 5km ⚓300m ⚓250m ⊗500m ⚓600m.

| ⚓S | Ste.Croix ⚓❄ | 23C3 |

Grand-Rue, L'Auberson. **GPS:** n46,82019 e6,47230. ⬆.

4 ☐free ⚡ ▢ Ch ⚡ (4x)free.
Location: Rural, simple. **Surface:** asphalted.
Distance: ⚓2km ⊗on the spot ⚓3km.

| △ | Vesenaz | 23B5 |

Pointe a la Bise. **GPS:** n46,24517 e6,19331.
⚓. ▢ 01/01-31/12

| △ | Zweisimmen | 23D4 |

Vermeille, Eygässli 2. **GPS:** n46,56265 e7,37766.
⚓. ▢ 01/01-31/12

Switzerland North

| ⚓S | Altikon ⚓ | 24C1 |

Stellplatz auf dem Bauernhof, Feldistrasse 18. **GPS:** n47,57337 e8,78391.
3 ☐CHF 10 ⚡CHF 1 ▢ Ch ⚡ CHF 4 ☐CHF 2. ⚓ **Surface:** metalled.
▢ 01/01-31/12
Distance: ⊗200m ⚓200m.
Remarks: Max. 48h.

| △ | Brunnen | 24B3 |

Hopfraeben. **GPS:** n46,99700 e8,59300.
⚓. ▢ 01/05-01/10

| △ | Engelberg | 24B3 |

Eienwäldli, Wasserfallstraße 108. **GPS:** n46,81009 e8,42243.
⚓. ▣ 01/11-30/11

| ⚓S | Frick | 24A1 |

Hotel Engel, Hauptstraße 101. **GPS:** n47,50576 e8,02430.

20 ☐free WC. **Surface:** gravel. ▢ 01/01-31/12
Distance: ⚓300m ⚓ 1,6km ⊗on the spot ⚓50m ⚓50m.
Remarks: Behind the hotel.

| ⚓ | Giswil | 24B3 |

Stellplatz an der Kirche, Panoramastrasse. **GPS:** n46,83230 e8,17900.
3 ☐free. **Surface:** asphalted. ▢ 01/01-31/12
Distance: ⚓on the spot ⊗on the spot ⚓on the spot.
Remarks: Max. 1 night.

| ⚓S | Hemmiken | 24A1 |

Stellplatz Bauernhof, Asphof 50. **GPS:** n47,49682 e7,88749.
3 ☐CHF 20 ⚡ ▢ Ch ⚡ ☐. **Location:** Isolated. **Surface:** unpaved.
▢ 01/01-31/12
Distance: ⚓1,4km.

| △ | Horw | 24B3 |

Steinibachried. **GPS:** n47,01100 e8,31100.
⚓. ▢ 01/04-01/10

| △ | Reinach | 24A1 |

Waldhort, Heideweg 16. **GPS:** n47,49923 e7,60296.
⚓. ▢ 15/03-15/10

| ⚓S | Weggis ⚓⚓⚓❄ | 24B2 |

Bauernhof Gerberweid, Eichistrasse 2. **GPS:** n47,03888 e8,41446.

15 ☐CHF 6-10 + CHF 6/pp + CHF 2,70/pp tourist tax ⚡CHF 1 ▢ Ch ⚡ CHF 3
☐CHF 2. **Surface:** grassy. ▢ 01/04-15/10
Distance: ⚓2km ⊗1km ⚓1km ⚓500m ⚓on the spot.

| ⚓S | Willisau | 24A2 |

Bisangmatt. **GPS:** n47,11937 e7,99829. ⬆.

4 ☐CHF 5 ⚡ ⚡ (4x)free. **Surface:** metalled. ▢ 01/01-31/12
Distance: ⚓800m ⊗800m ⚓800m.
Remarks: At fire-station.

| △ | Zug | 24B2 |

Zugersee, Chamer Fussweg 36. **GPS:** n47,17758 e8,49358.
⚓. ▢ 01/04-01/10
Remarks: Max. ^3.17m.

Switzerland East

Altstätten 🏔 24D1

Gasthausziel, Trogenerstrasse 99. **GPS**: n47,38892 e9,53457.
6 🅿 CHF 10, guests free ⛽ 🔌Ch 🚿 CHF 5/day. ♿ 🅿 01/01-31/12
🕐 Wed-Thu
Distance: 🚶3km ⊗ on the spot.

Andeer 24D3

Sut Baselgia. GPS: n46,60651 e9,42630.
🅿.

Appenzell 🌿☂🏕❄ 24D2

Restaurant Eggli, Egglistrasse. **GPS**: n47,32104 e9,46565.
10 🅿 ⛽🔌Ch guests free. **Surface:** asphalted. 🅿 01/01-31/12
Remarks: The most beautiful panorama of Appenzell.

Bivio ⛲❄ 24D4

Wohnmobil-Stellplatz Tua. GPS: n46,46304 e9,65597.

20 🅿 CHF 10-15 + CHF 2,50/pp tourist tax ⛽🔌Ch 🚿 CHF 7/day.
Surface: grasstiles.
🅿 01/01-31/12
Distance: 🚶Savognin 18km ⊗ on the spot. 🚠 Savognin 18km 🎿on the spot.
Remarks: Parking ski-lifts.

Breil/Brigels ⛲🏔❄🚡 24C3

Parkplatz der Bergbahnen. GPS: n46,77104 e9,06770. 🔼.

20 🅿 CHF 7 + CHF 3/pp tourist tax ⛽CHF 2/50liter 🔌Ch 🚿 CHF 3/day.
Surface: metalled. 🅿 01/04-30/11
Distance: 🚶600m ⛰ on the spot ⊗Imbiss on the spot, restaurants 600m
🚠600m ⊗ on the spot 🎿nearby.
Remarks: At Brigeler See.

Chur 🌿🏕 24D3

Stellplätze Camp Au, Felsenaustrasse 61. **GPS**: n46,86187 e9,50756.
🅿CHF 15 + CHF 1,20/pp tourist tax ⛽🔌Ch WC 🚿. 🅿 01/01-31/12
Distance: 🚶3km 🚲2km ⊗ on the spot 🚠 on the spot.
Remarks: Max. 1 night, oldest city of Switzerland.

Churwalden 24D3

Pradafenz, Girabodawag 34. **GPS**: n46,77636 e9,54178.
🅿. 🅿 01/01-31/12

Davos 🌿⛲🏔🏕❄ 24D3

Rinerlodge Talstation, Rinerhornbahn, Davos Glaris. **GPS**: n46,74150 e9,77814.
10 🅿CHF 29 ⛽🔌Ch 🚿 CHF 2. **Surface:** gravel.
Distance: 🚶1km ⛰ on the spot ⊗on the spot 🎿on the spot 🚠 on the spot.
Remarks: Max. 24h.

Tourist information Davos:
👁 Davos Alpengarten. Botanical garden. 🅿 01/05-30/09 9-17h.
⊗ Berghaus Stafelalp, Frauenkirch. 250 Year old inn where they still cook on a wood oven and shimmer paraffin lamps are lit.

Elm 24C3

Sportbahnen Elm, Schiesserblock. **GPS**: n46,91332 e9,16228.
50 🅿free. **Surface:** asphalted. 🅿 01/03-30/11
Distance: ⊗650m 🚠650m 🎿on the spot 🚡on the spot.

Ennetbühl 🍴🏕❄ 24C2

Stellplatz Gill, Schwägalpstrasse 1336. **GPS**: n47,24111 e9,21861.

20 🅿CHF 4 + CHF 3/pp ⛽🔌Ch 🚿 (9x)CHF 0,50/kWh WC 🚿CHF 1 🕐 📶CHF 3. **Surface:** metalled.
Distance: 🚶400m ⛰on the spot ⊗400m 🚠400m 🎿on the spot.
Remarks: Payment also in euros.

Eschenz 24C1

Hüttenberg. GPS: n47,64436 e8,85935.
8 🅿CHF 20 ⛽🔌Ch 🚿 WC 📶included. **Location:** Rural.
Surface: grassy/metalled. 🅿 01/01-31/12
Remarks: Payment also in euros.

Kreuzlingen 24C1

Fischerhaus, Promenadestraße 52. **GPS**: n47,64745 e9,19898.
🅿. 🅿 01/04-01/11

Kriessern 24D2

BP Kriessern, Lehenstrasse. **GPS**: n47,35919 e9,60866.
5 🅿free ⛽ 🚿 against payment. **Surface:** asphalted. 🅿 01/01-31/12
Distance: 🚶600m 🚲on the spot ⊗Bistro.

Müstair 25B3

Clenga. GPS: n46,62900 e10,45400.
🅿. 🅿 01/05-20/10

Neuhausen 🌿🏕 24B1

Parkplatz Fischacker, Nohlstrasse. **GPS**: n47,67373 e8,60866.

50 🅿€ 15 ⛽🔌Ch WC 🚿. **Surface:** grassy/metalled.
Distance: 🚶200m ⛰on the spot ⊗200m 🚠1km.

Tourist information Neuhausen:
👁 Der Rheinfall. Water falls.

Pontresina 25A4

Plauns. GPS: n46,46200 e9,93400.
🅿. 🅿 01/06-15/10, 15/12-15/04

Samnaun 25A3

Wohnmobilstellplatz Samnaun-Ravaisch, Sportplatzweg 13.
GPS: n46,94906 e10,36705.

18 🅿CHF 18-39/day, CHF 6,20/pp ⛽🔌Ch 🚿 WC 📶included.
🅿 01/01-31/12
Distance: ⊗750m 🚌200m 🎿on the spot.

CH

Remarks: At football ground.

Sankt Gallen	24D1

Paul-Grüninger-Stadion, Grütlistrasse. **GPS:** n47,43361 e9,40464.
2 CHF 2/9-19h, CHF 1/19-8h CHF 1/100liter CHF 0,50/kWh.
Surface: asphalted. 01/01-31/12
Distance: 2km 300m.
Remarks: Next to sports fields.

Sankt Moritz	24D4

Olympiaschanze. GPS: n46,47800 e9,82600.
15/05-01/10

Tourist information Sankt Moritz:
Clean Energy Tour. Hiking trail, nature, energy, climate and weather adventure. Sign up at Kur- und Verkehrsverein St. Moritz. 15/06-01/10 Wed 13.45h duration 2,5 hours.

Savognin	24D3

Veia Sandeilas. **GPS:** n46,59660 e9,59226.
15 CHF 15 + CHF 8/pp CHF 1 Ch CHF 2,50. **Surface:** gravel.
01/01-31/12
Distance: 500m.
Remarks: Near the chair-lift, summer: parking at campsite Julia.

Schiers	24D3

Restaurant Prättigauerhof, Flurystrasse 19. **GPS:** n46,97034 e9,68752.
2 free, use of a meal obligated . **Surface:** metalled.
01/01-31/12 Sa + Su
Distance: 300m on the spot 100m.

Sent	25A3

Camping Sur En. GPS: n46,81852 e10,36596.
10 CHF 15 + CHF 2,50/pp tourist tax CHF 3. 01/01-31/12
Distance: on the spot.
Remarks: Max. 1 night, 17-10h.

Splügen	24D4

Auf dem Sand. GPS: n46,54922 e9,31399.
01/01-31/12

Steckborn	24C1

Wohnmobilplatz Steckborn, Schützengraben. **GPS:** n47,66813 e8,98462.

8 CHF 12/24h Ch (8x)included. **Surface:** gravel.
01/01-31/12
Distance: 400m 200m 400m 300m.

Unterwasser	24D2

Hotel Restaurant Post, Postplatz. **GPS:** n47,19673 e9,30949.
6 CHF 15 + CHF 3/pp tourist tax, guests free (6x).
01/01-31/12
Distance: 300m on the spot 300m on the spot.

Vaduz/Liechtenstein	24D2

Rheinparkstadion, Rheindamm. **GPS:** n47,14022 e9,50945.

10 CHF 4,50, 19-07h free Ch WC free. **Surface:** asphalted.
01/01-31/12

Distance: 1,8km on the spot.
Remarks: Along the Rhine river, parking near stadium, max. 24h.

Tourist information Vaduz/Liechtenstein:
Liechtenstein Tourismus, Städtle 37, www.vaduz.li. Monarchy on the Austrian-Swiss border.
Skimuseum, Fabrikstrasse 5. 100 years ski history. Mo-Fri 14-18h.
Erlebniswelt Neugutsof, Neugutweg 30. Maize labyrinth with wild-west city.
15/06-30/09 Wed 13-18h, Sa-Su 10-20h, holidays Mo-Fri 10-20h, Sa-Su 10-22h.

Vals	24C3

Stellplatz Vals, Vallée. **GPS:** n46,60891 e9,17438.

10 CHF 17 + CHF 2,80/pp tourist tax WC.
Surface: metalled. summer
Distance: 300m on the spot 300m 300m on the spot.
Remarks: Parking funicular railway.

Zizers	24D3

K. Lüthi, Rappagugg. **GPS:** n46,91937 e9,56270.
5 free Ch. **Surface:** metalled.
Distance: 1,6km on the spot.
Remarks: At motorhome dealer.

Zürich	24B2

Seeburcht, Seestrasse 559. **GPS:** n47,33641 e8,53960.
01/05-01/10

Tourist information Zürich:
Zürich Tourismus, Im Hauptbahnhof, www.zuerich.com. Historical city with large pedestrian area.

Switzerland South

Agno	24C5

Eurocampo, Via di Molinnazzo. **GPS:** n45,99547 e8,90063.
01/04-01/10

Avegno	24C5

Piccolo Paradiso. GPS: n46,20100 e8,74300.
01/03-01/11

Bellinzona	24C5

Centro Sportivo, Viale Giuseppe Motta. **GPS:** n46,20116 e9,01729.

7 CHF 20 CHF 1/20liter Ch. **Surface:** asphalted. 01/01-31/12
Distance: 1,5km 4km.
Remarks: Max. 48h.

Tourist information Bellinzona:
Castelgrande. 01/01-31/12 10-18h.
Castello di Montebello. 01/03-30/11 10-18h.
Castello di Sasso Corbaro. 01/03-30/11 10-18h.
Palestra di Roccia San Paolo, Palazo Civico. Climbing garden for beginners and experienced, 30.000^2m, 23 climbing trails.

Bouveret	23C4

Rive Bleue. GPS: n46,38645 e6,86041.

CH

🏖. ☐ 01/04-30/09

| △ | Brig | 24A4 |

Brigerbad. GPS: n46,29995 e7,93617.

🏖.

| 🏕S | Champéry ⛰ ❄ | 23C5 |

Route de la Fin. GPS: n46,17592 e6,87076.⬆.

6 🏖CHF 18 + 2,20/pp 🔌🔧Ch ✂ (4x)included. **Location:** Rural, simple.
Surface: asphalted. ☐ 01/01-31/12
Distance: ⊗100m 🚰on the spot 🚌200m ⚡200m.
Remarks: Parking supermarket, nearby the télépherique.

| △ | Evolène | 24A5 |

Evolène. GPS: n46,11075 e7,49654.
🏖. ☐ 01/01-31/12

| △ | Gordevio | 24C4 |

Bella Riva. GPS: n46,22293 e8,74313.
🏖. ☐ 01/04-01/10

| 🏕S | Grimentz ⛰🏔⛰🏕❄ | 24A5 |

Aire camping-car l'Ilôt Bosquet, Route de Moiry. **GPS:** n46,17432 e7,57271.➡.

20 🏖CHF 15 🔌🔧Ch 🚐CHF 3. 🏖🚙 **Location:** Rural, simple, quiet.
Surface: asphalted. ☐ 01/01-31/12
Distance: 🚶on the spot ⊗on the spot 🚰on the spot 🚌on the spot ⚡nearby ⛷nearby.
Remarks: Pay and coins at tourist office, public transport, free entrance swimming pool (summer).

Tourist information Grimentz:
ℹ Grimentz/St.Jean Tourisme, www.grimentz.ch. Many signposted cycle and hiking routes.
👁 La Maison bourgeoisiale. Life of the citizens of Grimentz. ☐ guided tour Mo.
🎫 free.

| 🏕S | Grimselpas ⛰🚣 | 24B4 |

Hotel Grimselblick, Totensee. **GPS:** n46,56115 e8,33673.
20 🏖CHF 10 🔌. **Surface:** asphalted.
Distance: ⚡on the spot.
Remarks: Service at hotel.

| 🏕 | Hérémence | 23D5 |

Val des Hérémence, Parking B,C,D en E, Le Chargeur. **GPS:** n46,08882 e7,40362.

15🏖free. **Surface:** unpaved. ☐ 01/01-31/12
Remarks: At artificial lake.

| △ | La Fouly | 23D5 |

Les Glaciers. GPS: n45,93351 e7,09361.
🏖. ☐ 15/05-30/09

| △ | Les Haudères | 24A5 |

Molignon. GPS: n46,09061 e7,50776.
🏖. ☐ 01/01-31/12

| 🏕S | Leuk | 24A4 |

Hexenplatzstrasse. GPS: n46,31082 e7,63436.
4 🏖CHF 15/24h 🔌🔧Ch ✂. **Surface:** asphalted. ☐ 01/01-31/12
Distance: 🚶400m ⚡on the spot 🚌on the spot ⊗400m ⚡400m.

| 🏕 | Leukerbad ⛰🚣❄ | 24A4 |

Winterstellplatz, Parkplatz Fischweiher. **GPS:** n46,38215 e7,63232.⬆.

30 🏖CHF 10/24h. 🚐 **Location:** Rural, simple. **Surface:** gravel/sand.
☐ 01/11-15/04
Distance: ⊗150m ⚡600m ⚡100m.
Remarks: Payment only with coins.

| 🏕 | Locarno ⛰🚣🏖 | 24C5 |

Parco della Pace, Via Gioacchino Respini. **GPS:** n46,16011 e8,80255.⬆➡.

50 🏖CHF 5/6h. **Surface:** gravel.
☐ 01/01-31/12
Distance: 🚶900m 🏊100m ⊗100m.
Remarks: Max. 24h.

Tourist information Locarno:
👁 Rasa. Touristic car-free miniature village, can be reached by first taking the Centrovall-track, till Verdasio, then the small telpher carrier to Rasa.
⛴ Tenero-Locarno-Tenero. Free boat service. ☐ 31/05-30/09.

| 🏕 | Martigny ⛰⛰❄ | 23D5 |

P1, Place de la Fondation Gianadda. **GPS:** n46,09585 e7,07143.⬆⬆.

5 🏖free. **Location:** Urban, simple. **Surface:** asphalted.

| △ | Martigny ⛰⛰❄ | 23D5 |

Les Neuvilles, Rue du Levant 68. **GPS:** n46,09787 e7,07930.
🏖. ☐ 01/02-31/12

Tourist information Martigny:
🥾 Gorges du Durnand. Hiking trail through the gorge of the river Durnand.

CH

| △ | Meride | 24C5 |

Parco al Sole. GPS: n45,88806 e8,94944.
🛇. ⬛ 01/05-01/10

| △ | Molinazzo di Montegio | 24C5 |

Tresiana. GPS: n45,98990 e8,81576.
🛇. ⬛ Easter-01/11

| △ | Muzzano-Lugano | 24C5 |

Piodella di Agnuzzo. GPS: n45,99463 e8,90857.
🛇. ⬛ 01/01-31/12

| △ | Raron | 24A4 |

Santa Monica, Kantonstrasse 56. **GPS:** n46,30007 e7,82374.
🛇. ⬛ 01/01-31/12

| △ | Reckingen | 24B4 |

Camping Augenstern, Im Ellbogen 21. **GPS:** n46,46500 e8,24500.
🛇. ⬛ 01/05-18/10 and 15/12-15/03

| S | Saas Fee | 24A5 |

Parkplatz P4. GPS: n46,11090 e7,93208.⬆

50 🛇CHF 26/24h 🚰🗑Ch included 💧CHF2 WC. 🚌 **Location:** Rural, simple, isolated, quiet. **Surface:** grassy/gravel.
⬛ 01/01-31/12 ⬤ service in winter
Distance: 🚶100m ⊗200m 🛒900m 🎿200m.

| ⚓ | Saillon | 23D5 |

Bains de Saillon, Route du Centre Thermal 16. **GPS:** n46,17353 e7,19372.
12 🛇free. **Surface:** grassy.
⬛ 01/01-31/12. **Distance:** 🚗4km. **Remarks:** Max. 48h.

| S | Sierre | 24A4 |

Chemin Du Grand-Lac. **GPS:** n46,28597 e7,54013.⬆.

4 🛇. **Location:** Rural, simple. **Surface:** grassy.
Distance: 🚗 on the spot ⛵100m ⊗on the spot.
Remarks: Max. 1 night.

| △ | Sierre | 24A4 |

Bois de Finges. GPS: n46,29362 e7,55777.
🛇. ⬛ 01/05-01/10

| S | Simplon | 24A4 |

Col du Simplon, Simplonstrasse. **GPS:** n46,24944 e8,03056.⬆.

18 🛇free 🚰🗑Ch WC free. **Location:** Rural, simple, isolated.

Surface: asphalted.
Distance: ⊗200m.

| S | Sion | 23D5 |

Botza, Route du Camping 1, Vétroz. **GPS:** n46,20585 e7,27855.
🛇. ⬛ 01/01-31/12

| S | Sonogno | 24C4 |

Camper Area Sonogno, Cioss. **GPS:** n46,35058 e8,78846.➡.
15 🛇€16/night 🚰🗑Ch included. **Location:** Rural, isolated, quiet.
Surface: grassy. ⬛ 01/01-31/12
Distance: 🚶200m ⊗200m 🛒200m.

| S | St.Léonard | 23D5 |

Place du Lac Souterrain. **GPS:** n46,25564 e7,42600.⬆➡.

15 🛇CHF 10/night 🚰🗑Ch 💧 (4x) WC included. **Location:** Rural, simple, central, quiet. **Surface:** asphalted/grassy. ⬤ service: 01/11-19/03
Distance: 🚗5,5km ⊗300m.
Remarks: Pay in at kiosk.

| S | Stampa | 24D4 |

Tankstelle Esso, Strada Principale. **GPS:** n46,34593 e9,59660.⬆.
8 🛇CHF 8 🚰CHF3 🗑Ch 💧CHF3. ⬛ 01/01-31/12
Distance: 🛒on the spot.
Remarks: Max. 24h.

| △ | Tenero | 24C5 |

Campofelice, Via Alle Brere 7. **GPS:** n46,17353 e8,85401.
🛇. ⬛ 01/04-27/10

| △ | Tenero | 24C5 |

Lido Mappo, Via Mappo. **GPS:** n46,17850 e8,84519.
🛇. ⬛ 15/03-01/11

| △ | Tenero | 24C5 |

Tamaro, Via Mappo 32. **GPS:** n46,17525 e8,84779.
🛇. ⬛ 15/03-01/11

| S | Trient | 23D5 |

Place de Repos Du Peuty, Le Peuty. **GPS:** n46,04645 e6,99499.⬆.

6 🛇CHF 3/pp 🚰🗑free. **Location:** Rural, simple, isolated, quiet.
Surface: grassy.
Distance: ⊗1,5km 🚶on the spot.

| S | Vétroz | 23D5 |

Restaurant L'As de Pique. GPS: n46,20556 e7,27833.
🚰🗑Ch 💧CHF 15, guests free.

AUSTRIA

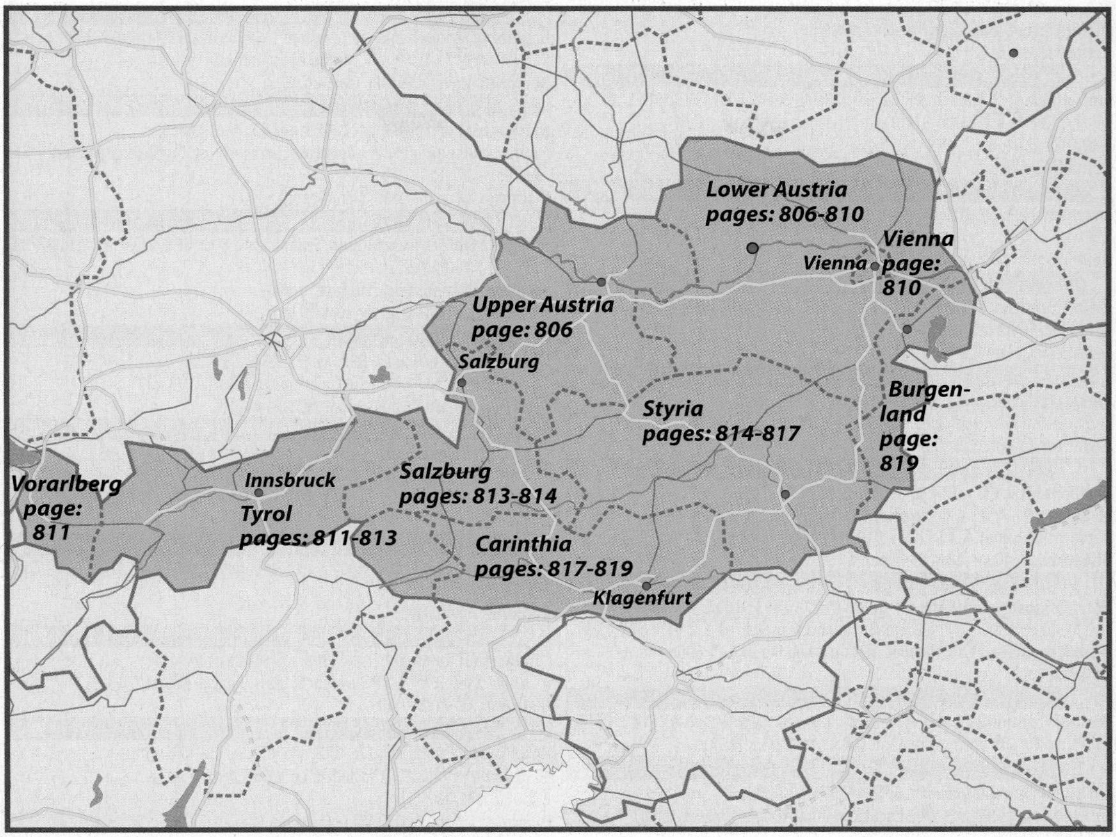

Lower Austria
pages: 806-810

Vienna
page: 810

Vienna

Upper Austria
page: 806

Salzburg

Burgen-
land
page:
819

Styria
pages: 814-817

Vorarlberg
page:
811

Innsbruck

Salzburg
pages: 813-814

Tyrol
pages: 811-813

Carinthia
pages: 817-819

Klagenfurt

AT

Capital: Vienna
Government: federal, parliamentarian, democratic
republic
Official Language: German
Population: 8,500,000 (2013)
Area: 83,857 km²

General information
Dialling code: 0043
General emergency: 112
Currency: Euro

Regulations for overnight stays
In general overnight parking is allowed, except: Tyrol,
Vienna, nature reserves and in areas where locally
prohibited. No "camping" activities allowed and
disposal wastewater must be at official places.

Additional public holidays 2015
January 6 Epiphany
May 1 Labor Day
June 4 Corpus Christi
August 15 Assumption of the Virgin Mary
October 26 National Holiday
November 1 All Saints' Day
December 8 Immaculate Conception

Upper Austria

♿ S   Ebensee   19C6
Am Traunsee, Trauneck. **GPS:** n47,81283 e13,77730.
5 ⛺free ⛽ 🚿 Ch 🔧 €3. **Surface:** asphalted.
Distance: 🚶500m 🛒on the spot ⊗300m.
Remarks: At lake.

♿ S   Ebensee   19C6
Freizeitanlage Rindbach, Strandbadstraße. **GPS:** n47,80934 e13,79002. ⬆.
30 ⛺€ 12 ⛽. ▢ 01/04-31/10
Distance: 🚶1,4km.
Remarks: At lake.

🏕   Eferding   19C4
Brandstatt, Pupping. **GPS:** n48,33503 e14,02698.
⛺.
Remarks: On the Danube river.

🏕   Gallneukirchen   27A1
Freizeitcentrum, Veitsdorfer Weg 10. **GPS:** n48,36045 e14,40797. ⬆.
10 ⛺free. **Surface:** asphalted. ▢ 01/01-31/12
Distance: 🚶1km ⊗on the spot 🍴1km.

🏕   Gmünden   19C6
Parkplatz des Toscanapark, Scharnsteiner Straße. **GPS:** n47,91186 e13,78708.
5 ⛺free. **Surface:** asphalted. ▢ 01/01-31/12
Distance: 🚶1km ⚓200m.

🍴 S   Gosau   19B6
Gasthaus Echo, Gosau 614. **GPS:** n47,55171 e13,51345.
10 ⛺free 🔧 €5 🐾. **Location:** Rural, simple, isolated, quiet.
Surface: asphalted. ▢ 01/05-31/10
Distance: ⚓400m ⊗on the spot.

🍴 S   Gosau   19B6
Hotel Gosauschmied, Gosau 57. **GPS:** n47,55072 e13,51607.
10 ⛺€ 10 ⛽🚿 Ch 🔧on demand. **Surface:** asphalted. ▢ 01/01-31/12
Distance: 🚶3km ⊗on the spot 🍴3km 🚃on the spot 🐾500m 🐕on the spot.

🍴 S   Haslach   19C4
Gasthof Furtmühle, Schwackerreith 20, St.Oswald. **GPS:** n48,60497 e14,01967.
15 ⛺free ⛽ 🔧against payment. ▢ 01/01-31/12 ▣ Tue

🍴 S   Hinterstoder   27A2
Gasthof Baumschlagerreith, Scheckau 14. **GPS:** n47,64525 e14,09632.
10 ⛺€ 8, guests free ⛽ 🔧. **Location:** Rural, simple, isolated, quiet.
▢ 01/01-31/12
Distance: 🚶9km ⊗on the spot.

🍴   Kefermarkt   27A1
Schloßbrauerei Weinberg, Weinberg 2. **GPS:** n48,44856 e14,53957.
5 ⛺guests free. **Surface:** asphalted. ▢ 01/01-31/12
Distance: 🚶800m ⊗on the spot.

🏕 S   Königswiesen   27A1
Freibad, Badgasse 4. **GPS:** n48,40450 e14,84080. ⬆.
3 ⛺€ 2 + € 2/pp ⛽ Ch WC. **Surface:** asphalted. ▢ 01/04-31/10
Distance: 🚶500m ⊗10m Freibadbuffet 🍴300m.
Remarks: Parking swimming pool.

🏕   Kremsmünster   27A2
Fischerparadies, Mairdorf 16. **GPS:** n48,06991 e14,11249.
10 ⛺€ 14, 2 pers incl. **Surface:** grassy. ▢ 01/01-31/12
Distance: 🚶3km ⛽on the spot.
Remarks: Fishing permit € 10.

🏕   Kremsmünster   27A2
Parkplatz Benediktiner Stift, Fuxjägerstraße. **GPS:** n48,05407 e14,12607.
⛺.
Distance: 🚶500m ⊗500m.

🏕 S   Kronstorf   27A1
Stellplatz Metzenhof, Dörfling 2. **GPS:** n48,12828 e14,43432.
10 ⛺€ 18, 2 pers incl ⛽ 🔧 WC 🐾included. **Location:** Rural, comfortable, isolated, quiet. ▢ 01/03-30/11
Distance: ⚓on the spot ⊗on the spot.
Remarks: At golf court.

🏕   Marchtrenk   27A1
Imbiß Koutek, Eichenstraße 2. **GPS:** n48,19055 e14,11893.
10 ⛺. ▢ 01/01-31/12
Distance: 🚶1km 🏊2,3km ⊗on the spot 🍴50m.

🦆   Mondsee ⛵   19B6
Geflügelhof Schweighofer, Schwand 10. **GPS:** n47,88186 e13,31105.
5 ⛺€ 13, 2 pers.incl ⛽🚿Ch 🐾included. **Surface:** grassy.
▢ 01/01-31/12

🐑 S   Naarn   27A1
Bauernhof Mostschenke, Dirnwagram 1. **GPS:** n48,21750 e14,61972.
5 ⛺€ 10 ⛽🚿 WC. **Surface:** asphalted.
Remarks: Arrival <19.30h, max. 4 days.

🍴 S   Naarn   27A1
Gasthof zur Post, Marktplatz 1. **GPS:** n48,22579 e14,60662.
5 ⛺€ 6, 2 pers incl ⛽ 🔧. **Location:** Simple, noisy. **Surface:** asphalted.
▣ Thu
Distance: 🚶on the spot ⊗on the spot.

🏕 S   Neumarkt   27A1
Stellplatz Einfach Ausspannen, Seisenbachweg 12. **GPS:** n48,43457 e14,47739.
2 ⛺€ 10 ⛽ 🔧 WC 🐾included.
Location: Isolated, quiet. **Surface:** grassy.
Distance: 🚶1km ⛽on the spot ⊗1km.

🏕 S   Ranshofen   19A5
Vereinslokal, Scheuhub 2. **GPS:** n48,23228 e12,99893.
10 ⛺free ⛽ Ch 🔧. **Surface:** grassy. ▢ 01/01-31/12
Distance: 🚶2km ⊗on the spot 🍴2km 🚃2km.

©S   Scharnstein   19C5
Camping Schatzlmühle, Viechtwang 1A. **GPS:** n47,91578 e13,97353.
5 ⛺€ 10 🔧 €3 🐾€2. ▢ 01/05-31/10
Distance: 🚶2km ⊗on the spot 🍴600m 🚃on the spot 🐾on the spot 🐕on the spot.

🏕   St.Pankraz   27A2
Parkplatz Klauser Stausee, Klaus an der Pyhmbahn. **GPS:** n47,82733 e14,15703.
⛺.
Remarks: Along river.

🍴 S   Straß im Attergau   19B6
Landgasthof Rosslwirt, Halt 4. **GPS:** n47,90488 e13,44677.
6 ⛺guests free ⛽ 🔧. **Surface:** grassy/gravel. ▢ 01/01-31/12
Distance: ⊗on the spot.

🍴 S   Suben   19B4
Hotel Suben, Etzelhofen 125. **GPS:** n48,40149 e13,42582. ⬆.
40 ⛺€ 10 ⛽🚿Ch 🐾included. **Location:** Simple, noisy.
▢ 01/01-31/12
Distance: 🏊on the spot ⊗on the spot.

🏕 S   Vöcklabruck   19C5
Hallenbad am Freizeitgelände, Hausruckstraße. **GPS:** n48,01107 e13,65299.
⛺.
6 ⛺guests free ⛽🚿 Ch 🔧. **Surface:** metalled. ▢ 01/01-31/12
Distance: 🚶500m.
Remarks: Max. 48h.

🏕 S   Waldhausen im Strudengau   27A1
Badesee, Schloßberg. **GPS:** n48,28420 e14,95883.
6 ⛺free ⛽€1/10minutes 🚿Ch 🔧€1/8h. **Location:** Rural, isolated, quiet.
Surface: gravel. ▢ 01/01-31/12
Distance: 🚶2km ⚓on the spot ⊗on the spot 🍴2km 🚃2km.

Lower Austria

🍴 S   Aggsbach Dorf   27A1
Gasthof Pension zur Kartause, Aggsbach-Dorf 38. **GPS:** n48,29638 e15,42604.
⬆.
10 ⛺free ⛽ 🔧. **Location:** Rural, isolated, quiet. **Surface:** grassy.
▢ 01/01-31/12
Distance: ⊗on the spot.

🏕 S   Aggsbach Markt   27A1
Badestrand. **GPS:** n48,29814 e15,40497. ⬆.

AT

16 ⌗ € 10 🚰 🖭 Ch ✏ €1. **Surface:** gravel. ◼ 01/03-31/10
Distance: 🚶500m ⊗50m Donaustüberl 🚊500m.
Remarks: On the Danube river.

🅂 Alland 27B1
ÖMV-tankstelle Groschner&KarrerOHG, Gewerbestraße 550.
GPS: n48,06734 e16,06364.

10 ⌗free 🚰 🖭 Ch against payment. **Location:** Highway. **Surface:** asphalted.
◼ 01/01-31/12
Distance: ✒ on the spot.
Tourist information Alland:
👁 Tropfsteinhöhle. Caves. ◼ 01/04-30/09 Sa, Su 9-17h, 01/07-31/08 Mo-Fri
15-16.30h Sa-Su 9-17h ◼ 01/11-31/03. 🎫 € 1,90/3.

🍴🅂 Altenmarkt an der Triesting 27B1
Gasthof Zum Kleinen Semmering, Hafnerberg 15. **GPS:** n48,01762 e16,01383.

10 ⌗free 🚰 WC. **Surface:** metalled.
Distance: 🚶2,3km ⊗on the spot 🚊2,3km.

🅂 Arbesbach 27A1
Am Ganser. GPS: n48,49123 e14,95683.⬆
15 ⌗€5 🚰🖭Ch ✏ included. **Surface:** gravel. ◼ 01/01-31/12
Distance: 🚶500m ⊿on the spot ⊗500m 🚊500m 🚮500m.
Remarks: Check in at town hall.

🅂 Ardagger 27A1
Stellplatz am Donauwellenpark, Markt 39. **GPS:** n48,17981 e14,82579.⬆
10 ⌗free 🚰€2 🖭Ch ✏ (8x)€1/kWh. ◼ 01/01-31/12
Distance: 🚶on the spot ⊿7km ⊗on the spot 🚊on the spot 🚲 on the spot.
Remarks: At Danube cycle route.

🅂 Armschlag 27A1
Mohndorf. **GPS:** n48,45222 e15,21944.
5 ⌗€ 7, 2 pers.incl. 🚰🖭Ch ✏. **Surface:** asphalted. ◼ 01/01-31/12
Distance: 🚶on the spot ⊗on the spot 🚊2km 🚶Mohnstrudelwandernetz.

💧🅂 Aschbach Markt 27A1
Fam. Edtbauer, Auckental 1 u. 2. **GPS:** n48,10682 e14,69988.
8 ⌗free 🚰🖭 ✏ €2. ◼ 15/04-30/10
Distance: 🚶7km ⊿3km 🚊7km.

📷 Bad Großpertholz 27A1
Busparkplatz Naturpark Nordwald, Scheiben. **GPS:** n48,61765 e14,81548.

⌗. **Location:** Rural. **Surface:** asphalted.

📷 Bernhardsthal 27B1
Am Bernhardsthaler Teich, Schulstrasse. **GPS:** n48,69402 e16,87481.⬆➡

5 ⌗free. **Surface:** grassy.
◼ 01/01-31/12
Distance: 🚶500m ⊿on the spot 🚲on the spot ⊗weekends only.

🅂 Eggenburg ☂ 💃 27B1
Stellplatz an der Stadtmauer, Erzherzog-Karl-Ring 19.
GPS: n48,64513 e15,81745.⬆

8 ⌗€ 4 🚰€1/10minutes 🖭Ch ✏ (8x)€1/6h. **Surface:** metalled.
◼ 01/04-31/10
Distance: 🚶on the spot ⊿4km ⊿creek ⊗300m 🚊200m 🚮500m
🚲on the spot 🚶300m.

🍴🅂 Erlauf 27A1
Gasthof Plaika Wirt, Plaika 1. **GPS:** n48,16866 e15,16436.
10 ⌗guests free 🚰⌗. ◼ Mon, Tue

📷 Gaming 27A2
Kartause. GPS: n47,92463 e15,08223.
⌗.

🅂 Gars am Kamp 27A1
Gföhler Strasse/Strandgasse, Thunau am Kamp. GPS: n48,59300 e15,65723.⬆

5 ⌗free ✏. **Surface:** gravel. ◼ 01/01-31/12
Distance: 🚶200m ⊗on the spot 🚊200m.
Remarks: At swimming pool.

📷 Göllersdorf 27B1
Parkplatz Barbara Heuriger, Spitalgasse 467. **GPS:** n48,49667 e16,11171.
10 ⌗free. **Surface:** gravel.
Distance: 🚶500m ⊿1km ⊗on the spot 🚊1km.

📷 Gumpoldskirchen 27B1
Brunngasse. **GPS:** n48,04212 e16,27820.⬆
10 ⌗free. **Surface:** asphalted.
Distance: 🚶500m ⊗500m.
Remarks: Max. 8M.

🅂 Gumpoldskirchen 27B1
Neustiftgasse. **GPS:** n48,04423 e16,27552.
🚰🖭Ch.

AT

Parkplatz an der Donau, Parkweg. **GPS**: n48,15110 e16,94440.

🅿. **Surface:** asphalted. 🄾 01/01-31/12
Distance: 🚰500m ⊗on the spot.

Hohenau/March 27B1
Freizeitzentrum, Kindergartenstrasse. **GPS**: n48,61095 e16,91010.

🅿free. **Surface:** asphalted. 🄾 01/01-31/12
Remarks: Swimming pool 200m.

Hollenstein/Ybbs 27A2
Naturpark Hollenstein, Wenten 1. **GPS**: n47,76884 e14,77270.
3 🅿€ 5 🚰 🍽 Ch 🧺. **Location:** Rural, isolated, quiet.
🄾 01/01-31/12
Distance: 🚰4km.

Hollenstein/Ybbs 27A2
Gasthof Staudach, Walcherbauer 5. **GPS**: n47,80703 e14,76687.
4 🅿€ 14, 4 pers.incl 🚰 🍽 Ch 🧺.
Distance: 🚰200m ⊗10m 🧺200m 🏃on the spot.

Karlstein an der Thaya 27A1
Sieghartser Straße. **GPS**: n48,88186 e15,40442.⬆
🅿. **Surface:** grassy. 🄾 01/01-31/12
Distance: 🚰200m 🧺200m.
Remarks: At tennis-court.

Klosterneuburg 27B1
Euromobil Campers, Bahnhofplatz 16, Kritzendorf. **GPS**: n48,33582 e16,29863.

4 🅿free 🍽 Ch. **Surface:** asphalted. 🄾 01/01-31/12
Distance: 🚲12,5km ⊗nearby 🧺nearby.
Remarks: Lock-up parking, guarded.

Laimbach am Ostrong 27A1
Bauernhof Stoiber, Wagmühle 34. **GPS**: n48,31711 e15,11636.⬆
5 🅿€ 12 🍽 Ch 🧺. **Surface:** grassy.
Distance: 🚰300m ⊗300m 🧺300m.

Langenlois 27A1
Reisemobilstellplatz Langenlois, Krumpöckallee 21.
GPS: n48,47063 e15,69782.⬆
7 🅿€ 6 + € 1,50/pp 🚰€1/10minutes 🍽 Ch 🧺(7x)€1/8h.
Surface: metalled.

Distance: 🚰1,5km ⊗1km 🧺1km.

Langschlag-Mitterschlag 27A1
Freizeitanlage Frauenwieserteich, Böhmerwald-Bundesstraße.
GPS: n48,58038 e14,83507.
10 🅿free. **Location:** Simple, isolated, quiet.
🄾 01/01-31/12
Distance: 🚰5km 🏊on the spot 🚣on the spot ⊗on the spot 🧺5km.

Mitterbach 27A2
Biobauernhof Sepplbauer, Bergstraße 11. **GPS**: n47,83216 e15,30648.
10 🅿€ 6 🧺€2. **Location:** Rural, isolated, quiet. **Surface:** grassy.
🄾 01/05-30/09
Distance: 🚰4km.

Mödling 27B1
Sportzentrum Mödling, Dr-Otto-Scheff-Weg 13. **GPS**: n48,08972 e16,29118.⬆
5 🅿free. **Location:** Urban. **Surface:** grasstiles. 🄾 01/01-31/12
Distance: 🚰1km ⊗200m 🧺400m.
Remarks: At sports park.

Orth/Donau 27B1
P2, Am Rosenhügel. **GPS**: n48,14523 e16,70383.⬆

🅿free. **Surface:** metalled. 🄾 01/01-31/12
Distance: 🚰on the spot ⊗250m 🧺1,2km.

Ottenschlag 27A1
Florianigasse. **GPS**: n48,42361 e15,22750.⬆

8-10 🅿€ 5 🚰€1/10minutes 🍽 Ch 🧺€1/8h. **Surface:** metalled.
Distance: 🚰500m ⊗Gaststätte 🧺500m.

Pillichsdorf 27B1
Am Tennisclub, Bahnstraße 8A. **GPS**: n48,36167 e16,53750.➡

8 🅿free, use facilities € 10 🚰 🍽 Ch 🧺 WC 🧺. 🄾 01/01-31/12
Distance: 🚰500m, Vienna 15km ⊗300m 🧺500m 🚌on the spot.
Remarks: Use facilities clubhouse possible.

Plaika 27A1
Gasthaus zum Plaikawirt, Plaika 1. **GPS**: n48,16878 e15,16416.⬆
5 🅿free 🚰 🧺. 🄾 01/01-31/12
Distance: 🚲5km ⊗on the spot.

Pulkau 27B1
Rat-Cumfe Straße. **GPS**: n48,70430 e15,86637.⬆➡

8 ⬜€ 5 ⛽€1/10minutes 🚿Ch 💧€1/6h. **Surface:** gravel.
📅 01/01-31/12
Distance: 🛒500m ⊗300m 🍴on the spot 🚊on the spot.

| 🏞 | Reichenau/Rax | 27B2 |

Kaiserbrunn, Bundesstraße Höllental 27. **GPS**: n47,73480 e15,79188.

⬜free. **Surface:** metalled.

| 🍴🚻S | Reichenau/Rax | 27B2 |

Gasthof Flackl Wirt, Hinterleiten 12. **GPS**: n47,69056 e15,82778.

5 ⬜€ 14 breakfest incl ⛽ 💧according consumption WC at restaurant.
Distance: 🛒1,5km ⊗on the spot.

| 🏞S | Retz | 27B1 |

Parkplatz Alter Sportplatz, Jahnstraße. **GPS**: n48,75382 e15,95105.

5 ⬜€ 3 ⛽€1/10minutes 🚿Ch 💧€1/8h. **Surface:** asphalted.
📅 01/04-31/10 ⬛ last weekend of Sep
Distance: 🛒500m 🚊500m.

| 🏞S | Rossatzbach | 27A1 |

Wohnmobilplatz Artner, Aggsteiner-Bundesstraße. **GPS**: n48,38750 e15,51722.

18 ⬜€ 10 ⛽🚿Ch 💧(12x) WC included. **Surface:** gravel.
📅 01/01-31/12
Distance: 🛒300m ⊿on the spot 🚊1,5km.
Remarks: Vinotheek 300m.

| 🏞S | Rust | 27B2 |

Reisebus-Parkplatz, Amhafen. **GPS**: n47,80405 e16,67873.

6 ⬜ ⛽🚿Ch.

| 🏞 | Schiltern bei Langenlois | 27A1 |

Erlebnisgärtner Kittenberger, Laabergstraße 15. **GPS**: n48,51180 e15,63277.
⬆.
3 ⬜. 📅 01/01-31/12
Distance: 🛒500m ⊗500m.

| 🏞S | Schönberg | 27A1 |

Freizeitzentrum, Badgasse. **GPS**: n48,52063 e15,69377.

5 ⬜€ 5/night ⛽🚿 💧(1x) WC included ⬜€1.
Surface: asphalted.
📅 01/01-31/12, service Easter-01/11
Distance: 🛒200m ⟵on the spot ⊗on the spot 🚊200m 🚲Kamptalradweg.
Remarks: Shower during opening hours. Along river.

| 🏞 | Schrems | 27A1 |

Parkplatz Kulturhaus, Josef-Widy-Straße. **GPS**: n48,79225 e15,06852.
3 ⬜free. **Surface:** asphalted. 📅 01/01-31/12
Distance: 🛒on the spot.

| 🏞 | Schrems | 27A1 |

Parkplatz Stadthalle, Doktor-Karl-Renner-Straße. **GPS**: n48,79167 e15,07120.
3 ⬜free. **Surface:** asphalted. 📅 01/01-31/12
Distance: 🛒on the spot 🚊500m.

| 🏞S | St.Martin am Ybbsfelde | 27A1 |

Gemeindeparkplatz, St. Martin. **GPS**: n48,16465 e15,01995.
⬜free ⛽ 💧. **Surface:** grasstiles. 📅 01/01-31/12
Distance: 🛒on the spot.
Remarks: Parking in front of church.

| 🏞S | Stockerau | 27B1 |

Hallenbad Wellness Oase, Pestalozzigasse. **GPS**: n48,39385 e16,21912. ⬆➡

AT

6 ⌂ free ⚡€2 ▣ Ch WC ⊐ sanitary in swimming pool. **Surface:** gravel. ▣ 01/01-31/12
Distance: ⌂1,5km ⚓500m ⊐50m.

| 🛁 | **Stockerau** | 27B1 |

Alte Au, Zum Spitzgarten. **GPS:** n48,38366 e16,20394.⬆️.
3 ⌂ free. **Surface:** gravel. ▣ 01/01-31/12
Distance: ⌂1km ⊗50m.
Remarks: At sports centre.

| 🛁 | **Weistrach** | 27A1 |

Parkplatz Sportplatz. GPS: n48,05475 e14,58167.⬆️.
10 ⌂ free. **Surface:** asphalted. ▣ 01/01-31/12
Distance: ⌂200m ⊗on the spot ⊐200m.
Remarks: Near sports fields.

| 🛁 | **Weitra** | 27A1 |

Freizeitzentrum Hausschachen, Promenade. **GPS:** n48,70414 e14,89343.⬆️.
10 ⌂ free. **Surface:** metalled. ▣ 01/01-31/12
Distance: ⌂600m ⊗600m.
Remarks: Max. 1 night.

| 🛁 | **Wiener Neustadt** | 27B2 |

Parkplatz Stadion, Stadionstrasse. **GPS:** n47,82156 e16,25629.

20 ⌂. **Location:** Urban. **Surface:** asphalted. ▣ 01/01-31/12
Distance: ⌂500m ⊐on the spot.

| 🛁S | **Wilfersdorf** | 27B1 |

Schloss Wilfersdorf, Parkplatz am Schloss. **GPS:** n48,58600 e16,64514.⬆️.

3 ⌂€4 ⚡━ ▣ WC. ▣ 01/01-31/12
Distance: ⌂100m ⊗300m ⊐on the spot.
Remarks: Check in at Schloss, 10-16h tue/su.

| 🛁 | **Ybbs an der Donau** | 27A1 |

Donauufer, Donaulände. **GPS:** n48,17979 e15,08387.⬆️.
5 ⌂ free. **Surface:** metalled. ▣ 01/01-31/12
Distance: ⌂700m ⊗700m.

| 🍴S | **Zwettl** | 27A1 |

Wirtshaus zur Minidampfbahn, 47, Teichhäuser bei Zwettl.
GPS: n48,66278 e15,15444.⬆️➡️.

10 ⌂€5 ⚡━ ▣ Ch ✎ €2,50. **Surface:** grassy/metalled. ▣ 01/01-31/12
Distance: ⌂2km ⟋200m ⊗on the spot ⊐2,5km.

Vienna

| 🛁S | **Wien** 🌿🍴🍞 | 27B1 |

Reisemobilstellplatz Wien - Wien

office@reisemobilstellplatz-wien.at - http://www.reisemobilstellplatz-wien.at

Excellent location for city visit
Open all year
Bread-service

Reisemobilstellplatz Wien, Perfektastraße 49-53, Vienna (Wien).
GPS: n48,13698 e16,31582.⬆️.
167 ⌂€21 ⚡━ ▣ Ch ✎ (167x) WC ⊐included 🚿€2/24h.
Location: Comfortable. ▣ 01/01-31/12
Distance: ⌂on the spot ⚓4km ⊗30m ⊐30m 🚇metro 150m 🚲100m.

| 🛁 | **Wien** 🌿🍴🍞 | 27B1 |

Kurpark Oberlaa, Filmteichstrasse 5, Vienna (Wien). **GPS:** n48,15211 e16,39767.
⌂ free. **Surface:** grassy/metalled. ▣ 01/01-31/12
Distance: 🚌centre > bus 68A Reumannplatz > tram U1 Stefansdom.
Remarks: No camping activities.

| 👣S | **Wien** 🌿🍴🍞 | 27B1 |

Weingut Heuriger Schilling, Langenzersdorferstraße 54, Wien-Strebersdorf,
Vienna (Wien). **GPS:** n48,29856 e16,38421.

2 ⌂€5, guests free ⚡━ ▣ Ch ✎ WC. **Surface:** grassy/gravel.
▣ Feb, Apr, Jun. Aug, Oct ◉ other months
Distance: ⌂Vienna 15km 🚌on the spot.
Remarks: Max. 3 days.

Tourist information Vienna (Wien):
ℹ️ Overnight parking prohibited.
ℹ️ Tourist-Info, Albertinaplatz 1, info.wien.at/. Imperial city, many curiosities,
capital of the classic music.
ℹ️ Wien-Karte. Card gives 72h entrance to public transport and discounts on
museums, curiosities. Available at Tourist-Info and hotels. 🎫 € 19,90.
👁 Spanische Hofreitschule, Michaelerplatz 1. Spanish Riding School, morning-

AT

training can be visited without reservation. ⏰ 9.40-12.30h.

Ⓜ Kunsthistorisches Museum, Maria Theresien-Platz. Important painting collection. ⏰ Tue-Su 10-18h, Thu 10-21h. 🎫 € 14.

☺ Wurstelprater. Amusement park. ⏰ 15/03-15/10 10-24h.

Vorarlberg

| 🅢 | Dornbirn | 24D1 |

Stellplatz Mathis, Obere Härte 27. **GPS**: n47,40577 e9,72492.
3 (7-8-10m) ⛽ € 15 + tourist tax € 1/pp 🚰 💧 Ch 🚐 📶 included. **Location:** Comfortable. **Surface:** grasstiles. ⏰ 01/01-31/12
Distance: 🚶on the spot 🚲 2km 🚴 on the spot 🏃 on the spot.

| 🍴🅢 | Hard 🏔️💧 | 24D1 |

Gasthaus Sternen, Landstraße 49. **GPS**: n47,48442 e9,68698.
8 ⛽ customers free 🚰. **Surface:** asphalted. 🅿️ Mo
Distance: 🚶Bregenz 4,5km ⊗on the spot.

| 🅢 | Schoppernau | 25A2 |

Breganzerwaldstrasse. **GPS**: n47,31674 e10,00835.

10 ⛽free. **Surface:** metalled.
Distance: 🚶600m ⊗on the spot 🛒600m 🚐on the spot 🏃on the spot.
Remarks: Parking ski-lifts.

Tyrol

| ©🅢 | Achenkirch 🏔️💧🍴❄️ | 25C1 |

Wohnmobilhafen Achensee, Achenkirch 17. **GPS**: n47,49947 e11,70655.
20 ⛽from € 14 2 pers incl 🚰 💧 Ch 🔌 WC 🚐included.
Surface: gravel.
⏰ 01/01-31/12
Distance: 🏊on the spot 🛒on the spot.
Remarks: Max. 1 night, dog € 4,50, extra pers € 7, electricity winter € 0,70/kWh.

| ©🅢 | Aschau im Zillertal 🏔️ | 25D1 |

Reisemobilhafen Aufenfeld, Aufenfeldweg. **GPS**: n47,26318 e11,90063.
20 ⛽€ 17 🚰 💧 Ch 🔌 WC 🚐 ⏰ 01/01-31/12

| © | Biberwier 🏔️💧 | 25B1 |

Wohnmobilhafen Arienberg, Marienbergstrasse 15. **GPS**: n47,37512 e10,89082.

15 ⛽€ 15-22, 2 pers.incl, tourist tax € 1,60/pp 🚰 💧 Ch 🔌€3 🚐included.
Surface: grassy. ⏰ 01/01-31/12
Distance: 🚶on the spot 🛒2km 🏃on the spot 🎿on the spot.

| 🅢 | Bichlbach | 25B1 |

Almkopfbahn. **GPS**: n47,42367 e10,78116.

15 ⛽. ⏰ 01/01-31/12
Distance: 🚶5km ⊗on the spot 🚐on the spot 🏃on the spot.
Remarks: Parking next to valley station.

| △ | Breitenwang | 25B1 |

Seespitze. **GPS**: n47,47417 e10,78472.
⛽. ⏰ 01/05-15/10

| △ | Breitenwang | 25B1 |

Sennalpe. **GPS**: n47,48639 e10,83972.
⛽. ⏰ 15/12-15/10

| ©🅢 | Ehrwald | 25B1 |

Tiroler Zugspitze, Obermoos. **GPS**: n47,42731 e10,94096.
10 ⛽ 22-24/20-10h 🚰 💧 Ch 🔌€0,80/kWh WC. ⏰ 01/01-31/12
Distance: 🚶3,5km ⊗on the spot 🚊on the spot 🏃on the spot.

| △ | Feichten/Kaunertal | 25B2 |

Kaunertal. **GPS**: n47,05333 e10,75056.
⛽. ⏰ 01/05-30/09

| ©🅢 | Fügen | 25D1 |

Zillertal Hell, Fügen 212. **GPS**: n47,35934 e11,85198.
10 ⛽against payment 🚰 💧 Ch 📶against payment. **Surface:** metalled.
⏰ 01/01-31/12

| 🅢 | Galtür 🏔️❄️ | 25A2 |

Silvretta-Bundesstraße, B188, Wirl. **GPS**: n46,96570 e10,16390.

⛽€ 20 🚰 💧 Ch. **Surface:** metalled. ⏰ winter
Distance: ⊗100m 🚐on the spot 🏃on the spot 🎿on the spot.
Remarks: Free skibus to Ischgl.

| 🍴🅢 | Galtür ❄️❄️ | 25A2 |

Zeinisee, Zeinisjochstrasse. **GPS**: n46,97824 e10,12738.
⛽€ 23-25,50 incl. 2 pers, dog € 3 🚰 💧 Ch 🔌€0,70/kWh WC 🚐included 📶against payment. **Location:** Rural. **Surface:** grassy/gravel.
⏰ Whitsuntide-05/10
Distance: 🚶Galtür 8,5km ⊗on the spot.
Remarks: Silvrettacard incl., one night stay + € 5.

| 🍴🅢 | Gerlos 🏔️❄️ | 25D2 |

Bauernhof Schönachhof, Schönachtal 242. **GPS**: n47,22639 e12,05476.

10 ⛽€ 15, winter € 30 + tourist tax, dog € 4 🚰 💧 Ch 🔌 WC 🚐.
⏰ 01/01-31/12

AT

Tourist information Gerlos:
☺ Activ Wellness. Free wellness program. ◻ 01/07-30/09.

| 🍴 S | **Gries am Brenner** | 25C2 |

Gasthof Humler-Hof, Nößlach 483. **GPS:** n47,06660 e11,47187.
50 🛏 free ╱═ WC free. ◢ 1km. ◻ 01/01-31/12
Distance: 🚠 Gries 5km ◢ 1km.

| 🎫 S | **Hall in Tirol** 🌊⛺🏔❄ | 25C2 |

Wohnmobilpark, Scheidensteinstraße 24. **GPS:** n47,28444 e11,49665. ⬆.

10 🛏 € 10-15 + € 1/pp + tourist tax ╱═ 🔌 Ch ╱ included.
Surface: metalled. ◻ 01/01-31/12
Distance: 🚠 400m ⊗ 200m Gaststätte 🛒 300m.
Remarks: Max. 1 night.

| 🛟 S | **Heiterwang** 🏔❄ | 25B1 |

Ferienhof Sunnawirt, Mühle 4. **GPS:** n47,44951 e10,74812.
30 🛏 € 7 + tourist tax ╱═ 🔌 Ch ╱ €3 🚿.
Distance: 🚠 200m ⊿ Heiterwanger See 1,6km ⊗ 200m 🛒 200m 🚶 on the spot 🎿 3km 🐕 on the spot.
Remarks: Bread-service.

| 🍴 | **Heiterwang** 🏔❄ | 25B1 |

Enet der Ach 10. **GPS:** n47,44806 e10,74250.
🛏 € 5, guests free. **Surface:** unpaved. ◻ 01/01-31/12
Distance: 🚠 on the spot ⊿ 2km Heiterwanger See ⊗ on the spot.

| 🎫 S | **Hochfilzen** | 26A1 |

Schulgasse. **GPS:** n47,47000 e12,62250. ⬆ ➡.

5 🛏 free ╱═ 🔌 Ch ╱ free WC ⌗. **Surface:** gravel. ◻ 01/05-01/10
Distance: 🐕 on the spot.
Remarks: Behind fire-station, max. 3 nights.

| 🛟 S | **Ischgl** 🏔❄ | 25A2 |

Mathoner Straße 5, Ischgl-Mathon. **GPS:** n46,98967 e10,24751.
15 🛏 € 15 + tourist tax ╱═ 🔌 Ch ╱ ⌗. **Surface:** gravel.
◻ 01/01-31/12
Distance: 🚠 1km ⊗ 100m.
Remarks: Free skibus to Ischgl and Galtür.

| 🍴 S | **Jenbach** | 25D1 |

Gasthof Rieder, Fischl 3. **GPS:** n47,40131 e11,77500.

5 🛏 free ╱═.

Remarks: Guests only.

| 🎫 S | **Kramsach** | 25D1 |

Camping Seehof, Moosen 42. **GPS:** n47,46138 e11,90685.
20 🛏 € 15-19, 2 pers.incl, tourist tax € 2/pp ╱═ 🔌 Ch included ╱ €2,80/kWh 🚿 against payment. ◻ 01/01-31/12
Distance: ⊿ on the spot 🚂 on the spot 🐕 on the spot.

| 🍴 S | **Leutasch** | 25C1 |

Am Kreithlift, Weidach 381. **GPS:** n47,36392 e11,16657.
20 🛏 free, 15/12-15/03 € 22 ╱═ 🔌 Ch ╱ included. ◻ 01/01-31/12
⦿ service: summer
Distance: 🚠 1,5km ⊗ on the spot 🎿 on the spot 🐕 on the spot.
Remarks: Loipenplakette, drying room for skis and sauna included.

| 🛏 | **Matrei** | 26A2 |

Matreier Tauernhaus, Nähe Tauer 22. **GPS:** n47,11833 e12,49778.
20 🛏 € 5/24h. **Surface:** gravel. ◻ 01/05-30/11
Distance: ⊗ on the spot.

| ⛺ S | **Nassereith** | 25B2 |

Roßbach, Roßbach 325. **GPS:** n47,31153 e10,85270.

🛏 € 20,50 ╱═ 🔌 Ch ╱ included. **Surface:** grassy. ◻ 01/01-31/12
Distance: 🛒 500m.

| 🍴 S | **Obsteig** | 25B2 |

Gasthof zum Lenz, Gschwent 282. **GPS:** n47,30930 e10,94482.

6 🛏 € 15 ╱═ 🔌 Ch ╱ ⌗ included. ◻ 01/01-31/12, service 01/05-01/10
Distance: 🚶 on the spot 🐕 on the spot.

| 🎫 S | **Pettneu am Arlberg** 🏔 | 25A2 |

Camping Arlberg, Pettneu am Arlberg 235. **GPS:** n47,14506 e10,33816.
50 🛏 € 15-19 + tourist tax, dog € 3 ╱═ 🔌 Ch included ╱ €1.
◻ 01/01-31/12
Remarks: Winter: skibus.

| 🛏 S | **Pfunds** | 25B2 |

Wohnmobilplatz Via Claudiasee, Rauth 714. **GPS:** n46,95429 e10,51171. ⬆.
🛏 € 10 + € 1,50/pp tourist tax, dog € 1,50 ╱═ €1 🔌 Ch ╱ €0,60/kWh
WC ⌗ sanitary €3/pp 🚿 from €0,50. **Surface:** grassy/metalled.
◻ 01/01-31/12
Distance: 🚠 2km 🚂 on the spot ⊗ 200m 🚴 on the spot 🚶 on the spot.
Remarks: Bread-service.

| 🛏 S | **Schwaz** | 25C1 |

Wohnmobilstellplatz Königfeld, Königfeldweg. **GPS:** n47,34655 e11,70436. ⬆.

10 ⌇€4 ⟋€2 ⛶Ch.▯🏠 **Surface:** asphalted.
◻ 01/01-31/12
Distance: ⟍500m ⟋1,9km ⊗Gaststätte 50m ⛾50m.
Tourist information Schwaz:
👁 Schwazer Silberbergwerk. ◻ 01/05-31/10.

🚲🅂	Seefeld in Tirol	25C1

Wildseepromenade. **GPS:** n47,32486 e11,18718.
⌇free. **Surface:** gravel. ◻ 01/01-31/12
Distance: ⟍200m.

🚐🅂	St.Johann im Tirol	26A1

Michelnhof. **GPS:** n47,51056 e12,40893.
⌇€ 22-32 ⟋⛶Ch ⚡WC ⛽€0,50/time ▨ 📶. **Location:** Rural.
Surface: gravel. ◻ 01/01-31/12
Distance: ⊗on the spot.

🍴🅂	Steinach am Brenner	25C2

Gasthaus Wolf, Brennerstraße 36. **GPS:** n47,06704 e11,48574.
5 ⌇guests free ⟋. **Surface:** asphalted.
Distance: ⟍2km ⊗on the spot.
Remarks: At the old Brennerstraße.

🍴	Stumm	25D1

Gasthof Rißbacher Hof, Ahrnbachstraße 37. **GPS:** n47,27951 e11,89347.

3 ⌇€ 10. ▣ Wed

🍴🅂	Wenns/Piller 🏔❄	25B2

Gasthof Sonne, Piller 41. **GPS:** n47,13581 e10,69390.

5 ⌇€ 5, guests free ⟋. **Surface:** gravel. ◻ 01/01-31/12
Remarks: Altitude 1350m.

⛺	Wiesing	25D1

Inntal. **GPS:** n47,40585 e11,80536.

⌇. ◻ 01/01-31/12

Salzburg

🚲🅂	Altenmarkt im Pongau	26B1

Bauernhof Kellerbauer, Kellerdörfl Palfen 7. **GPS:** n47,37015 e13,42923.
10 ⌇€ 10 ⟋⛶Ch ⚡€2. **Location:** Simple, isolated, quiet.
Surface: grassy/gravel. ◻ 01/01-31/12
Distance: ⟍1,5km.

🚐🅂	Golling	19B6

Wohnmobil-Park Aqua Salza, Mösslstraße 199. **GPS:** n47,59543 e13,17222.⬆.
15 ⌇€ 9,90 + € 1/pp tourist tax ⟋€1/80liter ⛶Ch ⚡€0,50/kWh.
Surface: asphalted. ◻ 01/01-31/12
Distance: ⟍500m ⊗300m.
Remarks: Max. 5 days, check in on arrival.

🚲🅂	Hüttschlag	26B2

Bauernhof Stockham-Camping, See 5. **GPS:** n47,14775 e13,28947.⬆.
5 ⌇€ 15,60, 2 pers.incl ⟋⛶Ch ⚡€1,50 WC ⛽€1. ◻ 01/04-31/10
Distance: ⟍6km ⊗150m ⛾6km.

🍴🅂	Krimml	25D2

Hotel Krimmlerfälle, Wasserfallstraße 42. **GPS:** n47,21617 e12,17185.

10 ⌇€ 11, tourist tax excl., dog € 4 ⟋⛶Ch ⚡(4x)€3.
◻ 15/05-25/10
Distance: ⟍500m ⊗on the spot.

⌇🅂	Leogang	26A1

Leoganger Bergbahnen, Hütten 39. **GPS:** n47,43963 e12,72040.
50 ⌇€ 8 + € 1,10/pp tourist tax ⟋⛶Ch ⚡(9x) WC ⛽€2 📶.
Location: Comfortable, quiet.
Distance: ⟍3,5km ⊗on the spot ⛷on the spot.

⌇🅂	Maria Alm	26A1

Wohnmobilstellplatz Stegerbauer, Stegen 16. **GPS:** n47,39765 e12,90350.

10 ⌇€ 10-12 + tourist tax € 1/pp ⟋⛶Ch ⚡(10x)€2,50. **Surface:** gravel.
◻ 01/01-31/12
Distance: ⟍1km ⟍on the spot ⊗500m ⛾1km ⟍200m 🚶on the spot
⛷1km 🚡on the spot.

🍴🅂	Neukirchen	25D2

Panoramastellplatz, Scheffau 96. **GPS:** n47,23862 e12,24083.

AT

9 ☐€ 7, guests free ⚡🚰Ch ✦€1,50 📶. **Location:** Rural, isolated, quiet. **Surface:** gravel. 📅 01/01-31/12
Distance: 🚶4km ⊗on the spot 🚴Tauernradweg 🎿on the spot ☂on the spot 🏊on the spot.
Remarks: Bread-service.

4 ☐€ 8, guests free. **Location:** Rural, simple. **Surface:** grasstiles. 📅 01/01-31/12
Distance: 🚶1,8km 🚲3,2km ⊗on the spot.

| 🏔 | | **Tweng** | 26C1 |

Landhotel Postgut, Tweng 2. **GPS:** n47,19058 e13,60210.

| 🍴S | **Deutsch Goritz** | 27B3 |

Pechmann's Alte Ölmühle, Ratschendorf 188. **GPS:** n46,75072 e15,81337. ⬆.
15 ☐customers free ⚡➕according consumption. **Surface:** metalled.
Distance: 🚶850m ⊗on the spot.

| 🏔S | **Deutschfeistritz** | 27A2 |

Sportclub Union. GPS: n47,20116 e15,32710.

5 ☐€ 10. **Surface:** metalled. 📅 01/01-31/12
Distance: 🚶on the spot ⊗on the spot.

Styria

| 🏔S | **Bad Gams** 🚴🎪🎯🏞 | 27A3 |

Freizeitzentrums GamsBad, Bad Gams 2. **GPS:** n46,86730 e15,22743.⬆.

6 ☐€5 ⚡🚰Ch. **Surface:** grasstiles/metalled. 📅 01/01-31/12
Distance: 🚶200m ⊗on the spot ⊗200m 🚇100m 🚂200m.
Remarks: Check in at Gamsbad.

20 ☐€ 11, 2 pers.incl ⚡🚰Ch ✦€2 WC ☐included ⊡. **Surface:** grassy.
📅 01/04-01/11
Remarks: At manege, check in on arrival, bread-service.

| 🏔S | **Deutschlandsberg** 🌿🎪🍽🏞 | 27A3 |

Koralmhalle, Höhe Frauentalerstraße 51. **GPS:** n46,81783 e15,22248.⬆.

| ⓒS | **Bad Radkersburg** | 27B3 |

Camping Alt-Weindörfl, Altneudörfl 144. **GPS:** n46,69444 e15,98991.
☐€ 4 + € 3/pp WC included. **Surface:** gravel.
Distance: 🚶750m ⊗on the spot 🚇750m.

| ⓒ | **Bad Waltersdorf** | 27B2 |

Thermenland Camping, Campingplatzweg 316. **GPS:** n47,16246 e16,02296.
10 ☐Mondscheinplätze € 9,50/18-9h, 2 pers. incl. + tourist tax.
📅 01/01-31/12
Distance: 🚶1,6km 🚲3km ⊗Stüberl.

2 ☐free. **Surface:** asphalted. 📅 01/01-31/12
Distance: 🚶200m ⊗on the spot 🚇100m 🚂on the spot.
Remarks: Max. 3 days.

| 🏔S | **Gaishorn am See** | 27A2 |

Sportzentrum, Sieberer Weg, B113. **GPS:** n47,48583 e14,54803.
10 ☐€ 11, 2 pers.incl ⚡🚰Ch ✦(6x)€4 WC ☐included. 🚿 **Surface:** gravel.
📅 15/04-30/09
Distance: 🚶500m 🚲4,6km ⛵Gaishorner See 100m.

| 🏔S | **Gamlitz** | 27B3 |

Wohnmobilstellplatz Gamlitz, Untere Hauptstraße 455.
GPS: n46,72028 e15,56833. ⬆➡.

| 🍴 | **Bad Waltersdorf** | 27B2 |

Gasthof Erhardt, Am Waltersdorfberg 99. **GPS:** n47,16687 e15,98921. ⬆.

AT

30 ⌇€ 20 ⤶liter ⌇Ch⌇stay ⤳€1/2kWh WCincluded. ⛗ **Location:** Rural, comfortable. **Surface:** gravel. ◻ 01/04-31/10
Distance: ⌇1km ⤳5km ⤳on the spot ⨂on the spot ⤳on the spot.
Remarks: Parking at Motorikpark.

| ⌇S | **Gamlitz** | 27B3 |

Buschenschank Loar-Moar, Untere Hauptstraße 21. **GPS:** n46,72196 e15,56495. ➡.

9 ⌇€ 22 ⤶⌇Ch⤳included. **Location:** Rural. **Surface:** grassy. ◻ 01/05-31/10
Distance: ⌇900m ⤳5,5km.

| ⌇S | **Gosdorf** | 27B3 |

Hof Schönwetter, Haus 5. **GPS:** n46,72630 e15,79652.
6 ⌇€ 10 ⤶. **Surface:** grassy. ◻ 01/01-31/12
Distance: ⨂500m ⌇2km.

| ⌇S | **Graz** 🎋🏛🍲 | 27B2 |

Stellplatz Wölfl, Steinfeldgasse 47. **GPS:** n47,06527 e15,42046.
5 ⌇€ 12 ⤳€2/day. **Location:** Simple. **Surface:** asphalted. ◻ 01/01-31/12
◉ Sa-Su
Distance: ⌇1,5km ⤳3,7km.
Remarks: At motorhome dealer, check in during opening hours.

Tourist information Graz:
Ⓜ Freilichtmuseum, Stübing. Open air museum. ◻ 01/04-31/10.
✖ Schloß Eggenberg, Eggenberger Allee 90. ◻ 01/04-31/10 Tue-Su 10-17h.
Ⓣ € 6.

| ⌇S | **Großlobming** | 27A2 |

Murinsel, Teichweg 1. **GPS:** n47,19326 e14,80422.
16 ⌇€ 9/18-10h 2 pers.incl, 1 hour € 1 ⤶⌇Ch⤳included.
Surface: grassy. ◻ 01/01-31/12
Remarks: Reservation in winter peak season.

| ⌇S | **Hieflau** | 27A2 |

Gasthaus zum Harmonika Wald, Wandau 9. **GPS:** n47,62255 e14,75411.
5 ⌇guests free ⤶included. **Surface:** asphalted.
◻ 01/01-31/12 ◉ Wed
Distance: ⌇1,8km ⨂on the spot.

| ⌇S | **Jagerberg** 🏛 | 27B3 |

Am Freibad. GPS: n46,85152 e15,74655.➡.

6 ⌇free ⤶€0,50/60liter ⌇Ch. **Location:** Rural, simple.
Surface: asphalted/gravel.
Distance: ⌇500m ⨂500m ⌇500m.

| ⌇S | **Jagerberg** 🏛 | 27B3 |

Kindergarten Vorplatz, Jagerberg 98. **GPS:** n46,85692 e15,74292.⬆➡.

15 ⌇free ⤶liter ⤳ (1x). **Location:** Rural, simple. **Surface:** gravel.
◻ 01/01-31/12
Distance: ⌇400m ⨂400m ⌇400m ⤳400m.

| ⌇S | **Judenburg** 🏛 | 27A2 |

Erlebnisbad, Fichtenhainstraße. **GPS:** n47,16407 e14,65308.⬆➡.

5 ⌇€ 5 ⤶⌇Ch WCfree. **Surface:** gravel. ◻ 01/01-31/12
Distance: ⌇500m ⨂200m ⌇200m.
Remarks: Check in at swimming pool.

| ⌇S | **Kaindorf** 🏞🏛 | 27B2 |

Buschenschank Schleiss, Obertiefenbach 42. **GPS:** n47,23839 e15,84498.

4 ⌇€ 6, guests free ⤶⌇Ch. **Location:** Rural, simple. **Surface:** asphalted.
◻ 01/03-15/12
Distance: ⨂on the spot.

| ⌇S | **Leutschach** 🏛 | 27B3 |

Buschenschank Krampl, Schloßberg 9. **GPS:** n46,63898 e15,45872.
10 ⌇⤶⌇Ch⤳. ◻ 01/03-30/11
Distance: ⌇6km.

| ⌇S | **Leutschach** 🏛 | 27B3 |

Ölpresse Resch, Schlossberg 89. **GPS:** n46,65170 e15,47114.⬆.
6 ⌇€ 13 ⤳ WCincluded. **Location:** Rural, simple. **Surface:** asphalted.
◻ 01/04-30/11
Distance: ⌇2km.

| ⌇S | **Leutschach** 🏛 | 27B3 |

Weinbau Peter Grill, Kranach 48. **GPS:** n46,68478 e15,47191.⬆.
4 ⌇free ⤶⌇included ⤳€3. **Surface:** grassy. ◻ Easter-01/11
Distance: ⌇4,5km.

| ⌇S | **Liezen** | 27A2 |

Sportzentrum, Friedau. **GPS:** n47,56500 e14,23333.⬆➡.

AT

AT

3 ⌇free ⊐🚰 ⌐€1. **Surface:** gravel. ◻ 01/01-31/12
Distance: 🚶1km 🏊5,3km ⊗300m 🍴1km 🚌on the spot.

| Ⓒ | Mureck ♿ | 27B3 |

Wohnmobilstellplätze Mureck, Hauptplatz 30. **GPS:** n46,70489 e15,77240.➡

5 ⌇€ 12,40-19. **Location:** Urban, simple. **Surface:** metalled.
◻ 01/04-01/11
Distance: 🚶350m 🚲10km.
Remarks: Max. 5 days.

| 🏕 S | Murfeld | 27B3 |

Gasthof Dorfheuriger Rom Thomas, Dorfstrasse 1, Unterschwarza.
GPS: n46,71557 e15,67624.⬆➡.

40 ⌇€ 10 ⊐🚰 Ch 🔌 WC ⊐ 📶included. 🚿 **Location:** Comfortable.
Surface: grassy. ◻ 01/01-31/12
Distance: 🚶200m 🚲2,5km ⊗on the spot.
Remarks: Check in at restaurant, bread-service, wifi code: Camping01, entrance code: camp1.

| 🏕 S | Oberrakitsch | 27B3 |

Ölmühle Sixt, Oberrakitsch 115. **GPS:** n46,73863 e15,74605. ⬆ .

10 ⌇€ 10 ⊐🚰 Ch 🔌 WCincluded. 🚿 **Location:** Rural, simple.
Surface: gravel. ◻ 01/01-31/12
Distance: 🚶1km ⊶on the spot ⊗1km 🍴3km 🚌4km.
Remarks: Bread-service.

| 🏞 S | Passail | 27B2 |

Almenland Stellplatz, Auen 61. **GPS:** n47,28217 e15,55711.⬆.

4 ⌇free ⊐🚰€0,50/60liter ⊐ Ch 🔌 €0,50/kWh. **Location:** Rural, comfortable.
Surface: asphalted. ◻ 01/01-31/12
Distance: 🚶Passail 3,5km.

| 🍴 | Pichl-Kainisch | 19C6 |

Sportstüberl Andrea, Pichl 57. **GPS:** n47,56711 e13,85207.
3 ⌇guests free. **Surface:** metalled. ◻ 01/01-31/12 ◉ Wed

| 🏕 | Pölfing-Brunn 🏊♿ | 27A3 |

Kipferlbad, Badstraße 13. **GPS:** n46,72422 e15,29268. ⬆ .

10 ⌇free. **Location:** Rural, simple. **Surface:** grassy.
◻ 01/01-31/12
Distance: 🚶1km 🏊on the spot ⊗on the spot 🍴1km 🚌1km.

| 🏕 | Riegersburg | 27B2 |

P Seebad. GPS: n46,99677 e15,94107.⬆ .

10 ⌇free. **Location:** Rural, simple. **Surface:** asphalted.
◻ 01/01-31/12
Distance: 🚶500m 🏊on the spot 🍴500m.
Remarks: Swimming pool available.

| 🏕 S | Schwanberg 🏊♿ | 27A3 |

Freibad, Badstraße. **GPS:** n46,76361 e15,20639.

4 ⌇free, 16/05-14/09 € 6 ⊐🚰 Ch 🔌 included. **Surface:** gravel.
◻ 01/01-31/12
Distance: 🚶500m 🏊on the spot ⊗on the spot 🍴500m 🚌500m.

| 🏕 | Soboth ♿ | 27A3 |

Parkplatz Soboth-Stausee. GPS: n46,68142 e15,03805. ⬆ .

🏕free. **Location:** Rural, simple. **Surface:** asphalted.
Distance: 🚶5km 🏊on the spot ⊗200m 🏃on the spot.
Remarks: Parking at artificial lake.

🏕S	St. Stefan im Rosental 🌳	27B2

Schichenauerstraße 6. **GPS:** n46,90634 e15,71431.⬆️➡️

15 🏕free 🚰€1/100liter 🗑Ch ⚡(6x)€0,50/kWh. **Location:** Rural,
comfortable. **Surface:** gravel. ⬛ 01/01-31/12
Distance: 🚶200m ⊗200m 🚂200m.

🏕S	Stadl an der Mur	27A2

Da' Bräuhauser, Steindorf 23. **GPS:** n47,08885 e13,98824.
15 🏕€ 14-18, 2 pers.incl, tourist tax € 1/pp 🚰🗑Ch included ⚡€0,60/kWh
🗑. **Surface:** grassy. ⬛ 01/01-31/12
Distance: 🚶500m.

🏕	Stainz	27A3

Parkplatz 3, Ettendorfer Straße. **GPS:** n46,89377 e15,26823.

3 🏕free. **Surface:** metalled. ⬛ 01/01-31/12
Distance: 🚶100m ⊗100m 🚂100m.

Tourist information Stainz:
ℹ️ Region Süd-Weststeiermark, Hauptplatz 34, www.stainz.at. Das Land des
Schilcher, country of the Austrian rosé wine.
👁 Der Stainzer Flascherlzug. Narrow-gauge steam train. ⬛ 01/05-31/10 Sa-Su 15h.
😊 Ren(nt)t a Traktor, Anton Nettwall, Sommereben 95, St. Stefan ob Stainz.
With a tractor through Schilcherland. 🎫 € 50 1/2 day.

🏕S	Unterlamm 🌳	27B2

Sieglhof, Magland 44. **GPS:** n46,98152 e16,09172.⬆️➡️

10 🏕€ 5 🚰on demand. **Location:** Rural, simple. **Surface:** grassy/gravel.
⬛ 01/01-31/12 ⬛ Tue + Wed
Distance: 🚶4km ⊗on the spot 🚂1,5km 🚌on the spot.

🏕	Veitsch	27A2

Marktgemeindeamt, Obere Hauptstraße 18. **GPS:** n47,57896 e15,48961.⬆️

2 🏕free. **Surface:** asphalted. ⬛ 01/01-31/12
Distance: 🚶300m ⊗100m 🚂100m 🚌100m.

🏕S	Vordernberg	27A2

Hauptplatz 2. **GPS:** n47,48617 e14,99202.⬆️

6 🏕 🚰€1/10minutes 🗑Ch ⚡€1/8h. **Surface:** gravel.
⬛ 01/04-31/10
Distance: 🚶500m ⊗500m 🚂500m 🚌on the spot.

😊S	Vordernberg	27A2

Traktormuseum, Böhlerstraße 8. **GPS:** n47,47364 e14,98741.
5 🏕€ 5, free with a meal 🚰. **Surface:** grassy.
⬛ 01/01-31/12 ⬛ Restaurant: Mo-Tue
Distance: ✈13km ⊗on the spot
Remarks: Parking nearby museum.

Carinthia

🏕	Bad Sankt Leonhard im Lavanttal	27A3

Bachwegbrücke. **GPS:** n46,96037 e14,79358.

8 🏕free. ⬛ 01/01-31/12
Remarks: Parking behind Spar-supermarket.

🏕	Bleiburg	27A3

Grabenstraße. **GPS:** n46,59095 e14,79550.

AT

4 🚐 free. **Surface:** grasstiles. ⏺ 01/01-31/12
Distance: ⊗100m 🚰on the spot 🚮200m.

🚐S **Ferlach** 🗑 27A3
Messeparkplatz Schloß Ferlach. GPS: n46,52633 e14,29750. ⬆→.

30 🚐€ 4/24h 🚰€1/10minutes 🗑Ch ✏(10x)€1/10h. 🚮 **Location:** Urban, simple. **Surface:** metalled. ⏺ 01/01-31/12
Distance: 🚶500m 🚲on the spot ⊗300m 🚰300m 🚮300m.
Remarks: Max. 24h, no camping activities.

🍴 **Glödnitz** 27A3
Gasthof Hochsteiner, Laas Straß2 9. **GPS:** n46,87226 e14,11655.
20 🚐€ 3, guests free. **Surface:** asphalted.
⏺ 01/01-31/12 ⬤ Restaurant: Mo
Distance: ⊗on the spot.

© **Heiligenblut** 26B2
Möllfluss-Camping, Pockhorn 30. **GPS:** n47,02371 e12,86180.
🚐€ 16 2p incl. + tourist tax. **Surface:** asphalted.
⏺ 15/06-01/09

©S **Hermagor** ⛵🏔🏞❄ 26C3
Schluga, Vellach 15. **GPS:** n46,63147 e13,39532.
6 🚐€ 13 2 pers.incl, dog € 3,10 🚰🗑Ch ✏(6x)€3 WC ⎕included.
Surface: gravel. ⏺ 01/01-31/12
Distance: 🚮winter free shuttle to piste.
Remarks: Peak season max. 3 days, max. 7 days.

Tourist information Hermagor:
⬇ Presseggersee. Nature reserve, no motor boats allowed.

🍴S **Kötschach–Mauthen** 26B3
Gasthof Gailberghöhe, Gailberg 3. **GPS:** n46,71525 e12,96753.

70 🚐€ 14,50, 2 pers.incl. 🚰🗑Ch ✏ WC included.
Surface: asphalted/gravel. ⏺ 01/05-15/11, 15/12-15/03
Distance: 🚶7km ⊗on the spot 🚰7km 🎿2km 🚡7km.

⛺ **Ledenitzen** 27A3
Ferien am Walde. GPS: n46,57046 e13,95161.
🚐. ⏺ 01/05-01/10

🍴S **Mörtschach** 26B2
Gasthaus Schwaiger, Mörtschach 35. **GPS:** n46,92287 e12,91348.

4 🚐 guests free 🚰 ✏. **Surface:** grassy.

🍴S **Rosegg** 27A3
Gasthof Roseggerhof, Schulweg 4. **GPS:** n46,59026 e14,02037. ⬆.

30 🚐€ 10,50-12 + € 1,20/pp tourist tax 🚰🗑 ✏included ⎕€2.
Location: Rural, simple. **Surface:** grassy. ⏺ 01/04-01/11
Distance: 🚲8km ⊗on the spot 🚰bakery 150m.

🍴 **Sachsenburg** 26B2
Restaurant Auszeit, Obergottesfeld 79. **GPS:** n46,79959 e13,35137. ⬆.

10 🚐guests free. **Location:** Rural, simple. **Surface:** gravel.
⏺ 01/01-31/12 ⬤ week after Easter, week after All Saints' Day
Distance: 🚲9km ⊗on the spot.

🍴 **Wernberg** 27A3
Landgasthof Fruhmann, Triester Straße 1. **GPS:** n46,62501 e13,92933. ⬆.

5 🚐guests free. **Location:** Rural, simple. **Surface:** gravel.
⏺ 01/01-31/12
Distance: 🚶Villach 6,5km 🚲1,2km ⊗on the spot 🚰bakery + butcher.

🍷S **Zlan** 🍴 26C3
Nagelerhof, Ziebl 4. **GPS:** n46,74042 e13,57707. ⬆.

AT

8 ⌁ € 17,20 + € 1,50/pp tourist tax ⌁ ⊞ Ch ⌁ € 1,50 WC ⌁ included. ⛟
Location: Simple. **Surface:** grassy. ◻ 01/03-31/10
Distance: ⌁ 8km.
Remarks: Not suitable for motorhomes +7m.

Burgenland

△ S	Andau	27B2

Pusztasee. GPS: n47,77536 e17,03265.
⌁ € 17 ⌁ ⊞ Ch ⌁. ◻ 15/04-15/10

▣ S	Bad Tatzmannsdorf ♨	27B2

Thermencamping, Am Campingplatz 1, Oberschützen.
GPS: n47,33912 e16,21892.
15 ⌁ € 13-19,40 + € 1,50/pp tourist tax ⌁ ⊞ Ch ⌁ according consumption
WC ⌁ included ▣. **Surface:** gravel.

⚓ S	Breitenbrunn am Neusiedlersee	27B1

Parkplatz Yachthafen und Bad. GPS: n47,91806 e16,76314.
12 ⌁ € 3,20, € 3,20/pp ⌁ ⊞ Ch. **Location:** Isolated. **Surface:** gravel.
◻ 01/04-31/10
Distance: ⌁ Breitenbrunn 3,8km ⌁ 14km ⌁ on the spot.
Remarks: Service on campsite.

⌁ S	Deutsch Jahrndorf	27B1

Söldnergasse 19. **GPS:** n48,00777 e17,11073. ⬆➡.

17 ⌁ voluntary contribution ⌁ ⊞ Ch. **Surface:** grassy. ◻ 01/04-31/10
Distance: ⌁ 500m ⊗ 500m ⌁ on the spot.
Remarks: Max. 3 nights.

⌁ S	Horitschon	27B2

Weingut Duschanek, Hauptstraße 104. **GPS:** n47,59162 e16,53493. ⬆.

10 ⌁ € 5, guests free ⌁ ⊞ Ch ⌁ € 3 WC. **Surface:** metalled.
◻ 01/01-31/12
Distance: ⌁ 600m ⊗ on the spot ⌁ 600m ⌁ on the spot.

⌁ S	Illmitz	27B2

Wohnmobilstellplatz Pustablick, Ufergasse 42. **GPS:** n47,75851 e16,79606. ⬆.
8 ⌁ voluntary contribution ⌁ ⌁ € 2. **Surface:** grassy. ◻ 01/04-01/11
Distance: ⌁ 900m ⊗ 900m ⌁ bakery 500m.

⌁ S	Jois	27B1

Bioweingut Edelhof, Hauptplatz 6. **GPS:** n47,95922 e16,79012.

5 ⌁ € 15 ⌁ ⊞ Ch ⌁ included. ◻ 01/03-31/10
Remarks: In the courtyard of a medieval farmstead.

⌁	Moschendorf	27B2

P Weinmuseum-Kulturverein Moschendorf, Moschendorf 95.
GPS: n47,05784 e16,47713.
⌁. **Surface:** asphalted. ◻ 01/01-31/12

⌁ S	Oslip	27B1

Kulturzentrum Gasthof Cselly Mühle, Sachsenweg 63.
GPS: n47,84119 e16,62510.
5 ⌁ free ⌁ ⊞ Ch ⌁. **Location:** Isolated. **Surface:** grassy.
◻ 01/01-31/12
Distance: ⌁ 1,2km ⊗ on the spot.
Remarks: Check in on arrival.

⌁ S	Podersdorf	27B1

Weingut Schaller, Frauenkirchnerstraße 20. **GPS:** n47,85032 e16,83934. ⬆.
5 ⌁ € 8 ⌁ ⊞ Ch included ⌁ € 2. **Surface:** grassy.

⌁ S	Podersdorf	27B1

Weingut Sloboda, Alte Satz 1. **GPS:** n47,85020 e16,83091.
11 ⌁ € 10 ⌁ ⊞ Ch ⌁ included. **Surface:** grassy. ◻ 01/03-31/10
Distance: ⌁ 500m ⌁ 13,5km ⌁ 500m Neusiedler See ⌁ 1km.

ITALY

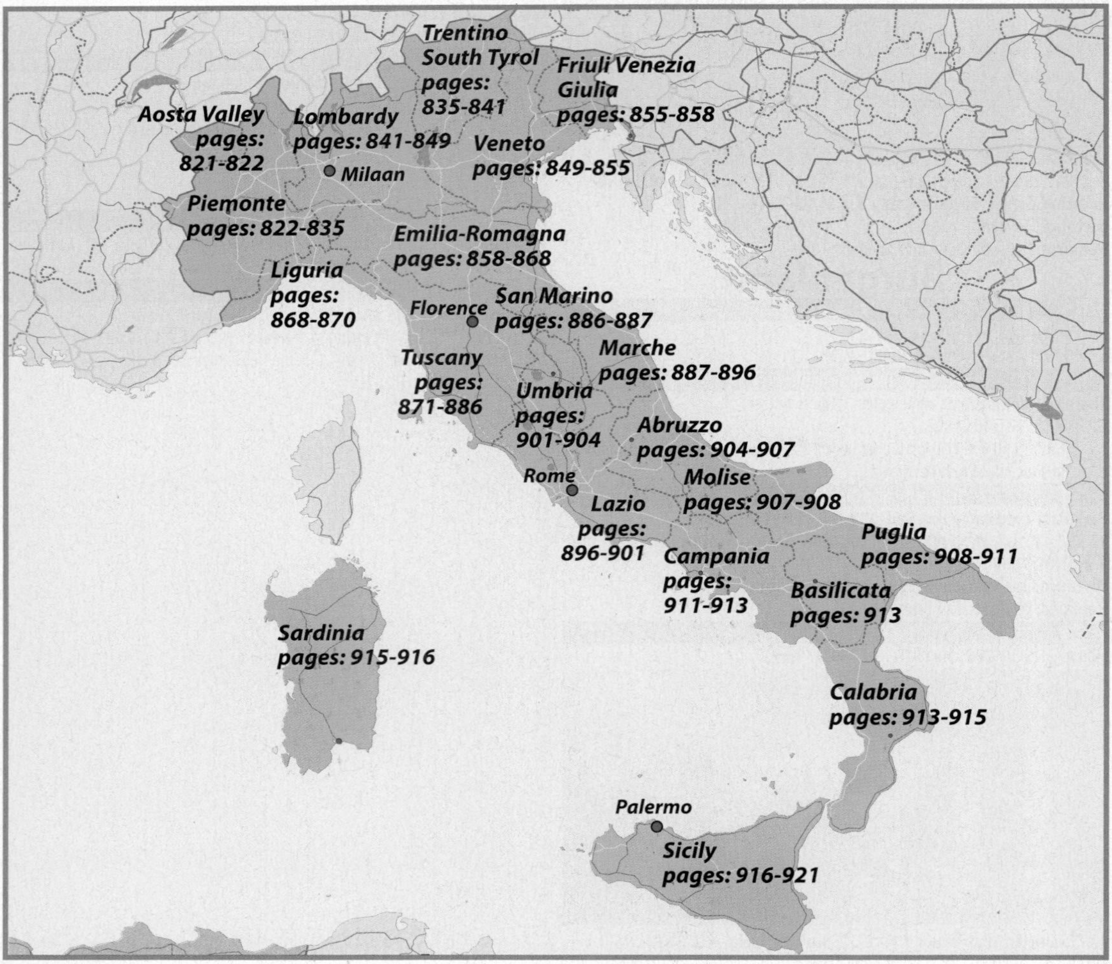

Trentino
South Tyrol
pages: 835-841

Friuli Venezia
Giulia
pages: 855-858

Aosta Valley
pages:
821-822

Lombardy
pages: 841-849

Veneto
pages: 849-855

Milaan

Piemonte
pages: 822-835

Emilia-Romagna
pages: 858-868

Liguria
pages:
868-870

Florence

San Marino
pages: 886-887

Tuscany
pages:
871-886

Marche
pages: 887-896

Umbria
pages:
901-904

Abruzzo
pages: 904-907

Rome

Molise
pages: 907-908

Lazio
pages:
896-901

Campania
pages:
911-913

Puglia
pages: 908-911

Basilicata
pages: 913

Sardinia
pages: 915-916

Calabria
pages: 913-915

Palermo

Sicily
pages: 916-921

Capital: Rome
Government: parliamentarian republic
Official Language: Italian
Population: 61,680,000 (2014)
Area: 301,318 km²

General information
Dialling code: 0039
General emergency: 112
Currency: Euro
Credit cards are accepted almost everywhere.

Regulations for overnight stays
Wild camping is allowed with permission of
municipality, police or property owner when no
problems occur.

Additional public holidays 2015
January 6 Epiphany
April 25 Liberation Day
May 1 Labor Day
June 2 Festa della Republica, National Holiday
August 15 Assumption of the Virgin Mary
November 1 All Saints' Day
November 2 Armistice Day
December 8 Immaculate Conception

Italy

Aosta Valley

S Antey-Saint-André 24A6

Località Filey, SR46. **GPS**: n45,81246 e7,58898.
15 free Ch. **Surface:** metalled. 01/01-31/12
Distance: 850m.

S Aosta 23D6

Via Cadutti del Lavoro. **GPS**: n45,73600 e7,33035.

30 € 12/24h € 1/100liter €2 Ch € 1/kWh. **Location:** Urban, noisy.
Surface: asphalted. 01/01-31/12
Thu-morning closed because of market
Distance: on the spot 4,5km 200m. **Remarks:** Parking closes at 22h.

S Aymavilles 23D6

Strada Comunale del Moulins. **GPS**: n45,70125 e7,23960.
20 € 8/24h . **Surface:** metalled. 01/05-31/10
Distance: on the spot 2km.

S Bionaz 23D5

Area Attrezzata Bosco di Lexert. **GPS**: n45,87458 e7,42381.
€ 10/night Ch.
Remarks: Picnic area at small lake.

S Brusson 24A6

Foyer du Ski, Rue Vollon. **GPS**: n45,76617 e7,71117.

50 € 10/24h Ch included. **Surface:** grassy/metalled.
01/01-31/12
Distance: on the spot.
Remarks: At lake.

S Cervinia/Breuil 24A5

GPS: n45,92614 e7,62026.

50 € 7/24h Ch. **Surface:** asphalted. 01/01-31/12
Distance: 1km Lago Blu 400m on the spot.
Remarks: Shuttle bus to city centre.

S Champorcher 24A6

Area pic-nic, Loc. Chardonney. **GPS**: n45,62153 e7,60654.
free free. **Surface:** grassy/metalled.
Remarks: Nearby parking funicular railway.

S Chatillon 24A6

Area Camper attrezzata Chatillon, Località Chopine. **GPS**: n45,74889 e7,62388.
€ 6/12h Ch . **Surface:** metalled. 01/01-31/12
Distance: historical centre 500m.

S Cogne 23D6

Fraz. Lillaz. **GPS**: n45,59602 e7,38815.

38 € 8,50, Jul-Aug and 24/12-6/1 € 10,50, tourist tax excl Ch.
Surface: asphalted. 01/01-31/12
Distance: 100m on the spot 100m 100m on the spot 1km.
Remarks: Altitude 1650m.

S Cogne 23D6

Fraz. Revettaz. **GPS**: n45,60840 e7,35830.

120 € 8, 1/7-31/8 + 24/12-6/1 € 10 Ch € 2. **Surface:** asphalted.
01/01-31/12 water disconnected in winter

Tourist information Cogne:
Parco Nazionale Gran Paradiso, Vall d'Aosta. Nature reserve, information centres: Dégioz, Rhêmes-Notre-Dame and Cogne.

S Courmayeur 23D6

Funivia Val Veny. **GPS**: n45,81428 e6,95612.
free . **Surface:** metalled. 01/01-31/12
Distance: 3km on the spot.

S Gressoney 24A5

P Weissmatten, Via Bildschocke, Saint Jean. **GPS**: n45,76028 e7,83556.

15/12-31/03 - 01/07-31/08 € 10/24h . **Surface:** asphalted.
01/01-31/12
Remarks: Parking funicular railway.

S Gressoney 24A5

Tschaval, La Trinité. **GPS**: n45,85657 e7,81362.

IT

36 ⬛€ 12/24h, May-Oct € 10 ⬛⬛Ch⬛€3 WC ⬛. **Surface:** metalled. ⬛ 01/01-31/12, 24/24h
Distance: ⬛2 restaurants ⬛300m ⬛on the spot ⬛on the spot ⬛on the spot ⬛200m.

⬛S	Hône ⬛	24A6

Via Raffort. **GPS:** n45,61169 e7,73262.⬛
10 ⬛€8 ⬛⬛Ch⬛included. **Surface:** metalled. ⬛ 01/01-31/12
Distance: ⬛350m ⬛7km.
Remarks: Max. 48h.

⬛S	La Thuile ⬛⬛❄	23D6

Area Azzura. GPS: n45,70823 e6,95335.

75 ⬛€ 12/24h ⬛⬛Ch⬛(45x)€3 ⬛. **Surface:** metalled. ⬛ 01/01-31/12
Distance: ⬛500m ⬛500m ⬛100m.

⬛	Pont-Saint-Martin	24A6

Piazzale Palazzetto dello Sport. GPS: n45,60025 e7,79338.
⬛free. **Surface:** asphalted.
Distance: ⬛1km.

⬛S	Rhemes Notre Dame	23D6

Loc. Chanavey. **GPS:** n45,57960 e7,12392.
⬛€5 ⬛⬛⬛ included. **Surface:** metalled.
Distance: ⬛on the spot.

⬛	Rhemes Notre Dame	23D6

Frazione Bruil. **GPS:** n45,57148 e7,11848.
20 ⬛free. **Surface:** asphalted.

⬛S	Saint-Denis ⬛	24A6

Strada Regionale del Col Saint Pantaléon, Loc. Plaù. **GPS:** n45,77129 e7,56092.
10 ⬛free ⬛⬛Ch⬛free. **Surface:** grasstiles/grassy.
Distance: ⬛16km.

⬛S	Saint-Oyen ⬛❄	23D6

Rue de Flassin. **GPS:** n45,82133 e7,20822.⬛
⬛€ 12/24h ⬛⬛Ch⬛ WC included ⬛€1. ⬛ 01/01-31/12
Distance: ⬛22km ⬛on the spot ⬛on the spot.

⬛S	Torgnon	24A6

Plan Prorion. **GPS:** n45,80397 e7,55490.⬛➡.
25 ⬛€ 8/24h ⬛⬛Ch⬛. **Surface:** asphalted. ⬛ 01/01-31/12
Distance: ⬛50m.

⬛S	Valgrisenche ⬛	23D6

Frazione Bonne. **GPS:** n45,61931 e7,05930.

20 ⬛€ 10/24h ⬛⬛Ch⬛€3. **Surface:** grassy/sand.
Remarks: At weir.

⬛S	Valsavarenche ⬛	23D6

GPS: n45,59229 e7,20839.⬛
⬛€5 /12h ⬛⬛Ch. **Surface:** grasstiles. ⬛ 01/01-31/12
Distance: ⬛100m.
Remarks: Check in at town hall Tabaccheria or Bar Lo Fourquin, with registration number motorhome.

⬛S	Verrès	24A6

Via Stazione. **GPS:** n45,66214 e7,69356.⬛

6 ⬛€5 ⬛⬛free. **Surface:** asphalted.
Distance: ⬛200m ⬛1,5km.

Piedmont

⬛S	Acqui Terme ⬛⬛⬛	31B2

Area comunale, SS456, Viale Einaudi. **GPS:** n44,66533 e8,47228.⬛

150 ⬛€5 ⬛⬛Ch⬛(16x)included WC.⬛
Location: Urban, comfortable, central, noisy. **Surface:** grasstiles/metalled. ⬛ 01/01-31/12
Distance: ⬛1,5km ⬛25km ⬛50m ⬛250m.

⬛S	Aglié	31A1

Via della Gula. **GPS:** n45,36662 e7,76381.
40 ⬛free ⬛free. **Location:** Urban, simple. **Surface:** metalled. ⬛ 01/01-31/12
Distance: ⬛on the spot.

⬛S	Alba ⬛⬛	31A2

Alba Village, Corso Piave 219, loc. San Cassiano. **GPS:** n44,68537 e8,01019.➡

IT

20 ☜ € 8 + € 0,50/pp tourist tax ⛽ € 0,50/30liter ☱ Ch 📶 free 📹.
Location: Urban, comfortable, central. **Surface:** grassy.
◘ 01/01-31/12
Distance: 🚲 2,5km 🏊 1km ⊗ on the spot ⛽ 100m 🚌 on the spot.
Remarks: Nearby Hotel&Camping Alba Village, max. 48h, check in at reception, monitored parking.

☜ S	Alessandria	31B1

Area comunale, Viale Teresa Michel. **GPS:** n44,92075 e8,62722. ⬆.

25 ☜ free ⛽ ☱ Ch. **Location:** Urban, simple. **Surface:** asphalted.
◘ 01/01-31/12
Distance: 🚲 2km 🏊 2km ⊗ on the spot ⛽ 500m 🚌 on the spot.

☜ S	Arona	24B6

Via Michelangelo Buonarotti. **GPS:** n45,76879 e8,54495.
20 ☜ free. **Surface:** metalled. ◘ 01/01-31/12
Distance: 🚲 2km ⊗ 200m ⛽ 2km.

☜ S	Asti 🍇	31B2

Piazza Campo del Palio. **GPS:** n44,89712 e8,21057. ⬆.
>50 ☜ free ⛽ ☱. **Location:** Urban, simple, central, noisy. **Surface:** asphalted.
◘ 01/01-31/12 ◉ Wed-Sa
Distance: 🚲 on the spot ⊗ on the spot ⛽ on the spot.

☜ S	Avigliana 🍇🏔	30D1

Piazzale Grande Torino, Via Pontetto. **GPS:** n45,07342 e7,39075.

☜ free ⛽ ☱ Ch free. **Surface:** asphalted.
Distance: 🚲 1km 🏊 4,6km.
Remarks: Nearby sports complex.

Tourist information Avigliana:
⛩ ◘ Thu.

☜ S	Bairo	31A1

SP 41, Via Cornaletto. **GPS:** n45,38681 e7,75796.

☜ free ⛽ ☱ Ch free. **Surface:** gravel. ◘ 01/01-31/12
Distance: 🚲 200m.

☜ S	Barge	30D2

Via Fiorita. **GPS:** n44,72684 e7,32028. ⬆ ➡.

5 ☜ free ⛽ ☱ Ch free. **Surface:** asphalted.
Distance: 🚲 800m 🚌 on the spot.

☜ S	Battifollo	31A3

Pian del Mondo, Via Crosa. **GPS:** n44,31994 e8,01858. ⬆ ➡.
30 ☜ € 10 ⛽ ☱ Ch ⚡ WC 🚿 included 📶. **Location:** Rural, comfortable.
Surface: gravel. ◘ 01/01-31/12
Distance: 🚲 700m ⛽ 500m.

☜ S	Baveno	24B5

Area Comunale, Piazza Umberto Giordano. **GPS:** n45,91139 e8,50056. ⬆.

40 ☜ € 12/24h ⛽ ☱ Ch WC included. 🚿 **Surface:** metalled.
◘ 01/01-31/12
Distance: 🚲 500m 🏊 2,8km ⛵ Lago Maggiore 300m ⛽ 300m.
Remarks: Behind railway station, max. 72h, no camping activities, weekend: noisy.

☜ S	Bibiana	30D2

Viale Rimembranza. **GPS:** n44,79581 e7,29366.
8 ☜ free ⛽ ☱ Ch. **Location:** Urban, simple. **Surface:** metalled.
Distance: 🚲 500m ⊗ 500m.

☜ S	Biella	24B6

Area Comunale, Piazzale Sandro Pertini. **GPS:** n45,55559 e8,06760. ⬆.

30 ☜ free ⛽ ☱ free. **Location:** Urban. **Surface:** asphalted.

IT

◘ 01/01-31/12
Distance: 🚰on the spot ⊗100m 🚉station 100m.
Remarks: Square next to station F.S San Paolo.

| 🏕 S | Bielmonte 🏔 ⚡ 🍴 | 24B6 |

Piazzale 2, SS232. **GPS:** n45,66250 e8,08472.
8 🚿€3,50 🚰 🗑 Ch included ⚡€3,50.

| 🏕 S | Borgo San Dalmazzo | 31A3 |

P Area Camper, Strada Communale Del Cimitero. **GPS:** n44,32889 e7,49167. ⬆
➡

🚿free 🚰 🗑 Ch free. **Location:** Urban. **Surface:** asphalted.
◘ 01/01-31/12
Distance: 🚰100m.
Remarks: At sports park.

| 🏕 S | Borgosesia | 24B6 |

Piazza Valentino milanaccio, Via Varallo. **GPS:** n45,72005 e8,27408. ⬆

8 🚿free 🚰 🗑 Ch free. **Location:** Urban. **Surface:** asphalted.
◘ 01/01-31/12 ◉ Jun
Distance: 🚰300m.
Remarks: Market Saturday.

| 🏕 S | Candelo | 24B6 |

Area Comunale, Via C. Pavese/Via F. Bianco. **GPS:** n45,54244 e8,11524. ⬆

10 🚿free 🚰 🗑 Ch free. **Location:** Urban, quiet. **Surface:** gravel.
◘ 01/01-31/12
Distance: 🚰400m ⊗400m 🚉100m.
Remarks: Nearby sports center.

| 🏕 S | Candelo | 24B6 |

Area Ricetto, Via Mulino. **GPS:** n45,54624 e8,11573. ⬆

25 🚿free 🚰 🗑 Ch ⚡ 📶free. **Location:** Comfortable. **Surface:** metalled.
◘ 01/01-31/12
Distance: 🚰400m ⊗400m.

| 🏕 S | Canelli 🌿 🏛 | 31B2 |

Piazza Unione Europea. GPS: n44,72039 e8,29369. ⬆

15 🚿free 🚰 🗑 Ch free. **Location:** Urban, simple, noisy. **Surface:** asphalted.
◘ 01/01-31/12
Distance: 🚰500m ⊗on the spot 🛒on the spot 🚉on the spot.

| 🏕 S | Cannobio | 24C5 |

Area Comunale, Via Al Fiume / Via San Rocco. **GPS:** n46,06179 e8,69242. ⬆➡

20 🚿€ 15/24h 🚰 🗑 Ch WC free. 🅿 **Location:** Rural. **Surface:** grasstiles.
◘ 01/01-31/12
Distance: 🚰500m 🛒on the spot ⊗500m 🛒300m.
Remarks: Along river, max. 3 days.
Tourist information Cannobio:
🛈 Su.

| 🏕 S | Carcoforo 🌿 🏔 ⚡ ☀ | 24B5 |

Le Giare, SP11, Loc. Tetto Minocco. **GPS:** n45,90769 e8,05130. ⬆

100 🚿€ 10/day, € 15/weekend, € 40/week 🚰 🗑 Ch free ⚡ (16x)€ 1,50
WC 🗑€ 1. 🚿 **Surface:** grassy. ◘ 01/03-30/09
Distance: 🚰on the spot ⊗50m 🛒300m.
Remarks: Along the Egua river.

| 🏕 S | Casale Monferrato 🌿 🏛 | 31B1 |

Palazzetto dello Sport Paolo Ferraris, Via Visconti. **GPS:** n45,12556 e8,46194.
✈.

15 🛏free 🚰💧 in shopping centre. **Location:** Rural. **Surface:** asphalted.
🅿 01/01-31/12
Distance: 🚶1,5km 🚲3,6km ⊗200m 🚰200m.
Remarks: At sports centre.

| 🏕 | Casale Monferrato 🌿⛲ | 31B1 |

Parcheggio Castello, Piazza Castello. **GPS:** n45,13722 e8,44806. ⬆.

>10 🛏free. **Location:** Urban, simple, central, noisy. **Surface:** asphalted.
🅿 Tue, Fri 6-16h (market)
Distance: 🚶200m 🚲4km ⊗100m 🚰250m 🛒on the spot 🚌on the spot.

| 🏕S | Casaleggio Boiro | 31B2 |

Via Castello. **GPS:** n44,63354 e8,73254. ⬆➡.

8 🛏free 🚰🔌Chfree 🧹 (6x)included. **Location:** Rural, comfortable, quiet.
Surface: gravel. 🅿 01/01-31/12
Distance: 🚶250m 🚲10km ⊗150m 🚰250m.

| 🏕S | Castelletto Stura | 31A2 |

Via Cuneo. **GPS:** n44,44194 e7,63444.

🛏free 🚰🔌free. **Surface:** gravel.
Remarks: Nearby sports park.

| 🏕 | Castiglione Falletto | 31A2 |

Area comunale, Piazzale Muntelier. **GPS:** n44,62379 e7,97486. ⬆.

10 🛏free 🚰🔌Chfree 💧. **Location:** Rural, comfortable, quiet.
Surface: metalled. 🅿 01/01-31/12
Distance: 🚶100m ⊗100m 🚰100m.

| 🏕S | Castiglione Tinella | 31B2 |

Camperstop Ai Ciuvin, Agriturismo, Strada Manzotti 3.
GPS: n44,73357 e8,18140. ⬆.

12 🛏€ 20 🚰🔌Ch 🧹 WC 🚰. **Location:** Rural, comfortable, isolated, quiet.
Surface: grassy. 🅿 01/01-31/12
Distance: 🚶15km 🚲20km ⊗on the spot 🚰15km.
Remarks: Max. 48h.

| 🏕S | Cavour | 30D2 |

Via Vigone. **GPS:** n44,78766 e7,37660. ⬆➡.

18 🛏€ 5/24h 🚰🔌Chfree. **Surface:** metalled.
Distance: 🚶400m ⊗100m.

| 🏕S | Ceresole Reale | 30D1 |

Borgata Chiapili Inferiore, SP50. **GPS:** n45,45142 e7,18587. ⬆.
🛏€ 8 🚰€4 🔌Ch 🧹€3. **Surface:** unpaved.
Distance: 🚶4km ⊗Ristorante Lo Sciatore 🚰2km.
Remarks: Along the Orco river, national Park 'Gran Paradiso'.

| 🏕S | Ceresole Reale | 30D1 |

Borgota Villa, SP50. **GPS:** n45,44053 e7,21066.

40 🛏free 🚰WC free. **Surface:** grassy/gravel.
Distance: 🚶Ceresole Reale 2km ⛵on the spot ⊗200m.
Remarks: At lake, national park 'Gran Paradiso', altitude 1350m.

🚐S **Cesana Torinese** 🏔❄ 30D2

Area Sosta Camper Casa Cesana, Viale Sen. Bouvier. **GPS**: n44,94782 e6,79516. ⬆.

12 🛏 € 10/24h 🚰 🔌 Ch included 🔌 (12x)€3/day,6Amp. **Surface**: asphalted. ⬛ 01/01-31/12
Distance: 🛒300m ⊗50m 🍴100m.

🚐S **Cherasco** 🍄🏕 31A2

Parking Area Camper, Piazza Giovanni Paolo II. **GPS**: n44,64946 e7,85529. ⬆.

9 🛏 free 🚰 🔌 Ch free 🔌 (8x)against payment WC.
Location: Rural, simple, quiet. **Surface**: asphalted. ⬛ 01/01-31/12
Distance: 🛒400m 🏊 3,7km ⊗200m 🔌300m.
Remarks: Max. 48h.

🚐S **Chianocco** 30D1

Area Camper Giraude. **GPS**: n45,14110 e7,16592. ⬆➡.
20 🛏 €3 - €6 🚰 🔌 Ch WC. **Location**: Rural, comfortable.
Surface: grassy/gravel.
Distance: 🛒1km.

🚐S **Chieri** 31A1

Piazza Quarini, via Bernardo Vittone. **GPS**: n45,00488 e7,82724.

12 🛏 free 🚰 🔌 Ch free. **Surface**: asphalted. ⬛ 01/01-31/12
Distance: 🛒on the spot 🚌200m > Turin.
Remarks: Behind Barracks, tuesday market.

🚐S **Chieri** 31A1

Strada San Silvestro. **GPS**: n45,01460 e7,83214. ⬆.
10 🛏 free 🚰 🔌 Ch free. **Location**: Simple. **Surface**: asphalted.
Distance: 🛒on the spot.

🚐S **Chiusa di Pesio** 31A3

Via Provinciale (SP42). **GPS**: n44,27233 e7,66361.

8 🛏 €4 🚰 🔌 Ch.
Distance: 🏊on the spot ⊗300m 🔌700m 🚌on the spot 🚶on the spot.

🚐S **Chiusa di San Michele** 30D1

Via Pragallo. **GPS**: n45,10294 e7,33034. ⬆.
5 🛏 €7 🚰 🔌 Ch 🔌 included. **Surface**: concrete. ⬛ 01/01-31/12
Distance: 🚲8km ⊗600m.
Remarks: Max. 48h, to be paid at Uffici Comunali, Piazza Bauchiero 2.

🚐S **Chivasso** 31A1

Piazza Libertini, Via Gerbido. **GPS**: n45,18514 e7,89296. ⬆.

🛏 free 🚰 €2 🔌. **Location**: Urban. **Surface**: asphalted.
Distance: 🛒300m 🔌Carrefour 100m.
Remarks: Parking swimming pool.

🚐S **Collegno** 31A1

Collegno Area Sosta Camper, Corso Pastrengo. **GPS**: n45,08070 e7,58313. ⬆.

30 🛏 free 🚰 €0,50 🔌 Ch 🔌 €0,50. **Surface**: asphalted.
Distance: 🚲4km 🚌on the spot.
Remarks: Coins at Autolavaggio Il Draghetto, video surveillance.

🚐S **Cortemilia** 31B2

Strada San Roco. **GPS**: n44,57848 e8,18567.
10 🛏 free 🚰 🔌 Ch free. **Location**: Simple. **Surface**: gravel.
Distance: 🛒500m ⊗500m.
Remarks: Max. 48h.

🚐S **Cravagliana** 24B5

Pian delle Fate, Loc. Brugarolo, SP di Valle Mastallone. **GPS**: n45,85223 e8,22473. ⬆.

IT

826 *Italy*

30 ☕ € 14/24h ⛽ 🚰 Ch ⚡ (4x) WC ⬛included. **Surface:** grassy.
⬛ 15/03-15/10
Distance: 🚶on the spot ⊗on the spot.

| 🏔S | Crissolo | 30D2 |

Via Ruata. **GPS:** n44,69771 e7,15931.
10 ☕ € 5 ⛽ 🚰 Ch WC included. **Location:** Simple. **Surface:** gravel.
Distance: ⊗on the spot.

| 🌿S | Cuceglio | 31A1 |

Area Camper Erbaluce, Via Porta Pia 69/71. **GPS:** n45,34724 e7,81168.
☕free ⛽. **Surface:** metalled.

| 🏔S | Cuneo 🌺 ❄ | 31A3 |

Via Discesa Bellavista. **GPS:** n44,39495 e7,54878. ⬆➡.

☕free ⛽🚰 Chfree. **Surface:** asphalted.
Distance: 🚶250m.
Remarks: Dir Torino/Saluzzo, before the old bridge over the Stura river.

Tourist information Cuneo:
⛺ Piazza Galimberti. ⬛ Tue.

| 🏔S | Donato | 24A6 |

Area Camper Fabrizio de André, Via S. Pertini, SP405. **GPS:** n45,52774 e7,90944.
⬆.

6 ☕ € 3/night ⛽ 🚰 WC free. **Location:** Rural. **Surface:** grasstiles.
⬛ 01/01-31/12
Distance: 🚶300m ⊗300m.
Remarks: Pay at Tabaccheria in the village.

| 🏔S | Entracque | 31A3 |

Area C'era una Volta, SS22. **GPS:** n44,25151 e7,38975. ⬆.

20 ☕ € 15 ⛽ 🚰 Ch ⚡ included WC ⬛€5/day 📶.
Surface: unpaved.
⬛ 01/01-31/12
Distance: 🚶1km 🏊river-beach ⊗on the spot 🚌> Cuneo 🚲on the spot.

| 🏔S | Entracque | 31A3 |

Parcheggio Camper Real Park, Ponterosso. **GPS:** n44,26111 e7,37750. ⬆.

66 ☕ € 6 ⛽ ⚡ included. **Surface:** grassy.
Distance: 🚶3km ⊗on the spot 🚌on the spot 🚲6km.
Remarks: Recreation park, max. 2 days.

| 🏔S | Entracque | 31A3 |

Via del Mulino. **GPS:** n44,23389 e7,39723.
60 ☕ € 12/24h, € 20/48h ⛽ 🚰 ⚡ (50x)included.
Distance: 🚶300m.

| 🏔S | Fenestrelle | 30D1 |

Le Casermette. GPS: n45,03671 e7,05090.
25 ☕ € 10 ⛽ 🚰 Ch ⚡ € 3. **Surface:** unpaved.

| 🏔S | Fenestrelle | 30D1 |

GPS: n45,03889 e7,04583.

9 ☕free. **Surface:** grassy.
Remarks: Next to cemetery.

| 🏔S | Frabosa Soprana 🏔 | 31A3 |

Grotta di Bossea, Loc.Bossea 10. **GPS:** n44,24077 e7,83939. ⬆.
5 ☕free ⛽ 🚰 Chfree WC. **Location:** Rural, simple, isolated.
Surface: asphalted. ⬛ 01/01-31/12
Distance: 🚶12km 🚌on the spot ⊗on the spot 🍴12km 🥾on the spot.
Remarks: Parking at the caves.

| 🏔 | Garessio | 31A3 |

Area Comunale, Str.Provinciale del Colle di San Bernardo (P582).
GPS: n44,19927 e8,02587. ⬆.

30 ☕free ⛽ 🚰 Chfree. **Location:** Rural, simple. **Surface:** asphalted.
⬛ 01/01-31/12
Distance: 🚶1km 🏊22km ⊗1km 🍴1km.

| 🏭S | Genola | 31A2 |

Grosso Vacanze, Via Divisione Alpina Cuneense 2, SS20. **GPS:** n44,59751 e7,65982.
☕free ⛽🚰Ch⚡. **Surface:** metalled. ⬛ 01/01-31/12
Remarks: Motorhome dealer, accessory shop.

| 🏔S | Giaveno | 30D1 |

SP187, via Torino. **GPS:** n45,04154 e7,36096.

IT

⏚free 🚰🝙free. **Surface:** asphalted.
Distance: ⊗100m.

🝙S **Grinzane Cavour** 31A2
Piazza Ugo Genta, Via Bricco. **GPS:** n44,65515 e7,98936. ➡️.

3 ⏚free 🚰🝙 Ch free. **Location:** Rural, simple, isolated, noisy.
Surface: asphalted. 🔲 01/01-31/12
Distance: 💧500m ⊗500m 🛒2km 🚶on the spot.

🝙S **Ivrea** 24A6
La Dora d'Ivrea, Via Dora Baltea. **GPS:** n45,46334 e7,87621.

8 ⏚€5 🚰€3 🝙Ch. **Surface:** asphalted. 🔲 01/01-31/12
Distance: 💧500m ⚓4,5km 🛒Ipermercato 800m 🚌350m.
Remarks: Beside river.

S **Locana** 31A1
Via Nusiglie. **GPS:** n45,41361 e7,46278.
€5/24h 🚰 ⚡€3/24h WC.

🝙S **Macugnaga** 🏔️ 24A5
Pecetto, Di Iacchine Pierluigi Loc. Pecetto. **GPS:** n45,97015 e7,95352. ⬆️.

28 ⏚€10, 2 nights €15 🚰🝙Ch WC free. 🛁 **Location:** Rural, simple, quiet.
Surface: concrete. 🔲 01/05-30/11
Distance: 💧1km ⊗100m 🛒500m 🚌100m 🚶on the spot.
Remarks: At ski-lift.

🝙S **Madonna del Sasso** 24B6
Area Comunale, Via Santuario, Fraz. Boleto. **GPS:** n45,78974 e8,37222. ⬆️.

8 ⏚free 🚰🝙Ch free. **Surface:** grasstiles. 🔲 01/01-31/12
Distance: 💧200m ⛵Lago d'Orta 700m ⊗100m 🚌50m.
Remarks: Narrow entrance, view at Lago d'Orta.

🝙 **Maglione** 🌿 31A1
SP78, Via Cigliano. **GPS:** n45,34338 e8,01456.

20 ⏚free. **Surface:** grassy.
Distance: 💧on the spot ⊗50m.
Remarks: Art city.

🝙S **Marsaglia** 31A2
Via della Stazione, SP115. **GPS:** n44,45228 e7,97929.
18 ⏚€13 🚰🝙Ch ⚡WC. **Surface:** asphalted/grassy. 🔲 01/01-31/12
Distance: 💧on the spot.
Remarks: Inspection june 2013: closed because of renovation.

🝙S **Melle** 30D2
SP8. **GPS:** n44,56245 e7,31739. ⬆️.
25 ⏚€3-€5 🚰🝙Ch WC included.
Location: Comfortable. **Surface:** metalled.
Distance: ⊗250m.

🝙S **Mirabello Monferrato** 31B1
SS31. **GPS:** n45,03016 e8,52946. ⬆️.

8 ⏚free 🚰€2 🝙Ch€1. **Location:** Simple, isolated, quiet.
Surface: asphalted. 🔲 01/01-31/12
Distance: 💧900m ⚓10km ⊗800m 🛒50m 🚌50m.

🝙S **Mombarcaro** 31A2
SP103. **GPS:** n44,46900 e8,08352.
8 ⏚€5 🚰🝙Ch ⚡included. **Location:** Rural, comfortable.
Surface: metalled. 🔲 01/01-31/12
Distance: ⊗500m.

🝙S **Mombaruzzo** 31B2
Club Agrisportivo Mombaruzzo, SP4. **GPS:** n44,77993 e8,45061.
⏚€10 🚰🝙Ch ⚡€2 WC. 🔲 01/01-31/12
Distance: 💧1,5km.

🝙S **Mondovì** 🌿 31A3
Piazza le Giardini. **GPS:** n44,39430 e7,82370. ⬆️➡️.
⏚free 🚰🝙Ch free. **Location:** Simple, noisy. **Surface:** asphalted.
🔲 01/01-31/12

Distance: 🚶500m.
Remarks: Nearby bus station, parking under railway bridge.

| 🔲S | Mondoví 🌿 | 31A3 |

Piazza Republica. **GPS:** n44,38964 e7,81930.⬆️.
🏕free. **Location:** Urban, simple, central. **Surface:** asphalted.
🅾 01/01-31/12
Distance: 🚶400m 🚲5km ⊗50m 🚊100m 🚌on the spot.
Remarks: Nearby the old station.

| 🔲S | Mondoví 🌿 | 31A3 |

Mondovicino Outlet Center. **GPS:** n44,41889 e7,84966.⬆️➡️.
🏕free 🔌 Ch. **Location:** Simple. **Surface:** asphalted. 🅾 25/12, 01/01
Distance: 🚶4km 🚲1,2km 🚊on the spot.
Remarks: Parking at Outlet Center and Centro Commercial.

| 🔲S | Mongrando | 24A6 |

Area Comunale, Via dei Giovanni. **GPS:** n45,52543 e8,00595.⬆️.

15 🏕€4/24h 🔌 Ch ⚡included. 🐾 **Location:** Urban, quiet.
Surface: grasstiles. 🅾 01/01-31/12
Distance: 🚶900m.
Remarks: At sports centre.

| 🔲S | Montiglio Monferrato | 31A1 |

Via Padre Carpignano. **GPS:** n45,06261 e8,10045.
25 🏕free 🔌.

| 🔲S | Niella Tanaro | 31A2 |

Agriturismo i Fornelli, Via Fornello 1. **GPS:** n44,41418 e7,90988.⬆️.

3 🏕€5 🔌€3,50 🔌 Ch ⚡€2,50/24h WC 🚽. **Location:** Rural, simple,
isolated, quiet. **Surface:** grassy/gravel. 🅾 01/01-31/12
Distance: 🚶4km 🚲2km ⊗1km 🚊10km.
Remarks: Farm products.

| 🔲S | Nizza Monferrato 🌿 | 31B2 |

Parking Camper Piazzale S.Pertini, Piazzale Sandro Pertini.
GPS: n44,77140 e8,35346.⬆️.

14 🏕€5 🔌 Ch ⚡ Service, electricity incl. €3. 🐾 **Location:** Urban,
comfortable, central, quiet. **Surface:** grassy. 🅾 01/01-31/12
Distance: 🚶200m 🚲20km ⊗500m 🚊500m.
Remarks: Gate closed, first call Motorhome Club Nicese between 9-20h.

| 🔲S | Novi Ligure | 31B2 |

Viale Pinan Cichero, zona stadio comunale. **GPS:** n44,77006 e8,78200.⬆️.

25 🏕free 🔌 Ch free. **Location:** Urban, simple, noisy. **Surface:** asphalted.
🅾 01/01-31/12
Distance: 🚶1,5km 🚲2km ⊗on the spot 🚊600m.
Remarks: Parking gymnasium.

| 🔲S | Occimiano | 31B1 |

Via Circonvallazione. **GPS:** n45,05834 e8,50940.⬆️.

5 🏕€5 🔌 Ch ⚡included. **Location:** Rural, comfortable.
Surface: asphalted. 🅾 01/01-31/12
Distance: 🚶250m 🚲15km ⊗250m 🚊400m.
Remarks: To be paid at bar Concordia.

| 🔲S | Oggebbio | 24C5 |

Fiesta, Via Martiri Oggebbiesi 6. **GPS:** n45,99680 e8,65304.⬆️➡️.

20 🏕€18/24h 🔌 Ch ⚡ WC included 🚽€1 🚿€5,/24h.
Location: Luxurious. **Surface:** gravel.
🅾 01/06-31/12
Distance: ⚓on the spot ⊗700m.
Remarks: Attention: narrow road, view on Lago Maggiore.

| 🔲S | Omegna | 24B5 |

Lido di Omegna, Via Caduti di Bologna. **GPS:** n45,86340 e8,39840.⬆️.

25 🏕€8-15 🔌 Ch ⚡€3. **Surface:** metalled. 🅾 01/01-31/12
Distance: 🚶1,8km ⚓beach.
Remarks: Caution key electricity € 30.

IT

🏕️S **Ormea** 🌿🏔️🎠 **31A3**

Via Orti della Rana. **GPS:** n44,14532 e7,90751.➜.

10 🅿️€ 10 🚰🔌Ch. **Location:** Rural, comfortable, quiet. **Surface:** grasstiles.
🚾 01/01-31/12
Distance: 🛒1km ⊗500m 🚉1km.

🏕️S **Oropa** 🌿⛵🎠 **24A6**

Area di Santuari, Via Santuario di Oropa. **GPS:** n45,62864 e7,97530.⬆️➜.

31 🅿️€ 10, 01/05-30/09 € 15, 01/07-31/08 € 21 🚰🔌Ch 🧹 WC 🗑️.
Location: Rural. **Surface:** metalled. 🚾 01/01-31/12 ❄️ snow
Distance: ⊗500m.

🏕️ **Orta San Giulio** **24B6**

Via Panoramica. **GPS:** n45,79729 e8,41527.⬆️.

20 🅿️€ 10/24h. 🏠 **Surface:** asphalted. 🚾 01/01-31/12
Distance: 🛒500m 🏊Lago d'Orta 500m 🚉100m.

🏕️S **Ovada** **31B2**

Via Gramsci. **GPS:** n44,64084 e8,64920.➜.

25 🅿️free 🚰🔌free. **Location:** Simple, central. **Surface:** metalled.
🚾 01/01-31/12
Distance: 🛒300m ⚓3km ⊗100m 🚉500m.

🏕️S **Piatto** **24B6**

Area Comunale, Fraz. Malina. **GPS:** n45,58908 e8,13630.⬆️.

10 🅿️free 🚰🔌Ch. **Location:** Urban. **Surface:** asphalted.
🚾 01/01-31/12
Remarks: At sports park.

🏕️S **Pietraporzio** **30D3**

Via Nazionale, SS21. **GPS:** n44,34868 e7,01831.
10 🅿️€ 5/24h 🚰🔌Ch 🧹. **Surface:** asphalted. 🚾 01/01-31/12

🏕️S **Pollone** ⛵🎠 **24A6**

Burcina di Pollone, Via Felice Piacenza. **GPS:** n45,58548 e8,00521.⬆️➜.

20 🅿️€ 10/24h 🚰🔌Ch 🧹 WC included 🗑️€2. 🏠 **Location:** Rural,
comfortable. **Surface:** grasstiles. 🚾 01/01-31/12
Distance: 🛒600m ⊗on the spot.
Remarks: At parco Naturale Burcina.

🏕️S **Pombia** **24C6**

Safari Park, SS 32 km 23,4. **GPS:** n45,64167 e8,61740.
🅿️free 🚰 WC. **Surface:** asphalted.

🏕️S **Ponderano** **24B6**

Area Comunale, Strada Vicinale al Cimitero. **GPS:** n45,53683 e8,04949.⬆️.

10 🅿️free 🚰🔌free. **Location:** Urban, simple. **Surface:** gravel.
🚾 01/01-31/12
Distance: 🛒400m.
Remarks: Nearby sports park.

🏕️S **Pont Canavese** **31A1**

Via Roma. **GPS:** n45,42153 e7,60020.
12 🅿️€ 7 🚰€2 🔌Ch 🧹€2. **Surface:** grassy. 🚾 01/01-31/12
Distance: 🏊on the spot.
Remarks: Max. 48h.

🏕️S **Pontechianale** **30D2**

Area Camper, Fraz Maddalena. **GPS:** n44,62158 e7,02776.
🅿️€ 8/24h 🚰🔌. **Surface:** grassy.

🏕️ **Pontechianale** **30D2**

Chianle, SP 251. **GPS:** n44,65055 e6,99280.
15 🅿️free. **Location:** Simple, isolated. **Surface:** grassy/gravel.
Distance: 🛒4km 🏊on the spot.

🏕️S **Pragelato** **30D1**

Villagio GoFree, SS23. **GPS:** n45,02187 e6,94914.
🅿️€ 16-21, 4 pers.incl 🚰🔌Ch 🧹€1,50 WC 🗑️📶. 🚾 01/01-31/12

Distance: 🚵 on the spot ⚲ on the spot 🏊 on the spot ⛷ on the spot.
Remarks: Spa, ski, tennis, golf.

🏕 S   Pragelato   30D1
Fraz. Pattemouche, Valtroncea. **GPS:** n44,98736 e6,92090.

🏕 € 8/24h 🚰 🗑 Ch 🚿. **Surface:** unpaved. 🅿 01/01-31/12
Distance: 🏊 on the spot.
Remarks: Former campsite, service only during winter period.

🏕 S   Prali ❄   30D2
Fraz.Ghigo. **GPS:** n44,89176 e7,04956.⬆.

🏕 free 🚰 🗑 Ch free. **Surface:** grassy.
Distance: 🚶 300m ⛵ on the spot.
Remarks: Altitude 1450m, along river.

🏕 S   Prarostino   30D2
Porto di Montagne, Via Piani. **GPS:** n44,86488 e7,26970.⬆.
15 🏕 €7 🚰 🗑 Ch 🚿 included. **Location:** Comfortable.
Surface: grassy/gravel.
Distance: ⊗300m 🍺200m.

🏕 S   Prato Nevoso ❄   31A3
Area Stalle Lunghe, Via Corona Boreale. **GPS:** n44,25200 e7,78192.⬆.

🏕 € 15-20 🚰 🗑 Ch 🚿. **Surface:** asphalted. 🅿 01/01-31/12
Distance: 🚶 on the spot ✈ A6 33km ⊗on the spot 🍺50m 🏊 on the spot.

🏕   Prato Nevoso ❄   31A3
Piazza G. Dodero. **GPS:** n44,25200 e7,78192.⬆➡.

10 🏕 free. **Location:** Rural, simple, central. **Surface:** asphalted.
🅿 01/01-31/12

Distance: 🚶 on the spot ⊗on the spot 🏊 on the spot ⛷ on the spot.

🍴 S   Rimasco   24B5
Il Laghetto, Strada del Lago. **GPS:** n45,86109 e8,06450.⬆.

20 🏕 € 10/24h 🚰 🗑 Ch 🚿 €2/day WC 🗑 included. **Surface:** grassy.
🅿 01/05-30/09 ◉ Restaurant: Tue
Distance: ⛵on the spot ⊗on the spot.

🍴 S   Riva Valdobbia   24A6
Area Lo Chalet, Fraz Gabbio. **GPS:** n45,83467 e7,95469.⬆.

48 🏕 € 13/24h 🚰 🗑 Ch 🚿 €3 WC included 🗑. **Surface:** grassy/metalled.
🅿 01/04-31/10
Distance: ⛵on the spot ⊗on the spot.
Remarks: Along river.

🏕 S   Rivoli   31A1
Campo sportivo, Via Isonzo. **GPS:** n45,08147 e7,51037.⬆.

🏕 free 🚰 🗑 Ch free. **Surface:** asphalted.
Distance: 🚶 1km ✈ 1,5km.
Remarks: Parking sports park.

🏕   Rivoli   31A1
Piazzale Mafalda di Savoia. **GPS:** n45,06994 e7,51097.
🏕 free. **Surface:** asphalted.
Distance: 🚶 500m ✈ 2,5km.
Remarks: Parking castle.

🏕 S   Romano Canavese   31A1
Piazza Bachelet, via Montalenghe, SP82. **GPS:** n45,38782 e7,86396.⬆.

8 🏕 free 🚰 🗑 🚿 (2x). **Surface:** grassy/metalled. 🅿 01/01-31/12

IT

Distance: 🏄 2,2km.

🛁 S	Rosta	31A1

Via Buttigliera Alta 2, Via Piave. **GPS:** n45,07106 e7,46333.
🛁free 🚰 €2 ♨ Ch€2. **Surface:** asphalted. 🔓 01/01-31/12
Distance: 🍴on the spot 🚃train > Turin 19min.

🛁 S	Saluzzo 🌿	31A2

Area Bodoni, Via Olivero Matteo. **GPS:** n44,63886 e7,49192.⬆️.
🛁free 🚰♨ Chfree. **Surface:** grasstiles. 🔓 01/01-31/12
Distance: 🚶700m ⊗200m.

🛁 S	Saluzzo 🌿	31A2

Via Cuneo 16. **GPS:** n44,63739 e7,49740.
±10 🛁free 🚰free. **Surface:** asphalted/grassy. 🔓 01/01-31/12
Distance: 🚶1km.

🛁 S	San Damiano d'Asti 🌿	31A2

Via Monsignor Franco. **GPS:** n44,82659 e8,05921.⬆️.

50 🛁free 🚰♨ Ch. **Location:** Rural, simple. **Surface:** gravel.
🔓 01/01-31/12
Distance: 🚶1km ⊗1km 🍴1km.
Remarks: At cemetery.

🛁 S	San Damiano d'Asti 🌿	31A2

Azienda Agricola Cascina Piana, Fraz S.Grato. **GPS:** n44,85136 e8,07417.

25 🛁€ 8-10 🚰♨ Ch🔧 (8x) WC 🗑 included. **Location:** Rural, comfortable,
isolated, quiet. **Surface:** grassy. 🔓 01/01-31/12
Distance: 🚶1,5km ⊗1,5km 🍴500m.
Remarks: Farm products.

🛁 S	Sanfront	30D2

Via Montebracco, SP26. **GPS:** n44,64944 e7,32056.⬆️➡️.

🛁free 🚰♨ Chfree. **Surface:** gravel.
Remarks: At sports park, max. 24h.

🛁 S	Santa Maria Maggiore 🚠	24B5

Area Verde Attrezzata, Via Alfredo Belcastro/via Pineta.
GPS: n46,13219 e8,45500.⬆️➡️.

32 🛁€ 15/24h 🚰♨ Ch🔧 . 🏳 **Location:** Rural. **Surface:** gravel.
🔓 01/01-31/12
Distance: ⊗200m 🚲 on the spot.
Remarks: Max. 48h.

🛁 S	Santa Maria Maggiore 🚠	24B5

Agriturismo Al Piano delle Lutte, Via Domodossola 57.
GPS: n46,13569 e8,44753.

3 🛁€ 10/24h 🚰♨ Ch🔧 according consumption WC 🗑. 🚲 **Location:**
Rural, simple. **Surface:** grassy/gravel. 🔓 01/01-31/12
Distance: 🍴on the spot.

🍴 S	Sant'Antonino di Susa	30D1

Area Sosta Il Sentiero Dei Franchi, Borgo Cresto 16/1.
GPS: n45,09973 e7,27754.
20 🛁€ 10 🚰♨ Ch🔧 €2. **Surface:** grassy/gravel. 🔓 01/01-31/12
Distance: ⊗on the spot.

🛁 S	Sestriere 🏔 ❄	30D1

Lago Losetta, Strada Azzurri d'Italia. **GPS:** n44,96465 e6,88141.
120 🛁€ 10/24h 🚰♨ Ch🔧 . **Surface:** gravel. 🔓 01/01-31/12
Distance: 🚶800m 🚌 Shuttle bus to ski-piste.

🛁 S	Sommariva Perno	31A2

Area comunale, Loc.Piano, SP0. **GPS:** n44,75126 e7,89667.⬆️➡️.

10 🛁free 🚰♨ Chfree. **Location:** Rural, simple, noisy. **Surface:** gravel.
🔓 01/01-31/12
Distance: 🚶500m 🏄 13km ⊗250m 🍴250m.

🛁 S	Susa	30D1

Piazza Repubblica. **GPS:** n45,13861 e7,05389.

12 🛏free 🚰🧺Ch 🛁 free. **Surface:** asphalted. ⬛ 01/01-31/12
Distance: 🚶300m.

| 🛏S | **Tagliolo Monferrato** | 31B2 |

Str. del Varo. **GPS:** n44,63760 e8,67029.
21 🛏€ 5/24h 🚰🧺Ch. **Location:** Rural, simple, quiet.
Surface: grassy/gravel.
⬛ 01/01-31/12
Distance: 🚶250m 🚴2km ⊗200m 🛒400m.
Remarks: Max. 72h, keycard barrier at Bar/Tabac, caution € 10.

| 🛏S | **Torino** 🌿🧺 | 31A1 |

Corso Casale 327. **GPS:** n45,08084 e7,72993.
🛏free 🚰🧺free. **Location:** Noisy. **Surface:** asphalted.
Distance: 🚶800m ⊗100m 🛒150m.

| 🛏S | **Torino** 🌿🧺 | 31A1 |

Parco Ruffini, Corso Lione/Corso Carlo Piaggia, Turin (Torino).
GPS: n45,05686 e7,63166.
🛏free 🚰🧺free. **Surface:** asphalted.
Distance: 🚶city centre 5km.

Tourist information Turin (Torino):
Ⓜ Mole Antonelliana. National Film museum.
Ⓜ Museo Nazionale dell'Automobile, Corso Unità d'Italia 40. Museum of
motor-cars. 🕐 Tue-Sa, 10-18.30h, Su 10-20.30h 🔴 Mo.
Ⓜ Palazzo Madame. Historical art.
✠ Palazzo Reale. Royal palace.
✝ Cathedral, 1498.
✝ Basilica di Superga. Baroque basilica.

| 🛏S | **Usseaux** 🌿⛰ | 30D1 |

Fraz. Fraisse-Pourrieres, SR23. **GPS:** n45,04170 e6,98518.
🛏€ 15 🚰🧺Ch 🛁 WC 🍽. **Surface:** grassy.

| 🛏S | **Usseaux** 🌿⛰ | 30D1 |

Area sosta Usseaux, Fraz. Fraisse-Pourrières. **GPS:** n45,04146 e6,98500.
🛏€ 15 🚰🧺Ch WC 🍽. **Surface:** grassy.

| 🛏S | **Usseaux** 🌿⛰ | 30D1 |

Lago di Laux, Via Lago 7. **GPS:** n45,04166 e7,02222.
100 🛏€ 15/24h 🚰€3 🧺€3 Ch 🛁€2,50. **Surface:** grassy.
⬛ 01/01-31/12
Distance: 🚶500m 🚣200m ⊗on the spot 🛒5km.
Remarks: Pay at restaurant, in winter time not always easy to reach.

| 🛏S | **Valdieri** ⛰🐂 | 30D3 |

Centro Alpino S.Anna, Loc. S. Anna. **GPS:** n44,24513 e7,32548. ⬆➡.

40 🛏€ 12 🚰🧺Ch 🛁 included. **Surface:** grassy/gravel.
Distance: 🚶100m 🚣on the spot ⊗100m.
Remarks: Narrow entrance (bridge).

| 🛏S | **Valdieri** ⛰🐂 | 30D3 |

Parco Alpi Marittime, Terme di Valdieri. **GPS:** n44,20546 e7,26840.
🛏€ 10 🚰🧺Ch 🛁. **Surface:** gravel. ⬛ 01/01-31/12

| 🛏S | **Valle Mosso** | 24B6 |

Piazza Alpini d'Italia. **GPS:** n45,63316 e8,14629. ⬆.

3 🛏free 🚰🧺Ch free. **Location:** Urban. **Surface:** asphalted.
⬛ 01/01-31/12
Distance: 🚶on the spot 🛒Conad 20m 🛒50m.

| 🛏S | **Varallo** | 24B6 |

Area Comunale, Via Sant'Antonio. **GPS:** n45,81797 e8,24857. ⬆.

8 🛏€ 10/24h 🚰🧺Ch 🛁 included. **Location:** Urban, quiet.
Surface: gravel/sand. ⬛ 01/01-31/12
Distance: 🚶500m ⊗500m.
Remarks: To be paid at town hall.

| 🛏S | **Venaria Reale** | 31A1 |

Relax and Go, Via Scodeggio 15. **GPS:** n45,14108 e7,62404.
15 🛏€ 15 🚰🧺Ch 🛁. **Surface:** grassy.
Distance: ⊗650m 🚌bus GTT, tram 11>Turin.

| 🛏S | **Venasca** | 31A2 |

SP8, Via Provinciale. **GPS:** n44,56620 e7,39328. ⬆.

20 🛏free 🚰free. **Surface:** sand.
Distance: 🚶600m.

| 🛏S | **Verbania** 🌊 | 24B5 |

Area Comunale, Viale Sant´Anna. **GPS:** n45,92896 e8,56468. ⬆.

6 🛏free 🚰🧺free. **Location:** Urban, simple. **Surface:** asphalted.
⬛ 01/01-31/12
Distance: 🚶on the spot 🚣100m ⊗200m.

IT

Verbania 〚S〛 24B5

Area Zone Arena, Via San Bernardino. **GPS**: n45,93143 e8,57106.⬆.
13 🛏 € 10/24h 🚿 included. 🍴 **Location**: Simple. **Surface**: asphalted.
⬜ 01/01-31/12
Distance: 🚶600m 🏊50m ⊗100m 🍺250m.

Vercelli 〚S〛 31B1

Via Trento, c/o piazzale Pala-hockey. **GPS**: n45,33417 e8,41861.⬆.

10 🛏free 🚿 🔧free. **Location**: Urban, simple. **Surface**: asphalted.
⬜ 01/01-31/12
Distance: 🚶1,5km 🚲6km ⊗50m 🍺1,5km 🚌on the spot.

Tourist information Vercelli:
✝ Basilica di Sant'Andrea. Basilica, part of abbey.

Vergne 〚S〛 31A2

Piazza della Vite e del dell Vina. **GPS**: n44,61298 e7,92064.⬆.
6 🛏free 🚿 Chfree. **Location**: Simple. **Surface**: metalled.
Distance: 🚶on the spot ⊗on the spot.

Vialfrè 〚S〛 31A1

Via Luigi Emanuel, SP55. **GPS**: n45,38298 e7,81754.⬆.

🛏free 🚿 🔧free. **Surface**: metalled.
Distance: 🚲6km ⊗300m 🍺300m.

Vidracco 〚S〛 31A1

Damanhur Crea, Via Baldissero 21. **GPS**: n45,42884 e7,75327.⬆.

30 🛏 € 8/24h 🚿 Ch 🔧(24x) WC 🔧included. **Surface**: asphalted.
Distance: ⊗cafetaria 🍺on the spot.

Tourist information Vidracco:
👁 Damanhur Crea, Via Baldissero 21. Extraordinary Italian artistic and spritual community.

Villar Focchiardo 〚S〛 30D1

Area Camper Villar Focchiardo, Via Fratta, SS24. **GPS**: n45,11336 e7,22408.⬆.
➡.

54 🛏 € 3, € 15/week 🚿 Chfree. **Surface**: grassy. ⬜ 01/01-31/12
⬛ camper service: 01/11-31/03
Distance: 🚲4,5km.

Villar Pellice 〚S〛 30D2

Parco Flissia, Via Cave del Fin. **GPS**: n44,80472 e7,15083.

20 🛏 € 6 🚿 🔧free.
Location: Rural, simple, isolated. **Surface**: grassy.
Distance: 🚶500m 🏊on the spot 🎣fishing permit obligatory 🍴agriturismo.

Vinadio 〚S〛 30D3

Area di Sosta Communale, Bagni di Vinadio, Fraz. Strapesi. **GPS**: n44,28747 e7,07534.⬆.

30 🛏 € 11/24h 🚿 🔧 Ch 🔧free. **Surface**: gravel.
Distance: 🚶300m, Vinadio 10km 🏊on the spot 🦢on the spot.
Remarks: Altitude 1350m, parking at the spa resort of Strapeis.

Vinadio 〚S〛 30D3

Piazza d'Armi, SS21. **GPS**: n44,30667 e7,17083.⬆.

🛏1/6-31/8 € 5 🚿 Chfree. **Surface**: asphalted.
Distance: 🚶400m.

Volpedo 〚S〛 31C2

Lungo Curone Matteotti. **GPS**: n44,88512 e8,98707.⬆➡.

IT

6 🚐free 🚰 🚽 Chfree. **Surface:** grassy/gravel.
Distance: 🏘600m.
Remarks: At sports park.

🍇 [S] **Zubiena** 24A6

Prà Gros Agriturismo, SS338, Casale Montino. **GPS**: n45,49812 e7,98934.⬆.

6 🚐 🚰 🚽. **Location:** Rural. **Surface:** gravel/metalled.
Distance: 🍴on the spot.

Trentino South Tyrol

🚐 [S] **Andalo** 25C4

Via Rindole, 6, Loc. Rindole. **GPS**: n46,16113 e11,00647.

80 🚐€ 15 🚰 🚽 Ch 🔌 €5. **Surface:** asphalted. ☐ summer
Distance: 🏘200m 🍴on the spot.
Remarks: Service passerby € 5, beautiful view.

🚐 **Arco** 25B5

Piazzale Carmellini, Viale Paolina Caproni. **GPS**: n45,92232 e10,89032.⬆.

14 🚐€ 1,50/4h, max. € 10/24h. **Surface:** asphalted.
☐ 01/01-31/12
Distance: 🏘200m 🍴200m.
Remarks: Max. 72h.

[S] **Arco** 25B5

Viale Rovereto. **GPS**: n45,91820 e10,89225.⬆.
🚰 🚽 Chfree. ☐ water disconnected in winter

🚐 [S] **Barbiano** ⛰ 25C3

Kollmann Stop, Frazione Colma, SS12. **GPS**: n46,58728 e11,52401.⬆.

15 🚐€ 10, in envelope in mail box 🚰 🚽 Ch 🔌 included. **Location:** Simple, noisy. **Surface:** gravel. ☐ 01/01-31/12
Distance: 🏘300m ⛽9km 🍴300m 🛒300m 🚌on the spot 🚲on the spot.
Remarks: Along through road, max. 48h.

🚐 **Baselga di Pine** 25C4

Ice Rink Piné, Via Dello Stadio. **GPS**: n46,12617 e11,25382.⬆.

10 🚐free. **Surface:** metalled.

🚐 [S] **Bolzano/Bozen** 🌿 ⛰ 25C4

Parking Fiera Messe, Via Bruno Buozzi. **GPS**: n46,47417 e11,32617.⬆.

30 🚐free 🚰 🚽 Chfree. **Location:** Urban, simple, noisy. **Surface:** asphalted.
☐ 01/01-31/12
Distance: 🏘centre 4km ⛽1,1km 🍴on the spot 🛒4km 🚌on the spot.
Remarks: Along railwayline.

🚐 [S] **Bolzano/Bozen** 🌿 ⛰ 25C4

Via Maso della Pieve. **GPS**: n46,47327 e11,33693.⬆.

8 🚐€ 0,70/h mo-fr 8-19h, sa 8-13, overnight stay free 🚰 🚽 Ch.
Location: Urban, simple, noisy. **Surface:** asphalted. ☐ 01/01-31/12
Distance: 🏘city centre 3km 🛒100m 🚌on the spot.

🚐 [S] **Borgo Valsugana** 🌿 ⛰ 25C5

Via Tommaso Temanza. **GPS**: n46,05444 e11,46361.

IT

18 ⬛€ 10/24h 🚰🚽 Ch 🧹 included. **Surface:** metalled.
Distance: 🚶100m 🏊20m 🚋20m ⊗100m 🛒100m.
Remarks: Max. 48h, service passerby € 5.

🅿 Braies 🌲⛪🏔 25D3
P2, Lago di Braies, Fraz. San Vito. **GPS:** n46,70265 e12,08520. ➡

30 ⬛€ 10, Jul € 13, Aug € 15 🚰🚽 🧹€6. **Surface:** asphalted.
⬛ 01/04-30/09
Distance: 🚶2km ⊗200m 🛒2km.

Caldonazzo 🌊 25C5
Via al Lago. **GPS:** n46,00501 e11,26307. ⬆

25 ⬛€ 5-15 🚿€0,50. 🏊 **Location:** Rural, simple, quiet. **Surface:** gravel.
⬛ 30/05-31/10
Distance: 🚶Braies 5km 🏊Lago di Braies 250m ⊗250m 🛒5km
🚴 on the spot 🚶 on the spot.

🅿S Brentonico 🌲⛪🏔 25C5
Via al Dosset. **GPS:** n45,81540 e10,95581. ⬆➡

30 ⬛€ 8/6-22h (01/04-30/9), € 10/night. **Surface:** grassy/sand.
⬛ 01/01-31/12
Distance: 🏊50m ⊗300m.
Remarks: Payment only with coins.

🅿S Cavalese 🌊 25C4
P Fondovalle, SP232. **GPS:** n46,28438 e11,47256. ⬆

11 ⬛€7 🚰€2 🚽 Ch 🧹€3. **Surface:** asphalted. ⬛ 01/01-31/12
Distance: 🚶400m 🚲 10km ⊗250m 🛒300m.

🅿 Brunico/Bruneck 🌲🏔❄ 25D3
P2, Piazza Mercato di Stegona. **GPS:** n46,79558 e11,93006. ⬆.

50 ⬛€ 10 🚰🚽. **Location:** Simple. **Surface:** grasstiles/metalled.
⬛ 01/01-31/12

©S Chiusa 🌲🏔❄ 25C3
Gamp, Via Gries 10. **GPS:** n46,64128 e11,57244. ➡

>25 ⬛free. **Location:** Urban, simple, noisy. **Surface:** gravel.
⬛ 01/01-31/12
Distance: 🚶800m ⊗500m 🛒500m 🚌on the spot 🚴on the spot
🚶 on the spot.

Tourist information Brunico/Bruneck:
ℹ Associazione Turistica, Via Europa,24. Fortified city, 14th century.
Ⓜ Regional museum.
⬛ Annual fair. ⬛ last week Oct.

🅿S Caldes 25B4
Rafting Val di Sole, Loc. Contrè. **GPS:** n46,36139 e10,94528.

20 ⬛€ 14,50-16/24h 2 pers. + 2 children incl, dog € 2 🚰🚽 Ch 🧹included.
Location: Rural, simple. **Surface:** grassy. ⬛ 01/01-31/12
Distance: 🚶300m 🚲 800m ⊗on the spot 🛒mini market 🚌100m
🚴 on the spot 🚶 on the spot.

🅿 Corvara in Badia 25D3
P Corvara, Strada Planac SS244. **GPS:** n46,54105 e11,88388. ⬆.

10 🛏 free. **Location:** Rural, simple, isolated. **Surface:** gravel.
🕐 01/01-31/12
Distance: 🚶3,5km. 🚂3,5km.

| 🛏 S | **Dimaro** | 25B4 |

Camper Solander, Loc. Rovina. **GPS:** n46,32488 e10,86215.⬆.

10 🛏 € 20/24h, € 10/night 🚰🔌 Ch 🔌 WC 🚮 included. **Surface:** gravel.
🕐 01/01-31/12
Distance: 🚶500m ⊗ on the spot.
Remarks: Near campsite Dolomiti.

| 🛏 S | **Dimaro** | 25B4 |

Hotel Belvedere, SS239. **GPS:** n46,29734 e10,86765.
🛏 € 15/24h 🚰🔌 Ch 🔌 included. **Surface:** asphalted. 🕐 01/01-31/12

| S | **Folgaria** ⛷🏊🏔🌳❄ | 25C5 |

Area Sosta Bucaneve, Via Negheli 87. **GPS:** n45,91849 e11,19255.⬆.
25 🛏 € 8. **Surface:** grassy/metalled. 🕐 01/01-31/12
Distance: 🚶300m 🚵 mountainbike trail 🎿100m.
Remarks: Golf court, shuttle bus.

| S | **Folgaria** ⛷🏊🏔🌳❄ | 25C5 |

Osteria Carador, Via Neghelli 58. **GPS:** n45,91748 e11,19094.⬆.
🛏 € 8/24h 🔌 €5. **Surface:** gravel/sand. 🕐 01/01-31/12
Distance: ⊗ on the spot 🎿 on the spot.
Remarks: Golf court.

| S | **Folgaria** ⛷🏊🏔🌳❄ | 25C5 |

SS3501. **GPS:** n45,91397 e11,17081.⬆.
🚰€1 🔌 Ch.

| 🛏 S | **Gargazzone** ⛷🏔🌳 | 25C3 |

Weisshof-Törgelle-Keller, Landstrasse 65 SS38. **GPS:** n46,58500 e11,20528.⬆.

10 🛏 € 10 🚰🔌 Ch 🔌 €2/24h WC 🚮 €1.
Location: Rural, simple, quiet. **Surface:** grassy/gravel.
🕐 01/01-31/12
Distance: 🚶2km 🚲1,5km ⊗500m 🚂2km 🚗 on the spot 🚵 on the spot
🏊 on the spot.
Remarks: Reservation for Christmas holidays, tel.: +39 (0)473 292448.

Tourist information Gargazzone:
ℹ Consorzio Turistico, Via Maria Trost, 5, Merano, www.meranerland.com. Place
with medicinal sources.

🏛🍴 Castel Tirolo, 4km N. de Merano. Regional museum. 🕐 01/03-31/12.
🍴 Merano. 🕐 Tue, Fri.
🎉 Festa della Città, Merano. 🕐 1st weekend Aug.

| 🛏 S | **Glorenza** | 25B3 |

Glurms Camping im Park, > SS41. **GPS:** n46,67067 e10,54520.⬆➡.

40 🛏 € 12 🚰🔌 Ch 🔌 €2 WC 🚮. **Surface:** grassy.
Distance: 🚶500m ⚓ on the spot.
Remarks: Along the Adige river.

| 🛏 S | **La Villa in Badia** 🏔❄ | 25D3 |

Odlina, Strada Ninz, 49. **GPS:** n46,58889 e11,90028.➡.

45 🛏 summer € 25, winter € 30 🚰🔌 Ch 🔌 WC 🚮 included 🔘€5 🌐€3. 🚐
Location: Rural, luxurious, quiet. **Surface:** metalled. 🕐 01/01-31/12
Distance: 🚶400m ⊗150m 🚂150m 🚗 on the spot 🚵 on the spot
🏊 on the spot 🎿300m.
Remarks: Reservation for Christmas holidays: info@odina.it, use of sauna
against payment.

| 🛏 S | **Lago** | 25C4 |

Via Tresselume. **GPS:** n46,28291 e11,52557.

30 🛏 free 🚰€1 🔌€2 Ch 🔌1 🚮 (12x)€2/8h. 🚐 **Location:** Rural, simple.
Surface: metalled. 🕐 01/01-31/12
Distance: 🚶200m ⊗200m.

| 🛏 S | **Lavarone** 🏕🏔🌳❄ | 25C5 |

Prà Grando, Via Padova. **GPS:** n45,93602 e11,27099.

40 🛏 € 14 May/June/July, € 15 Aug, € 18 Dec-April 🚰🔌 Ch 🔌 included.
Surface: grassy/gravel. 🕐 01/05-30/09, 01/12-31/03

IT

Distance: 300m 32km Lago di Lavarone 1km 1km 300m
300m 300m 1km 1km.

	S	Lavarone		25C5

SS 349, Loc Moar. **GPS:** n45,94575 e11,26397.

10 € 0,40/h €0,50 Ch.
Location: Simple. **Surface:** metalled.
Distance: 800m Lago di Lavarone 1,9km 500m.

	S	Levico Terme		25C5

Area Sosta Camper Valsugana, Loc Pleina. **GPS:** n46,00691 e11,28706.

50 € 25 Ch WC. **Surface:** grassy. 01/01-31/12
Distance: 1,3km 200m, Lido di Levico 1,1km 50m 50m
on the spot.
Remarks: Max. 3 nights, check in at reception campsite.

	S	Levico Terme		25C5

Area 47, SP1. **GPS:** n46,00415 e11,28880.
24 € 15, 01/06-30/09 € 25 Ch included.
Distance: 1,3km on the spot.
Remarks: Including access to swimming pool and private beach.

	S	Moena		25D4

Bar Il Giardino, SS 48 Forno di Moena. **GPS:** n46,35238 e11,63149.

50 € 10-12 Ch included €4/24h. **Location:** Rural, comfortable,
central. **Surface:** grassy/metalled. 01/01-31/12
Distance: 3,5km 500m 2km 300m on the spot on the spot
on the spot.
Remarks: Max. 48h, skibus comes at parking.

	S	Molveno		25B4

Area attrezzata per camper Lago di Molveno, Via Lungolago, 25, Loc. Ischia.
GPS: n46,14018 e10,96011.

50 € 12-28 Ch included. **Surface:** metalled. 01/01-31/12
Distance: 800m 200m 200m 100m.

	S	Molveno		25B4

Via Lungolago,Loc. Ischia. **GPS:** n46,14165 e10,95727.

20 € 9-22 Ch included. **Surface:** metalled. 01/01-31/12
Distance: 1km 400m 200m 100m.

	S	Pergine Valsugana		25C5

Soleando Camperparking, Via al lago 23/A. **GPS:** n46,05184 e11,22494.

10 €12/day Ch.
Surface: gravel.
Distance: 600m Lago di Caldonazzo 1km 300m 300m 100m
on the spot.
Tourist information Pergine Valsugana:
www.apt.trento.it. City at the foot of the Dolomites with historical centre.
Palazzo Pretorio, Trento. Ecclesiastical museum.

	S	Predazzo		25D4

Latemar 2200, SS48, dir Moena. **GPS:** n46,32582 e11,59970.

50 free, peak season € 7-10/24h Ch included.
Location: Rural, simple, noisy. **Surface:** asphalted/gravel. 01/01-31/12
Distance: 2,5km 2,5km on the spot on the spot on the spot
on the spot on the spot.
Remarks: Parking ski-lifts.

	S	Rabbi		25B4

Area camper Plan, Loc. Plan, Bagni di Rabbi. **GPS:** n46,40619 e10,82629.

IT

105 🛏 € 14-21, 2 pers.incl. ⚡💧 Ch 🔌 WC included ⬜against payment 🅿.
Surface: metalled. 🅾 01/06-30/09
Distance: 🚃600m.
Remarks: Former campsite, max. 48h.

| 🅿🆂 | Racines ⛰ | 25C3 |

Sportzone Ratschings, Belprato, Stanghe. **GPS:** n46,88254 e11,38383. ⬆.

20 🛏 free.
Location: Rural, simple. **Surface:** gravel.
🅾 01/01-31/12
Distance: 🚃400m 🚴5km ⊗400m 🚃400m 🚶400m 🅰Gilfenklammroute.

| 🅿🆂 | Riva del Garda 🚵🏊 | 25B5 |

Via Monte Brione. **GPS:** n45,87986 e10,85872. ⬆.

41 🛏 € 0,50/h, max. € 24/48h ⚡💧 Ch 🔌 included. **Surface:** grasstiles.
🅾 01/11-07/12
Distance: 🚃1,5km 🏊200m.
Remarks: Max. 48h.
Tourist information Riva del Garda:
Ⓜ Museo Civico, Piazza Battisti.

| 🅿🆂 | Rovereto 🚵 | 25C5 |

Area Camper Quercia, Via Palestrina. **GPS:** n45,90232 e11,03704. ⬆➡.
15 🛏 € 8/12h, € 16/24h ⚡💧 Ch 🔌 WC ⬜🅿. **Surface:** metalled.
🅾 01/01-31/12
Distance: 🚃1,5km 🚴2km.
Remarks: Caution € 5, bicycle rental.
Tourist information Rovereto:
Ⓜ Castello di Rovereto. War museum. 🅾 Tue-Su 🅾 01/01-28/02.
✖ Castel Beseno. 🅾 Tue-Su.

| 🅿🆂 | San Candido ⛰❄ | 26A3 |

Area di Sosta Camper, Via Prato alla Drava, 1/A. **GPS:** n46,73924 e12,36559. ➡.

90 🛏 € 15 ⚡💧 Ch 🔌 WC included ⬜€2. 🛁 **Location:** Rural, comfortable, quiet. **Surface:** gravel. 🅾 01/01 - 31/12
Distance: 🚴6km ⊗on the spot 🚃500m 🚃on the spot 🚲on the spot 🚶on the spot 🚵2km 🏊500m.
Remarks: Bicycle rental, shuttle bus San Candido and skipistes € 1/pp.

| 🅿🆂 | San Guiseppe al Lago 🌊 | 25C4 |

Posteggio Camper Lago di Caldero, San Guiseppe 18.
GPS: n46,39038 e11,25663.➡.

35 🛏 € 15/night ⚡💧 Ch 🔌 WC ⬜. 🛁 **Location:** Rural, comfortable, quiet.
Surface: gravel. 🅾 13/03-15/11
Distance: 🚴5km Caldero 🏊Private beach ⊗50m 🚃Nearby campsite.
Remarks: Next to campsite, max. 4 days.

| 🅿🆂 | San Martino di Castrozza ⛰❄ | 25D4 |

Area camper Tognola, Loc.Tognola. **GPS:** n46,25373 e11,80158.⬆.

80 🛏 € 12 ⚡💧 included Ch ➕€1/80minutes. 🛏 **Location:** Rural, comfortable, quiet. **Surface:** gravel. 🅾 01/01-31/12
Distance: 🚴1,5km ⊗500m on the spot 🚶on the spot 🚲on the spot.
Remarks: Next to ski-lift, free shuttle.

| 🍴🆂 | San Vigilio di Marebbe ⛰❄ | 25D3 |

Restaurant Pizzeria Rittenkeller, Ras-Costa 2. **GPS:** n46,70630 e11,92920.➡.

120 🛏 01/04-30/11 € 20, 01/12-31/03 € 25 ⚡💧 Ch 🔌 included.
Location: Rural, simple, quiet. **Surface:** gravel. 🅾 01/01-31/12
Distance: 🚴600m 🚴500m ⊗on the spot 🚃600m 🚃600m 🚲on the spot 🏊600m.
Remarks: Next to ski-lift, reservation for Christmas holidays: info@ritterkeller.it.

IT

IT

Santa Cristina Valgardena 🏔 25D3
P1 Monte Pana, Strada Pana. **GPS**: n46,55174 e11,71624. 🚡 .

50 🛏 free, peak season € 4/day. 🅿 **Location:** Simple, isolated, quiet.
Surface: gravel. ⬛ 01/01-31/12
Distance: 🚲 2,5km. 🛒 2,5km.
Remarks: Altitude 1650m, max. 7 days, narrow entrance.

Selva di Val Gardena 🏔 ❄ 25D3
Piz Sella, Strada Plan de Gralba. **GPS**: n46,53204 e11,77230. ⬆ .

15 🛏 free, Winter € 6/day, € 6 night. **Location:** Rural, simple. **Surface:** gravel.
⬛ 01/01-31/12
Distance: 🚲 4km ⊗ 150m 🚶 on the spot 🚲 on the spot.
Remarks: Inclining pitches.

© S Sesto/Sexten 🏔 ❄ ⚒ 26A3
Caravanpark Sexten, SS52 St Josefstrasse 54. **GPS**: n46,66741 e12,39996. ➡ .

36 🛏 € 23-29 ⛽ 🔧 Ch 🚿 WC included 🚽 ▣ €4 🚿 €2. **Location:** Rural,
luxurious, quiet. **Surface:** grasstiles. ⬛ 01/01-31/12
Distance: 🚲 3km ⊗ on the spot 🚉 on the spot 🚌 on the spot 🚴 on the spot
🚶 on the spot 🚲 900m ⛵ on the spot.
Remarks: Sauna and spa.

S Silandro 🏔 25B3
Via Ospedale, Silandro/. **GPS**: n46,62721 e10,78185.

🛏 free. **Surface:** grasstiles.
Distance: 🚲 500m ⊗ 500m.

S Siusi 🌿🏕🏔🌲❄ 25C3
Seiseralm, Via Rosegarten. **GPS**: n46,54048 e11,56600. 🚡 .

>25 🛏 free WC. **Location:** Rural, simple, quiet. **Surface:** gravel.
Distance: 🚲 500m ⊗ on the spot 🛒 500m 🚌 on the spot 🚶 on the spot
🚲 on the spot.
Remarks: Parking at Seiseralm-lift.

S Smarano 🏕🏔🎯 25C4
Area Sosta Ostaria del Filò, Viale Merlonga 48/a. **GPS**: n46,34962 e11,10956. ⬆ .

43 🛏 € 10-13-15 ⛽ 🔧 Ch 🚿 WC 🚽 ▣ . **Surface:** grassy. ⬛ 01/01-31/12
Distance: 🚲 1km ⊗ on the spot.
Remarks: Check in at restaurant.

S Solda 🏔 25B4
GPS: n46,51448 e10,59578.
25 🛏 free. **Location:** Simple. **Surface:** gravel. ⬛ 01/01-31/12
Distance: 🚲 1km ⊗ 100m 🚶 on the spot 🚲 on the spot.

S Tirolo 25C3
Via principale. **GPS**: n46,68636 e11,15904. ⬆ .

15 🛏 € 10,50/night ⛽ WC. 🚿 **Location:** Rural, simple, quiet.
Surface: asphalted. ⬛ 01/01-31/12
Distance: 🚲 200m ⊗ 50m 🛒 200m 🚌 50m 🚴 on the spot 🚶 on the spot.

⛲ S Tirolo 25C3
Schneeburghof, Monte Benedetto 26. **GPS**: n46,67789 e11,16495.

20 🛏 € 23 ⛽ 🔧 Ch 🚿 included. **Location:** Comfortable. **Surface:** grassy.
Distance: 🏊 on the spot.

🍴 [S] **Tonadico** 25D4

Lanterna Verde, Via Zocchet 10. **GPS**: n46,18216 e11,84318.➡.

45 🚐€ 15 🚰 Ch 🔌 included WC. **Location:** Rural, comfortable, quiet.
Surface: grasstiles. ☐ 01/01-31/12
Distance: 🏘1km 🍴100m 🛒1km 🚌on the spot 🚲on the spot 🚶on the spot ⛷15km ⛷15km.
Remarks: Max. 48h, check in at restaurant.

🚐 [S] **Trento** 25C5

P Zuffo, Loc. Vela. **GPS**: n46,07650 e11,11050.⬆➡.

20 🚐€ 5 🚰€1 Ch. **Surface:** asphalted. ☐ 01/01-31/12
Distance: 🏘1,8km ⛽150m 🚌200m.

🚐 [S] **Trento** 25C5

Camper Trento Park, Via Brennero, 181. **GPS**: n46,09438 e11,11335.
200 🚐€ 12/24h 🚰 Ch 🔌 included 🚿€1 📶.
Surface: asphalted.
☐ 01/01-31/12
Distance: 🏘city centre 3km ⛽2km 🍴400m 🚌400m bus 3-11-17 > centre.

🚐 [S] **Trento** 25C5

Parking Trentino, Via Santi Cosma e Damiano 64. **GPS**: n46,07674 e11,10411.⬆.

20 🚐€ 15 🚰 Ch 🔌 included. **Location:** Urban. **Surface:** grasstiles.
☐ 01/01-31/12
Distance: 🏘1,8km ⛽300m 🍴300m 🚌bus > centre 15 min.
Remarks: Call for entrance code: 3389004343 Mr. Pisetta.

🚐 **Trento** 25C5

P3 Giardino Botanico Fondo Viote, SP85. **GPS**: n46,02445 e11,03973.

100 🚐€ 4-10/10h, overnight stay free. **Location:** Rural, simple, isolated, quiet.
Surface: asphalted. ☐ 01/01-31/12
Distance: 🏘18km Trento 🍴150m 🚌on the spot 🚲on the spot 🚶on the spot ⛷on the spot.
Remarks: Max. 48h.

🚐 [S] **Tres** 25C4

A Monte del Paese, SP della Predaia. **GPS**: n46,32040 e11,10202.⬆.

15 🚐€ 10/24h 🚰 Ch 🔌 WC included. **Surface:** gravel.
☐ 01/01-31/12
Distance: 🏘800m.

Lombardy

🚐 [S] **Alzano Lombardo** 24D6

Via Europa. **GPS**: n45,73690 e9,72007.⬆➡.

3 🚐 🚰. **Surface:** asphalted. ◙ Sa 6-15h market
Remarks: At sports park.

🚐 [S] **Biassono** 24D6

Via al Parco/Via della Sciavatera. **GPS**: n45,63102 e9,28865.⬆➡.

10 🚐free 🚰 Ch free. **Location:** Rural, simple, isolated. **Surface:** asphalted.
☐ 01/01-31/12
Distance: 🏘500m 🛒Centro Commerciale Vilasanta 4km
🚌train > Milan 500m.

🚐 [S] **Borgofranco sul Po** 32A1

Via Filipo Turati. **GPS**: n45,04775 e11,20524.⬆➡.

4 🚐free 🚰 Ch free. **Location:** Simple, quiet. **Surface:** grassy.

IT

■ 01/01-31/12 ◉ water: frost
Distance: 🚲600m ⛵1km ⊗200m 🛒300m 🚏200m 🚶200m.

🚐S **Bormio** 🌿⛰❄ **25A4**
Bormio 2000, Via Battaglion Morbegno. **GPS:** n46,46260 e10,37190.⬆

🚐€ 8/24h 🚰🗑Ch included. **Surface:** sand. ■ 01/01-31/12
Distance: 🚲500m ⊗500m 🚲on the spot.
Remarks: Parking funicular railway, service passerby € 5.

Tourist information Bormio:
ℹ Ufficio Informazioni e di Accoglienza Turistica, Via Roma, 131/b. Alps city, large winter sport area, also summer skiing.
🌿 Parco Nazionale dello Stelvio. Region with 50 glacier lakes and high mountain peaks. Access around Bormio.

🚐S **Campione** **25B5**
Area Camper Campione del Garda, Via Verdi. **GPS:** n45,75651 e10,74985.⬆

30 🚐€ 15/24h 🚰. **Surface:** unpaved. ■ 01/04-31/10
Distance: 🚲500m ⛵on the spot ⊗200m.

🚐S **Capo di Ponte** **25A5**
Concarena, Via Santo Stefano. **GPS:** n46,02447 e10,34325.⬆➡

12 🚐€ 8/24h, 1/10-28/2 free 🚰🗑Ch 🚿WC included.
Surface: asphalted. ■ 01/01-31/12
Distance: 🚲300m ⊗300m 🛒300m.

🚐S **Certosa di Pavia** 🏛 **31C1**
Parking Certosa, Via di Vittorio, SP27. **GPS:** n45,25735 e9,14161.⬆

20 🚐€ 4/night, € 5/day 🚰🗑Ch WC free. 🏠**Location:** Simple.
Surface: grassy/gravel. ■ 01/01-31/12 ◉ water disconnected in winter

Distance: 🚲1km ⊗200m 🛒on the spot 🚶on the spot.
Remarks: Monastery Certosa di Pavia 450m.

🚐S **Certosa di Pavia** 🏛 **31C1**
Località Certosa Monumento. **GPS:** n45,25574 e9,14632.⬆

🚐€ 4/night, € 4/day 🚰🗑Ch WC free. **Surface:** sand.
■ 01/01-31/12
Distance: ⊗500m.
Remarks: Monastery Certosa di Pavia 80m.

🚐S **Chiavenna** **24D4**
Piazzale Leonardo da Vinci, Via A. Moro, SS36. **GPS:** n46,31424 e9,39631.⬆➡

🚐free 🚰🗑Ch free. **Surface:** asphalted.
Distance: 🚲800m 🛒200m.

🚐S **Chiesa in Valmalenco** **25A4**
Loc. Vassalini. **GPS:** n46,27020 e9,85670.⬆.

🚐free 🚰€3 🗑. **Surface:** gravel.
Distance: 🚲1km 🚲200m.

🚐S **Clusone** **25A5**
Busgarina, Via Vago 6, loc Fiorine. **GPS:** n45,87312 e9,91642.⬆

80 🚐€ 13 🚰🗑Ch 🚿(33x)€2 🗑€1/7minutes. ■ 01/01-31/12
Distance: 🛒on the spot.

🚐S **Clusone** **25A5**
Viale Vittorio Emanuele. **GPS:** n45,88926 e9,95812.⬆

5 ⬛free ⛽🔌Chfree. **Surface:** asphalted. 🅿 01/01-31/12
Distance: 🚶600m 🅿on the spot.
Remarks: Max. 48h.

⬛S **Colico** 24D5
L'Ontano, Via Montecchio Nord. **GPS:** n46,14213 e9,37452. ⬆➡.

25 ⬛€ 15/24h ⛽🔌 Ch 🚿 WC ▯€1/3minutes. **Surface:** metalled.
🅿 01/02-31/12
Distance: 🚶500m 🅿on the spot ⊗on the spot.
Remarks: View on Lake Como.

⬛S **Cremona** 31D1
Piazzale della Croce Rossa, Via Mantova. **GPS:** n45,13744 e10,03464. ⬆.

⬛free ⛽🔌Chfree. **Location:** Simple. **Surface:** asphalted.
🅿 01/01-31/12
Distance: 🚶on the spot 🚲3km ⊗on the spot 🍺200m 🚌on the spot.
Remarks: Nearby stadium.

🍴S **Desenzano del Garda** 25B6
Pit-Stop La Spiaggia, Via Valtenesi, 19. **GPS:** n45,48783 e10,52468. ⬆.

100 ⬛€ 10/24h ⛽🔌Chincluded. **Surface:** unpaved.
🅿 01/01-31/12
Distance: 🅿200m ⊗Pizzeria Stella Del Garda 🚌10m.

🍴S **Esine** 25A5
Parco e Ristorante Le Fontanelle, Via Toroselle 12, SS42.
GPS: n45,90302 e10,21820.

15 ⬛ ⛽🔌Ch. **Surface:** grassy. 🅿 01/01-31/12
Distance: 🚶4km ⊗on the spot.

⬛S **Gandino** 25A5
Via Giovanni Pascoli. **GPS:** n45,81286 e9,90538. ⬆➡.

2 ⬛free ⛽🔌Chfree. **Surface:** metalled. 🅿 01/01-31/12
Distance: 🚶historical centre 250m.
Remarks: Max. 48h.

⬛S **Gavirate** 24C5
Via Cavour. **GPS:** n45,83913 e8,72105. ⬆➡.

30 ⬛€ 8/day ⛽€2 🔌Ch€1 🚿 €1/12h. ▯🅿 **Location:** Rural, simple, quiet.
Surface: grasstiles. 🅿 01/01-31/12
Distance: 🚶200m 🅿10m ⊗on the spot 🚲on the spot 🚶on the spot.
Remarks: At lake of Varese, friday market.

⬛S **Germignaga** 24C5
Via A. Bodmer. **GPS:** n45,99630 e8,72421. ⬆.

6 ⬛€ 1,50/h, € 15/24h ⛽€1 🔌Ch 🔌€3 WC. ▯🅿 **Location:** Simple, central,
quiet. **Surface:** asphalted. 🅿 01/01-31/12
Distance: 🚶500m 🅿on the spot 🚲on the spot ⊗500m 🍺500m.
Remarks: Max. 48h, key electricity at pay-desk.

⬛ **Iseo** 25A6
Viale Europa. **GPS:** n45,65396 e10,04449.

IT

🏕free. **Surface:** unpaved. ⬛ 01/01-31/12
Distance: 🚶1km ⛰250m ⊗600m.
Tourist information Iseo:
ℹ️ I.A.T. (Ufficio Informazioni e di Accoglienza Turistica), Lungolago Marconi,
2. Old fishermen's village. 🎪 Week market. ⬛ Fri.

🏕 S	Lecco	24D5

Via Arturo Toscanini, Loc. Bione di Lecco. **GPS:** n45,83136 e9,40779. ⬆️.

12 🏕free 🚰🗑Chfree. **Surface:** asphalted. ⬛ 01/01-31/12
Distance: 🚶2,8km.
Remarks: At lake Garlate, cycle routes.

🏕 S	Livigno 🏔❄	25A4

Aquafresca, Via Palipert 374. **GPS:** n46,50713 e10,11952. ⬆️.
🏕 🚰🗑Ch🔧 WC ⬛. ⬛ 01/01-31/12
Distance: 🚴on the spot 🚵on the spot.
Remarks: Free shuttle.

🏕 S	Livigno 🏔❄	25A4

Stella Alpina, Via Palipert 570. **GPS:** n46,50515 e10,11958. ⬆️.

28 🏕€ 15 🚰🗑Ch🔧€3 WC ⬛📷📶. **Surface:** gravel.
⬛ 01/01-31/12
Distance: 🚶400m 🚌Free bus 🚴on the spot.
Remarks: Free shuttle to ski-lifts.

🏕 S	Livigno 🏔❄	25A4

Trepalle, SS301. **GPS:** n46,52655 e10,17578. ⬆️.

50 🏕€ 10 🚰🗑Chfree. **Surface:** asphalted.

Distance: 🚶Livigno 6,6km ⊗200m 🚌bus to Livigno every 40 minutes
🚴on the spot.
Remarks: Altitude 2000m.
Tourist information Livigno:
👁 Latteria di Livigno, Via Pemonte 911. Discover the secrets of dairy products
from Livigno. On Wednesday the possibility of preparing meals, costs € 7, from
14h. ⬛ summer Mo-Fr 8-20h.

🏕 S	Lodrino	25A6

Via Kennedy, Localité Dade. **GPS:** n45,71450 e10,28107. ⬆️.

3 🏕free 🚰🗑Ch 🔧free. **Surface:** asphalted. ⬛ 01/01-31/12
Distance: 🚶500m.

🏕 S	Luino	24C5

Via Gorizia. **GPS:** n45,97255 e8,75275. ⬆️➡️.

16 🏕€ 9 Ch. **Location:** Rural, isolated, quiet. **Surface:** asphalted/grassy.
⬛ 01/01-31/12
Distance: 🚶3km ⊗on the spot 🚤3km.
Remarks: At sports grounds.

🏕 S	Maccagno	24C5

Via Virgilio Parisi. **GPS:** n46,04010 e8,73545. ⬆️➡️.

18 🏕free 🚰free.
Location: Rural, simple, central, quiet. **Surface:** gravel.
Distance: 🚶300m ⛰200m 🚶200m ⊗300m 🚤300m 🚌300m
🚲on the spot 🚶on the spot.
Remarks: At sports centre, max. 72h, friday market.

🏕 S	Magnacavallo	32A1

Via Salvador Allende. **GPS:** n45,00587 e11,17906. ⬆️➡️.

IT

4 ⑤free ⟶ ⬛Chfree. **Location:** Simple. **Surface:** asphalted.
⬛ 01/01-31/12
Distance: 200m ⊗200m ⚑200m 🚲50m.
Remarks: At sports park.

| ⑤S | | Mandello del Lario | 24D5 |

Area Cima, Via Giulio Cesare. **GPS:** n45,91830 e9,31589.➡.

12 ⑤€10 ⟶ ⬛ Ch. **Surface:** asphalted. ⬛ 01/01-31/12
Distance: 800m ⊿Lago di Lecco 400m.

| ⑤S | | Mantova ⬭ | 32A1 |

Parco Paganini, Via Fiera 11, Grazie di Curtatone. **GPS:** n45,15333 e10,69111.
⬆➡.

108 ⑤€12 ⟶ ⬛ Ch ⚿ WC ⬛included. ⬛ **Location:** Simple, central.
Surface: asphalted/grassy. ⬛ 01/03-13/11
Distance: 300m, Mantova 6km ⊗300m ⚑4km, bakery 300m.

| ⑤S | | Mantova | 32A1 |

Sparafucile, Via Legnago 1/a. **GPS:** n45,16336 e10,81244.⬆➡.
54 ⑤€ 10/12-12h, € 15/24h ⟶ ⬛Chincluded ⚿ WC ⬛.⬛
Location: Luxurious. **Surface:** grassy/metalled. ⬛ 01/01-31/12
Distance: 1km ⚓4km.

| ⬛ | | Mantova ⬭ | 32A1 |

Anconetta. **GPS:** n45,15322 e10,79864.⬆.

⑤free. **Location:** Urban, simple. **Surface:** asphalted. ⬛ 01/01-31/12
Distance: centre 800m ⊿on the spot.
Remarks: Marina.

| ⑤ | | Menaggio | 24D5 |

Via Armando Diaz 12. **GPS:** n46,02454 e9,23900.
20 ⑤free. ⬛ 01/01-31/12
Distance: 550m ⊿on the spot ⚑on the spot.

| ⑤S | | Merate | 24D6 |

Via Papa Giovanni Paolo I, loc. Sartirana. **GPS:** n45,71326 e9,41865.⬆.

10 ⑤€ 5,50 ⟶ ⬛Ch ⚿. **Surface:** grasstiles.
Remarks: Max. 72h.

| ⑤S | | Milano ✹⚘⬭ | 31C1 |

Ripamonti SNC, Via Ripamonti 481, Milan (Milano). **GPS:** n45,40914 e9,20937.

30 ⑤€ 20/24h ⟶ ⬛ Ch ⚿ €5 WC ⬛included. **Surface:** asphalted.
Distance: ⬛on the spot ⚑Milan 40min.
Remarks: Monitored parking.

| ⑤ | | Milano ✹⚘⬭ | 31C1 |

Camper Village Linate Parking, Viale Enrico Forlanini, 123, Milan (Milano).
GPS: n45,46245 e9,27024.⬆.
⑤€ 20/24h. **Location:** Urban. **Surface:** metalled. ⬛ 01/01-31/12
Distance: centre 7km ⚑N 74 > centre.

Tourist information Milan (Milano):
Ⓜ✖ Castello Sforzesco.
⬆ Duomo. History of Gothic architecture. ⬛ Tue-Su.
⚘ Via Fauché. ⬛ Tue, Sa.
⚘ Mercatone del Naviglio Grande, Naviglio Grande. Antiques market, 400 stalls.
⬛ last Su of the month.
⬭ Galleria.

| ⑤ | | Moglia | 32A1 |

Via Tazio Nuvolari. **GPS:** n44,93639 e10,91582.⬆.

14 ⑤free ⟶ ⬛Chfree. **Surface:** asphalted. ⬛ 01/01-31/12
Distance: 300m ⚓A22 7km ⊗300m.
Remarks: At swimming pool.

| ⬛ | | Monte Marenzo | 24D6 |

Via Papa Gionvanni. **GPS:** n45,77639 e9,45222.⬆.

IT

6 🅼free ⛽🚽free. **Surface:** gravel. ⭕ 01/01-31/12
Distance: 🚉300m.

🅼S · · · · · · · · · · · · **Monzambano** · · · · · · · · · · 25B6
Area attrezzata camper Comunale di Monzambano, Via Degli Alpini n. 9.
GPS: n45,38916 e10,69277.⬆➡.

140 🅼€ 12/24h ⛽🚽🚿(24x)🔌included 📶€1/12h. **Surface:** gravel.
⭕ 01/01-31/12
Distance: ⊗100m 🚉300m, bakery 100m.
Remarks: Max. 48h.

🅼S · · · · · · · · · · · · **Morbegno** ❄️🏔❄ · · · · · · · · 24D5
Area Sosta Camper Morbegno, Via del Foss. **GPS:** n46,14419 e9,57500.⬆.
22 🅼€ 10 ⛽🚽Ch🚿📶included. **Location:** Rural. **Surface:** grasstiles.
⭕ 01/01-31/12
Distance: 🚉historical centre 500m ⊗100m 🚌Skibus 🚲 on the spot.

🅼S · · · · · · · · · · · · **Niardo** · · · · · · · · · · · · · 25A5
Area di sosta Mr. Sanders, Località Crist. **GPS:** n45,97690 e10,31959.⬆.

20 🅼€ 10 ⛽🚽Ch🚿€2 WC🔌. **Surface:** metalled. ⭕ 01/01-31/12
Distance: 🚉Niardo 1,3km ⊘on the spot ⊗on the spot.
Remarks: Bread-service.

🅼S · · · · · · · · · · · · **Nova Milanese** 🛑 · · · · · · · 24D6
Via G. Brodolini. **GPS:** n45,58298 e9,19668.⬆➡.

25 🅼free. **Surface:** grassy/gravel. ⭕ 01/01-31/12
Distance: 🚉800m ⊘40m 🚽800m 🚲on the spot.
Remarks: At lake Mezzola, signposted cycle routes.

🅼S · · · · · · · · · · · · **Olginate** · · · · · · · · · · · 24D6
Via Cesare Cantù. **GPS:** n45,79523 e9,41610.⬆.

46 🅼€ 8/12h ⛽🚽Ch🚿. **Surface:** metalled. ⭕ 01/01-31/12
⭕ Thu>16h-Fri<16h (market)
Distance: 🚉200m ⊘on the spot.
Remarks: At Olginate lake.

🅼S · · · · · · · · · · · · **Pizzighettone** · · · · · · · · 31D1
Via De Gasperi. **GPS:** n45,18538 e9,79402.⬆➡.

4 🅼free ⛽🚽Chfree. **Location:** Simple. **Surface:** gravel.
⭕ 01/01-31/12
Distance: 🚉400m ⊗300m 🛒Lidl 100m.

🅼S · · · · · · · · · · · · **Rovetta** · · · · · · · · · · · · 25A5
Campo sportivo, Via Papa Giovanni XIII. **GPS:** n45,88892 e9,98224.⬆.

🅼free ⛽🚽Ch. **Surface:** asphalted.
Distance: 🚉400m.
Remarks: Parking at gymnasium.

🍴🅼S · · · · · · · · · · · · **Ruino** 🛑🏔🏕🎾 · · · · · · · · 31C1
Agriturismo Adriana Tarantani, Loc. Tre Venti. **GPS:** n44,92833 e9,26311.⬆.

4 🅼free ⛽🚽free. **Location:** Urban, simple. **Surface:** asphalted.
⭕ 01/01-31/12
Distance: 🚉500m 🚲1,6km ⊗200m.
Remarks: Video surveillance.

6 ⌇free with a meal ⌂ 🗑Ch ⚡. **Location:** Rural, simple.
Surface: grassy/gravel. ⬛ 01/01-31/12
Distance: 🚶1km ⊗on the spot ⚊1km 🚌100m.

| ⌇S | Sabbioneta ⚓ | 32A1 |

Via Piccola Atene. **GPS:** n44,99459 e10,48849.⬆️➡️.

15 ⌇free ⌂ 🗑Chfree. **Location:** Simple, quiet. **Surface:** metalled.
⬛ 01/01-31/12
Distance: 🚶200m ⊗400m ⚊500m.

| ⌇S | San Benedetto Po ⚜ | 32A1 |

Via Cardinal Ruffini. **GPS:** n45,04292 e10,93432.⬆️.
4 ⌇free ⌂ 🗑Chfree. **Surface:** asphalted. ⬛ 01/01-31/12
Distance: 🚶500m ⊗on the spot.

| ⌇S | Santa Caterina Valfurva | 25B4 |

Baita de Naségn, Via Forni, loc. Nassegno. **GPS:** n46,40917 e10,50833.⬆️➡️.

⌇€ 12 ⌂ 🗑Ch ⚡ €3. **Surface:** grassy.
Distance: 🚶500m 🏊on the spot 🎿on the spot.

| ⌇S | Saronno | 24C6 |

Via E.H.Griegh. **GPS:** n45,61265 e9,04274.⬆️.

2 ⌇free ⌂ €1/100liter 🗑Ch. **Location:** Simple, simple. **Surface:** asphalted.
⬛ 01/01-31/12
Distance: 🚶1,5km ⚡3,5km ⊗500m ⚊200m.

| ⌇S | Saronno | 24C6 |

Via Dalmazia 11. **GPS:** n45,62446 e9,02469.⬆️.

2 ⌇free. **Location:** Urban, central. **Surface:** concrete.
⬛ 01/01-31/12
Distance: 🚶on the spot ⚡2km ⊗1km ⚊1km.
Remarks: Max. 24h.

| ⌇S | Sartirana Lomellina | 31B1 |

Via Cavour. **GPS:** n45,11337 e8,66936.⬆️➡️⬆️.

3 ⌇free ⌂ €2/100liter 🗑Ch. **Location:** Simple. **Surface:** asphalted.
⬛ 01/01-31/12 🔘 Sa-morning market
Distance: 🚶100m ⊗200m ⚊100m 🚌on the spot.

| ⌇⌇S | Sirmione ⚜ | 25B6 |

Camper Park Sirmione, Via Cantarane. **GPS:** n45,46083 e10,63333.⬆️.

150 ⌇€ 20/24h, € 11/20.30-9.30h ⌂ 🗑Ch ⚡ €3 📶included.
Surface: gravel. ⬛ 15/03-31/10
Distance: 🚶1,5km ⛵Lake Garda ⊗100m ⚊1km 🚌100m.

| ⌇S | Sirmione ⚜ | 25B6 |

Piazzale Montebaldo. **GPS:** n45,48694 e10,61028.⬆️➡️.

21 ⌇from € 2,50 1/2h till-€ 21/24h ⌂ 🗑Ch WC. **Surface:** asphalted.
⬛ 01/01-31/12
Distance: 🚶200m ⛵on the spot ⊗50m ⚊200m.

| ⌇S | Sondrio ⛰❄ | 25A5 |

Area Sportiva, Via Vanoni. **GPS:** n46,16064 e9,86957.⬆️.

IT

6 ⛺free 🚰🔌Ch free. **Surface:** asphalted.
Distance: 🚶600m.
Remarks: Parking sports park.

🏕S   **Stezzano**   **24D6**
Via Pietro Mascagni. **GPS:** n45,65594 e9,65301.⬆️.

⛺free 🚰🔌Ch free. **Surface:** asphalted.

🏕S   **Sulzano**   **25A6**
Parking Gerolo, Via Tassano 14. **GPS:** n45,63546 e10,07665.⬆️➡️.

25 ⛺€ 15/24h, € 10/night 🚰🔌Ch WC 🚿. **Surface:** grassy.
🔲 01/01-31/12
Distance: 🚶300m ⛵Lago Iseo 400m 🛒300m.

🏕S   **Ternate** 🚤   **24C6**
Via Roma. **GPS:** n45,78006 e8,69780.⬆️➡️.

8 ⛺free 🚰🔌Ch 🚿(4x)free. **Location:** Simple, central, quiet.
Surface: unpaved. 🔲 01/01-31/12
Distance: 🚶200m ⛵on the spot 🎣on the spot ✖on the spot 🛒200m
🚲on the spot 🏊on the spot.
Remarks: At Comabbio lake.

🏕S   **Tirano** 🚂   **25A4**
Area Camper Tirano, Via Polveriera/Via Sala Piero. **GPS:** n46,21361 e10,15722.
⬆️➡️.

20 ⛺€ 10/24h 🚰🔌Ch 🚿 included. **Location:** Comfortable.
Surface: metalled.
Distance: 🚶1km 🚉station 800m.
Tourist information Tirano:
  ℹ️ Bernina Express. The highest-altitude trans-Alpine line in Europe, with one of the steepest gradients in the world between Tirano (It) and Chur (Ch). UNESCO's List of World Heritage. 🎫 ± € 100/pp return ticket (Tirano-Chur), ± € 45/pp return ticket (Tirano-Pontresina).

🏕S   **Torbole** 🎿🚣⛰️🌳   **25B5**
Tr@ns.it, Via Al Cor. **GPS:** n45,87264 e10,87260.⬆️➡️.

120 ⛺€ 20-33 🚰🔌Ch 🚿WC 🚿 📶included. **Surface:** grassy.
🔲 01/01-31/12
Distance: 🚶on the spot ⛵on the spot ✖on the spot 🛒on the spot.
Remarks: Along Lake Garda.

©S   **Toscolano Maderno** 🚤   **25B6**
Area Sosta Maderno, Via Promontorio. **GPS:** n45,63487 e10,61103.⬆️➡️.

25 ⛺€ 25 🚰🔌Ch 🚿WC 🚿included 🚿. **Surface:** grassy.
🔲 01/01-31/12
Distance: ⛵500m.

🏕S   **Treviglio**   **24D6**
Via al Malgari. **GPS:** n45,53142 e9,59710.⬆️.

4 ⛺free 🚰🔌Ch free. **Surface:** metalled. 🔲 01/01-31/12
Distance: 🚶700m 🛒400m.
Remarks: At sports park.

Varzi 31C2

Strada Circonvallazione. **GPS:** n44,82172 e9,19727. ⬆️➡️.

30 🅿️ free, summer € 5 🚰 ⚡ Ch WC free. 🛶 **Location:** Simple, central.
Surface: asphalted/metalled. ☀️ 01/01-31/12
Distance: 🚂 200m 🚲 50m 🧍 50m.
Remarks: Along the Staffora river, friday market.

Veneto

Arquà Polesine 32B1

Ostello Canalbianco, SS 16, n15. **GPS:** n44,99665 e11,76243.
12 🅿️ € 10 🚰 ⚡ Ch 💦 WC 🔧.
Distance: ❌ on the spot.

Asiago 25C5

P Verdi Mosele, SS349, Via Giuseppe Verdi. **GPS:** n45,87129 e11,50026. ⬆️.

20 🅿️ € 1/h, € 4/day. **Surface:** asphalted. ☀️ 01/01-31/12
Distance: 🚂 300m 🧍 500m.

Asolo 25D5

Area Camper Communale, Via Forestuzzo. **GPS:** n45,79637 e11,91283. ⬆️➡️.

13 🅿️ € 7/24h 🚰 ⚡ Ch 💦 (14x)included. **Surface:** grassy/sand.
☀️ 01/01-31/12
Distance: 🚂 400m ❌ 400m 🧍 400m.
Remarks: Access 8-19.30h, barbecue place, picnic area.

Auronzo di Cadore 26A3

Taiarezze, SR48, Via Reaneloc. **GPS:** n46,56217 e12,41640. ⬆️.

30 🅿️ € 8, 20/07-31/08 and 24/12-06/01 € 12 🚰 ⚡ Ch included. 🚐

Location: Rural, simple, quiet. **Surface:** asphalted. ☀️ 01/01-31/12
Distance: 🚂 1,5km 🅿️ on the spot ❌ on the spot 🧍 on the spot 🚐 on the spot 🛶 on the spot 🧍 on the spot 🏊 1,6km 🚲 1,6km.
Remarks: Max. 48h, payment only with coins.

Barbarano Vicentino 25D6

Viale Vittorio Veneto 66. **GPS:** n45,40725 e11,54654. ⬆️.

3 🅿️ free 🚰 ⚡ free. **Surface:** asphalted. ☀️ 01/01-31/12
Distance: 🚂 200m ❌ 200m 🧍 200m.

Bassano del Grappa 25D5

Parcheggio Gerosa, Via Alcide de Gasperi. **GPS:** n45,75831 e11,73091. ⬆️➡️.

20 🅿️ € 12/24h 🚰 ⚡ Ch 💦 included. **Surface:** asphalted.
☀️ 01/01-31/12
Distance: 🚂 300m ❌ 300m 🧍 300m 🚐 on the spot.
Remarks: Max. 48h.

Bassano del Grappa 25D5

Prato Santo Caterina, Via Chini 6. **GPS:** n45,76009 e11,73413.
🅿️ free.
Distance: 🚂 on the spot.

Belluno 26A4

Rio Cavalli, Via Sagrogna 74. **GPS:** n46,15646 e12,26136. ⬆️.

20 🅿️ € 10, electricity included € 15 🚰 💦 ⚡ €5 📶.
Location: Comfortable, central, quiet. **Surface:** grassy/sand.
☀️ 01/01-31/12
Distance: 🚂 3km 🚲 6km 🛶 on the spot ❌ on the spot 🧍 3km 🚐 on the spot.

Belluno 26A4

Viale dei Dendrofori, loc. Lambioi. **GPS:** n46,13712 e12,21371. ⬆️➡️.

IT

12 🚐8-18 € 0,80/h, overnight stay free 🚐 💺 Ch free. **Location:** Simple, central, noisy. **Surface:** grasstiles/metalled. 🔲 01/01-31/12
Distance: 🚶100m ⊗100m 🛒100m.
Remarks: Nearby swimming pool and skating rink.

🚐 S	**Bibione**	26B5

Strada Brussa. **GPS:** n45,62458 e12,95866.⬆.

4 🚐 free. **Location:** Simple, central, quiet. **Surface:** sand.
🔲 01/05-31/10
Distance: 🚶1km ⚓on the spot 🛒on the spot ⊗on the spot 🛒1km 🚌300m.
Remarks: Beach parking.
Tourist information Cavallino-Treporti:
⛺ Week market. 🔲 Tue-Thu morning.

🚐 S	**Chioggia**	32C1

2 Palme, Lungomare Adriatica. **GPS:** n45,22122 e12,29624.⬆.

100 🚐€ 7/day, overnight stay free 🚐 WC 🗑. **Location:** Rural, simple, isolated, quiet. **Surface:** grassy. 🔲 25/04-31/09
Distance: ⚓sandy beach 250m.
Remarks: Guarded during the day, dog permitted on the beach.

🚐 S	**Borghetto di Valeggio sul Mincio** 🌿	25B6

Camper parking Visconteo, Strada provinciale 55. **GPS:** n45,35537 e10,72017.⬆.
60 🚐€ 10/24h 🚐€3 💺 Ch 🔌€1/12h.
Location: Rural, comfortable. **Surface:** gravel.
Distance: 🚶on the spot ⚓Lake Garda 13km ⊗250m 🚲on the spot 🏃on the spot.
Remarks: Borghetto 200m.

🚐	**Caorle** 🏖	26B5

Area di sosta Ai Parchi, Via Traghete. **GPS:** n45,60490 e12,88500.⬆.

65 🚐€ 11-16/24h 🚐 💺 Ch 🔌(60x)€4/kWh WC 🗑€1/3minutes 📶.
Location: Comfortable, isolated, noisy.
Surface: gravel.
🔲 01/01-31/12
Distance: 🚶historical centre 1,1km ⚓500m ⊗300m 🛒300m 🏧350m 🚌150m.
Remarks: Max. 72h, monitored parking, Luna Park 150m, Parco Acquatico 150m.

🚐	**Cavallino-Treporti** 🏖	26A6

Spiaggia di Cà Ballarin, Via Gabrielle Berton. **GPS:** n45,45998 e12,51659.⬆.

100 🚐€ 12, peak season € 20, Su/holidays € 15 🚐 💺 Ch 🔌 (100x) WC included 🗑€0,50. 🚲 **Location:** Urban, simple, central.
Surface: grassy/gravel. 🔲 01/01-31/12
Distance: 🚶centre 1,8km ⚓200m.
Remarks: Chioggia: little Venice.

🚐 S	**Colà di Lazise** 🍃	25B6

Villa dei Cedri, Via Possoi. **GPS:** n45,46777 e10,74972.⬆.

200 🚐€ 1/h, 5 hours min 🚐 💺 Ch 🔌 📶included. 🚐 **Location:** Rural.
Surface: grasstiles. 🔲 01/01-31/12
Remarks: Parco Termale 300m.

🚐 S	**Conegliano** 🍷	26A5

Area de Sosta Campeggio Club Conegliano, Via Don Bosco, SS13.
GPS: n45,87799 e12,30111.⬆➡.

30 🚐€ 12/24h 🚐 💺 Ch 🔌(16x)included WC 🗑. **Location:** Simple, central, quiet. **Surface:** grassy. 🔲 01/01-31/12
Distance: 🚶2km ⊗nearby 🛒on the spot.

IT

Domegge di Cadore Belluno 26A3

Camping Cologna, Vallesella di Cadore. **GPS**: n46,44605 e12,40658.

30 € 10 Ch. **Location:** Rural, simple, quiet. **Surface:** grassy. 01/05-20/10
Distance: 1km At the lake on the spot on the spot 1km 1km on the spot on the spot.
Remarks: Max. 24h, narrow entrance.

Feltre 25D5

Area Camper Vincheto, Via Casonetto 158C. **GPS**: n46,03124 e11,95911.
12 € 15 Ch included €3. **Surface:** grassy/metalled. 01/01-31/12

Feltre 25D5

Piazale Pra del Vescovo, Viale A. Gaggia. **GPS**: n46,02013 e11,90792.

15 free Ch free. **Surface:** metalled. 01/01-31/12
Distance: 500m 500m 500m 500m.
Remarks: Max. 48h.

Ferrara di Monte Baldo 25B6

Via Chiesa. **GPS**: n45,67794 e10,85491.

16 free Ch (16x). **Location:** Rural, simple, isolated, quiet.
Surface: gravel. 01/01-31/12
Distance: 300m 300m 300m on the spot on the spot.

Garda 25B6

P Centro, SS249. **GPS**: n45,57501 e10,71019.

20 € 13/24h WC. **Surface:** metalled. 01/01-31/12
Distance: 200m on the spot on the spot.

Garda 25B6

Via Preite. **GPS**: n45,57620 e10,71404.
30 € 15/24h Ch. **Surface:** metalled. service: Easter-31/10
Distance: 300m Lake Garda 300m.

Lazise 25B6

Parking Lazise Dardo, Via San Martino, SP31. **GPS**: n45,50623 e10,73584.

15 € 17/24h. **Surface:** asphalted. 01/01-31/12
Distance: 200m 5,8km 200m 200m 200m.

Lido di Jesolo 26B6

Area camping Albatros, Via Correr 102/A. **GPS**: n45,52477 e12,68995.

131 € 9-17 Ch WC included. **Location:** Comfortable, isolated, quiet. **Surface:** grassy. 01/03-31/10
Distance: 500m 700m 100m 100m 100m 100m.

Lido di Jesolo 26B6

Boscopineta, Via Vettor Pisani. **GPS**: n45,52278 e12,69178.

250 € 10-20 Ch WC. **Location:** Comfortable, central.
Surface: grassy. 01/01-31/12
Distance: 400m.

Lido di Jesolo 26B6

Camping Park dei Dogi, Viale Oriente. **GPS**: n45,52146 e12,68828.

200 € 14-26, 4 pers.incl. Ch WC included €0,50.
Location: Comfortable, central, quiet. **Surface:** grassy. 01/01-31/12
Distance: 200m sandy beach 200m 40m 40m 20m.

IT

Lido di Jesolo — 26B6
Jesolo Camper Don Bosco, Via Oriente/via G.Don Bosco.
GPS: n45,52188 e12,68943.⬆️➡️.

250 € 10-20 🚰🗑️ Ch ⚡€3/kWh WC 🚽€1 🚿€5. **Surface:** grassy/gravel.
📅 01/01-31/12
Distance: 🚌within walking distance 🏖️100m ⊗on the spot 🛒100m
🍴on the spot. **Remarks:** Bus to Venice stops in front of motorhome parking.

Lido di Jesolo — 26B6
Parcheggio Mare d'Oriente, Viale Oriente, Lido di Jesolo est.
GPS: n45,52083 e12,68556.⬆️.

€ 10/24h, € 13/Sunday, Aug 🚰🗑️ Ch ⚡included 🚿. **Location:** Simple,
central, quiet. **Surface:** grassy. 📅 summer
Distance: 🚌100m 🏖️100m ⊗on the spot 🛒on the spot 🍴on the spot.
Remarks: Servicepoint at Don Bosco, incl.

Livinallongo del Col di Lana — 25D3
Sportbar del Ghiaccio, Via Piagn,6 Arabba. **GPS:** n46,49678 e11,87692.⬆️.

50 € 10/24h, Jul-Aug-Dec € 14 🚰🗑️ Ch ⚡(17x)€3/24h WC 🚽€3.
Location: Rural, comfortable, quiet. **Surface:** grassy/gravel.
📅 01/01-31/12
Distance: 🚌on the spot ⊗on the spot 🛒200m 🍴200m 🚲on the spot
🏃on the spot 🚴200m.
Remarks: At the skating rink, check in at bar.

Malcesine — 25B5
Camping Lombardi, Via Navene, loc. Campagnola. **GPS:** n45,78429 e10,82187.
⬆️.

20 € 17/24h, 28/06-01/09 € 20/24h 🚰€1 Ch ⚡ WC 🚽€1.
Surface: unpaved. 📅 01/04-31/10
Distance: 🚌3km 🏖️Lake Garda 500m.
Remarks: Max. 48h.

Marghera — 26A6
Parcheggio Terminal Service, Via dei Petroli 1/3 angolo via della Libertà.
GPS: n45,46806 e12,26589.

€ 10/24h. **Location:** Simple, central, quiet.
📅 01/01-31/12
Distance: 🍴> Venice.
Remarks: Monitored parking.

Mirano — 26A6
Camper Club Mirano, Via viasana, 4. **GPS:** n45,49322 e12,08968.⬆️.

€ 12/24h 🚰🗑️ Ch ⚡.
Location: Comfortable. **Surface:** grasstiles.
Distance: 🚌historical centre 1,5km 🚆8km 🍴300m Padua-Venice.
Remarks: For entrance email: camperclubmirano@libero.it of
phone 3479831010.

Misurina — 26A3
Piazzale Loita, Via Monte Piana. **GPS:** n46,58839 e12,25737.➡️.

50 € 14 🚰🗑️ Ch included. 📷 **Location:** Rural, simple, simple, central,
noisy. **Surface:** gravel. 📅 01/01-31/12
Distance: 🚌300m 🏖️500m ⊗50m 🛒300m 🍴on the spot 🚲on the spot
🏃on the spot 🚴3km.
Remarks: Max. 48h.

Misurina — 26A3
P camper Rifugio Auronzo, Rifugio Auronzo. **GPS:** n46,61267 e12,29342.➡️.

IT

40 ⃠€ 33 toll road incl., extra night € 15. 🅿 **Location:** Rural, simple, isolated. **Surface:** gravel. ⬛ 01/05-30/10 **Distance:** 🚴Misurina 12km ⊗on the spot 🚊12km 🚌on the spot 🥾 Tre Cime di Lavadero 🚠15km. **Remarks:** Beautiful view.

50 ⃠€ 3,50. 🏖 **Location:** Rural, quiet. **Surface:** grassy/sand. **Distance:** 🏖50m. **Remarks:** Beach parking.

| 📷S | Punta Sabbioni 🚣🍴 | 26A6 |

Parking Dante Alighieri, Dante Alighieri 26. **GPS:** n45,44132 e12,42131. ⬆.

| 📷S | Montagnana 🌿 | 32B1 |

Via Circonvallazione. **GPS:** n45,23528 e11,46639. ⬆➡.

20 ⃠free 🔌🗑ChWCfree. **Surface:** asphalted. ⬛ 01/01-31/12 **Distance:** 🚴200m ⊗200m 🚊200m. **Remarks:** At sports centre.

36 ⃠€ 17-20 + € 3/pp 🔌🗑Ch🚿€3 WC 🗑⬛€3. **Location:** Simple, central, quiet. **Surface:** grassy. ⬛ 01/01-31/12 **Distance:** 🚴on the spot 🏊1,5km 🚊700m 🚌free shuttle to beach. **Remarks:** Arrival <22h, monitored parking, ferry boat to Venice 500m.

| 📷S | Padova 🌿 | 25D6 |

P1, Piazza della Pace Ytzhak Rabbin, Via cinquantottesimo Fanteria, Padua (Padova). **GPS:** n45,39686 e11,87673. ⬆. ⃠8-20h € 10, 20-8h € 10, 18-10h € 20. **Surface:** asphalted. ⬛ 01/01-31/12 **Distance:** 🚴on the spot 🚲6km ⊗on the spot 🚊on the spot 🚌on the spot.

Tourist information Padua (Padova): 👁 Caffè Pedrocchi, Via Oberdan. Café, meeting point for students. 👁 Capella degli Scrovegni. Chapel.

| 🏖📷S | Punta Sabbioni 🚣🍴 | 26A6 |

Agricamping da Scarpa, Via Pealto 17. **GPS:** n45,44279 e12,44055.

| 📷S | Peschiera del Garda | 25B6 |

Area camper Peschiera, Via Milano. **GPS:** n45,43995 e10,68474. ⬆. 100 ⃠€ 12-15/24h 🔌🗑Ch🚿 included WC 🗑€1 🚿. 🅿 **Surface:** gravel. ⬛ 01/01-31/12 **Distance:** 🚴500m ⊗400m. **Remarks:** Monday-morning market.

| 📷S | Peschiera del Garda | 25B6 |

P4, Via Milano 67. **GPS:** n45,44141 e10,67892. ⬆.

15 ⃠€ 14-16 + € 5/pp 🔌🗑Ch🚿WCincluded 🗑. **Surface:** grassy. ⬛ 01/01-31/12 **Distance:** 🏊500m ⊗on the spot 🚊500m 🚌ferry Venice 1,5km.

| 📷S | Recoaro Terme 🚣🏔🍴❄ | 25C6 |

Area Communale, Via Della Restistenza. **GPS:** n45,70430 e11,22902. ⬆➡.

33 ⃠€ 15/24h 🔌🗑Chfree. **Surface:** gravel. ⬛ 01/01-31/12 **Distance:** 🚲5km 🏊Lake Garda 300m ⊗100m 🚌nearby. **Remarks:** Parking nearby campsite Bella Italia.

Tourist information Peschiera del Garda: ℹ Tourist town at Lake Garda. 🥾 ⬛ Mo-morning.

| 📷 | Porto Tolle 🍴 | 32C1 |

Via strada del Mare, loc. Barricata, SP38. **GPS:** n44,84997 e12,46342. ⬆.

16 ⃠€ 5/24h 🔌🗑€0,10/10liter 🗑Ch (16x)€0,50/2h,6Amp. ⬛ 01/01-31/12 **Distance:** 🚴on the spot ⊗on the spot 🚊on the spot 🚌on the spot 🚠on the spot.

| 📷S | Santo Stefano di Cadore 🏔🍴 | 26A3 |

Albergo Gasperina, Loc. Cima Canale, Val Visdende. **GPS:** n46,60835 e12,63053. ⬆➡.

IT

49 🚐 € 11/24h, Aug € 12 ⚓ 🔌 Ch ⚡ (49x)€3/day WC included 🚰€2. **Surface:** gravel.
🅾 25/04-01/10
Distance: 🛒12km ➳300m ⊗on the spot ⚓6km ♨on the spot 🅰on the spot.
Remarks: Check in at restaurant, bread-service, 10% discount at restaurant.

🚐S	**Sappada** 🏔❄	26A3

Area Camper, Borgata Palù. **GPS:** n46,56254 e12,67991.⬆➡

60 🚐 € 10/24h ⚓ 🔌 Ch ⚡ (24x)included. 🚰 **Location:** Rural, simple, quiet.
Surface: gravel. 🅾 01/01-31/12
Distance: 🛒1,1km ➳500m ⚡1km ♨on the spot 🅰on the spot ♒100m.
Remarks: Keycard at townhall, caution € 5.

🚐S	**Schio** ⛵🏔♨❄	25C5

Parking Palasport, Viale dell'Industria. **GPS:** n45,71389 e11,37599.⬆

4 🚐free ⚓ 🔌 Ch free. **Surface:** asphalted. 🅾 01/01-31/12
Distance: 🛒1km ⊗1km ⚡1km ♒on the spot ⚓on the spot.

🚐S	**Sernaglia della Battaglia**	26A5

Area attrezzata Le Grave, Via Passo Barca, Falzè di Piave.
GPS: n45,85676 e12,16566.⬆➡

26 🚐 € 5/12h, € 8/24h ⚓ 🔌 Ch included ⚡€2/24h. **Location:** Simple.
Surface: grassy. 🅾 01/01-31/12
Distance: 🛒150m ⚓on the spot ⊗100m ⚡150m ♒300m.

🚐S	**Soave** 🌺🍇	25C6

Via Invalidi del Lavoro. **GPS:** n45,42340 e11,24541.⬆➡

8 🚐 € 5 ⚓ 🔌 Ch ⚡ (8x)free,16Amp. 🚰 **Surface:** grasstiles.
🅾 01/01-31/12
Distance: 🛒200m ⚡ 3km ➳on the spot ⊗200m ⚡200m ♒300m.

🚐S	**Torre di Mosto**	26B5

Agriturismo La Via Antiga, Via S. Martino 13. **GPS:** n45,64389 e12,67056.⬆

8 🚐 € 15/day ⚓ 🔌 Ch ⚡ (5x)included. **Location:** Simple, isolated, quiet.
Surface: grassy/gravel. 🅾 01/03-30/09
Distance: 🛒7km.

🚐S	**Treviso** 🌺	26A5

Parking ex Foro Boario, Via Castello d'Amore. **GPS:** n45,67014 e12,25733.⬆

13 🚐free ⚓ 🔌 Ch free. **Surface:** metalled. 🅾 01/01-31/12
Distance: 🛒500m ⚡ 11,5km ⊗500m ⚡500m ♒200m.
Remarks: Max. 48h.

🚐S	**Treviso** 🌺	26A5

Via Giovanni Boccaccio. **GPS:** n45,66769 e12,26361.⬆➡

40 🚐free ⚓ 🔌 Ch free. **Location:** Simple, central, noisy. **Surface:** asphalted.
🅾 01/01-31/12
Distance: 🛒1km ⊗500m ⚡500m ♒300m.
Remarks: Along railwayline.

Tourist information Treviso:
🅰 Sile. Fish-market on island.

🚐S	**Venezia** 🌺⛵🏛🍴🍇	26A6

Parcheggio Al Tronchetto, Venice (Venezia) . **GPS:** n45,44146 e12,30514.⬆

🚐€ 21/0-12h, 12-24h € 16 🚰 ⬇ Ch 🚿.
Location: Urban, simple, central, quiet. **Surface:** asphalted.
📅 01/01-31/12
Distance: 🏙2km 🌊on the spot 🚌ferry Venice.

[🚐] [S] Venezia — 26A6

Parco di San Giuliano, Via San Giuliano, Venice (Venezia).
GPS: n45,46742 e12,27916.⬆.

100 🚐€ 10/24h 🚰€3 ⬇ Ch 🔌 WC 🚿. **Location:** Simple, central, quiet.
Surface: grassy. 📅 01/01-31/12
Distance: 🚌ferry Venice 100m.

Tourist information Venice (Venezia):
[i] A.P.T. (Azienda di Promozione Turistica), www.turismovenezia.it. Historical city consits of 117 islands, 150 canals and 400 bridges.

[🚐] [S] Verona — 25C6

Area sosta camper Porta Palio, Via dalla Bona. **GPS**: n45,43354 e10,97879.⬆.

37 🚐€ 5/4h, € 10/24h 🚰 ⬇ Chincluded. **Surface:** asphalted.
📅 01/01-31/12
Distance: 🏙500m 🍴Pizza (ordering service) 🚌bus 62 > centre.

[🍇] [S] Verona — 25C6

Agricamping Corte Finiletto, Strada Bresciana, 41. **GPS**: n45,44651 e10,91917.
⬆.

🚐€ 18, 2 pers.incl 🚰 ⬇ Ch 🔌€2 WC 🚿. **Surface:** grassy/gravel.

Tourist information Verona:
👁 Arena. Large anfiteatro, in July/August opera performances.
👁 Via Capella. Known for the love drama of Romeo and Juliet.
🏪 Piazza dellen Erbe. 📅 daily.

[🚐] [S] Vicenza — 25D6

Park Interscambio CentroBus, Via Bassano, Zona sud-est.
GPS: n45,54321 e11,55886.

40 🚐€ 10/24h 🚰 ⬇ 🔌 WCincluded. **Surface:** asphalted.
📅 01/01-31/12 ⛔ during event
Distance: 🏙2km 🍴on the spot 🚌Free bus to centre, every 15 min.
Remarks: At stadium.

[🚐] [S] Vicenza — 25D6

Park Interscambio CentroBus, Viale Cricoli, Zona nord.
GPS: n45,56418 e11,54903.➡.

18 🚐€ 8,40/24h 🚰 ⬇ Ch 🔌 WCincluded. **Surface:** asphalted.
📅 01/01-31/12
Distance: 🏙1,6km 🍴on the spot 🍞on the spot 🚌Free bus to centre.

Tourist information Vicenza:
👁 Quartiere delle Barche. District with palaces in Venetian style.

Friuli Venezia Giulia

[🚐] [S] Andreis — 26A4

SP20. **GPS**: n46,19880 e12,61157.⬆➡.

🚐€ 5/day 🚰 ⬇. **Location:** Simple. **Surface:** grassy/gravel.
Distance: 🌊little stream.

[🚐] [S] Barcis — 26A4

Loc. Portuz, SS251. **GPS**: n46,19055 e12,56507.⬆.

IT

20 🍴 € 12/24h 🚰 🔌 Ch 🔧. **Location:** Comfortable, isolated, quiet.
Surface: grasstiles/metalled. 🔲 01/01-31/12
Distance: 🚶400m 🅿on the spot ⊗500m 🚉500m.
Remarks: At the lake of Barcis.

| 📷 S | Corno di Rosazzo | 26C4 |

Via dei Pini. **GPS:** n45,98955 e13,43917. ⬆➡.

8 🍴free 🚰 🔌. **Location:** Rural, simple, quiet. **Surface:** asphalted.
🔲 01/01-31/12
Distance: 🚶300m.

| 📷 S | Dolegna del Collio | 26C4 |

Frazione Vencò. **GPS:** n46,00370 e13,47700. ⬆.

🍴free 🚰 🔌 Ch 🚾. **Surface:** asphalted.
Distance: 🚶Dolegna del Collio 4km.
Remarks: 50m from border with Slovenia, picnic area.

| 📷 S | Forni di Sopra 🏔 ⛄ ❄ | 26A3 |

Santa Viela, SS52. **GPS:** n46,42500 e12,57036. ❄.

20 🍴 € 7-9 🚰 🔌 Ch free. 🏕 **Location:** Rural, simple, noisy.
Surface: asphalted. 🔲 01/01-31/12
Distance: 🚶800m ⊗on the spot 🚉800m 🚌400m 🚴on the spot
🚶on the spot 🎿on the spot 🎣on the spot.
Remarks: No camping activities.

| 📷 S | Gemona del Friuli | 26B4 |

Piazzale Mons. Battista Monai. **GPS:** n46,27585 e13,13728. ⬆.
🍴free 🚰 🔌 Ch free.
Location: Simple, central, noisy. **Surface:** asphalted.
Distance: 🚶on the spot 🚲3,3km.

| 📷 S | Gorizia 🏛 | 26C4 |

Viale Oriani. **GPS:** n45,94554 e13,61603. ⬆.

30 🍴free 🚰 🔌 Ch free. **Location:** Simple, quiet. **Surface:** asphalted.
🔲 01/01-31/12
Distance: 🚶centre 500m.

| 📷 S | Gradisca d'Isonzo | 26C5 |

Viale Trieste. **GPS:** n45,88577 e13,49582. ⬆.

3 🍴free 🚰 🔌 Ch free. **Location:** Central. **Surface:** asphalted.
Distance: 🚶on the spot 🚲2,3km ⊗on the spot 🚉on the spot.
Remarks: Max. 48h.

| 📷 S | Grado | 26C5 |

Viala Italia. **GPS:** n45,68218 e13,41230. ⬆➡.

40 🍴 € 12 🚰 🔌 Ch 🚾 included. 💶 **Location:** Simple. **Surface:** asphalted.
🔲 01/01-31/12
Distance: 🚶1km 🚲24km 🚉600m.

| 📷 S | Montereale Valcellina | 26A4 |

Via dell'Omo. **GPS:** n46,15168 e12,66122. ⬆➡.

15 🍴free 🚰 🔌 Ch. **Location:** Urban. **Surface:** asphalted.
🔲 01/01-31/12
Distance: 🚶500m 🚉300m.

| 📷 S | Pordenone | 26A5 |

Agip, SS13, Pordenone. **GPS:** n45,97236 e12,64332. ⬆.

IT

8 ⊞ € 3/24h 🚱 Ch. **Location:** Urban, simple, isolated, quiet.
Surface: asphalted. ◻ 01/01-31/12
Distance: 🚶1km 🚲 3km ⊗200m 🚉200m.
Remarks: To be paid at petrol station.

⊞ S **San Daniele del Friuli** 🛁 26B4

Via Udine, SP16. **GPS:** n46,15610 e13,01368. ⬆.

20 ⊞ free 🚱 Ch free. **Location:** Comfortable, central, quiet.
Surface: grasstiles. ◻ 01/01-31/12
Distance: 🚶300m ⊗on the spot 🚉300m 🚌200m.
Remarks: Parking sports park.

⊞ S **San Vito al Tagliamento** 26B5

Area di sosta San Vito al Tagliamento, Via Pulet. **GPS:** n45,91224 e12,86590.
⬆➡.

12 ⊞ € 5/12h, € 8/24h, € 15/48h 🚱€1 Ch 🚿.
Location: Rural, simple, isolated, quiet. **Surface:** asphalted. ◻ 01/01-31/12
Distance: 🚶500m 🚲 15km ⊗500m 🚉500m 🚌500m.
Remarks: Gate can be opened manually.

⊞ S **Sauris** 🏔 26A3

Prosciuttificio Wolf Sauris, Sauris di Sotto 88. **GPS:** n46,46756 e12,70833. ⬆.
10 ⊞ free 🚱 free WC . **Location:** Rural, simple, quiet.
Surface: asphalted.
Distance: 🚶on the spot ⊗150m 🚶on the spot.

⊞ S **Tarcento** 26B4

Plein-air Torre, Via Sotto Colle Verzan. **GPS:** n46,21496 e13,22503. ⬆.

10 ⊞ free 🚱 Ch 🚿 free.

Location: Simple, quiet. **Surface:** grasstiles.
Distance: 🚶200m ⊗200m 🚉200m.
Remarks: Nearby sports center, max. 72h, no camping activities.

⊞ S **Tarvisio** 🛁 🏔 ❄ 26C3

Parcheggio P3, Via Armando Diaz. **GPS:** n46,50426 e13,57157. ⬆➡.

25 ⊞ € 0,60/h 🚱 Ch. **Location:** Urban, simple, central.
Surface: metalled.
Distance: 🚶on the spot ⊗100m 🚉100m.

⊞ S **Trieste** 🌊 🛁 🍽 26C5

Via Von Bruck, Torre del Lloyd. **GPS:** n45,63710 e13,76990. ⬆➡.

50 ⊞ € 4 🚱 Ch free. **Location:** Highway, simple, noisy. **Surface:** asphalted.
◻ 01/01-31/12
Distance: 🚶3km 🚌shuttle to centre.
Remarks: Max. 72h, pitches under motorway.

⊞ **Trieste** 🌊 🛁 🍽 26C5

Piazzale 11 settembre 2001, Viale Miramare. **GPS:** n45,68250 e13,75138.

20 ⊞ free. **Location:** Urban, simple, quiet. **Surface:** metalled.
Distance: 🚶on the spot.
Remarks: In front of porticciolo di Barcola, quiet at night, crowdy during the day.

⊞ **Trieste** 🌊 🛁 🍽 26C5

Via Ottaviano Augusto. **GPS:** n45,64599 e13,75654.

⊞ free. **Location:** Urban. **Surface:** asphalted. ◻ 01/01-31/12
Distance: 🚶centre 500m ⊗100m 🚌on the spot.
Remarks: In opposite of Piazza Unitá d'Italia.

Tourist information Trieste:

IT

👁 Grotta del Giganta. Caves. 🅾 Tue-Su, 01/07-31/08 Mo-Su.

| 🚐S | **Udine** | 26B4 |

Via Chiusaforte. **GPS:** n46,08115 e13,22317.⬆️.
50 🚐free 🔧🗑 Chfree. **Surface:** grasstiles. 🅾 01/01-31/12
Distance: 🚶city centre 2km 🚲3,5km 🚌line 1 > centre.

| 🚐S | **Zoppola** | 26B5 |

Via Manteghe. **GPS:** n45,96502 e12,78019.⬆️➡️.

2 🚐free 🔧🗑 Chfree. **Location:** Rural, isolated, quiet. **Surface:** metalled.
🅾 01/01-31/12
Distance: 🚶centre 800m.
Remarks: At gymnasium.

Emilia-Romagna

| 🚐S | **Anita** | 32C2 |

Agriturismo Prato Pozzo, Via Rotta Martinella 34/a. **GPS:** n44,54892 e12,13322.
⬆️➡️.

20 🚐€ 5 + € 5/pp, guests free 🔧🗑 Ch 🔌 (12x)€ 2,50/day WC ⬜included
📷. **Location:** Rural, comfortable, isolated, quiet. **Surface:** grassy/metalled.
🅾 01/01-31/12
Distance: 🚶1km 🏖500m 🚉500m ⊗on the spot 🛒1km 🚌1km.

| 🚐S | **Argenta** | 32B2 |

Area Golf Club, Via Poderi. **GPS:** n44,63027 e11,81112.⬆️.
5 🚐€ 5 🔧🗑 Ch 🔌 included. **Surface:** gravel/metalled. 🅾 01/01-31/12
Distance: 🚶3km.
Remarks: Key at Golf Club.

| 🚐S | **Argenta** | 32B2 |

Via Galassi. **GPS:** n44,61265 e11,83972.⬆️➡️.

10 🚐free 🔧🗑free. **Surface:** metalled. 🅾 01/01-31/12
Distance: 🚶200m ⊗200m 🛒200m 🚌200m.
Remarks: At tennis-courts.

| | **Bagno di Romagna** 🏔🏕 | 32C3 |

Via Lungo Savio 1. **GPS:** n43,84108 e11,96532.

10 🚐free. **Surface:** metalled. 🅾 01/01-31/12
Distance: 🚶500m 🚲1km ⊗500m 🛒500m.
Remarks: Parking swimming pool.

Tourist information Bagno di Romagna:
🏛 Week market. 🅾 Fri 7.30-12.30h.

| 🚐S | **Bellaria-Igea Marina** 🏖🌊 | 32C3 |

Parking delle Robinie, Via Pinzon 258, Igea Marina, Zona sud.
GPS: n44,12783 e12,48873.

106 🚐€ 10-12, Apr-Sept € 14,00-16,50 🔧🗑 Ch 🔌 €2,50/day ⬜€1/
time. **Location:** Rural, comfortable, central, quiet. **Surface:** grassy/gravel.
🅾 15/03-05/10, 08-23h
Distance: 🏖10m ⊗200m 🛒100m 🚌50m.

| 🚐S | **Bellaria-Igea Marina** 🏖🌊 | 32C3 |

Mare d'Inverno, Via Murri, 13. **GPS:** n44,11639 e12,49972.⬆️.

45 🚐€ 8, peak season € 10, holidays + € 2 🔧🗑 Ch 🔌 €2,50/day ⬜€1/time.
Location: Rural, comfortable, quiet. **Surface:** grassy.
🅾 Easter-30/09
Distance: 🚶800m 🏖200m ⊗800m 🛒1,5km, bakery 800m 🚌100m.

| 🚐S | **Bellaria-Igea Marina** 🏖🌊 | 32C3 |

Area di sosta Rio Pircio, Via Benivieni 4, Igea Marina. **GPS:** n44,12688 e12,48849.

68 🚐€ 10-18/24h 🔧🗑 Ch 🔌 €2/day WC€1/time ⬜hot shower€1.
Location: Rural, comfortable, central, quiet. **Surface:** grassy.
🅾 01/01-31/12
Distance: 🏖100m ⊗200m 🛒250m.

IT

Bellaria-Igea Marina — 32C3

L'Adriatico Parking, Via Benivieni, 12. **GPS**: n44,12644 e12,48740.

60 € 10-16/24h Ch €2,50/day 1/time against payment €1/24h,€5/week. **Location:** Rural, comfortable, quiet. **Surface:** grassy. Easter-Oct
Distance: 250m.

Berceto — 31D2

Via P. Salas. **GPS**: n44,51123 e9,98589.

20 € 7 Ch WC included. **Surface:** asphalted. 01/01-31/12
Distance: 200m 4km 200m on the spot on the spot.
Remarks: Caution € 20, key at kiosk in front of restaurant Rina.

Bertinoro — 32C3

Via Superga, SP 83, Loc. Fratta Terme. **GPS**: n44,13749 e12,10313.

free Ch free. **Surface:** asphalted. 01/01-31/12
Distance: 1km 1km 1km 300m.
Remarks: Near spa resort and sports centre.

Bomporto — 32A2

Piazza dello Sport, Via Verdi. **GPS**: n44,72886 e11,03585.

10 free free.
Location: Urban, simple. **Surface:** metalled.
Distance: 500m 500m.
Remarks: Parking at sports park.

Brisighella — 32B2

Piazzale Donatori di Sangue. **GPS**: n44,22168 e11,77883.

18 € 8 Ch free €2/12h. **Surface:** asphalted. 01/01-31/12
Distance: 1km 1km 1km 500m.

Carpi — 32A2

Piazzale delle Piscine. **GPS**: n44,78444 e10,86817.

free Ch free. **Surface:** metalled.
Distance: 300m 50m on the spot.
Remarks: Parking swimming pool.

Casal Borsetti — 32C2

Area Sosta Camper Mare e Parco, Via Ortolani. **GPS**: n44,55000 e12,27997.

238 € 9, 01/06-01/09 € 11 Ch included €3/24h WC.
Location: Rural, comfortable, central, quiet. **Surface:** grassy/metalled. 01/01-31/12
Distance: 150m 150m.

Casola Valsenio — 32B3

Via don Milani/Via Antonio Gramsci. **GPS**: n44,22597 e11,62953.

3 free free. **Surface:** asphalted. 01/01-31/12
Distance: 300m 500m 500m.
Remarks: At swimming pool.

Casola Valsenio — 32B3

Viale Domenico Neri. **GPS**: n44,22483 e11,62392.
4 free free. **Surface:** asphalted. 01/01-31/12
Distance: 100m 500m 100m.

Castel San Pietro Terme — 32B2

Via Oriani. **GPS**: n44,39725 e11,59197.

IT

8 free €1 Ch WC €0,20. **Surface:** asphalted. 01/01-31/12
Distance: 300m 4,2km 200m 250m 250m 250m.
Remarks: Nearby hospital.

S Castellarano 32A2

Parco Don Reverberi, Via Don Reverberi. **GPS**: n44,50777 e10,73419.

5 free Chfree. **Location:** Rural, simple. **Surface:** asphalted.
01/01-31/12
Distance: 500m 500m 500m 500m 500m.

S Castelnovo ne' Monti 32A2

Impianti Sportivi, Zona PEP, Via Fratelli Cervi, SS63. **GPS**: n44,43277 e10,41133.

4 free Chfree. **Location:** Simple, quiet. **Surface:** asphalted.
01/01-31/12
Distance: 500m on the spot.

S Cervia 32C2

Via Aldo Ascione, Cervia-nord. **GPS**: n44,28151 e12,32459.

50 free Chfree. **Location:** Simple, isolated, noisy. **Surface:** asphalted.
01/01-31/12
Distance: 3km 3km 1,3km.

S Cervia 32C2

Viale Tritone, Fraz. Pinarella. **GPS**: n44,23984 e12,35883.

40 free Chfree. **Location:** Urban, simple, noisy.
Surface: asphalted/metalled. 01/01-31/12
Distance: 750m 900m on the spot.

S Cervia 32C2

Terme di Cervia, Viale C. Forlanini, Cervia-nord. **GPS**: n44,27335 e12,32964.

50 € 8/24h €2. **Location:** Rural, quiet. **Surface:** grassy/gravel.
01/04-30/11
Distance: 3km 3km 50m.
Remarks: Parking spa resort.

Tourist information Cervia:
Week market. Thu.

S Cesena 32C3

Zona Ippodromo, Via G. Ambrosini. **GPS**: n44,14549 e12,22865.
free €1 €2 Ch. **Location:** Urban. **Surface:** grasstiles.
Distance: 500m.

S Cesena 32C3

Agriturismo Macin, Via San Mauro 5280. **GPS**: n44,13592 e12,16953.

4 € 5, free for clients Ch WC included.
Surface: grassy/metalled. 01/01-31/12
Distance: 5km 8,4km 5km 5km.

S Cesenatico 32C2

Piazzale della Rocca. **GPS**: n44,19855 e12,39086.

35 free Chfree. **Location:** Simple. **Surface:** metalled.
01/01-31/12
Distance: 500m 2km 200m 500m 200m.

C S Cesenatico 32C2

Via Mazzini, zona Ponente. **GPS**: n44,21408 e12,38008. ⬆.

21 € 12/24h Ch included. **Location:** Rural, simple.
Surface: grassy/gravel. 01/01-31/12
Distance: centre 3,5km 800m.
Remarks: At entrance campsite Cesenatico, max. 48h.

S Civitella di Romagna 32C3

Agriturismo Acero Rosseo, Via Seggio. **GPS**: n44,00200 e11,97539. ⬆➡.

20 guests free free. **Surface:** grassy. 01/01-31/12
Distance: 5km on the spot 5km.

S Collecchio 31D2

Via Spezia. **GPS**: n44,75178 e10,22265. ⬆➡.

8 free Ch. **Location:** Simple. **Surface:** asphalted.
01/01-31/12
Distance: 500m.

S Comacchio 32C2

Area di sosta Cavallari, Via Villaggio San Carlo 9. **GPS**: n44,70297 e12,16862. ⬆.

90 € 13 Ch Service € 4 included WC € 2/time. **Location:** Rural,
luxurious, quiet. **Surface:** grassy. 01/01-31/12
Distance: 1km.

S Comacchio 32C2

Via Fattibello. **GPS**: n44,69095 e12,18447. ⬆➡.

13 free. **Location:** Rural, central, quiet. **Surface:** asphalted.
01/01-31/12
Distance: 300m.

S Conselice 32B2

Agriturismo Massari, Via Coronella 110, Chiesanuova di Conselice.
GPS: n44,53167 e11,81856. ⬆➡.

10 € 9/pp, guests free Ch WC included.
Surface: metalled. 01/01-31/12
Distance: 1,5km 200m on the spot 1,5km.

S Cusercoli 32C3

Agriturismo Ca'Bionda, Via San Giovanni 41. **GPS**: n44,04153 e11,97544. ⬆➡.

20 free Ch free WC. **Surface:** metalled.
01/01-28/02 in case of snow. **Distance:** 3,5km on the spot 3,5km.
Remarks: Last 3km narrow road, swimming pool.

S Faenza 32B2

Via Proventa. **GPS**: n44,31272 e11,89289. ⬆➡.

2 free Ch free. **Surface:** asphalted. 01/01-31/12
Distance: 4km 2km.

S Faenza 32B2

Agriturismo Trerè, Via Casale 19. **GPS**: n44,29968 e11,80368. ⬆➡.

IT

5 ⌗ € 8 + € 5/pp, guests free ⌂ ⊟ Ch ⚊ €2 WC ⌷. **Surface:** metalled. ⬛ 01/01-31/12
Distance: ⚓7km ⚓on the spot ⚓200m ⊗on the spot.
Remarks: Dog € 1, swimming pool € 5.

20 ⌗ free ⌂ ⊟ Ch ⚊ (16x) WC free. **Surface:** asphalted. ⬛ 01/01-31/12
Distance: ⚓300m ⚓6km ⊗200m ⚓500m.

⌗ S	Farini	31C2

Viale dei Sassi Neri. **GPS:** n44,70994 e9,56611. ⬆➡.

	Forlimpopoli	32C3

Via De Gasperi. **GPS:** n44,19044 e12,12608.

50 ⌗ free ⌂ ⊟ Ch free. **Surface:** grassy/gravel. ⬛ 01/01-31/12
Distance: ⚓400m ⚓on the spot.

⌗ S	Ferrara 🏖 ⛺ ☕	32B1

Via Rampari di San Paolo. **GPS:** n44,83544 e11,61090. ⬆➡.

30 ⌗ € 6/24h ⌂ €1/100liter ⊟ €2 Ch €1 ⚊ € €5/2h 🛜. **Location:** Central, noisy. **Surface:** metalled. ⬛ 01/01-31/12
Distance: ⚓800m ⚓6,5km ⊗250m ⚓500m ⚓50m.

Tourist information Ferrara:
Ⓜ Museo della Cattedrale. Ⓣ gift.
🏰 Castello Estence.
🏰 Palazzo Scifanoia.
⛲ ⬛ Mo, Fri.

⌗ free. **Surface:** asphalted. ⬛ 01/01-31/12
Distance: ⚓100m ⚓100m ⚓100m ⚓100m.
Remarks: Nearby railway station.

S	Forlimpopoli	32C3

Palazzetto dello Sport, Via del Tulipano. **GPS:** n44,18534 e12,11960. ⌂ ⊟ Ch free.

⌗ S	Gropparello 🏖 💧	31D2

Via D. Aligieri. **GPS:** n44,83521 e9,73051. ⬆➡.

⌗ S	Fontanellato 🏖	31D1

Via Caduti di Cefalonia. **GPS:** n44,88195 e10,17762. ⬆.

30 ⌗ free ⌂ ⊟ free. **Location:** Simple, quiet. **Surface:** asphalted. ⬛ 01/01-31/12
Distance: ⚓centre 500m ⚓5,4km ⚓500m.
Remarks: At cemetery.

⌗ S	Fontanellato 🏖	31D1

Via Nazionale Emilia. **GPS:** n44,87797 e10,16987. ⬆➡.

⌗ € 10 ⌂ ⊟ free. 🅿 **Location:** Rural, simple, quiet. **Surface:** asphalted. ⬛ 01/01-31/12
Distance: ⚓100m ⊗500m.
Remarks: Castello di Gropparello 300m.

⌗ S	Guastalla 🏖 🍽	32A1

Piazzale Ugo Foscolo. **GPS:** n44,92364 e10,65148. ⬆.

⌗ free ⌂ ⊟ free ⚊ (6x)€3. **Surface:** asphalted. ⬛ 01/01-31/12
Distance: ⚓historical centre 300m ⚓1,5km ⊗600m ⚓100m.
Remarks: Cycle route along the Po river.

⌗ S	Imola 🏖 ⛺	32B2

Via Pirandello. **GPS:** n44,34628 e11,70922.

IT

30 🛏free 🚰🔌free. **Surface:** grassy/sand. ☐ 01/01-31/12
Distance: 🛒700m 🚉50m ⊗80m 🚰50m supermercato Famila.
Remarks: In front of the Ferrari Circuit.

30 🛏€6 🚰🔌Ch included. **Surface:** grassy. ☐ 01/04-30/09
Distance: 🛒100m ⛱100m ⊗50m 🚰200m 🚰50m.

Tourist information Imola:
🏛 Piazza Gramsci. ☐ Mo-Thu, Sa 8-12.30h.

Maranello 32A2
Area Camper Maranello, Via Fondo Val Tiepido 77, Torre Maina.
GPS: n44,50008 e10,87384.⬆.

Lagosanto 32C1
Ristorante Il Varano, Via Valle Oppio 6, Marozzo di Lagosanto.
GPS: n44,78167 e12,12533.⬆.

10 🛏€5 🚰🔌Ch 🔧 WC 🚿. **Location:** Rural, comfortable, quiet.
Surface: unpaved. ☐ 01/01-31/12
Distance: ⊗on the spot 🚌shuttle Bologna-Modena 🚲on the spot.
Remarks: Entrance code available at bar.

36 🛏€15, guests free 🚰🔌Ch 🔧(36x) WC 🧺. **Location:** Rural, comfortable, quiet. **Surface:** gravel. ☐ 01/01-31/12
Distance: 🛒3km ⛱12km ⊗on the spot 🚰500m.

Marzaglia 32A2
Area di sosta Marzaglia, Strada Pomposiana 305. **GPS:** n44,63514 e10,80733.
⬆➡.

Langhirano 31D2
Salumificio La Perla, Quinzano. **GPS:** n44,58748 e10,23783.⬆.

50 🛏free 🚰🔌. **Location:** Rural, simple, quiet. **Surface:** gravel.
☐ 01/01-31/12
Distance: 🛒3km ⊗on the spot 🚰3km 🥾on the spot.
Remarks: Producer Parma ham.

30 🛏€5/pppd 🚰🔌Ch 🔧€1,50/day WC 🚿.🏪 **Location:** Rural, comfortable, quiet. **Surface:** gravel. ☐ 01/01-31/12
Distance: 🛒Modena 10km 🏖7km.

Langhirano 31D2
La Fazenda, Cascinapiano di Langhirano. **GPS:** n44,63322 e10,27410.⬆.

Mesola 32C1
Oasi Park II, Via Cristina 84, SP27, Bosco Mesola. **GPS:** n44,86822 e12,24898.➡.

50 🛏€10, guests €5 🚰🔌 🔧 WC included. **Location:** Simple, quiet.
Surface: grassy/gravel. ☐ 01/01-31/12
Distance: 🛒1km 🚉on the spot ⊗on the spot 🚰500m.

130 🛏€8-15 🚰🔌Ch 🔧(100x)€2/day WC 🚿🧺against payment
🚿included. **Location:** Rural, comfortable, quiet. **Surface:** grassy.
☐ 01/03-01/11
Distance: ⊗400m 🚰1km. **Remarks:** Free bicycles available.

Lido di Dante 32C2
Via Marabina 208. **GPS:** n44,38867 e12,31364.

Mesola 32C1
Via Beatrice d'Este. **GPS:** n44,92331 e12,23469.⬆.

IT

IT

6 ⌗free ⚡⚹ Ch free. **Location:** Rural, simple. **Surface:** asphalted.
◻ 01/01-31/12
Distance: ⚡400m ⊗400m ⚑150m.
Remarks: Parking sports park.

Mesola 32C1
Agriturismo Ca'Laura, SP 27, Bosco Mesola. **GPS:** n44,87122 e12,24444. ⬆.

6 ⌗€ 15 ⚡⚹ Ch ⚘ WC ⌐. **Location:** Luxurious, quiet. **Surface:** metalled.
◻ 01/01-31/12
Distance: ⌂10km ⚹on the spot ⚑1km ⚌1km.
Remarks: Swimming pool, training golf course.

Mirandola 32A1
Via Luigi Galvani. **GPS:** n44,89812 e11,06199. ⬆.
10 ⌗free ⚡⚹ Ch free. **Location:** Simple, quiet. **Surface:** gravel.
Distance: ⚡500m ⊗1km ⚑1km ⚌500m.
Remarks: At cemetery.

Misano Adriatico 32D3
Centro Caravan Misano, Via Taveleto 53. **GPS:** n43,96694 e12,67306.

12 ⌗€ 18 ⚡⚹ Ch ⚘ (12x)€2,6Amp WC ⌐€0,50 ▣ 📶included. **Location:**
Luxurious, quiet. **Surface:** grassy. ◻ 01/01-31/12
Distance: ⚡500m ⚡5km ⌂2km ⊗500m ⚑500m.
Remarks: Caution key € 10, video surveillance.

Modena 32A2
Camper Club Mutina, Strada Collegarola 76/A, zona Vaciglio.
GPS: n44,61361 e10,94444. ⬆.

32 ⌗€ 15/24h ⚡⚹ Ch ⚘ WC ⌐ 📶included. **Location:** Rural, comfortable,

luxurious, quiet. **Surface:** asphalted. ◻ 01/01-31/12
Distance: ⚡600m ⚡3km 🚲600m 🚶on the spot.

Modena 32A2
Ristorante Pizzeria Taverna Napoleone, Via San Lorenzo 44.
GPS: n44,57567 e10,96415.

10 ⌗free ⚡⚹ free. **Location:** Rural. **Surface:** metalled.
◻ 01/01-31/12
Distance: ⚡5km ⚡2,8km ⊗pizzeria ⚑5km.
Remarks: 10% discount at restaurant.
Tourist information Modena:
Ⓜ Galleria Ferrari, Via Dino Ferrari 43, Maranello. Museum of motor-cars.

Monticelli d'Ongina 31D1
Piazza Resistenza. **GPS:** n45,09050 e9,93537. ⬆➡.

10 ⌗free ⚡⚹ Ch free. **Location:** Simple, quiet. **Surface:** asphalted.
◻ 01/01-31/12
Distance: ⚡centre 300m ⚡6,2km ⊗300m ⚑300m.

Parma 31D2
Area Camper Parma, Largo XXIV Agosto 1942, n° 21/a.
GPS: n44,80931 e10,28495. ⬆➡.

30 ⌗€ 1/8-22h, € 8/night ⚡⚹ Ch ⚘ WC ⌐€1.
Surface: grasstiles.
◻ 01/01-31/12
Distance: ⚡centre 3,5km ⚡7km ⚑Lidl 100m ⚌100m.
Remarks: Monitored parking, motorhome washing place 50m.
Tourist information Parma:
👁 Palazzo Pilotta. ◻ morning.
⚘ Via Verdi. Week market. 👁 Wed-Sa 7-14h.

Pavullo nel Frignano 32A2
Via Degli Abeti. **GPS:** n44,34294 e10,83309. ⬆.

12 ⌇free ⌤ ⌷ Ch free.
Location: Comfortable, quiet. **Surface:** gravel/sand.
Distance: ⌿700m ⊗600m ⌁600m ⇦600m.
Remarks: Picnic area.

| ⌇ S | Porto Corsini ⌗ | 32C2 |

Pro Loco, Via G. Guizzetti. **GPS:** n44,49620 e12,27950. ⬆️➡️.

155 ⌇ 01/04-30/09 € 9, 01/06-30/09 € 11 ⌤ ⌷ Ch ⌿ €3/day WC.
Location: Rural, comfortable, quiet. **Surface:** grassy. ◫ 01/04-30/09
Distance: ⌿500m ⌁200m ⌿300m ⊗300m ⌁300m.

| ⌇ S | Portomaggiore ⌇ | 32B2 |

Via Giuseppe Mazzini. **GPS:** n44,69584 e11,81389. ⬆️.

10 ⌇free ⌤ ⌷ free. **Surface:** asphalted. ◫ 01/01-31/12
Distance: ⌿500m ⊗500m ⌁500m.
Remarks: Nearby cemetery.

Tourist information Portomaggiore:
⌇ Valli di Comacchio. Nature reserve, in winter whereabouts birds.

| | Premilcuore | 32B3 |

Parcheggio Fluviale, Loc. Fontanalba. **GPS:** n43,97618 e11,77615.

30 ⌇free ⌤ ⌷ free. **Location:** Urban, simple. **Surface:** grasstiles.
◫ 01/01-31/12
Distance: ⌿Ravenna centre 6km.
Remarks: Nearby basilica.

| ⌇ S | Ravenna ⌇⌂⌷ | 32C2 |

Piazza della Resistenza. **GPS:** n44,41433 e12,18852. ⬆️.

10 ⌇ € 0,50/h, € 2,50/24h ⌤ ⌷ Ch free. ▮▮ **Location:** Urban, simple, central.
Surface: grasstiles. ◫ 01/01-31/12
Distance: ⌿historical centre 500m ⌁5km ⊗150m ⌁500m ⇦50m.
Remarks: Max. 24h.

| ⌇ S | Ravenna ⌇⌂⌷ | 32C2 |

Via Pomposa. **GPS:** n44,43002 e12,20827. ⬆️.

10 ⌇free ⌤ ⌷ Ch free. **Surface:** asphalted. ◫ 01/01-31/12
Distance: ⌿city centre 2km ⇦100m ⌁on the spot.

| ⌇ S | Ravenna ⌇⌂⌷ | 32C2 |

Via Teodorico. **GPS:** n44,42317 e12,20981.

10 ⌇free ⌤ ⌷ Ch free. **Location:** Urban, simple, quiet. **Surface:** asphalted.
◫ 01/01-31/12
Distance: ⌿500m ⊗on the spot.
Remarks: In front of the Mausoleum.

| ⌁ | Ravenna ⌇⌂⌷ | 32C2 |

Via Brancaleone/circonvallazione S. Gaetanino. **GPS:** n44,42339 e12,20478. ⬆️.

⌇ € 1. **Surface:** metalled. ◫ 01/01-31/12
Distance: ⌿500m ⌁20m ⊗500m ⇦50m.
Remarks: Along river.

| ⌇ S | Ravenna ⌇⌂⌷ | 32C2 |

Parking Bus-Camper, Via E.Ferrari. Loc.Classe. **GPS:** n44,37849 e12,23461. ⬆️➡️.

IT

25 🆓free. **Location:** Urban, simple, noisy. **Surface:** metalled.
🅾 01/01-31/12
Distance: 👤200m 🏖5km 🏊100m ⊗200m 🍴200m 🚌10m.
Remarks: Next to Rocca Brancaleone.

| 🅾S | Ravenna 🌊🏕🍧 | 32C2 |

Area Camper Atrezzata, Eurolandia, SS16. **GPS:** n44,33533 e12,26949.⬆

68 🆓€ 10/day, € 15/2 days 🚰 🚿 Ch included. 🅿 **Location:** Rural, simple.
Surface: gravel. 🅾 01/01-31/12

| 🅾S | Ravenna 🌊🏕🍧 | 32C2 |

Parco Divertimenti Mirabilandia, SS16, via Romea Sud 463.
GPS: n44,33290 e12,26966.⬆

400 🆓€ 15 🚰 🚿free.
Location: Rural, simple, noisy. **Surface:** gravel.
Distance: 👤Ravenna centre 10km ⊗McDonalds.
Remarks: Max. 48h.

Tourist information Ravenna:
ℹ U.I.A.T. (Ufficio Informazioni e di Accoglienza Turistica), Via Salara, 8/12, www.turismo.ravenna.it. City of the mosaics, historical city with many curiosities.
🎪 Piazza Garibaldi. Antiques market.
🅾 3rd weekend of the month.
😊 Parco Divertimenti Mirabilandia, SS16, via Romea Sud 463. Amusement park.
🅾 01/04-15/09.

| 🆑S | Reggio nell'Emilia | 32A2 |

Parking Ex Foro Boario, Via XX Settembre. **GPS:** n44,70941 e10,62463.⬆➡

200 🆓free 🚰 🚿 Ch free. **Location:** Urban, simple. **Surface:** grasstiles.

🅾 01/01-31/12
Distance: 👤1km 🏖3,7km 🏊100m 🍴500m 🚌Free bus to centre.

| 🆑S | Riccione 🏕🍧 | 32D3 |

Piazza 1° Maggio. GPS: n44,00392 e12,65115.⬆➡

10 🆓free 🚰€4 🚿 Ch. **Location:** Urban, simple, central, quiet.
Surface: asphalted. 🅾 01/01-31/12 🔌 Service: winter
Distance: 👤100m 🏖500m ⊗500m 🍴100m 🚌50m.

| 🆑S | Rimini 🌊🏕🍧 | 32C3 |

Park Settebello, Viale Roma 86. **GPS:** n44,06068 e12,57572.⬆➡

300 🆓€ 10/24h 🚰€2 🚿€2 🚿(80x)€3/day. **Location:** Urban, simple, central, noisy. **Surface:** metalled. 🅾 01/01-31/12
Distance: 👤200m 🏖500m.
Remarks: Next to cinema Settebello.

| 🆑S | Rimini 🌊🏕🍧 | 32C3 |

Sostaverde La Valletta, Via Della Lama 47, SS 16. **GPS:** n44,09889 e12,49867.
⬆➡

150 🆓€ 10/24h 🚰 🚿€3 WC 🚿 included. **Location:** Rural, noisy.
Surface: grassy/gravel. 🅾 01/04-30/09
Distance: 👤Rimini 11km 🏖3,8km 🏊2km ⊗800m 🍴800m.
Remarks: Shuttle bus to beach.

| 🆑S | Rimini 🌊🏕🍧 | 32C3 |

P30 Chiabrera, Via Chiabrera. **GPS:** n44,04803 e12,59548.⬆
🆓01/05-30/09 € 12,10. **Location:** Urban, simple, central, noisy.
Surface: asphalted.

Tourist information Rimini:
⊗ Cása Zanni, Via Casale, 205, Villa Verucchio. Restaurant with authentic Italian cuisine.

| 🆑S | Ro 🍧 | 32B1 |

Mulino sul Po. GPS: n44,95498 e11,75668.⬆

IT

4 ⌒free ⚡ ⚡ (4x)free.
Location: Rural, simple. **Surface:** metalled.
Distance: 🚶1km 🚴on the spot 🧍on the spot.
Remarks: Along the Po river.

🄢🅂 **Rocca San Casciano** 🍴 32B3
GPS: n44,06173 e11,84604.⬆️.
4 ⌒free ⚡€1/100liter ⚡Ch ⚡€1/4h. **Location:** Rural. **Surface:** metalled.
◻️ 01/01-31/12
Distance: 🚶300m ⊗100m.

🄢🅂 **Rubiera** 32A2
Via della Chiusa. **GPS:** n44,64229 e10,77765.⬆️➡️.

⌒free ⚡⚡Ch. **Location:** Simple, quiet. **Surface:** asphalted.
◻️ 01/01-31/12
Remarks: At sports park.

🄢🅂 **Sala Baganza** 31D2
Via Vittorio Emanuele, 42. **GPS:** n44,70856 e10,23070.⬆️.

2 ⌒free ⚡⚡Ch ⚡ (4x)free. **Location:** Rural, simple, quiet.
Surface: asphalted. ◻️ 01/01-31/12
Distance: 🚶500m ⚡15km 🛒500m.

🄢🅂 **Salsomaggiore Terme** ♨️ 31D2
Via Antonio Gramsci. **GPS:** n44,82005 e9,98981.⬆️.

20 ⌒free ⚡⚡free. **Location:** Urban, simple, quiet. **Surface:** gravel.
◻️ 01/01-31/12
Distance: 🚶800m.
Remarks: Parking next to station.

🄢🅂 **San Piero in Bagno** 32C3
Via G.Mazzini. **GPS:** n43,86353 e11,97692.⬆️.

5 ⌒free. **Surface:** asphalted. ◻️ 01/01-31/12
Distance: 🚶500m ⚡1km ⊗500m 🛒500m 🚌200m.

🄢🅂 **Santa Sofia** 🏔️ 32C3
Piazzale K. Marx. **GPS:** n43,94165 e11,90930.⬆️.

⌒free ⚡⚡Chfree. **Surface:** asphalted. ◻️ 01/01-31/12
Distance: 🚶200m.
Tourist information Santa Sofia:
🌲 Foreste Casentinesi. National nature reserve.

🄢🅂 **Serramazzoni** 🌿🏔️♨️ 32A2
Piazza Olimpico. **GPS:** n44,42223 e10,79402.⬆️➡️.

20 ⌒free ⚡⚡Chfree. **Location:** Urban. **Surface:** asphalted.
◻️ 01/01-31/12
Distance: 🚶300m ⊗100m 🗑️300m 🛒300m 🧍300m 🚲800m.

🄢🅂 **Serramazzoni** 🌿🏔️♨️ 32A2
Via Giardini Nord, Montagnana di Serramazzoni. **GPS:** n44,47250 e10,82005.⬆️.

15 ⌒free ⚡⚡. **Location:** Rural, simple, quiet. **Surface:** gravel.
◻️ 01/01-31/12
Distance: 🚶8km Maranello 🛒8km.
Remarks: Maranello: Ferrari factory and museum.

🄢🅂 **Soragna** 🌿 31D1
Via Matteotti / via Gramsci. **GPS:** n44,92988 e10,12566.⬆️.

IT

IT

10 ⛺free 🚰🔧Chfree. **Location:** Urban, simple, quiet. **Surface:** asphalted.
🅿 01/01-31/12
Distance: 🚶120m ⊗200m 🚉200m.

Suviana 32A3
Via Lungo Lago. **GPS:** n44,12039 e11,04592.

60 ⛺Free, hollidays € 9. 🐕
Location: Rural, simple, quiet. **Surface:** asphalted.
Distance: 🏊on the spot 🍴on the spot ⊗on the spot.
Remarks: At lake Suviana.

Terenzo 🌿🏔🍽 31D2
Loc. Bardone. **GPS:** n44,62528 e10,10083. ⬆.

10 ⛺€ 13 🚰🔧Ch🔧 WC🚽included. 🐕 **Location:** Rural, comfortable, quiet. **Surface:** metalled. 🅿 01/01-31/12
Distance: 🚶200m 🚲12km 🚌12km 🚶on the spot.

Tredozio 🏔🍽 32B3
Area Le Volte, Via Salvo D'Acquisto. **GPS:** n44,07431 e11,73228. ⬆➡.

Vergato 32A2
SS 64, Bologna-Pistoia. **GPS:** n44,28952 e11,11270. ⬆.

25 ⛺free 🚰🔧Chfree. **Location:** Rural, simple. **Surface:** asphalted.
🅿 01/01-31/12
Distance: 🚶400m ⊗400m 🚉500m 🚌500m.

Vezzano Sul Crostolo 🍽 32A2
Area Sosta Camper Matildica, SS63. **GPS:** n44,58960 e10,53608.
10 ⛺ 🚰🔧Ch 🔧. **Surface:** asphalted. 🅿 01/01-31/12
Distance: 🚶1,5km 🚌on the spot 🚴on the spot 🚶on the spot.
Remarks: Eco Parco di Vezzano, keycard at Bar Sport, Via Roma, SS63, n44,59963, o10,54542.

Liguria

Borghetto Santo Spirito 31B3
Via Tevere. **GPS:** n44,11548 e8,23758. ⬆➡.

150 ⛺€ 10/24h, Jul-Aug-Dec € 13 🚰🔧Ch 🔌(50x)€3/day,16Amp.
Surface: gravel.
Distance: 🚶1,1km 🚲2,5km 🏊400m.
Remarks: Along the river Varatella.

Castelnuovo Magra 31D3
Agriturismo Cascina dei Peri, Via Montefrancio 71. **GPS:** n44,10355 e10,00734.
⬆➡.

6 ⛺€ 8,50/pp, children free 🚰🔧Ch 🔧€3 WC🚽included 📺€5 🧺.
Surface: grassy/gravel. 🅿 01/01-31/12
Distance: 🚶2,4km.
Remarks: Dinner € 20/pp wine incl. (to order <16h), selling of wine and olive oil, swimming pool from june.

Cengio 31B2
Area Attrezzata Cengio Isole, Via Isole. **GPS:** n44,39083 e8,20194. ⬆➡.

40 ⛺€ 5 🚰🔧Ch 🔧€2,50. **Surface:** metalled. 🅿 01/01-31/12
Distance: 🚶1,5km ⊗200m camping 🚉1,5km.
Remarks: Next to campsite Le Volte, max. 48h, discount at restaurant/ swimming-pool.

Tresigallo 32B1
Fraz. Finale di Rero. **GPS:** n44,81643 e11,90050.
⛺free 🚰🔧.
Remarks: Nearby sports park.

🛏free 🚰💧Ch free. **Surface:** asphalted.
Distance: 🚶600m ⚓on the spot ⊗on the spot.
Remarks: Nearby sports park.

🛏S **Cervo** 31A3
Camper Cervo, Via Steria. **GPS:** n43,92833 e8,10527.⬆➡.

130 🛏€ 12-15/day 🚰💧Ch included 🔑€3/24h. **Surface:** gravel.
◻ 01/01-31/12
Distance: 🚶2,5km.

🛏S **Diano Marina** 31A3
Oasi Park, Via Sori 5. **GPS:** n43,90667 e8,07083.⬆➡.

300 🛏€ 8-15/day 🚰💧Ch 🔑€3 WC €1 ◉📶. **Surface:** grassy/gravel.
◻ 01/01-31/12
Distance: 🚶600m 🚲6,8km ⚓800m ⊗600m 🛒600m 🚐600m
🚵 mountainbike trail.
Remarks: Beachshuttle with bar/restaurant.

🛏S **Diano Marina** 31A3
Il bowling di Diano, Via Diano S. Pietro, 71 - Diano Castello.
GPS: n43,91683 e8,07576.⬆.

🛏€ 18/day 🚰💧Ch 🔑€4. **Surface:** unpaved. ◻ 01/01-31/12
Distance: 🚶1km 🚲5,5km ⚓1,2km ⊗on the spot 🛒50m.
Remarks: Narrow entrance, swimming pool, bar, bowling.

🛏S **Diano Marina** 31A3
Al Roseto, Via Case Parse, San siro, Diano Castello. **GPS:** n43,91983 e8,07733.⬆.

🛏€ 12-15 🚰💧Ch 🔑 WC €2 📶. ◻ 01/01-31/12
Distance: 🚲5,5km.
Remarks: At Floriculturist, shuttle bus to beach.

🛏S **Finale Ligure** 31B3
Area Caprazoppa, Via Aurelia, SS1. **GPS:** n44,16549 e8,33750.⬆.

40 🛏€ 18/24h 🚰💧Ch included. **Surface:** gravel/sand.
◻ 01/01-31/12
Distance: 🚶500m 🚲4km ⚓700m.

🛏 **Imperia** 31A3
Francy Park, Via dei Giardini. **GPS:** n43,86917 e8,00010.⬆.

32 🛏€ 10, 01/06-30/09 € 13.🚽 **Surface:** metalled. ◻ 01/01-31/12
Distance: 🚶centre 4km ⚓sea 150m ⊗150m.

🛏S **La Spezia** 🏖⚓🚢 31D3
Viale San Bartolomeo. **GPS:** n44,10417 e9,85917.

100 🛏€ 5 🚰💧free. **Surface:** grassy. ◻ 8-20h ◉ 12.30-13.30h
Distance: 🚶4km.
Remarks: Monitored parking.

Tourist information La Spezia:
ℹ Lerici. Former fishing village, nowadays holiday resort.
ℹ Cinque Terre. Protected coast area.
⛫ Castello di Lerici, Lerici. ◻ 01/04-31/10.
🎣 Lerici. ◻ Sa-morning.

🛏S **Levanto** 31C3
SP556, Loc. Moltedi. **GPS:** n44,17476 e9,61836.⬆➡.

16 🚐 € 12/12h, € 15/24h, € 20/36h 🚰 🔋 Ch free. 🅿 01/01-31/12
Distance: 🚶500m ⚓1km 🚂train 100m.
Remarks: Behind railway station, well situated for visiting the Cinque Terre by train.

La Sosta, Via delle Fornaci, 31. **GPS:** n44,13115 e8,24111.⬆
41 🚐 € 15 🚰 🔋 Ch 🔌 WC 🗑 🕸included. 🏧 **Surface:** gravel.
🅿 01/01-31/12
Distance: ⚓2km ⊗400m.
Remarks: Shuttle bus.

Tourist information Loano:
👁 Grotta di Santa Lucia, Toirano. Stalactites and stalagmites.
⌒ Grotta della Basura, Toirano. Man and beast from the stone age.

Area Camper, Via Crispi 43. **GPS:** n44,15484 e8,28397.⬆➡

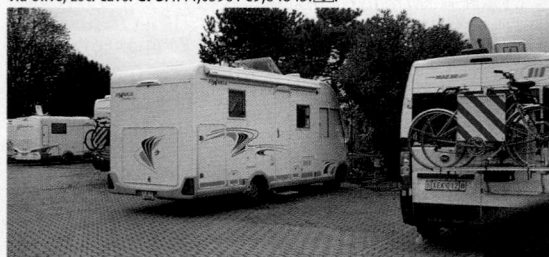

53 🚐 € 13/24h, 01/06-30/09 € 16/24h 🚰 🔋 Ch 🔌 (53x)included
WC 🗑€0,70. **Surface:** gravel.
Distance: ⚓200m.

Via Olivo, Loc. Cavo. **GPS:** n44,05961 e9,84843.⬆

20 🚐 € 1,85/h 8-20h, overnight stay free 🚰 🔋 Ch. 🏧 **Surface:** metalled.
🅿 01/01-31/12
Distance: 🚶2km ⚓750m ⊗600m 🚂50m.

Area Camper Il Pozzo, Via Gaetano Salvemini. **GPS:** n43,85512 e7,96083.⬆➡

30 🚐 € 15-23 🚰 🔋 Ch 🔌 WC 🗑 🖥€4 🕸included. **Location:** Luxurious.
Surface: gravel.
Distance: 🚶400m ⚓600m ⊗400m.
Remarks: Max. 7m.

Viale Franco Molfino, Camogli. **GPS:** n44,33472 e9,16084.

9 🚐 € 9/8-20h. **Surface:** asphalted.
Distance: ⊗150m 🚂on the spot.
Remarks: Marked hiking trails in Parco di Portofino (45min-2h).

Camper Village, Strada Porsani. **GPS:** n43,84378 e7,90824.⬆

60 🚐 € 12-30/24h 🚰 🔋 Ch 🔌€3 WC 🗑. **Surface:** gravel.
Distance: 🏄10km ⚓800m 🚂on the spot.
Remarks: Free shuttle, swimming pool.

Marina degli Aregai, Via Gianni Cozzi. **GPS:** n43,83723 e7,90581.

± 30 🚐 € 1,50/h, € 5-10/day. 🏧 **Surface:** asphalted.
Distance: 🚶on the spot ⚓Sandy beach ⊗on the spot 🚲on the spot.

Area Comunale Piscina, Via degli Alpini. **GPS:** n44,51667 e9,16000.➡

10 🚐free 🚰 🔋 Ch free. **Surface:** grasstiles.
Distance: 🚶200m.
Remarks: Next to swimming pool, market Saturday.

Tuscany

🚿S **Alberese** 32B6

Parco Naturale della Maremma, Via del Bersagliere.
GPS: n42,66944 e11,10416. ⬆️

50 🚐 € 9/day, € 6/½day 🚰 ♨ Ch free. **Surface:** sand.
🅿 01/04-30/09
Distance: 🚶100m ⛵7km ⊗on the spot.

🚿S **Anghiari** 32C4

Via Campo della Fiera. **GPS:** n43,53904 e12,05291. ⬆️

8 🚐 free 🚰 ♨ Ch free. **Surface:** asphalted.
Distance: 🚶on the spot ⊗on the spot 🍽on the spot.

🚿S **Anghiari** 32C4

Agriturismo Val della Pieve, Via della Fossa 8. **GPS:** n43,53657 e12,05131. ⬆️
➡️

10 🚐 € 18/24h 🚰 ♨ Ch 💨 included WC 🗑 ◉ ♨. **Surface:** gravel.
🅿 01/01-31/12
Distance: 🚶300m ⊗300m 🍽300m 🚎300m.
Remarks: Swimming pool € 3/pppd.

🍴S **Anghiari** 32C4

Agriturismo La Taverna dei Sorci, San Lorenzo. **GPS:** n43,51467 e12,07799. ⬆️

20 🚐 free 🚰. **Surface:** metalled. 🅿 01/01-31/12
Distance: ⊗on the spot.

🚿S **Arcidosso** 32B5

Parco Faunistico Monte Amiata, Località Poderi. **GPS:** n42,83740 e11,52922.

15 🚐 free ♨ Ch. **Location:** Rural, simple, central, quiet. **Surface:** grassy.
🅿 01/01-31/12
Distance: 🚶10km.
Remarks: Nature reserve.

🚿S **Arezzo** 🍇 32C4

Via Da Palestrina/via Tarlati (centro-nord). **GPS:** n43,47213 e11,88773.

30 🚐 € 0,80/h, € 8/24h 🚰 ♨ Ch ♨ free. **Surface:** asphalted.
Distance: 🚶historical centre 1km.
Remarks: Escalator to city centre.

🚿 **Arezzo** 🍇 32C4

P Tarlati, Via Guido Tarlati. **GPS:** n43,47237 e11,88362. ⬆️

50 🚐 free. **Location:** Urban, central. **Surface:** grasstiles.
🅿 01/01-31/12
Distance: 🚶city centre 1km ⊗500m 🚎300m.
Tourist information Arezzo:
⛺ Week market.

🚿S **Barberino di Mugello** 🏔 🎭 32B3

SS65, Fraz. Monte di Fó. **GPS:** n44,07613 e11,28062. ⬆️

30 🚐 free 🚰 ♨ Ch free. **Surface:** metalled.
Distance: 🚶4km ⊗150m (camping) 🍽150m (camping).
Remarks: In front of campsite Il Sergente.

🚿S **Barga** 32A3

Area San Cristoforo, Via Hayange. **GPS:** n44,07234 e10,48131. ⬆️➡️

IT

€ 10/24h Ch (10x) WC 200m.
Distance: centro storico within walking distance.

S Bibbiena 32C3

Agricola Casentinese, Loc. Casanova 63. **GPS**: n43,71669 e11,85173.

€ 15, 01/05-30/09 € 20 2 pers. Incl Ch WC included
€5, ironing services €5. **Surface:** gravel. 15/03-01/11, Christmas
Distance: 4km on the spot on the spot.
Remarks: Swimming pool € 5/pp (free with a meal).

S Borgo a Mozzano 32A3

Via I° Maggio, SP2. **GPS**: n43,97612 e10,54113.

4 free Ch (4x)free. **Surface:** gravel.
Distance: 200m Serchio river.
Remarks: At tourist office.

Buonconvento 32B5

Viale della Liberta. **GPS**: n43,13854 e11,48109.

free. **Location:** Simple. **Surface:** unpaved.
Distance: 50m 50m.
Remarks: At the city walls.

S Buonconvento 32B5

Viale Ferruccio Parri. **GPS**: n43,13065 e11,48349.

€1 Ch. 01/01-31/12

S Calci 32A4

Via Brogiotti. **GPS**: n43,72769 e10,51722.

6 € 8/24h Ch included. **Surface:** asphalted. 01/01-31/12
Distance: 100m 200m.
Remarks: At sports park, payment only with coins.

S Campiglia Marittima 32A5

Parcheggio La Pieve, Via di Venturina. **GPS**: n43,05672 e10,61439.

4 free Ch free. **Location:** Rural. **Surface:** asphalted.
Distance: 350m 450m 500m.
Remarks: In front of cemetery, near gymnasium.

S Capraia e Limite 32A3

Via delle Ginestre, zona industriale, loc. Capraia Fiorentina.
GPS: n43,73660 e11,00442.
free Ch free. **Surface:** metalled.

S Casola in Lunigiana 31D3

Area La Linea del Drago. **GPS**: n44,19916 e10,17333.

20 € 7 + € 5/pp Ch WC included. **Surface:** grassy.
01/01-31/12
Distance: on the spot.
Remarks: At little stream with swimming area.

S Castagneto Carducci 32A5

Camperesort, Via Aurelia 373/B. **GPS**: n43,15630 e10,56097.

50 ⬛€ 10 + € 7/pp, 16/09-14/06 € 5/pp ⛽🚰 Ch ✦ WC ⬛€0,50 ⬛€3 ➰included. **Location:** Luxurious. **Surface:** grassy/gravel. ⬛ 01/01-31/12
Distance: ⚓1,2km ⊗on the spot.
Remarks: Swimming pool incl.

⬛S **Castagneto Carducci** 32A5
Via del Seggio, Marina di Castagneto. **GPS:** n43,18401 e10,54841.⬆️

30 ⬛€ 10/24h ⛽🚰 Chfree. **Surface:** unpaved.
Distance: 🚰2km ⚓500m ⊗2,5km 🏖2,5km.

⬛S **Castagneto Carducci** 32A5
Viale delle Palme, Marina di Castagneto. **GPS:** n43,19323 e10,54152.⬆️

20 ⬛€ 10/24h ⛽🚰 Ch. **Surface:** unpaved.
Distance: ⚓100m.
Remarks: Max. 48h, dogs beach.

⬛S **Castel del Piano** 🏔☂🏔 32B5
Via Po. **GPS:** n42,88872 e11,53733.➡️

30 ⬛free ⛽🚰 Chfree. **Location:** Rural, simple. **Surface:** asphalted.
⬛ 01/01-31/12
Distance: 🚰500m.

⬛S **Castelfiorentino** 32A4
Ara Comunale, Via Che Guevara, circonvallazione Ovest.
GPS: n43,60885 e10,96365.⬆️

5 ⬛free ⛽🚰free. **Location:** Simple, isolated. **Surface:** asphalted.
Distance: 🚰1,5km ⊗1,5km 🏖1,5km.

⬛S **Castellina in Chianti** 32B4
La Strada del Chianti, SR222. **GPS:** n43,47330 e11,28760.⬆️➡️

15 ⬛€ 10/24h, 01/11-31/03 free ⛽€0,20/10liter 🚰 Ch ✦ (8x) included WC €0,50. 🏠 **Location:** Rural, comfortable. **Surface:** asphalted.
⬛ 01/01-31/12
Distance: 🚰200m.

Tourist information Castellina in Chianti:
⛵ Via IV Novembre. Week market. ⬛ Sa-morning.

⬛S **Castelnuovo di Garfagnana** 32A3
Via Valmaira. **GPS:** n44,11447 e10,40304.⬆️

⬛free ⛽🚰 Chfree. **Surface:** metalled. ⬛ 01/01-31/12
Distance: 🚰1km.
Remarks: At sports park.

⬛S **Castelnuovo di Val de Cecina** 32A5
Via della Fonte, Sasso Pisano. **GPS:** n43,16748 e10,86586.⬆️

10 ⬛free ⛽€2 🚰 Ch ✦ €3/12h. **Location:** Rural. **Surface:** metalled.
⬛ 01/01-31/12
Distance: 🚰100m ⊗200m.

⬛S **Castiglion Fiorentino** 32C4
Piazza Garibaldi, viale Marconi. **GPS:** n43,34465 e11,92278.⬆️ .

IT

20 ⬚free 🚰 ≅ Chfree WC. **Location:** Rural, simple. **Surface:** asphalted.
🔲 01/01-31/12 🔘 Fri-morning market
Distance: 🛒on the spot ⊗on the spot.

| 🔲 S | Castiglione della Pescaia 🌊⛵≈ | 32A5 |

Rocchette Serignano, Via Rio Palma, Rocchette.
GPS: n42,77970 e10,79955. ⬆➡.

± 50 ⬚€ 22/day 🚰≅ Ch 🔌 (18x)included 🗑€ 1. **Surface:** unpaved.
🔲 01/04-30/09
Distance: 🛒Castiglione della Pescaia 7km ⚓200m ⊗200m.
Remarks: Beach parking, unguarded.

| 🔲 S | Castiglione della Pescaia 🌊⛵≈ | 32A5 |

Viale Kennedy, SS158. **GPS:** n42,77447 e10,84395. ⬆➡.

5 ⬚free 🚰≅ free. **Location:** Rural, simple. **Surface:** gravel/sand.
🔲 01/01-31/12
Tourist information Castiglione d'Orcia:
✠ Rocco d'Orcia. Medieval citadel.

| 🔲 S | Certaldo | 32A4 |

Area Comunale, Piazza dei Macelli. **GPS:** n43,54629 e11,04611. ⬆➡.

10 ⬚free 🚰≅ Chfree. **Location:** Rural. **Surface:** metalled.
🔲 01/01-31/12
Distance: 🛒medieval centre 150m (elevator) ⊗150m 🍴250m.

| 🔲 S | Chifenti | 32A3 |

Area sosta Chifenti, SS12. **GPS:** n44,00492 e10,56337.
10 ⬚free 🚰≅ Chfree. **Surface:** asphalted/gravel. 🔲 01/01-31/12
Distance: 🛒500M.

| 🔲 S | Chiusdino | 32B5 |

Abbazia San Galgano, SS441. **GPS:** n43,15283 e11,15137. ⬆.

40 ⬚Apr-Jun, Sep € 12, Jul/Aug € 15 🚰≅ Ch. **Surface:** asphalted.
🔲 01/04-30/09
Distance: 🛒4km ⚓500m ⊗4km 🍴4km.

| 🔲 S | Castiglione della Pescaia 🌊⛵≈ | 32A5 |

Via Andromeda. **GPS:** n42,76888 e10,89079. ⬆.
9 ⬚free. **Surface:** asphalted. 🔲 01/01-31/12
Distance: 🛒1km.

| ⚓ | Castiglione della Pescaia 🌊⛵≈ | 32A5 |

Via Ponte Giorgini. **GPS:** n42,76515 e10,88545. ⬆.
⬚€ 1,50/h 8-24h. **Surface:** asphalted. 🔲 01/01-31/12
Distance: 🛒on the spot.
Remarks: Market Saturday.

| 🔲 S | Castiglione d'Orcia 🌊⛰ | 32B5 |

Area Pro Loco, Viale Marconi. **GPS:** n43,00292 e11,61552. ⬆.

15 ⬚€ 1,50/h, 🚰 10/8-20h, overnight stay free 🔌 (9x)free.
Location: Rural, isolated, quiet. **Surface:** grasstiles. 🔲 01/01-31/12
Distance: 🛒12km ⊗300m.
Remarks: Abbey of San Galgano 300m.

| 🔲 S | Chiusi | 32C5 |

Via Torri del Fornello. **GPS:** n43,01461 e11,94972. ⬆.

5 ⬚free 🚰≅ free. **Surface:** asphalted.
Distance: 🛒100m 🚂4,5km.
Remarks: Next to school.

IT

	Chiusi	32C5

Loc. Sbarchino. **GPS:** n43,05049 e11,95756.⬆️.
10 🅿️free. ◻️ 01/01-31/12
Distance: ⊗Pesce d'Oro 🚲 on the spot 🚶 on the spot.

	Cutigliano	32A3

Via di Risorgimento/Sp37. **GPS:** n44,09877 e10,75450.
14 🅿️€ 1,50/h, € 15/24h ⛽🚰Ch🚿included. 📶 **Surface:** metalled.
Remarks: Max. 48h.

	Dicomano	32B3

SS67, Tosco Romagnola. **GPS:** n43,89407 e11,53715.⬆️.
4 🅿️free ⛽🚰Chfree. **Surface:** asphalted. ◻️ 01/01-31/12
Distance: 🚶1km ⊗200m.

	Equi Terme	31D3

Via della Stazione. **GPS:** n44,17009 e10,15513.⬆️➡️.

40 🅿️€ 10/night ⛽🚰Ch🚿included. **Surface:** gravel.
Distance: ⊗100m.
Remarks: Near spa resort (100m), caves (500m) and marble quarry.

	Firenze	32B3

FiPark, Viale Europa, Fraz. Bagno a Ripoli, Florence (Firenze).
GPS: n43,75554 e11,30609.⬆️.

40 🅿️7-19h € 2/h, 19-7h € 1/h, € 15/24h ⛽🚰Ch. **Surface:** metalled.
◻️ 01/01-31/12
Distance: 🚌bus 23/33 > centre.

	Firenze	32B3

Area sociale 'Flog', Via M Mercati 24/b, zona Careggi, Florence (Firenze).
GPS: n43,79491 e11,24835.

25 🅿️€ 15/24h ⛽€3🚰Ch. **Surface:** gravel. ◻️ 01/01-31/12
Distance: 🚶city centre 2km ⊗Pizzeria 🚌centre : bus 4, 6-24h.

	Firenze	32B3

Florence Park Scandicci, Via di Scandicci 241, Florence (Firenze).
GPS: n43,76267 e11,20875.⬆️.

25 🅿️€ 15 ⛽🚰Ch📶included. 🚐 **Location:** Urban, comfortable, central.
Surface: metalled. ◻️ 01/01-31/12
Distance: 🚶4km 🚲5km 🚶150m.
Remarks: Video surveillance.

	Firenze	32B3

Gelsomino SCAF, Via del Gelsomino 11, Florence (Firenze).
GPS: n43,75173 e11,24388.
40 🅿️€ 15/24h ⛽🚰Ch🚿 included. **Surface:** asphalted.
◻️ 01/01-31/12
Distance: 🚶2km 🚌bus 37 > centre.

Tourist information Florence (Firenze):
ℹ️ U.I.A.T. (Ufficio Informazioni e di Accoglienza Turistica), Piazza Stazione, 4, www.firenze.turismo.toscana.it. Renaissance city with many curiosities.
👁 Ponte Vechio. Famous bridge with jeweller's shops.
✝ Cappella Brancacci, Santa Maria del Carmine. Renovated frescoes.
🛍 The Mall, le griffe, Via Europa 8, Leccio Reggello. Factory outlet.

	Firenzuola	32B3

Area Picnic, Loc. Badia a Moscheta. **GPS:** n44,07586 e11,42064.🎏.

10 🅿️free. **Surface:** gravel. ◻️ 01/01-31/12
Distance: 🚶Firenzuola 8km ⊗500m agriturismo Badia di Moscheta.

	Firenzuola	32B3

Loc. Pieve di Camaggiore. **GPS:** n44,14594 e11,45361.🎏.

20 🅿️free. **Surface:** grasstiles. ◻️ 01/01-31/12
Distance: 🚶Firenzuola 10km 🏊river 100m.
Remarks: Playground.

	Fivizzano	31D3

Agriturismo Ristorante Al Vecchio Tino, Loc. Germalla 1, Monte dei Bianchi.
GPS: n44,17155 e10,13325.
6 🅿️€ 12 ⛽🚰Ch🚿 included. **Surface:** gravel. ◻️ 01/01-31/12

	Foiano della Chiana	32C4

Outlet Village Valdichiana, Via Enzo Ferrari 5, loc. Farniole.
GPS: n43,22489 e11,80291.⬆️.

IT

10 ⌂free. **Location:** Simple. **Surface:** asphalted. ☐ 01/01-31/12
Distance: ⊗on the spot ⚲on the spot.
Remarks: Motorhome parking at Outlet.

⌂S | **Follonica** | 32A5
Eucalyptus Camper Park, Via Sanzio. **GPS:** n42,92804 e10,77569.

40 ⌂€ 10 🚰€4 🗑Ch ✎ included ⬚€1.♨
Distance: 🏖beach 1,8km ⊗1km ⚲1km.

⌂S | **Gaiole in Chianti** | 32B4
Via Michelangelo Buonarroti. **GPS:** n43,46434 e11,43440. ⬆➡.

⌂free 🚰🗑Ch free. **Location:** Rural, simple. **Surface:** metalled.
☐ 01/01-31/12
Remarks: At footballstadium.

⌂S | **Gallicano** | 32A3
Via dei Cipressi. **GPS:** n44,05827 e10,44565. ⬆➡.

4 ⌂free 🚰🗑Ch ✎ (2x)free. **Surface:** metalled. ☐ 01/01-31/12
Distance: 500m.
Remarks: Grotta del Vento.

⌂S | **Greve in Chianti** | 32B4
Monte S. Michele, Via Montebeni. **GPS:** n43,59066 e11,31355. ⬆➡.

17 ⌂free 🚰🗑free. **Location:** Rural, comfortable, quiet. **Surface:** metalled.
☐ 01/01-31/12
Distance: 500m ⚲500m.
Tourist information Greve in Chianti:
⛺ ☐ Sa-morning.

⌂S | **Isola dElba** | 32A5
Area Camper Cavo, San Bennato, Cavo, Elba (Isle) (Isola dElba).
GPS: n42,85459 e10,42267.⬆.
50 ⌂€ 18/24h 🚰🗑Ch ✎€2 ⬚€1. **Surface:** gravel. ☐ 01/04-30/10
Distance: 600m ⚲400m.

⌂S | **Isola dElba** | 32A5
Loc. Bocchetto, Porto Azzurro. **GPS:** n42,77114 e10,39985.
60 ⌂free, peak season € 10/24h 🚰🗑Ch free. **Surface:** asphalted.
Distance: city centre 1km.
Remarks: Nearby cemetery.

⌂S | **Isola dElba** | 32A5
Sighello, area La Pila, Marina di Campo. **GPS:** n42,75905 e10,23645.⬆.
20 ⌂€ 15 🚰🗑Ch ✎€3. **Surface:** unpaved. ☐ 01/05-30/09
Distance: 1,5km.
Remarks: At sports park.

⌂S | **Larciano** | 32A3
Residence Poggetto, Via Stradella 1489. **GPS:** n43,83319 e10,88042.⬆.

25 ⌂€ 15/24h, free with a meal 🚰🗑Ch ✎. **Surface:** grassy/gravel.
☐ 01/01-31/12
Distance: 1km ⊗1km.

⌂S | **Livorno** | 32A4
Il Cavalluccio, Via G. Pascoli 12, Fraz Quercianella. **GPS:** n43,46027 e10,36222.

44 ⌂€ 18/night 🚰🗑Ch ✎ WC ⬚included. **Surface:** unpaved.
Distance: 🏖sea 50m.

⌂S | **Livorno** | 32A4
Piazza Ordoardo Borrani, Viale d'Antignano. **GPS:** n43,50465 e10,32144.⬆.

50 🛏free. **Location:** Rural. **Surface:** asphalted.
Distance: 🚲400m Antignano ⛱100m 🛒300m.

Tourist information Livorno:
ℹ️ Ufficio Informazioni, Piazza del Municipio. Medieval port city.

🚐🅂	Lucca 🌿⛱🍴	32A3

Il Serchio, Via del Tiro a Segno 704, loc. Sant'Anna. **GPS:** n43,85000 e10,48583.⬆️

66 🛏€ 25/24h, dog € 1 🚰🗑Ch 🔌(66x),4 WC 🚿€€4,50 📶included.
Surface: grasstiles. ⬛ 01/03-31/01
Distance: 🚲1km ⛱2km 🛒500m ⊗on the spot 🛒2km on the spot.
Remarks: Waste dump € 2/day, shuttle € 1/pp, swimming pool € 5/pp.

🚐🅂	Lucca 🌿⛱🍴	32A3

Area Sosta Lucca, Viale Gaetano Luporini. **GPS:** n43,84028 e10,48878.⬆️➡️

65 🛏€ 10/24h, peak season € 14/24h, € 3/h 🚰🗑Ch 🔨included.
Surface: asphalted.
Distance: 🚲5 min walking 🏖2km.

Tourist information Lucca:
👁 Casa di Puccini, Via di Poggio. Birth place of the composer. ⬛ Tue-Su.
⛺ ⬛ Wed, Sa, 3rd Su of the month antiques market.

🚐🅂	Lucignano 🌿⛱	32B4

SP19. **GPS:** n43,27664 e11,74512.⬆️➡️

20 🛏free 🚰🗑Ch 🔌(9x)free. **Location:** Rural, simple. **Surface:** grassy.
⬛ 01/01-31/12
Distance: 🚲500m.
Remarks: At the edge of village.

🚐🅂	Marina di Cecina ⚓🌊	32A4

Parcheggio Aqua Park, Marina di Cecina. **GPS:** n43,30070 e10,49948.⬆️

100 🛏01/03-15/11 € 8 🚰🗑Ch. **Location:** Rural. **Surface:** metalled.
⬛ 01/01-31/12
Distance: 🚲2km ⛱1km ⊗200m 🛒200m.

🚐🅂	Marina di Cecina ⚓🌊	32A4

Via della Cecinella. **GPS:** n43,29278 e10,50785.⬆️

30 🛏1/3-15/11 € 8/24h 🚰🗑Ch. **Location:** Rural, simple, quiet.
Surface: asphalted. ⬛ 01/01-31/12
Distance: 🚲2km ⛱300m ⊗2km 🛒2km.

🚐🅂	Marina di Grosseto	32B5

Oasi di Maremma, SP158 delle Collacchie Km 34,4. **GPS:** n42,72611 e10,99055.
⬆️➡️

100 🛏€ 15, peak season € 18, 4 pers.incl 🚰🗑Ch 🔌(100x)€2 WC 🚿€1
🚿€3. **Surface:** grassy. ⬛ 01/04-30/09
Distance: 🚲1km ⛱1km ⊗1km 🛒1km on the spot.
Remarks: Water at each pitch, shuttle € 1,50/pp.

🚐🅂	Marina di Grosseto	32B5

Area di sosta l'Oàsi, S332 > dir San Vincenzo d'Elba. **GPS:** n42,73466 e10,97483.
⬆️➡️

50 🛏Jun € 14, Jul/Aug € 18, Sep € 12, 4 pers.incl 🚰🗑Ch 🔌€2 WC 🚿€2 🧺.
Surface: grassy. ⬛ Easter-30/09
Distance: 🚲Marina 1,5km ⛱1,1km ⊗400m 🛒nearby.

🚐	Marina di Grosseto	32B5

Via Costiera, SP158. **GPS:** n42,73722 e10,96388.⬆️➡️

50 🛏free. **Surface:** gravel. 📷 01/01-31/12
Distance: 🚶2km 🏖400m.

Tourist information Marina di Grosseto:
🌿 Parco Naturale della Maremma. Nature reserve.
📷 Wed, Sa, Su 9h 01/06-30/09 guided walk 7h, 16h.

🅂 Marina di Pisa 31D4
Parcheggio Camper Pisamo, Viale Gabriela d'Annunzio.
GPS: n43,67908 e10,27830.
130 🛏€ 15/24h ⚓🍽 Ch 🚿. **Surface:** sand. 📷 01/01-31/12
Distance: 🏖sea 1km.

🅂 Marradi 32B3
Area sosta Marradi, Via San Benedetto. **GPS:** n44,07347 e11,61166.⬆️

30 🛏free ⚓100liter🍽 Ch 🚿 8kWh,Service€5. **Surface:** asphalted.
📷 01/01-31/12
Distance: 🚶50m.
Remarks: Caution key service € 7.

🅂 Massa Marittima 32A5
Viale del Risorgimento. **GPS:** n43,04530 e10,89050.⬆️➡️

7 🛏free ⚓🍽 Chfree. **Surface:** asphalted. 📷 01/01-31/12
Distance: 🚶historical centre 650m ⊗600m 🚰500m 🚐on the spot.

🅂 Montalcino 32B5
Geen, Via Osticcio. **GPS:** n43,04913 e11,48749.⬆️➡️

30 🛏€ 5/24h ⚓🍽 Chfree. 🏠 **Location:** Rural, comfortable, quiet.
Surface: asphalted/metalled. 📷 01/01-31/12
Distance: 🚶700m ⊗700m 🚰700m.

🅂 Monte San Savino 32B4
Via del Casalino. **GPS:** n43,33177 e11,72204.⬆️

20 🛏free ⚓🍽 Chfree. **Location:** Rural, simple. **Surface:** gravel.
📷 01/01-31/12
Distance: 🚶on the spot 🚲4,2km ⊗200m.
Remarks: Steep ramp.

🅂 Montecatini Terme ♨ 32A3
Piazza Pietro Leopoldo, SS 436. **GPS:** n43,88286 e10,76386.
40 🛏free. **Surface:** asphalted. 📷 01/01-31/12 ⚫ Thu (market)
Distance: 🚲3km ⊗500m 🚉500m.
Remarks: In front of stadium, tuesday market.

🅂 Montemignaio 32B3
Via Molino. **GPS:** n43,73989 e11,62024.⬆️➡️
🛏free ⚓🍽 free. **Surface:** gravel. 📷 01/01-31/12
Distance: ⊗150m.

🅂 Montepulciano 32C5
P5, Piazza Pietro Nenni. **GPS:** n43,09577 e11,78684.⬆️➡️

32 🛏€ 10/24h ⚓🍽 free. 🏠 **Location:** Rural, simple. **Surface:** asphalted.
📷 01/01-31/12 ⚫ Thu-morning closed because of market
Distance: 🚶200m ⊗100m 🚰400m.

🅂 Monteriggioni 32B4
Strada di Monteriggioni. **GPS:** n43,38801 e11,22511.⬆️

12 🛏€ 1/h 8-20h, max. € 5, overnight stay free. 🏠 **Location:** Rural,
comfortable. **Surface:** gravel. 📷 01/01-31/12
Distance: 🚶300m 🚲1,4km ⊗300m 🚰on the spot.

🅂 Monteroni d'Arbia 32B4
Via San Giusto. **GPS:** n43,23048 e11,42371.⬆️➡️

IT

🏕free ⚡🔌Chfree. **Location:** Rural, simple. **Surface:** sand. ▢ 01/01-31/12
Distance: 🚶50m.
Remarks: P centre.

50 🏕€ 10/motorhome, € 8/pp, € 5/child ⚡🔌 Ch 🔧 (40x)included WC 🚿.
Surface: grassy/gravel. ▢ 01/01-31/12
Distance: 🚶Orbetello 5km 🏊50m ⊗200m 🛒alimentari.
Remarks: Max. 72h.

⬛S **Montespertoli** 32B4
Molino del Ponte, Via Volterrana Nord. **GPS:** n43,65606 e11,08445. 🔼 .

⬛S **Palazzuolo sul Senio** 🌿⛰️ 32B3
Parcheggio Casone, Via Casone. **GPS:** n44,11073 e11,54968. 🔼➡️

5 🏕free ⚡€1/100liter 🔌€2 Ch. **Location:** Rural. **Surface:** metalled. ▢ 01/01-31/12
Distance: 🚶Montespertoli 2,3km ⊗on the spot 🛒400m.

100 🏕free ⚡🔌Chfree. **Surface:** asphalted. ▢ 01/01-31/12
Distance: 🚶100m ⊗100m 🛒100m.
Remarks: Narrow entrance.

⬛S **Montevarchi** 32B4
Via B. Latini. **GPS:** n43,53052 e11,56784. 🔼

⬛S **Palazzuolo sul Senio** 🌿⛰️ 32B3
Via Francesco Pagliazzi. **GPS:** n44,11551 e11,54984. 🔼 .

🏕free ⚡🔌free. **Location:** Urban, simple. **Surface:** asphalted.
Distance: ✈7km 🛒Coop.
Remarks: Nearby stadium.

6 🏕free. **Surface:** metalled. ▢ 01/01-31/12
Distance: 🚶on the spot.
Remarks: Next to cemetery, upper part of the parking.

⬛S **Montopoli in Val d'Arno** 32A4
Piazza Amerigo Vespucci, Via di Masoria. **GPS:** n43,67333 e10,75222. 🔼

⬛S **Pecciolì** 32A4
Parco Preistorico, Via Cappuccini. **GPS:** n43,55694 e10,71889. 🔼

31 🏕free ⚡🔌Chfree. **Surface:** metalled. ▢ 01/01-31/12
Distance: 🛒within walking distance.

⬛S **Orbetello** 32B6
Lanino Parco Sosta, Loc. Santa Liberata. **GPS:** n42,43346 e11,15959. 🔼➡️

15 🏕free, after 2 days € 5/day ⚡🔧WC. **Location:** Rural, simple.
Surface: gravel. ▢ 01/01-31/12
Distance: 🚶500m ⊗500m 🛒2km.
Remarks: Picnic area, playground.
Tourist information Pecciolì:
🅘 Parco Preistorico, Via Cappuccini. ▢ 01/01-31/12.

⬛S **Pienza** 🌿⛰️ 32B5
Via Mencattelli e Foro Boario. **GPS:** n43,07799 e11,68087. 🔼➡️

🅿8-20h: € 1,50/1h, € 5/4h, € 10/8h, overnight stay free ⛽🚰Ch ⚡ included WC . 🚐 **Location:** Rural, simple. **Surface:** asphalted. ⬛ 01/01-31/12 ⦿ Fri-morning market **Distance:** 🚶100m.

150 🅿€ 2/h, € 17/8-20h, overnight stay free ⛽🚰Ch. **Location:** Isolated, quiet. **Surface:** grassy. ⬛ 01/01-31/12 **Distance:** 🚶Piombino 9km ⛵1,5km. **Remarks:** Beach parking, camper service 8-20h, no camping activities, shuttle bus.

🅿🆂 **Pieve Santo Stefano** 32C3

Grey camper, Via della Verna. **GPS:** n43,67058 e12,03729.⬆️.

🅿🆂 **Piombino** 🏖 32A5

Perelli 1-3, Loc. Perelli. **GPS:** n42,95527 e10,61944.⬆️.

20 🅿€ 10 ⛽🚰Ch ⚡ WC included 🗑€ 1. **Location:** Noisy.
Surface: metalled. ⬛ 01/01-31/12
Distance: 🚶on the spot ⛵1,7km.
Remarks: Nearby viaduct E45.

50 🅿€ 2/h, € 16/8-20h, overnight stay free ⛽🚰Ch free. 🚐
Location: Quiet. **Surface:** grassy/sand.
⬛ 01/06-30/09
Distance: ⛱Sandy beach ⊗Perelli 1.
Remarks: Beach parking, service: Perelli 3, no camping activities, dogs beach.

🅿🆂 **Piombino** 🏖 32A5

Camperoasi, Loc. Mortelliccio, Riotorto. **GPS:** n42,95416 e10,66638.⬆️➡️.

🅿🆂 **Piombino** 🏖 32A5

Via della Pace. **GPS:** n42,93777 e10,52194.⬆️.

93 🅿€ 20, Apr-Jun, Sep € 30, Jul/Aug € 40 ⛽🚰Ch ⚡ WC included 🗑€0,50 📷🅿 **Location:** Comfortable. **Surface:** grasstiles/grassy.
⬛ 01/01-31/12 ⦿ 01/10-31/03 Mo-Thu
Distance: ⛱200m 🏪50m 🚏50m.
Remarks: Water/drainage at each pitch, 10% discount on presentation of the guide 2012, reception open: 9.30-12.30 14-19.30.

15 🅿free ⛽€0,10/10liter 🚰Ch. **Location:** Urban, noisy. **Surface:** metalled.
⬛ 01/01-31/12
Distance: 🚶500m ⛵1km ⊗700m 🚏800m.

🅿🆂 **Piombino** 🏖 32A5

Carbonifera 1, Loc. Torre Mozza. **GPS:** n42,94750 e10,69277.⬆️➡️.

🅿🆂 **Pisa** 32A4

Parcheggio camper, Via di Pratale 78. **GPS:** n43,72106 e10,42066.⬆️.

± 75 🅿€ 2/h, € 18/24h 🚰Ch included. 🚐 **Surface:** grassy/gravel.
Distance: ⛱50m.
Remarks: Beach parking, no camping activities.

100 🅿€ 12/night, € 1/h, € 5/6h ⛽€3 🚰Ch ⚡. **Location:** Quiet.
Surface: asphalted.
Distance: 🚶800m ⛵7km 🚏on the spot.
Remarks: Monitored parking.

🅿🆂 **Piombino** 🏖 32A5

Parcheggio Caldanelle, Loc. Caldanelle. **GPS:** n43,00216 e10,52816.⬆️.

🅿🆂 **Pistoia** 32A3

Via Marino Marini/via della Quiete. **GPS:** n43,94389 e10,91556.⬆️➡️.

IT

50 🛏free ⛽ 🗑. **Surface:** asphalted.
Distance: 🚶city centre 1km 🚲6km 🚌on the spot.
Remarks: At sports park.

🛏S | **Pistoia** | 32A3

Agricamper Podere Campofossato. GPS: n43,99503 e10,89520.
8 🛏€ 20 ⛽🗑Ch ✂included.
Distance: 🚌50m.
Remarks: Regional products.

🛏S | **Poggibonsi** | 32B4

Via Fortezza Medicea, loc. Vallone. **GPS:** n43,46203 e11,14593. ⬆➡.

± 15 🛏free ⛽€0,10/10liter 🗑Ch ✂(6x)€1/12h. **Location:** Rural.
Surface: gravel. 🅿 01/01-31/12
Distance: 🚶centre 500m ⊗400m 🚊500m.

Tourist information Poggibonsi:
ℹ Monteriggioni. Walled small town.

🛏S | **Pontassieve** | 32B3

Viale Hanoi/viale Lisbona. **GPS:** n43,77370 e11,42764.
🛏free ⛽Chfree. **Surface:** asphalted.
Distance: 🚶500m.

🛏S | **Poppi** | 32B3

La Crocina, Viale dei Pini. **GPS:** n43,71982 e11,76529. ⬆.

12 🛏free ⛽🗑Chfree ✂€3/5h. **Surface:** asphalted.
🅿 01/01-31/12
Distance: 🚶historical centre 500m ⊗300m.

🛏S | **Porto Ercole** 🏖 | 32B6

Le Miniere, SP di Porto Ercole. **GPS:** n42,41749 e11,20386. ⬆➡.

130 🛏€ 25/24h, Aug € 30, Sep € 20 ⛽🗑 Ch ✂ WC included 🚿€0,50 🔌€5
📶. **Surface:** grassy. 🅿 Easter-30/09
Distance: 🚶Porto Ercole 2km ⚓800m ⊗800m.
Remarks: Bread-service, borrow cycles for free, free shuttle to beach every 30 minutes.

🛏S | **Porto Ercole** 🏖 | 32B6

Parking Da Renzo, SC della Feniglia. **GPS:** n42,41527 e11,20777. ⬆➡.

150 🛏€ 18 ⛽€7 Ch ✂ €3. **Surface:** grassy.
🅿 Easter-01/10
Distance: 🚶Porto Ercole 3km ⚓beach 1km ⊗800m.
Remarks: No camping activities, bike/car rental, beach shuttle (August).

🛏S | **Pratovecchio** | 32B3

Via Uffenheim. **GPS:** n43,78680 e11,71932. ⬆➡.

12 🛏free ⛽🗑Ch ✂free. **Surface:** asphalted. 🅿 01/01-31/12
Distance: 🚶50m ⊗100m 🚊100m.
Remarks: Along river, follow signs instead of GPS.

🛏S | **Radda in Chianti** 🍂 | 32B4

Viale 20 Settembre. **GPS:** n43,48643 e11,37543. ⬆➡.

6 🛏€ 12/24h ⛽🗑WCfree. 🚐 **Location:** Rural, simple. **Surface:** metalled.
🅿 01/01-31/12
Distance: 🚶200m (stairs).

🛏S | **Radicofani** | 32C5

Via della Mossa. **GPS:** n42,89427 e11,77598. ⬆.

5 🛏free ⛽🗑Chfree. **Location:** Rural, simple. **Surface:** grassy/gravel.
🅿 01/01-31/12
Distance: 🚶400m.

🛏S | **Radicondoli** | 32B4

Il Pianetto. GPS: n43,25888 e11,04250. ⬆➡.

IT

⌾€ 1/1h, >1 hour € 0,50/h ⌁⌁Ch ⌁ (16x). **Surface:** unpaved.
⌾ 01/01-31/12
Distance: ⌁medieval centre 300m ⊗300m ⌁2km.

Villa dei Boschi, Loc. Villa dei Boschi 50, Fraz San Gimignanello, SP10.
GPS: n43,22829 e11,65429.⌁.

20 ⌾€ 15, free with a meal ⌁ ⌁ WC ⌁included. **Location:** Rural, simple.
Surface: grassy. ⌾ 01/01-31/12
Distance: ⊗on the spot.

Area di sosta Le Terme, Via Trieste. **GPS:** n43,29243 e11,60752.⌁.

64 ⌾€ 5/6h, € 8/12h, € 12/24h ⌁⌁Ch ⌁ WC ⌁included ⌁€2.⌁⌁
Location: Rural, comfortable. **Surface:** gravel/metalled.
⌾ 01/01-31/12
Distance: ⌁500m ⊗50m ⌁200m.
Remarks: Terme Antica Querciolaia 50m.

Molino a Fuoco, Via dei Cavalleggeri Antica, Vada. **GPS:** n43,32816 e10,46005.
⌁⌁.

70 ⌾1/4-15/9 € 10 ⌁⌁Ch. **Surface:** grassy/gravel.
Distance: ⌁400m ⌁500m ⊗400m ⌁400m.
Remarks: Max. 72h.

Il Fortullino, Loc. Castiglioncello. **GPS:** n43,42889 e10,39750.

150 ⌾€ 15/night, Jul-Aug € 20 ⌁⌁Ch ⌁⌁included. **Surface:** unpaved.
⌾ 01/04-30/09
Distance: ⌁Castiglioncello 4km, Livorno 20km, Pisa 40km ⌁150m
⊗Pizzeria 100m ⌁5km.

SP39, Via Aurelia, Loc Caletta. **GPS:** n43,39900 e10,42807.

18 ⌾€ 8 ⌁⌁free. **Surface:** metalled.
Distance: ⌁on the spot ⌁300m ⌁100m.
Remarks: Along busy road, max. 48h.

Parcheggio del Lillatro, Via Fratelli Gigli, loc Lillatro. **GPS:** n43,38380 e10,43206.
⌁.

40 ⌾€ 9. **Location:** Simple, isolated, quiet. **Surface:** sand.
⌾ Easter-31/10
Distance: ⌁50m ⊗50m.

Sportiva Vada, Via Mare Mediterraneo, Vada. **GPS:** n43,35208 e10,45183.⌁⌁.

75 ⌾€ 10/day. **Location:** Rural, quiet. **Surface:** unpaved.
⌾ 01/04-01/10
Distance: ⌁400m ⌁200m ⊗200m ⌁400m.

Via Della Pineta. **GPS:** n42,86530 e11,87383.⌁.

IT

15 🛏free. **Location:** Rural, simple. **Surface:** gravel/sand.
🅾 01/01-31/12
Distance: 🚶500m.

🛏 S **San Casciano dei Bagni** 🌊⛵🏔♨ 32C5
Piazzale del Ponte. **GPS:** n42,87024 e11,87742.⬆.

15 🛏€ 6/12h, € 12/24h 🚰🍽Ch.🚐 **Surface:** asphalted.
🅾 01/01-31/12
Distance: 🚶100m.
Remarks: Near spa resort.

🛏 S **San Casciano in Val di Pesa** 32B4
Parco Il Poggione. **GPS:** n43,65395 e11,18768.⬆.

5 🛏€ 8 🚰🍽free.🚐

🛏 S **San Gimignano** 🌊⛵ 32A4
Area di Sosta Santa Chiara, Via di Castel San Gimignano, Loc. Fprmace.
GPS: n43,45572 e11,03476.⬆➡.

30 🛏€ 22/24h 🚰€2 🍽Ch.🚿WC🗑included. 🚌 **Location:** Rural, luxurious.
Surface: gravel. 🅾 01/01-31/12
Distance: 🚶3km ⊗osteria/bar 🍺1,5km 🚌shuttle.
Remarks: Free shuttle bus to San Gimignano, tenniscourt.

🛏 S **San Gimignano** 🌊⛵ 32A4
Park Santa Lucia, Loc. Santa Lucia. **GPS:** n43,45205 e11,05586.⬆➡.

± 30 🛏€ 1/h, € 15/24h 🚰🍽Ch 🚿 (14x)included. 🚐 **Location:** Rural,
simple. **Surface:** gravel.
Distance: 🚶3km 🚌Citybus Linea 1.
Remarks: Next to swimming pool, 24/24 video surveillance, shuttle bus to city
centre.

🛏 S **San Miniato Basso** 32A4
Piazza G. Impastato, Via Pestalozzi/Via G. Pizzigoni, zona industriale.
GPS: n43,69417 e10,83638.⬆.

🛏 € 0,50/h 🚰🍽free. **Surface:** asphalted. 🅾 01/01-31/12
Distance: 🛒800m ⊗50m 🍺Superal.

🛏 S **San Miniato Basso** 32A4
Area Camper Il Salice, Via Pier delle Vigne 28/A, loc. La Catena.
GPS: n43,68434 e10,82224.⬆.

20 🛏€ 15/24h 🚰🍽Ch 🚿WC🗑. **Surface:** gravel. 🅾 01/01-31/12
Distance: 🚶1km 🚌on the spot.
Remarks: Max. 3 days, shuttle bus to city centre.

🛏 S **San Piero a Sieve** 32B3
GPS: n43,96260 e11,32732.⬆.
🛏free 🚰€2 🍽Ch. **Surface:** metalled.
Distance: 🚶500m ⊗250m.

San Quirico d'Orcia 🌊♨ 32B5
Via delle Scuole. **GPS:** n43,05607 e11,60682.⬆➡.

30 🛏€ 10/24h 🚰🍽free. 🚐 **Location:** Rural, simple. **Surface:** asphalted.
🅾 01/01-31/12
Distance: 🚶200m.

IT

Remarks: Picnic area, playground.

⛲ **San Quirico d'Orcia** 🛶🎣 **32B5**
Strada di Bagno Vignoni, Bagno Vignoni. **GPS:** n43,02904 e11,62450. ⬆️➡️.

± 20 🏕free.
Location: Rural, simple, quiet. **Surface:** unpaved.
🅿️ 01/01-31/12
Distance: ⊗350m.
Remarks: Parco dei Mulini: natural hot springs, free entrance, 400m.

🏕S **San Romano in Garfagnana** **31D3**
Via Campo Sportivo/via Prà di Lago. **GPS:** n44,17243 e10,34199. ⬆️➡️.

15 🏕free ⛽🍽Chfree. **Surface:** grassy. 🅿️ 01/01-31/12
Remarks: At sports park, Parco Avventura Selva del Buffardello 100m.

🏕S **San Vincenzo** **32A5**
Via Biserno. **GPS:** n43,08790 e10,54134. ⬆️.

90 🏕€ 10/24h ⛽🍽free. 🛶 **Surface:** sand. 🅿️ 01/01-31/12
Distance: 🚶1km ⚓beach 200m ⊗50m 🏖50m.
Remarks: Beach parking, no camping activities.

🏕S **Sansepolcro** 🛶⛳ **32C4**
Viale Alessandro Volta. **GPS:** n43,56976 e12,13727.
20 🏕free ⛽🍽Chfree. **Location:** Urban, simple. **Surface:** asphalted.
🅿️ 01/01-31/12
Distance: 🚶200m.

🍴S **Sansepolcro** 🛶⛳ **32C4**
Podere Violino, Loc. Gricigmano. **GPS:** n43,55539 e12,12312. ⬆️➡️.

8 🏕€ 6 + € 5/pp ⛽🍽Ch 🛠 WC 🗑included 🧺.

Surface: grassy.
Distance: 🚶2km ⚓river ⊗on the spot 🏖500m.
Remarks: Restaurant closed on Sunday, swimming pool available.

🏕S **Santa Fiora** **32B5**
Strada di San Rocco. **GPS:** n42,83531 e11,58397. ⬆️➡️.

20 🏕free ⛽🍽Chfree 🛠 (6x)€1/2h. **Location:** Rural, simple.
Surface: gravel/sand. 🅿️ 01/01-31/12
Distance: 🚶450m.

🏕S **Saturnia** 🎣 **32B5**
L'Alveare dei Pinzi, Strada della Peschiera, Saturnia. **GPS:** n42,65597 e11,50368.
⬆️➡️.

400 🏕€ 14/24h ⛽🍽Ch 🛠 (120x)€2 WC included 🗑€0,50 📷€6 🧺.
Surface: metalled. 🅿️ 01/01-31/12
Distance: 🚶Saturnia 3km ⚓1,5km ⊗on the spot.
Remarks: Panoramic view, free shuttle to spa resort and Saturnia,
bar/snack/fruit, terme di Saturnia (sulfur baths) 1,7km, Cascate del Mulino
(water fall, free entry) 2,5km.

🏕S **Saturnia** **32B5**
La Quercia, Via Aurina 15. **GPS:** n42,66667 e11,50457. ⬆️➡️.

30 🏕€ 15/24h ⛽🍽Ch 🛠 WC 🗑€0,50 🧺. **Surface:** gravel.
🅿️ 01/01-31/12
Distance: 🚶200m ⊗100m 🏖100m.
Remarks: Shuttle bus, terme di Saturnia (sulfur baths) 1,7km, Cascate del
Mulino (water fall, free entry) 2,5km.

🍴S **Scarperia** 🏔🎪 **32B3**
Ranch Ricavo, Via di Galliano 21. **GPS:** n44,01189 e11,30681. ⬆️.

20 🛏 € 10 🚐🚽 Ch ⚓ 🚿included. **Surface:** grassy. 🌑 01/01-31/12
Distance: 🛒5km ⊗on the spot 🚰5km.

| 🛏 S | Sestino | 32C3 |

Via Travicello. **GPS:** n43,71223 e12,30356. ⬆➡.

12 🛏 free 🚐🚽 ⚓ free. **Surface:** grasstiles.
Distance: 🛒2km.
Remarks: Nearby sports park.

| 🛏 | Sesto Fiorentino | 32B3 |

Area Antica Etruria, Via Ferruccio Parri. **GPS:** n43,84150 e11,17667. ⬆.

50 🛏 € 18/24h 🚐🚽 Ch ⚓ WC ⬇included. **Surface:** asphalted.
🌑 01/01-31/12
Distance: 🚲1,5km ⊗400m 🚆30m > Florence.
Remarks: Monitored parking.

| 🛏 S | Sesto Fiorentino | 32B3 |

Viale Ariosto. **GPS:** n43,83238 e11,18997. ⬆ .

15 🛏 free 🚐🚽 Ch free. **Surface:** asphalted. 🌑 01/01-31/12
Distance: 🚲3km 🚰on the spot 🚆train 100m.
Remarks: In front of Lidl supermarket, 20 mins to Florence by train.

| 🛏 S | Siena 🌿⛲ | 32B4 |

P1, Palasport, Via Achille Sclavo. **GPS:** n43,33323 e11,31739. ⬆.

75 🛏 € 20/motorhome (8.00-20.00h) 🚐🚽 Ch WC free. **Location:** Urban,
simple. **Surface:** metalled. 🌑 01/01-31/12
Distance: 🚶on the spot.

| 🛏 S | Siena 🌿⛲ | 32B4 |

P2, Il Fagiolone, Via di Pescaia. **GPS:** n43,31456 e11,31760. ⬆.

🛏 € 20/motorhome (8-20h), overnight stay free 🚐🚽 WC free.
Location: Urban, simple, noisy. **Surface:** metalled. 🌑 01/01-31/12
Distance: 🚶on the spot.
Remarks: Along busy road.

| 🛏 | Siena 🌿⛲ | 32B4 |

Acqua Calda, Via Fausto Coppi. **GPS:** n43,33627 e11,29695. ⬆ .

🛏 free. **Location:** Urban, simple. **Surface:** asphalted. 🌑 01/01-31/12
Distance: 🚲650m 🚌bus 10 centre Siena.

| 🛏 | Siena 🌿⛲ | 32B4 |

Via delle Province/via Napoli. **GPS:** n43,34168 e11,30512. ⬆ .

🛏 free. **Location:** Urban, simple, noisy. **Surface:** asphalted. 🌑 01/01-31/12
Distance: ⊗200m McDonalds 🚶on the spot.

Tourist information Siena:
- 👁 Palazzo Publico. Gothic town hall from 1342.
- 👁 Torre del Mangia. Bell tower. 🌑 daily.
- ✝ Duomo. Romanesque Gothic cathedral.
- ✿ La Lizza. Week market. 🌑 Wed morning.
- ✴ Palio, Piazza del Campo. Famous historical horse race. 🌑 02/07, 16/08.

IT

Stia — 32B3

Parco comunale del Canto della Rana, Via Londa, SP556. **GPS:** n43,80407 e11,70282. ⬆️➡️.

18 🅿️free 🚰🗑️Ch 🧹free. **Surface:** gravel. 📅 01/01-31/12
Distance: 🚶500m.

Suvereto — 32A5

Via dei Forni. **GPS:** n43,07572 e10,67802. ⬆️.

12 🅿️free 🚰🗑️free. **Location:** Rural, simple, quiet. **Surface:** grassy.
📅 01/01-31/12
Distance: 🚶medieval centre 200m ⊗300m 🚉300m.

Torrita di Siena — 32C4

Via di Ciliano. **GPS:** n43,16475 e11,77173. ⬆️.

6 🅿️free 🚰🗑️Ch 🧹free. **Location:** Rural, comfortable, quiet.
Surface: grasstiles/metalled. 📅 01/01-31/12
Distance: 🚶400m ⊗200m.

Venturina — 32A5

Parco Termale Calidario, Via del Bottaccio. **GPS:** n43,03666 e10,60000. ➡️.

20 🅿️free 🚰€0,10/10liter 🗑️Ch. **Location:** Quiet. **Surface:** metalled.
📅 01/01-31/12
Distance: 🚶800m ⊗50m 🚉800m.
Remarks: Thermal centre 50m.

Viareggio — 31D3

Via Martiri di Belfiore. **GPS:** n43,88120 e10,25080. ⬆️.

44 🅿️€ 15/24h 🚰🗑️Ch 🧹included. **Surface:** asphalted.
📅 01/01-31/12
Distance: 🚶1km ⛵2,5km.
Remarks: Check in at All Events Festival Puccini Viareggio, Viale Regina Margherita 1, 43,8673339 10,2431529, terrain with video surveillance.

Vinci — 32A3

Via Girolamo Calvi. **GPS:** n43,78080 e10,92830. ⬆️.
12 🅿️free 🚰🗑️Chfree. **Surface:** metalled. 📅 01/01-31/12
Distance: 🚶300m.
Remarks: At sports park.

Volterra — 32A4

Parking P3, Fonti Docciola, Viale Dei Filosofi. **GPS:** n43,40306 e10,86417. ⬆️.

15 🅿️€ 8/24h 🚰🗑️Chfree. 🏠 **Location:** Urban. **Surface:** gravel.
Distance: 🚶historical center 100m ⊗200m 🚉300m.

San Marino

San Marino — 32C3

Camper Stop, Via del Serrone 94. **GPS:** n43,92057 e12,45056. ⬆️.
🅿️free 🚰🧹. **Surface:** grassy.
Distance: 🚶city centre 3km 🚌on the spot.

San Marino — 32C3

P13, Baldasserona, Borgo Maggiore. **GPS:** n43,94054 e12,44289. ⬆️.

50 🅿️free 🚰🗑️Ch. **Surface:** asphalted. 📅 01/01-31/12
Remarks: Service 300m.

San Marino — 32C3

Strada Genghe di Atto, Acquaviva. **GPS:** n43,94491 e12,42963. ⬆️.

5 ⌂free ⌖ ▦ Ch WC free. **Surface:** asphalted.

San Marino 32C3

P10, Via Napoleone Boneparte. **GPS:** n43,93567 e12,44362. ⬆

20 ⌂€ 8/24h. **Surface:** asphalted. ◉ 01/11-31/03
Remarks: Elevator to centre 50m.

Tourist information San Marino:
ℹ Borgo Maggiore. Week market. ⬛ Thu.

Marche

Amandola 33B2
Piazzale Sandro Pertini. **GPS:** n42,97085 e13,35488.
⌂€ 8,50 ⌖ ▦ Ch ⚡ WC ⊐included. **Surface:** asphalted. ⬛ 01/01-31/12
Distance: ⊗850m.

Ancona 33C1
Via Sanzio Blasi, Loc. Posatore. **GPS:** n43,59964 e13,48530. ⬆→

30 ⌂€ 12-13 ⌖ ▦ Ch ⚡ (24x)included. **Location:** Simple.
Surface: asphalted/grassy. ⬛ 01/01-31/12
Distance: ⊾4,5km ⇒10m.
Remarks: Max. 72h, entrance between 8-22h.

Ancona 27A10
Centro Commerciale Auchan, Via Scataglini, Zona Industriale Baraccola, SS16, Ancona-sud. **GPS:** n43,55133 e13,51506. ⬆→

25 ⌂free ⌖ ▦ free. **Location:** Simple. **Surface:** grasstiles.
⬛ 01/01-31/12
Distance: ⊾8km ⛵ 3,6km.

Tourist information Ancona:
ℹ Riviera del Conera. Touristic peninsula with beaches and several bathing resorts.

Apecchio 32C4
Via Isidoro Pazzaglia. **GPS:** n43,55938 e12,41969. ⬆→
30 ⌂free ⌖ ▦ Ch ⚡ (6x)free. **Surface:** metalled. ⬛ 01/01-31/12
Distance: ⊾100m ⛁50m.

Tourist information Apecchio:
ℹ Week market. ⬛ Fri-morning.

Ascoli Piceno 33C2
Ex Seminario, Viale Alcide Gasperi. **GPS:** n42,85222 e13,58222. ⬆→

20 ⌂€ 3/night,20/h, night € 3 ⌖ ⚡. **Location:** Urban. **Surface:** asphalted.
Distance: ⊾centre 500m ⊗200m ⛁200m.
Remarks: Guarded parking.

Ascoli Piceno 33C2
Bed & Breakfast Chartaria, Via Adriatico. **GPS:** n42,84792 e13,57306. ⬆.
7 ⌂€ 15 ⌖ ⚡ €3. **Surface:** grassy.

Tourist information Ascoli Piceno:
ℹ City with many monumental bldg.
ℹ ⬛ Wed, Sa.

Camerino 33B2
Via Macario Muzio. **GPS:** n43,13677 e13,06718. ⬆

8 ⌂free ⌖ ▦ Ch free ⚡ €1/4h WC ⊐. **Location:** Rural. **Surface:** asphalted.
⬛ 01/01-31/12
Distance: ⊾centre 500m ⊗350m.
Remarks: Beautiful view, escalator to city centre.

Carpegna 32C3
Via Aldo Moro. **GPS:** n43,78083 e12,34040. ⬆

10 ⌂free ⌖ €1 ▦ Ch ⚡ €0,60/h. **Surface:** concrete. ⬛ 01/01-31/12
Distance: ⊾300m ⛁300m.

Castelfidardo 33C1
Croce Verde, Via Lumumba/via Donato Bramonte. **GPS:** n43,46603 e13,55563. ⬆→

IT

3 🛏free 🚰 🗑free. **Location:** Simple. **Surface:** asphalted.
🗓 01/01-31/12
Distance: 🚶200m.
Remarks: Max. 48h.

10 🛏€ 13, guests € 10 🚰 🗑Ch 🔧 WC,on camp site 🗑included,on camp site.
🚿 **Location:** Rural, simple. **Surface:** grassy.
🗓 01/01-31/12
Distance: 🚶5km ⊗on the spot.

🚐S	Cerreto D'Esi	33B1

Via Dante Alighieri. **GPS:** n43,32714 e12,99114.➡

🚐S	Cossignano	33C2

Via Gallo. **GPS:** n42,98050 e13,69213.⬆

6 🛏€6 🚰€3 🗑Ch 🔧included. **Location:** Simple. **Surface:** metalled.
🗓 01/01-31/12
Distance: ⊗500m.

🚐S	Cupramontana	33B1

Verdicchio, SP 11. **GPS:** n43,43934 e13,11837.⬆➡

10 🛏free 🚰 🗑. **Location:** Simple. **Surface:** metalled.
🗓 01/01-31/12
Distance: 🍺500m.

🚐S	Colmurano	33B2

Via Piero della Francesca, Contrada Peschiera. **GPS:** n43,16260 e13,35828.⬆➡

10 🛏free 🚰 🗑free Ch 🔧 (10x). **Location:** Simple, noisy. **Surface:** metalled.
🗓 01/01-31/12
Distance: ⊗100m 🍺500m.
Remarks: Beautiful view of Monte San Vicino.

🚐S	Fabriano 🏛 👣	33B1

Fraz. Poggio San Romualdo. **GPS:** n43,36473 e13,02534.⬆

8 🛏free 🚰 🗑 Ch WCfree. **Surface:** asphalted. 🗓 01/01-31/12
Distance: 🚶400m.
Remarks: Near sports park and historical centre.

🚐S	Corinaldo 🌿	32D3

Viale Dante. **GPS:** n43,64703 e13,04910.⬆

35 🛏free 🚰 🗑free. **Location:** Rural, simple, quiet. **Surface:** grassy.
🗓 01/01-31/12
Distance: 🚶3,5km 🚶on the spot.

🚐S	Fabriano 🏛 👣	33B1

Via Bruno Buozzi. **GPS:** n43,34650 e12,91645.➡

8 🛏free 🚰 🗑Chfree. **Location:** Simple. **Surface:** asphalted.
🗓 01/01-31/12
Distance: 🚶400m 🍺50m.

🚐S	Corinaldo 🌿	32D3

Ristorante Camping Colverde, Via per Montalboddo 52.
GPS: n43,63504 e13,09743.⬆➡

18 🛏free 🚰€0,20/10liter 🗑Ch 🔧 (6x)€3/12h. **Location:** Simple.
Surface: grassy. 🗓 01/01-31/12
Distance: 🚶3km.

IT

Remarks: Next to sports centre.

🚐 S   **Falerone**   33C2

Ex-stazione FS di Piane di Falerone, Via Togliatti. **GPS:** n43,09944 e13,49944. ⬆.

15 🚐free 🚰🔌Ch🚿free. **Surface:** metalled. ◉ 1st Su of the month
Distance: 🚶100m ⊗200m.
Remarks: Nearby the old station and theatre Romano.

🚐 S   **Fano** 🚲⛵⛴🏖   32D3

Lungomare Sassonia, Via Ruggeri. **GPS:** n43,84238 e13,03197. ⬆.

60 🚐€ 7-8,50 🚰🔌included 🚿(20x)€2/day WC🚽 📶€0,50/day.🚿
Surface: grassy/gravel. ◻ 01/01-31/12
Distance: 🚶1km 🚗2km ⛱50m ⊗50m 🛒600m.

🚐 S   **Fano** 🚲⛵⛴🏖   32D3

Area di Sosta Adriatico, SS16, Torrette di Fano. **GPS:** n43,80789 e13,08198. ⬆.

30 🚐€ 13-20, Camperstop 18-9h€ 8-10 🚰🔌Ch🚿(12x) WCincluded
🚽€0,50 ◉€3/time.🚿 **Location:** Comfortable. **Surface:** grassy/gravel.
◻ 24/04-15/09
Distance: 🚶4km 🚗9km ⛱200m ⊗50m 🛒500m.
Remarks: Service passerby € 5.

🚐 S   **Fano** 🚲⛵⛴🏖   32D3

Viale Kennedy. GPS: n43,84557 e13,01133. ➡.

16-20 🚐free 🚰🔌Chfree. **Location:** Simple. **Surface:** asphalted.
◻ 01/01-31/12
Distance: 🚶200m 🚗2,7km ⛱800m.
Remarks: Nearby cemetery.

🚐 S   **Fano** 🚲⛵⛴🏖   32D3

Campo Nunzia, SS Adriactica Sud-Loc. Torrette di Fano.
GPS: n43,80444 e13,08472. ⬆➡.

28 🚐€ 10-15 🚰🔌Ch🚿€3/24h WC🚽€3. **Location:** Comfortable.
Surface: grassy/gravel. ◻ 24/04-01/09
Distance: 🚶7km 🚗10km ⛱150m.

🍴   **Fano** 🚲⛵⛴🏖   32D3

BarRistorante La Tratta, Via Fratelli Zuccari 37. **GPS:** n43,83589 e13,04182. ⬆.

14 🚐€ 6.🚿 **Location:** Simple, quiet. **Surface:** grassy. ◻ 01/04-01/10
Distance: 🚶2,5km ⛱50m ←on the spot ⊗on the spot.
Remarks: P camper.

Tourist information Fano:
🛈 ◻ Wed, Sa.

🚐 S   **Fermo**   33C1

Area Camper 2004, Lungomare Marina Palminese. **GPS:** n43,15085 e13,81382. ⬆.

64 🚐€ 10, electricity included € 12 🚰🔌Ch🚿(32x)included
🚽hot shower against payment. **Surface:** grassy. ◻ 01/04-30/09
Distance: 🚗2,5km ⛱on the spot.

🚐 S   **Fermo**   33C1

Baia dei Gabbiani, Viale A. de Gasperi, Lido S. Tomasso.
GPS: n43,22158 e13,78113. ⬆➡.

50 🚐€ 13-15, Aug € 20 🚰🔌Ch🚿🚽€0,50 ◉. **Surface:** grassy/gravel.
◻ 01/04-30/09
Distance: 🚗6,6km ⛱Private beach.

IT

Fermo — 33C1
Onda Verde, Via Usodimare, Lido di Fermo. **GPS**: n43,20289 e13,78825.

100 € 10-€ 18 (Aug) Ch 2Amp WC included. **Surface:** grassy. 01/04-30/09
Distance: Fermo 10km 5,4km 10m 10-500m 200m.

Fossombrone — 32D3
Via Oberdan. **GPS**: n43,69301 e12,81835.

8 free Ch free. **Surface:** asphalted. 01/01-31/12
Distance: 500m 1,4km.

Tourist information Fossombrone:
Week market. Mo.

Genga — 33B1
Frasassi, Fraz San Vittore. **GPS**: n43,40321 e12,97597.

50 free WC free. **Location:** Simple, quiet. **Surface:** gravel. 01/01-31/12
Distance: 7km on the spot.
Remarks: Nearby pay-desk Gole di Frasassi, free shuttle to the caves.

Gradara — 32D3
Parking P1, Piazza Paolo e Francesca. **GPS**: n43,94083 e12,77083.

14 € 10/24h Ch WC free. **Location:** Simple, central. **Surface:** asphalted. 01/01-31/12
Distance: historical center 100m 7,3km on the spot 400m.
Remarks: Parking centre.

Grottammare — 33C2
Sosta Camper 43° Parallelo, Via Carlo Alberto dalla Chiesa. **GPS**: n42,96673 e13,87694.
40 € 15 Ch WC . **Surface:** asphalted.
Distance: 2,7km 500m 500m 100m on the spot.
Remarks: Behind centro commerciale Cityper, along railwayline.

Grottammare — 33C2
Briciola di Sole, Contr. Granaro 19. **GPS**: n42,98278 e13,84000.

14 € 15, guests free Ch included. **Surface:** gravel/metalled. 01/04-31/10
Distance: 2,5km sea 5km on the spot 2km.
Remarks: Restaurant with traditional kitchen, located on estate.

Jesi — 33B1
Via Zannoni. **GPS**: n43,51882 e13,24180.

10 free free. **Location:** Simple, quiet. **Surface:** asphalted. 01/01-31/12
Distance: 500m centro storico.

Tourist information Jesi:
Area with many vineyards.
Grotte di Frasassi. Caves.

Loreto — 33C1
Area Camper Pro Loco, Via Maccari. **GPS**: n43,44125 e13,61491.

65 € 12/24h Ch included (20x)€3/day WC €1/time.
Location: Comfortable. **Surface:** grasstiles. 01/01-31/12
Distance: 150m 15km.
Remarks: Max. 48h.

Loreto — 33C1
Parking P1, Via Benedetto XXV. **GPS**: n43,44129 e13,60756.

6 ⌧€ 6/day, overnight stay free WC. 🚻 **Surface:** asphalted.
Distance: 🚶300m ⊗50m.
Remarks: Parking at city wall.

| ⌧S | Macerata | 33B1 |

Stadio Helvia Recina, Via dei Velini. **GPS:** n43,30701 e13,43722.⬆️

80 ⌧€ 8-11 🔌 Ch 💧 (80x)€2/24h WC 🚻included,cold. 🛁 **Location:**
Simple. **Surface:** grassy. ⬛ 01/04-30/09
Distance: 🚶500m ⛵1,5km 🚲50m ⊗on the spot.
Remarks: Between coast road and railwayline.

| ⌧S | Matelica 🌿🏔 | 33B1 |

Porte Capamante, Via Circonvallazione. **GPS:** n43,25917 e13,01083.➡️

20 ⌧free 🔌€1/15minutes 🚿free. **Location:** Urban, simple.
Surface: asphalted. ⬛ 01/01-31/12
Distance: 🚶3,5km.

| ⌧S | Macerata Feltria | 32C3 |

Loc. San Gasparre. **GPS:** n43,80098 e12,42886.

6-8 ⌧free 🚿 free. **Location:** Simple. **Surface:** asphalted.
⬛ 01/01-31/12
Distance: 🚶200m ⊗200m 🍽200m.

| 🍴S | Matelica 🌿🏔 | 33B1 |

Country House Salomone, Località Salomone 437. **GPS:** n43,29635 e13,00031.
⬆️➡️

4 ⌧free 🔌 Ch WC 🚻free. **Surface:** metalled. ⬛ 01/01-31/12
Distance: 🚶1km 🏊on the spot ⊗Pizzeria.
Remarks: Along Aspa river.

Tourist information Macerata Feltria:
🏕 Week market. ⬛ Tue.

20 ⌧€ 7, free with a meal 🔌🚿 💧(16x)included WC at restaurant. 🛁
Location: Rural, simple. **Surface:** grassy/gravel. ⬛ 01/01-31/12
Distance: ⊗on the spot.

| ⌧S | Mergo | 33B1 |

Area Sosta Comunale, Via Colli. **GPS:** n43,47394 e13,03598.⬆️➡️

| ⌧S | Marina di Montemarciano 🌊 | 33B1 |

Lungomare Alfredo Cappellini. **GPS:** n43,65936 e13,32780.

40 ⌧€ 0,70/h 🔌 Ch 💧 (32x)€2. 🚻 **Location:** Simple, noisy.
Surface: gravel. ⬛ 15/05-15/09
Distance: 🚶4km ⛵9km 🏖pebbled beach 60m ⊗100m.
Remarks: To coast road and railwayline.

| ⌧S | Marotta 🌊 | 32D3 |

Area di Sosta Marotta, Lungomare Colombo 157, Mondolfo.
GPS: n43,76067 e13,15312.⬆️

10 ⌧free 🔌🚿 Ch free 💧 (8x). **Location:** Simple. **Surface:** concrete.
⬛ 01/01-31/12
Distance: 🚶300m.
Remarks: Nearby sports park.

| ⌧S | Mondavio 🌿 | 32D3 |

Borgo Gramsci. **GPS:** n43,67487 e12,96700.⬆️

IT

5 🛒free ⟋▬🔌WCfree,50m. **Location:** Simple. **Surface:** metalled.
◻ 01/01-31/12
Distance: 🚶historical center 100m ⊗100m 🍴200m.
Remarks: Nearby old town and medieval citadel Roveresca.

Tourist information Mondavio:
↗ Week market. ◻ Mo.

🛒S	Montalto delle Marche 🌿	33C2

Via Cuprense. **GPS:** n42,98726 e13,60870.⬆.

6 🛒free ⟋▬🔌free. **Surface:** metalled. ◻ 01/01-31/12
Distance: 🚶100m.

🛒S	Monte San Giusto	33C1

Campo Sportivo, Via Magellano, Villa San Filippo. **GPS:** n43,26343 e13,60070.
⬆➡.

20 🛒free ⟋▬🔌Chfree. **Surface:** asphalted. ◻ 01/01-31/12
Distance: 🚶1km.
Remarks: Outlet center leather and shoes.

🛒S	Monte Vidon Corrado	33C2

Viale Trento e Trieste. **GPS:** n43,12205 e13,48381.⬆.

4 🛒free ⟋▬Chfree. **Surface:** metalled. ◻ 01/01-31/12
Distance: 🚶200m ⊗200m.

🛒S	Montecosaro	33C1

Via Martiri della Libertà Ungherese. **GPS:** n43,31779 e13,63653.

30 🛒free ⟋▬🔌Chfree. **Surface:** concrete. ◻ 01/01-31/12
Distance: 🚶100m ⊗100m 🍴100m �e50m.

🛒S	Montefiore dell'Aso 🌿🏔	33C2

Piazza Pietro Nenni. **GPS:** n43,04992 e13,75021.

10 🛒free ⟋▬🔌Chfree. **Surface:** sand. ◻ 01/01-31/12
Distance: 🚶200m.

🛒S	Montefiore dell'Aso 🌿🏔	33C2

Agricamper Il Poggio del Belvedere, Contrada Aso no. 11.
GPS: n43,04611 e13,72500.⬆.

6 🛒🟢€ 8/pp ⟋▬🔌 Ch 🔌 WC ▯included. **Surface:** metalled.
◻ 01/01-31/12

🛒S	Montelupone 🌿	33C1

Loc. San Firmano. **GPS:** n43,36383 e13,54950.⬆.

20 🛒free ⟋▬🔌free. **Location:** Simple. **Surface:** asphalted.
Distance: 🚶500m.
Remarks: Parking sports park.

🛒S	Montelupone 🌿	33C1

Via Allesandro Manzoni. **GPS:** n43,34300 e13,57080.⬆.

IT

10 ᠍free 🚰🗑free. **Location:** Simple. **Surface:** asphalted.
🚻 01/01-31/12
Remarks: Parking city park.

🅂 Morro d'Alba 33B1
Area Comunale, Via degli Orti. **GPS:** n43,60198 e13,21263. ⬆️➡️.

10 ᠍free 🚰🗑free.
Location: Simple, quiet. **Surface:** asphalted.
🚻 01/01-31/12
Distance: 🚶500m.
Remarks: Access with electronic card, Bar Pro Loco or town hall.

🅂 Offida 💱 33C2
Via Tommaso Castelli. **GPS:** n42,93689 e13,69180. ⬆️.

3 ᠍free 🚰🗑free. **Surface:** unpaved. 🚻 01/01-31/12
Remarks: At the city walls.

Pedaso 33C2
Via Martiri della Libertà. **GPS:** n43,09985 e13,84272.
᠍free. **Surface:** asphalted. 🚻 01/01-31/12
Distance: 🚶on the spot 🏊on the spot ⊗150m.
Remarks: Parking at the beach.

🅂 Pesaro ⚓🚢 32D3
Via dell Aquedotto. **GPS:** n43,90842 e12,90097. ⬆️.

12 ᠍free 🚰🗑Chfree ⚡(12x)€1. **Surface:** asphalted.
Distance: 🚶1km 🏖7,5km.

Pesaro ⚓🚢 32D3
Waterfront Parking, Via Calata Caio Duilio. **GPS:** n43,92244 e12,90657. ⬆️.

20 ᠍€12. 🚻 01/01-31/12
Distance: 🏊on the spot.
Tourist information Pesaro:
🎪 Week market. 🚻 Tue.

🅂 Petritoli 33C2
Impianti Sportivi. GPS: n43,07306 e13,65139. ⬆️.

10 ᠍free 🚰🗑Chfree. **Surface:** sand. 🚻 01/01-31/12
Distance: 🚶1km.
Remarks: At sports park.

🅂 Piandimeleto 32C3
Via Giacomo Leopardi. **GPS:** n43,72541 e12,41328. ⬆️➡️.

9 ᠍free 🚰🗑Chfree. **Surface:** grassy. 🚻 01/01-31/12
Distance: 🚶100m.

🅂 Pietrarubbia 32C3
Vulcangas, Via Montefeltresca 107, Ponte Cappuccini. **GPS:** n43,80278 e12,36667.
⬆️.

2 ᠍free 🚰🗑WCfree. **Surface:** metalled. 🚻 01/01-31/12
Distance: 🚶200m.

🅂 Pievebovigliana 33B2
Via Rancia. **GPS:** n43,06583 e13,08526. ⬆️.

10 ᠍free 🚰🗑Ch⚡. **Surface:** asphalted. 🚻 01/01-31/12
Distance: 🚶300m.

🅂 Pioraco 33B2
Loc. Buchetto, SS361 km77. **GPS:** n43,18010 e12,97422. ⬆️.

IT

Distance: ⚓beach 200m ⊗300m.
Remarks: Shuttle bus.

🛁 S | **Potenza Picena** | 33C1
Via Togliatti, Porto Potenza Picena. **GPS:** n43,36167 e13,69306. ⬆

45 🍴€ 7/24h, € 10/48h, € 15/72h 🚰🍽 Ch included 🚿(12x)€2.
Surface: asphalted. ☐ 01/01-31/12
Distance: 🚶200m ⚓600m ⊗200m 🛒200m.
Remarks: Thursday market.

🛁 S | **Recanati** | 33C1
Camperclub Recanati, Viale Giovanni XXIII. **GPS:** n43,40245 e13,55777. ⬆➡

30 🍴free 🚰🍽 🚿(22x)free. **Location:** Urban, simple. **Surface:** asphalted.
☐ 01/01-31/12
Distance: 🚶500m.

🛁 S | **San Benedetto del Tronto** | 33C2
Viale dello Sport. **GPS:** n42,92312 e13,89527. ⬆

20 🍴€ 5, Jul/Aug € 8 🚰🍽 Ch 🚿included. **Surface:** asphalted.
Distance: 🚲4,3km ⚓500m 🚌on the spot.
Remarks: Along railwayline, under viaduct.

🛁 | **San Ginesio** | 33B2
Via Ciarlatini. **GPS:** n43,10945 e13,31801.

8 🍴free. **Surface:** gravel. ☐ 01/01-31/12
Distance: 🚶200m ⊗200m 🛒200m 🛒1km.

🛁 S | **San Severino Marche** | 33B1
P7, Viale Mazzini. **GPS:** n43,22757 e13,18836. ⬆➡

18 (+20) 🍴€ 13 🚰🍽 🚿(16x) WC included. ⚑ **Location:** Rural,
comfortable, quiet. **Surface:** gravel. ☐ 01/01-31/12
Distance: 🚶700m 🛒on the spot ⊗summer 🏃on the spot.

🛁 S | **Pollenza** 🌿 | 33B1
Contrada Morazzano. **GPS:** n43,26482 e13,34614. ⬆➡

8 🍴free 🚰🍽free. **Location:** Simple. **Surface:** asphalted.
☐ 01/01-31/12
Distance: 🚶500m.
Remarks: Nearby elevator to centre, max. 48h.

🛁 S | **Porto Recanati** 🏖 | 33C1
Karting Club Pista del Conero, Viale Scarfiotti, loc. Scossicci.
GPS: n43,47067 e13,64246. ⬆

80 🍴€ 15/24h 🚰🍽 Ch 🚿(80x) WC included 🍽€1 🚿free. ⚑
Location: Simple, noisy. **Surface:** gravel. ☐ 01/04-30/09
Distance: 🚶100m ⊗200m.

🛁 S | **Porto Recanati** 🏖 | 27A11
Pro Loco, Viale Scarfiotti, loc. Scossicci. **GPS:** n43,44605 e13,65639. ⬆

40 🍴€ 10/24h 🚰🍽included Ch 🚿(8x)€2 WC 🍽€1. ⚑ **Location:** Simple.
Surface: grassy. ☐ 01/04-30/09
Distance: 🚶500m 🚲3km ⚓50m ⊗200m 🛒1km.
Remarks: Max. 72h.

🛁 S | **Porto San Giorgio** | 33C1
La Perla Adriatico, Via San Martino 13. **GPS:** n43,16400 e13,80836.
75 🍴€ 12/18 🚰🍽 Ch 🚿 WC 🍽🚿. **Surface:** unpaved.
☐ 01/01-31/12

IT

12 ⌚free 🚰🍽free 🔌 (12x)€0,50/4h. **Location:** Simple, quiet. **Surface:** asphalted. ⚫ 01/01-31/12
Distance: 🚶800m.
Remarks: Parking sports park.

⛽S　　　　**Sant'Agata Feltria** 〰️⛱️🏔️　　32C3
Piazzale Europa. **GPS:** n43,86386 e12,20549. ⬆️➡️.

40 ⌚€ 8/24h 🚰🍽 🔌 (6x)free. **Surface:** asphalted.
Distance: 🚶100m.

⛽S　　　　　　**Sarnano**　　　　　33B2
Via Corridoni. **GPS:** n43,03444 e13,29972.⬆️.

15 ⌚free 🚰🍽 Ch WC free. **Surface:** asphalted. ⚫ 01/01-31/12
Distance: 🚶100m ⊗100m 🚆100m.

⛽S　　　　　**Sassoferrato**　　　　33B1
Via Raffaello Sanzio. **GPS:** n43,43122 e12,85471.⬆️.

7 ⌚free 🚰🍽free 🔌(6x)€1/day. **Location:** Simple. **Surface:** asphalted.
⚫ 01/01-31/12
Distance: 🚶500m.

⛽S　　　　　**Senigallia**　　　　32D3
Via F. Podesti 234, SS16, Senigallia-sud. **GPS:** n43,70483 e13,23764.⬆️.

14 ⌚free 🚰🍽free. **Location:** Simple, noisy. **Surface:** asphalted.
⚫ 01/01-31/12
Distance: 🚶3km 🏊3,3km ⛵150m.
Remarks: Along busy road, next to petrol station, max. 48h.

⛽S　　　　　**Tolentino**　　　　33B1
Viale Foro Boario. **GPS:** n43,20773 e13,28784.

15 ⌚free 🚰🍽free. **Surface:** asphalted. ⚫ 01/01-31/12
Distance: 🚶200m ⊗200m.

⛽S　　　　　**Urbania** 〰️　　　　32C3
Area camper Barco, Loc. Barco Ducale Colonia. **GPS:** n43,67916 e12,51277. ⬆️
➡️
65 ⌚free 🚰🍽Ch 🔌free.
Location: Rural.
Surface: gravel/sand.
Distance: 🚶1km.
Remarks: Biking trail, behind former summer residence of dukes of Urbania.

⛽S　　　　　**Urbania** 〰️　　　　32C3
Piazzale Fosso del Maltempo, Viale Michelangelo. **GPS:** n43,66482 e12,52191.
⬆️➡️.

50 ⌚free 🚰🍽Ch 🔌free. **Surface:** asphalted. ⚫ 01/01-31/12
Distance: 🚶500m.
Tourist information Urbania:
🎪 Week market. ⚫ Thu.

⛽S　　　　　**Urbino** 〰️　　　　32D3
Via Pablo Neruda. **GPS:** n43,73333 e12,62722. ⬆️➡️.

IT

10 ᗭfree 🚰🔧🗑Chfree. **Surface:** asphalted. ⬛ 01/01-31/12
Distance: 🚶historical centre 2,5km.
Remarks: Shuttle bus to city centre.

| ♨S | **Urbino** 🌿 | 32D3 |

Corte della Miniera, Via Miniera, 10. **GPS:** n43,78336 e12,59091.
5 ᗭguests free 🚰🗑Ch🧹.
Distance: 🚶Urbino 11km ⊗on the spot.

Tourist information Urbino:
⚘ Week market. ⬛ Sa.

| ♨S | **Urbisaglia** 🌿⛲ | 33B1 |

Abbadia di Fiastra, P4. **GPS:** n43,22111 e13,40722.⬆️.

20 ᗭfree 🚰🗑Ch🧹 free. **Surface:** metalled.
⬛ 01/01-31/12
Distance: 🚶4km ⊗50m.
Remarks: Parking monastery, archaeological park Urbs Salvia 3km, hiking area.

| ♨S | **Visso** 🏔 | 33B2 |

Largo Gregorio XIII. GPS: n42,93139 e13,09141.⬆️➡️.

15 ᗭfree 🚰🗑Chfree 🧹€0,80/h. **Surface:** asphalted.
Distance: 🚶800m.

Lazio

| ♨S | **Acquapendente** | 32C5 |

Agriturismo Buonomore, SS2 via Cassia km 130. **GPS:** n42,73367 e11,88361.⬆️.

8 ᗭ€ 15, Aug € 30 🚰🗑Ch🧹 WC⬜included 🍽.
⬛ 01/01-31/12
Distance: 🚶3km ⊗on the spot.

| ♨S | **Acquapendente** | 32C5 |

Via Campo Boario. **GPS:** n42,74203 e11,86240.⬆️.

ᗭfree 🚰🗑Chfree. **Surface:** asphalted/metalled.
Distance: 🚶250m 🚊250m.

| ♨S | **Albano Laziale** | 33B4 |

Piazza Guerucci, Via Riccardo Lombardi. **GPS:** n41,73206 e12,65213.
ᗭfree 🚰🗑Ch. **Surface:** asphalted.
Distance: 🚆train > Rome 55min.
Remarks: Next to post office and sports park.

| ♨S | **Amatrice** | 33B3 |

AgriCamper Amatrice, Località Retrosi. **GPS:** n42,62349 e13,31788.
20 ᗭ€ 13 🚰🗑Ch🧹. **Surface:** gravel.
Remarks: Located in national nature reserve Gran Sasso.

| ♨S | **Bolsena** 🌿⛲ | 32C5 |

Guadetto, Via della Chiusa. **GPS:** n42,63604 e11,98695.⬆️.

30 ᗭ€ 15/24h 🚰🗑Ch🧹 included WC⬜🚿. **Surface:** grassy/sand.
⬛ 01/01-31/12
Distance: 🚶500m ⛱10m 🚣on the spot ⚓on the spot.

| ♨ | **Bolsena** 🌿⛲ | 32C5 |

Via Santa Maria. **GPS:** n42,63898 e11,98562.⬆️➡️.

50 ᗭ€ 5/12h, € 10/24h. **Surface:** asphalted. ⬛ 01/01-31/12
Distance: 🚶800m ⛱100m on the spot ⊗400m 🚊400m 🚣100m.

| ♨S | **Bolsena** 🌿⛲ | 32C5 |

Agricampeggio Le Calle, Via Cassia km 111,200. **GPS:** n42,63029 e11,99716.⬆️.
ᗭ€ 15-19, 2 pers.incl 🚰🗑Ch🧹 WC⬜included. ⬛ 01/04-01/11
Distance: 🚶1km ⊗on the spot.

Tourist information Bolsena:
ℹ Citadel and ramparts.

| ♨S | **Bracciano** | 33A4 |

Le Mimose, Via del Lago 25. **GPS:** n42,10856 e12,17893.
50 ᗭ€ 14/24h 🚰🗑Ch🧹€3. **Surface:** gravel. ⬛ 01/01-31/12
Distance: 🚶800m ⛱Lago di Bracciano 250m ⊗150m.

| ♨S | **Capodimonte** 🏖 | 32C6 |

Temporanea. GPS: n42,55979 e11,88714.⬆️.

50 ⌁€ 10/24h ⚡🔌Ch. **Surface:** grassy. ☐ 01/01-31/12
Distance: ⛵2km 🚶on the spot.
Remarks: At lake Bolsena, check in at bar.

Cassino 33C5
Parking Europa, Via Agnone 5. **GPS:** n41,48289 e13,83750.

⌁€ 13,50 ⚡€2 🔌€2 Ch€2 ⚡€3 🔌. **Surface:** grassy/gravel.
Distance: ⛵800m 🚂station 1km.

Castel di Tora 33B3
Via Turano, SP34. **GPS:** n42,21362 e12,96888.
15 ⌁€ 5/24h ⚡🔌Ch ⚡. **Surface:** gravel. ☐ 01/01-31/12
Distance: ⛵1km 🚶on the spot.
Remarks: At Turano lake.

Castel Gandolfo 33B4
Parcheggio Bus Lago Albano, Via Spiaggia del Lago. **GPS:** n41,75797 e12,65359. ⬆.
⌁€ 10/24h. **Surface:** asphalted. ☐ 01/01-31/12
Distance: 🚶on the spot ⊗on the spot 🚂800m > Rome.
Remarks: At lake Albano.

Castel Gandolfo 33B4
Ristorante I Quadri 2000, Via dei Pescatori 21. **GPS:** n41,74930 e12,65384.
10 ⌁€ 15/24h ⚡🔌Ch ⚡. **Surface:** sand. ☐ 01/01-31/12
Distance: 🚶on the spot ⊗on the spot.
Remarks: Private beach at Lago di Albano.

Civita Castellana 33A3
Via Terni. **GPS:** n42,29905 e12,41520.

+50 ⌁free ⚡🔌free. **Surface:** asphalted. ☐ 01/01-31/12
Distance: ⛵500m 🚋50m.
Remarks: At cemetery.

Tourist information Civita Castellana:
👁 Palazzo Farnese, Caprarola. Pentagonal country house, accessed by winding staircase.

Colle di Tora 33B3
Via Maria Letizia Giuliani. **GPS:** n42,20898 e12,94915.
15 ⌁€ 5/24h ⚡🔌Ch. **Surface:** gravel. ☐ 01/01-31/12
Distance: ⛵on the spot 🚶on the spot ⊗on the spot.
Remarks: At Turano lake.

Colleferro 🦋 33B4
Viale Europa. **GPS:** n41,72540 e13,00989.
⌁free ⚡🔌Chfree.
Distance: ✈5km 🚂train > Rome.
Remarks: Next to swimming pool.

Tourist information Colleferro:
ℹ Anagni. Region with number of old settlements.

Farfa in Sabina 33B3
Abbazia di Santa Maria, SP41A. **GPS:** n42,22166 e12,71603.
⌁free ⚡🔌Chfree. **Surface:** gravel. ☐ 01/01-31/12
Distance: ⛵4,7km.

Gaeta 33C5
Playa Colorada, Torre S.Agostino, SS 213, Sperlonga>Gaeta.
GPS: n41,22812 e13,50281.

30 ⌁€ 25-30, 2 pers.incl ⚡🔌Ch ⚡ WCincluded 🛢€1 🔌.
Surface: grassy/gravel. ☐ 01/04-30/09
Distance: ⛵50m ⊗bar/restaurant 🚋on the spot.

Gaeta 33C5
Sosta Camper Internationale, Via Flacca km 20.500. **GPS:** n41,23598 e13,49045.

30 ⌁€ 20-25 ⚡🔌Ch ⚡ WCincluded 🛢€1. **Surface:** gravel.
Distance: 🚶on the spot ⊗on the spot.
Remarks: Monitored parking.

Gaeta 33C5
Copacabana Beach, Via flacca Km 20.350, S.agostino Gaeta.
GPS: n41,23743 e13,48781. ⬆.
14 ⌁€ 20-30, 4 pers.incl ⚡🔌Ch ⚡ WC 🛢 🔲.
Distance: ⛵6km 🚶on the spot ⊗on the spot.
Remarks: Shuttle to Gaeta.

Gaeta 33C5
Oasi Camper Service, Via Flacca km. 20,643, Loc. riviera di Ponente.
GPS: n41,23583 e13,49048. ⬆.

22 ⌁€ 25 ⚡🔌Ch ⚡ WC 🛢. **Surface:** gravel. ☐ 01/04-01/10
Distance: ⛵6km ⛵50m 🚋500m.

Gradoli 32C6
Parcheggio camper San Magno, Strada di Gradoli, SP114 km 6+137.
GPS: n42,59925 e11,86547. ⬆.

IT

50 ⌧€ 10 🚰🗑Ch🚿. **Surface:** grassy. ⬛ 01/01-31/12
Distance: 🚶7km 🏊on the spot ⊗500m.
Remarks: At lake Bolsena.

♿Ⓢ **Ladispoli** 33A4

Oasi del Camper, Via Roma 139. **GPS:** n41,95954 e12,05282.⬆.

300 ⌧8-20h € 6, 20-8h € 6 🚰€3 🗑Ch➕€3 WC⬜€0,50.
Surface: grassy/sand. ⬛ 01/01-31/12
Distance: 🚶1,2km 🏊on the spot ⊗on the spot 🛒2km.
Remarks: At the beach.

♿Ⓢ **Ladispoli** 33A4

Area Sosta Lady Beach, Via Roma. **GPS:** n41,95829 e12,05585.⬆.
30 ⌧€ 10/24h 🚰🗑Ch🚿€3 WC⬜€0,50. **Surface:** grassy/sand.
Distance: 🚶800m 🏊on the spot.

♿Ⓢ **Latina** 33B5

Area Camper Alta Marea, Strada Lungomare 3253, SP39, Loc. Foce Verde.
GPS: n41,41043 e12,86008.

100 ⌧€ 12-15 🚰🗑Ch🚿⬜included. **Surface:** grassy.
⬛ Easter-30/09
Distance: 🚶on the spot 🏊50m ⊗on the spot.

☺Ⓢ **Latina** 33B5

Museo di Piana delle Orme, Strada Migliara 43 Mezza.
GPS: n41,44452 e12,98479.
25 ⌧🚰🗑Ch. **Surface:** gravel. ⬛ 01/01-31/12
Distance: 🚶Latina 10km.

♿Ⓢ **Leonessa** 33B3

GPS: n42,56436 e12,96172.⬆.

---

50 ⌧free 🚰🗑Ch. **Surface:** asphalted. ⦿ Market day
Distance: 🚶500m ⊗500m 🛒500m 🚌300m.

♿Ⓢ **Lubriano** 32C5

Parco Paime, Piazza Palme. **GPS:** n42,63500 e12,10512.⬆.

17 ⌧€ 6/24h 🚰🗑🚿(36x). **Surface:** grasstiles.
⬛ 01/01-31/12
Distance: 🚶1km ⊗on the spot.
Remarks: Nights closed with barrier.

♿Ⓢ **Lunghezza** 33B4

Camper Club Mira Lago Roma Est, Via Lunghezzina 75.
GPS: n41,93159 e12,67642.
⌧€ 18/24h 🚰🗑Ch🚿€2 WC⬜. **Surface:** grassy.
Distance: 🚲700m 🏊on the spot.
Remarks: At 2 small lakes.

♿Ⓢ **Montalto di Castro** 32B6

Via Arbea, Marina di Montalto di Castro. **GPS:** n42,32981 e11,57699.⬆➡.

50 ⌧€ 10/24h, € 5 01/10-31/12 🚰🗑Chfree. 🏠**Location:** Rural.
Surface: grassy/gravel. ⬛ 01/01-31/12
Distance: 🚶250m 🏊200m ⊗200m 🛒200m.

♿Ⓢ **Montalto di Castro** 32B6

Via Torre Marina, Marina di Montalto di Castro. **GPS:** n42,32137 e11,59015.⬆➡.

64 ⌧€ 5, 15/05-15/09 € 10 🚰🗑Ch🚿included. 🏠**Surface:** sand.
⬛ 01/01-31/12
Distance: 🚶500m 🏊200m ⊗400m 🛒300m.

🅂 **Montefiascone** 32C6

Cantina di Montefiascone, Via Grilli 2. **GPS**: n42,53346 e12,04293.⬆️.

30 🍴free 🚰🗑️Ch🛠️. **Surface**: metalled. ⬜ 01/01-31/12
Distance: 🚶1km.

🅂 **Montefiascone** 32C6

Agricamper Bella Cima, Strada Limitone. **GPS**: n42,52241 e12,00767.⬆️➡️.

18 🍴€ 15/24h 🚰🗑️Ch🛠️ included. **Surface**: gravel.
⬜ 01/01-31/12
Distance: 🚶4km ⊗4km 🛒4km.
Remarks: Swimming pool.

🅂 **Nettuno** 33B5

Area Sosta L'Ippocampo, Via Palestrina 9. **GPS**: n41,47354 e12,68916.
50 🍴€ 10 🚰🗑️Ch🛠️. **Surface**: gravel. ⬜ 01/01-31/12
Distance: 🌊3km.

🅂 **Oriolo Romano** 33A4

Via degli Artigiani. **GPS**: n42,16699 e12,13902.
🍴free 🚰🗑️ free. **Surface**: asphalted. ⬜ 01/01-31/12
Distance: 🚶850m 🛒on the spot 🚆station 600m Roma-Viterbo.

🅂 **Pescia Romana** 32B6

Area La Pineta, Loc. Marina di Pescia Romana. **GPS**: n42,36367 e11,49738.⬆️.

50 🍴€ 10-22 🚰🗑️Ch🛠️€3 🍴€1. **Surface**: grassy. ⬜ Easter-30/09
Distance: 🚶Pescia Romana 7km 🌊100m ⊗100m.

🅂 **Pescia Romana** 32B6

Campeggio Club degli Amici. **GPS**: n42,36717 e11,48828.⬆️.
20 🍴€ 6/10 + € 6/10,50/pp 🚰🗑️Ch🛠️WC🍴included 🍴€4.
Surface: sand. ⬜ 01/05-3rd Su Sep
Distance: 🌊lava beach 100m 🛒on the spot.

🅂 **Rieti** 33B3

Via Fonte Cottorella. **GPS**: n42,39548 e12,86463.⬆️➡️.

10 🍴free 🚰🗑️. **Surface**: asphalted. ⬜ 01/01-31/12
Distance: 🚶historical center 100m.

🅂 **Roma** 33B4

Area Attrezzata LGP Roma, Via Casilina 700, Rome (Roma).
GPS: n41,87595 e12,55515.⬆️.

200 🍴€ 17/<8m, € 22/8><10m, € 30/10><15m 🚰🗑️Ch🛠️ included 🧺.
Surface: grassy. ⬜ 01/01-31/12
Distance: ⊗100m 🚆100m 🚌bus service to city centre day and night.
Remarks: Accessory shop, trailer/additonal car € 15 on separate parking € 7,
repairs. Exit 18 ring road (G.R.A.), follow Roma centro, ± 4km dir centre, company
is on the left side of the road, turning after 2nd lights.

🅂 **Roma** 33B4

Oasi del Camper, Via dell'Ippodromo di Tor di Valle 1, Rome (Roma).
GPS: n41,82021 e12,43545.⬆️➡️.

🍴€ 20 🚰🗑️Ch🛠️ included.
Surface: gravel.
⬜ 01/01-31/12, 24/24h
Distance: 🚶city centre 10km ⊗150m Arbino 🚇metro 150m.
Remarks: Terrain with video surveillance. Exit 28 ring road (G.R.A.), follow Roma
centro, keep right Roma Ostiense, further indicated.

🅂 **Roma** 33B4

Prato Smeraldo, Via Ardeatina/Via di Tor Pagnotta 424, Rome (Roma).
GPS: n41,80970 e12,52857.
🍴€ 16 🚰🗑️Ch🛠️📶included.
⬜ 01/01-31/12, 24/24h
Distance: ⊗on the spot 🛒on the spot 🚌on the spot.
Remarks: Exit 25 ring road (G.R.A.), second light to the right, Via di Tor Pagnotta.

🅂 **Roma** 33B4

Le Terrazze, Via di Fioranello 170, Rome (Roma). **GPS**: n41,79250 e12,54083.
300 🍴€ 20, max. 4 pers.incl 🚰€2 🗑️Ch🛠️(40x)included.
Surface: metalled. ⬜ 01/01-31/12
Remarks: Car rental, excursions. Exit 25 ring road (G.R.A.), dir Santuario Divino
Amore.

🅂 **Roma** 33B4

Parcheggio IAT, Air terminal Ostiense, Piazza G. da Verrazzano 9, Zone Mercati
Generali, Rome (Roma). **GPS**: n41,86931 e12,48944.

IT

⚡€ 1,50, at least € 6, € 27/24h ⚡🗒Ch✏included.
Surface: asphalted.
🔲 01/01-31/12
Distance: 🚇metro 1km.
Remarks: Motorhome and Coach Parking.
Tourist information Rome (Roma):
ℹ️ Città del Vaticano. Domicile of the pope. Independent state since 1929.
ℹ️ A.P.T. (Azienda di Promozione Turistica), Via Parigi, 11. Capital of the country, a lot of curiosities in the old town centre. Roma Archeologica Card: 7-days ticket € 27,50, free entrance to Roman National Museum, Colosseum, Palatine, Baths of Caracalla, Tomb of Cecilia Metella and Villa of the Quintili.
👁 Piazza del Campidoglio.
👁 Palatino, Via di S. Gregorio, 30. Archeological site. 🔲 9h-sunset. 🎟 € 8, incl. Colosseum.
👁 Subiaco.
Ⓜ Musei Vaticani, Città del Vaticano. Paintings and art objects.
✝ Basilica di San Pietro. Basilica with Sistine Chapel.
⋂ Colosseo, Piazza del Colosseo. Colosseum, anfiteatro, the most important monument of ancient Rome. 🔲 9h-sunset. 🎟 € 8.
⋂ Foro Romane, Via dei Fori Imperiali. Novel Forum, the political, economic, and religious centre of ancient Rome. 🔲 9h-sunset. 🎟 free.
⋂ Pantheon, Piazza della Rotonda. Church of Santa Maria ad Martyres.
🔲 8.30-19.30h, Su 9-18h, Mass Sa 17, Su 10.30h, 16.30h. 🎟 free.
☀ Città del Vaticano. Pope blesses the mob for the window of the library.
🔲 Su 12h.
🛒 Piazza di Spagna.

🏕S — San Felice Circeo — 33B5
Circeo Camper, Viale Europa 1. GPS: n41,24095 e13,10426.

60 ⚡€ 20-33, 4 pers.incl ⚡🗒Ch✏€3 WC 🔄📶included. **Surface:** grassy.
🔲 01/04-20/09
Distance: 🚶100m ⛱10m ⊗100m 🚌100m.

🏕S — San Felice Circeo — 33B5
Area Camper La Rosa dei Venti, Viale Europa 9A. GPS: n41,24387 e13,10819.

50 ⚡€ 24/12-12h ⚡€3 🗒Ch✏. **Surface:** gravel. 🔲 01/01-31/12
Distance: 🚶500m ⛱10m ⊗on the spot 🚌600m 🚌600m.

🏕S — San Felice Circeo — 33B5
CirceMed, Via della Molella 2/A. GPS: n41,25684 e13,12089.⬆
⚡€ 16-24 ⚡🗒Ch📶included. **Surface:** grassy. 🔲 01/04-30/09
Distance: ⛱400m 🚌200m.
Tourist information San Felice Circeo:
🎯 🔲 Tue-morning.

🏕 — Tarquinia — 32C6
Largo Barriera San Giusto. GPS: n42,25307 e11,75410.⬆ .

5 ⚡free. **Surface:** asphalted. 🔲 01/01-31/12
Distance: 🚶100m ⊗100m 🚌100m.
Remarks: Archeological site 1km.

🏕S — Tarquinia — 32C6
Viale Andrea Doria/via Odisseo, Lido di Tarquinia. GPS: n42,22516 e11,70897.⬆
⚡.
Distance: ⛱sandy beach 450m.

🏕S — Tivoli — 33B4
Via Aquaregna. GPS: n41,95841 e12,80465.
30 ⚡free ⚡🗒Ch. **Surface:** asphalted.
🔲 01/01-31/12 🔘 Wed, market
Distance: 🚶400m.
Remarks: Along the Aniene river.
Tourist information Tivoli:
👁 Villa d'Este. Country house with gardens and fountains, 16th century.
⋂ Villa Adriana. Roman villa.

🏕S — Tuscania — 32C6
Via Nazario Sauro. GPS: n42,42217 e11,87520.⬆ .
12 ⚡free ⚡🗒free. **Surface:** grasstiles/metalled. 🔲 01/01-31/12
Distance: 🚶250m ⊗250m 🚌250m.

🏕S — Villa San Giovanni in Tuscia — 32C6
Via P.M. Liberati. GPS: n42,28160 e12,05282.
⚡free ⚡🗒Ch. **Surface:** asphalted. 🔲 01/01-31/12
Distance: 🚶200m.

🏕S — Viterbo — 32C6
Piazza Mariano Romiti, loc. Belcolle. GPS: n42,40897 e12,11049.⬆
50 ⚡free ⚡🗒free. **Surface:** asphalted. 🔲 01/01-31/12
Distance: 🚶Lazise centre 300m 🚌on the spot.

🍴 — Viterbo — 32C6
Bed&breakfast Axia, Strada Procoio 2/C. GPS: n42,41157 e12,05061.

30 ⚡€ 12 ⚡Ch✏€3. **Surface:** grassy. 🔲 01/01-31/12
Distance: 🚶Viterbo 4km.
Remarks: 10% discount at entrance Terme dei Papi (900m).

🍴 — Viterbo — 32C6
Agriturismo Monteparadiso, Loc. Monterazzano. GPS: n42,43192 e12,03004.
⬆.

5 guests free. **Surface:** gravel.
Distance: 7km.
Remarks: Near Termale Bullicame and Terme dei Papi.

| Viterbo | 32C6 |

Terme dei Papi, Strada Montarone. **GPS:** n42,41487 e12,06351.

100 free. **Surface:** grassy/gravel. 01/01-31/12
Distance: 3km.
Remarks: At Terme dei Papi.

| Vitorchiano | 32C6 |

SP23 Via della Teverina. **GPS:** n42,47152 e12,17212.

10 free. **Surface:** asphalted. 01/01-31/12
Distance: 500m.

Umbria

| S | Amelia | 32D6 |

Piazzale del Mercato, Via Rimembranze. **GPS:** n42,55200 e12,41880.
10 free Ch free. **Surface:** asphalted. 01/01-31/12 Mo-morning (market)
Distance: 50m 50m 50m.

| S | Assisi | 33A2 |

Via Giosuè Borsi, loc. Santa Maria degli Angeli. **GPS:** n43,05972 e12,58747.

€ 16/24h, € 1,60/h Ch . **Surface:** asphalted.
01/01-31/12
Distance: 2km bus >Assisi 20min (retour € 1,80).

| Assisi | 33A2 |

Area San Vetturino, SS147. **GPS:** n43,07710 e12,59957.

30 € 14/24h, € 2/h. **Surface:** asphalted. 01/01-31/12
Distance: 500m.
Remarks: Convento di San Francesco 1km.

| Assisi | 33A2 |

Viale Vittorio Emanuele II/SS147. **GPS:** n43,06864 e12,61420.

10 € 20/24h. **Surface:** gravel. 01/01-31/12
Distance: city centre 100m.

| Bevagna | 33A2 |

Piazza dell'Accoglienza, Via Raggiolo. **GPS:** n42,93417 e12,60639.

50 free Ch WC free. **Surface:** gravel.
Distance: 100m 100m 100m.

| Borghetto | 32C4 |

Via Pontile. **GPS:** n43,18415 e12,02372.

4 free free. **Surface:** asphalted. 01/01-31/12
Distance: 150m 100m.
Remarks: At lake Trasimeno.

| S | Cannara | 33A2 |

Via Giaime Pintor, Loc. Casone. **GPS:** n42,99272 e12,57840.

IT

20 🛆free 🚰🔌Chfree. **Surface:** asphalted.
Distance: 🚶300m 🚱300m 🚲on the spot.
Remarks: At sports park XXV Aprile, cycle routes.
Tourist information Cannara:
👁 Assisi. Historical city.

| 📷S | Cascia | 33B2 |

Piazzale Papa Leone XIII, Via della Molinella. **GPS:** n42,71968 e13,01605.⬆➡.

14 🛆€ 8/day, overnight stay free 🚰🔌 Ch 🔋free. **Surface:** asphalted.
🅿 01/01-31/12 🅿 Service: winter
Distance: 🚶300m ⊗300m 🚱300m 🏊100m 🚲100m.
Remarks: Escalator to city centre.

| 📷S | Cascia | 33B2 |

Strada Statale Discascia. **GPS:** n42,72139 e13,01778.
20 🛆€ 7/24h ✂included. **Surface:** gravel. 🅿 01/01-31/12
Distance: 🚶1km.

| 🏕 | Castelluccio di Norcia | 33B2 |

Pian Grande. GPS: n42,80045 e13,18947.

🛆free. **Surface:** grassy. 🅿 01/01-31/12
Distance: 🚶Castelluccio 5km.
Remarks: Parco Nazionale dei Monti Sibilini.

| 📷S | Castiglione del Lago 🏖 | 32C5 |

Viale Divisione Partigiani Garibaldi. **GPS:** n43,12389 e12,05054.⬆.

🛆free, summer € 12 🚰🔌 Ch ✂included. **Surface:** asphalted/sand.
🅿 01/01-31/12
Distance: 🚶800m 🚣on the spot.

Remarks: At lake Trasimeno.

| 📷S | Città di Castello | 32C4 |

Piazzale E. Ferri, Viale Nazario Sauro. **GPS:** n43,45892 e12,23465.⬆➡.
🛆free 🚰€0,10/10liter 🔌Ch. **Location:** Urban. **Surface:** asphalted.
🅿 01/01-31/12
Distance: 🚶300m ⚓ 1,5km.
Remarks: Escalator to city centre.

| 📷S | Città di Castello | 32C4 |

La Fontana del Boschetto, Via Aretina 38. **GPS:** n43,45737 e12,22882.
20 🛆€ 12 🚰🔌Ch✂🔌.
Distance: 🚶2km ⊗on the spot.
Remarks: Free shuttle.

| 📷S | Ferentillo | 33B3 |

Loc. Precetto. **GPS:** n42,61802 e12,79347. 🛗.
5 🛆free 🚰🔌. **Surface:** asphalted.
Distance: 🚶200m.

| 📷S | Ficulle | 32C5 |

Parco Cittadino, Via Orvieto SR 71. **GPS:** n42,83044 e12,06828.⬆➡.

25 🛆free 🚰🔌Chfree. **Surface:** gravel.
Distance: 🚶500m ⚓ 10km ⊗1km 🚱500m.

| 📷S | Gualdo Cattaneo | 32D5 |

Parco Acquarossa, Via Bonifacio 6. **GPS:** n42,89168 e12,53591.⬆.
🛆€ 5 🚰🔌Ch 🔌 WC 📶included.
Location: Rural. **Surface:** gravel.
Distance: 🚶on the spot ⊗on the spot.
Remarks: Excursions, regional products.

| 📷S | Gualdo Tadino | 33B1 |

Piazza Federico II di Svevia. **GPS:** n43,23143 e12,78062.
🛆free 🚰🔌Chfree. **Surface:** asphalted. 🅿 Thu (market)

| 📷S | Gualdo Tadino | 33B1 |

Via Perugia. **GPS:** n43,23756 e12,77235.
100 🛆free 🚰🔌free.
Distance: ⊗400m 🚱20m.
Remarks: Nearby stadium.

| 📷S | Gubbio 🌾 | 32D4 |

Camperclub Gubbio, Via del Bottagnone. **GPS:** n43,35000 e12,56389.⬆.

80 🛆free, 20-8h € 5 🚰🔌Chfree 🔌 (8x)€ 1/h. **Surface:** asphalted.
🅿 01/01-31/12
Distance: 🚶historical centre 1,5km ⊗100m 🚱200m.
Remarks: Teatro Romano 500m.

| 📷S | Monte Castello di Vibio 🌾🏛🏘👥 | 32C5 |

Via Bartolomeo Jacopo della Rovere. **GPS:** n42,84185 e12,35076.➡.

10 🛏free 🚰🔌Ch free. **Surface:** gravel. ⬛ 01/01-31/12
Distance: 🚶350m ✖50m.

| �re S | **Montefalco** 🌿⛲👪 | 33A2 |

Viale delle Vittoria. **GPS:** n42,89230 e12,64791.⬆

15 🛏free 🚰🔌Ch ➕€1/h WC 🚽. **Surface:** grasstiles.
Distance: 🚶100m.

| �re S | **Montone** | 32C4 |

Via Aldo Bologni. **GPS:** n43,36346 e12,32499.
🛏€ 10/24h 🚰🔌Ch 🔧. **Surface:** asphalted. ⬛ 01/01-31/12
Distance: 🚶200m ✖250m.
Remarks: At sports park.

| �re S | **Orvieto** 🌿⛲🍴👪 | 32C5 |

Area Sosta Camper Orvieto, Strada della Direttissima, Piazza delle Pace.
GPS: n42,72562 e12,12736.⬆.

50 🛏€ 18/day 🚰🔌Ch 🔧 WC 🚽included 🔲.
Surface: metalled.
⬛ 01/01-31/12
Distance: 🚶funicular (retour € 1,60) 5 min 🏖2,4km ✖50m pizzeria 🚌50m.

Tourist information Orvieto:
ℹ U.I.A.T. (Ufficio Informazioni e di Accoglienza Turistica), Piazza Duomo, 24.
City on volcanic plateau.
🔔 Del Crocifisso del Tufo. Ruins of Etruscan city.

| ☎ S | **Panicale** 🌿⛲ | 32C5 |

Area Camper, Viale della Repubblica. **GPS:** n43,02806 e12,10222.⬆➡.

8 🛏€ 8/24h 🚰€0,50 🔌Ch 🔧 €0,50/kWh. **Surface:** grasstiles.

⬛ 01/01-31/12
Distance: 🚶100m ✖100m 🔲50m.

| ☎ S | **Passignano sul Trasimeno** | 32C4 |

Airone Area Camper, Lungolago Giappesi. **GPS:** n43,18445 e12,14526.⬆.
🛏€ 15 🚰🔌Ch 🔧 WC 🚽€0,50 🛜included. **Surface:** grassy.
⬛ 01/01-31/12
Distance: 🚶500m 🏖beach 200m ✖50m.
Remarks: At lake Trasimeno.

| ☎ S | **Passignano sul Trasimeno** | 32C4 |

Via Europa, SS75bis, km 35,8. **GPS:** n43,18509 e12,14348.⬆.

4 🛏free 🚰€0,30/100liter 🔌Ch 🔧€0,30/h WC. **Surface:** asphalted.
⬛ 01/01-31/12
Distance: 🚶400m 🏖100m.
Remarks: At lake Trasimeno.

| ☎ S | **Perugia** 🌿 | 32C5 |

Il Bove, Via Giovanni Ruggia. **GPS:** n43,09810 e12,38386.⬆➡.

50 🛏€ 5/12h, € 18/24h 🚰🔌Ch 🔧 WC 🚽 🛜 🚐
Location: Urban. **Surface:** asphalted. ⬛ 01/01-31/12
Distance: 🚶1,5km 🏖500m 🚇100m 🚌200m 🚲on the spot.
Remarks: Parking police station.

Tourist information Perugia:
🏛 Palazzo dei Priori.
🍴 ⬛ Tue.

| ☎ S | **San Gemini** | 33A3 |

Via della Libertà. **GPS:** n42,61200 e12,54372.

16 🛏 🚰🔌Ch 🔧 WC 🚽 🛜. **Surface:** metalled. ⬛ 01/01-31/12
Distance: 🚶300m ✖100m.

| ☎ | **Sant'Anatolia di Narco** | 33B2 |

Purchetta, SP209. **GPS:** n42,73599 e12,83598.
8 🛏free 🚰 🔧. ⬛ 01/01-31/12
Distance: ✖on the spot 🚇on the spot 🚲on the spot.

| ☎ S | **Scheggia e Pascelupo** | 32D4 |

Camper Scheggia, Via Campo Sportivo. **GPS:** n43,40007 e12,66674.
🛏€ 12/24h 🚰🔌Ch 🔧included. **Surface:** gravel. ⬛ 01/01-31/12
Distance: 🚶450m ✖500m.

⬛S | **Spello** | 33B2
Via Centrale Umbra. **GPS**: n42,99371 e12,66730.⬆.

70 ⬛€6/24h ⛽🗑Ch. **Surface:** asphalted.
Distance: ⛲500m ⚓1,1km ⊗500m ⚱500m.
Remarks: Parking sports park.

⬛S | **Spello** | 33B2
Terme Francescane Village, Via Fonte Citerna. **GPS**: n43,00619 e12,62116.⬆.
30 ⬛€13 ⛽🗑Ch ⚡€3 WC. **Surface:** gravel. ☐ 01/01-31/12
Distance: ⛲Spello 6km.

⬛ | **Spoleto** | 33B2
Parcheggio Ponciano, Via del Tiro a Segno. **GPS**: n42,73687 e12,74212.➡.

20 ⬛€1/h, €5/24h. **Surface:** gravel. ☐ 01/01-31/12
Distance: ⛲500m ⊗500m ⚱500m.
Remarks: Escalator to city centre.

⬛S | **Spoleto** | 33B2
Via dei Filosofi. **GPS**: n42,74619 e12,73214.⬆➡.

⬛free ⛽🗑free. **Surface:** gravel.
Distance: ⛲800m.
Tourist information Spoleto:
👁 Montefalco. Village worth seeing, parking outside village, narrow streets.
👁 Ponte delle Torri. Aqueduct, 14th century.
🎪 ☐ Tue, Fri.
🎆 Art festival. ☐ 01/06-31/07.

⬛S | **Terni** | 33B3
Via Lombardo Radice. **GPS**: n42,56634 e12,63577.⬆.

⬛€4/48h ⛽€0,50 ⛽🗑Ch ⚡ included. **Surface:** asphalted.
Distance: ⛲50m ⊗50m.

⬛ | **Terni** | 33B3
Piazzale Felice Fatati, SR209. **GPS**: n42,55690 e12,72006.

⬛free. **Surface:** unpaved.
Distance: ⛲Terni 7km ⊗on the spot.
Remarks: Along river, nearby waterfalls.

⬛S | **Todi** | 32C5
Area Porta Orvietana, Viale di Montesanto. **GPS**: n42,78120 e12,40168.⬆.

16 ⬛€14/24h, €3/h ⛽🗑Ch. **Surface:** asphalted. ☐ Sa-morning market
Remarks: Elevator (free) to centre.

⬛S | **Torgiano** | 32C5
Via Perugia. **GPS**: n43,02917 e12,43833.⬆.

10 ⬛free ⛽🗑Chfree. **Surface:** asphalted. ☐ 01/01-31/12
Distance: ⛲200m ⚓3,5km ⊗200m ⚱300m.

⬛S | **Trevi** | 33B2
Via Costa San Paolo. **GPS**: n42,87829 e12,75221.⬆➡.

20 ⬛free ⛽🗑Chfree. **Surface:** grasstiles. ☐ 01/01-31/12
Distance: ⛲500m ⚓5,1km.
Remarks: At swimming pool.

Abruzzo

⬛S | **Anversa degli Abruzzi** | 33C4
Il Sagittario, Loc. Ponte delle Fornaci. **GPS**: n41,99995 e13,80960.⬆.
10 ⬛€12 ⛽🗑Ch ⚡ WC. **Surface:** gravel. ☐ 01/01-31/12

Distance: 1km 1km 1km.

S | **Anversa degli Abruzzi** | 33C4

Bioagriturismo La Porta dei Parchi, Piazza Roma 3. **GPS:** n42,00014 e13,79899.

4 € 10, free with a meal Ch WC included.
Surface: metalled. 01/01-31/12
Distance: on the spot.

S | **Campotosto** | 33C3
Via Lago, SR557. **GPS:** n42,56208 e13,34805.
€ 5 . **Surface:** grassy. 01/01-31/12
Distance: Campotosto 3km on the spot.
Remarks: At lake Campotosto.

S | **Casalbordino** | 33D3
Portobello, SS16, km 503, Lido di Casalbordino. **GPS:** n42,17070 e14,63928.

8 against payment Ch (8x). **Surface:** asphalted. 01/01-31/12
Distance: 1,5km 3km.
Remarks: Check in at bar.

| | **Casalbordino** | 33D3
Via Alessandrini. **GPS:** n42,19952 e14,61800.
20 € 5. **Surface:** grassy/sand. 01/01-31/12
Distance: on the spot on the spot on the spot.

S | **Casalbordino** | 33D3
Area di sosta Ass Villa Sarda, Contr. Piana Sabelli. **GPS:** n42,17773 e14,59994.
20 Ch WC . **Surface:** grassy. 01/01-31/12
Distance: 1km on the spot.

S | **Fossacesia** | 33D3
Area Camper, Via Lungomare 16b. **GPS:** n42,24067 e14,52988.

24 € 10 Ch included. **Surface:** gravel/sand. 01/03-30/11
Distance: 6,5km on the spot.
Remarks: Pebbled beach.

S | **Isola del Gran Sasso** | 33C3
S.Gabriele dell Addolorata. **GPS:** n42,51712 e13,65634.

free Ch. **Surface:** gravel/sand.
Distance: on the spot 4km on the spot on the spot.
Remarks: Nearby basilica.

S | **Lanciano** | 33D3
Area Attrezzata, Strada provinciale Lanciano-Frisa, Lancianovecchia.
GPS: n42,23385 e14,39106.

50 free Ch WC free. **Surface:** asphalted.
Sa-morning market
Distance: 300m (stairs and elevator).
Remarks: At city walls, upper part of the parking, escalator to city centre.

Tourist information Lanciano:
Historical city with medieval Jewish district, Ripa Sacca.

S | **L'Aquila** | 33C3
Via porta Napoli. **GPS:** n42,34175 e13,39510.
10 free Ch. 01/01-31/12
Distance: 700m 500m.

S | **L'Aquila** | 33C3
Via Strinella. **GPS:** n42,35323 e13,40708.
10 free Ch free. **Surface:** asphalted. 01/01-31/12
Distance: 500m.
Remarks: In front of Hotel Federico II, adjacent Parco del Castello.

S | **Notaresco** | 33C2
Via Martiri della Libertà. **GPS:** n42,65527 e13,89578.
10 free Ch free against payment. **Surface:** asphalted.
Distance: on the spot.
Remarks: At tennis-courts.

S | **Penne** | 33C3
Agriturismo Il Portico, Contrada Colle Serangelo 26. **GPS:** n42,45592 e13,95165.

15 € 10, free with a meal Ch (7x)€3 WC included.
Surface: grassy.

S | **Pescasseroli** | 33C4
Area Camper S.Andrea, Loc. Sant'Andrea. **GPS:** n41,79888 e13,79222.

IT

🚐€ 15, 2 pers.incl 🚰🔌Ch🛁WC🛢included. 🅿 8-13h, 14.30-20h
Remarks: Free shuttle to centre.
Tourist information Pescasseroli:
🚶 Parco Nazionale d'Abruzzo. Nature reserve.

🚰 S	Pineto	33C2

Sand stone beach, Via Tremiti, fraz. Scerne. **GPS:** n42,64270 e14,04505. ⬆
🚐 🚰 Ch WC 🛢. **Surface:** grassy. 🅿 01/05-31/10
Distance: 🏊on the spot 🚲 on the spot.

🍴	Pineto	33C2

Ristorante Aria e Sole, Borgo Santa Maria. **GPS:** n42,60891 e14,04341.
Distance: 🚲200m.

🍴 S	Roccaraso ⛰❄	33D4

Hotel Park Il Poggio, SS17, C.da Poggio, 1 , Loc Il Poggio.
GPS: n41,82638 e14,10111. ⬆➡.

18 🚐€ 20 🚰🔌Ch🛁(18x)included. 🅿 01/01-31/12
Distance: ⊗on the spot.
Remarks: Shuttle bus to ski-piste.

🚐 S	Roseto degli Abruzzi	33C2

Area di Sosta Camper Romeo, Via degli Orti 13, loc. Cologna Spiaggia.
GPS: n42,72287 e13,98076. ⬆

40 🚐€ 20/24h 🚰🔌Ch🛁(40x) WC included 🛢€1. **Surface:** grassy.
🅿 01/01-31/12
Distance: 🚲200m 🏊750m ⊗on the spot 🍽100m.

🚐 S	Roseto degli Abruzzi	33C2

Area di sosta Isola del Sole, Piana degli Ulivi. **GPS:** n42,66902 e14,01189. ⬆➡.

11 🚐€ 20 🚰🔌Ch🛁(11x)€2 WC🛢included. **Surface:** metalled.
🅿 01/01-31/12
Distance: 🚲3km 🏊3km.
Remarks: Swimming pool (summer).

🚐 S	Roseto degli Abruzzi	33C2

Palazzo dello Sport. GPS: n42,66012 e14,02382. ⬆➡.

🚐free 🚰🔌Chfree. **Surface:** asphalted. 🅿 Tue
Distance: 🚲200m.
Remarks: Tuesday market.

🚐 S	San Demetrio nei Vestini	33C3

La Grotta di Stiffe, Via del Mulino, Fraz. Stiffe. **GPS:** n42,25567 e13,54811. ➡.

🚐free 🚰€2,50 🔌Ch🛁€2,50. **Surface:** metalled/sand.
Distance: 🚲l'Aquila 18km.

🚐 S	San Salvo Marina 🏖	34A1

Parking on the Beach, Via Amerigo Vespucci 20. **GPS:** n42,07233 e14,76945. ⬆
➡.

35 🚐€ 15/30 🚰🔌Ch🛁(30x)€3 WC🛢included 🅿€8. **Surface:** asphalted.
🅿 01/01-31/12
Distance: 🚲2km 🏊50m sandy beach ⊗50m 🛒Centro Commerciale 2km.

🚐 S	San Salvo Marina 🏖	34A1

Area Sosta Communale per Autocaravan. GPS: n42,07195 e14,76289. ⬆.

IT

30 ⏚ € 16/24h, € 20/48h, € 30/72h ⏚ 🔌 Ch WC included ⏚ cold shower.
Surface: grassy. 🅿 01/05-15/09
Distance: 🚶300m 🚲 2,2km 🏖 300m.

| 🍴 S | Santo Stefano di Sessanio 🌿 | 33C3 |

GPS: n42,34706 e13,64545.
⏚ free. 🅿 01/01-31/12

| 🍴 S | Santo Stefano di Sessanio 🌿 | 33C3 |

Ostello del Cavaliere, Piazza Della Giudea. **GPS:** n42,34429 e13,64314. ⬆.
5 ⏚ guests free ⏚. **Surface:** metalled.
Distance: 🚶300m.

| S | Sant'Egidio alla Vibrata | 33C2 |

Zona industriale. **GPS:** n42,81937 e13,69915. ⬆➡.

⏚ free ⏚ 🔌 Ch free. **Surface:** asphalted.

| S | Torino di Sangro | 33D3 |

Area camper Vitale, Lido le Morgie. **GPS:** n42,20403 e14,60349. ⬆.
100 ⏚ € 15/24h ⏚ 🔌 Ch included 🔌 €2 WC ⏚ €0,50.
Surface: grassy/sand.
Distance: 🚲 8km 🏖 beach 70m 🏪 on the spot.

| S | Tortoreto Lido | 33C2 |

Via Napoli. **GPS:** n42,78552 e13,95013.
30 ⏚ € 12/24h ⏚ 🔌 Ch 🔌 WC ⏚ 🚿. **Surface:** asphalted.
🅿 01/01-31/12
Distance: 🏖 beach 200m.

| S | Villalago 🏔 | 33C4 |

SP82b. **GPS:** n41,92255 e13,85621. ⬆.

13 ⏚ free ⏚ 🔌 Ch free. **Surface:** asphalted.
Distance: 🏖 on the spot.
Remarks: At lake Scanno, nearby beach and kosk.

Molise

| S | Campobasso | 34A2 |

Area di sosta Dominick Ferrante, Contrada Macchie 1.
GPS: n41,56886 e14,65118. ⬆➡.

20 ⏚ € 10/24h, € 15/48h ⏚ 🔌 Ch 🔌 included. **Surface:** gravel.
Distance: 🚶800m.

| 🍴 S | Monteroduni | 33D4 |

Oasi San Nazzaro. GPS: n41,53448 e14,15924.

40 ⏚ € 10, free with a meal ⏚ 🔌 Ch 🔌 (6x)included. **Surface:** grassy.
🅿 01/01-31/12
Distance: 🎣 Fish lake 🍽 on the spot.

| S | Petacciato Marina | 34A1 |

Villagio la Torre, SS16 Adriatica km535,5, Termoli ri Vasto.
GPS: n42,02432 e14,88739. ⬆.

60 ⏚ € 10-20 ⏚ 🔌 Ch 🔌 (50x)included WC ⏚. **Surface:** gravel/sand.
🅿 01/01-31/12
Distance: 🏖 on the spot 🍽 on the spot 🛒 on the spot.
Remarks: Access via gate next to tower ruins.

| S | Petacciato Marina | 34A1 |

Parking spiaggia, Via del Mare, SS16. **GPS:** n42,03543 e14,85337. ⬆.

40 ⏚ € 6, 8-20h ⏚ against payment. **Surface:** asphalted.
Distance: 🚲 9,5km 🏖 50m.
Remarks: Reserved place for motorhomes.

| S | Petacciato Marina | 34A1 |

Parking Tolomei, Via Marinelle, SS 16. **GPS:** n42,03219 e14,85844. ⬆.
50 ⏚ € 15 ⏚ 🔌 Ch 🔌 WC ⏚ 🚿. **Surface:** gravel. 🅿 01/01-31/12
Distance: 🏖 Direct access.
Remarks: Shuttle bus.

IT

Termoli 34A1
Centro Commerciale Sannicola, SS 87 Sannitica, km216-256.
GPS: n41,93880 e14,98754.

20 ⬛free 🚰⬛Ch free. **Surface:** asphalted. ⬛ 01/01-31/12

Puglia

Alberobello 34C1
Parcheggio Nel Verde, Via Cadore. **GPS:** n40,78266 e17,23418.

60 ⬛€ 15-18/24h, € 10/12h, € 8/6h 🚰⬛Ch ⚡€3 📶included.
Surface: grassy/gravel. ⬛ 01/01-31/12
Distance: Trulli-centre 50m ⊗50m 🛒100m.
Tourist information Alberobello:
ℹ️ Centre of the Trulli-region. Trulli houses are curious houses built without motor.
⛺ ⬛ Thu-morning.

Bari 34C1
Area Hobby Park Wash, Via Giovanni del Conte. **GPS:** n41,11581 e16,88501.
⬛€ 15/24h 🚰⬛Ch ⚡. **Surface:** metalled. ⬛ 01/01-31/12
Distance: centre 500m ⚓700m.
Remarks: Monitored parking.

Bari 34C1
Gran Parcheggio Alberotanza, Via Alberotaza, 43A. **GPS:** n41,09520 e16,87868.

250 ⬛€ 15 🚰€0,50/30liter ⬛€2,50 Ch ⚡€0,50/kWh 🚿.
Surface: asphalted. ⬛ 01/01-31/12
Distance: ✈7,8km ⊗500m 🛒500m.
Remarks: Monitored parking.

Brindisi 34D1
Area Attrezzata, Strada Minnuta 6. **GPS:** n40,63517 e17,91824.

⬛€ 10 🚰⬛Ch ⚡€3 WC ⬛included. **Surface:** asphalted. ⬛ 01/01-31/12
Remarks: 24/24 surveillance.

Castellana Grotte 34C1
Area Sapori & Sapori, Via Turi. **GPS:** n40,88560 e17,15722.
10 ⬛free 🚰⬛Ch free. **Surface:** asphalted.
Distance: 1km.
Remarks: Caves 1,8km.

Castellana Grotte 34C1
Le Grotte di Castellana, SS32. **GPS:** n40,87543 e17,14900.

⬛€ 5. **Surface:** grassy/gravel. ⬛ 01/01-31/12
Remarks: Parking at the caves of Castellana, overnight stay allowed.

Gallipoli 34D2
GPS: n40,06000 e18,03939.
⬛€ 13 🚰⬛Ch ⚡€5.
Distance: 5km.

Lecce 34D1
Camperpark Fuori Le Mura, Via S.Oronzo Fuori Le Mura, 20.
GPS: n40,39340 e18,16581.

21 ⬛€ 15/24h 🚰⬛Ch ⚡ WC ⬛. ⬛ 01/01-31/12
Distance: city centre 3km 🚌300m.
Remarks: Shuttle bus to city centre.

Lesina 34A1
Oasi, Via Ludovica Ariosto. **GPS:** n41,86472 e15,35806.

15 ⬛€ 12, Sept-Mar-Apr € 15, May/Aug € 18 🚰⬛Ch ⚡ WC ⬛included.
Surface: asphalted. ⬛ 01/01-31/12

IT

Distance: 300m ⊗on the spot 🚿500m.

| 🅂 | Lucera 〰 | 34A1 |

Via Montello. **GPS:** n41,49987 e15,33223.⬆.

100 🏕free 🚐🗑. **Surface:** asphalted. ◗ 01/01-31/12
Remarks: At station.

| 🅂 | Lucera 〰 | 34A1 |

Centro sportivo Casanova, Strada Contrada Casanova.
GPS: n41,48849 e15,26008.⬆.
🏕€ 10 🚐🗑 Ch. **Location:** Isolated. ◗ 01/01-31/12
Distance: Lucera 9km.

| 🅂 | Margherita di Savoia | 34B1 |

Lido Baywatch, Via Barletta. **GPS:** n41,36222 e16,17361.⬆➡.

12 🏕€ 15, Aug € 20 🚐🗑 Ch 🔌 WC ☐included. **Surface:** gravel/sand.
◗ 01/01-31/12
Distance: 2km ⚓on the spot ⊗on the spot.

| 🅂 | Massafra | 34C1 |

Area di Sosta La Stella, SS7, SS Appia km 633, Le Forche.
GPS: n40,59201 e17,09904.⬆.

20 🏕€ 10/16-12h, € 20/24h 🚐🗑 Ch 🔌 (18x) WC included ☐€1.
Surface: grassy. ◗ 01/01-31/12
Distance: 1km ⊗500-700m 🚿1km.
Remarks: Beachshuttle € 2.

| 🅂 | Mattinata 🏖 | 34B1 |

Punta Grugno, SS89dirB. **GPS:** n41,69797 e16,06236.⬆➡.

80 🏕€ 11, Jun € 13, Jul € 16, Aug € 20 🚐🗑 Ch 🔌€2,50 WC ☐€0,80.

Surface: grassy/sand. ◗ 01/04-01/10
Distance: Mattinata 2km ⚓pebbled beach ⊗on the spot 🚿2km.

| 🅂 | Mattinata 🏖 | 34B1 |

Eden Park, Porto di Mattinata, SP53. **GPS:** n41,70667 e16,06556.⬆.

25 🏕€ 10, Jul/Aug € 20 🚐🗑 Ch WC included ☐€0,50. **Surface:** grassy/sand.
◗ 01/06-31/08
Distance: 1km ⚓pebbled beach 🚣on the spot ⊗1km 🚿1km.

| 🅂 | Melendugno | 34D1 |

Area Camper Salento I Faraglioni, SP366 km 20.5, Sant'Andrea.
GPS: n40,25550 e18,43748.
15 🏕€ 12-27/24h 🚐🗑 Ch 🔌 WC ☐. ◗ 01/01-31/12
Distance: 700m 🚿on the spot.
Remarks: Shuttle bus to beach.

| 🅂 | Melendugno | 34D1 |

Gran Pasha, Strada provinciale Lecce-Melendugno-San Foca, km.18.
GPS: n40,27724 e18,40510.
50 🏕€ 10-15, 20/07-31/08 € 25 + tourist tax 🚐🗑 Ch 🔌€3 WC ☐.
Surface: unpaved. ◗ 01/01-31/12
Distance: 1,5km.
Remarks: Free shuttle.

| 🅂 | Monopoli | 34C1 |

Area du Sosta Camper Lido Millennium, SP90, Loc. Capitolo, SS16 km850 Uscita
Capitolo. **GPS:** n40,90374 e17,35261.⬆➡.

100 🏕€ 12-15-18 🚐🗑 Ch 🔌 6Amp WC ☐included. **Surface:** gravel.
◗ Easter-30/09
Distance: 500m ⚓50m ⊗50m 🚿50m.
Remarks: Private beach.

| 🅂 | Otranto | 34D1 |

Oasy Park, Via Renis. **GPS:** n40,13795 e18,48922.⬆➡.

50 🏕€ 20 3 pers.incl 🚐🗑 Ch 🔌 (70x),16Amp WC included ☐€1 ⊙€4.
Surface: grassy/gravel. ◗ 01/01-31/12
Distance: 400m ⚓700m ⊗400m 🚿400m.

| 🅂 | Otranto | 34D1 |

Area Camper Fontanelle, Sp366, km28. **GPS:** n40,19159 e18,45494.

IT

🛏€ 15, Jul-Aug € 20, 4 pers incl. + tourist tax 🚰🔌Ch🚿€2 WC included 🚽€0,50.
Distance: 🚶Otranto 5km 🏖beach 200m.
Remarks: Shuttle bus to Otranto.

📷S	Peschici 🌊⛵🏄	34A1

Camper Marina Picola, Loc. Pantanello, Baia di Peschici.
GPS: n41,94528 e16,00528.⬆️

45 🛏Apr € 12, May € 13, Jun/Sep € 15, Jul € 20, Aug € 25 🚰🔌
Ch🚿WC included 🚽€0,50. **Surface:** grassy/sand. ☀️ 01/04-30/09
Distance: 🚶2,5km, walking 800m (stairs) 🏖sandy beach 50m.

📷S	Peschici 🌊⛵🏄	34A1

AgriCamper Pane e Vino, SS89 km 2,6. **GPS:** n41,92372 e16,01534.
20 🛏€ 10 🚰🔌Ch🚿WC 🚽. **Surface:** sand.
Distance: 🚶3,5km ⊗on the spot.

📷S	Peschici 🌊⛵🏄	34A1

Area attrezzata per camper Dattoli, Via Spiaggia, SS89.
GPS: n41,94522 e16,01138.
14 🛏€ 15-20 🚰🔌Ch🚿WC included 🚽€0,50. **Surface:** unpaved.
Distance: 🚶Old city 300m (stairs) 🏖100m ⊗100m.

😀	Putignano	34C1

Grotte di Putignano, SS172. **GPS:** n40,85706 e17,10944.
🛏free. ☀️ 01/01-31/12

📷S	Rodi Garganico	34A1

Area sosta camper Isola Bella, Via delle More. **GPS:** n41,92444 e15,84166.⬆️
➡️

30 🛏€ 15-20, Aug € 25 🚰🔌Ch🚿WC 🚽included. **Surface:** grassy/sand.
☀️ 01/06-15/09
Distance: 🚶Lido del Sole 1,5km, Rodi Garganico 3,8km 🏖sandy beach 10m 🚶⊗100m 1,5km.

📷S	San Giovanni Rotondo 🌊⛵🏔	34A1

Coppa Cicuta, Strada Comunale Pozzocavo-Tre Carrini. **GPS:** n41,69599 e15,70423.
⬆️➡️

30 🛏€ 12 🚰🔌Ch🚿(30x)€1,50/night WC 🚽included 📷€10.
Surface: gravel. ☀️ 01/01-31/12
Distance: 🚶3km ⊗on the spot.
Remarks: Shuttle € 2/pp.

📷S	San Giovanni Rotondo 🌊⛵🏔	34A1

Lo Chalet, Viale Padre Pio. **GPS:** n41,70658 e15,69799.⬆️
🛏€ 15/24h 🚰🔌Ch🚿WC 🚽.📷 **Surface:** metalled.
☀️ 01/01-31/12
Distance: ⊗on the spot.
Remarks: Free shuttle, santuario 300m.

🍴S	San Giovanni Rotondo 🌊⛵🏔	34A1

Di Cerbo, Circonvallazione Sud, SP45bis. **GPS:** n41,69725 e15,73097.

20 🛏€ 5,20/day, € 7,80/night 🚰🔌Ch🚿WC 🚽€0,50 📷€1.
Surface: asphalted. ☀️ 01/01-31/12
Distance: 🚶1km ⊗on the spot 🏖on the spot 🚐on the spot.
Remarks: Shuttle bus.

P	San Giovanni Rotondo 🌊⛵🏔	34A1

Viale Padre Pio. **GPS:** n41,70679 e15,69927.
150 🛏€ 2,50, overnight stay free. **Surface:** asphalted.
Remarks: Shrine Padre Pio 200m.

📷S	San Pietro in Bevagna 🏄	34D1

La Salina, SP122, Manduria. **GPS:** n40,30121 e17,72630.⬆️
🛏€ 14-20, 4 pers.incl 🚰🔌Ch🚿€2,50 WC 🚽included. **Surface:** gravel.
☀️ 01/06-30/09
Distance: 🏖on the spot.

📷	San Pietro in Bevagna 🏄	34D1

La Marina, Via Favignana, Manduria. **GPS:** n40,30888 e17,67750.⬆️

80 🛏€ 20/24h. **Surface:** unpaved.
Distance: 🏖300m.

📷	Sannicola 🏄	34D2

Campo delle Bandiere, Loc. Padula Bianca. **GPS:** n40,09681 e18,01297.
🛏€ 20 🚰🔌Ch WC 🚽. **Surface:** sand. ☀️ 01/06-01/09
Distance: 🏖Sandy beach.

📷S	Santa Maria al Bagno	34D1

Area Camper Mondonuovo, Via Torre Mozza. **GPS:** n40,13494 e18,00166.⬆️➡️
30 🛏€ 15 🚰🔌Ch🚿🚿. **Surface:** grassy. ☀️ 01/01-31/12

Distance: 🏖beach 500m.

📷S | **Torre Canne di Fasano** | 34C1

Lido Tavernese, SS379, uscita Torre Canne Sud. **GPS:** n40,82023 e17,49875.

100 🛏€ 15-22 🚰🔌Ch🧹 (80x)€2 WC included 🚿€1. **Surface:** grassy.
Distance: 🚲3,5km 🏖on the spot ⊗01/07-31/08.

📷S | **Torre Canne di Fasano** | 34C1

Il Privilegio Camper Service, Via Appia, SP90 > Savelletri.
GPS: n40,84363 e17,46359.

🛏€ 15-20 🚰🔌Ch🧹WC🚿. **Surface:** gravel.
Distance: 🏖on the spot.
Remarks: Beach club.

📷S | **Troia** | 34A1

Campo della Fiera, Via Sant'Antonio. **GPS:** n41,36158 e15,30616.

12 🛏free 🚰🔌Ch🧹. **Surface:** asphalted. ◻ 01/01-31/12
Distance: 🚲200m.
Remarks: Near the cathedral.

📷S | **Vico del Gargano** | 34A1

Lido Azzurro. GPS: n41,94208 e15,98303.⬆.

80 🛏Oct-Apr € 10, May-June € 15, Jul/Aug € 25 🚰🔌Ch🧹€3,(Aug)
WC included 🚿. ◻ 01/01-31/12
Distance: 🚲Valazzo 4km 🏖Sandy beach 🛒1km (camping).

📷S | **Vieste** 🌴🏖🚂 | 34B1

Fusilo Rosina, Contrada S.Lucia. **GPS:** n41,91028 e16,12944.⬆.

70 🛏Jun-Sep € 15, Jul € 20, Aug € 27,50 🚰🔌Ch🧹 (70x)included
WC🚿€0,50. **Surface:** grassy. ◻ 01/06-15/09

Distance: 🚲4km 🏖300m ⊗50m 🛒100m 🚌50m.

📷S | **Vieste** 🌴🏖🚂 | 34B1

Area Eden Blu, Lungomare Enrico Mattei. **GPS:** n41,85985 e16,17396.⬆.
40 🛏🔌22 🚰Ch🧹WC🚿. **Surface:** unpaved. ◻ 01/04-31/10
Distance: 🏖on the spot.

Tourist information Vieste:
⛺ ◻ Mo.

📷S | **Zapponeta** | 34B1

Zapponeta Beach, Via del Mare. **GPS:** n41,45694 e15,96083.⬆➡.

30 🛏€ 10, 1/7-15/7, 15/8-31/8 €12, 15/7-15/8 € 15/2 pers incl 🚰🔌
Ch🧹€2 WC included 🚿€0,50. **Surface:** grassy/metalled. ◻ 01/04-30/09
Distance: 🚲250m 🏖on the spot 🍴on the spot ⊗500m 🛒500m.
Remarks: Narrow entrance.

Campania

📷S | **Bacoli** | 33D6

Sea Oasis Village, Via Strada Romana, loc. Fusaro. **GPS:** n40,82194 e14,04791.
± 100 🛏€ 15/20/24h, 4 pers.incl 🚰🔌Ch🧹€5 WC🚿€1 🚿.
Surface: grassy/sand.
Distance: 🏖on the spot.
Remarks: At the beach.

📷S | **Bacoli** | 33D6

Sea Oasis Village, Via Strada Romana. **GPS:** n40,82194 e14,04791.
100 🛏€ 18-20, 4 pers.incl. **Surface:** grassy.
Distance: 🏖on the spot ⊗on the spot.

📷S | **Bacoli** | 33D6

Parco Naturale Agriturismo Fondi di Baia, Via Fondi di Baia.
GPS: n40,81132 e14,07518.

20 🛏€ 10 🚰🔌Ch🧹 included. **Surface:** asphalted. ◻ 01/01-31/12
Distance: 🚲3km ⊗Baia 700m 🚌100m.

📷S | **Baia e Latina** | 33D5

Country Village Il Baglio, Via Sciuliarelle. **GPS:** n41,30386 e14,24754.⬆.
🛏guests free 🚰🔌Ch🧹WC🚿. ◻ 01/01-31/12
Distance: 🚲village 2km ⊗on the spot.

📷S | **Benevento** 🌴 | 34A2

Sannio Camper Club, Via Domenico Mustilli. **GPS:** n41,13141 e14,78960.⬆.

IT

50 � € 10/24h ⌗ ᷤ Ch ⚡ included. ☐ 01/01-31/12
Distance: ⛰500m ✈1,8km ⚓300m.

Tourist information Benevento:
⌖ Piazza Risorgimento en Piazza Santa Maria. ☐ Wed, Sa 8-13h.

| | Casalbore | 34A2 |

Agriturismo Le Mainarde. GPS: n41,24516 e15,00242.⬆
30 ⌗ € 15. ☐ 01/01-31/12
Distance: ⊗on the spot.

| | Cava de' Tirreni ♨ | 34A2 |

Via Ido Longo, loc. Sant'Arcangelo. GPS: n40,69984 e14,69553.
⌗free ⌗ ᷤ Chfree. Surface: grasstiles. ☐ 01/01-31/12
Distance: ✈2,3km.

Tourist information Cava de' Tirreni:
ⓘ Salerno. City with medieval centre.
Ⓜ Museo Civico, Amalfi. Museum with Tavole Amalfitane, the old Law of the Sea. ☐ 8-14h, Sa 8-12h ◉ holiday.

| | Contursi Terme ♨ | 34B2 |

Agriturismo Il Giardino, Loc. Prato. GPS: n40,64891 e15,23002.
⌗ € 10 ⌗ ᷤ Ch ⚡. Surface: metalled.
Distance: ✈4,4km ⊗on the spot.
Remarks: Le Terme Vulpacchio 50m.

| | Marina di Camerota | 34B3 |

Parcheggio Europa, Via Sirene. GPS: n40,00302 e15,36493.
⌗ € 18 ⌗ ᷤ ⚡ 🗑. Surface: unpaved. ☐ Easter-30/09
Distance: ⚓300m.

| | Napoli ♨⛴🍴 | 33D6 |

Parking IPM, Via Colli Aminei 27, Naples (Napoli). GPS: n40,87038 e14,24616.

⌗7-21h € 10 21-8h €10 ⌗ ᷤ Ch included. ⚡€2. Surface: asphalted.
☐ 01/01-31/12
Distance: ✈1,2km 🚌bus R4 centre Napoli 30m.
Remarks: Monitored parking.

| | Napoli ♨⛴🍴 | 33D6 |

Parking Patry, Via Nuova Poggioreale 120, Naples (Napoli).
GPS: n40,86788 e14,29436.⬆
⌗ € 24/24h ⌗ ᷤ Ch ⚡ included. Location: Urban. Surface: metalled.
☐ 01/01-31/12
Distance: 🚇metro 300m.
Remarks: Monitored parking.

Tourist information Naples (Napoli):
ⓘ A.A.C.S.T.(Azienda Autonoma di Cura Soggiorno e Turismo), Palazzo Reale, www.regione.campania.it. Capital of the province with many monuments and cultural treasures.
👁 Vesuvio. Volcano, observatorium on western edge of the crater. Visit with guide possible.
👁 Mergellina. Small peninsula with fishing-port and marina.
👁 Teatro San Carlo. Opera building.
Ⓜ Museo Nazionale Archeologico di Napoli, Piazza Museo Nazionale 19. Antique hellenic-roman civilisation. ☐ Tue-Su 9-14h.
🏠 Palazzo Reale. Royal palace. ☐ 9-13.30h ◉ Mo.
✝ Duomo San Gennaro. Cathedral with original interior.
∩ Ercolano/Herculaneum. Ancient city buried together with Pompeii.
☐ 9-14.45h, holidays 9-18.15h.
⌖ Mercato Corso Malta. ☐ Mo, Fri.

| | Paestum ♨ | 34B3 |

Camper Village Maremirtilli, Via Linora di Paestum, SP278.
GPS: n40,37607 e15,00119.
70 ⌗€ 15-25 ⌗ ᷤ Ch ⚡ WC 🗑. Surface: grassy. ☐ 01/01-31/12
Distance: ⚓on the spot.

| | Paestum ♨ | 34B3 |

Camper Park Zone Archeologica, Via Magna Grecia, Capaccio Paestum.
GPS: n40,41851 e15,00697.⬆.
30 ⌗€ 10 ⌗ ᷤ Chincluded. Surface: unpaved. ☐ 01/01-31/12
Distance: ⛰300m ⚓1,6km ⊗50m.
Remarks: Paestum Excavations 200m.

| | Paestum ♨ | 34B3 |

Gli Eucalipti Area di Sosta, Via Linora, 76, Capaccio. GPS: n40,38565 e15,00308.
25 ⌗€ 14/17 ⌗ ᷤ Ch ⚡ included. Surface: grassy. ☐ 01/05-01/10
Distance: ⚓4km ⚓50m.

| | Paestum ♨ | 34B3 |

Fattoria del Casaro, Via Licinella 5, Capaccio Paestum.
GPS: n40,41504, o15,00505.
100 ⌗€ 12/24h ⌗ ᷤ Ch ⚡ 🗑included.
Distance: ⛰600m ⚓beach 1,8km ⊗on the spot.
Remarks: Paestum Excavations 300m, regional products and bread.

Tourist information Paestum:
ⓘ A.A.C.S.T.(Azienda Autonoma di Cura Soggiorno e Turismo), Via Magna Grecia, 151. Old city, founded by the Greeks. In the surroundings many vestiges from that time. ☐ 9h-sunset.

| | Palinuro | 34B3 |

Via Palorcio. GPS: n40,03722 e15,30944.
⌗€ 20/24h ⌗ ᷤ Ch WC 🗑included.
Distance: ⚓700m.

| | Pompei ♨ | 33D6 |

Parking Plinio, Via Plinio 98. GPS: n40,74710 e14,48756.

30 ⌗8-20h € 10, 8-8h € 19, 20-8h € 12. Surface: asphalted.
☐ 01/01-31/12
Distance: ⛰Archeological site Pompei 250m ⚓300m.
Remarks: Monitored parking.

| △ S | Pompei ♨ | 33D6 |

Camping Pompei, Via Plinio 113.
GPS: n40,74675 e14,48496.⬆.
⌗€ 15,50-20, 2 pers.incl ⌗ ᷤ Ch ⚡ WC 🗑 📶included.
Location: Urban. Surface: grassy.
☐ 01/01-31/12
Remarks: Entrance acient city 150m.

Tourist information Pompei:
ⓘ Ancient city at the foot of Vesuvius. ☐ 9h-sunset ◉ holiday.

| | Pozzuoli | 33D6 |

Castagnaro Parking - Pozzuoli - Napoli

info@castagnaroparking.it - www.castagnaroparking.it
Paved and flat motorhome pitches
Beautiful view
Electricity/water/drainage at each pitch

Castagnaro Park, Via del Castagnaro 1. **GPS:** n40,86942 e14,12165.
85 ⬛€ 15 ☂━ ⚒ Ch ⚒ (80x)€2/24h WC included ⬛€1,50.
Surface: grassy/gravel.
⬛ 01/01-31/12
Distance: ⚓300m ✦4km ⊗300m ⬛300m ⬛200m.
Remarks: Monitored parking, reservation during Christmas period.
Tourist information Pozzuoli:
ℹ Cuma. Archeological site. ⬛ 9-14.45h, summer 18h.

Sala Consilina 34B2

Via Santa Maria della Misericordia. **GPS:** n40,41376 e15,56397.⬆.
20 ⬛€ 5/night ☂━ Ch ⚒ included.
Surface: metalled.
⬛ 01/01-31/12
Distance: ⚓1,5km ✦300m ⊗500m ⬛2,5km ⬛1,5km ⬛15km ⬛15km.
Remarks: Behind hotel Vallis Dea.

Tramonti 34A2

Agriturismo Costiera Amalfitana, Via Falcone, 12 - Frazione Pietre.
GPS: n40,69929 e14,61811.⬆.

10 ⬛01/09-14/06 € 22, 15/06-31/08 - 23/12-06/01 € 30 ☂━⚒
Ch ⚒ WC ⬛included. **Location:** Rural, comfortable. **Surface:** grassy/gravel.
⬛ 01/01-31/12
Distance: ⚓50m ✦15km ⬛6km ⊗on the spot ⬛30m ⬛500m
⬛on the spot.
Remarks: Amalfi Coast.

Basilicata

Grumento Nova 34B2

Agriturismo Al Parco Verde, Contrada Spineto, Moliterno-Grumento.
GPS: n40,28110 e15,90563.⬆➡.
20 ⬛€ 20 ☂━ Ch ⚒ WC ⬛included ⬛. **Surface:** grassy.
⬛ 01/06-01/10
Distance: ⚓8km ⬛2km ⬛5km ⬛on the spot ⬛2km ⬛1km.
Remarks: Archeological site 200m.

Metaponto 34C2

Camper parking Nettuno, Viale Magna Grecia, Metaponto Lido.
GPS: n40,35693 e16,83221.⬆.

50 ⬛€ 13/24h, Jul/Aug € 18 ☂━⚒ Ch ⚒ WC included ⬛€1.
Surface: grassy/gravel. ⬛ 01/01-31/12
Distance: ⬛50m ⊗on the spot ⬛300m.
Tourist information Metaponto:
ℹ Archeological site. ⬛ 9h-sunset.

Calabria

Amantea 34C3

Garden Park Caterina, SS. 18, loc Coreca. **GPS:** n39,09383 e16,08508.⬆.
10 ⬛€ 20-25, 4 pers.incl ☂━⚒ Ch ⚒ €2,50 WC included ⬛€1 ⬛€5.
Surface: grassy. ⬛ 15/06-15/09
Distance: ⚓on the spot ⬛on the spot ⬛on the spot ⊗nearby.

Bova Marina 34D5

Mafalda's Camper Park, Via Sotto Ferrovia, loc. San Pasquale.
GPS: n37,92422 e15,94800.⬆.
20 ⬛€ 10-20 ☂━ Ch ⚒ included. **Surface:** gravel/sand.
Distance: ⚓3km ⬛on the spot ⬛on the spot ⊗200m ⬛500m.
Remarks: Acces via unmetalled road along the beach.

Catanzaro Marina 34D3

Il Chioschetto, Via Carlo Pisacane 24. **GPS:** n38,83321 e16,64862.

10 ⬛free ☂━ ⚒. **Location:** Simple. **Surface:** sand.
Distance: ⬛Sandy beach.

Cirella 34C3

Area Camper Ulisse, SS 18 km 270, Diamante. **GPS:** n39,72500 e15,80930.

130 ⬛€ 8-25, 4 pers.incl ☂━⚒ Ch ⚒ WC ⬛included ⬛.
Surface: grassy/sand. ⬛ 01/04-31/10
Distance: ⚓800m ⬛on the spot ⬛on the spot ⊗on the spot ⬛on the spot
⬛on the spot.

Cirella 34C3

Lido Alexander, SS 18, Diamante. **GPS:** n39,72168 e15,81097.⬆.

50 ⬛€ 8-17 ☂━⚒ Ch ⚒ €3 WC included ⬛€1 ⬛€3. **Surface:** grassy/gravel.
⬛ 01/01-31/12
Distance: ⚓1,5km ⬛on the spot ⬛on the spot ⊗on the spot
⬛on the spot.

Cirella 34C3

Lido delle Sirene, SS 18, Contr. Riviere. **GPS:** n39,71822 e15,81137.➡.

100 ⬛ ☂━⚒ Ch ⚒ WC ⬛. **Surface:** grassy. ⬛ 01/06-20/09

IT

Distance: 🚶1km ⛱on the spot 🏊on the spot ✕on the spot 🍽1km.

🛏 S **Cirella** 34C3

Lido Tropical, Viale Glauco, 9, Diamante. **GPS**: n39,69222 e15,81556.⬆️

200 🚐 € 8-30, 4 pers.incl 🚰 🔌 Ch ⚡ WC 🚿. **Surface**: grassy/sand.
🅿 01/01-31/12

Distance: 🚶1,5km ⛱on the spot 🏊on the spot ✕200m 🍽200m 🚌shuttle to town.

🛏 S **Cirò Marina** 34D3

Via Maddalena. **GPS**: n39,35998 e17,12910.
25 🚐 € 6, 01/06-31/08 € 12 🚰 ⚡. **Surface**: unpaved. 🅿 01/01-31/12
Distance: 🚶1,2km ⛱50m.

🛏 S **Cittadella del Capo** 34C3

Torre Parise, Via Parise. **GPS**: n39,56580 e15,87399.⬆️
16 🚐 € 15, Jul/Aug € 18 🚰 🔌 Ch ⚡ WC included. **Surface**: grassy.
🅿 01/01-31/12
Distance: 🚶1,5km ⛱200m ✕500m.
Remarks: Swimming pool.

🛏 S **Condofuri Marina** 34D5

Agriturismo Antonino Gemelli, Via Salinella 37. **GPS**: n37,92372 e15,85150.⬆️
20 🚐 € 15-20 🚰 🔌 Ch ⚡ WC 🚿. **Surface**: gravel/sand.
🅿 01/01-31/12
Distance: 🚶500m ⛱100m.

🍴 S **Corigliano Calabro** 34C3

B&B Club Tepee, Contrada Sant'Agata 42, SS106bis > Cantinella.
GPS: n39,64140 e16,38617.
🚐 € 10 🚰 🔌 Ch ⚡.
Distance: 🚶Corigliano 14km.

🛏 S **Cropani Marina** 34D3

Sena Park, Viale Venezia 34. **GPS**: n38,91143 e16,80963.⬆️➡️
25 🚐 € 12-28, 2 pers.incl 🚰 🔌 Ch ⚡ WC 🔌€0,50 🚿 included.
Surface: grassy/sand. 🅿 01/01-31/12
Distance: 🚶500m ⛱400m 🏊400m ✕ristorante/pizzeria 🍽500m.
Remarks: Washing motorhome € 20.

🛏 S **Crotone** 34D3

Hera Lacinia Mare, Via Filippo, 47, Campione III. **GPS**: n39,00311 e17,16984.⬆️
10 🚐 € 25 🚰 🔌 Ch ⚡. **Surface**: gravel/metalled.
Distance: 🚶on the spot ⛱on the spot 🏊on the spot ✕100m 🍽200m.

🛏 S **Morano Calabro** 34C3

Via Gaetano Scorza. **GPS**: n39,84098 e16,13731.⬆️➡️

40 🚐free 🚰 🔌. **Surface**: asphalted. 🅿 01/01-31/12
Distance: 🚶200m 🚲7km ⛱200m 🍽200m.
Remarks: Next to church of San Bernardino, panoramic view.

🛏 S **Palmi** 34C4

Sosta Camper Prajola, Lungomare Donna Canfora. **GPS**: n38,39333 e15,86277.
⬆️➡️

25 🚐 € 15/24h 🚰 🔌 Ch ⚡ WC included 🚿. **Location**: Simple.
Surface: gravel. 🅿 01/01-31/12
Distance: ⛱on the spot.

🛏 S **Praia a Mare** 34B3

Nuova Playa, Contr. Fiucci. **GPS**: n39,86885 e15,78943.⬆️

15 🚐 € 15, peak season € 30 🚰 🔌 Ch ⚡ included. **Surface**: grassy.
🅿 01/01-31/12
Distance: 🚶2km ⛱on the spot 🏊on the spot ✕100m 🍽2km.
Remarks: Black sandy beach, in front of Dino island.

🛏 S **Praia a Mare** 34B3

Punto Mare, Loc. Fiuzzi. **GPS**: n39,87633 e15,78727.⬆️

30 🚐 € 6 🚰€2,50 🔌€2,50 Ch ⚡€2. **Surface**: grassy. 🅿 01/06-30/09
Distance: 🚶800m ⛱600m 🏊600m ✕500m 🍽500m 🚿on the spot.

🛏 S **Rossano** 34D4

Sosta Camper Il Faro, C. da Foresta Faro Campo Trionto.
GPS: n39,62148 e16,75146.⬆️

12 🚐 € 13-25 🚰 🔌 Ch ⚡ WC included. **Location**: Comfortable, isolated.
Surface: grassy. 🅿 01/01-31/12
Distance: 🚶2km, Rossano 12km ⛱Sandy beach ✕on the spot.

🛏 S **Scalea** 34B3

Dolce Vita, Via Fiume Lao 7. **GPS**: n39,79667 e15,79265.⬆️

IT

100 € 16-21 Ch €5 WC €0,50.
Surface: grassy.
01/05-30/09
Distance: on the spot on the spot on the spot on the spot 800m.

S **Scalea** 34B3

Lido Zio Tom, Corso Mediterraneo km 261,7. **GPS**: n39,81306 e15,78917.

140 € 10-18 Ch included,4Amp WC hot shower against payment. **Surface:** grassy/gravel. 15/04-15/10
Distance: on the spot 300m 1km 1,5km.

S **Scalea** 34B3

Lido Aqua Mar Sosta Camper Martina, Corso Mediterraneo.
GPS: n39,80092 e15,79087.
€ 20/24h Ch WC €0,50.
Distance: on the spot.

Sardinia

S **Aglientu** 31C4

Oasi Gallura, Localita'Vignola Mare 19, SP 90 km 53. **GPS**: n41,12556 e9,06167.
70 € 13,50-19 Ch €2,50 WC hot shower €1 €5.
Distance: 50m on the spot on the spot.

S **Alghero** 31B5

Camperpark I Platani, Ss 291 Km 32,5 S.Maria la Palma - Fertilia.
GPS: n40,60693 e8,27522.

€ 16, Jul €18, Aug € 20 Ch WC included €5.
Distance: Alghero 7km 1,5km.
Remarks: Monitored parking 24/24, shuttle bus to beach, swimming pool.

S **Alghero** 31B5

Paradise Park, Loc. Le Bombarde. **GPS**: n40,59180 e8,25610.

100 ± € 18 Ch WC included.
Distance: 350m 350m on the spot on the spot 50m.

S **Bosa** 31C5

S'Abba Drucche Spiagge, SP49 Alghero-Bosa km 38+800.
GPS: n40,31671 e8,47368.
€ 20-24 Ch WC €1 €7. **Surface:** unpaved.
01/04-30/09
Distance: on the spot on the spot.

S **Buggerru** 31C6

Area Terrazze. **GPS**: n39,40317 e8,40250.

50 € 20/24h Ch €5. **Surface:** sand. 01/01-31/12
Distance: 200m on the spot.
Remarks: Beach parking.

S **Buggerru** 31C6

Loc. Cala Domestica. **GPS**: n39,41757 e8,41147.
20 € 25 cold shower. **Surface:** sand.
Distance: 4km sandy beach 50m 50m.
Remarks: Beach parking.

S **Domus de Maria** 31C6

Loc. Spartivento, Chia. **GPS**: n38,88962 e8,86437.
€ 17/24h Ch €0,50, cold shower. **Surface:** sand.
Easter-30/09
Distance: on the spot on the spot on the spot.
Remarks: In front of Hotel Su Giudeu.

S **Ghilarza** 31C5

Via Rosario. **GPS**: n40,12604 e8,83942.
2 free Ch. **Surface:** forest soil. 01/01-31/12
Distance: 500m.

S **Nuoro** 31C5

P.le Anfiteatro cittadino, Piazza Veneto. **GPS**: n40,31447 e9,32807.
30 free Ch free. 01/01-31/12

S **Oristano** 31C5

Stadio Tharros, Via Dorando Petri. **GPS**: n39,89710 e8,58927.
free Ch free. 01/01-31/12
Distance: 500m 500m Porta Nuova 650m.

S **Oristano** 31C5

Zona sportiva Sa Rodia, Viale Repubblica. **GPS**: n39,90605 e8,57878.
free Ch free.
Distance: historical centre.
Remarks: Parking in front of swimming pool.

San Teodoro 31C4

Via Donat Cattin. **GPS**: n40,76658 e9,66884.
30 free. **Surface:** asphalted.

S **Sorso** 31C4

Camp Site, Via degli Oleandri, SP 81 km 13, Platamona Lido.
GPS: n40,81565 e8,46462.
50 € 12-18 Ch WC . 01/01-31/12

IT

Distance: ⚓300m 🛒nearby 🚌on the spot.

♿S · **31B4**

La Pineta, Loc. Pozzo S.Nicola, SP34. **GPS:** n40,86843 e8,23610.⬆️

📷€ 19, Aug € 21 ⛽ 🗑Ch ✎ WC included 🚿hotshower€ 1.

Surface: grassy/sand.

Distance: ⚓3,5km ⊗on the spot.

Remarks: Free shuttle to beach.

🍴S · **Tonara** · **31C5**

Ostello delle Gioventù, Via Muggianeddu, 2. **GPS:** n40,02855 e9,17542.

📷€ 10 ⛽ 🗑Ch ✎. ⬜ 01/01-31/12

Distance: 🚶500m ⊗on the spot.

♿S · **Valledoria** · **31C4**

Punto Maragnani, Via Cristoforo Colombo, Loc. Maragnani.

GPS: n40,92470 e8,79548.

📷€ 18/24h ⛽ 🗑Ch ✎ WC 🚿included. ⬜ 01/01-31/12

Distance: ⚓50m 🛒200m.

♿S · **Villaputzu** · **31C6**

Area di sosta camper Turimar, Via Nazionale 236, SS125.

GPS: n39,46017 e9,60290.

📷 ⛽ 🗑Ch ✎ WC 🚿against payment.

Distance: 🚶Villaputzu 6km ⚓50m ⊗on the spot.

♿S · **Villasimius** · **31C6**

Gli Aranci, Viale dei Carrubi, loc. Pranu Zinnigas. **GPS:** n39,14997 e9,51292.

100 📷€ 22 ⛽ 🗑Ch ✎ WC 🚿included. ⬜ 01/05-30/09

Distance: 🚶2km ⚓3km.

Remarks: Shuttle bus to beach.

Sicily

♿S · **Agrigento** 🏖🏄 · **34B6**

Sosta Camper Quality, Via delle Dune, San Leone. **GPS:** n37,24566 e13,61114.⬆️

50 📷€ 20 ⛽ 🗑Ch ✎ WC 🚿📶included. **Location:** Comfortable, quiet.

Surface: sand. ⬜ 01/06-31/10

Distance: 🚶Dune ⚓sandy beach 10m ⊗50m.

♿S · **Agrigento** 🏖🏄 · **34B6**

Valle dei Templi, Viale Caduti di Marzabotto. **GPS:** n37,28881 e13,58181.

50 📷€ 5. **Location:** Simple. **Surface:** sand. ⬜ 01/01-31/12

Remarks: Near entrance and pay-desk of Valle dei Templi.

♿S · **Augusta** · **34C6**

Area Attrezzata Camper Nelly, SS114 - Km 118,5, Contrada Agnone Bagni.

GPS: n37,31148 e15,09260.

📷€ 13, July € 14, Aug € 15/day ⛽ 🗑Ch ✎ WC 🚿included.

⬜ 01/01-31/12. **Distance:** 🚴6km.

♿S · **Caccamo** · **34B6**

SS 285. **GPS:** n37,93410 e13,66115.⬆️.

10 📷free ⛽ 🗑Ch ✎free.

Location: Simple. **Surface:** gravel/metalled.

Distance: 🚶900m ⊗300m.

📷 · **Caltagirone** 🏖 · **34C6**

Piazzale San Giovanni, Loc. San Giovanni. **GPS:** n37,23949 e14,50717.⬆️.

📷free. **Surface:** asphalted. ⬜ 01/01-31/12

Distance: 🚶historical centre 700m.

♿S · **Caltanissetta** · **34B6**

Via Guastaferro. **GPS:** n37,48959 e14,04515.⬆️➡️.

25 📷free ⛽ 🗑Chfree.

Location: Urban, simple, noisy. **Surface:** asphalted.

Distance: 🚶2km ⊗on the spot 🛒on the spot.

♿S · **Castelbuono** · **34B5**

Via Guiseppe Mazzini. **GPS:** n37,93694 e14,09296.⬆️.

10 📷free ⛽ 🗑Ch. **Location:** Simple, quiet.

Distance: 🚶700m ⊗700m.

♿S · **Castellammare del Golfo** · **34A6**

Playtime, Viale Leonardo da Vinci, SS187. **GPS:** n38,02494 e12,89086.⬆️➡️.

📷€ 15/24h ⛽ 🗑Ch ✎ WC 🚿⬜. **Surface:** grassy.

Distance: 🚶200m ⚓1km.

♿S · **Castelluzzo** · **34A6**

Parcheggio Trinacria, Via Calazza. **GPS:** n38,10694 e12,72861.⬆️➡️.

± 40 📷against payment ⛽ 🗑 ✎. **Surface:** gravel. ⬜ summer

Distance: ⚓400m ⊗500m 🛒500m.

Remarks: Beach parking.

📷 · **Castelluzzo** · **34A6**

Parking Macari, SP16. **GPS:** n38,13564 e12,73638.

📷free. **Surface:** sand.

📷 · **Castelluzzo** · **34A6**

SP16. **GPS:** n38,12166 e12,72666.

📷free. **Surface:** gravel.

Distance: ⚓on the spot.

Remarks: Beach parking, beach train.

♿S · **Enna** 🏔 · **34C6**

Ennacamper, C/da S.Giuseppe, Pergusa. **GPS:** n37,52277 e14,29000.⬆️.

30 📷€ 20/24h ⛽ 🗑ChService€ 5 ✎€ 4 📶. **Location:** Simple.

Surface: sand.

Remarks: Free shuttle, cleaning motorhome € 5.

📷S · **Francavilla di Sicilia** · **34C5**

Maremonti, Via Cappuccini. **GPS:** n37,90855 e15,14347.⬆️➡️.

±50 📷gift ⛽. **Surface:** unpaved. ⬜ 01/01-31/12

Distance: 🚶400m ⚓Riverbed.

Remarks: Gole dell'Alcantara 6km.

♿S · **Furnari** ⚓ · **34C5**

Tonnarella, Corso Palermo 6. **GPS:** n38,13218 e15,12469.⬆️.

IT

44 ⓈE 13-24 ⌐🔲 Ch ✍ WC included 🔲€0,50 🔲€4. **Location:** Simple.
Surface: gravel. 🔲 01/01-31/12
Distance: 🏖on the spot 🏊on the spot ⊗150m ⚓250m.
Remarks: Monitored parking, excursion to the Eolie-islands.

80 ⓈE Jun € 15, Jul € 20, Aug € 25 ⌐🔲 Ch ✍ WC 🔲included.
Surface: gravel.
Distance: 🏖Licata 9km 🏊on the spot ⊗on the spot.
Remarks: Stairs to sandy beach.

| 🏕S | Gangi 🌿🏔 | 34B5 |
SS14. **GPS:** n37,79203 e14,21079.⬆.
15 Ⓢfree ⌐🔲 Ch ✍ free. **Surface:** gravel/sand. 🔲 01/01-31/12
Distance: 🏖750m ⊗750m.

| 🏕S | Gela | 34C6 |
Meridiana Park, Via Torre di Manfria, Contrada Piano Marina.
GPS: n37,11166 e14,12444.⬆➡.
80 ⓈE 15/day ⌐🔲 Ch ✍ WC 🔲. **Surface:** grassy.
Distance: 🏖Gela 14km 🏊1,2km.
Remarks: Swimming pool, sandy beach.

| 🏕S | Marina di Ragusa 🏖🌊 | 34C6 |
Marina Caravan, Via Portovenere 57. **GPS:** n36,78472 e14,56486.⬆.

| 🏕S | Giardini Naxos ⛱🌊 | 34C5 |
Parking Lagani, Via Stralcina 22, zona Recanati. **GPS:** n37,82092 e15,26753.⬆
➡.

30 ⓈE 15-30 ⌐🔲 Ch ✍ WC included 🔲€1,(summer) 🔲€5 🔊.
Surface: metalled.
🔲 01/01-31/12
Distance: 🏖on the spot 🏊200m ⊗50m ⚓200m 🚌Bus to Taormina 300m.
Remarks: Special tariff for long stay during the winter, bar, view on Etna and Taormina.

58 ⓈE € 10, 01/06-30/09 € 17,50 ⌐🔲 Ch ✍ WC 🔲included 🔲€4 🔊.
Surface: grassy. 🔲 01/01-31/12
Distance: 🏖500m 🏊300m ⊗100m ⚓100m 🚌200m.
Remarks: Water/drainage at each pitch.

| 🏕S | Marina di Ragusa 🏖🌊 | 34C6 |
Tanto per Camper, Via Donnalucata. **GPS:** n36,78944 e14,56666.⬆➡.

| 🏕S | Giardini Naxos ⛱🌊 | 34C5 |
Eden Parking, Via Stracina. **GPS:** n37,82188 e15,26701.⬆.
30 ⓈE 7-25 ⌐🔲 Ch ✍ €0,35/kWh WC 🔲€1 🔊. **Surface:** grassy.
🔲 01/01-31/12
Distance: 🏊500m 🚌> Taormina.

40 ⓈE 15/9-14/6 € 10, 15/6-26/7 € 14, 27/7-30/8 € 18, 2 pers.ind ⌐🔲
Ch ✍ WC included 🔲€1 🔲€4. **Surface:** grassy/gravel. 🔲 01/01-31/12
Distance: 🏖800m 🏊1,5km ⊗100m ⚓800m.
Remarks: Beachshuttle € 0,50.

| 🏕S | Giardini Naxos ⛱🌊 | 34C5 |
Holiday Sun, Viale Stracina 20. **GPS:** n37,82109 e15,26784.
30 ⓈE 7-25 ⌐🔲 Ch ✍ WC 🔲 🔊. **Surface:** grassy/gravel.
Distance: 🏊beach 500m ⊗on the spot 🚌> Taormina.

Tourist information Giardini Naxos:
⛺ 🔲 Sa-morning.

| 🏕S | Marsala | 34A6 |
Beach Sibiliana, Contrada Fossarunza 205/z 14. **GPS:** n37,73520 e12,47497.⬆.
100 ⓈE 20 ✍ 🔲 Ch ✍ WC 🔲 🔊included. **Surface:** unpaved.
Distance: 🏊50m.

| 🏕S | Ispica | 34D6 |
Associazione Camper Club Porto Ulisse. **GPS:** n36,69761 e14,98647.⬆.
Ⓢ 🔲 Ch 🔲. **Surface:** grassy. 🔲 01/01-31/12
Distance: 🏊100m.

| 🏕S | Marsala | 34A6 |
Nautisub Club S. Teodoro, Contrada Birgi. **GPS:** n37,91046 e12,46178.⬆➡.

| 🏕S | Licata 🌊 | 34B6 |
Ristorante La Sorgente, Loc. Pisciotto. **GPS:** n37,12666 e13,85194.⬆➡.

± 50 ⓈE 15/20 ⌐🔲 Ch ✍. **Surface:** grassy. 🔲 01/05-30/09
Distance: 🏖5km 🏊Sandy beach ⊗on the spot.

IT

Marsala 34A6
Via Colonnello Maltese. **GPS:** n37,79497 e12,43270.
free Ch. **Surface:** asphalted. 01/01-31/12
Distance: 500m on the spot.

Mineo 34C6
Le Bave di Bacco, Strada Provinciale 86. **GPS:** n37,24137 e14,72239.
customers free . **Location:** Rural, simple, isolated. **Surface:** grassy.
01/01-31/12

Montallegro 34B6
Vizzi Parking, Via Lungomare, SP87. **GPS:** n37,38206 e13,30932.
€ 15 €3 Ch €2. **Surface:** gravel. 01/06-01/10
Distance: 100m.

Montallegro 34B6
Agriturismo Torre Salsa, Bove Marina. **GPS:** n37,37583 e13,32222.

20 € 17-24 €4 Ch according consumption WC €1 €6
€1,50/h. **Surface:** grassy. 01/01-31/12
Distance: 700m.
Remarks: Also pitches on the beach without service, estate 300 acres, hiking and mountain bike trails.

Montevago 34A6
Agricamper Mastragostino - Villa dei Pini. GPS: n37,70083 e12,98000.
€ 15 Ch included. 01/01-31/12
Distance: 200m.

Montevago 34A6
Centro Terme Acqua Pia, Loc. Acque Calde. **GPS:** n37,70602 e12,98092.
20 against payment. 01/04-31/10

Motta Camastra 34C5
S185, fraz. Ficarazzi. **GPS:** n37,87876 e15,17615.

10 € 10, Jul/Aug € 15 Ch WC included. **Surface:** grassy/gravel.
Distance: 300m 1km.
Remarks: In front of entrance of Gole dell'Alcantara.

Mussomeli 34B6
Piazzale Mongibello. GPS: n37,58343 e13,74956.
free Ch.
Distance: historical centre.

Noto 34D6
Airone, Via San Corrado, Lido di Noto. **GPS:** n36,85916 e15,11555.

50 Jun/Sep € 14-16, Aug € 18 Ch €2 WC hot shower €0,50.
Surface: grassy/sand. 01/04-30/09
Distance: 100m 100m 750m Bus to Noto 100m.

Noto 34D6
Il Canneto, Viale Lido di Noto, Lido di Noto. **GPS:** n36,86083 e15,11944.

55 € 10-18 Ch €2 WC . **Surface:** grassy/sand.
Distance: on the spot 1,2km.
Remarks: Bread-service and meals, direct access to the sandy beach.

Noto 34D6
NotoParking, Contrada Faldino, Noto. **GPS:** n36,88353 e15,08595.

40 € 18 Ch €3 WC €1.
Surface: grassy/gravel.
01/01-31/12
Distance: 1km 3km 200m 200m.
Remarks: Organised excursions in the surroundings, free shuttle bus to Noto.

Noto 34D6
Oasi Park Falconara, Viale Ionio, Lido di Noto. **GPS:** n36,87001 e15,12872.
50 € 15, 01/06-31/10 € 16-20 Ch WC included. **Surface:** gravel.
01/01-31/12
Distance: Noto 4km beach 700m pizzeria 50m.
Remarks: Shuttle bus to Noto and beach.

Noto 34D6
Parcheggio Calamosche, Oasi di Vendicari. **GPS:** n36,81611 e15,09888.

40-50 € 14 WC included. **Surface:** grassy. 01/06-30/09
Distance: Noto 10km 20 min walking bar/restaurant.

Oliveri · 34C5

Azimut Sosta Camper, Corso Cristoforo Colombo. **GPS:** n38,12840 e15,05833. ⬆
100 🛏€ 12-15-20-22 🚰🚽 Ch 💧 (100x),6Amp WC 🛁 included. **Location:**
Comfortable. **Surface:** grassy/gravel. 🅿 01/03-31/10
Distance: 🏪500m, Tindari 1,2km 🏖2,5km ⛱beach 50m 🚉50m ⊗50m
🚉200m 🚌10m 🚏100m 🚲100m 🚶200m.

Pachino · 34D6

Dragomar, Strada Marzamemi Portopalo di Capo Passero, Marzamemi.
GPS: n36,72732 e15,12083. ⬆➡

30 🛏€ 10-15 🚰🚽 Ch 💧 WC 🛁. **Surface:** gravel. 🅿 01/01-31/12
Distance: ⛱on the spot ⊗400m 🏪600m.
Remarks: Seaview, no beach.

Pachino · 34D6

La Cabana Service, Viale le Aloha, Contrada Granelli. **GPS:** n36,70562 e15,00689.
⬆➡

200 🛏€ 15, Jul/Aug € 20 🚰🚽 Ch 💧 WC included 🛁hot shower€1.
Surface: grassy/sand. 🅿 01/01-31/12
Distance: 🏪Pachino 7km ⛱on the spot 🍴on the spot.
Remarks: Bar, sandy beach.

Palermo · 34B6

Green Car Palermo, Via Quarto dei Mille 11b. **GPS:** n38,11016 e13,34307. ⬆
🛏€ 20/24h 🚰🚽 Ch 💧 included.
Location: Simple. **Surface:** asphalted.
Distance: 🏪piazza Indipendenza 300m.

Palermo · 34B6

Parking Ospedale Cervello, Via Trabucco. **GPS:** n38,15619 e13,31354.
🛏🚰🚽. **Location:** Simple, isolated.
Remarks: Nearby hospital.

Palermo · 34B6

Via Uditore 17. **GPS:** n38,13140 e13,32515. ⬆
🛏🚰🚽 Ch 💧 WC 🛁. **Surface:** gravel.
Remarks: Monitored parking, shuttle bus to city centre.

Palermo · 34B6

Piazza Alcide De Gasperi. **GPS:** n38,15170 e13,33944.
🛏free. **Surface:** asphalted.
Distance: 🚉on the spot.
Remarks: Nearby stadium.

Palermo · 34B6

Freesbee Parking, Via Imperatore Federico 116. **GPS:** n38,14722 e13,35277. ⬆
100 🛏€ 15-18 🚰🚽 Ch 💧 WC 🛁€1. **Surface:** asphalted.
Distance: 🏪Cathedral Palermo 400m 🏖2km 🚏150m.
Remarks: At motorhome dealer, 24/24 surveillance.

Tourist information Palermo:
ℹ U.I.A.T. (Ufficio Informazioni e di Accoglienza Turistica), Piazza Castelnuovo, 34, www.regione.sicilia.it/turismo. Capital of Sicily, port and economical heart of the Island.
👁 San Giovanni degli Eremiti.

👁 Santa Catarina.
🎭 Vucciria, Via Cassari-Argenteria. Palermo's most famous, picturesque and historic market.

Piazza Armerina · 34C6

Via G. Lo Giudice. **GPS:** n37,38711 e14,37041.
🛏free. **Location:** Simple. **Surface:** asphalted. 🅿 01/01-31/12
Distance: 🏪200m.

Piazza Armerina · 34C6

Agricamper Valle Dell'Elsa, SS65. **GPS:** n37,30173 e14,39605.
12 🛏€ 15/24h 🚰🚽 Ch 💧 WC 🛁 included. **Location:** Rural, comfortable, isolated, quiet. **Surface:** metalled. 🅿 01/01-31/12
Distance: 🏪Piazza Armerina 20km ⊗on the spot.

Piazza Armerina · 34C6

Agriturismo Agricasale, Contrada Ciavarina. **GPS:** n37,34032 e14,38840.
40 🛏€ 15 🚰🚽 Ch 💧 included.
Location: Rural, comfortable, isolated, quiet.
Distance: 🏪Piazza Armerina 13km ⊗bar/restaurant.
Remarks: Swimming pool € 3/pppd.

Piazza Armerina · 34C6

Agriturismo Gigliotto, SS 117bis km60. **GPS:** n37,29051 e14,38721.
20 🛏€ 20, 01/04-31/10 € 30 🚰🚽 Ch 💧 WC 🛁 included.
Location: Comfortable, quiet. **Surface:** gravel. 🅿 01/01-31/12
Distance: 🏪Piazza Armerina 13km.
Remarks: Swimming pool incl.

Piazza Armerina · 34C6

SP90. **GPS:** n37,36805 e14,33421. ⬆
20 🛏€ 15/24h 🚰🚽 Ch 💧 included. **Location:** Simple.
🅿 01/01-31/12
Distance: 🏪Piazza Armerina 4,5km ⊗on the spot.
Remarks: Villa Romana del Casale 400m.

Porto Empedocle · 34B6

Punta Piccola Park, Scala dei Turchi, SP68. **GPS:** n37,28916 e13,49250. ⬆➡

99 🛏May € 18, Jun € 20, 1-15 Jul € 23 15 Jul-31 Aug € 23 🚰🚽 Ch 💧 (65x)
WC 🛁€1. **Surface:** gravel. 🅿 25/04-30/09
Distance: 🏪2,5km ⛱on the spot ⊗200m 🍴1km.
Remarks: Direct access to the sandy beach.

Tourist information Porto Empedocle:
ⓝ Valle dei Templi, Agrigento. The Valley of The Temples, archeology.

Portopalo di Capo Passero · 34D6

Cicogna. **GPS:** n36,68333 e15,13638. ➡
20 🛏Jun/Sep € 10, Jul/Aug € 15 🚰🚽 Ch 💧 (20x)included 🛁.
Surface: gravel.
Distance: 🏪50m ⛱sandy beach 300m.

Pozzallo · 34C6

Il Giardino di Epicuro, SP67. **GPS:** n36,73128 e14,86240. ⬆➡

50 🛏€ 8, Jun € 10, Jul/Aug € 13 🚰🚽 Ch 💧 (22x)€2 🛁cold shower.
Surface: grassy/sand. 🅿 01/05-30/09

Distance: 🏖500m ⚓on the spot ⊗50m 🚰300m.
Remarks: Sandy beach.

📷S | **Pozzallo** | 34C6

Salvamar, Zona Porto di Pozzallo. **GPS**: n36,71541 e14,82240. ⬆.

30 🛒€ 10-€ 20 (Aug) 🚰🗑Ch🧹€3 🚿€1. **Surface:** grassy.
⬛ 01/01-31/12
Distance: ⚓200m 🏖500m 🚰1km.

📷S | **Realmonte** 🏖 | 34B6

Sosta camper Zanzibar, C/o Capo Rossello. **GPS**: n37,29495 e13,45438. ⬆➡.

100 🛒€ 12-22, 01/10-30/03 € 10 🚰🗑Ch🧹 WC included 🚿hot shower€1.
Surface: gravel. ⬛ 01/01-31/12
Distance: ⚓sandy beach ⊗on the spot 🚰150m.
Remarks: Bus to Valle dei Templi (€ 7/pp, min. 4 pers).

📷S | **Reitano** 🏖 | 34B5

Via Lungomare Colonna. **GPS**: n38,01407 e14,33081. ⬆.
70 🛒€10 🚰🗑Ch🧹🚿€0,50. **Location:** Simple.
⬛ 15/07-18/09
Distance: 🏖500m ⚓on the spot.

©S | **Ribera** | 34B6

Kamemi, SS115, Secca Grande. **GPS**: n37,43840 e13,24469.
🛒Camperstop € 8 🚰🗑Ch. ⬛ 01/01-31/12 ◉ 01/08-24/08 No
Camperstop

📷S | **Roccalumera** | 34C5

Park Jonio, Via Collegio, SS114 Roccalumera > Nizza di Sicilia.
GPS: n37,97943 e15,39752. ⬆➡.

60 🛒€ 13/24h, Jul/Aug € 15 🚰🗑Ch🧹 (60x) 🚿. **Surface:** gravel.
Distance: 🏖within walking distance ⚓250m ⊗Bar/snack 🍴on the spot.
Remarks: In front of Centro Sportivo.

🍴 | **San Giovanni La Punta** | 34C5

Entertainmentcity Isivillage, Via Fisichelli 63. **GPS**: n37,58929 e15,08612.
🛒guests free. **Surface:** asphalted.

📷S | **San Vito Lo Capo** | 34A6

Via Faro 36. **GPS**: n38,18472 e12,73277.

30 🛒Jun € 15, Jul € 20, Aug € 25 🚰🗑Ch🧹 included 🚿hot shower€1.
Surface: asphalted/grassy.
Distance: 🏖1km ⚓on the spot ⊗300m 🚰1km.
Remarks: Terrace on the sea, no beach, sandy beach 400m.

📷S | **San Vito Lo Capo** | 34A6

Via Savoia 13. **GPS**: n38,16222 e12,73666. ⬆.

90 🛒€ 10, Jun € 12, Jul € 15, Aug € 18 🚰🗑Ch🧹 (90x) WC 🚿€0,50 ◉€5.
Surface: gravel. ⬛ 01/01-31/12
Distance: 🏖300m ⚓1,4km ⊗1km 🚰1km.
Remarks: Free shuttle to beach.

📷 | **San Vito Lo Capo** | 34A6

Via la Piana. **GPS**: n38,16886 e12,74307.

🛒free. **Surface:** unpaved.
Distance: 🏖800m ⚓800m.
Remarks: Free shuttle to centre.

📷S | **Scicli** 🏖 | 34C6

Club Piccadilly, Via Mare Adriatico, Donnalucata. **GPS**: n36,74750 e14,66306. ⬆.
🛒€ 15-30 🚰🗑Ch🧹 WC 🚿 🍴. ⬛ 01/01-31/12
Distance: 🏖3km ⚓sandy beach 100m.

📷S | **Scopello** 🌿🏖 | 34A6

Fontana Andrea, Contrada Ciauli, SS 187. **GPS**: n38,05492 e12,84290. ⬆.
🛒€ 12/24h 🚰🗑Ch🧹 included. **Surface:** grassy. ⬛ 01/04-01/10
Distance: ⚓beach 300m.

📷S | **Scopello** 🌿🏖 | 34A6

Azienda agricola Plaia Antonella, Fraz. Scopello. **GPS**: n38,06777 e12,81777.
⬆➡.

20 € 15-20 Ch. **Surface:** metalled.

50 € 20/24h Ch included €1.
Surface: gravel.
01/05-30/09
Distance: historical centre 200m 1,5km 100m 400m.
Remarks: Farm products, shuttle to beach and Riserva dello Zingaro € 2,50/pp.

Siracusa 34D6

Parcheggio Von Platen, Via Augusto Von Platen 38. **GPS**: n37,07692 e15,28738.
€ 0,90/h.
Remarks: Near archeological site and museum.

S **Siracusa** 34D6

Via Procione 6, zona Golfetto, Fontane Bianche. **GPS**: n36,96361 e15,22027.
€ 20 Ch WC . **Surface:** unpaved.
Distance: Siracusa 15km on the spot on the spot.
Remarks: Bus to Siracusa, natural swimming pool in sea.

Siracusa 34D6

Area sosta Siracusa, Via Rodi 15. **GPS**: n37,06436 e15,28710.
€ 0,60/h, night € 1. **Surface:** asphalted. 01/01-31/12
Distance: Ortigia 500m 50m.

S **Sutera** 34B6

Piazza Rettore Carruba. **GPS**: n37,52450 e13,72960.
free Ch. **Surface:** asphalted.
Distance: on the spot on the spot.

S **Taormina** 34C5

Sosta Camper Pier Giovanni, Trappitello, Via Spagnuolo.
GPS: n37,82196 e15,24502.

15 € 10-15 Ch WC included. **Surface:** grassy/metalled.
01/01-31/12
Distance: 500m 4km 300m 300m.

S **Terme Vigliatore** 34C5

Area Trinacria, Via Lungomare Marchesana. **GPS**: n38,14018 e15,14596.

120 € 15, Aug € 18 Ch included. **Surface:** grassy.
01/01-31/12
Distance: 50m pizzeria 200m 200m.
Remarks: Excursion to the Eolie-islands.

S **Trapani** 34A6

Hotel Le Saline, SP21 km4, contrada Nubia-Paceco. **GPS**: n37,98304 e12,53106.

IT

SLOVENIA

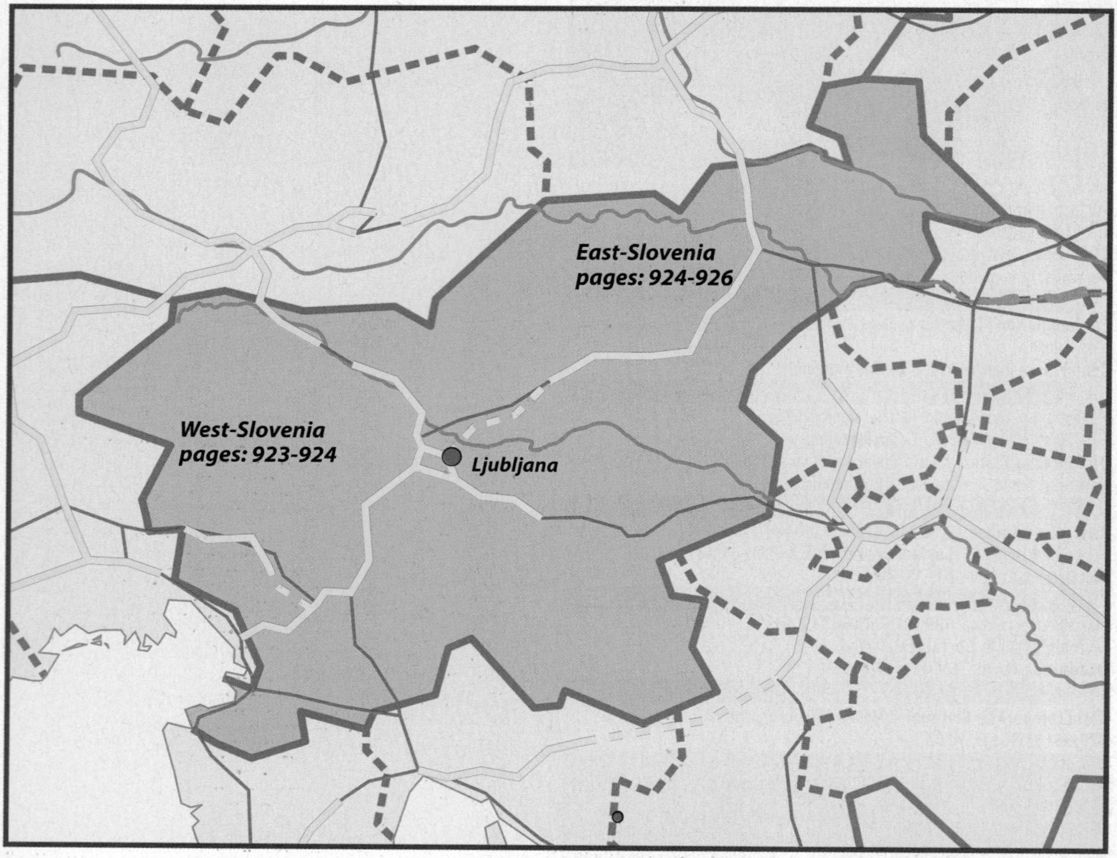

East-Slovenia
pages: 924-926

West-Slovenia
pages: 923-924

Ljubljana

Capital: Ljubljana
Government: parliamentarian republic
Official Language: Slovenian
Population: 2,060,000 (2013)
Area: 20,273 km²

General information
Dialling code: 00386
General emergency: 112
Currency: Euro
Credit card are accepted almost everywhere.

Regulations for overnight stays
There is no regulation against overnight camping, but it is not yet generally accepted. In the National Park Triglav wild camping is forbidden.

Additional public holidays 2015
February 8 Prešern Day - Slovenian cultural festival
April 27 Uprising against the Occupation Day
May 1-2 Labour Day
June 25 National Holiday
August 15 Assumption of the Virgin Mary
October 31 Reformation Day
November 1 All Saints' Day
December 26 Independence Day

S l o v e n i a

Slovenia West

⛺S   Bled 🌿⛰🏞   27A3
Bled, Kidričeva 10 c. **GPS:** n46,36162 e14,08221.
🛁€ 28,50-€ 31,50 🚰🔌Ch♿💳🚿.
⬤ 01/04-15/10
Distance: 🏊on the spot � on the spot ⊗on the spot 🍴on the spot.
Tourist information Bled:
Ⓜ Bled Castle. Exhibition about the history of Bled, during the summer also open-air concerts. ⬤ 8-17h.
🚶 Soteska Vintgar Gorge, TD Gorje, Podhom 0, Gorje. Trail over bridges and galleries along a river.

⛺S   Bohinjsko jezero ⛰🏞   27A3
Zlatorog. GPS: n46,27917 e13,83611.
🛁🚰🔌Ch♿ ⬤ 01/05-30/09
Distance: 🏊on the spot ⊗on the spot 🍴150m.
Tourist information Bohinjsko jezero:
🌊 Savica Falls. Water falls.

🛁S   Bovec ⛰🎯❄   26C4
Kanin Cable Car Station, Dvor. **GPS:** n46,33306 e13,53944.⬆➡

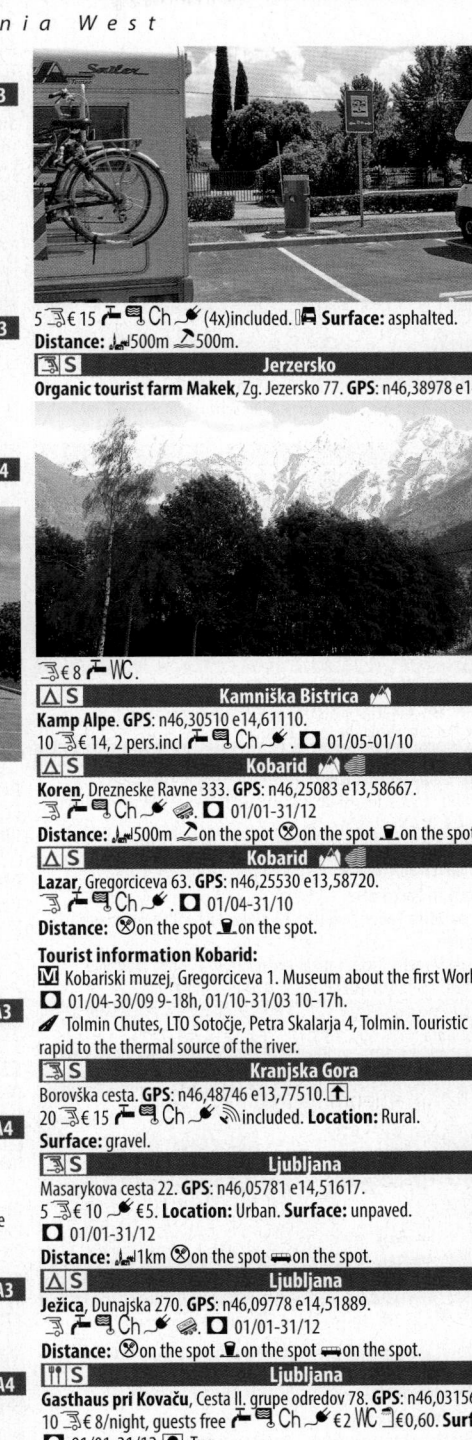

14 🛁€ 9/24h, € 12/36h 🚰🔌Ch♿ included.🏠
Location: Rural.
Surface: asphalted.
Distance: 🚴on the spot.
Remarks: Max. 36h.
Tourist information Bovec:
ℹ Triglav National Park, Dom Trenta, Soča. Information centre.
🏰 Kluže Fortress, Trg golobarskih žrtev 8. Fort above gorge.
🚶 Soča Trail, Soča.
Hiking trail along the Soca river.

5 🛁€ 15 🚰🔌Ch♿ (4x)included. 🏠 **Surface:** asphalted.
Distance: 🚶500m 🏊500m.

🛁S   Jerzersko   27A3
Organic tourist farm Makek, Zg. Jezersko 77. **GPS:** n46,38978 e14,50835.

🛁€ 8 🚰WC.

⛺S   Kamniška Bistrica ⛰   27A3
Kamp Alpe. GPS: n46,30510 e14,61110.
10 🛁€ 14, 2 pers.incl 🚰🔌Ch♿ ⬤ 01/05-01/10

⛺S   Kobarid ⛰   26C4
Koren, Drezneske Ravne 333. **GPS:** n46,25083 e13,58667.
🛁🚰🔌Ch♿💳. ⬤ 01/01-31/12
Distance: 🚶500m 🏊on the spot ⊗on the spot 🍴on the spot.

⛺S   Kobarid ⛰   26C4
Lazar, Gregorciceva 63. **GPS:** n46,25530 e13,58720.
🛁🚰🔌Ch♿. ⬤ 01/04-31/10
Distance: ⊗on the spot 🍴on the spot.
Tourist information Kobarid:
Ⓜ Kobariski muzej, Gregorciceva 1. Museum about the first World War.
⬤ 01/04-30/09 9-18h, 01/10-31/03 10-17h.
🚶 Tolmin Chutes, LTO Sotočje, Petra Skalarja 4, Tolmin. Touristic route along the rapid to the thermal source of the river.

🛁S   Kranjska Gora   27A3
Borovška cesta. GPS: n46,48746 e13,77510.⬆
20 🛁€ 15 🚰🔌Ch♿📶included. **Location:** Rural.
Surface: gravel.

🛁S   Ljubljana   27A3
Masarykova cesta 22. GPS: n46,05781 e14,51617.
5 🛁€ 10 ♿€5. **Location:** Urban. **Surface:** unpaved.
⬤ 01/01-31/12
Distance: 🚶1km ⊗on the spot 🚏on the spot.

🛁S   Ljubljana   27A3
Ježica, Dunajska 270. **GPS:** n46,09778 e14,51889.
🛁🚰🔌Ch♿💳 ⬤ 01/01-31/12
Distance: ⊗on the spot 🍴on the spot 🚏on the spot.

🍴S   Ljubljana   27A3
Gasthaus pri Kovaču, Cesta II. grupe odredov 78. **GPS:** n46,03156 e14,60428.
10 🛁€ 8/night, guests free 🚰🔌Ch♿ €2 WC🚿€0,60. **Surface:** grassy.
⬤ 01/01-31/12 🅾 Tue
Distance: 🚶8km 🚴2,5km ⊗on the spot 🚏on the spot.
Tourist information Ljubljana:
ℹ Ljubljana Tourist Card. Card offers among other things free public transport, free access at museums and discount in restaurants, shops etc. Available at Tourist Office, railway station and several hotels. 🎫 € 35/72h.
🏰 Ljubljana Castle. Medieval fortress, tourist train at town centre.
⬤ 01/10-30/04 10-21h, 01/05-30/09 9-22h.
🗼 Vodnikov trg. ⬤ daily, summer 6-18h, winter 6-16h.

🛁S   Domžale   27A3
ACG Autocenter Glavan, Češminova ulica 1a. **GPS:** n46,14671 e14,60082.
6 🛁free 🚰🔌🚿 voluntary contribution. **Location:** Simple.
Surface: asphalted. ⬤ 01/01-31/12
Distance: 🚶3km ⊗150m 🍴150m.

🛁S   Dornberk   27A4
Vina Saksida, Zalošče 12a. **GPS:** n45,88997 e13,74711.
10 🛁€ 10/pp 🚿WC🍴📶. **Location:** Rural, isolated.
Surface: metalled.
Distance: 🏊350m 🚶350m ⊗on the spot 🍴1km 🚴on the spot 🚶on the spot.
Remarks: Covered picnic area, swimming pool available.

⛺S   DovjeMojstrana   27A3
Kamne. GPS: n46,46444 e13,95778.
🛁🚰🔌Ch♿. ⬤ 01/01-31/12
Distance: ⊗1km 🍴1km.

🛁S   Hruševje   27A4
Penzion & Wellness Mirjam, Razdrto 19. **GPS:** n45,75690 e14,06126.⬆
5 🛁€ 11, 2 pers.incl, extra pers € 2 🚰🔌Ch♿🍴€1. **Location:** Rural.
Surface: grassy/gravel.
Distance: 🚶on the spot 🚶1km.

🍴S   Ilirska Bistrica   27A4
Okrepčevalnica Grill Danilo, Bazoviška cesta 46. **GPS:** n45,55822 e14,24311.
⬆➡
8 🛁€ 11, 2 pers.incl 🚰🔌Ch♿WC🍴. **Location:** Rural.
Surface: asphalted. ⬤ 01/01-31/12
Distance: 🚶800m ⊗on the spot.

🛁S   Izola   27A4
Cankarjev Drevored. **GPS:** n45,53806 e13,66444.⬆

SL

☺ Zoo Ljubljana. Zoo. ◘ summer 9-19h, winter 9-16h.

Locatec 27A4
A1. **GPS:** n45,89854 e14,25570.

6 ⌇free ⌁ WC ⌐free.
Distance: ◢100m. **Remarks:** Guarded parking petrol station LOM II, on both sides of the highway PO-LJ.

Luče 27A3
Camp Smica, Luče 4. **GPS:** n46,35644 e14,74290.
⌇ ⌁ Ch ⌁ ⌁. ◘ 01/05-30/10
Distance: ⌂on the spot ⊗on the spot ⌁900m.

Lukovica 27A3
OMV Istrabenz. GPS: n46,16690 e14,69380.⬆
2 ⌇free. **Location:** Highway, noisy.
Distance: ◢on the spot ⊗on the spot.
Remarks: Parking petrol station OMV Istrabenz.

Portorož 27A4
Strunjan, Strunjan 23. **GPS:** n45,52570 e13,61087.
⌇ ⌁Ch ⌁⌁. ◘ 01/01-31/12
Distance: ⌂on the spot ⊗on the spot ⌁100m.

Portorož 27A4
Marina Portorož, Cesta solinarjev 8. **GPS:** n45,50342 e13,59439.
⌇€ 16, 15/04-30/09 € 23 + tourist tax € 0,50/pp ⌁⌁Ch ⌁⌁included.
Surface: gravel. ◘ 01/01-31/12
Distance: ⌂on the spot ⌁on the spot ⊗on the spot ⌁on the spot.
Remarks: Swimming pool available.

Tourist information Portorož:
ℹ Turistična organizacija Koper, Verdijeva 10, Koper. City with a Venetian past and a lot of curiosities.
Ⓜ Pomorski muzej Sergej Mašera, Cankarjevo nabrežje 3, Piran. Maritime museum. ◘ 9-12h, 15-18h, 01/07-31/08 9-12h, 18-21h ◉ Mo.

Postojna 27A4
Park Postojnska Jama, Veliki Otok. **GPS:** n45,78066 e14,20322.⬆

20 ⌇€ 18/24h ⌁⌁Ch ⌁(20x)included. 🚐 **Surface:** concrete.
◘ 01/04-30/09
Distance: ⌁1km ◢3km.
Remarks: Postojna caves 300m.

Tourist information Postojna:
👁 Križna jama, Bloška polica 7, Grahovo. Largest water caves of Slovenia.
🏰 Perdjama Grad. Castle, 16th century and caves. ◘ 01/05-30/09 9-18, 01/10-30/04 10-16h.
⌒ Postojnska Jama, Jamska cesta 30. Postojna caves. ◘ 01/05-30/09 9-18, 01/10-30/04 10-16h.

Šmarje 27A4
Garni Mimosa, Srgaši 38a. **GPS:** n45,50870 e13,70576.⬆
10 ⌇€ 10. **Location:** Rural. **Surface:** metalled. ◘ 01/01-31/12
Distance: ⊗on the spot ⌁on the spot ☖on the spot.

Smlednik 27A3
Hotel Kanu, Valburga 7. **GPS:** n46,16932 e14,42185.⬆
15 ⌇€ 10 ⌁⌁Ch ⌁included. ⌁ **Location:** Rural, isolated, quiet.
Surface: grasstiles. ◘ 01/01-31/12
Distance: ◢5km ⊗on the spot.

Tolmin 27A3
Kamp Siber, Klanec 8. **GPS:** n46,18082 e13,73792.

50 ⌇€ 6/pp ⌁⌁Ch ⌁WC ⌐included. **Location:** Rural.
Surface: grassy/gravel. ◘ 01/01-31/12
Distance: ⌁1km ⌂on the spot ⌁1km.

Slovenia East

Braslovče 27A3
Najem & Kamping, Preserje 16b. **GPS:** n46,28918 e15,05492.
⌇€ 4/24h ⌁⌁Ch ⌁€5/day. **Location:** Rural, isolated.
Surface: grassy/gravel.
Distance: ⊗400m ⌁1km ⌁10km.
Remarks: At motorhome dealer.

Brestanica 27B3
Bazen Brestanica, Jetrno selo 2. **GPS:** n46,00124 e15,47492.
⌇ ⌁Ch ⌁. **Surface:** gravel.
Remarks: At swimming pool.

Brestanica 27B3
Ribiška družina Brestanica, Raztez 1a. **GPS:** n46,00504 e15,49751.
⌇. **Location:** Isolated, quiet. **Surface:** gravel.
Distance: ⌁on the spot ⌁on the spot.
Remarks: Fishpond.

Celje 27B3
Parking Glazija, Ljubljanska cesta 20. **GPS:** n46,23059 e15,26010.
4 ⌇€ 10 ⌁⌁included. 🚐 **Surface:** metalled.

Celje 27B3
Glavan center karavaninga, Obrtna cesta. **GPS:** n46,24406 e15,30217.⬆
5 ⌇€ 5/24h ⌁€1/100liter ⌁Ch ⌁€0,50/kWh. 🚐 **Surface:** gravel.
◘ 01/01-31/12
Distance: ⌁2km ⊗2km ⌁2km.
Remarks: At motorhome dealer.

Cirkulane 27B3
Herman Lederhaus, Dolane 8. **GPS:** n46,37114 e15,99682.
10 ⌇€ 10 ⌁⌁Ch ⌁WC ⌐. **Surface:** grassy/gravel. ◘ 01/01-31/12
Distance: ⌂on the spot ⌁on the spot ⊗on the spot ⌁50m.
Remarks: Restaurant and leather factory.

Dolenjske Toplice 27A4
Kamp Polje, Meniška vas. **GPS:** n45,76739 e15,05151.⬆

25 ⌇€ 8/24h ⌁⌁Ch. ⌁ **Location:** Rural, comfortable. **Surface:** unpaved.
◘ 01/03-15/11
Distance: ⌁800m ⌂on the spot ⌁on the spot ⊗800m ⌁800m ⌁on the spot ☖on the spot.
Remarks: Along the Krka river, terme Dolenjske Toplice 800m.

🏕️S Ivanjkovci 🏔️ 27B3

Vinoteka Svetinjska Klet, Svetinje 5. **GPS:** n46,46220 e16,16990. ⬆️.

5 🚐free 🔧. **Surface:** metalled.
Distance: ⊗on the spot.

🍴 Kamnica ⛵ 27B3

Gostilna Koblarjev Zaliv, Na otok 20. **GPS:** n46,56560 e15,61908.

20 🚐free, use of a meal desired. **Surface:** grassy.
🅿️ 01/01-31/12
Distance: 🚶Maribor 2km 🏊on the spot 🎣on the spot ⊗on the spot 🍴2km 🚌300m.
Remarks: Walking and bicycle area along the Drava river to Maribor centre.

S Krško 27B3

Raceland. **GPS:** n45,92977 e15,53500. ⬆️.
🚐🚰🍽️Ch🔧. **Location:** Rural, isolated. **Surface:** asphalted.
Distance: ⊗on the spot.
Remarks: Parking at Karting.

S Krško 27B3

Stadium Matija Gubec, Cesta krških žrtev 130a. **GPS:** n45,94691 e15,48832. ⬆️.
🚐. **Surface:** gravel. 🅿️ 01/01-31/12

🍴 Krško 27B3

Gostilna Stanislava Pečnik, Gunte 8. **GPS:** n45,98645 e15,46572.
🚐. 🅿️ Su
Distance: 🏊on the spot 🎣on the spot ⊗on the spot.

🍴S Laško 🏊⛲🍷 27B3

Wellness park Laško, Zdraviliška cesta 6. **GPS:** n46,16188 e15,23132. ⬆️.
14 🚐€ 10/day 🚰Ch🔧(4x)€4. **Surface:** metalled. 🅿️ 01/01-31/12
Distance: 🚶on the spot ⊗on the spot 🍴on the spot.
Remarks: Check in at reception.

🏕️S Laško 🏊⛲🍷 27B3

Zdraviliške Laško, Zdraviliška cesta 4. **GPS:** n46,15944 e15,23143.

4 🚐€ 10/day 🚰🔧(4x)€4 🗑️. 🅿️ 01/01-31/12 🔴 2nd week Jul
Distance: 🚶on the spot ⊗on the spot 🍴on the spot 🚌on the spot.

🏕️S Lendava 🍷 27B3

Terme Lendava. **GPS:** n46,55396 e16,45813. ⬆️.
🚐€ 24, 2 pers.incl 🚰🍽️Ch🔧€4. 🅿️ 01/01-31/12
Remarks: Including access spa resort.

🍴🍴S Ljutomer 27B3

Gostilna Trnek, Mota 76. **GPS:** n46,55516 e16,21929. ⬆️.

25 🚐guests free 🔧€3 WC 🍽️📶. **Location:** Rural, isolated, quiet.
Surface: grassy. 🅿️ 01/01-31/12
Distance: 🏊on the spot 🎣on the spot ⊗on the spot.

🏕️S Maribor 27B3

Avtobusna postaja Maribor, Mlinska ulica 1. **GPS:** n46,55852 e15,65573. ⬆️.
4 🚐€ 10 🔧. **Location:** Noisy. **Surface:** asphalted.
Distance: 🚶on the spot ⊗on the spot 🍴on the spot 🚌on the spot.
Remarks: Nearby bus station P4.

🍴S Moravske Toplice 27B3

Kamp Moravske Toplice, Kranjčeva ulica 12. **GPS:** n46,68298 e16,21953.
🚐€ 32, 2 pers.incl 🚰🍽️Ch🔧€4 🗑️. 🅿️ 01/01-31/12
Distance: ⊗100m 🍴200m.
Remarks: Including access spa resort 3000.

Tourist information Moravske Toplice:
🌿 Goričko Regional Park, Ulica ob igrišču 3, www.park-goricko.org. Information centre.

🏭S Obrežje Jug 27B3

OMV Istrabenz. **GPS:** n45,85517 e15,68513.
2 🚐free. **Location:** Noisy.
Distance: 🔧on the spot.
Remarks: Parking petrol station OMV Istrabenz.

🏕️S Ormož 27B3

Ob ribniku. **GPS:** n46,40588 e16,15963.
5 🚐free 🚰🔧. **Location:** Rural. **Surface:** asphalted. 🅿️ 01/01-31/12
Distance: 🏊on the spot 🎣on the spot.

🏕️S Podbočje 27B4

Turistična kmetija Hribar, Podbočje 36. **GPS:** n45,86190 e15,47110. ⬆️.
5 🚐. **Surface:** gravel.
Distance: 🚶400m.

🏕️ Podčetrtek 27B3

Golf Klub a Podčetrtek, Olimje 24. **GPS:** n46,14400 e15,56493. ⬆️.
5 🚐€ 10. **Location:** Isolated, quiet. **Surface:** asphalted/gravel.
Distance: ⊗on the spot 🚴on the spot 🏔️on the spot.
Remarks: At golf court, bicycle rental.

🍴S Podčetrtek 27B3

Terme Olimia Kamp Natura, Zdravilška cesta 24. **GPS:** n46,15830 e15,60690.
15 🚐€ 15,50/pp 🚰🍽️Ch🔧€3,20 🗑️. **Surface:** metalled.
🅿️ 21/04-30/09
Distance: ⊗on the spot 🍴on the spot.
Remarks: Including access spa resort € 30,80.

Tourist information Podčetrtek:
👁️ Sedovška Homestead, Aškercev trg 24, Šmarje pri Jelšah. Traditional farmstead.
✝️ Olimje Monastery and Pharmacy, Olimje 82. Monastery and one of the oldest pharmacies in the world.

🏕️S Podsmreka 27A3

A2. **GPS:** n45,94805 e14,77065.
5 🚐free 🚰free.
Distance: 🔧100m.
Remarks: Guarded parking petrol station Petrol Podsmereka, highway Novo Mesto-Ljubljana.

🔺S Prebold 27A3

Dolina, Dolenja Vas 147. **GPS:** n46,24018 e15,09268.
🚐🚰🍽️Ch🔧. 🅿️ 01/01-31/12
Distance: ⊗200m 🍴200m.

Camping Terme Ptuj - Ptuj

⛽S **Ptuj** 🏖️🍴 **27B3**

kamp@terme-ptuj.si - www.camping-slovenia.com

Located nearby spa
Excellent location for city visit
Medieval town

Camping Terme Ptuj, Pot v toplice 9. **GPS:** n46,42109 e15,85585.
20 🍴 € 23 6 pers incl 🚰 Ch 🔌(2x),16Amp WC 🚿included 🔌€5/5 🚿.
Location: Simple. **Surface:** gravel.
📅 01/01-31/12
Distance: 🏊800m 🏄 3km 🛒500m ⊗100m 🚌1km 🚲 on the spot 🚴25km.
Tourist information Ptuj:
ℹ️ Maribor Tourist Board, Partizanska 47, Maribor, www.maribor-tourism.si. Old
city with historical centre.
🏛️🎭 Mariborski Grad, Maribor. Castle, 15th century, regional museum.
📅 01/04-31/12 Tue-Sa 9-17h, Su 9-14h 🔲 Mo.
🏛️🎭 Ptujski Grad. Castle, 11th century with regional museum.
📅 01/05-31/10 9-18h.

△S **Rečica ob Savinji** **27A3**
Menina. GPS: n46,31167 e14,90917.
🍴 🚰 Ch 🔌 🚿. 📅 01/01-31/12
Distance: 🏊 on the spot ⊗on the spot 🍺300m.
Tourist information Rečica ob Savinji:
👁️ Mozirski gaj, Hribernikova 1, Mozirje. Botanical garden. 📅 01/04-31/10.
🅼 Musej Premogovništva, Stari jašek - Koroška cesta, Velenje. Coal mining
museum.

⛽S **Rogla** **27B3**
Rogla. **GPS:** n46,45259 e15,33117.⬆️.

🍴 🚰 Ch 🔌. **Surface:** gravel.
Distance: 🏊Zreče 10km.
Remarks: Altitude 1517m.

⛽S **Slovenj Gradec** **27A3**
Camperstop Slovenj Gradec, Ozare 18. **GPS:** n46,51418 e15,07678.⬆️➡️.

6 🍴€5 🚰 Ch 🔌(4x) 🚿included. **Location:** Comfortable, quiet.

📅 01/01-31/12
Distance: 🏊500m ⊗500m 🍺500m 🚲on the spot.
Remarks: At youth hostel.

⛽S **Solcava** **27A3**
Park Logarska Dolina, Logarska Dolina 9. **GPS:** n46,39870 e14,63100.⬆️.
🍴€ 10 🚰 🏕️ **Location:** Isolated.
Distance: 🚲on the spot 🚶on the spot.

⛽S **Stahovica** **27A3**
Pri Jurju, Kamniska Bistrica 5. **GPS:** n46,32695 e14,58685.
20 🍴€5 🚰 Ch 🔌 🚿 🏕️ **Location:** Simple, isolated, quiet.
Surface: grassy. **Distance:** 🚲on the spot 🚶on the spot.

⛽S **Tepanje** **27B3**
GPS: n46,34776 e15,48695.
5 🍴free 🚰free. **Location:** Noisy.
Distance: 🔌 on the spot.
Remarks: Guarded parking petrol station Petrol Tepanje I, on both sides of the
highway Maribor-Ljubljana.

⛽S **Visnja Gora** **27A3**
Kopaliska Ulica 25. **GPS:** n45,95258 e14,75210.

20 🍴 🚰 Ch 🔌 WC 🚿. **Location:** Rural. **Surface:** grassy/sand.
📅 01/01-31/12
Distance: 🏊on the spot 🚲1,7km ⊗on the spot.

⛽S **Žalec** **27A3**
Mestni trg. **GPS:** n46,25427 e15,16294.⬆️➡️.
🍴free 🚰 Ch free. **Surface:** metalled. 📅 01/01-31/12
Distance: 🏊500m ⊗500m 🍺700m.
Remarks: At sports park.

⛽S **Zdole** **27B3**
Etnoart tourism Špiler, Kostanjek 18. **GPS:** n46,01018 e15,54409.
🍴 🚰 🔌.
Distance: ⊗on the spot.

⛽S **Zdole** **27B3**
Gostilna pri Dularju, Kostanjek 20. **GPS:** n46,00975 e15,54155.
🍴 🚰 Ch 🔌.
Distance: ⊗on the spot.

⛽S **Zrece** **27B3**
Thermal Spa, Cesta na Roglo. **GPS:** n46,37096 e15,39021.

4 🍴€ 15 + tourist tax € 1,30/pp 🚰 🔌included. **Surface:** asphalted.
Remarks: 20% reduction swimming pool.

CROATIA

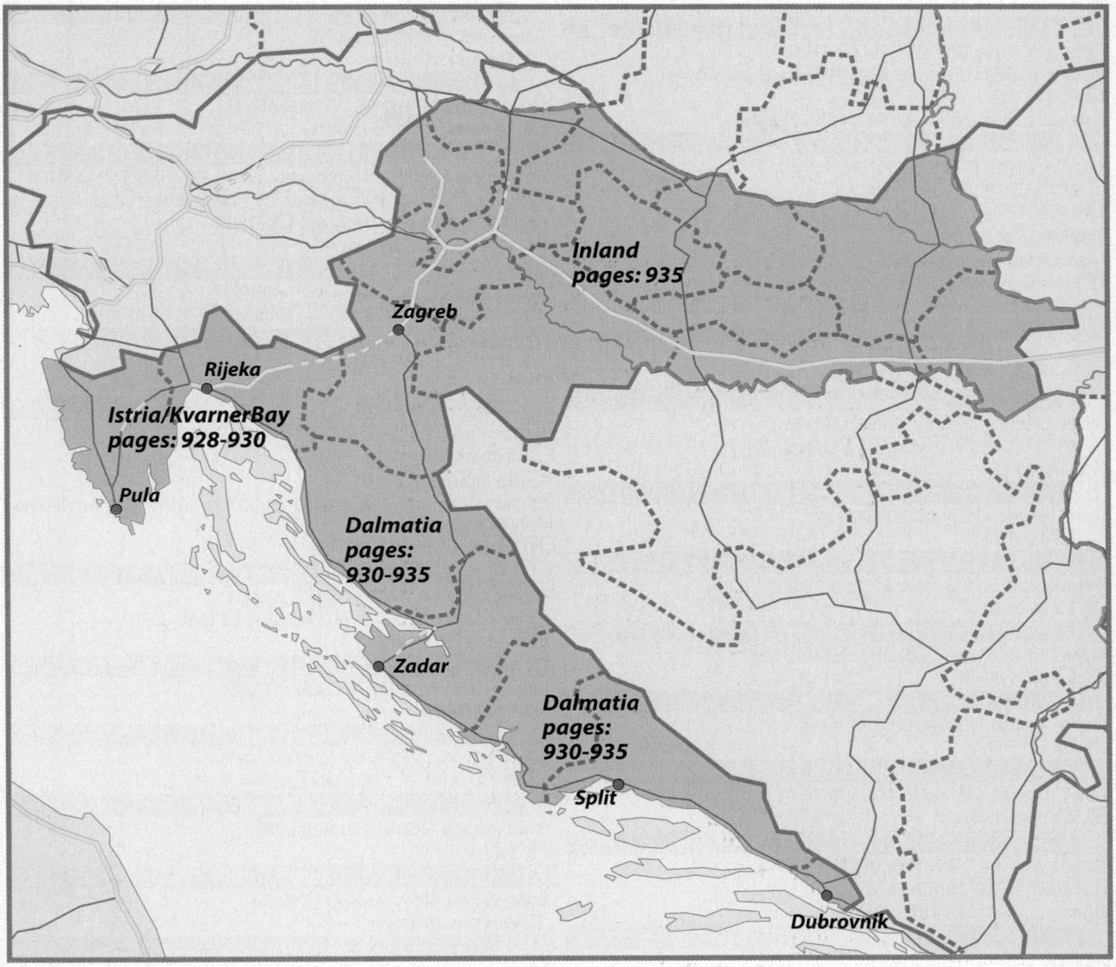

Map of Croatia showing regions:
- Istria/KvarnerBay pages: 928-930 (with Rijeka, Pula)
- Zagreb
- Inland pages: 935
- Dalmatia pages: 930-935 (with Zadar, Split, Dubrovnik)

Capital: Zagreb
Government: parliamentarian democracy
Official Language: Croatian
Population: 4,253,000 (2013)
Area: 56,594 km².

General information
Dialling code: 00385
General emergency: 112
Currency: Kuna, kn, 1 kuna = 100 lipa
1kn = € 0,13, € 1 = 7,64 kn (October 2014)
1kn = £0,10, £ 1 = 9,70 kn (October 2014)
Credit card are accepted almost everywhere.

Regulations for overnight stays
Wild camping is forbidden.

Additional public holidays 2015
January 6 Epiphany
May 1 Labor Day
June 4 Corpus Christi
June 22 Dan antifasisticke borbe, Anti-Fascist Resistance Day
June 25 Dan drzavnosti, National Holiday
August 5 Victorie Day and National Thanksgiving
August 15 Assumption of the Virgin Mary
October 8 Independence Day

Croatia

Istria/Kvarner Bay

🏕️S | **Baderna** | 27A4
Farm Pino, Olives & Oil, Katun 1. **GPS**: n45,21913 e13,72903.
20 🛏 € 10 + € 3/pp 🚿€4 🍽 Ch. **Surface**: metalled/sand.

🏕️ | **Bašanija** 🚤 | 26C6
Svjetionicarska ulica. **GPS**: n45,49064 e13,49190.
15 🛏 8-16. 🏖 **Location**: Rural, simple. **Surface**: grassy/gravel.
🅾 01/01-31/12
Distance: ⚓on the spot 🚐on the spot ⊗100m.

△S | **Cres/Cres** 🚤🚤 | 27A4
Kovačine, Melin I, 20. **GPS**: n44,96278 e14,39694.
🛏 🚿🍽 Ch 🛒 WC 🗑 📶included.
🅾 15/04-15/10
Distance: ⚓on the spot.

Tourist information Cres/Cres:
ℹ️ Turisticka zajednica, Riva Creskih Kapetana, www.tzg-cres.hr. Island can be reached with ferry service from Brestova, south of Rijeka and Valbiska, west Krk.

△S | **Cres/Martinščica** | 27A5
Slatina. **GPS**: n44,82091 e14,34238.
🛏 🚿🍽 Ch 🛒 WC 🗑 🧺. 🅾 15/04-31/10

△S | **Cres/Nerezine** | 27A5
Baldarin, Punta Križa. **GPS**: n44,61680 e14,50834.
🛏 🚿🍽 Ch 🛒 WC 🗑included. 🅾 15/04-01/10
Distance: ⚓3,5km ⚓on the spot.

△ | **Cres/Nerezine** | 27A5
Lopari, Nerezine. **GPS**: n44,68253 e14,39846.
🛏. 🅾 15/04-30/09

△ | **Cres/Nerezine** | 27A5
Preko Mosta, Osor 76, Nerezine. **GPS**: n44,69250 e14,39167.
🛏. 🅾 01/04-30/09

△ | **Cres/Nerezine** | 27A5
Rapoća, Rapoća, Nerezine. **GPS**: n44,66357 e14,39756.
🛏. 🅾 01/05-30/09

△ | **Cres/Valun** | 27A5
Zdovice, Valun bb. **GPS**: n44,90297 e14,36338.
🛏. 🅾 15/05-01/10

△ | **Crikvenica** 🏖🚤🚤 | 27A4
Kacjak, Kacjak BB. **GPS**: n45,16703 e14,70511.
🛏. 🅾 15/05-15/09

🏕️S | **Fažana** | 27A5
Ul.1.Maja. **GPS**: n44,92880 e13,80255.⬆️
15 🛏200kn WC. 🏖 **Surface**: asphalted.
Distance: ⚓400m ⚓on the spot ⊗on the spot.

△ | **Fažana** | 27A5
Bi Village, Dragonja 115. **GPS**: n44,91750 e13,81111.
🛏. 🅾 01/04-15/11

△ | **Fažana** | 27A5
Pineta Fažana, Perojska cesta bb. **GPS**: n44,93835 e13,79554.

🅾 22/04-30/09

Tourist information Fažana:
🌿 National Parc Brijuni, Brijuni. Nature reserve, boat connection from Fažana. 🅾 daily.

△ | **Ičiči** | 27A4
Opatija. **GPS**: n45,31083 e14,28472.
🛏. 🅾 01/04-01/10

🏕️S | **Jadruhi** | 27A4
Agroturizam Jadruhi, Jadruhi 11. **GPS**: n45,30084 e13,75017.⬆️➡️
5 🛏€ 7 🚿. **Location**: Rural, comfortable. **Surface**: gravel.
Distance: ⊗on the spot.

△ | **Klenovica** | 27A4
Klenovica, Zidinice BB. **GPS**: n45,09788 e14,84393.
🛏. 🅾 01/05-30/09
Distance: ⚓on the spot 🚐on the spot.

△ | **Koromačno** | 27A4
Tunarica. **GPS**: n44,96917 e14,09889.
🛏. 🅾 20/05-05/09

△ | **Kraljevica** | 27A4
Ostro. **GPS**: n45,27109 e14,56402.

🛏. 🅾 01/05-30/09

△ | **Krk/Baška** 🚤🚤 | 27A4
Zablace, Emila Geitslicha 34, Baška. **GPS**: n44,96694 e14,74528.
🅾 01/05-01/10

△ | **Krk/Klimno** | 27A4
Slamni. **GPS**: n45,15351 e14,61770.
🛏. **Remarks**: Mini-camp.

△ | **Krk/Klimno** | 27A4
Slamni, Klimno 8a. **GPS**: n45,15364 e14,61721.
🛏. **Remarks**: Mini-camp.

🏕️S | **Krk/Krk** 🏖🚤🚤 | 27A4
Camper Stop Felix, Ulica Narodnog preporoda 51. **GPS**: n45,02928 e14,58149.
12 🛏€ 25 🚿🍽 Ch 🛒 WC included 🗑 📶. 🏖 **Location**: Urban, comfortable. **Surface**: grassy/gravel. 🅾 01/01-31/12
Distance: 🚐300m ⚓300m.

△S | **Krk/Krk** 🏖🚤🚤 | 27A4
Jezevac, Plavnička bb. **GPS**: n45,01877 e14,56684.
🛏from € 20,30 🚿🍽 Ch 🛒 WC 🗑included. 🅾 01/05-30/09

△ | **Krk/Krk** 🏖🚤🚤 | 27A4
Bor. **GPS**: n45,02250 e14,56194.
🛏. 🅾 01/01-31/12

△ | **Krk/Krk** 🏖🚤🚤 | 27A4
Marta, Škrbcici 29. **GPS**: n45,04930 e14,48940.
🛏. **Remarks**: Mini-camp.

Tourist information Krk/Krk:
ℹ️ Tourist Information, Vela placa 1/1, www.krk.hr. Krk accessible via toll-bridge south-east from Rijeka.
🎵 Jazz-festival, Kamplin. 🅾 Aug.

△S | **Krk/Malinska** 🚤🚤 | 27A4
Glavotok, Glavokok 4. **GPS**: n45,09472 e14,44111.
🛏from € 20 🚿🍽 Ch 🛒 WC 🗑included. 🅾 01/05-30/09
Distance: ⚓on the spot.

△ | **Krk/Malinska** 🚤🚤 | 27A4
Draga, Palih Boraca 4. **GPS**: n45,12052 e14,52494.
🛏. **Remarks**: Mini-camp.

△S | **Krk/Njivice** | 27A4
Njivice, Primorska bb. **GPS**: n45,16963 e14,54740.
🛏 🚿🍽 Ch 🛒 WC 🗑included. 🅾 20/04-01/10

△ | **Krk/Omišalj** | 27A4
Pusca, Pušča bb. **GPS**: n45,23613 e14,55108.
🛏. 🅾 01/06-30/09

△ | **Krk/Pinezici** | 27A5
Amar, Njivine 8. **GPS**: n44,96484 e13,93448.
🛏. **Remarks**: Mini-camp.

△S | **Krk/Punat** 🚤🚤 | 27A4
Pila, Setalište Ivana Brusića. **GPS**: n45,01581 e14,62860.
250 🛏from € 20 🚿 Ch 🛒 included. 🅾 15/04-30/09

△S | **Krk/Punat** 🚤🚤 | 27A4
Škrila, Stara Baška. **GPS**: n44,96611 e14,67389.
350 🛏 🚿🍽 Ch 🛒. 🅾 01/05-30/09

△ | **Krk/Punat** 🚤🚤 | 27A4
Maslinik, Nikole Tesle 1. **GPS**: n45,01809 e14,63478.
🛏. **Remarks**: Mini-camp.

Tourist information Krk/Punat:
✝ Otočić Košljun. Monastery.

△ | **Krk/Šilo** | 27A4
Tiha Šilo, Konjska bb. **GPS**: n45,14876 e14,67150.
🛏. **Remarks**: Mini-camp.

🏕️ | **Labin** 🏖 | 27A4
Tunarica, Rudarska 1. **GPS**: n44,96933 e14,09979.
🛏.

△ | **Labin** 🏖 | 27A4
Marina. **GPS**: n45,03333 e14,15806.
🛏.
🅾 15/04-30/09

Tourist information Labin:
Ⓜ Narodni muzej, N. Katunara 6. Ethnological museum. 🅾 daily 10-13h, 17-19h.

HR

Lošinj/Mali Lošinj — 27A5
Kredo. GPS: n44,53444 e14,44751.

🛅. ⬛ 01/01-31/12
Distance: 🚶2km 🏖on the spot. **Remarks**: Mini-camp.

Lošinj/Mali Lošinj — 27A5
Čikat. GPS: n44,53750 e14,45056.
940 🛅from € 18,40 🔌 Ch WC included. ⬛ 15/04-15/10

Lošinj/Mali Lošinj — 27A5
Poljana. GPS: n44,55556 e14,44167.
🛅from € 17,85 🔌 Ch WC included. ⬛ 01/05-30/09

Tourist information Lošinj/Mali Lošinj:
☀ Dolphins day, action day with possibility for adoption of a dolphin.

Medulin — 27A5
Kazela. GPS: n44,80695 e13,95015.
🛅🔌 Ch WC included. ⬛ 01/04-15/10

Medulin — 27A5
Medulin. GPS: n44,81417 e13,93194.
1500 🛅🔌 Ch WC included. ⬛ 03/04-09/10

Medulin — 27A5
Indie, Banjole. **GPS**: n44,82398 e13,85090.
🛅. ⬛ 01/05-01/10

Medulin — 27A5
Kranjski Kamp, Runke 52, Premantura. **GPS**: n44,80694 e13,91616.
🛅. **Remarks**: Mini-camp.

Medulin — 27A5
Piškera, Indie 49, Banjole. **GPS**: n44,82332 e13,84855.
🛅. **Remarks**: Mini-camp.

Medulin — 27A5
Pomer, Pomer. **GPS**: n44,82064 e13,90205.
🛅. **Remarks**: Mini-camp.

Medulin — 27A5
Postolovic, Bumbište 10. **GPS**: n44,82037 e13,85749.
🛅. **Remarks**: Mini-camp.

Medulin — 27A5
Runke, Premantura. **GPS**: n44,80742 e13,91632.
🛅. ⬛ 01/05-30/09

Medulin — 27A5
Širola, Rupice Bd. **GPS**: n44,82113 e13,85872.
🛅. **Remarks**: Mini-camp.

Medulin — 27A5
Stupice, Premantura. **GPS**: n44,79779 e13,91354.
🛅. ⬛ 01/05-25/09

Medulin — 27A5
Tasalera, Premantura. **GPS**: n44,81425 e13,91275.
🛅. ⬛ 01/04-30/09

Tourist information Medulin:
ℹ Premantura. Most Southern place of Istria.
👁 Banjole. Fisherman's village with natural harbour.

Moščenička Draga — 27A4
Draga. GPS: n45,24023 e14,25021.
🛅. **Remarks**: Mini-camp.

Moščenička Draga — 27A4
Draga. GPS: n45,24000 e14,25028.
165 🛅. ⬛ 15/04-15/10

Motovun — 27A4
Motovun, Rizanske skupstine. **GPS**: n45,33507 e13,82498.

---

10 🛅 € 23,40 🔌 Ch WC 📶free. **Location**: Rural, comfortable.
Surface: gravel. ⬛ 01/01-31/12
Distance: 🚶50m 🏖50m.

Novi Vinodolski — 27A4
Autocamp Sibinje, Sibinj. **GPS**: n45,04405 e14,87751.
🛅.
Distance: 🏖on the spot ⊗50m 🚊50m. **Remarks**: Mini-camp.

Novi Vinodolski — 27A4
Punta. GPS: n45,11587 e14,84725.
🛅. ⬛ 01/06-30/09
Distance: 🏖on the spot 🚊3km. **Remarks**: Mini-camp.

Novigrad (Istria) — 26C6
Mareda. GPS: n45,34149 e13,54610.
800 🛅from € 17 🔌 Ch WC included. ⬛ 15/04-30/09

Novigrad (Istria) — 26C6
Sirena. GPS: n45,31528 e13,57556.
🛅🔌 Ch WC included. ⬛ 01/04-30/09

Tourist information Novigrad (Istria):
🌿 Farmers market. ⬛ daily.
☀ Pelegrinus, Umag. ⬛ 23/05.

Poreč — 27A4
30. Travinja/Karla Huguesa. **GPS**: n45,22186 e13,60700.

🛅120kn 🔌. **Surface**: asphalted.
Distance: 🚶800m ⊗400m.

Poreč — 27A4
Bijela Uvala. GPS: n45,19139 e13,59667.
2000 🛅from € 20 🔌 Ch WC included. ⬛ 01/04-15/10

Poreč — 27A4
Laternacamp. GPS: n45,29639 e13,59444.
3000 🛅from € 22,65 🔌 Ch WC included. ⬛ 01/04-15/10

Poreč — 27A4
Puntica, Funtana. **GPS**: n45,17749 e13,60406.
250 🛅🔌 Ch 🛠. ⬛ 11/04-13/10

Poreč — 27A4
Zelena Laguna. GPS: n45,19611 e13,58917.
1000 🛅from € 20 🔌 Ch WC included. ⬛ 01/04-15/10

Poreč — 27A4
Materada, Materada. **GPS**: n45,24628 e13,59600.
🛅. **Remarks**: Mini-camp.

Tourist information Poreč:
ℹ Turisticka zajednica, Zagrebacka 9, www.istra.com/porec. Old city, centre tourist and cultural.
👁 Decumanus. Roman main street with palazzi from the Venetian time.
Ⓜ🏛 Zavicajnog muzeja poreštine. Native museum of Porec.
⬛ daily 10-13h, 18-22h.
✝ Eufrazijeva bazilika. Basilica, 6th century, in the centre.

HR

HR

daily 7-19h.

| △ S | Pula | 27A5 |
Puntižela. GPS: n44,89806 e13,80722.
Ch WC included. 01/05-31/10

| △ S | Pula | 27A5 |
Stoja. GPS: n44,86000 e13,81472.
750 Ch WC included.
03/04-02/11

Tourist information Pula:
M Arheoloski Muzej Istre, Carrarina 3. Archeological museum.
winter Mo-Fri 9-14h, summer Mo-Sa 9-19h.
Amfiteatar. Large anfiteatro from Roman time. daily 8-21h.
Ljetni klasicni Festival, Amfitheatar. Opera festival. Aug.

| △ | Rab | 27A5 |
Mel, Kampor 319. GPS: n44,79390 e14,70302.
Remarks: Mini-camp.

| △ | Rab | 27A5 |
Planka, Kampor 326. GPS: n44,78049 e14,72048.
Remarks: Mini-camp.

| △ S | Rabac | 27A4 |
Oliva. GPS: n45,07960 e14,14777.
300 Ch WC. 15/03-30/09
Distance: on the spot.

| △ | Rijeka | 27A4 |
Preluk Katalinic, Preluk 1. GPS: n45,35340 e14,33235.
Remarks: Mini-camp.

Tourist information Rijeka:
Tourist Information, Kastav 47, Kastav. Walled city with rich history.
M Pomorski i povijesni muzej, Muzejski trg 1. Navy museum. Mo-Fri 10-13h, 18-21h.
Velika trznica. Market opposite to Modello palace.
Carnival of Rijeka. Feb.

| △ S | Rovinj | 27A4 |
Aleja Ruera Boskovica. GPS: n45,08861 e13,64478.
30 25kn 6-23h Ch. Location: Urban. Surface: asphalted.
01/01-31/12
Distance: centre 1,2km 300m.

| © S | Rovinj | 27A4 |
Camping Polari. GPS: n45,06300 e13,67480.

87kn-174kn, Fr-Sa + 20% Ch. Surface: grassy.
22/03-02/10
Distance: on the spot.
Remarks: Camperstop max. 48h.

| △ S | Rovinj | 27A4 |
Mon Paradiso, Uvala Veštar. GPS: n45,04947 e13,69000.
40 Ch. 01/06-30/09 Remarks: Mini-camp.

| △ S | Rovinj | 27A4 |
Polari. GPS: n45,06258 e13,67477.
2150 Ch WC included. 01/04-30/09

| △ S | Rovinj | 27A4 |
Porton Biondi. GPS: n45,09410 e13,64232.
Ch WC included. 01/04-30/09

| △ S | Rovinj | 27A4 |
Valdaliso. GPS: n45,10389 e13,62500.
400 Ch WC included. 20/04-15/10

| △ S | Rovinj | 27A4 |
Vestar. GPS: n45,05389 e13,68639.
800 Ch WC included. 15/04-30/09

| △ S | Rovinj | 27A4 |
Ulika, Polari Bd. GPS: n45,06528 e13,67583.
01/04-01/10 Remarks: Mini-camp.

| © S | Rovinj | 27A4 |
Cesta ža Valaltu-Lim. GPS: n45,10500 e13,64608.

15 10 Ch WC included. Location: Quiet. Surface: grassy.
01/05-31/08
Distance: 1km 500m 1km 500m.

Tourist information Rovinj:
Turisticka zajednica, Budicin 12, www.istra.com/rovinj. City has been a cultural monument since 1963.
Aquarium, Obala G. Paliage 5. daily 9-21h.
Palazzo Califfi, Trg Marsala Tita 11. Tue-Su 10.30-14h, summer 18-20h.
Market.
Grisia, Grisia. Art festival. 2nd week Aug.

| △ S | Savudrija | 26C6 |
Pineta. GPS: n45,48667 e13,49250.
from € 16,50 Ch WC included. 15/04-30/09

| △ | Savudrija | 26C6 |
Ravna Dolina. GPS: n45,49246 e13,50490.
01/05-30/09

| △ | Savudrija | 26C6 |
Veli Jože, Borozija. GPS: n45,49556 e13,50444.
01/04-30/09

| △ | Selce | 27A4 |
Selce. GPS: n45,15408 e14,72533.
01/04-31/10

| △ | Umag | 26C6 |
Finida. GPS: n45,39278 e13,54194.
Ch WC included. 15/04-30/09

| △ S | Umag | 26C6 |
Stella Maris. GPS: n45,45056 e13,52278.
400 Ch WC included. 15/04-15/10

| © S | Vrsar | 27A4 |
Camping Valkanela. GPS: n45,16509 e13,60871.

€ 10, Jun € 14,50, Jul-Aug € 20 + tourist tax Ch included.
Surface: grassy. 23/04-23/09
Distance: on the spot.
Remarks: Camperstop, max. 48h, use camp-site facilities incl.

| △ S | Vrsar | 27A4 |
Porto Sole. GPS: n45,14139 e13,60222.
800 Ch WC included. 15/04-30/09

Dalmatia

| △ | Babino Polje | 27D6 |
Marina, Ropa 11. GPS: n42,73543 e17,54650.
Remarks: Mini-camp.

Babino Polje — 27D6
Mungos. GPS: n42,73885 e17,53441.
€ 31. **Remarks**: Mini-camp.

Baška Voda — 27C6
Basko Polje. GPS: n43,34878 e16,96478.
. 15/05-30/09

Bibinje — 27B5
Andela. GPS: n44,06889 e15,29464.
. **Remarks**: Mini-camp.

Bibinje — 27B5
Dido, Težački put. **GPS**: n44,05670 e15,29008.
. **Remarks**: Mini-camp.

Bibinje — 27B5
Kero, Punta Bibinje. **GPS**: n44,05730 e15,28918.
. **Remarks**: Mini-camp.

Bibinje — 27B5
Punta, Težački put. **GPS**: n44,05680 e15,29162.
. **Remarks**: Mini-camp.

Biograd na Moru — 27B5
Dijana & Josip, Put Solina 26. **GPS**: n43,93422 e15,44828.
. **Remarks**: Mini-camp.

Biograd na Moru — 27B5
Ljutic, Put Solina. **GPS**: n43,92654 e15,45353.
. **Remarks**: Mini-camp.

Biograd na Moru — 27B5
Mia, Put Solina 47. **GPS**: n43,93441 e15,44803.
. **Remarks**: Mini-camp.

Biograd na Moru — 27B5
Soline, Put Kumenta. **GPS**: n43,92756 e15,45595.
. 01/05-30/09

Bol — 27C6
Kito, Ante Radića 1. **GPS**: n43,26407 e16,64820.
. 01/05-31/10

Drace-Pelješac — 27C6
Plaža, Janjina. **GPS**: n42,92477 e17,43079.
. **Remarks**: Mini-camp.

Dubrovnik — 27D6
Solitudo, Vatroslava Lisinskog 17. **GPS**: n42,66178 e18,07052.

01/04-31/10

Tourist information Dubrovnik:
Aquarium, D. Jude 2. Mo-Sa 9-13h.
City Walls, Gunduličeva poljana 2. City wall surround the entire Old City.
10-15h, 01/04-31/10 9-18.30h.
Place Stradun. Main street with Onofrio-fountain and Sveti Frane monastery.
Dubrovacki Muzej, Pred Dvorom 3. History of the city.
Mo-Sa 9-14h.
Pomorski Muzej, Sveti Ivan. Shipping museum. Tue-Sa 9-13h.
Summer Festival. 10/07-25.08.

Dugi Rat — 27C6
Ivo, Duce Rogac. **GPS**: n43,44111 e16,65778.
. **Remarks**: Mini-camp.

Dugi Rat — 27C6
Luka, Duce Rogac. **GPS**: n43,44164 e16,65347.
. **Remarks**: Mini-camp.

Dugi Rat — 27C6
Orij, Orij, Duce Rogac. **GPS**: n43,44631 e16,63429.
. **Remarks**: Mini-camp.

Grebaštica — 27B6
Ante&Toni, Brodarica. **GPS**: n43,63833 e15,95833.
. 01/05-01/10
Distance: 100m on the spot. **Remarks**: Mini-camp.

Grebaštica — 27B6
Tomas, D8. **GPS**: n43,62986 e15,95443.
.
Distance: on the spot. **Remarks**: Mini-camp.

Kaštel Kambelovac — 27C6
U Dragama, A. Starcevica 39. **GPS**: n43,55053 e16,37676.
. **Remarks**: Mini-camp.

Kaštel Štafilic — 27C6
Koludrovac, Resnik Bb. **GPS**: n43,54281 e16,31844.
. **Remarks**: Mini-camp.

Kaštel Stari — 27C6
Adria. GPS: n43,55143 e16,35349.
. **Remarks**: Mini-camp.

Kaštel Stari — 27C6
Kamp- Biluš Josip. GPS: n43,55162 e16,34978.
. **Remarks**: Mini-camp.

Kolan — 27B5
Sveti Duh. GPS: n44,51518 e14,95525.
. **Remarks**: Mini-camp.

Korčula — 27C6
Kalac. GPS: n42,95056 e17,14500.
. 01/06-01/10

Korčula — 27C6
Oskorušica, Oskorušica 27/ VI, Račišce. **GPS**: n42,96795 e17,07335.
. **Remarks**: Mini-camp.

Korčula — 27C6
Vela Postrana, Lumbardra 142. **GPS**: n42,92230 e17,17266.
. **Remarks**: Mini-camp.

Tourist information Korčula:
Turisticka zajednica, Obala Tudmana, www.korcula.net. City with historical centre, birth-place Marco Polo.
Marco Polo fest. 09/07-11/07.
Sword dance festival. daily 04/07-23/08.

Korenica — 27B5
Bistro Marina. GPS: n44,74702 e15,70464.
10 . **Location**: Urban. **Surface**: metalled.
Distance: 100m.
Remarks: Guests free.

Kornati/Murter — 27B5
Slanica, Jurija Dalmatinca 17. **GPS**: n43,81682 e15,57733.
from € 14,30 WC included. 01/05-15/10

Kornati/Murter — 27B5
Jazina, Tisno. **GPS**: n43,80940 e15,62760.
. 01/05-30/09

Kornati/Murter — 27B5
Jezera-Lovišča, Jezera. **GPS**: n43,79370 e15,62867.
. 15/04-15/10

Kornati/Murter — 27B5
Kosirina, Betina. **GPS**: n43,79727 e15,61004.
. 01/05-30/09

Kornati/Murter — 27B5
Plitka Vala, Betina. **GPS**: n43,80515 e15,61284.
. 15/04-15/10

Kucište — 27C6
Palme. GPS: n42,97639 e17,12917.
. 01/06-01/10

Kucište — 27C6
Plaža, Viganj 4, Od Gaja. **GPS**: n42,97935 e17,10400.
. **Remarks**: Mini-camp.

Lokva Rogoznica — 27C6
Danijel, Ruskamen bb. **GPS**: n43,40973 e16,74529.
. **Remarks**: Mini-camp.

Lokva Rogoznica — 27C6
Linda. GPS: n43,40817 e16,75485.
. **Remarks**: Mini-camp.

Lovište — 27C6
Lupiš. GPS: n43,02790 e17,03012.
. **Remarks**: Mini-camp.

Lukoran — 27B5
Novi Kamp, Punta 28. **GPS**: n44,10538 e15,15518.
. **Remarks**: Mini-camp.

Mlini — 27D6
Kate, Tupina 1. **GPS**: n42,62472 e18,20806.
. **Remarks**: Mini-camp.

Mlini — 27D6
Kupari, Kupari bb. **GPS**: n42,62462 e18,18833.

HR

🏕 🔲 01/04-30/09 **Remarks:** Mini-camp.

Mlini	27D6

Matkovica, Srebreno 8. **GPS:** n42,62450 e18,19295.
🏕. **Remarks:** Mini-camp.

Mlini	27D6

Paradiso Laguna, Za Gospom, Plat. **GPS:** n42,60759 e18,22838.
🏕. **Remarks:** Mini-camp.

Mlini	27D6

Porto, Srebreno. **GPS:** n42,62433 e18,19107.
🏕. **Remarks:** Mini-camp.

Mljet	27C6

Marina, Marina Matana,Ropa 11. **GPS:** n42,75260 e17,46000.
🏕. **Remarks:** Mini-camp.

Mokalo	27C6

Adriatic. **GPS:** n42,97694 e17,22500.
🏕. 🔲 01/04-31/10

Molunat	27D6

Adriatic II. **GPS:** n42,45327 e18,43582.
🏕. **Remarks:** Mini-camp.

Molunat	27D6

Adriatic I, Višnjici 4, Đurinici. **GPS:** n42,45341 e18,43554.
🏕. **Remarks:** Mini-camp.

Molunat	27D6

Monika, Molunat 10. **GPS:** n42,45284 e18,42871.
🏕. **Remarks:** Mini-camp.

Nin	27B5

Dišpet, Put Ždrijaca 13. **GPS:** n44,24618 e15,18971.
🏕. **Remarks:** Mini-camp.

Nin	27B5

Nin, Put Venere Anzotike 41. **GPS:** n44,24541 e15,17401.
🏕. **Remarks:** Mini-camp.

Nin	27B5

Ninska Laguna, Put blata 10. **GPS:** n44,24639 e15,17389.
🏕 11 - € 18. **Remarks:** Mini-camp.

Tourist information Nin:
Ⓜ Arheološka zbirka Nin, Trg Kraljevac 8. Archeological museum.
🔲 01/10-31/5 8-14h, 01/06-30/09 8-22h.

Novigrad (Dalmatia)	27B5

Adria-Sol Mulic. **GPS:** n44,18472 e15,54944.
🏕. **Remarks:** Mini-camp.

Omiš	27C6

Galeb. **GPS:** n43,44061 e16,68128.
🏕.

Omiš	27C6

Lisičina, Lisičina 2. **GPS:** n43,44737 e16,69038.
🏕. 🔲 01/01-31/12 **Remarks:** Mini-camp.

Opuzen	27D6

Rio, Put Zlatinovca 23. **GPS:** n43,02227 e17,55136.
🏕. 🔲 01/05-01/10

Orašac	27D6

Pod Maslinom, Put prema moru b.b. **GPS:** n42,69907 e18,00592.
🏕. 🔲 01/05-30/09 **Remarks:** Mini-camp.

Pag	27B5

Košljun, Košljun B.B.. **GPS:** n44,39849 e15,07936.
🏕. **Remarks:** Mini-camp.

Pag	27B5

Pere, Dinjiška. **GPS:** n44,35939 e15,18641.
🏕. **Remarks:** Mini-camp.

Pag	27B5

Porat, Stjepana Radića bb., Povljana. **GPS:** n44,34551 e15,10869.
🏕. **Remarks:** Mini-camp.

Pag	27B5

Simuni, V. Nazora b.b, Simuni. **GPS:** n44,43766 e15,05408.
🏕. 🔲 04/04-01/10.

Pakoštane	27B5

Kozarica. **GPS:** n43,90970 e15,49881.
🏕from € 15,70 🔌 Ch WC included. 🔲 15/04-15/10

Pakoštane	27B5

Blaž. **GPS:** n43,90763 e15,50089.

🏕. **Remarks:** Mini-camp.

Pakoštane	27B5

Marin. **GPS:** n43,90445 e15,51750.
🏕. **Remarks:** Mini-camp.

Pakoštane	27B5

Nordsee. **GPS:** n43,90525 e15,51617.
🏕. 🔲 01/04-03/10

Pakoštane	27B5

Oaza Mira, Dr. Franje Tuđmana bb, Drage. **GPS:** n43,88607 e15,53290.
🏕. **Remarks:** Mini-camp.

Pakoštane	27B5

Oaza, Drage. **GPS:** n43,87035 e15,55917.
🏕. 🔲 01/04-15/10 **Remarks:** Mini-camp.

Pakoštane	27B5

Pakoštane. **GPS:** n43,91258 e15,49772.
🏕. **Remarks:** Mini-camp.

Pelješac/Orebić	27C6

Glavna Plaža. **GPS:** n42,97583 e17,18917.
🏕from € 15 🔌 Ch WC included. 🔲 15/05-01/10

Pelješac/Orebić	27C6

Trstenica, Šetalište Kneza Domagoja 50. **GPS:** n42,98095 e17,19435.
🏕 🔌 Ch WC included. **Remarks:** Mini-camp.

Pelješac/Orebić	27C6

Paradiso. **GPS:** n42,97475 e17,23497.
🏕. **Remarks:** Mini-camp.

Pelješac/Orebić	27C6

Paradiso, Obala Pomoraca 70 A. **GPS:** n42,96693 e17,24230.
🏕. **Remarks:** Mini-camp.

Pelješac/Orebić	27C6

Perna. **GPS:** n42,97638 e17,13272.
🏕. 🔲 17/04-30/09

Pelješac/Trpanj	27C6

Divna. **GPS:** n43,00944 e17,26806.
🏕. **Remarks:** Mini-camp.

Pelješac/Trpanj	27C6

Vrila. **GPS:** n43,00360 e17,28467.
🏕. 🔲 20/05-10/10

Petrcane	27B5

Pineta, Punta Radman 21. **GPS:** n44,18362 e15,16291.
🏕. **Remarks:** Mini-camp.

Podgora	27C6

Sutikla. **GPS:** n43,23590 e17,07833.
🏕. 🔲 01/05-30/09

Podstrana	27C6

Car, Sv. Martin 180. **GPS:** n43,47479 e16,56624.
🏕. **Remarks:** Mini-camp.

Podstrana	27C6

Tamaris, Sv.Martin 114. **GPS:** n43,47551 e16,56383.
50 🏕from € 16,50. 🔲 01/01-31/12
Distance: on the spot. **Remarks:** Mini-camp.

Tourist information Podstrana:
Sinjska alka, Sinj. Knight celebration. 🔲 5th August.

Posedarje	27B5

Bristi. **GPS:** n44,21231 e15,48038.
🏕. **Remarks:** Mini-camp.

Posedarje	27B5

Kristina. **GPS:** n44,00000 e15,47961.
🏕. **Remarks:** Mini-camp.

Povijana	27B5

Mali Dubrovnik, Kralja P. Svacica 1. **GPS:** n44,34931 e15,10060.
🏕. **Remarks:** Mini-camp.

Povijana	27B5

Porat, Ante Starcevica Bb. **GPS:** n44,34560 e15,10897.
🏕. **Remarks:** Mini-camp.

Primošten	27B6

Zagrebacka ul.. **GPS:** n43,58854 e15,92632.
10 🏕 € 7/24h.
Distance: 200m 200m 200m 200m.

HR

△S	Primošten	27B6

Adriatic, Huljerat b.b.. **GPS:** n43,60645 e15,92193.
🛏from € 24 🚐🍴Ch🔌 WC ⬛included 🚿. ⬛ 08/04-31/10

△S	Privlaka	27B5

Dalmacija, Ivana Pavla II 40. **GPS:** n44,25613 e15,12557.
🛏🚐🍴Ch🔌 included. ⬛ 01/05-15/10

△	Privlaka	27B5

Medanić, Put Brtalica 47. **GPS:** n44,24887 e15,13379.
🛏. **Remarks:** Mini-camp.

△	Ražanac	27B5

Kamp Miočić, Rtina I 139, Rtina. **GPS:** n44,29219 e15,30179.
🛏.

	Ražanac	27B5

Kamp Odmoree, Rtina Stošići bb. **GPS:** n44,30040 e15,28881.

△	Ražanac	27B5

Planik. **GPS:** n44,27778 e15,34472.
🛏€ 5,07-12, € 3,33-5,33/pp. ⬛ 15/05-30/09 **Remarks:** Mini-camp.

△	Ražanac	27B5

Puntica. **GPS:** n44,28389 e15,34306.
🛏€ 12 -20. **Remarks:** Mini-camp.

△	Rovanjska	27B5

Tamaris. **GPS:** n44,25037 e15,53735.
🛏. **Remarks:** Mini-camp.

△	Senj	27A4

Skver. **GPS:** n44,99389 e14,89978.
40 🛏 🚐🍴Ch🔌 WC ⬛. **Location:** Comfortable. **Surface:** gravel/metalled.
⬛ 01/04-01/10
Distance: 🚶500m ⚓on the spot ⊗on the spot 🍴150m.

△	Senj	27A4

Bunica, Bunica 33. **GPS:** n45,02607 e14,88630.
🛏. **Remarks:** Mini-camp.

△	Senj	27A4

Ujca, M. Cihlar Nehajeva, 4. **GPS:** n44,96833 e14,92167.
🛏. ⬛ 01/05-01/10
Distance: ⚓on the spot. **Remarks:** Mini-camp.

△	Šibenik	27B5

Krka. **GPS:** n43,79463 e15,68120.⬆.

🛏free. ⬛ 01/01-31/12
Remarks: 1km from Krka waterfalls.

△S	Šibenik	27B5

Solaris. **GPS:** n43,69917 e15,87795.
🛏🚐🍴Ch🔌. ⬛ 15/03-30/11

△	Šibenik	27B5

Solaris-Zablaće, Obala palih boraca 2a. **GPS:** n43,70524 e15,86850.
🛏. ⬛ 01/05-30/09

Tourist information Šibenik:
🌟 Internationaal kinderfestival. ⬛ 22/06-06/07.
🌿 Nacionalni Park Krka, Krka. Nature reserve.

△	Slano	27D6

Baldo. **GPS:** n42,79683 e17,84989.
🛏. **Remarks:** Mini-camp.

△	Slano	27D6

Bambo. **GPS:** n42,77513 e17,88500.
🛏. **Remarks:** Mini-camp.

△	Slano	27D6

Banja, Put Od Banje. **GPS:** n42,77414 e17,88405.
🛏. **Remarks:** Mini-camp.

△	Slano	27D6

Rogac, Grgurici. **GPS:** n42,78229 e17,87536.
🛏€ 4-5 + € 2-2,50/pp. ⬛ 01/04-31/10 **Remarks:** Mini-camp.

△	Slano	27D6

Sladenovici, Sladenovici 9. **GPS:** n42,78450 e17,86104.
🛏. **Remarks:** Mini-camp.

△	Slatine	27C6

Domic, Put Porta 71, Ciove. **GPS:** n43,49784 e16,34060.
🛏. **Remarks:** Mini-camp.

△	Split	27C6

Stobreč. **GPS:** n43,50401 e16,52644.

🛏. ⬛ 01/01-31/12
Distance: 🚶centre 7km ⚓on the spot.

Tourist information Split:
Ⓜ Arheoloski Muzej, Zrinjsko-Frankopanska 25. Findings from Roman time and Middle Ages. ⬛ Tue-Fri 9-14h, Sa-Su 9-13h, 01/06-30/09 Tue-Fri 9-12, 13-20h, Sa-Su 9-13h.
Ⓜ Galerija Ivana Mestrovica, Setaliste I. Mestrovica 46. Gallery. ⬛ Mo-Sa 10-18h, Su 10-14h.
Ⓜ Muzej Hrvatskih Arheoloskih Spomenika, S. Gunjace bb. Archeological findings. ⬛ Mo-Sa 9-20h.
✠ Dioklecijanova palača. Roman palace.

△S	Starigrad/Paklenica	27B5

Camp National Park, Paklenica. **GPS:** n44,28832 e15,44573.
🛏🚐Ch🔌. ⬛ 15/03-15/10 **Remarks:** Mini-camp.

△	Starigrad/Paklenica	27B5

Jaz, Seline, Paklenica. **GPS:** n44,28323 e15,46028.
🛏. ⬛ 01/05-30/09 **Remarks:** Mini-camp.

△	Starigrad/Paklenica	27B5

Marko, Paklenicka 7, Paklenica. **GPS:** n44,28851 e15,45261.
🛏. ⬛ 01/01-31/12 **Remarks:** Mini-camp,

△		

Pinus, Ive Senjanina 5, Paklenica. **GPS:** n44,30928 e15,42320.
🛏. **Remarks:** Mini-camp.

△	Starigrad/Paklenica	27B5

Pisak, Paklenica. **GPS:** n44,27285 e15,47806.
🛏. **Remarks:** Mini-camp.

△	Starigrad/Paklenica	27B5

Plantaža, Put Plantaže 2, Paklenica. **GPS:** n44,30056 e15,43211.
🛏. **Remarks:** Mini-camp.

△	Starigrad/Paklenica	27B5

Vesna, Paklenicka 103, Paklenica. **GPS:** n44,28610 e15,45243.
🛏. ⬛ 01/01-31/12 **Remarks:** Mini-camp.

Tourist information Starigrad/Paklenica:
ℹ Nacionalni park "Paklenica". Nature reserve, 150 km biking ad hiking trails, bird observation, tunnels and caves. 🎫 30kn/day.

△	Ston	27D6

Prapratna. **GPS:** n42,81778 e17,67611.
🛏. ⬛ 01/06-30/09

△	Ston	27D6

Vrela, Brijesta 10. **GPS:** n42,90397 e17,53266.
🛏. **Remarks:** Mini-camp.

△	Sukošan	27B5

Brajde. **GPS:** n44,04256 e15,30755.
🛏. **Remarks:** Mini-camp.

△	Sukošan	27B5

Kaj. **GPS:** n44,04278 e15,30655.
🛏. **Remarks:** Mini-camp.

HR

Sukošan 27B5
Malenica, Vl. Milan Gašparović. **GPS:** n44,03658 e15,32790.
Remarks: Mini-camp.

Sukošan 27B5
Oliva. **GPS:** n44,04247 e15,30805.
Remarks: Mini-camp.

Supetar 27C6
Waterman Beach. **GPS:** n43,38076 e16,56439.
01/05-30/09

Sutivan 27C6
Mlin, Brac. **GPS:** n43,38316 e16,47795.
Remarks: Mini-camp.

Sutivan 27C6
Sutivan, Gorana Pavlova 12. **GPS:** n43,38523 e16,48460.
01/01-31/12

Sv. Filip I Jakov 27B5
Djardin, Sveti Filip i Jakov bb. **GPS:** n43,96139 e15,42750.
from € 18 Ch included. 01/05-30/09

Sv. Filip I Jakov 27B5
Filip, Put Primorja 10a. **GPS:** n43,96055 e15,42910.
from € 15,20 Ch included. **Remarks:** Mini-camp.

Sv. Filip I Jakov 27B5
Ante, Turanj. **GPS:** n43,99637 e15,37915.
Remarks: Mini-camp.

Sv. Filip I Jakov 27B5
Antonio, Turanj. **GPS:** n43,97488 e15,39990.
Remarks: Mini-camp.

Sv. Filip I Jakov 27B5
Bepo, Turanj. **GPS:** n43,96562 e15,41254.
Remarks: Mini-camp.

Sv. Filip I Jakov 27B5
Bozo, Sv. Petar. **GPS:** n43,99688 e15,37838.
Remarks: Mini-camp.

Sv. Filip I Jakov 27B5
Jugo, Turanj. **GPS:** n43,96605 e15,41173.
Remarks: Mini-camp.

Sv. Filip I Jakov 27B5
Livada. **GPS:** n43,95976 e15,43108.
Remarks: Mini-camp.

Sv. Filip I Jakov 27B5
Maestral, Turanj 90. **GPS:** n43,96611 e15,41162.
Remarks: Mini-camp.

Sv. Filip I Jakov 27B5
Milan, Sv. Petar. **GPS:** n44,00205 e15,36859.
Remarks: Mini-camp.

Sv. Filip I Jakov 27B5
Moce, Put Primorja 8. **GPS:** n43,95968 e15,42915.
Remarks: Mini-camp.

Sv. Filip I Jakov 27B5
R & B, Turanj. **GPS:** n43,96592 e15,41196.
Remarks: Mini-camp.

Sv. Filip I Jakov 27B5
Rio, Put Primorja. **GPS:** n43,95583 e15,43500.
Remarks: Mini-camp.

Tkon 27B5
Adriana. **GPS:** n43,91734 e15,42596.
Remarks: Mini-camp.

Tkon 27B5
Brist. **GPS:** n43,92312 e15,41493.
Remarks: Mini-camp.

Tribanj 27B5
Ante, Krušcica. **GPS:** n44,34469 e15,32842.
Remarks: Mini-camp.

Tribanj 27B5
Punta Šibuljina, Šibuljina. **GPS:** n44,33631 e15,34627.
Remarks: Mini-camp.

Trogir 27C6
Vranjica Belvedere, Seget Vranjica. **GPS:** n43,51196 e16,19159.
from € 20 Ch WC. 15/04-15/10

Trogir 27C6
Seget, Seget Donji. **GPS:** n43,51904 e16,22430.
50 from € 21. 01/03-31/10
Distance: 800m on the spot. **Remarks:** Mini-camp.

Tourist information Trogir:
Tourist Information, Ivana Pavla II Square, www.trogir-online.com. City with rich culture from Greek, Roman and Venetian time.
M Town Museum, Fanfogna palace, Garagnin. History of the city. 16/09-14/06 by request 8-14h, 15/06-15/09 9-21h.
M Zbirka Kairos. Ecclesiastical art collection. 15/6-15/9 8-13, 15-19h.
Fort Kamerlengo. 15/6-15/9 9-20h.
Katedrala St. Lawrence. Bell-tower of Cathedral of St. Lawrence, 47m. 15/6-15/9 9-12, 16-19h. 5kn.

Vela Luka 27C6
Mindel, Stani 193. **GPS:** n42,98369 e16,67060.
01/01-31/12

Viganj 27C6
Antony Boy. **GPS:** n42,97889 e17,10752.
01/01-31/12

Vir 27B5
Luka. **GPS:** n44,29610 e15,10605.
Remarks: Mini-camp.

Vir 27B5
Sapavac, Put Bunara 101. **GPS:** n44,29432 e15,07640.
Remarks: Mini-camp.

Vodice 27B6
Imperial, Vatroslava Lisinskog 2/I. **GPS:** n43,75287 e15,78992.
from € 22 Ch. 21/03-11/11

Vransko Jezero 27B5
Crkvine. **GPS:** n43,93035 e15,51012.
15/04-15/10

Vrsi 27B5
Mulic, Mulo. **GPS:** n44,26174 e15,21246.
Remarks: Mini-camp.

Zaboric 27B6
Jasenovo. **GPS:** n43,65116 e15,95025.
50 from € 13 Ch WC. 01/05-01/10
Distance: on the spot. **Remarks:** Mini-camp.

Zadar 27B5
Rosmari, Emanuela Vidovica 2. **GPS:** n44,13250 e15,20861.
20 Ch WC.
Distance: on the spot on the spot. **Remarks:** Mini-camp.

Zadar 27B5
Borik, Radovana 7. **GPS:** n44,13528 e15,21528.
01/05-30/09

Tourist information Zadar:
Trg Pet Bunara. Square of the five fountains.
M Arheoloski Muzej, Simuna Kozicica Benje bb. Archeological findings. Mo-Sa 9-13h, 18-20h.
Music nights at St. Donatius of Zadar. 01/07-15/08.

Zaostrog 27C6
Uvala Borova, Mkarska. **GPS:** n43,13123 e17,28750.
01/05-30/09

Zaton 27B5
Zaton. **GPS:** n44,23385 e15,16671.
01/05/30/09

Ždrelac 27B5
Ruža. **GPS:** n44,00925 e15,28067.
Remarks: Mini-camp.

Živogošče 27C6
Dole. **GPS:** n43,17118 e17,19669.
01/05-30/09

Žrnovo 27C6
Tri Žala, Uvala Tri Žala 808. **GPS:** n42,96407 e17,09104.
Remarks: Mini-camp.

Žrnovo 27C6
Vrbovica, Vrbovica bb. **GPS:** n42,95882 e17,11394.
Remarks: Mini-camp.

| △ | Žuljana | 27C6 |

Vucina. GPS: n42,88257 e17,45135.
🦌. **Remarks:** Mini-camp.

Inland

| 🦌S | Kopačevo 🚐 | 27D3 |

Family-Camperstop, Ferenca Kiša 7. **GPS:** n45,59832 e18,78467.
20 🦌 against payment 🚿 ✗. ▢ 01/04-30/09

| 🦌S | Koprivnica | 27C3 |

Cerine, Miroslava Krleze 81. **GPS:** n46,15361 e16,84250. ⬆ ➡.
11 🦌 € 12 🚿 ▤ Ch ✗ WC. **Location:** Comfortable. **Surface:** grasstiles.
▢ 01/01-31/12
Distance: 🏊1,5km ⊗300m 🏖1km.
Remarks: Parking spa resort.

| △ | Lipovac | 27D4 |

Spacva. GPS: n45,04593 e18,99682.
🦌. ▢ 01/05-01/10

| 🦌S | Plitviča | 27B4 |

Bear, Seliste Dreznicko 52. **GPS:** n44,94804 e15,63639.

15 🦌 € 23 🚿 ▤ Ch ✗ WC ▢ included. **Surface:** grassy. ▢ 01/04-01/11
Remarks: Baker every morning, water falls Plitvica 5km.

| 🦌S | Plitviča | 27B4 |

Cvetkovic, Jezerce 28. **GPS:** n44,86338 e15,63967.

20 🦌 € 20 🚿 ▤ Ch ✗ WC ▢ included ▥ free. **Surface:** grassy/gravel.
Remarks: Water falls Plitvica 2km.

| △ | Plitviča | 27B4 |

Korana. GPS: n44,99260 e15,64916.
🦌 € 6 + € 5/pp.

Tourist information Plitviča:
🌿 Nacionalni Park Plitviča Jezera, www.np-plitvicka-jezera.hr. National park
Plitvice lakes. ▢ 9-17h.

| △ | Racovica | 27B4 |

Turist, Grabovac 102. **GPS:** n44,97222 e15,64750.
🦌 € 23. ▢ 01/05-31/10

| 🦌S | Zagreb | 27B4 |

Camp-Zagreb, Jezerska 6. **GPS:** n45,80253 e15,82622. ⬆.
40 🦌 € 23-€31 🚿 ▤ Ch ✗ WC ▢ included. **Location:** Urban, luxurious.
Surface: metalled.
Distance: 🏊 on the spot 🚌 on the spot ⊗ on the spot 🎣 on the spot 🚶 on the
spot.

Tourist information Zagreb:
ℹ www.zagreb-touristinfo.hr. Capital, surface 64133 km ^{2}, inhabitants 885,000,
11 theaters and 22 museums.
Ⓜ Archeological Museum, 19 Nikola Subic Zrinski Square. ▢ Tue-Fri 10-17h,
Sa-Su 10-13h.
Ⓜ Atelje Mestrovic, Mletacka 8. Former dwellinghouse of sculptor Ivan
Mestrovic. ▢ Tue-Fri 10-18h, Sa-Su 10-13h.
Ⓜ Ethnographic Museum, Mazuranicev trg 14. ▢ Tue-Thu 10-18h, Fri-Su

10-13h.
Ⓜ Muzej Grada Zagreb, Opaticka 20. City museum.
▢ Tue-Fri 10-18h, Sa-Su 10-13h.
Ⓜ Tehnicki Muzej, Savska cesta 18. Technical museum.
▢ Tue-Fri 9-15h, Sa-Su 9-13h.
🎆 Medjunarodna Smotra Folklora. International folk festival.
▢ 20/07/05-24/07/05.
🎆 Zagreb Summer Festival.
▢ 01/07-15/08.
🌿 Park Prirode Kopacki Rit. Nature reserve, boat rental.
▢ daily 8-16h.

HR

GREECE

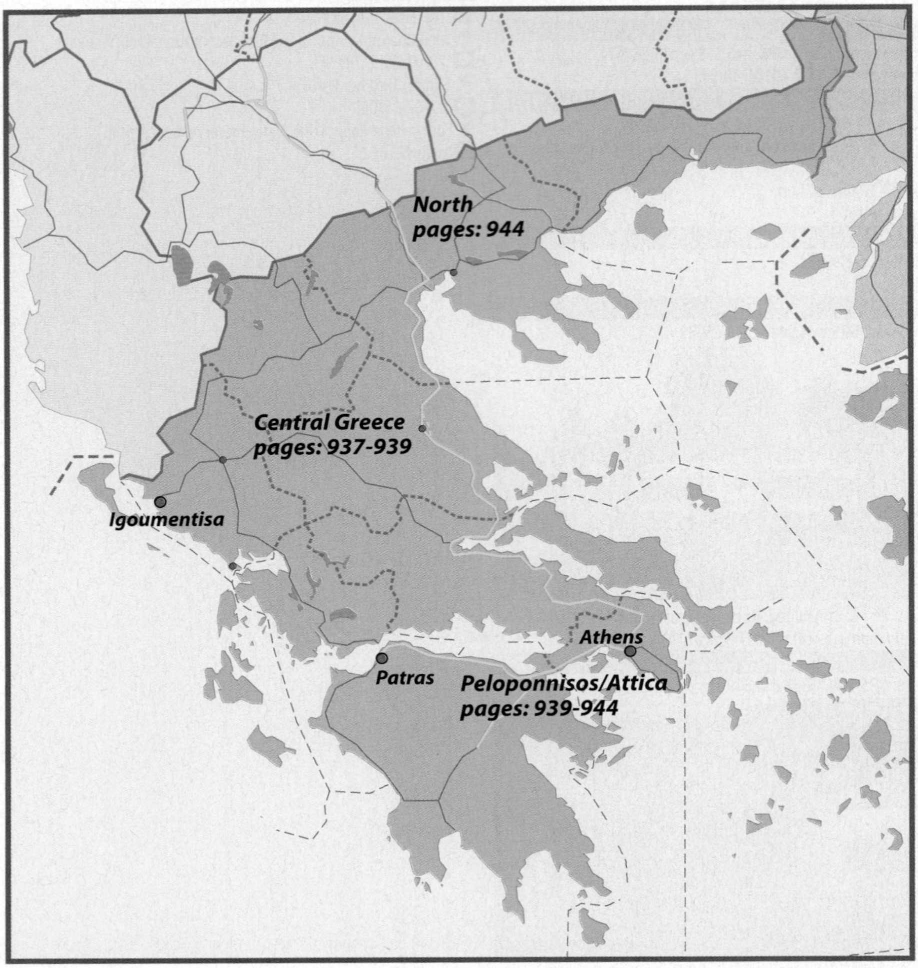

North
pages: 944

Central Greece
pages: 937-939

Igoumentisa

Patras

Athens

Peloponnisos/Attica
pages: 939-944

Capital: Athens
Government: Parliamentary democracy
Official Language: Greek
Population: 11,300,000 (2013)
Area: 131,990 km²

General information
Dialling code: 0030
General emergency: 112
Currency: Euro

Regulations for overnight stays
Wild camping and overnight parking is not officially
allowed. Overnight parking places mentioned here
are not official motorhome stopovers but
tolerated areas.

Additional public holidays 2015
January 6 Epiphany
February 23 Ash Monday, 41 days before Easter
March 25 Independence Day
April 10 Orthodox Easter
May 1 Labor Day
August 15 Assumption of the Virgin Mary
October 28 National Holiday, Ochi day

Greece

Central Greece

Achillio — 35C4
Epar. Od. Archilliou-Glifas. **GPS**: n39,00943 e22,95758.
Distance: on the spot on the spot on the spot.

Agios Nikolaos — 35B4
GPS: n38,34959 e22,15661.
01/10-30/04
Remarks: Parking at harbour.

Ammoudia — 35A4
GPS: n39,23636 e20,48073.

Surface: gravel/sand.
Distance: on the spot 50m on the spot 100m 250m.
Remarks: At harbour.

Ammoudia — 35A4
GPS: n39,23989 e20,48116.

Surface: sand.
Distance: on the spot on the spot on the spot 200m 50m.
Remarks: Beach parking.

Arahova — 35C4
GPS: n38,47948 e22,58164.
01/01-31/12

Arillas — 35A4
Restaurant Soukas, Aglias-Platarias. **GPS**: n39,35278 e20,28861.
free for clients . **Location:** Rural. **Surface:** grassy/sand.
01/05-01/10
Distance: on the spot on the spot.

Boukka — 35B4
GPS: n38,93125 e21,14200.

Surface: sand.
Distance: on the spot 100m.
Remarks: Next to sports fields, beach parking.

Corfu — 35A4
Dionysus, Dassia. **GPS**: n39,66472 e19,84440.
Ch. 15/04-15/10

Corfu — 35A4
Dolphin Camping, Sidari. **GPS**: n39,78890 e19,72354.
Ch. 15/04-31/10

Corfu — 35A4
Karda Beach, Dassia. **GPS**: n39,68611 e19,83861.
Ch.
01/04-15/10
Distance: on the spot.

Tourist information Corfu:
Esplanada, Kerkyra (Corfu). Meeting point for inhabitants and tourists.
Kerkyra (Corfu).
Frurion, Kerkyra (Corfu). Citadel, 1550.
Aqualand, Corfu Water Park, Ag.Ioannis. Leisure pool park.

Delphi — 35C4
Apollon. GPS: n38,48388 e22,47550.
Ch. 01/01-31/12

Delphi — 35C4
Delphi Camping. GPS: n38,47833 e22,47450.
Ch. 20/03-30/11

Delphi — 35C4
Chrissa. GPS: n38,47267 e22,46206.
01/01-31/12

Tourist information Delphi:
Site of Delphi. Archeological site. 7.30-17.30h holiday. € 6.

Eratini — 35B4
N48/E65 km 47. **GPS**: n38,33769 e22,19198.

Surface: grassy/sand.
Distance: on the spot on the spot.
Remarks: Beach parking, max 3,5t.

Erétria — 35C4
Milos Camping. GPS: n38,39139 e23,77556.
Ch.

Tourist information Erétria:
Seaside resort and archological site Antique Eretria.

Gliki — 35A4
Taverne Panorama. GPS: n39,32726 e20,61568.

guests free WC . **Surface:** grassy.
Distance: 500m 500m.
Remarks: Along the Acheron river.

Hiliadou — 35B4
GPS: n38,39408 e21,92096.

GR

🛏 🚰 🔌. **Surface:** gravel.
Distance: 🚶Nafpaktos 7km 🏖on the spot.
Remarks: Beach parking.

🏢 Igoumenítsa 🚉🚤 35A4
GPS: n39,51278 e20,25741.
🛏.
Distance: 🚶on the spot 🚢 600m 🚂on the spot.
Remarks: Parking supermarket at the ring-road 6, dir Ioánnina.

Tourist information Igoumenítsa:
⛰ Goumani (titani). Archeological site.

🛏 Ioánnina 🏔🚤 35A3
Sta Papagou 7. **GPS:** n39,67319 e20,85476.
30 🛏 €8. **Surface:** metalled. 📅 01/01-31/12
Distance: 🚶100m 🚏100m ⊗100m.
Remarks: Monitored parking.

🔺 Ioánnina 🏔🚤 35A3
Limnopoula. **GPS:** n39,67770 e20,84280.
🛏.
📅 01/04-15/10

Tourist information Ioánnina:
ℹ Capital of Epirus, important city in the Turkish time.
👁 Perama. Caves. 📅 daily.

🔺 Itea 35C4
Ayannis, Kirra. **GPS:** n38,42440 e22,45880.
🛏.
Tourist information Itea:
Ⓜ Nautical Museum, Mouseio, 4, Galaxídi.

🍴🅂 Kastrosikia 🚤 35A4
Taverna Lulu, Kastrosikia Beach. **GPS:** n39,09441 e20,63725.
25 🛏 guests free 🚰
Location: Rural, simple. **Surface:** grassy.
Distance: 🏖on the spot ⊗on the spot.

🏢 Krioneri 35B4
GPS: n38,34397 e21,58823.

🛏. **Surface:** gravel. 📅 01/01-31/12
Distance: 🏖on the spot 🚏on the spot ⊗300m.

🏢 Levkas 35A4
Vlycho. **GPS:** n38,68318 e20,69819.
🛏.
Distance: 🚏on the spot.
Remarks: Parking on the quay.

🔺 Levkas 35A4
Dessimi Beach, Vlicho, Lefkada (Levkas). **GPS:** n38,67250 e20,71100.
🛏. 📅 01/04-30/11

GR

🔺 Levkas 35A4
Poros Beach, Poros, Lefkada (Levkas). **GPS:** n39,64095 e20,69700.
🛏. 📅 01/05-30/09

Mesolóngi 🚤 35B4
GPS: n38,36358 e21,42016.
🛏. 📅 01/01-31/12
Remarks: Parking in harbour.

🔺🅂 Metéora 🏔⛰ 35B4
Meteora Garden, Kalambaka. **GPS:** n39,70869 e21,60915.
🛏 🚰 Ch. 📅 01/01-31/12

🔺🅂 Metéora 🏔⛰ 35B4
Rizos International, Kalambaka. **GPS:** n39,69010 e21,64564.
🛏 🚰 Ch. 📅 01/01-31/12

🔺🅂 Metéora 🏔⛰ 35B4
Vrachos Kastraki, Kastraki. **GPS:** n39,71338 e21,61588.
🛏 🚰 Ch. 📅 01/01-31/12

🍴🅂 Metéora 🏔⛰ 35B4
Taverna Arsenis, East Street, Kalambaka. **GPS:** n39,69923 e21,64109.
8 🛏 guests free 🚰 €5 WC.
📅 01/01-31/12

Tourist information Metéora:
✝ Important cultural inheritance, 24 monasteries built on enormous sandstone
peaks, of which 6 can be visited. 📅 9-13h, 15-17h. 🅣 against payment.

🏢 Métsovo 🏔🚉❄ 35A3
GPS: n39,76898 e21,17749.
🛏.
Tourist information Métsovo:
ℹ Traditional mountain village.
Ⓜ Archotiko Tositsa. Restored 18th century mansion, museum or folk art.
📅 8.30-13h, 16-18h. 🅣 €2.

🍴🅂 Mytikas 🚤 35A4
Restaurant Delphina. **GPS:** n38,67410 e20,96708.
5 🛏 €10 🚰 Ch included. **Location:** Rural. **Surface:** grassy.
Distance: 🚶3km 🏖on the spot ⊗on the spot.

🏢 Nafpaktos 🏔🚤 35B4
Xiliadou, N48/E65 km 80,5. **GPS:** n38,38139 e21,81661.
🛏.
Surface: gravel/sand.
Distance: 🏖on the spot 🚏on the spot ⊗nearby.
Remarks: Parking at the beach.

Tourist information Nafpaktos:
ℹ Old city with Venetian Castle and circular walled harbor.

🔺🅂 Parga 🚉🚤 35A4
Enjoy Lichnos. **GPS:** n39,28358 e20,43340.
🛏 🚰 Ch. 📅 01/05-15/10

🔺🅂 Parga 🚉🚤 35A4
Valtos Camping. **GPS:** n39,28556 e20,38972.
🛏.
📅 01/05-30/09

Tourist information Parga:
ℹ Lively bathing resort.
⛰ Necromanteion of Ephyra. Oracle of death.

🔺🅂 Pilion 🏔🚉🚤 35C3
Olizon, Milina. **GPS:** n39,16472 e23,21666.
🛏 🚰 Ch. 📅 01/05-15/10

🔺🅂 Pilion 🏔🚉🚤 35C3
Sikia Fig Tree, Kato Gatzea. **GPS:** n39,31025 e23,10977.
🛏 🚰 Ch. 📅 01/04-15/10

Tourist information Pilion:
ℹ Mythological peninsula, beautiful nature, authentic mountain villages and
fishing towns.
👁 Makrinitsa. Village worth seeing, car-free.
Ⓜ Miliés. Folk museum. 📅 01/04-31/10 Tue-Su, 01/11-31/03 Wed-Su.
Ⓜ Archeological Museum, Athanasáki 1, Vólos. 📅 Tue-Su 🔴 holiday.

Plataria 35A4
GPS: n39,44606 e20,27409.

🏕. **Surface**: grassy/sand. ⬛ 01/01-31/12
Distance: 🏖500m ⛱on the spot ⬅on the spot ⊗200m 🍴250m.
Remarks: Parking at the beach.

⛰S Plataria 35A4
Nautilos. **GPS**: n39,44389 e20,25806.
🏕 ⛪Ch. ⬛ 01/04-20/10

⛱S Préveza 🛶🌊 35A4
Mitikas. **GPS**: n39,01719 e20,71555.

🏕 ⛪🚿. **Surface**: asphalted/gravel.
Distance: 🏖Preveza 7km ⛱on the spot ⬅on the spot ⊗500m.
Remarks: Parking at the beach.

Préveza 🛶🌊 35A4
GPS: n38,95008 e20,75498.
🏕.

Tourist information Préveza:
⛰ Kassópi, Kassópi. Archeological site.
⛰ Nikopolis. Old Roman city.

🍴 Vagia 35C4
Restaurant Ynaiopio, Palaia Ethniki Odos Athinon-Lamias.
GPS: n38,34331 e23,19378.
🏕free with a meal.

⛱S Vonitsa 35A4
Agio Sotiriou. **GPS**: n38,93302 e20,91937.

🏕 ⛪🚿. **Surface**: grassy.
Distance: 🏖Vonitsa 3km ⛱lake ⬅on the spot ⊗taverne 🍴3km.

Vonitsa 35A4
Marina. **GPS**: n38,92172 e20,88482.
5 🏕free. **Location**: Simple. **Surface**: gravel.
Remarks: Near marina.

Peloponnisos/Attica

Agia Kyriaki 35C6
GPS: n36,71883 e23,02305.
🏕.

Remarks: At the beach.

⛱S Agios Andreas 35C5
GPS: n37,37120 e22,78262.

🏕 ⛪WCfree. **Surface**: gravel.
Distance: 🏖3km ⛱on the spot ⬅on the spot ⊗on the spot.
Remarks: At harbour.

⛰ Agios Andreas 35C5
Camping Agios Andreas. **GPS**: n36,86664 e21,92087.⬆
🏕. ⬛ 20/04-30/09
Distance: ⛱on the spot.

Agios Fokas 35C6
GPS: n36,59565 e23,06108.

5 🏕. **Surface**: sand.
Distance: 🏖Monemvasia 13km.
Remarks: Parking at pier.

Agios Kiriaki 35B5
Filiatra, Epar.Od.Filiatron. **GPS**: n37,11963 e21,57611.
🏕. ⬛ 01/01-31/12

⛰ Assini 35C5
Kastraki. **GPS**: n37,52861 e22,87556.
🏕. ⬛ 01/04-01/10

Athens 🌐🛶🍴 35C4
GPS: n37,96987 e23,72263.
🏕. ⬛ 01/01-31/12
Remarks: Parking of the Acropolis, guarding after authorization Probably only outside the main season.

⛰S Athens 🌐🛶🍴 35C4
Athens camping, Leoforis Athinon. **GPS**: n38,00889 e23,67222.
🏕€ 26, 2 pers.incl ⛪🚿Chincluded 🔌€4.
⬛ 01/01-31/12

Tourist information Athens:
👁🚶🍴 Monasteraki. Old district with Athenian flea market. ⬛ Su 8-14h.
👁 Panathenaic Stadium. Stadium of the first Olympic Games in 1896.
👁👁 Plaka. Old district around the Acropolis.
👁 Tomb of the Unknown Soldier, Plateía Syntágmatos. Sunday 11h changing of the guard.
⛰ Acropolis. Archeological site.
⬛ 01/05-31/10 Mo-Fri 8-18.30h, Sa-Su 8.30-14.30h, 01/11-30/04 8.30-16.30h
⬛ 01/05, 28/10, holiday.

Diakofto 35B4
GPS: n38,19747 e22,20167.

🥾. **Surface:** asphalted.
⭕ 01/01-31/12
Distance: ⬡on the spot ⬡on the spot ⊗on the spot 🛢500m.
Remarks: Parking at harbour.

Tourist information Diakofto:
👁 Rack railway, Kalavryta. Train journey with rack-railway.

| 🛏 | Dimitsána | 35B5 |

Kefalari tou Ai-Yanni. GPS: n37,59058 e22,04286.
4 🥾.
Remarks: Parking water museum.

| 🍴 | Dimitsána | 35B5 |

Taverna Koustenis, Eparchiaki Odos Kato Davias. **GPS:** n37,58650 e22,04459.⬆
5 🥾free.
Location: Rural, simple. **Surface:** gravel.
Distance: 🚶9km ⊗on the spot.

Tourist information Dimitsána:
⬇ Loúsios-kloof. 5km long and 300m deep, marked trails.

| 🛏 | Elefsina | 35C4 |

GPS: n38,04235 e23,53942.
🥾. ⭕ 01/01-31/12
Remarks: Parking in front of the ruins in the city center.

| 🛏 S | Epidaurus | 35C5 |

GPS: n37,59675 e23,07444.

🥾 🚰WCfree.
Surface: gravel.
Remarks: Overnight stay on parking at the Ancient theater is generally tolerated.

Tourist information Epidaurus:
⌒ Ancient Epidaurus. Archeological site. ⭕ 8-19h.

| 🏕 | Ermioni | 35C5 |

Hydras Wave. GPS: n37,40583 e23,31556.
🥾. ⭕ 15/4-15/10

| 🛏 | Galatas | 35C5 |

Epar.Odos Ermionis. **GPS:** n37,49491 e23,45546.
20 🥾.
Distance: 🚶on the spot ⊗on the spot.
Remarks: At the quay.

| 🛏 | Gerolimenas | 35C6 |

GPS: n36,48230 e22,39969.

3 🥾. **Surface:** asphalted.
Distance: ⬡on the spot ⬡on the spot ⊗50m 🚶on the spot.
Remarks: Parking at the beach.

| 🏕 S | Gialova Pylou | 35B6 |

Navarino Beach. GPS: n36,94770 e21,70620.
🥾🚰♨Ch➕. ⭕ 01/04-31/10

| 🏕 S | Glifa Kyllini | 35B5 |

Ionion. GPS: n37,83640 e21,13340.
🥾🚰♨Ch➕📶. ⭕ 01/01-31/12

| 🛏 | Gythion | 35C6 |

GPS: n36,78883 e22,58225.
🥾. **Surface:** sand.
Distance: ⊗on the spot.
Remarks: At the beach, ± 5km from Gythion dir Skala.

| 🏕 S | Gythion | 35C6 |

Gythion Bay. GPS: n36,72920 e22,55243.
🥾🚰♨Ch➕. ⭕ 01/01-31/12

| 🛏 | Kakovatos | 35B5 |

GPS: n37,45721 e21,63869.
🥾. **Surface:** metalled.
Remarks: Parking at the beach.

| 🛏 S | Kalogria | 35B5 |

Kalogria Camper Stop, Kalogria Peloponnes. **GPS:** n38,15986 e21,37162.

40 🥾€ 10, 16/07-31/08 € 12 🚰♨Ch♨ (20x)€3/day WC🚽📶included.
Surface: unpaved. ⭕ 01/05-31/10
Distance: 🚶5km 🚗11km ⬡250m 🚶300m ⊗50m 🛢on the spot 🚌on the spot 🚲on the spot 🚶on the spot.

Tourist information Kalogria:
⬇ Kotychi, Lapas. Visitors centre, swamp area.

| 🛏 | Kamares | 35C6 |

GPS: n36,68203 e22,52090.

🥾. **Surface:** sand.
Distance: ⬡on the spot ⬡on the spot ⊗350m.

| 🏕 | Kameras Irion | 35C6 |

Poseidon. GPS: n36,68826 e22,51753.
🥾.

	Karavostasi	35C6

Taverna O Faros. GPS: n36,69733 e22,38073.
15 free on demand. **Location:** Rural, simple. **Surface:** gravel.
Distance: on the spot on the spot.

	Kastro	35B5

Loutra Kilinis. GPS: n37,86533 e21,10903.
WC free.
Remarks: Parking at the beach.

	Kastro	35B5

Killinis Beach. **GPS:** n37,87413 e21,10748.

. **Surface:** grassy/sand.
Distance: 2km on the spot on the spot Beach taverne.

Tourist information Kastro:
Chlemoutsi. Medieval castle.

	Kato Alissos	35B5

Kato Allissos. GPS: n38,14986 e21,57740.
€ 19 Ch 01/04-20/10

	Kifisiá	35C4

Dionissiotis. GPS: n38,10535 e23,81355.
ChWC. 01/01-31/12
Remarks: 18km north of Athens, route Athens dir Lamia.

Tourist information Kifisiá:
Holiday resort of the Athenian since the Roman time.
Goulándris, Levidou 13. History of nature.

	Killini	35B5

Epar Od. Andravidas-Killinis. **GPS:** n37,92598 e21,16699.
.
Distance: 2km.
Remarks: Parking at the beach.

	Korfos	35C5

GPS: n37,76361 e23,13302.

. **Surface:** gravel.
Remarks: At fishing port.

	Korinthos	35C5

Afrodites Waters, Ancient Corinth. **GPS:** n37,91139 e22,87861.

30 € 10 Ch WC . 01/01-31/12

Distance: 350m 350m 350m.

	Korinthos	35C5

GPS: n37,88983 e22,86761.
.
Remarks: Parking Akrokorinth.

	Korinthos	35C5

Ancient Korinthos. GPS: n37,90750 e22,87806.

	Korinthos	35C5

Blue Dolphin, Lecheon. **GPS:** n37,93460 e22,86490.
Ch. 01/04-15/10

	Korinthos	35C5

Isthmia Beach, Isthmia. **GPS:** n37,88950 e23,00530.

15/04-15/10

Tourist information Korinthos:
Important trade centre.
Korinth Canal. Canal, 23m wide.
Acrocorinth. Fortress. 8-19h.
free.

	Koroni	35B6

GPS: n36,79729 e21,96002.

.
Remarks: Parking at harbour.

	Koroni	35B6

Camping Koroni. GPS: n36,81168 e21,93303.
.
Distance: 600m on the spot on the spot.

Tourist information Koroni:
Port city with Venetian castle, 1206.

	Kosmas	35C5

Epar.Od.Leonidiou-Kosma. **GPS:** n37,09180 e22,74043.
. **Surface:** metalled.
Distance: on the spot on the spot on the spot.
Remarks: Behind church.

	Kotronas	35C6

GPS: n36,61899 e22,49367.

GR

free. **Surface:** concrete.
Distance: on the spot on the spot 50m.
Remarks: Parking at pier.

Lambiri 35B4
Tsolis, Old National Road. **GPS**: n38,32083 e21,97194.
. 15/04-30/09

Legrena 35D5
GPS: n37,66206 e23,99772.
. 01/01-31/12

Marathon 35D4
Ramnous. GPS: n38,13139 e24,00722.
.
01/04-31/10

Tourist information Marathon:
www.marathon.gr. The name marathon, course of 41 km, comes from this town.

Mayroyouni/Gythion 35C6
Meltemi. GPS: n36,72986 e22,55360.
.

Tourist information Mayroyouni/Gythion:
Tourist Information Areópoli, Vasiléos Pávlou 21, Máni. Peninsula.
Pýrgos Diroú, Máni. Caves.

Monemvasía 35C6
GPS: n36,68240 e23,03821.
.
Remarks: Parking harbour.

Monemvasía 35C6
GPS: n36,68875 e23,05076.
.
Surface: asphalted.
Distance: on the spot on the spot shuttle to old town.

Tourist information Monemvasía:
Fortified city, lower town have been restored.
Agía Sofia. Church 13th century.

Mycenae 35C5
Atreus. GPS: n37,71911 e22,74114.
.
01/01-31/12

Tourist information Mycenae:
Archeological Museum, Argos.
Archeological site. 1/4-31/10 8-19h, 1/11-31/3 8-17h holiday.
Agora Argos, Argos. Archeological site. summer 8.30-15h.

Nafplio 35C5
GPS: n37,56823 e22,80170.

.
Surface: asphalted.
Distance: 500m 300m.
Remarks: Parking marina.

Tourist information Nafplio:
Tourist information, Ikostispémtis Martiou 2. First Greek capital.
Archeological Museum. Tue-Su 8.30-15h Mo.
Palamídi. Citadel 18th century.

Neo Itylo 35C6
GPS: n36,69246 e22,38969.

. **Surface:** asphalted.
Distance: on the spot on the spot 50m.
Remarks: Not in front of hotel.

Olympia 35B5
Alphios. GPS: n37,64360 e21,61930.
. 01/04-31/10

Tourist information Olympia:
Archeological Museum. Important Greek archeological museum.
Mo 11-19h, Tue-Su 8-19h.

Paralia Astros 35C5
GPS: n37,44475 e22,74800.

. **Surface:** gravel.
Distance: on the spot on the spot 200m.
Remarks: At the beach.

Paralia Platanou 35B4
GPS: n38,17104 e22,26828.

. **Surface:** gravel.
Distance: on the spot.
Remarks: At the beach.

Paralia Rizomilos 35B4
GPS: n38,21898 e22,14745.

free. **Surface:** gravel.
Distance: on the spot on the spot on the spot mini market

(summer).
Remarks: Not in front of hotel.

△ **Pátra** 🍴🏖 **35B5**

Golden Sunset, Old national Road km 19. **GPS:** n38,14389 e21,58778.
🚐. 🅾 01/04-15/10

Tourist information Pátra:
👁 Archaïa Klauss. First commercial producer of wine of Greece.

🅿 **Perahóra** **35C4**

GPS: n38,03188 e22,87293.
🚐.
Distance: 🏊on the spot ⊗on the spot.
Remarks: At the lake.

🅿 S **Petalidi** **35B6**

GPS: n36,95871 e21,93418.
🚐 🚰. **Surface:** asphalted.
Remarks: Nearby port.

🅿 **Petalidi** **35B6**

GPS: n36,95915 e21,92870.

🚐. **Surface:** asphalted.
Distance: ⊗on the spot.
Remarks: Parking in village, near the sea.

🅿 S **Plaka** 🏖🏊 **35C5**

GPS: n37,14824 e22,89222.

40 🚐 € 5/24h 🚰🚽 💧 WC ❚included. **Surface:** asphalted.
Distance: 🏊on the spot 🚶on the spot ⊗50m 🛒50m 🍽on the spot.
Remarks: Narrow entrance.

🍴 **Porto Kagio** **35C6**

Taverna Porto. GPS: n36,42811 e22,48697. ⬆.
max. 3 🚐guests free. **Surface:** grassy.
Distance: 🏊on the spot 🚶on the spot ⊗on the spot 🛒mini market.

🅿 **Pylos** **35B6**

GPS: n36,91633 e21,69524.

🚐. **Surface:** concrete.
Distance: 🏊100m ⊗100m.
Remarks: Parking at pier.

🅿 **Rafina** 🛥🏖 **35D4**

GPS: n38,01835 e24,01227.
🚐. 🅾 01/01-31/12

🅿 **Salandi** **35C5**

GPS: n37,44748 e23,12474.

🚐. **Surface:** gravel.
Distance: 🚶Didyma 5km 🏊on the spot 🚶on the spot.
Remarks: At the beach.

🅿 **Savalia** **35B5**

Savalia Beach. GPS: n37,79685 e21,25578.

🚐. **Surface:** asphalted.
Distance: 🏊on the spot 🚶on the spot.

🅿 **Skoutari** **35C6**

GPS: n36,65921 e22,49962.

max. 3 🚐. **Surface:** concrete.
Distance: 🏊on the spot 🚶on the spot ⊗within walking distance.
Remarks: Near fishing-port.

△ **Sounion** 〰 **35D5**

Camping Bacchus. GPS: n37,67694 e24,04750.
🚐.
🅾 01/01-31/12

Tourist information Sounion:
Ⓜ Mineralogical Museum, Lavrió. Old mine shaft of the silvermines. 🅾 Wed,
Sa-Su.
⌒ Archeological site.

🅿 S **Tolo** **35C5**

GPS: n37,51469 e22,85662.

GR

🛇 ⌐ WC. **Surface:** asphalted.
Distance: 🚶500m 🏊100m 🛒on the spot ⊗200m.
Remarks: Near fishing-port.

| ⍾ | Tyrchu | 35C5 |

Taverne Ostria. GPS: n37,31414 e22,82054.

3 🛇guests free. **Surface:** gravel. ⬛ 15/05-30/09
Distance: 🚶Tyros 10km 🏊on the spot 🛒on the spot ⊗on the spot.
Remarks: At the beach, attention: via steep path.

| ♿S | Zacharo | 35B5 |

Wohnmobil-Stellplatz. GPS: n37,47994 e21,62237.⬆

50 🛇€ 17 ⌐🍽Ch 🚿 WC⬛included ▣€2. **Surface:** grassy/gravel.
⬛ 01/01-31/12
Distance: 🚶2km 🏊50m 🛒on the spot ⊗300m ♨2km.

| 🛏 | Zacharo | 35B5 |

GPS: n37,51917 e21,60248.

🛇.
Distance: 🏊on the spot.

| △ | Zacharo | 35B5 |

Tholo Beach. GPS: n37,41160 e21,66830.
🛇. ⬛ 01/04-31/10

Greece North

| △ | Ag.Mamas Moudania | 35C3 |

Ouzoni Beach. GPS: n40,21611 e23,31833.
🛇. ⬛ 01/05-30/09

| △ | Akt Armenistis Sithonia | 35C3 |

Armenistis. GPS: n40,15222 e23,91361.
🛇. ⬛ 01/05-15/09

| 🛏 | Alexandroúpoli 🏖🌊 | 35D2 |

GPS: n40,84364 e25,87693.
🛇.
Remarks: Parking harbour.

| 🛏 | Alexandroúpoli 🏖🌊 | 35D2 |

Apollonias. GPS: n40,84342 e25,86477.
🛇.
Surface: asphalted.
Remarks: Parking near stadium.

Tourist information Alexandroúpoli:
ℹ Tourist Information, Mákris. Large holiday resort, beautiful beach.

| △ | Gerakani | 35C2 |

Kouyoni. GPS: n40,26464 e23,46347.
🛇. ⬛ 01/05-30/09

| 🛏S | Kalamaria | 35B2 |

Zampetaz, Tessaloniki-Perea. **GPS:** n40,50289 e22,97053.⬆
10 🛇free ⌐🍽Ch 🚿 🛶free.
Location: Simple. **Surface:** asphalted.
Distance: 🚶10km 🚤3km 🚌on the spot.

| 🛏S | Kastoriá 🌿 | 35A3 |

GPS: n40,50461 e21,27977.
🛇against payment ⌐.
Remarks: Voluntary contribution.

| △ | Metamorphosi | 35C3 |

Sunny Bay. GPS: n40,22694 e23,58944.
🛇. ⬛ 01/05-31/10

| 🛏S | Moustheni | 35C2 |

Moystheni Station. GPS: n40,84413 e24,11506.
10 🛇free ⌐🍽Ch 🛶.
Surface: asphalted.
Distance: 🚤10m ⊗on the spot 🛒mini market.
Remarks: Special part for motor homes, shop, restaurant, station 24/24.

| △ | Ouranoupoli | 35C2 |

Ouranoupoli. GPS: n40,33944 e23,97056.

| ⍾S | Paralia Epanomi 🌊 | 35B2 |

Golden Beach. GPS: n40,40469 e22,89925.
10 🛇€ 10 ⌐🚿€5. **Location:** Rural, simple. **Surface:** grassy/sand.
Distance: 🏊on the spot ⊗on the spot.

| 🛏S | Porto Lagos | 35D2 |

GPS: n41,00633 e25,12028.

5 🛇free ⌐. **Surface:** asphalted.
Distance: ⊗on the spot.
Remarks: Parking at pier.

| 🛏S | Vergina | 35B2 |

Parking, Aristotelos 25. **GPS:** n40,48506 e22,31978.⬆➡
25 🛇€4 ⌐🚿€2. **Location:** Urban, simple. **Surface:** asphalted.
Distance: 🚶on the spot ⊗200m ♨450m.

INDEX

INDEX